THEATRE

Volume two

This volume is published
by Hill and Wang
for The Repertory Theater
of Lincoln Center, Inc.

THEATRE

The Annual of the Repertory Theater of Lincoln Center

Barry Hyams, editor

Hill and Wang · *New York*

Foreword

LAST YEAR the publication of *Theatre: Volume I* implied by the numeral in its title the arrival of subsequent issues. With *Theatre: Volume II*, the process of parturition has begun. The term *theatre* is used in preference to *drama* because the latter generically denotes a literary form while *theatre* more accurately designates the total and sentient collaboration between stage practitioners and their audience. *Theatre* addresses itself to both.

The initial book was an account of the germination of the Repertory Theater of Lincoln Center, of an idea in evolution: a company emerging inchoate, the impulses that brought it into existence and some of the obstacles, material and environmental, that had, and still have, to be hurdled. The present volume is intended as the first step into the area of wider considerations—towards the development of an annual of creative thinking about the theatre and towards the revival of the tradition of criticism.

Theatre criticism has gradually lost the informed objectivity prevalent in the eighteenth and nineteenth centuries that could still be imbued with impassioned commitment. Over the past fifty years, with few exceptions, it has degenerated into cults of opinion, each representing the narrow view of the academician, the modernist or the avant-gardist, or of journalism, no matter how responsible or good willed, that is bound by obligations other than to the theatre. Under these conditions, criticism has become idiosyncratic and misleading. In addition, the blessings of social equality, having made natural the extension of its prerogatives into the arts, have resulted in the confusion of the amateur with the professional and have fostered the I-don't-know-what-it-means-but-I-know-what-I-like standard of the populist. This attitude makes for a serious problem because, being uninformed—and tickets being relatively costly—it leads readily to alienation from the theatre. A physician would not presume to try a case before the Supreme Court any more than an attorney would have the temerity to wield a scalpel in the operating room, though he might sit respectfully or even marvel at a performance in a theatre of surgery. The doctor and the lawyer feel themselves unqualified to adjudge each other yet neither is inhibited in his appraisal of the theatre. These professions are not singled out here; they are used simply to illustrate that the appreciation of a discipline is made more accurate, even heightened, by special knowledge.

Thus, the purpose of *Theatre* is to enlighten and stimulate the playgoer and the player with an annual forum. There is a need to encourage criticism freely expressed less in the sense of opinion and more as a synthesis of the past and present. It is necessary to supply information with which to test popular or singular concepts in the hope of pollinating thought rather than sterilizing it with dogma. Theatre standards require periodic judgment to be rendered without sentence being pronounced. When scholarship is summoned, it must refrain from pedantry. It, too, must learn to deal with the realities of the theatre without resorting to preciosity or retreating into attitudes of rectitude. In short, *Theatre* will attempt to explore the collective experience that unites the playgoer with the creative process backstage and in performance for their mutual enrichment and understanding.

The publication of *Theatre* is a nonprofit enterprise of the Repertory Theater of Lincoln Center. I wish to make grateful acknowledgement to all the writers herein whose cooperation has made this volume possible.

B. H.

January, 1965

Contents

Preface

by Alan Pryce-Jones

IT MAY SEEM odd that I have been chosen to write a preface for this book. To begin with, I am a foreigner who only arrived as a permanent resident of the United States at the age of fifty. I have thus no pretension to that knowledge of the American theatre and its problems which can only come from a lifetime of work within it. Then, my work in the theatre has mainly been as a critic, and critics, as we know, are an irritating tribe of perfectionists and fault-finders who can seldom be trusted with practical decisions in a sphere notoriously temperamental.

However, I was a director of the Old Vic Trust for a number of years in which the possible foundation of a National Theatre in Great Britain was busily being discussed. The arguments for and against repertory were part of my weekly diet for a decade; likewise the difficulties which arise, once the value of repertory is accepted, in seeing what to do next when a large company has been assembled under a permanent director.

Then again, I was brought to the United States by the Ford Foundation as someone supposedly familiar with the condition of the arts today. I was not invited as a theatre man only but as one who had spent his grown-up life both as an observer and a participant in the revolution which has affected each of the arts in Europe (and latterly in the United States as well) over the last half century: the revolution of consciousness which has enlarged the frontiers of language in painting, music, drama, fiction, poetry, and architecture.

I can at any rate claim objectivity. Having spent the last five years exploring, among other enticements, what has been happening in the theatre with a view to recommending financial help, or later—once my work with the Ford Foundation was through—to enlarging my own education, I can at least confirm the verdicts reached by Harold Clurman and Kenneth Tynan about the unique value of the repertory system if serious theatre is to continue at all. And I can apply to what is a relatively new factor in American theatre some of the lessons which Europe has taught me.

What chiefly concerns me here is the problem of establishing a repertory of suitable plays. The great theatres of the world—the Comédie Française, the Berliner Ensemble, the Moscow Art Theatre, and the rest—have each a separate personality and it must, therefore, be taken for granted that any American theatre of a comparable kind has to find a style and a function appropriate to itself alone.

So far in the United States, repertory has been in the hands of a few dedicated individuals such as Nina Vance of the Alley Theater, Houston, and Zelda Fichandler of the Arena Stage, Washington. Sir Tyrone Guthrie in Minneapolis and Elia Kazan and Robert Whitehead in the Repertory Theater of Lincoln Center subscribed to the same tradition within which each had a different set of problems to face. Lack of funds in one city, apathy in another, an *embarras de richesse* in New York itself are only a few of the obstacles to be overcome in a theatre community where most of the limelight is fixed steadily on a single city.

No obstacle is greater than the choice of suitable plays. There is no American Kleist or Büchner, no American Chekhov or Ibsen, no American Congreve or Racine. Nor is there any reason for establishing an American tradition for the production of foreign masterpieces unless they fall, like Shakespeare or Aeschylus, into that category of the universal which transcends all frontiers.

Good plays, and great ones more emphatically, are likely to engender other good or great plays by the force of example. There is every reason, therefore, for keeping as many as possible in the repertory. It would be absurd to ban Pirandello or Shaw from Lincoln Center simply because they are outsiders to an American tradition. At the same time, the creation of such a tradition is essential if Lincoln Center and the other repertory groups throughout the country are to justify themselves.

[x]

One way to do this is to cajole as many writers as possible to try their hands at playwriting. Generous attempts have been made to make the theatre attractive to poets and novelists. A Henry James of today, far from eating out his heart at the difficulty of gaining recognition in the theatre, would have been given a substantial check to act as observer, another to underwrite the cost of production should he actually compose an actable piece, free lodging in the mountains during the period of gestation, and a professorship when it failed.

It does not look, however, as though this were the way to get good new plays. The serious theatre is a kind of madness. Those who venture into it, successfully or no, are seldom the people who have to be encouraged by checks: it is more often restraint they need than a prod.

If encouragement has to be applied, it must, I think, be in the direction of bestowing on new writers a sense of mission. They must feel that the act of writing a play is in itself important. Like Sartre, they must feel that they are addressing themselves to other people for the good of the other people. Otherwise they might just as well take a gambler's risk on Broadway or Shaftesbury Avenue or the Paris boulevards and aim at cooking up a diversion for the hell of it—plus the money.

But, you may say, this is by no means the kind of play toward which writers are drawn nowadays. If there is one constant theme which recurs with boring solemnity in all critical writing about theatre it is "lack of communication." We are supposed, all of us, to talk incessantly but within a solitude of our own, addressing ourselves to no one in particular, solipsists one and all.

Yet it is only about ten years since the "well-made play" (another boring concept now I come to think of it) fell into final disrepute. Until then, there had survived enduring examples of the kind of theatre in which Somerset Maugham, Noel Coward, Lillian Hellman, S. N. Behrman, and other proficient craftsmen—perhaps Terence Rattigan is the youngest—had made their name.

This was the theatre of elegant comedy. It was played behind a proscenium arch and usually conceived in a three-act form. It employed the paraphernalia of upper-middle-class life, such as a white telephone in constant use, a cocktail tray, and a confidential manservant. In these plays the weather was always good so as to make maximum use of French windows leading to a wisteria-hung terrace. The summit of the drama was often reached in evening clothes or a dressing gown (which sounded more sophisticated than wrapper). Nobody on stage re-sembled anybody in life, just as none of the rooms in smart decorators' magazines resemble anything seen in a real house.

Yet the best of these plays—and I have deliberately exaggerated tics which only apply to the common run—had a legitimate theatrical message to convey. Maugham's *The Circle*, Coward's *Hay Fever*, Behr-man's *The Second Man*, Rattigan's *The Deep Blue Sea* convey an honor-able degree of theatrical experience. It is a rounded experience, ad-mittedly, and a psychological purist might object that life is no rounded matter. On the other hand, *The Importance of Being Earnest* and *Le Misanthrope* are carefully rounded too. It does not seem wise to dismiss plays simply because they are ingeniously equipped with a beginning, a middle, and an end.

About the time of John Osborne's *Look Back in Anger*, a convulsive change took place. Plays were adapted to one or no interval. The French windows were replaced by the kitchen sink. Four-letter words crept into the dialogue, which was often designed to show that even if com-munication were impossible the belch and the roar of protest still carried on some degree of bridge-building activity between people. Harold Pinter was the hero of the hour; and when a play of the older layout, such as Enid Bagnold's *The Chinese Prime Minister*, reached the stage in London or New York, it administered a sense of shock. How strange, people said, to hear such literate speech. How extraordinary to witness an action which proceeded by logical steps from start to finish.

Outside these activities, of course, the enduring theatre has gone its own way. Audiences have begun to feel slightly dissatisfied with, say, Tennessee Williams, if only on the implicit ground that a screw which can be turned no tighter has, in a sense, fulfilled its function. Chekhov's shares have constantly been rising in the intellectual market, but I do not remember that Ibsen has lately been blamed for asserting the ancient virtues of good construction, poetic vision, and truth to life.

It is just that a kind of moral wall has come to divide plays of ac-cepted merit from plays aiming at a contemporary statement. Wilde is accepted because he was writing over sixty years ago; O'Neill because he is the obvious giant among American playwrights, and dead into the bargain. But a contemporary is expected to write in the manner of *The Caretaker* or *Endgame*; to flesh his propaganda with dogged realism, like Arnold Wesker in *Roots*, or to confect an apocalyptic scheme, as John Arden did in *Sergeant Musgrave's Dance*, in order to balance the crackling scattiness of such playwrights as N. F. Simpson or Jack Gelber. There can—there just can—be a positive content to comedy. But it must never be explicit, the modern rule goes, for fear of being dismissed as middlebrow.

I am describing the period of the "Theatre of the Absurd." It presupposes an ultimate lack of design in personal or social life. We must not expect a Beckett or an Adamov or a Pinter to air problems after the example of O'Neill or Shaw, let alone solve them like Sartre by an application of doctrine. Better to take Alfred Jarry for master and turn out latter-day versions of *Ubu Roi*.

Now there is nothing wrong in this. The Theatre of the Absurd has had an excellent purgative effect on stagecraft as well as turning out some memorable experiences. I was an early and have remained a constant admirer of Pinter and I have derived most grateful pleasure from borderline plays in which the Absurd is set out as a comment on real life, such as Albee's *The American Dream* or Ann Jellicoe's *The Sport of My Mad Mother*.

Unluckily, though, the Absurd is not capable of unlimited extension. Its use of satire or irony is soon exhausted since these arts require a fixed basis of some kind if they are to do more than expend random whiffs of grapeshot against the world, and a fixed basis is just what is forbidden to the Absurd. Then again, the Absurd is invariable. It cannot be anything but Absurd. The playwright of the Absurd is like a mathematician constructing simultaneous equations. He can alter the digits but not the procedure, and into the bargain he has to do without the equal sign since the Absurd can never employ the formula $a + b = c$, its whole point being to add a to b without ever concluding the sum.

Playwrights are perfectly aware of this impasse. It is significant that the more alert of them are already turning to other techniques. The Ann Jellicoe of *The Knack* is quite unlike her earlier self. The realists with some sense of social purpose, like Arnold Wesker, are getting more and more involved in that purpose—witness *Chips With Everything*—and the philosophy of despair in Beckett's most recent works is far more explicit than in *Waiting For Godot*.

Presumably, then, the Absurd is for the moment played out. It did a fine thing in cleansing the palate, as it were. The comedy of mechanical formula has been driven off the stage—we need only remember the astonished exasperation which greeted Rattigan's last play, *Man and Boy*—along with the brand of commuters' fantasy which delighted matinee audiences for more than half a century.

But what comes now? The function of a repertory theatre is quite different from that of Broadway or off-Broadway. To the former it can safely leave pure entertainment in the form of the musicals and farces which are now Broadway's staple fare. To the latter, it can leave the early stages of experiment, the uncharted areas of the offbeat and the kind of intellectual whisper which becomes inaudible in any but a minute theatre.

Outside New York, repertory theatres have a certain duty to local talent. If a California or a Texas writer has an acceptable play on the stocks, he can legitimately expect the most intelligent theatre in his state to uphold him by presenting it. For Lincoln Center the problem is different and harder. It is inevitably going to be a showcase for "the American theatre." It is going to take its place, whether it will or no, in an international contest of talent. And whatever it does it will be criticized with the bitterness which is felt toward a relation who is both a late-comer into the family and, on the surface, a favorite of fortune.

Unluckily, a great play is, in the nature of things, a rarity. Like all great works of art, it obeys no law but its own: it cannot be planned for. All the same, acceptable drama needs the reconciliation of several elements: a sense of period (the poetic plays of T. S. Eliot, for instance, could never have been conceived in the poetic theatre which attracted Tennyson or Swinburne); the power to demand attention; the urge to speak out; some kind of coherent technique, however surrealist. For a good play to succeed—a great play is another matter—the tide has to be running the right way and taken the right way by the dramatist. It would not surprise me if the shock value of *Look Back in Anger* were repeated by another young playwright but with a difference. *Look Back in Anger* succeeded mainly because Osborne has a beautiful sense of language. His characters had some important things to say but nothing important to do. They expressed themselves with the freshness of ozone on a sultry day; they breathed life onto a dead stage. Suppose, now, someone came along with an equal power of language allied to a burning cause? May it not be that the theatre of the near future, having looked back to Chekhov as its ancestor in the last decade, will turn to the other great progenitor of modern drama and remember Ibsen, the Old Crusader, so that we switch from the Theatre of the Absurd to the Theatre of the Absolute?

Such plays, if they come into being, cannot be the sole concern of Lincoln Center. They have to be seen in relation to the past. I am not sure, even, that it is an important part of a balanced program in a theatre such as this to keep closely in touch with what is new. To set a standard, proved material is wanted and the merely fashionable need play no part. Kenneth Tynan, writing of the British National Theatre in this volume, says, "Success at the box office is no longer the only criterion. We would rather have a first-rate work playing to less than capacity than a third-rate one filling the house."

A major repertory company has, then, to concentrate on the first-rate, but this need not prevent it keeping one eye on the future. If there is no way of coaxing good new plays into existence by direct encouragement, the past can at least be raided for the best already there. When I said earlier that an American theatre comparable to the great permanent institutions of Europe has to find a style and a function of its own, I was not asking that every new production be stretched on some Procrustean bed labeled "American."

The Berliner Ensemble concentrates on Brecht, a writer whose work has a curious tendency to evaporate once it is translated out of German. The Comédie Française operates like a Breguet watch: a flawless, expensive, dead accurate mechanism which can be applied to any fraction of the theatrical calendar be it only French, from Corneille to Sardou and Henri Bernstein. The Royal Shakespeare Company lives up to its name. It would seem right, I think, that American repertory prefer to such chosen limitations a careful eclecticism. New York, after all, is the melting pot of the world and a New York theatre with a permanent company ought to reflect that fact by building up, without haste and without too much regard for immediate popularity, a conspectus of the first-rate in different modes of drama.

It has to be remembered that very few members of the ordinary public anywhere have any notion of what the theatre has to offer them. Again to quote Tynan, he remarks that "out of more than two dozen plays running in the West End, only three had been written before 1950." This refers to the London of a year or two back. In the winter of 1964 in New York there is not even one such production on Broadway, but off-Broadway there is a play apiece to be seen by Euripides, Marlowe, and Shakespeare, as well as *The Changeling* at Lincoln Center. There is nothing, however, anywhere to bridge a gap of over three hundred years between 1623 and the present moment.

The melancholy in this is not only that it deprives the theatre-going public of immense resources of pleasure, but that it emasculates the theatre itself. When we hear that the public is being wooed away from living theatre first by the movies and now by television, this only means that the theatre is not offering the public what it wants. When, from time to time, a modern play turns up on a serious theme—*Andorra, The Deputy, The Physicists*—the public is uncertain how to react and the playwright himself is conscious of having lost the sense of expectation on which Shaw, say, could still count forty years ago. Only in a repertory theatre skillfully conducted can that sense be recaptured. Only a repertory theatre, by lifting the emphasis away from the box office, can make it possible for playwrights to give back to the drama that numinous quality which first brought it into being at all. The influence on Brecht of having his own company plus a high degree of freedom from financial anxiety is to the point. We do not wish to use the drama for the propagation of tracts, naturally, but we also must wish it to recapture its contacts with real life instead of exploring endlessly artificial worlds of farce, spectacle, and the Absurd.

THEATRE

Molière

"Tartuffe"

by Henri Peyre

Iᴛ ɪs an idle question to ask which of Molière's comedies or of Shakespeare's tragedies is the greatest. We can decide with a fair degree of certainty which is the more enigmatic: *Dom Juan* or *Hamlet*. The best built and in a sense the most classically structured among the chief tragedies would be *Othello*; among the serious comedies, *Le Misanthrope*. We may venture to submit that as *King Lear* appears most tantalizingly to fascinate the audiences and the readers of the nineteen sixties looking for a mirror to their nihilistic anguish or to the sneer of "absurdists," *Tartuffe* holds the strongest appeal to the moderns who like to denounce sham. It has a broader universality than *The School for Women*; it plumbs tragic depths which *The Would-Be Gentleman* and even *The Miser* merely skirt. In that superb comedy over which Molière worked longer than any of his productions, circumstances having forced him to withdraw the first version of *Tartuffe* for nearly five years, unaided by any Latin or Italian predecessors as he had been in *The Miser*, or by borrowing the theme of *Dom Juan* from an Italian distortion of Tirso de Molina's play, the Frenchman created one of the few universal literary types bequeathed by his countrymen.

Tartuffe has enjoyed an uninterrupted success with French audiences for three centuries, both in the popular theatres and on the official subsidized stages to which habitués and students flock to absorb culture and to scrutinize every gesture and insinuation in the acting of a play they know by heart. Unsophisticated audiences are gripped by the vivid exposition, by the unique portrait of a middle-class family in the age of Louis XIV, by the dramatic suspense contrived by masterly Elmire, cool and self-possessed like a French bourgeoise in her salon or at the counter of her shop, and by the naïve relief of applauding the archcheater tricked in the end. The play has been performed recently in the original, in London and in New York. Exactly three hundred years after the first performance of *Tartuffe* at Versailles in May, 1664, it was fitting that this masterpiece of world comedy be staged again at the most classical and most adventurous theatre in New York.

The English, and the Americans after them, have never evinced the same resistance to Molière as they had, until our own age, to Corneille and Racine. His prestige was immense with the Restoration comic writers and with the eighteenth century, which launched the Shakespeare idolatry. Partial as Coleridge and Hazlitt could be to *All's Well That Ends Well*, *Much Ado About Nothing*, even to the less airy and more coarsely farcical *Merry Wives of Windsor*, they never claimed for Shakespeare the same sovereignty over comic writers of the French nation as they did for the tragedies in which the idolized genius never "abides our question." Few men have praised Molière's urbane, rational, serious comedy as Meredith in his thoughtful *Essay on Comedy* or, as recently as 1959, D. B. Wyndham Lewis in *Molière: the Comic Mask*. The most concise and most pregnant small volume on Molière is by an Oxford don, William G. Moore, and until Jacques Guicharnaud's exhaustive and literally definitive analysis of *Tartuffe*, the best monograph on that play was in English by an American, Hugh Gaston Hall (London, 1960). Performances of the great comedies of Molière written in verse, especially *Le Misanthrope* and *Tartuffe*, demand a dynamic and at the same time delicately imaginative rendering. They also require a translation which conveys the masterly structure of the play, omits nothing, alters the original as little as possible, and is both actable and poetical in the sense that Molière's conception of his characters is more poetical than it is realistic or impeccably geometric.

The American stage today is fortunate in having one of its finest and most original poets who proves pliable and modest enough (Goethe was in the past, and Pasternak) to be a faithful translator: Richard Wilbur. Others have deemed it advisable to treat the original with the liberties of a lover or of an unrepressed creator, impelled to transfigure Anouilh (Christopher Fry) or Racine's *Phèdre* (Robert Lowell) so as to adapt the foreign drama to the local public or to their own style and

[4]

mannerisms. It may not be a source of too great embarrassment to deal thus with works unfamiliar to critics and to cultivated readers and so exotic as not to bear transplantation without being grafted on our own native trees; as Chinese, Arabic, and even Russian or Scandinavian plays. But a number of persons in any audience have been, as we euphemistically put it, exposed to French in their youth. They are liable to reopen their Molière and to confront the translation with the original. Fidelity to the text is the first duty of the honest and expert translator, presupposing an intimate reflection on the meaning of each line. Wilbur's new translation of *Tartuffe*, published in 1961 by Harcourt, Brace & World, is remarkable for its faultless understanding of the language of the play, of the connotations and ambiguities of many a line, and for its re-creation in English of the tone of the original.

It is also a poetical translation in verse. One may condone a rendering into prose of very delicate and evocative poetry, be it Heine, Baudelaire, Valéry, or Rilke. The translator in such cases abandons any pretence of conveying poetry, which is music wedded to sense, into another medium. He can only play the part of a modest adjuvant to the reader who will master the meaning of the text, assisted by the prosaic version, while trying to respond to the metaphorical and musical spell of the original. Molière, however, wrote no lyrical drama. He worked no enchantment on his readers, as did Racine. His facility and flowing inventiveness were the subject of admiration for his contemporaries. Boileau, in a famous poem, appealed to Molière to impart to him his secret for rhyming with unimpeded ease. His comedies, for the most part already remote from the pastoral conventions of the Renaissance and from the lyrical exuberance of the sixteenth century, did not allow for any interruption of action as do those of Shakespeare, with their rapturous songs. The characters seem unaware of forests and brooks and flowers; the maidens in love are no Perdita or Rosalind, and the wives no Imogen. They do not exhale their joy at being loved in ecstatic lyrics or deplore the ingratitude of lovers nor those wasted kisses, "seals of love but sealed in vain," once offered to sweetly forsworn lips. There is no lullaby, no "sing willow, willow, willow" refrain, no romantic description in the French classical theatre of an Ophelia drowning. The poetry is more subdued, more rational, and blended with the speeches of the characters as in Tartuffe's declarations in a style both mystical and *précieux*. It can be conveyed through the veil of another language. It is here, with admirable restraint on the part of the translator.

In his endeavor not to allow that classical language ever to become overeloquent or wordy, Richard Wilbur has, if anything, toned down the original. His rhymed pentameter clings as closely as possible to the rhymed couplets of Alexandrines of Molière. No other line could have been substituted for it. But occasionally the English lines fall a little flat and lose the density and the balanced plenitude of the original.

> I bide your judgment and, as you think best,
> I shall be either miserable or blest.

These lines in Tartuffe's declaration to Orgon's wife, the polite but firm dilemma in which the hypocrite, sincere in his desire, tries to ensnare the married lady, lack the gallant, "precious" resonance of the word *seul*, emphasized by its position in lines 959–60 of the original:

> *Et je vais être enfin, par votre seul arrêt,*
> *Heureux, si vous voulez, malheureux, s'il vous plaît.*

With two untranslatable French words, *les gens* and *on*, the enveloping lines 996–97

> *Mais les gens comme vous brûlent d'un feu discret*
> *Avec eux, pour toujours, on est sûr du secret.*

were equally impossible to render in their sly suggestiveness, the half-repressed, lecherous grin on the face of the "false devout" promising a discreet adultery. Richard Wilbur's words

> Men of my sort, however, love discreetly,
> And one may trust our reticence completely.

omit perforce the verb *brûler* and the rich substantive *secret* and fall short of the original. Like many translators and like most Frenchmen expressing themselves in English, forced to render *on* (with its vagueness, its allusion to the social group, its suggestion of the universal) and finding "one" alien to the English tongue, Richard Wilbur had to resort

[6]

to "I" or "me," sharper, too direct, deprived of the magnifying force of the French nasal sound. Some of the vivacious definitiveness of Molière's language had to be sacrificed in the more brusque and concise comic passages, such as the masterly portraits sketched by rancorous Madame Pernelle in the opening scenes of the play, or in Dorine's robust, earthy remarks on the gluttony of *le pauvre homme*, unavoidably weakened as "poor fellow."

Vous êtes un sot en trois lettres, mon fils,

coined like a medal and soon to become proverbial in French, loses some of its flavor when flattened into

You, boy, grow more foolish every day.

Nevertheless, the dramatic motion of the original is preserved throughout. This accurate and intelligent translation is also adapted to the stage. The worst pitfall in any rendering of a French seventeenth-century text, into which Robert Lowell jumped joyfully when he offered his adaptation of *Phèdre*, is here eschewed; there is never any suspicion of vulgarity, and the tone as well as the tempo of Molière's text is preserved.

The French classical century has often been exalted in English to the position of the supreme age of reason for the Western world. Reasonableness is, to be sure, proposed as an ideal by the reasoner in many a comedy: here Orgon's brother, Cléante, assumes the role corresponding on a more static and prosaic plane to that of the Greek chorus, or even to the "parabasis" in Aristophanes' comedies where the author intervened in an impatient outburst to denounce the ridiculed evil. A certain social order in which the state and the absolute monarchy are never questioned, with common sense prevailing in the families and assuring each member of his independence, appears to be what Molière advocates or takes for granted as the one legitimate order. Infringements upon that natural pursuit of reasonable happiness by upstarts, swindlers, unscrupulous nobles, selfish and tyrannical fathers, and pretentious and pedantic mothers are the butt of his satire. But it would be a gross mistake to imagine that the order advocated by Molière mirrored that of a hierarchical, rigidly organized France in which, as Pope hinted with a little irony,

> The rules a nation born to serve obeys.

Molière and his "classical" contemporaries aspired to that orderly wisdom because it had long been conspicuously absent from their private lives and from their country. Soon after Pascal's death in 1662 and while Corneille was still composing his late masterpieces, the decade from 1660 to 1669, during which Bossuet, La Rochefoucauld, La Fontaine, Boileau, and Racine were going to set French literature as the model for Europe, was not an age of staid ceremony and of frigid conventionality. Still remote were Versailles, the Sun King's folly of grandeur, and his belated piety when, surrounded by his legitimate and illegitimate progeny, he was to share the remorse through which Mme de Maintenon curbed his mettle. Louis XIV was then closer to the *libertins* and could laugh at Molière's indictment of false piety. The civil feuds of the two Frondes were not far off and Orgon had proved loyal to the throne during those months of crisis. The unruliness of the Three Musketeers, the conspiracies of many great ladies tempted by warlike adventures, the passion for dueling, and the ghastly cruelty of the Thirty Years' War lingered in the memories of those who, like Molière, La Fontaine and Pascal, reached the age of forty as the young king assumed the full control of the state. The issue of the century's conflict between classicism and the baroque, between reason and unreason, anarchy and absolutism still hung in the balance. Unlike the Spaniards and the Italians, the French enjoyed the advantage of a growingly self-assertive middle class. Ceasing to strain for saintliness or to scale a heaven peopled with angels and ecstatic madonnas dear to the baroque compatriots of El Greco and Bernini, the French writers of 1660 desired in their works a certain degree of psychological realism and of truth to nature. After Molière's early success heralded the spirit of the new literary age, La Fontaine voiced the creed of his generation:

> *Et maintenant il ne faut pas*
> *Quitter la nature d'un pas.*

Molière, born in Paris in 1622, had returned to the capital in the

[8]

late 1650s from his long wanderings in the provinces. Still availing himself of the mold provided by the animated, gesticulating farce of the Italians and their expressive masks (he himself acted the part of the servant Mascarille, grimacing with his "little mask" and pretending to be a noble), in 1659 Molière struck success with the robust middle class and the shopkeepers and artisans who applauded him resoundingly. The play, *Les Précieuses Ridicules*, transformed the traditional, boisterous farce into a comedy of manners. It was a frontal attack against pretentiousness, snobbery, the artificiality of the "literary exquisites" of the time. It indicted falsely ludicrous metaphors and farfetched circumlocutions. An earthy man whose private life had been the disorderly one of many a comedian in those days, incessantly harassed by his treble career of author, actor, and director (to which would soon be added the worries of a diplomatic courtier negotiating to keep his theatre open), Molière would not put up with the elaborate courtship made fashionable by the *précieuses*. He resented the attempts of those fastidious ladies to refine men through raising artificial hurdles between desire and fulfillment. He was probably a sensuous man by temperament, dimly aware of the threat of consumption hovering over him and eager to love and live impetuously. His first crashing triumph with the Parisians had been an onslaught on hypocrisy in language, manners, and sex.

At the age of forty, having just married a much younger woman, Armande, whose sister had been perilously close to him, apprehensive of her infidelity (and justified in that fear), Molière had objectively mocked his own plight in his second brilliant victory, *The School for Women*. The selfish husband, in dread of being jilted, molding a naïve virgin to his own uses, teaching her innocence and ignorance, proclaiming to her the commandments of obedience to her lord and master, was both despicable in his egotism and pitiable in his helpless passion. But Molière aroused the ire of the devouts in town and at the court. They denounced his parody of the Ten Commandments, fearing like many males in Latin countries the mockery of religiosity in women, regarded as the strongest rampart against extramarital temptation. From then on, he became suspect to the clerical party.

That party was powerful, well organized, and made up of men of

[9]

sincere good will with a sprinkling of fanatics and deceivers with less good faith in them than religious conviction. The French classical age was a devout one with vast numbers of mystics to whom Abbé Bremond has devoted several volumes of his great history of religious feeling in that era; many of them were champions of the Counter Reformation or of diverse reforms inside Catholicism; all advocated strictness of dogma and austerity of behavior as a counteroffensive to the skeptical *libertins*. Religious orders such as the Oratorians and the Sulpicians had been founded by the French early in the seventeenth century. Jansenism had aroused hot debates in Paris just before Molière returned there to live. Pascal in his *Provincial Letters* had provided him with the first models of comic dialogue and with a piercing wit which left nothing unscathed in men's involuntary and sanctimonious self-deceptiveness. They had appeared as letters to a supposedly uninformed inhabitant of the provinces in 1656–57 while Molière was traveling in those remote parts with his theatrical company. Polemics raged in those days when doctrinal disputes channeled into those flammable subjects the debating zeal we have since expended on political dissents and sports events.

It was then common for dutiful persons like Orgon to go to church every day and pray or to attend early mass. The Jesuits, founded in Montmartre in 1534, had gained much of their power through confessing kings and influential persons and attempting to direct their policies. When dealing with a sovereign like the young king of France who devised the first performance of *Tartuffe* in 1664 as part of the sumptuous festivities for his mistress, Mlle de La Vallière, confessors had to accommodate human, and superhuman, frailties and to indulge in casuistry: a prudent weighing of the circumstances surrounding each case was advisable and many a sin had to be labeled "venial," allowing of "graceful" pardon. But with less regal personages, confessors or scrutinizers of behavior were less inhibited.

In 1627, a Congregation, or a Company as it called itself, of the Holy Sacrament had been founded. It consisted of pious men who settled in the homes of the middle class and the aristocrats—as parsons did in the households of English squires in the eighteenth century—to save them from the snares of sin and to teach observance of ecclesiastical precepts. They acted as advisers on the education of children, interpreted the dogma, prohibitions, and rituals of the faith. They also, incidentally, kept a jealous vigil on the virtue of the wife, seeing to it that the husband was duly informed or warned of infringements of the rules of faithful obedience. They succeeded in converting, among others, the Prince of Conti, once Molière's patron, who promptly turned against his former protégé and against all actors. Those lay gentlemen, visiting or dwelling in the homes they presumed to guide, agreed that comedians, a dangerous and immoral breed, would be admitted to communion only as sinners. As the Puritans had done across the Channel in 1642 when they closed the theatres, the Company of the Holy Sacrament centered its main attack on the stage.

Molière could not but resent them, their excess of devout zeal, their fanaticism, and the hypocrisy which at times paraded as piety. Some twenty-five years later, La Bruyère sketched a portrait of the "false devout" as a social type which had become current around the court and the city. Modern historians have pointed out that the Abbé Charpy de Sainte-Croix, author of a treatise on mystical life and close to Molière, had been found guilty of forgery, swindling, and adultery with the wife of the man in whose house he had been invited to live. Like Orgon, the husband had to be shaken forcibly from his blind faith in his conscientious director. In 1667, life once more imitating literature, the story of *Tartuffe* was enacted on the very street in the center of Paris on which Molière lived: an Italian actor saw his wife seduced by an Italian priest whom he had received and trusted. While Molière waged a five-year-long battle to have his play publicly performed and the Cabal of the Devout ferociously opposed him and his "infamous" comedy, Molière's friends, mostly to be found among the unbelievers and the admirers of Lucrèce's and Gassendi's Epicureanism, could fathom the extent to which the free expression of views and the rights of literature to treat any subject were imperiled.

Molière first drafted *Tartuffe* in three acts for the King and court on May 12, 1664. The text of that earlier play is no longer extant, and we do not know for certain whether it corresponded to the first three acts of the final play printed in 1669 or to the present Acts I, III, and IV, as John Cairncross vigorously contended in his *New Light on Molière*

(1956) and in a subsequent volume in French (1963). The evidence is contradictory. It seems likely that the original *Tartuffe* was not a truncated play but already complete, perhaps hastily put together for the festivities, *Les Plaisirs de l'Ile Enchantée*, that the monarch was offering to the royal favorite. Certainly the last act, with its intervention by the King whose exemption saves Orgon from the snare in which he has enmeshed himself, was a 1669 addition to thank the King for his long awaited permission to allow the performance of that dreaded comedy. Even before its first performance on May 12, 1664, the members of the Compagnie du Saint-Sacrement had planned in April to work for "the suppression of the wicked comedy of Tartuffe." Soon after its presentation for the King's guests, all further performances were forbidden.

After such a blow, Molière feared his company might be reduced to starvation and that his actors, out of work, might be lured to rival troupes. He read his *Tartuffe* before several distinguished persons, hoping in vain for their intercession. He wrote several pleas, or *placets*, to the King to have the ban lifted. Hastily, he composed his *Dom Juan* (1665) on a theme then in vogue into which he slipped an incidental indictment of religious hypocrites. *Le Misanthrope* followed in June, 1665, and scored only a moderate success; the audience wanted more entertainment. Molière gave a new title to *Tartuffe*; as *Panulphe ou l'Imposteur* it was performed on August 5, 1667, at the Palais-Royal and acclaimed by the public. The court at once forbade further performances. The text of that second version, which may have differed from the first and third, has not come down to us. At last, after a political agreement concluded between the Pope and the French monarchy put an end to a number of differences, on February 5, 1669, Louis XIV intervened directly and allowed the play to be performed and printed.

The Church party was not disarmed. In a richly documented volume, an American scholar, Herman P. Salomon, has traced the history of *Tartuffe devant l'opinion française* (Paris, 1962). He recalled how the archbishop of Paris in 1667 forbade the faithful to attend a performance of *Tartuffe* under pain of excommunication. The interdiction had to be lifted through an agreement between Colbert and

Church authorities before Louis XIV would restore to Molière permission to produce the play. The most popular of the preachers, the eloquent Jesuit Bourdaloue, delivered a sermon "on hypocrisy" in which he indicted "these damnable inventions intended to humiliate worthy people and to render them all suspect" and denounced Molière as the satirizer of all devouts, false and true. Bossuet, who delivered lessons to kings and princes, thundered, "Woe unto you that laugh now, for you shall weep!" Later on, he wrote a whole volume of reprobation of all theatre as dangerous to faith and to morals. At the end of the seventeenth century, in Quebec, Bishop Saint-Vallier prohibited the faithful from attending a performance of *Tartuffe* planned by Governor Frontenac. He even gave a hundred pistols to the Governor (who apparently distributed them to the poor) to persuade him to desist from such an unholy project. The performance was called off. Napoleon I, who liked the play and offered it repeatedly to the court, confessed on St. Helena his astonishment that Louis XIV had ever tolerated it. "If the play had been composed in my time," he added, "I would not have allowed it to be performed." A liberal Catholic novelist and dramatist, François Mauriac (whom his enemies have charged with *tartuferie*) thought fit in a small volume entitled *Three Great Men Before God* (1930) to vituperate Molière and the desolate gloom of his life, which he ascribed to God's absence from his universe. He had a kind word for Orgon, "a passionate Christian" ridiculed for being thus and because he distrusts nature and instinct. But nature is radically corrupt. Molière, who advocated following nature, was thereby, hinted the Academician, led to marry Armande and to much grief.

No other comedy of Molière, not even the baffling *Dom Juan* or the equally tragic *The Imaginary Invalid* which ended the playwright's career, has aroused such controversies. None has remained so popular with audiences and so widely praised by critics. *Tartuffe* is not an anticlerical pamphlet or a didactic play. It is primarily a serious and intense work in which Molière defends his view of life and upholds the right of the theatre to dramatize any subject and to disturb the prejudices or the convictions of the very audience that applauds him. It is a passionate play, concerned with a vital theme: the freedom of our consciences and the gains accruing to our sanity from a critical spirit and the power

[13]

to disbelieve. It is also an admirable work of art, structured with rare skill yet never mechanically contrived, which age has in no way withered.

In the context of a culture in which religion still encompassed the whole of daily life and with ethics and practical morality closely bound up with the prevalent Christian faith, the presentation of a pious hypocrite on a public stage represented such a bold undertaking that Molière had to take infinite care to alert his audience against any ambiguity. If the public could have entertained the slightest doubt as to who was the villain or as to the purity and earnestness of some of the motives prompting the falsely devout character, the result would have been catastrophic. The peculiar optics of the stage, where the light must needs be more glaring than in actual life and the obscurity of a poem or the suspense of a novel would be out of place, required that *Tartuffe* be displayed with some disregard of nuance. The moralist La Bruyère, in a portrait of a hypocrite, Onuphre, offered some twenty years later in his *Caractères*, took Molière to task for the exaggerated or misplaced concreteness of many details of *Tartuffe*. Hypocrisy had apparently re-fined its wiles by 1691 when La Bruyère wrote. The King was then over fifty and had begun thinking of the salvation of his soul; the courtiers naturally worshiped as the King did and discovered that they might also well buy a few guarantees in the next world. Onuphre, La Bruyère hinted, when making his entry, would not crudely shout of "his hair shirt and his scourge" and announce that he was off to the prison to distribute alms to the wretched. He would insinuate it more insidiously. And he would refrain from coveting the wife of the very man whose parasite he hoped to remain.

La Bruyère lacked a flair for the dramatic, and his subtle, restrained portrait has none of the tension and blinding clarity of Molière's dangerous villain. The requirements of the theatrical optics imposed upon Molière the forsaking of refined shades of characterization. His conception of a comedy which had to border on tragedy at every minute without ever becoming too tragic was indeed masterly. Spec-tators were meant to laugh at the demoralized family set at loggerheads by the intrusion of the hypocrite. They had first to be treated to a realistic description of Tartuffe eating "a leg of mutton and a brace of pheasants." The monstrous selfishness of the self-styled man of God had to be displayed in the ravage it wrought upon the stability and mental peace of a family. The name of Tartuffe, the very sound of which suggests the feline creeping upon an innocent prey, was alluring bait for the playgoer.

The opening scene has been praised by Goethe and by numberless critics. It is an animated "interior" depiction of a middle-class family such as has seldom been presented in classical literature. Sketched by Madame Pernelle's vigorous waspish tongue, it is also a gallery of portraits. The language, popular, vivacious, interspersed with folk sayings in the manner of an old woman from the country, fully conveys the tension which has been mounting in the assembled characters. The two chief ones, Tartuffe and his dupe, Orgon, are absent but vividly conjured up by those present. Mme Pernelle leaves the stage to return only at the end of the play. To berate every member of the family, she takes advantage of her venerable years, of the discreet reserve of her daughter-in-law, presumably much younger than Orgon whose second wife she is, and of her son's weakness. She upholds her son's smug admiration of the holy man Tartuffe, reproves in succession Damis, her grandson, Elmire's brother, Cléante, and chiefly the saucy maid, Dorine, whose blunt repartees point to the lechery half-hidden under Tartuffe's pious mask. The stormy leave-taking of the elderly lady has not only informed the audience of what it should know of the events preceding the raising of the curtain; it has built up an amused yet anxious tension. *Que d'eux je me délivre!* (Let me be freed from them!) The second half of the opening line of the play in the original immediately establishes the cleavage between "them": Tartuffe's foes, whose clear-sightedness has not been dimmed by the kneeling and praying and sanctimonious language of the hypocrite, and his two partisans, mother and son. At the same time, the intuitive playgoer, observing the actors' attitudes and intonations, may divine that Orgon, the son of such an imperious mother, still absent from the stage, has been stultified by her tyranny. Jealous of his second wife, she casts a few aspersions on her elegance, perhaps even on her virtue, aware that Orgon, lacking will and mind of his own, needs to cling to someone else as he used to cling to his mother in order to cover up his own vacuity.

The rest of the first act remains fully up to the admirable level of lively portraiture of characters tossed into the midst of a crisis set by the scene of exposition. Nowhere in his theatre has Molière blended entertainment and gravity more felicitously. After Mme Pernelle departs, promising to stay away from that unruly family for good, Dorine occupies the center of the stage. It is now her turn to describe Orgon and his almost amorous infatuation with the man of piety. We are now enlightened further on the plotting which Tartuffe has been concealing under his black, semiclerical garb and his invocations to heaven. He has persuaded his victim, Orgon, to oppose the marriage of his daughter, Mariane, to Valère. Soon it will be revealed that fearful for his own salvation, anxious to establish Tartuffe at the center of his family as the savior and guide of his soul, Orgon is determined to force his daughter to accept him as her husband.

After the maid's hilarious description of Tartuffe's earthy appetite to Orgon, who has just returned from an absence and cares only for news of him, Cléante attempts to reason with his infatuated brother-in-law. Where Dorine had proceeded with the blunt and robust vigor of a girl from the people, Cléante engages in a patient discourse in which he enlightens the audience but fails to disabuse Orgon. He addresses himself to the spectator in the name of Molière and in the name of the intelligent middle class of the second half of the seventeenth century, which was weary of religious feuds and of the mystical *élans* of the baroque and was attempting to secularize the faith.

The higher debate at the core of this play, and of the other great comedies, *Dom Juan* and *The Misanthrope*, composed at the same time by Molière, revolves around reality and illusion, truth and pretence, sincerity and deception. The counterfeiters who ape genuine devoutness and perhaps dupe themselves as well as their gullible victims are unequivocally denounced. The speeches of Cléante voice Molière's creed of moderation in religious convictions and common sense at the service of truth. The tone is didactic; comedy and much of the literature of the past and today have always been and continue to be didactic. Even art for art's sake was so, its enthusiasts proclaiming the banishment of moral predication from art and the reduction of the good to the beautiful. Closer to us, surrealists and existentialists alike have advocated commitment as their goal and revered *la morale* as their idol: that feminine word has received the worshipful tributes of André Breton. A passionate conviction lay behind the comedy of Aristophanes, behind that of Molière, of G. B. Shaw, and of Anouilh and Ionesco. Such a conviction tends to propagate itself to the reader and to the spectator. If the comic author exercises skill and restraint, the artistic quality of his work is not injured thereby. It may even be enhanced. In Molière, the will to convince never becomes obtrusive; it invites the audience to perceive the gravity of the theme tempered by humor and to be gripped by the suspense of the plot and its implications.

Behind the familiar issue of Latin and Italian comedy (Will the normal and mutual love of two young people be thwarted by the tyranny of a father?) to be debated in Act II, the graver problem put to the public is that of a father's right to impose his whim upon his family, and the even more momentous question of ascetic versus humane religious practice. The quarrels raging in France only a few years earlier, pitting the rigid Jansenist against the less rigorous morality of the Jesuits, were uppermost in the minds of many when *Tartuffe* was composed and staged. The Jansenists, to be sure, were no hypocrites or willful deceivers. They aimed at guiding the conscience of the faithful; their severe Augustinism deprived man of freedom in order to detract nothing from God's almightiness, spurning all compromise with human frailty and the modern world. The Jesuits and a few casuists among them whom Pascal flayed with his acid satire offered concessions to sinners and forsook the concept of an eternally irate and vengeful God. They compromised liberally with a world then beginning to accept tolerance, the diversity of faiths and moralities, and a relativistic point of view. Molière may not have consciously directed his indictment of fanaticism and hypocrisy at either of the two factions which then, and for many decades after, rent French Catholicism. Audiences, after years of prohibition and of controversy, flocking to *Tartuffe* in 1669 as they never flocked to any other comedy, did not have to seek far to find illustrations of Molière's comedy around them.

The second act of the play provides a period of relief and of expec-

[17]

tation. Mariane, trained to obey and to fear her father's will, protests weakly when her father imparts to her the result of his reflection: she must marry Tartuffe and forget about Valère, her suitor. Valère upbraids her submissiveness to her father's dicta and starts a lovers' quarrel, a staple commodity of old comedy. Dorine, the servant, through her robust language and impudence toward her master, dares encourage the daughter to revolt against her father's will. After that interlude, the audience, its impatience at a high pitch, is ready for the appearance of the impostor who has reduced a father to such a state of asinine blindness. That entry, in the second scene of Act III, is the most celebrated in the whole range of French comic theatre. It is preceded, in the opening scene of Act III, by a display of impetuousness on the part of Orgon's son, Damis, the one of his two children who judges him as mercilessly as he saw through the foolish stubbornness of his grandmother. Unrestrained and indignant at Tartuffe's lies, Damis shows himself ready to make an *éclat* that would upset the more patient strategy of Dorine, who places her confidence in her mistress Elmire, as one woman might trust another woman's artfulness. The character of Damis is lightly sketched, but in terms of the stage his presence at the beginning of the act is cleverly calculated. He will stay there while Tartuffe makes his sonorous entry; he will be there when the impostor makes his first attempt at seducing Elmire. After Elmire's cool rejection of Tartuffe's amorous advances, he will rush to report them to his father, who will disbelieve him. His role is to prolong the suspense of the audience, to reveal Orgon's perseverance in self-deception to the full, and to make more varied the picture of that animated and distressed family.

As Molière insisted in his letter on the play, no possibility whatever is left to the audience to mistake the criminal trumpery of Tartuffe's devoutness. As soon as he appears, he upbraids Dorine for showing too much of her bosom and suggesting unclean thoughts. She retorts with her familiar verve that his flesh must be weak indeed and detains him meanwhile so that Elmire may have a word with him. Elmire would ask him directly not to impede the marriage of her stepdaughter with Valère, but Tartuffe caressingly seizes her hand, touches her knee, pretends he is feeling the quality of her fine-woven dress. Restraining him, she questions his intention to accept Mariane's hand offered by her own father, and as the hypocrite equivocates, she pretends to be taken in by his unctuous evasiveness. There follow two long declarations of Tartuffe, comparable on a different key to Phèdre's double declaration to her stepson in Racine's tragedy. Compliments on Elmire's face and deportment are turned into mystical praise of God's work which produced such a rare marvel as this woman in whose home he has the bliss to eat and sleep. Tartuffe insinuates that he fought against the ardor aroused in him by so much beauty until he found he could to his own satisfaction reconcile it with his piety.

Egged on by a cool, ironical question from Elmire, who is surprised at the pietist turning to gallantry and with little scruple mixing the spiritual and carnal, Tartuffe lifts his mask. His second speech turns the baroque language of religious mysticism to the concrete expression of his desire. His imagination has been fired. The crescendo of his declaration grips the audience and perhaps leaves Elmire not totally unmoved. The impostor knows how contagious the poetical circumlocutions of an amorous appeal can be. He is intoxicated with his own flowery suavity. At the same time, like a man who must have had previous experience with such affairs, he reassures the married lady about the peril involved. Unlike indiscreet young lovers who cannot love and be loved without telling, he has long mastered the art of avoiding scandal. The pleasure he proposes will be untainted by fear.

Elmire's poise may be slightly embarrassing for the less sophisticated part of the audience. Many a husband would wonder how genuinely fond she can be of hers or how calculating she must be to restrain her anger at such an overt attack upon her wifely fidelity. Unruffled, she does not resort to indignant big words such as "virtue," "duty," "honor," or loving devotion to Orgon. She does not invoke any religious prohibition. Self-mastery and wisdom in this play and throughout Molière's comedies go hand in hand with lay ethics but do not stem from divine assistance. She is not one to go and pray. She returns to her plea that her overeloquent suitor renounce the marriage with Mariane. If he consents, she will not denounce or humiliate him. Clearly, she well knows that to disabuse Orgon's stubborn gullibility she will need more than reports and denunciations of his darling Tartuffe.

From his hiding place Damis has heard the declarations and steps forth to counteract his stepmother's promise of discreet silence. The impostor, dumbfounded at first, recovers his wits and holds his tongue. Orgon, entering, hears his son's report and begs Tartuffe to explain. Like Alceste indicating Célimène's treachery and imploring her to persuade him that she is not guilty, Orgon wants to disbelieve. Tartuffe, aware that the credulity of his dupe is boundless, engages in a gross simulation of Christian humility, pronounces himself base, abject, and falls to his knees. Orgon kneels too, a move which must have incensed the reverent in Molière's audience. From a naïve, almost pitiable gull, he now turns into a heartless father who curses his son and begs maligned Tartuffe to remain in his home, to appear openly and fearlessly "day and night" with Elmire, and to accept a clear deed and title to all his possessions. "In all things, let the will of Heaven be done," the hypocrite exults as Act III ends. But the audience of a comedy may suspect that his fall would soon follow.

The full display of Tartuffe's duplicity required such extreme measures on the part of Elmire that Molière had to prepare his audience for the climax throughout the admirable fourth act. The variety of the scenes in that act, the growing suspense, and the revelation of further complexities in the characters under stress are unmatched in any comedy. The tone and style of the repartees and longer speeches in this family drama indicate an adaptability to subtle characterization of words and the gestures that must accompany them testifying to Molière's elaborate calculation of every effect.

Cléante, apprised of the scandal and the fiery denunciation by Damis of Tartuffe's advances to his stepmother, attempts to reason with the impostor. He appeals to his sense of charity and Christian detachment from worldly goods. Is it becoming to a man of such piety to agree that a son be expelled by the father from his home and that the family be deprived of their property in favor of Tartuffe? The hypocrite's sanctimonious language and his refusal to accede to the reasonable request of the wise man of the household are marvelously in character and ingeniously theatrical. The hour strikes and Tartuffe departs to "attend to some pious duties."

Orgon appears. The opposition of his family to his autocratic stupidity has exasperated him. Like some weak-willed men, he has become obstinate in his foolishness and has developed a sadistic cruelty. He grins nastily before his anguished family, bearing the deed of the house he has donated to Tartuffe and the marriage contract which will give his daughter to the impostor. "This contract, child, contains your happiness," he announces to his heartbroken, imploring daughter. She begs to be allowed to enter a convent rather than marry a man she detests. Orgon, angered and diabolically intent upon his monstrous scheme, retorts that the more she loathes Tartuffe, the greater need she has to mortify her flesh through such a marriage. His will must be done.

After lecturing her husband on the composure with which a woman, confident in her honesty, should rebuff a man like Tartuffe, Elmire's last resort is to take things into her own hands. Patient in the presence of her husband's incredible infatuation, filled with scorn for such stupidity, she treats him like a pigheaded and self-abused child. The scene is famous. Hidden under a table, Orgon listens to a series of skilled and measured approaches made to Tartuffe by his own wife. The transformation from her previous coolness into a polished seductress, a scene worthy of an experienced courtesan, is made credible when the role is played by an actress attentive to every nuance of the text. At first taken aback, Tartuffe sniffs a pitfall; soon, convinced he is irresistible, reassured by Elmire's masterly use of the language of the salons mixed with expressions of religious misgivings, he falls into the trap. He allays the scruples she feigns about Heaven's wrathful punishment of adultery. Tartuffe dismisses her "ludicrous fears." He knows all the compromises with religion to be devised, and his concluding words expose him glaringly: "Comply with my desire. . . . The rest is my affair." Besides, Orgon is such a fool! Just good enough to be led by the nose.

At last, Orgon is disabused. As he orders the traitor and would-be adulterer out of the house, he is reminded that the house is no longer his. He had made a gift of it to Tartuffe. The impostor also has walked off with a strongbox full of important papers and money entrusted to Orgon by a friend and naturally confided to his religious adviser. The detail, probably Molière's afterthought, prepares the denouement.

[21]

The last act of the play, by now risen to a pitch of tragic intensity, could not but be an anticlimax. Some relief, difficult to make comic, had to be provided. Molière always experienced some trouble with his denouements; perhaps, like many authors, he had to finish his plays in a hurry and lost interest once the situation had been cleared up. Any comedy worthy of the name resists the author's attempt to conclude it logically. A tragic character may, after his ordeals, understand his own "tragic flaw," repent of his obdurate insolence, and like Theseus in *Phédre* or Oedipus, recognize his crimes or tame his haughty stubbornness. By nature, tragic characters may evolve and their failings, stemming as they do from passion or from unreason, do not totally destroy their intellectual power. They are seldom vain and stupid; if they were, they would provoke laughter and neither pity nor terror. They would not acquire heroic stature.

As Anatole France wittily put it, "The wicked man occasionally amends his ways and becomes good, the foolish man never." Any evolution would tempt the reader to sympathize with the plight of the foolish man since it would graphically depict the gradual stages of his folly. The onlooker might then identify himself with the very character who later turns out to be a scoundrel, a tyrant, or a cuckold deserving his cuckoldry. Orgon, the audience was informed at the outset, had once been a man of some wisdom. He had aligned himself with "the forces of order" and the cause of the king during the riots of the Fronde. He did, after all, win an intelligent and attractive wife and must have had some charm as well as other means to accomplish it. Like quite a few veterans of the wars and of the Resistance, he may have suffered a prolonged attack of arrested development. Molière makes it clear that piety, prompted by his weakness and fear for his soul, has stultified him. Madame Pernelle, who returns in the fifth act more gullible and opinionated than her son, may have had no mean share in his progressive fatuity, a tyrannized son turned despot of his own family. The *deus ex machina* of the final act was fittingly the King, who deserved Molière's thanks for allowing the play to be performed in spite of the magistrates and the zealots. The applause of the Parisian middle class, in those years ardently royalist, could not but be hearty.

Molière inserted a mildly amusing scene with the visit of M. Loyal,

Tartuffe's legal emissary, delivering the order of eviction. He, too, employs hypocritical circumlocutions; but his are legal while Tartuffe's were ecclesiastical. Even Madame Pernelle now sees the light. Orgon is ready to take flight when, in a sudden *coup de théâtre*, the King's officer arrests Tartuffe. Cléante, the sage, is the true Christian of the play. He forbears insulting the impostor and even hopes for his eventual repentance.

The greatness of this play, in no way worn by time, lies in its endowment with all the requirements a play should meet: namely, to be read studied, dissected as a classic, and acted for the most varied audiences, popular as well as sophisticated. The fact that it is in verse in no way detracts from the impact of the comedy upon audiences uninformed of the subtleties of French prosody. Both in the original and in Richard Wilbur's version the pace is swift, the crescendo of the scenes preserved and imparted to the audience, the style robust and concrete. The poetry constitutes a dynamic economy of means and effort. It strikes the listeners with electrical force. It also emphasizes the evocative and imaginative elements of *Tartuffe*, on first appearance a masterpiece of realism but also a play in which Molière, aware that realism must be symbolical and suggestive in an art where all is illusion, has distorted, stylized, and magnified reality and exalted it into truth. *Quelle vérité et quelle invraisemblance!* exclaimed Sainte-Beuve.

The structure of the play is its first outstanding quality. It has been analyzed with thoroughness and an unerring sense of the stage in the most recent and definitive French work on Molière by Jacques Guicharnaud, to whom any commentator on *Tartuffe*, *Dom Juan*, and *Le Misanthrope* will henceforth be indebted. The order of the acts and scenes is not the too meticulously contrived clockwork of the skilled playwrights in France during the last century. No undue attention is expended by Molière on arranging the entrances and exits of the characters to seem casual. The characters appear when needed and for purely theatrical effect. Scenes of digression are not ruled out if the psychological portrait of a certain person or his secret tension is thereby conveyed more fully. The spontaneous ebullience of farce in which Molière's career as actor and playwright originated is retained in this higher, serious kind of comedy. Played by Molière in 1669, Orgon has lingering features and contortions of Scaramouche and Sganarelle, whom the playwright had also impersonated in his early years of acting. Like them, Orgon clings to ready-made ideas with a stubbornness which arouses laughter. Like them, too, he nurtures his delusions and cultivates his infatuation until his whole universe collapses. The age-old theme of many a farce, medieval French or Italian, is revived in *Tartuffe:* the deceiver hoisted by his own petard, the traitor and impostor exposed. The trickster here is no entertaining smallfry, a Scapin we would forgive because he makes us laugh. He is a criminal plotter.

The characterization is no less worthy of praise. Contrary to many glib assertions currently made about the supposedly "cold" or "frigid" French classical drama, the characters are not abstract types. They are raised by the dramatist to a plane of universal truth. They are also individuals placed in a concrete environment. We see in the play an upper-middle-class family: a picturesque, garrulous, and gesticulating grandmother; Tartuffe drawing his chair close to Elmire and letting his hand wander on her knee; his gluttony over a leg of finely minced lamb, partridges, and a few more invigorating dishes for his morning repast. Stage directions in classical times were more succinct than in George Bernard Shaw's plays. The text itself was sovereign in the seventeenth century and suggested to the director the little he had to know from the author about props, movements, and attitudes.

Elmire is a disturbing character, sensible, sane, expert at listening to love declarations and at keeping them in place without undue *éclat*. Is her pride touched at all by Tartuffe's attentions, a married woman possibly bored with a foolish husband? Does a slight tremor of eyelashes or lips, a sudden flush on her cheeks reveal a change in her? What is her age and what could be her past? She cannot well have left a convent directly to marry Orgon and have remained innocent of the wiles of the world. She must be at least ten years older than her step-daughter and fifteen years or so younger than her husband. What a diplomat she shows herself to be when she elicits Tartuffe's second declaration exactly as she wishes! But of her love or affection for a husband she scorns, nothing is made clear. She is the mysterious character in the play.

[24]

Orgon is the comic hero, a prey to one fixed idea, a man obsessed with the fear of disorder, of disobedience, probably of death. It has been remarked that by changing one letter in his name (*o* to *a*), Molière had created in Argan, the imaginary invalid, a brother to Orgon: both incurably egocentric, both terrified by the dim prospect of salvation of either body or soul. Both count for nothing the ruination of their family and the unhappiness of a daughter in an unnatural marriage. But Orgon is even more tragic in his gullibility and foolishness. He becomes a sadist, delighting in curbing and oppressing his children and in inflicting pain on them. His affection for the character who has come to possess him is dangerously close to a lover's dotage. Are there faint lineaments in Orgon of a potential Baron de Charlus or of a Gidian "immoralist"; or of the ludicrously pathetic character in Gide's *Caves of the Vatican* who undertakes to liberate the supposedly imprisoned pope? Without stating it in the ironical terms Voltaire would have used, Molière did not conceal that religion lay at the source of Orgon's stultification.

Tartuffe himself ranks among the most admired portrayals in the whole range of comic literature. More subtle than Orgon, less predictable, he stands in bold relief in the play as one of the rare "round characters" of comedy, as E. M. Forster might have put it. He fills only the third and fourth acts of the play. For the rest, he is described chiefly as he appears to others. But that projection of his personality is highly revealing. The villain in him is exposed only at the end, though from the outset he had been a counterfeiter of religion. In the fashion of the French classical writers, his past is left in the dark. Balzac, perhaps even Shakespeare or Ibsen, would have revealed more about his earlier deeds as an adventurer and how he was, like Richard III, "determined to be a villain" and disguise his villainy under a mask of piety. Julien Sorel, during the French Restoration, would likewise reason that the "Red" of a military career having lost its glamor upon Napoleon's fall, the "Black" offers the better means to success in a society which apes piety and invests the Jesuits with the power to spy upon souls. But Julien soon shed his masks when love got the better of his frail heart and when the poet in him spurned the calculating hypocrite.

Tartuffe's self-mastery is astonishing. Was he once a confirmed

[25]

believer? How had he mastered the baroque language of the mystics which he converts to erotic purpose? He is repulsive in his crude manners, and had to be shown overplaying the personage Molière had assigned to him. Yet his power of attraction is also great. Tartuffe has duped Orgon and his mother. It is not certain that he does not exert some fascination even upon unromantic Elmire. His desire for his host's wife is not merely a sadistic calculation or pure lechery. Something in her cool, mature honesty attracts him; he appreciates her intellect or he would not compose those flowery and closely reasoned speeches with which he hopes to capture her. In his celebrated little book on *Laughter*, Henri Bergson noted that "Tartuffe has entered so thoroughly into his part that he plays it, so to speak, with sincerity." The ambiguity of his language, mystically devout and carnally insidious, has become natural and a mark of sincerity with him. His mask adheres so well to his face that he has become the one he endeavored to ape. Only toward the end of the play is he at last caught by imprudence with his mask disassociated from him. "Knavery's plain face is never seen till used," says Iago.

One of the most acute writers on the theatre in America, Eric Bentley, wrote in 1964 in *The Life of the Drama*: "Great drama has been a drama of ideas from the very first." Our age is an age of ideas, even more than was the century of Molière, often dubbed "the Age of Reason," or that of Voltaire and Rousseau. Our wars have been more ideological than the mere outcome of economic greed or of psychoanalytical frustrations. We have been gravely warned that peace is primarily a state of mind, a philosophy, that we shall not possess it securely unless we make it a continuous creation, willed by our minds and hearts. Books on the modern novel in France and elsewhere are entitled *The Novelist as Thinker* and *Literature as Philosophy*. Molière cannot be caricatured into a philosopher. He thought intensely as a painter, a sculptor, any artisan, any actor, and even a harassed theatrical director does; there is such a thing as a Swiss author has called "thinking with one's hands." Good theatre, earning plentiful box-office receipts as *Tartuffe* invariably does in Europe, may also be a thought-provoking and a poetical theatre. Only those who scorn man and wish to maintain

[26]

him in a state of passive receptivity to the baits of propaganda systematically underestimate the public. Molière thought better of man and of his contemporaries. He defined comedy as the most difficult of all the writing genres; it must entertain and correct audiences and, without antagonizing them, sharpen their critical view of others and of themselves.

The significance of *Tartuffe* is even more pregnant with implications today than when the play started its uproar among the devout. Molière shows in that masterpiece how many of us assume a mask and allow the mask to cling to us until all sincerity vanishes. Pedants, doctors, bad poets, teachers of philosophy and of dancing in *The Would-be Gentleman*, Monsieur Jourdain himself and the over-polite noblemen who swindle him, the effete *Précieuses*, all wear social masks and under these pretences their social or professional selves stifle any truthfulness they may have harbored. Etiquette, flattery, fashion, piety, conventionality of courtly life, even love conforming to rules of elaborate courtship were aspects of the masked ball danced by the nobles and upstarts around Louis XIV.

Molière had the audacity to indict the most redoubtable of his potential adversaries: the pious ones. Religion might be a pure affair of the heart, of silent, collective meditation or prayer in solitude. It might also then lead to mysticism, to the free examination of the Protestants, to disregard of rites and of hierarchy—all things suspicious to Bossuet, who denounced them in thundering tones. Religion is often a social function as well as a personal contrition or ecstasy; it entails rituals, ceremonies, care lavished on clothes and deportment and outward attitudes. Also, it carries with it the urge to spread to others the peace of mind the religious person may have gained. The Compagnie du Saint-Sacrement, which meddled with the private lives of people, accomplished much good. Even casuistry can be legitimate, since extenuating, or at least accompanying, circumstances exist in most "cases." When indicting false piety, Molière was bound to cast doubts and ridicule on true piety, too. Bourdaloue asked a relevant question when he pronounced in his sermon: "In tearing off the mask, does not comedy run the risk of scratching the face?" The answer is that in Molière's eyes tolerance is more moral than fanaticism; a straightforward, lay wisdom

[27]

such as Cléante and Elmire advocate and practice is preferable to an excessive piety which attempts to tyrannize others; a fair degree of intelligence is more admirable than the abdication of reason and of the critical spirit recommended by Pascal. His *Pensées*, kept in manuscript for ten years after his death, were being prepared for publication in 1670 when Moliére at last was allowed to stage *Tartuffe*.

False piety is less of an evil today in Christian countries than it once was. Hypocrisy, the sanctimonious pomposity of big words, catch phrases on "the ideal of service" or "the customer is always right" are very much with us. The jargon of our pedants, the euphemisms of financiers and economists gilding plain words like "deficit" or "waste," the circumlocutions of our political commentators drowning the issues of Congo or Vietnam, of the two Germanies or the evils of socialism, the obsessive repetitiousness of our "hidden" (but loudly deafening) persuaders; all that is very much with us. Tartuffes have not disappeared from our midst. Our contemporaries, subjected to universal education along with the systematic "decline of attention" perpetrated by mass media in the modern world, are almost as gullible as the hypocrite's victims. Molière is no stilted or old-fashioned satirist of a remote era. His fight against superficiality, falsehood, and intolerance is today as timely as ever. The author of the best English book on Molière, W. G. Moore, aptly wrote in 1937: "If Molière were alive today, writing with the same clear vision and unthinking disregard of contemporary 'verities,' the most revolutionary plays of our time would seem but a thin cackling by comparison with the broad laughter of his comic genius."

Is There a Tragic Sense of Life?

by Lionel Abel

For Merry Abel, 1940–1964, In Memoriam

Our Estimate of Writers with the "Tragic Sense"

WE SET a particular value on those writers of plays—sometimes of novels—who give expression to what has been called the "tragic sense of life." Do we overvalue them? The truth is, I think, that we value them in a very special way, for we see demonstrated in their works the possibility of viewing life other than with optimism or pessimism. And for ourselves, when we reflect, the only possible choice lies with one or the other of these extremes, so that it is not only the art of the writer of tragedy we admire, but some special insight, which we feel that we can achieve only through his intervention, and which he—for that is our assumption—enjoys by some peculiar privilege of rare wisdom, or intelligence, or some yet more mysterious endowment. He seems more *philosophic* than other writers of equal art or scope, so that by a kind of tacit consent philosophers have honored authors of tragedy as the most *philosophical* of writers. In this estimate of the writer of tragedy I think there is a misunderstanding of his very special achievement, hence also a misunderstanding of what he achieves, namely, tragedy. If we can correctly think out what we are right to admire the author of tragedy for, we may correct some wrong notions of what tragedy is.

Our Dissatisfaction with Optimism and Pessimism

Now it should be clear why optimism as an attitude toward life cannot satisfy us. It should be clear, too, that our dissatisfaction with it is mainly *intellectual*. For we are quite naturally optimistic insofar as we are active beings, living in time and planning the future which our very life structure requires us to think of as being capable of yielding to our purposes. But when we reflect, when we remember "things said

[29]

and done long years ago," and also the things we did not say or do, as well as those said and done by others, we realize—we have to—that there are a great many negative facts. Only a few of these, and there are a great many of them, would be enough to invalidate any optimistic hypothesis that the world as it is can be truthfully described as *good*. Instances of such negative facts may be remote or local: the unjust sentence passed on Socrates, or the fact raised by André Malraux at a congress of Soviet writers during the thirties of a man run over by a trolley car.[1] Such negative facts are able to render void all optimistic *generalizations* about the world, just as a few tiny facts which remain obdurate to explanation are sufficient to refute a whole scientific theory accounting for a multitude of others. So those who live by optimistic beliefs are like bad scientists, clinging, despite the evidence, to refuted theories.

But what about the negative facts? Do they at least justify pessimism? Not as a hypothesis, not as a generalized view. For the negative facts comprise merely one set of facts, and the world is such that no one set of facts is able to speak for it. We know that having heard one set out, we must listen to very different facts. Alas for the heartbreak of the defeated and the dead: if we do not straightway share their fate, we are forced to think of something else.

The Russian thinker Chestov—I will not call him a philospher—repeated again and again in his writings that the injustice done to Socrates was a fact he could not endure. He thought, too, that a fact of this sort should make us suspicious of any facts we ordinarily think of as positive. But even if the positive facts were far fewer than the negative, they could still not justify our electing for pessimism. (For Schopenhauer a preponderance of negative facts did justify pessimism; his argument lacks subtlety.) The positive facts remain, and they prevent us from resolving without artificiality in favor of a pessimistic view. A very few positive facts can make pessimism unacceptable. This is illustrated, I think, in the biblical story of Abraham's debate with

1. The reply made to Malraux was that the Soviet authorities would see to it that accidents of that sort decreased annually. The argument of the Soviet writers was for optimism, to them obligatory; the greater relative safety of future generations would more than make up for the absolute harm which had befallen one individual.

God when the Lord was intent on destroying the wicked cities of Sodom and Gomorrah. Abraham argued that if there were even ten good men in those cities, the Lord's proposed action would be unjust. And God finally conceded Abraham to be the better philosopher, admitting that if there were even fewer than ten good men in Sodom and Gomorrah, His pessimism about the two cities would be unjustified, notwithstanding all the wicked in them.

That the positive facts stand in the way of a resolve for pessimism is not in any sense an argument for being optimistic. Far from it! It is a sad fact indeed that sadness will bring us no closer than lightness of spirit to the heart of things.

What argues for optimism is that it is required by our life structure. If we plan to be optimistic, then at least we are not contradicting ourselves; but if we plan to be pessimistic—and since we live in time, to be pessimistic means to plan to be pessimistic—then we are contradicting ourselves; we are placing our trust in the view that things will be untrustworthy; we are reasoning that Failure cannot fail, and so, in a sense, can be depended on. Then too, except in cases of present or permanent distress, optimism is natural and spontaneous, while pessimism is inevitably theatrical. Life requires optimism; but optimism leaves out of account and quite disregards pain, frustration and death; such disregard is, of course, intellectually shallow. So we are back with our dilemma: we can be optimists or pessimists; but can we *want* to be either?

The Tragic Sense

The remedy is a fantastic one: it is a vision of the irremediable. We go to the theatre to see a tragedy. We see human action in the clearest light the mind can cast on it, and behold, we see the human person at his best. We do not disregard pain or frustration or death; in fact we give them our whole attention, and they do not make us pessimistic, they give us joy. As Aristotle said, we are relieved of pity and terror, the very emotions pessimism would yield to and optimism would avoid. We see life tragically; we have for the duration of the play at least and perhaps for some time afterward the tragic sense. Would that it were more lasting!

Can we make it so? Can we not make permanent the view of life we enjoyed in the theatre and in recollection afterward for however short a time? Can we not acquire or develop a sense of life such as the playwright himself must have had? Of course, we cannot be Sophocles, Shakespeare, or Racine. The question then is: can the tragic sense be acquired without the special genius of the writer of tragedy, and if so, how?

Why We Cannot Acquire the Tragic Sense

Suppose, though, for I think this true, that what we call the tragic sense does not form part of the playwright's genius and does not involve superior capacities of mind; then it must be the result of experience. Of what experience? The answer to this question is obvious; we should have thought of it immediately: the experience which leads to the tragic sense of life is the experience of tragedy; it is by undergoing tragedy that one arrives at the tragic sense. Or rather, the word "arrives" is misleading here, for one does not acquire or develop the tragic sense; it is not realized but imposed; one never possesses it, one has to be possessed by it.

We cannot add the tragic sense to our present sense of life, be that present sense optimistic or pessimistic. And without our present sense we have neither terms nor criteria with which to decide whether the tragic sense is worth what it will cost us. And from this it follows that no reason can ever be given for recommending the tragic sense, however good or great a thing the tragic sense may be.

Herbert J. Muller, in a recent book, *The Spirit of Tragedy*, has had the temerity to urge on us the acquisition of the tragic sense for reasons which he himself does not deny are frankly utilitarian. He writes: "We might not continue to get along as a free, open society without more of the tragic sense of life." I think the error he has fallen into is expressed in his use of the word "more." If we had *some* of the tragic sense of life then perhaps we could get still *more* of it, but it would not be the drastic thing it is if that were the way it could be come by. The prospect we would face, if we had not just "more" of the tragic sense but enough of it to have it, would be one of all or nothing.

So we cannot urge the tragic sense on ourselves or on others. To

[32]

try to attain it or to recommend it is comical and self-refuting, tragedy being real only when unavoidable. There would be no such things as tragedy if a tragic fate could be rationally chosen.

The Writer of Tragedy and the Philosopher

But what about the writer of tragedy? Must he not possess the tragic sense of life since he is able to make it available to us at least for the time we spend under his spell? Is there not reason for thinking that the writer of tragedy must have a more permanent relation to the tragic view than those who receive it from him? Does he have a special philosophy, a tragic philosophy if you please, permanently his, and which through his art he is able to share with us in some small measure? Now I do not think the writer of tragedy has to have any view of life drastically different from our own.

Supposing he were a philosopher, what difference would that make? He could not by means of philosophy resolve the question of optimism or pessimism, which we who are not philosophers face. For philosophers are also either optimistic or pessimistic. (Some philosophies are neutral, but this last attitude is finally comprised under pessimism. Neutrality to life really means pessimism about it.)

When the vision of a writer of tragedy is stated philosophically, it is always converted (I submit, necessarily) into a form of optimism or of pessimism. I shall give two examples. The first is taken from Matthew Arnold's famous poem *Dover Beach*. Arnold, looking out at the sea from Dover Beach and hearing in the cadence of the waves the "eternal note of sadness," thinks of Sophocles:

> Sophocles long ago
> Heard it on the Aegean, and it brought
> Into his mind the turbid ebb and flow
> Of human misery;

And the image of Sophocles hearing the note of "human misery" leads Arnold to this pessimistic declaration:

> Ah, love, let us be true
> To one another! for the world, which seems
> To lie before us like a land of dreams,

[33]

> So various, so beautiful, so new,
> Hath really neither joy, nor love, nor light,
> Nor certitude, nor peace, nor help for pain;

The view of life expressed here is not one that I, or any one else, could derive from seeing a performance of *Oedipus Rex*, *Oedipus at Colonus*, or *Antigone*. Perhaps Sophocles had such thoughts when he looked at the Aegean, but these are not the thoughts we think when witnessing his tragedies. And from the reports about Sophocles by his contemporaries, we are scarcely justified in calling to mind an individual contemplating human misery. The tragic poet was said to have been charming, gracious, genial, and with no better opinions about politics or life than other cultivated Athenians.

The wonderful Spanish writer and thinker Miguel de Unamuno, who is actually responsible for the phrase "the tragic sense of life," trying to state this "tragic sense" as a philosophical attitude, converts it, I think, into a refined and pleasing, though somber, form of optimism. Unamuno's tragic sense is even a misnomer; there is little tragic about it, for he is not urging us to set something above life; rather what he does urge us to set above life is nothing other than life, immortal life, the immortality of the soul, on which immortality he asks us to gamble the existence we are certain of. That this violently optimistic Christianity should attract us with its death-splashed Spanish cloak is due, of course, to our obscure recognition, even if we have not thought the matter through, that optimism presented simply as optimism would offer us only what we are well acquainted and dissatisfied with.

A novel and, I think, quite wrong view that thought, even philosophic thought, can have and has had a tragic cast is presented by Lucien Goldmann in his much-praised book on Pascal and Racine, *Le Dieu Cadré*. According to Goldmann there are certain philosophers whose thought can be characterized as tragic. He cites as instances Pascal and Kant. Why is their thought tragic? Because, says Goldmann, it expresses the conflict in them between alternatives and exclusive world views, the world view of mathematical science and the world view of revealed religion. But surely no character on the stage would be convincing in the tragic hero's part if his torment were due to nothing more drastic than his inability to choose between or mediate conflicting views. In fact, Kant and Pascal did both. What I mean is this: Kant opted for religion in his metaphysics and for science in his epistemology. And I think Pascal did the same in his distinction between *l'esprit géometrique* and *l'esprit de finesse*.

I submit that it is not through any particular philosophy that the tragic writer is able to give expression to his tragic sense of life, although this tragic sense does have for us, the audience, a virtue which has been called philosophic. Then is it by art alone that the writer of tragedy affects as he does?

The Writer of Tragedy Without the Philosopher

The very great probability is, I suggest, that the writer of tragedy is no more endowed with a tragic sense of life than are we to whom he makes it available. By which I mean that he, too, in his regular experience of life, is condemned to the same unsatisfactory choice between optimism and pessimism that we are, and that only in the act of writing a tragedy, only by making the tragic view available to us, is he himself enabled to envisage life in such terms. His creation then is a communion with us, in the experiencing of a view of things which we could not have without him, but which he in turn can only have insofar as he is capable of extending it to us.

Why could we not have the tragic sense without the *written* tragedy? Let us consider this point from a somewhat different angle. There is something we could have without the help of art, and which many people may confuse with the tragic sense, namely the feeling of a *pessimism that is justified*. This is all we can get from the lesser masters of the art of tragedy, from Euripides, Webster, and Tourneur at their best, and from Shakespeare in his unsuccessful tragedies such as *Troilus and Cressida, Coriolanus, Timon of Athens* and *King Lear*. Moreover, this justified pessimism appears at times even in the greatest works but it is not this which makes them tragic. When Richard in Shakespeare's *Richard II* complains of the vulnerability of kings,

> . . . for within the hollow crown
> That rounds the mortal temples of a king

[35]

> Keeps Death his court; and there the antic sits . . .
> Allowing him a breath, a little scene . . .
>   . . . and humour'd thus,
> Comes at the last, and with a little pin
> Bores through his castle wall, and farewell king!

he gives expression to a pessimism which in view of his situation he is certainly justified in feeling. And the greatness of the verse penetrates Richard's feeling completely; what he says seems all the more inevitable because said in lines of such power. Who can be secure if the best protected of men, the king, is not? It is to be noted that a negative fact, in this instance death, armed with so mean and trivial an instrument as a pin, is seen as rendering meaningless the highest state a man can aspire to, that of a kingliness. Later in the play Richard will say:

> . . . nor any man that but man is
> With nothing shall be pleas'd till he be eas'd
> With being nothing.

The feeling expressed here of life's meaninglessness we may all have felt, indeed must have felt, at some time or other and with some measure of poetry, too, for such feelings provide a verbal talent all by themselves. We would not need the art of tragedy to acquaint us with such a judgment of life nor even with the necessity to pronounce it consummately.

A judgment of life similar in its pessimism to Richard's and equally justified is uttered by Macbeth:

> Life's but a walking shadow, a poor player,
> That struts and frets his hour upon the stage
> And then is heard no more. It is a tale
> Told by an idiot, full of sound and fury,
> Signifying nothing.

This judgment, too, we could form for ourselves without either the experience of tragedy or Shakespeare's art. But what we could not get without actual or invented tragedy is the experience of resolution when nothing can follow from resolve, a resolution beyond optimism or pessimism, hope or despair. This we get from Macbeth's great words:

Though Birnam Wood be come to Dunsinane,
And thou opposed, being of no woman born,
Yet will I try the last.

Richard's speech about the death of kings is a protest against the weakness and impotence of the most highly placed. Macbeth's lines of resolution express a much more complicated feeling, one in which are allied, to use Heidegger's phrase, "utter impotence and super power." Richard's lines about the death of kings, justifying pessimism, point to the negative fact of death which renders optimistic notions of life invalid even for a king. Macbeth's lines of resolution refer to no negative facts at all, nor to anything common in human experience, not even to the common experience of kings, but exclusively to the withdrawal of their aid from him by those metaphysical beings, the witches, who had for a time supported him. Macbeth's lines are thrilling; Richard's are merely sad. What has to be explained is why Macbeth's lines thrill us, and why he had to pass through the experience of tragedy in order to be able to utter them. The weakness of Richard is evident, so is Macbeth's. But whence comes Macbeth's power?

What Is Tragedy?

In tragedy it is not the negative facts, rendering optimism invalid, which finally cause misfortune. Such negative facts as commonly threaten all of us are even converted by the mechanism of tragedy into positive goods. Blindness is an evil; yet Oedipus deliberately blinds himself; death we would think is to be avoided at all costs; yet Antigone elects to die and denies her sister, Ismene, the same privilege. Ajax, when told that if he spends the day in his tent he will be allowed to live, deliberately leaves his tent and falls on his sword. In the tragic universe the negative facts of experience are finally unimportant. What might lead us in ordinary life to be pessimistic is never the cause of tragedy.

What is the cause then of tragedy? It is the opposition, as Hegel affirmed, of two conflicting goods. Tragedy is never caused by what is unambiguously evil. It is the sheerly positive in conflict with the sheerly positive that destroys the tragic protagonist. In the Greek world it was the collision of the values of the family with those of the state. Those contrary values, as Aeschylus and Sophocles understood them,

[37]

could not be held to with equal fidelity in any superior experience of life. The superior man would inevitably violate the one or the other.[2] Perhaps it may be said that while this may have been true of the ancient Greek world, it was not true of the Shakespearean world. For in what sense can the witches who incite Macbeth to kill Duncan be called sheerly positive? In what sense can they be called representatives of the good? Are they not the expression of unmitigated evil?

If they were, *Macbeth* would not be a tragedy. It would be a melodrama, and Macbeth's story would merely be that of a villain defeated. But once again, in what sense can the witches be said to represent the good? In this sense: the witches in *Macbeth* are the only dramatic expression of the metaphysical. Duncan, the reigning king, is presented as kingly, just, morally right. But Macbeth and Banquo are the characters in the play who have direct contact with the representatives of the metaphysical, that is to say, the witches. Now in *Macbeth* the metaphysical does not coincide with the moral, but is at odds with it; yet both are to be valued. Since the justification for kingship was finally metaphysical—the Elizabethans believed in the divine right of kings as opposed to any merely moral right to kingship—how could an immoral deed of murder to attain kingship, when metaphysical forces, in this case, the witches, seemed to support that deed, be thought of as evil? And, in fact, we never feel Macbeth is evil. We think of him as suffering, suffering because he has violated moral values he cannot deny, in support of values neither he nor Shakespeare's age thought criticizable in moral terms. As in the Greek tragedies, we have in *Macbeth* good pitted against good, and the protagonist is the victim of their collision. What is dreadful then is never the mere negative facts ordinary experience fears. It is the good which is dreaded and has to be dreaded. Soren Kierkegaard, peculiarly sensitive to these matters, summed up

2. It may be asked: why is a collision of values different from a collision of world views? But a collision of views, even if we call them world views, takes place within *consciousness* and not within the *world*. Values such as the family and the state are not merely values; they are valued realities. I should like to point out here that one of the most interesting insights of Martin Heidegger—much more interesting than his remarks about anguish and guilt, which have become part of current twaddle—is his judgment that world views imply the absence of a world rather than a world's enduring presence. Tragedy takes place in a world, not in a consciousness which is uncertain as to what the world is.

what, I think, can be called the experience of tragedy when he said in his acute analysis of dread that it is fundamentally dread of the good.

What Has the Writer of Tragedy Seen?

So the tragic writer has to have seen some collision of good with good in order to have been able to arrange the events he describes into a tragedy. Was he predisposed to see some such collision of good with good? Not, I should say, if it were not there to be seen, even if only he saw it. For can we want to see what it is undesirable to see? Some of us may out of ambition or perversity, but not the writer of a proper tragedy. He sees what it is undesirable to see without desiring to see it. This is one of the things we admire him for. To be sure, there are others. But in any case, what must be understood here is that the object of his vision was given by his age or epoch and not created by him alone. The collision of good with good which he witnessed had then to be given him along with others to see; his part was to take what he saw, and what others may have seen, and fashion it into art.

Thus the tragic view, properly understood, means to have seen the necessity for tragedy, to have recognized it rather than to have created it. That the tragic vision results from a direct act of seeing, and not from the holding of any particular view, or from any predilection for interpreting reality tragically, is something we must understand in order to evaluate that vision and judge it for its true worth. Just as in the tragedy he is going to write, the dramatist will set forth a sequence of events whose connections are necessary, so he himself can only be stirred to set forth such a sequence of events by the sight of a fatality that was thrust upon his view and which was necessarily, not accidentally, there before him.

Once again: what did he see? A collision of good with good. Is it desirable that such a collision come within our view? Not in life. No. Nobody can genuinely say that he wants to see a tragedy enacted anywhere but on the stage. For it is a misfortune to a society or to a culture if its main values contradict one another. On the other hand, tragedy, that art which expresses the collision and not the harmony of such values, is in itself a positive aesthetic good. But this good, this aesthetic good, is achieved through an appropriate description of the ultimate in human misfortune: that man's values should contradict rather than support one another.

Once Again "The Tragic Thinker"

Perhaps it is right to say of the writer of tragedy that his thought, since it had to be equal to what he saw—what he saw was tragedy—is a kind of "tragic thinking." But this can only mean that the writer of tragedy has not permitted any philosophy or ideology to impede or obstruct his vision. But what about those thinkers who have been called "tragic," as for instance Pascal? As I indicated before, I think the term "tragic" when used to designate the thought of anyone not the writer of a tragedy is always wrongly used. Nonetheless, there are in Pascal's *Pensées* many dramatic characterizations of experience which give us a kind of thrill comparable to the kind we get from tragedy. My contention is that in the case of such *Pensées*, Pascal has merely created an abstract replica of the kind of collision of values we find embodied with ever so much more concreteness in tragic poetry. Here is one of the most famous of Pascal's thoughts:

Man is but a reed, the feeblest of Nature's growths, but he is a thinking reed. There is no need for the whole universe to take up arms to crush him; a breath, a drop of water, may prove fatal. But were the universe to kill him, he would still be more noble than his slayers; for man knows that he is crushed, but the universe does not know that it crushes him.

I think what we have here is an imitation in conceptual terms of the kind of event set forth in a real tragedy. It is to be noted that Pascal begins by saying men can be destroyed by a drop of water or a breath; but he chooses not to continue the thought that men can be destroyed by such small means. The drop of water, the breath, are tiny facts: acting negatively, they would be of no interest in tragedy. So in Pascal's thought they are expanded—in possibility, of course—into the universe. From the breath, the drop of water, Pascal goes to the whole universe, which he imagines in the act of overwhelming a man. Even then, says Pascal, the man would be nobler than his slayer. But, in any case, the slayer would be noble, being the universe. Insofar as Pascal's thought here may strike one as tragic, I should say that the event he has described was modeled on that structure of events always present in a true tragedy. For he who is destroyed in a true tragedy is always destroyed by something of worth. The drop of water, the breath, may be thought of, as I said before, as tiny facts behaving negatively but which Pascal had finally to forget about and obscure from his view in order to make a true judgment of man's nobility in misfortune.

What We Should Admire the Writer of Tragedy For

Let us turn from the "tragic thinker" to the writer of tragedy. Why do we admire him? Not for his philosophy, for he has none. If he does hold to one in his personal life, this is not pertinent to his achievement or to our judgment of it. Nor are we required to think of him as a master of experience, as wiser or more deeply human than ourselves. Let us admire him for his art; we should recognize, though, that what he gives us goes far beyond what art generally or regularly gives. And let us admire him for his luck, too, at having been given by his age the opportunity to see in his mind's eye certain paradigm instances of human adversity. Does not Pushkin say that the day after the flooding of Petrograd, "Khostov, poet, favorite of the heavens, already sang in verses never to die the griefs of Neva's shores"?[3]

Moreover, the effort the writer of tragedy makes has to be immense. He has seen the collision of the main values of his age or culture; he has seen the nonmeaning of meanings. Now the mind naturally seeks for meanings; the writer of tragedy has to deny and reverse this process in the very movement with which he yields to it.

His interest is, of course, an aesthetic one. May I speak for just one moment from a professional point of view? When you have written a play you are faced with this problem: what does this play mean? If it is meaningless, it is uninteresting. Suppose it does have a meaning, though. This is scarcely better. Have you not then reduced the action in your play to the illustration of an idea? Now illustrative art is scarcely better for many of us today than is meaningless art. Here the idea of tragedy exerts its fascination. For it is the kind of idea that attains to its truth only when represented in the work itself: the play, the tragedy.

---

3. From Pushkin's poem *The Bronze Horseman* in Edmund Wilson's translation.

We are much more clear about what tragedy is when we see a tragedy enacted than when we try to reason about tragedy.

And let us not forget that what the writer of tragedy gives, he himself gets in the very act of giving: communion with us in a privileged view of human adversity. We admire him then for what he makes us see, a world where the highest values collide and in which we know we could not live. We recognize this when the curtain comes down and we do not know where to go. We have to become optimists or pessimists again in order to think of going home.

"After the Fall": A View from the Director's Notebook

by Nancy and Richard Meyer

ONE DAY in the early spring of 1963, Elia Kazan stopped at the Yale University Co-op and purchased a notebook—a standard composition book with a black and white marbled cover familiar to students everywhere. He was on his way to the Connecticut home of Arthur Miller to continue their conversation about Miller's latest and still-unfinished play, *After the Fall*. Their discussion of the play had begun almost a year before when it was decided that the Miller play would be the opening production of the new Repertory Theater of Lincoln Center. Their plans had almost foundered more than once in frustrating postponements of construction of the theatre, but now it was settled that *After the Fall* would open in January, 1964, on a temporary stage. Now Kazan could turn his energies from his role as coproducer to his preferred position as director. Although rehearsals would not start until October, the purchase of the notebook signified the real beginning of production for Kazan. On its cover—in the space reserved for name, class, and subject—he wrote:

AFTER THE FALL
by A. Miller
A Man Recognizes His Humanity!

Kazan's notebook was a tool. It served as a repository for ideas as they occurred to him, as a point of reference when, weeks or even months later, he sensed that he had lost perspective and strayed from his interpretation.

There was a random quality to the entries; they varied in length, in form, and in style. An idea begun on one day in blue ink was later

[43]

expanded in green ink, all summed up and rephrased ten pages or ten days later in black ink. (He insists there is no significance in the color other than its suggestion of a time lapse.) Only a few of the entries were dated. There was no particular organization, and the author felt no compulsion to make the contents either consistent or comprehensive. For all the interest it might have to others and the promise it held for future editing and publishing, it was obviously a private device for personal use, and herein lay its value; for its literary merit was secondary to its spontaneity. It was grammatically casual, frequently repetitive, sometimes contradictory, shockingly candid, and rich with insight and dramatic imagination. In its unpolished form it was a rare glimpse of the mechanics of a mind, disclosing the probing behind the discovery, the thought behind the conclusion. Many of those conclusions were later abandoned, but each abortive effort had its place along the road to understanding of the script.

After the Fall was a difficult play by its very nature. The story of Quentin, a lawyer who puts his own life on trial, is unfolded in retrospect, not in flashbacks of factual reality but in the often-distorted memory of a man in torment. The scenes unfold in no chronological order, being called forth only as seemingly erratic memories which intrude themselves upon one man's burdened and anxious mind. The director's task was to make comprehensible to the audience the vagaries in time and space, the unrealistic characterizations, and the internal quality of the drama.

Kazan's problems were compounded as he set out to plan the production. His ideas on staging were being developed at a time when the stage itself was still only lines on the architect's drawing board. As he began his notebook, the play itself was still incomplete. His notes on *After the Fall* reflected the special difficulties involved in analyzing a character whose outcome was not yet clear and in interpreting a play whose theme was still shifting in its author's mind.

For Kazan, the director's duty was to convey the writer's intention, to produce the playwright as well as the play. He wrote on the flyleaf of the notebook:

> What is more heroic, more deeply
> *human*, than the spectacle of man

> looking into himself with fear,
> but finally without self-deception
> to find out who he is!—A man
> BRAVE enough to try to find out
> the truth about himself!!

Throughout the notebook Kazan expressed himself emphatically, centering a single thought upon a page; underlining once, twice, or three times; printing a significant word in large, bold letters; and spending exclamation points freely.

The two men worked closely together, punctuating Miller's periods of writing with regular conferences. They discussed the elusive theme of the play, the problems of staging, the possible revisions, suggestions Miller welcomed. Kazan used the notebook as a reminder of ideas he wanted to present to Miller, such as the item entered in March:

> I think, however concealed or
> inferred, ACT ONE should end with
> Quentin's unconscious or conscious
> determination to get away from his
> wife's puritanism.
>
> Now it's not really clear.

He frequently recorded significant snatches of their conversations, or summarized their outcome, as in the notes of a July meeting during which they discussed the essence of the play:

> . . . Persisting theme: everyone made Quentin
> feel superior, a God, special. And
> it turned out not to be so.
>
> . . . And now he wants the privilege of his
> faults. He wants to join the rest of the
> human race . . . *the fallible!*
>
> . . . Persisting theme: he went for the pose,
> so he cut off his connection and lost touch
> with his true feelings.

[45]

. . . Persisting theme: After the Fall!

There is no Eden—no perfect approval.
There is Murder in us all.

Kazan developed the murder theme more fully in a letter to scene designer Jo Mielziner. It read, in part:

August 5, 1963

Dear Jo,

The final pages of After the Fall make
clear what the subject matter, the theme
and the meaning of this play are. Miller
is dramatizing the fact that man survives
and always has survived by murder. He is
recognizing this in his hero and, so, in
himself and in all of us. He even goes so
far as to handcuff his hero and the Nazi mass
murderers. At the end of the play he, in
effect, says that we, the SURVIVORS, go
on only because others die. And finally,
that we need and unconsciously want the death
of others so we can survive!

On the personal level the play is about a
man who discovers that he has survived by
the deaths of other people with whom he's
been related, particularly those whom he
has known in bonds of love. These murders
came about, on his part, by a wish, by
his walking away at a critical moment, or
even by his accepting the death of someone
else as convenient.

So you will immediately recognize that the
mood of the play as Miller and I have come
to feel it and as I have tried to describe
above must be in the setting.

It should seem primordial, as old as
murder itself. . . .

It should be stained with old hatreds,
old bloodsheds. . . .

It should be where murder was discovered
by the murderer.

It should be cavernous, deep and dark.
It should be made up of the corners of
his memory into which his mind has never
penetrated before, because it never
dared to. . . .

It should be fragmented in the way a Braque
is fragmented, a spatial arrangement in
this case of Quentin's homes, beds, places
of going and coming, of living and of
crisis, of the memory of pain, hatred and
desperation and the arenas of Quentin's
agonies. Of course, unity is important.
But this should be a difficult unity, the
unity of complexities held together by
theme and meaning and the color of murder.
Each place suggested is where a murder took
place, and where Quentin managed to survive
while others did not. And the whole is the
place where these people—these guilts—
are brought forward by Quentin in front of
an audience to be recognized for what they
are, measured, judged, and finally disposed of.

E. K.

There were many artistic and practical considerations that influenced the course of the design. There was a steady progression toward the elimination of physical detail, and the characters themselves began to be relied upon to place the scene. In preparation for a conference with Miller, Mielziner, and coproducer Robert Whitehead, Kazan summarized his views on the production.

1. In this play the real is the unreal.
   The psychoanalyst, the only "real" person who
   is in the "present" with Quentin, is NOT THERE.

[47]

He is the least real. On the other hand, the
remembered figures are very real and affect
the action. They should not be treated as
spooks, given any mysterioso treatment,
wrapped in gauze, etc.

2. There is to be no scenery in this production,
   no furniture, and no projections to suggest
   "reality." The setting is the bare geography
   of the mind, the lava surface of some dead planet
   where the people from Quentin's past are still
   very much alive.

3. The REAL people, the remembered people,
   do not disappear. They merely retreat into the
   background. Nor do they stop "living." They
   continue. They are ready to assert themselves
   at any moment within Quentin's psyche.

4. When they are in the background they
   should be in unobtrusive attitudes that
   are characteristic and significant for
   Quentin, or in simple unobtrusive activities
   which are again the way Quentin remembers
   them most characteristically.

5. The "locale" for each remembered bit is
   created by the creation of environment, the
   behaviour of the background figures, sounds,
   props, especially hand props, living props,
   costumes and lights.

6. The RULE throughout: How Quentin's mind works,
   what *his* mind sees, remembers.

After the Fall presented a challenge in character analysis. Because
the play was contained within Quentin's mind, each part had not only
to carry its private conviction but had to have a psychological validity
in Quentin's memory as well. If the parts were distorted as he remembered them, there had to be visible cause for their distortion in addition
to sufficient indication of the pertinent facets of their true natures to
explain Quentin's reactions toward them.

As he had done in other plays before, Kazan searched for the

[48]

"spine" of each character, that lowest common denominator of personality that justifies even the most inconsistent details of behavior.

Kazan began with Quentin, who seemed at once to be a moral man who for some reason he did not understand himself had behaved immorally. Quentin's standards were high and inflexible—if they were exaggerated or pompous he did not see it—and his shortcomings were to him monstrous and inexcusable. While he recognized intellectually the advantages of reducing his self-demands to more workable levels, he was no more capable emotionally to settle for less than those about him. The internal conflict between his intentions and his failings had reduced him to an ineffectual man without faith in his own ability to behave responsibly and in dread of his own death-dealing future. Eden was the time when right was right and he was certain of his pursuit of it; now he was banished from Eden by his own weakness and he was frightened in a threatening new world where evil dwelt not only in him but in others as well. Yet there was a spark of humor in him and a spark of hope which brought him to the psychoanalyst and, finally, to his own past.

Kazan proceeded to isolate the many factors that determined his course, noting to himself at one time that these were "hard to list," that the character was not "color-ful." Quentin was complex, and the notebook gave evidence of continual realignment of his essential traits.

1. Bewildered . . . puzzling things out.
2. Troubled. Self-doubting.
3. Searching.
4. He's all intellectual . . . goes over and over and over his experiences, chewing them like a CUD.
5. Extremely inexperienced: Square. Innocent.
6. Feels sexually insufficient, uncertain, even inadequate.
7. Feels uncertain intellectually. This uncertainty is a *saving* grace. He also laughs at himself, *undercuts* his *pomposity* with humor.

8. Repressed, inhibited, "like a board."
   "Drives nails into himself because
   he can't feel enough."
9. Hard to connect with. He is always
   half-abstracted. He always seems
   REMOTE and judging and untouchable.
   He doesn't smile on cue. He has
   "other thoughts."
10. He once had a great "charm" (his smile)
    and he has realized that it was
    "they"-ism and has given it up.
    He had it in College.
11. Hard working . . . (up till when he quit
    the firm) . . . a Demon Beaver. But he
    worked as hard as he did mostly to
    avoid confronting his problems—his
    relationship with his wife, etc. The
    fact is that the only thing he got
    a lot out of is work.
12. Usually avoids direct confrontations . . .
    writes his anger . . . doesn't directly
    express it.
13. He is always full of longing.
14. He has given up the old "answers" . . .
    He has come to question everything he
    used to NOT QUESTION. But he is the
    sort of man who NEEDS "ANSWERS" . . .
    must have a firm and strong morality . . .
    cannot live *without* a rigid morality.

With each revision of the script, Kazan continued his efforts to catch and crystallize in his own words the elusive theme. Act Two was still incomplete when he wrote in his notebook:

THIS IS THE STORY OF A
MAN
WHOSE MORALITY HAS
BETRAYED HIM.
HE HAS FOUND IT FALSE

"For Kazan, the director's duty was to convey the writer's intention, to produce the playwright as well as the play." *Arthur Miller, left; Elia Kazan, right.*

"The two men worked closely together. They discussed the elusive theme of the play, the problems of staging, the possible revisions." By the lake in Connecticut. Kazan, left; Miller, right.

"*The mood of the play . . . must be in the setting.*" *Kazan, center, confers with designer Jo Mielziner, flanked by Robert Whitehead, left, and Arthur Miller, right.*

"The setting is the bare geography of the mind, the lava surface of some dead planet where the people from Quentin's past are still very much alive." Model setting for After the Fall *by Jo Mielziner.*

AND HE IS
SEARCHING
FOR A NEW ONE.
THIS PLAY DRAMATIZES HIS
BEWILDERMENT,
HIS SEARCH,
AND WHAT HE DOES
DISCOVER.

The central action of the play, the drama itself, involves this search. Kazan considered Quentin again with this in mind:

"Every morning I wake up full of hope!"
This is essential.

1. He is an *optimistic animal* . . . heads up . . . doesn't skulk.
2. A lawyer. He works on the problem of right and wrong, justice and injustice, what should endure, responsibility. Heads up . . . looks into things.
3. Trying to *save his life* . . . confronts. (Vs. hide, escape, dodge, evade.)
4. He is NOT BLAMING others . . . is for the first time (credit psychoanalysis) looking at himself. He is taking it "standing up."
5. He is pursuing truth at whatever cost. "I want a fact, a thing covered with blood, like all truth."
6. He goes over and over his old relationships to see and recognize what really took place. Finally he will get to the place where he can say: "I'm not afraid of you, because I know what you . . . are."
7. Comes to a recognition, an acceptance of the true nature of himself, of man, of Existence. He has all the facts. He must now confront them honestly.

All the other characters of the play, the "memory figures," were presented obliquely, through Quentin's nonobjective recollections. Kazan sought to comprehend them, one by one, as whole individuals with needs and desires of their own and to evaluate their effect upon the central figure.

About Felice, a casual acquaintance of Quentin who presumed to have her nose "fixed" because she thought he would like her better and whose intense interest in him is not returned, Kazan said:

FELICE:

A dancer

How to live? What is important? The mystery and wonder of existence. Dancing is a philosophy to her, not an exercise!

She married respectably, lived in the suburbs in a small house, began to feel CONDEMNED both to this way of life and to her husband. She had the guts to break it up.

So now she has a FANATICAL APPETITE for all that the world now affords her, for the first time can offer her.

But she needs someone to turn the key to light the light.

Quentin is the trigger to release some sort of wildness in her.

There is something frantic about Felice. Maniacal.

As Quentin experiences it—a girl who keeps wanting *something* from him that he can't satisfy . . . who sees him as an image that he can't meet.

After a time Quentin feels threatened by her worship.

The images of Quentin's earlier family life recurred intermittently throughout the play, called forth by more recent events that struck similar chords within him. There was Quentin's domineering mother, Rose, courageous in spite of disappointment in her marriage to his uneducated father, still exerting control over her son in spite of her death which Quentin felt he did not mourn sufficiently. Kazan considered not only her character but the means by which it could best be conveyed:

ROSE (Mother):

Love of life.

Zest.

"There's no depression for great people!"

Rose makes the excitement wherever she goes.

She fills Quentin with a sense of her potential.

She is full of *unused* sexuality . . . that overflows into everything—food, etc.

Seductive! His unconscious IDEA: Quentin feels it is a sinful betrayal of his mother to love anyone else!

Business:

she draws Quentin's picture
tastes cooking
feels her corset ⎫
rearranges people's clothing ⎬ incessantly
corrects people's stances ⎭

Quentin's father, Ike, a self-made man undone by the Depression, was injured even more acutely by Quentin's refusal to take over the failing family business. A man who loved his wife and struggled to live up to her high expectations, Ike was first seen on stage staggered by the news of her death.

IKE (Father):

A Businessman who built his life on money
and then lost it—2 parts—2 characters.

When IKE walks on ("I bought studs") you
should feel perfect competence. A businessman who manages his affairs well. In fact,
without visible strain. For instance, no one
in his business dealings *ever* finds out that
he can't read! Ever!

It was his country! His city! His terrain!

The first Big Non Survivor. They have killed
him and he lives to know it. So he alternates
between saving the last scraps of his business
and *reproaching* those (Quentin, National City
Bank) who let him down.

He has enormous energy—released now suddenly
. . . since it is suddenly not hitched to anything. He is constantly going over and over
his old records . . . especially his mistakes.

Naturally he resents those who survived.

He keeps hitting his head in a certain way *After
the Crash.*

IKE NEVER GETS OVER QUENTIN'S BETRAYAL!!!

Dan, the brother, stood by his father so that Quentin might leave.

DAN:

Loaded with responsibilities.

But deep underneath he is jealous, and even
angry, at Quentin.

He is too "nice a guy," too fair, too ethical
to let this be seen by Quentin.

But the fact is that he is disappointed in his
own life . . . and he did give it up for Quentin.

A man betrayed by his goodness and love.

Loves father and mother.

Loves his brother.

Overawed by his father.

His answer for the depression and the tragedy
of his father is loyalty and support.

To help out.

He admires Quentin and resents him.

People who sacrifice themselves for others
are not thanked.

Significant to Quentin's present condition were his relations with three friends: Lou, who asks Quentin to represent him when he is subpoenaed and refuses to speak; Elsie, Lou's wife; and Mickey, who threatened Lou's professional and personal security by agreeing to "name names." All of them took part in the test of convictions Quentin had failed in.

LOU:

A scholarly academician, gentle and innocent,
out of his depth in the threatening tenseness
of this crisis.

Is overwhelmed by his wife, who is *sure*.

Is always looking for LOVE, HELP, UNDERSTANDING.

Feels guilty as a witness or student for
having lied, and therefore is, in his heart,
not entirely sure of his position. (No more
than is Mickey.)

For the first time he feels isolated and ON THE SPOT.

So he wants more than anything else, the warmth of friendship. And this longing for togetherness is outraged. It is this Brotherliness that is outraged—nothing else as deeply.

Modest, withdrawing, doesn't want to inflict his problems on others.

Wants wife to be his Mother.

Thinks he's unattractive physically and socially dull . . . and that he's lowly before her.

ELSIE:

This is a woman who builds herself by "putting down" others. She is constantly laughing at Lou and at others. She must put other people down, because that is the only way she can become something herself.

She always starts in a burst of belief at and for someone. Then, at a predictable moment, she is *disappointed* with them.

Even casual bits of business are out of "to put down" i.e. tucks in Lou's shirt, corrects other items in his clothing.

Has had affairs. Lou's forgiven her. This ties her to him.

But she also resents this.

An old-time left-winger socialite. Positive of her morality, puritanical, narrow. But thinks of herself as broad.

Zest. Frank. Really very nice to her husband considering. . . .

MICKEY:

The Guiltless Man (as vs. Quentin).

A great and natural hedonist, full of energy
and pleasure . . . because he is not crippled
with puritanism and the consequent guilts.

Does Mickey expect Quentin to destroy him?
Keeps looking at him. Especially Mickey's last
look at Quentin.

It is then that he recognizes Quentin as a
killer.

He is not sure of his "position" (in his emotions).
No more than is Lou.

Kazan's notes on Quentin's first wife, Louise, reflected the complexity of her character. Although her scenes were limited to those which portrayed her only as partner to a failing marriage, the audience had to be made to see her as a woman with at least a suggestion of those attributes which originally attracted Quentin to her. Then they had to sense the effect she had upon Quentin and, in turn, the change that their conflict had wrought in her. Kazan considered her in light of the moral rigidity that has turned Quentin against her:

LOUISE:

Louise believes in certain rules of behaviour,
of right and wrong.

She is dominated by the "ought to" and the
"should."

Louise has been taught and believes if she
conforms to these rules, she'll come thru O.K.

Sin is absolute. She can't forget it.

Quentin is soiled, disgusting.

Every time Quentin blows his cork, Louise
smiles and enjoys his discomfort . . . and
also the reversal of their positions.
When she started with Quentin, it was all
his way . . . She let that go on too long.

She will not share the guilt. She will not
till the end admit the least part of it is
her fault. So either things have to be
perfect or not at all.

Louise has the INNOCENCE OF THE NON-PERFORMER.

On another page Kazan considered what Quentin had contributed
to their marital conflict:

1. Quentin has patronized her.
2. Quentin has used her—as a mother.
3. Quentin has used her as a servant.
4. Quentin has been totally selfish.
5. Quentin has made her feel insignificant.
6. Quentin has never granted her individuality.
7. Quentin has truly shared NOTHING with her!
8. Quentin wants to avoid her!! She is only
   a "thing," there when he needs it . . . But
   mostly he likes to work.
9. Quentin wants her SILENT. Not demanding
   not raising a ruckus.

She feels she let it go on too long. But now she
has to stop it—and take her place as an equal.

THEREFORE SHE WANTS REVENGE (as Quentin sees it).

A great deal of the audience's sympathy, or lack of it, for Quentin
rested upon their reaction to Louise. Her character had to tread the thin
line between a shrew and a neglected and misunderstood wife; she had
to be cold enough to explain his desire to leave her, yet warm enough
so that the audience would feel his guilt in the act. Kazan traced the

transition that had taken place between her earlier adoration of Quentin and her present distrust and condemnation of him.

> For Louise a *clear morality exists*:
> of right and wrong
> of left and right
> of purity and corruption.
>
> And this makes it possible to live without
> terror and confusion and internal bewilderment.
>
> As she sees it, Quentin is becoming mixed up,
> confused, corrupted.
>
> For Louise, "the answers" are not "all gone."
>
> For Louise, Quentin is changing for the worse,
> and away from her.
>
> Louise feels constantly rejected by Quentin.
>
> She feels he is "looking around longing."
>
> When she first got to know Quentin, he was a
> KNIGHT-IN-ARMOR, a *hero* fighting all immoral
> and corrupt society.
>
> *Now* he is changing—and becoming "confused."
> And therefore *as* corrupt as the society around
> him.
>
> The one thing she can't stand is the INSECURITY
> of life . . . to be in a precarious, threatened
> position.
>
> At bottom she has terrible, terrible doubts about
> her ATTRACTIVENESS AS A WOMAN!! About her
> sexuality. Anyone with sexuality is a tramp!
>
> She is frightened.
>
> Of all the characters in this play, Louise is the
> MOST INSECURE!—that's why she has to pretend
> she is the most secure!!—*SURE!!*

Kazan examined Louise and found her first morally confident, then increasingly insecure; then he took her one step farther. As the threat became more terrifying to her, Kazan analyzed her drive to become a "separate person."

> She has digested and put behind her the emotion of despair.
>
> She is NOT the complaining and neglected wife.
>
> She is far, far tougher.
>
> She is trying to make the marriage—not to break it. But above all, she is trying to get back her dignity and sense of worth.
>
> She is out to save *herself*, not the marriage.
>
> She is well past suffering, INTO ACTION.
>
> *FURTHERMORE*
>
> There is an outstanding element of REVENGE in Louise.
>
> Quentin has made her suffer. (Ditto her father and mother.)
>
> All three made her little, insignificant.
>
> Now she is both ASSERTING HERSELF and HITTING BACK for the first time.
>
> She is doing what she is doing TO SAVE HERSELF.
>
> She is taking her first awkward baby steps in independence.
>
> She is testing her new self.
>
> Some of her new steps are bound to be clumsy!!

As with each of the characters, Kazan returned again and again to Louise to add a new slant or a fresh insight, sometimes the result of a conference with Miller, sometimes an observation of his own made during a rehearsal.

Late Notes on LOUISE:

Louise and Guilt—She knows she hasn't done
her share! She knows *she is not without blemish*, and still
she says that *everyone should be without blemish!*

She always appeals to the
> MORALITY HE IS LEAVING,
> HE IS DISCARDING.

Yet she appeals to it as if he and it were still there.

LOUISE SHINES WITH MORAL IDEALISM.
What *ought* to be! Should!

Louise and Fighting—It is not easy for her to get
in there and SLUG.

She's afraid to get passionately aroused, because
there is sensuality in that. She doesn't want to
get into that.

RATIONALITY and MORALITY are her safeguards.

Make her SYMPATHETIC.

Louise was the center of the "loss of Eden" theme which ran
through the play; in fact, at one time it was to be the conclusive theme
of the play. Quentin's marriage, represented by Louise, was the symbol
of an existence in which goodness and propriety, certainty and happiness, faithfulness and fulfillment went hand in hand.

> Eden is where all is perfectly ordered and he
> knows his direction at all times.
>
> But Eden equals false innocence.
>
> He was trying to preserve an Eden, lying to
> himself to hold it together.

There had to be pain and intense conflict in his abandonment of Louise:

> Quentin is trying to hold the marriage together
> (without dying).

Quentin thinks she's right.

Quentin deeply respects her.
And for all these reasons he clings
very hard to the marriage . . . whatever
else it is, it is workable.

Still:

At end of Act One

Quentin in tears rejects
Louise, as much as
Louise's morality!

Act One was dominated by Louise, Act Two by Quentin's second wife, Maggie. The second act was not completed but its general direction was established in July when Kazan wrote:

I've been looking for the dramatic movement or
progression through the play:

Act I: Quentin blames others. (Psychoanalyst:
"You haven't told me one pertinent thing.
You've simply avoided the issue.")

[The lines attributed to the imaginary
"listener" are an example of a working
device Kazan uses regularly in his
probing below the level of the script.]

Act II: Quentin really gets down to his
complicity in his fall.

Quentin was attracted to Maggie for her animal-like innocence, her spontaneity, her beguiling sweetness, all in obvious contrast to the cool and inhibited Louise. From the beginning there was the hint of paradox in Maggie, a juxtaposition of purity and promiscuity that can be traced to her waifdom. Her sexuality was a device, but one essential to her survival. Her spine, the driving force behind both her strength and her weakness, was the desperate need "to make herself a thing of value."

The primary problem of the second act was to make understandable the hopelessness of Maggie, the inevitability of her downfall, and the part that Quentin did or did not play in her tragedy. Kazan's concern was to find what was basic to her character, to identify and convey the traits that explained both sides of the paradox. Insights were to come over a period of weeks, all contributing to the recognition of the seed of destruction that lay within her, an uncertainty of self, in Kazan's words, that was the very "opposite of spine."

> MAGGIE:
>
> An orphan who never had anything.
>
> She has had to accommodate, adapt herself, "be of service" in order to survive.
>
> Over the years the girl had no identity. She is whatever circumstances demand of her. What choice has she? She has to find protection, a roof.
>
> She was a girl who wanted to make people who originally thought her a worthless waif come to think of her WORTH.

Maggie's increasing desire to be of value led her from shameless promiscuity to her more meaningful affair with Judge Crandall and finally to Quentin. Her seduction of Quentin and her ensuing relationship with him were described by Kazan in a note to Barbara Loden, who played the role of Maggie.

> ". . . The main thing is that Maggie feels that Quentin is the first person, the first and only, who has ever aroused in her a sense of worth. And a sense of her potential as a human. Quentin says to her, 'Because you're so beautiful, Maggie. I don't mean only your face or your body.' And this is true, not only in the sense that he perceives it. But more importantly true in the

sense that FOR THE FIRST TIME IN HER LIFE SHE
FEELS THAT WAY. Through Quentin, she is on the
verge of discovery, and that discovery is that
she is somebody, that she has worth. And
following that, she must come to the realization,
which is the driving force of the scenes that
follow next: That Quentin is the only hope she
has for herself. That only through him can she
make it. And that's why he's like a God. Because
worshipping, emulating and serving a God, you can
partake to some extent in his erectness and value
and goodness and worth. She has found her saviour."

But Maggie's appetite for affection was insatiable, and her underlying need was increasingly desperate. Kazan drew upon his discussions
with Miller to define and paraphrase it.

"I will do whatever necessary to make you like me.
Because only if you like me will you protect me
and take care of me.

"And only if you protect me and take care of me,
will I be safe.

"And if you don't protect me and look after me,
BEFORE NIGHTFALL, I will have to get someone else
to do so.

"Men are pressing me—They want me—

"And I've got to have someone to silence the
terror, the creaks in the house—so HURRY!!
Hurry if you want me!! I'd rather have you—
but if not you, someone else!!

Maggie's station in life rose, but her relationship with Quentin was
one of deepening disappointment. To Maggie's mind, the world was
divided into those who were with her and those who were against her,
and any hint of limitation in Quentin's love was proof that he was an
enemy and a threat. The scenes of the second act illustrated Maggie's

outrage at the shortcomings of her savior, her disintegration and her consequent pursuit of self-destruction. Vengefulness in her was never far removed from helplessness.

> "I want you all for me."
>
> Voracious. Insatiable appetite. Never gets enough of everything!
>
> An orphan looking for support. She hoped for a miracle from Quentin (saviour) . . . Then no miracle happened. Quentin didn't live up to what *she thought he was.* (She had no right to call him faker. She is a desperate orphan who wanted to be saved . . . So he's either God or a fake.)
>
> Quentin, by bringing in the daylight, is threatening her world.
>
> Quentin: "If I leave her—i.e. withdraw my support— She will be back where she was, AT ANYONE'S MERCY, LOST ABANDONED AGAIN.

But at the same time, Maggie was to become a threat to Quentin. Her accusations of betrayal were to call forth the overwhelming sense of failure that he had felt too frequently before. While he was reluctant to add another desertion to his list, he saw in staying not her salvation but his own death. His back was to the wall.

> HE EITHER GIVES UP HIS GUILT
> IN RELATION TO HER
> OR
> SHE WILL KILL HIM!

Quentin escaped from Maggie physically, but he took the burden of guilt with him. However hopeless she seemed, the knowledge stayed with him that he had abandoned her to her death, making him an accessory to the crime. He was appalled at whatever in him kept him from forming a lasting relationship with those he thought he loved. He had lost faith in the world and in himself; he was disgusted with the context in which he saw himself.

Holga, the new woman in his life, offered a fresh context, a world in which his misdeeds might be viewed not as heinous but as human. Quentin had lived in a world of victims; Holga refused to be victimized, and she led Quentin to see that his treachery could be more than feared; it could be recognized and accepted and therefore controlled. Both the source of Holga's strength and the symbol of it was that she, a child of Nazis who knew full well the wrongs that they committed, could make a straightforward admission of error.

HOLGA:

She is not aware of her own beauty or simplicity or worth.

She knows how short, how fragile life is, how precious the minutes are.

"I don't know what will be a year from now.
I don't know next year, next month, next week,
ONLY TODAY—Maybe tomorrow—No, not tomorrow."

She is her history.

She has lived a life already.

It is as difficult for her to commit herself to hope as it is for Quentin.

Quentin: "I bless your uncertainty."
"All my women have been so goddam sure."
"You don't seem to be looking for some moral victory."

She has made up her mind to be self-sufficient, to live for her work.

And NOT to be helpless.

And NOT to need to be reassured every minute.

[66]

"*A girl who keeps wanting* something *from him he can't satisfy . . . who sees him as an image that he can't meet.*" *Zohra Lampert as Felice; Jason Robards as Quentin.*

"The first Big Non Survivor. They have killed him and he lives to know it." Left to right, Virginia Kaye as Rose, Jason Robards as Quentin, and Paul Mann as Ike.

"*In the distortion of one man's memory, the memory figures could not stand the test of reality. It's all stylized: as Quentin remembers it; as Quentin wants to remember it; as Quentin must remember it.*"

"*To pursue truth at* whatever *cost: going here and there, hounding,
uncovering, confronting, listening . . ." Kazan in discussion with actors
Barbara Loden, Jason Robards, Mariclare Costello, back to camera, and
playwright Arthur Miller.*

> Morality? Everyone thinks he's right.
>
> All evil is done in the name of good.
>
> Still, she has morality.
>
> But a morality that *permits* humanity.
> That has leeway.
> That recognizes the human condition.

Through Holga the final theme of the play was realized, the note of hope on which Quentin finally left the stage. The conclusion was a promise not bold but highly significant.

> They are all searching, wanting, waiting for
> an answer.
>
> Quentin (Miller, All of us) are in the habit
> of looking for the solution to our interior,
> intimate problems through someone else or
> something else: a woman, a cause, a religion,
> a conviction, a piece of work.
>
> The only true answer is through the recognition
> of our true natures—the truth of
> our behaviour. With this recognition, a
> true and safe way of living may be found
> that *partly* (but critically) may control the
> evil in us.
>
> The "saving grace" is not some outside element
> like a philosophy of Communism or love . . .
> not "others" or the right "they" . . . but con-
> frontation of one's self, and RECOGNITION
> of one's true nature.
>
> Quentin discovers that one has to find his
> strength NOT through a person or a cause, but
> IN ONE'S OWN BEING!

The persistent and unavoidable danger in the production of *After the Fall* was that the memory figures would become too solid, too well-developed, taking on lives of their own. If this happened, not only would the theme based upon self-confrontation be diminished but the characters themselves would lose their validity. Originally conceived in the distortion of one man's memory, the memory figures could not stand the test of reality. Many times, in one form or another, Kazan reminded himself:

IT'S ALL STYLIZED

"AS QUENTIN REMEMBERS IT."
"AS QUENTIN WANTS TO REMEMBER IT."
"AS QUENTIN MUST REMEMBER IT."

With this in mind, Kazan searched each character vertically, in depth; he laid them out side by side and viewed them horizontally, in terms of their significance to Quentin. Kazan saw them as "waiting evermore for Quentin," all wanting something of him: "encouragement, support, advice, money, coaching, love, friendship, household repairs, son-ness, husband-ness, father-ness, etc." Kazan approached them from one angle after another. He considered their continuous activities, those occupations with which they were associated in Quentin's mind:

> LOUISE: sitting, waiting, combing hair rather hope-
> lessly, playing solitaire, winding a clock,
> looking at wrist-watch ("Where is he?").
> An unhealthy stasis.
> LOU: walking around, reading brief, opening
> telegrams, running into Mickey.
> MICKEY: troubled, talking to himself, arguing it
> out with himself. He's still trying, and will
> be for years, to figure out whether he did
> right or he did wrong. Avidly reading
> newspapers, magazines . . . arguing,
> reading, running for the telephone.
> ELSIE: narcissistic tending face and body.
> Bawling out Lou . . . "idiot," etc. . . .
> sitting in a slump of despair, reverting to
> her body.

IKE (Father): telephone, fighting, making business deals, tearing up bills, stamping invoices, signing his name in connection with Dan.

DAN: book-keeping, sacrificing his life for Quentin.

ROSE (Mother): cooking, making a warm seductive house, giving gifts, giving food, tending, seducing. Driving him on to achievement . . . the achievement she missed with Ike.

FELICE: just staring at Quentin adoringly . . . writing him letters . . . looking at nose, reading books, doing dancing, radio. She hunts him out to worship him, but *she* needed it, enjoys it—NOT the God!

MAGGIE: groaning on bed ("What else have I got?"), sick, taking pills, calling on telephone— Trying to get someone on telephone— keeps trying to make some contact with someone. Playing Sinatra records, Ray Charles.

HOLGA: flower-picking, looking for Quentin. Always ready to travel, move on.

Kazan listed the props necessary to their activities and to the creation of the environment in which Quentin remembered them. He also sought to identify their objectives as they "wait":

LOUISE: watches each of his acts to JUDGE.

ROSE (Mother): measures each of his acts to DRIVE HIM ON.

FELICE: savours each of his acts to WORSHIP what she finds. Waits in attitude of adoration.

IKE (Father): takes in everything he does *instead* of doing for him, Ike. REPROACH.

MICKEY: ACCUSES him of abandonment, defection in friendship.

DAN: works for him and WAITS FOR THANKS.

MAGGIE: tries to WIN HIM BACK TO THE WAY

HE WAS, which was perfect and "all for her."

No! That is only in last scene.

[Such self-corrections are a part of the actual thinking process revealed throughout the notebook.]

HOLGA: DISCOVER—Where do I stand with you? Waits for Quentin's decision . . . on a hill.

LOU: ASKS FOR HELP . . . Waits for him . . . tries to get his attention. Tries to get him on phone. FIND HELP.

ELSIE: SCORN! (*Why*, he never finds out.)

On the other hand, Kazan considered how Quentin *thinks* they look at him:

MICKEY: accusingly.

ROSE (Mother): encouragingly, driving him on to achievement.

IKE (Father): reproaching him. (The reproach of the non-survivor.)

DAN: asking for appreciation.

LOUISE: disapproving, scolding, condemning, distrusting, judging.

MAGGIE: to join a family, to belong.

HOLGA: finding out where she really stands with him.

LOU: asking for his support and help (which finally didn't come through for him).

ELSIE: scornfully, superior, seductive.

FELICE: adoring him.

Throughout the play, the emphasis had to be on these figures not as individuals but as parts of Quentin's past, and his search was the central action of the play. In an entry made during lunch hour after the first rehearsal, Kazan attempted to define the nature of the search and to translate it to the stage.

Quentin is trying to deal with his past and
his situation truthfully and WITHOUT MERCY
on himself.

To PURSUE the truth at *whatever* cost:
going here and there
hounding
uncovering
confronting
listening
questioning this one and that one and back again
recalling
judging
probing
re-examining
contrasting people, comparing people
walking around and through the living statuary
of his PAST
re-living
re-experiencing
trying things out
repeating things just to see if he thinks of them
the same way
living among them.

He goes close and peers into their faces.
He stands alongside un-noticed and listens.
He pries, puzzles out the mystery.
He circles and inspects them from all angles.
He sits in on scenes, then walks away.

ALL IN PURSUIT

OF THE TRUTH

THAT MAY SAVE HIM

Comparing and contrasting all in pursuit of
the ELUSIVE thing—the truth.
Re-experiencing things, throwing himself
into things

THEN SUDDENLY WITHDRAW

AND LET SCENE GO ON

WITHOUT HIM

He starts scenes, then pulls out, once he's got
them going, and watches them.
Then he re-enters the scenes for awhile
Then he pulls out in order to see if he's stirred
up the ELUSIVE thing.

Quentin existed on two levels of experience, both of which were
important to capture:

1. What happened.
2. What is happening now.

He goes into a scene and behaves as he did then,
and then comes out of it and CHANGES COM-
PLETELY and is in his present situation.

He also remembers the way he was—and
NOW, OUTSIDE IT, he's amazed at the way he
behaved.

Although the final blocking was ultimately dependent upon
physical considerations and would not be completed until the play was
well into rehearsal, Kazan began months before to develop the idea of
the "freeze," a technique he would later put to use, at least partially.

Memories in Aspic

Doing something over and over. The one most
characteristic, most feeling, most eloquent
attitude, glimpse, activity.

They come out of one and into another like
Quick Dissolves in a film.

Black Outs   NO!
Try not to rely on them.
They are stereotyped and "empty."

Try to give entrances and exits to each character's every move. A continuing activity. Use
these continuing activities. Use the freezes—

In this way you will get the tangled interplay
of the mind. Memories and apperceptions
criss-crossing each other, living simultaneously, co-existing.

The unorthodox form of the play, combined with the lack of
realistic set, created a threat of obscurity. The director had to pay
constant attention to clarity. Though the play was not realistic in style,
Kazan was relentless in pursuing the realistic details from which his
imagination might then depart with confidence. He isolated the many
scenes and attempted to fix their dates, which he found to range from
1920 (Quentin's childhood scenes) to the future (Holga's arrival at the
airport). He made lists of scenes as to the sound effects they might employ, and other lists of the extras needed: hospital attendants, concentration camp guards, people in the park.

Although many of his ideas on staging were eventually revised or
abandoned, their inclusion in the notebook served to bring the vision
under closer control. Little by little, Kazan anchored each abstraction
to something tangible which could be recognized by the audience and
immediately understood.

Most of the notebook was completed before rehearsals began in
October; entries through December became briefer. Kazan continued
to refer to the book throughout rehearsals, but less and less did his ideas
find their way into its pages. Instead, they were squeezed into the
margins of his various versions of the script or dictated to the stage
managers for inclusion in their promptbooks, or scrawled on scraps of
paper and, once acted upon, discarded. More often they were passed
on verbally in private conferences with the actors, the designer, or the
costumer, as well as with his coproducer and the playwright.

The notebook reached no climax. Direct and unpretentious, it was
a sensitive and penetrating view of *After the Fall*; it revealed the
thoughtful side of a man of action. There was no final burst of insight,
no summing up, not even any indication of mounting anticipation of
opening night. The notebook was, for its author, a tool that had served
its purpose.

To Make a Play

by May Swenson

To make a play
is to make people,
to make people do
what you say;

to make real people
do and say
what you make;
to make people make

what you say real;
to make real
people make up
and do what you

make up. What you
make makes people
come and see
what people do

and say, and then
go away and do
what they see—
and see what

they do. Real
people do and say,
and you see and
make up people;

people come to see
what you do.
They see what *they*
do, and they

may go away undone.
You can make
people, or you
can unmake. You

can do or you
can undo. People
you make up make up
and make people;

people come to
see—to see
themselves real,
and they go away

and do what you
say—as if they
were made up,
and wore makeup.

To make a play
is to make
people; to make
people make

themselves; to
make people
make themselves
new. So real.

A Symposium: The New Repertory —A Socioartistic Experience

The National Theatre
by Kenneth Tynan

ON THE north bank of the Thames, alongside Hungerford Bridge, there is a building originally intended for theatrical performances. Over the door you can still read its name: the Playhouse. It closed down as a commercial theatre many years ago and became a B.B.C. studio. Directly opposite, on the south bank of the river, also alongside Hungerford Bridge, there is an empty site. On it, in the course of the next few years, the National Theatre will be built—a permanent, non-commercial home for the British theatre, whose doors (except during holidays, fires, floods, plagues, and nuclear wars) will never thereafter be closed.

In this riverside confrontation there are the makings of a hopeful symbol. On the rich northern bank, we have the money-making theatre that the public failed to support; on the poorer southern bank, the nonmoney-making theatre that the public is paying to build. If this is a valid symbol, if the people of this country have really switched their allegiance from the commercial to the noncommercial theatre, then I find myself in the unwonted posture of arguing with the tide of accepted opinion instead of against it.

But of course it isn't as clear-cut as that. Official opinion, in the course of the past hundred years or so, has slowly been coaxed, cajoled, and pressured into taking the view that we ought to have a National Theatre. But even today, I am convinced that the great majority of

[75]

people have only the vaguest idea of why we needed it. I doubt if they will actively attempt to sabotage the construction of the new theatre that Denys Lasdun is designing, but then they did nothing to sabotage the appalling Shell building that broods over the site like a bullet-riddled cenotaph. Apathy in these matters is no evidence of good judgment. Moreover, a few weeks ago I ran into outright hostility to the very idea of state-subsidized culture in a quarter where I had taken some kind of qualified sympathy for granted. I was talking to a well-known English novelist, who shall be Amis, about the National Theatre. He astonished me by saying that he objected on principle to all artistic ventures that were financed by the government. Art, he said, should rely on the laws of supply and demand: what the public wanted it would pay for out of its private pocket, and anything that could not pay its way was probably not good art. He challenged me to name a single great artist who did not prosper in his own lifetime. I whispered Mozart, whom he brushed aside as an exception; and I might have mentioned Brecht, who only achieved recognition when the East German government gave him a subsidized theatre to run.

Finally, my novelist chum told me that he would rather rely on the judgment of publishers who were profit-minded individualists than submit his manuscripts to a panel of faceless do-gooders employed by a Ministry of Culture. I tried to point out that public patronage was not intended to exclude private patronage, when suddenly I realized that we were arguing from different premises. He was talking as a novelist, who needs only time, talent, and a typewriter to produce a work of art. I, on the other hand, was concerned with the theatre, where, apart from this trio of prerequisites, a writer needs actors, directors, designers, carpenters, costumers, wigmakers, stagehands, electricians, and possibly singers, dancers, and musicians as well before his work can take on life and present itself for critical assessment. It costs infinitely less to publish a bad novel than to put on a bad play in the commercial theatre. And as soon as you begin to apply commercial criteria to the drama, you find that a play with two characters and one set, which runs for six months, must be considered "better" than a play with fifty characters and twelve sets which runs for a year, since the former will undoubtedly show a larger profit.

Ever since I had this unsettling chat, I have refrained from taking anything on trust when talking about the National Theatre. Hence the first question I'd like to deal with is: why do we need it?

Britain came late to the whole idea of state-aided theatre. One of the reasons for this is that our rulers have never officially concerned themselves with drama—and by rulers I mean royalty. Queen Elizabeth I enjoyed Shakespeare's plays, but she never paid for their upkeep. Louis XIV, by contrast, took Molière's actors under his fiscal wing and gave France the Comédie Française. Similarly, it was the rulers of the German city-states who founded the great German tradition of subsidized theatre; the provincial centers of German culture still compete with each other for theatrical supremacy.

Another reason for British backwardness is the lasting damage inflicted on the theatre by the Puritans in the seventeenth century. After their moral lacerations, acting came to be regarded as a form of clothed prostitution; and though Charles II subsidized actresses, he did not subsidize plays. Until Irving got his knighthood in 1895, acting remained a dubious profession, barely a stone's cast away from the brothel. And this mighty backlog of Puritan disapproval had to be dislodged before a British government could be persuaded to spend a penny of public money on an art so trivial. Nobody realized that the theatre had become trivial precisely because no public money had been spent to make it otherwise.

Twenty years ago, a prominent American playwright summed up what he felt about the Broadway theatre: "That the most exalted of the arts should have fallen into the receivership of businessmen and gamblers is a situation parallel in absurdity to the conduct of worship becoming the responsibility of a herd of water buffaloes. It is one of those things that a man of reason had rather not think about until the means of redemption is more apparent."

That was Tennessee Williams, talking about the American theatre in 1944. People in Britain have been arguing in the same way for more than a century, and elsewhere in Europe for more than three hundred years. The means of redemption became apparent a long time ago. The very idea that good theatre should be required to show a profit would seem indecent in Sweden, Denmark, Poland, Czechoslovakia, Hungary, Yugoslavia, Norway, Russia, Italy, both the Germanies, and France. You might as well insist that public libraries should profiteer or that the educational system should pay its way. Theatre in these countries is an amenity for which the state or the municipality—which are simply the individual writ large—must hold itself responsible. It is something the public needs and deserves, like art galleries, zoos, and parks for recreation.

Henry James wrote in 1872: "It is impossible to spend many weeks in Paris without observing that the theatre plays a very important part in French civilization; and it is impossible to go much to the theatre without finding it a copious source of instruction as to French ideas, manners and philosophy."

The same could not have been said of the British or the American theatre in the late nineteenth century. In London and New York, drama had been forced into the market place, there to compete with every other huckster. It had inevitably become a short-term art, dependent on quick financial returns, concerned only to produce what the public wants *now*—not what it might want over a period of five, ten, or twenty years. It was compelled to concentrate on easily digestible, un-controversial, ego-massaging, audience-ingratiating trifles, relieved on occasion by classical revivals tailored to fit star personalities. Box-office tyranny was absolute, and has remained so, apart from latter-day trickles of patronage from bodies like the Arts Council, ever since. As to the "instruction" of which Henry James spoke, it is a dirty word in the commercial theatre. Brecht once wrote an imaginary conversation in the course of which an actor says to a playwright: "You must under-stand that audiences in the theatre don't want to be sent back to school." To which the playwright replies: "In that case, your schools must be appalling—abolish them!"

Subsidy offers what commercialism negates: the idea of continuity, the guarantee of permanence. If a new production fails on first show-ing, it need not be lost forever; it can be shelved for a while and then, if public opinion changes, be revived on the crest of a new wave. Sub-sidy also enables the theatre to build a durable bridge, with free passage for traffic in both directions, between the past and the present. If Broad-way were subsidized, for instance, we would still be able to see Elia

[78]

Kazan's productions of *A Streetcar Named Desire* and *Death of a Salesman* —they would still be on view, alternating with a dozen other plays, old and new, performed by permanent acting troupes. The plays of Chekhov and Gorky have been in the repertoire of the Moscow Art Theatre for sixty years, with occasional changes of cast. In this way each new generation of playgoers is kept in touch with history. The storehouse of past achievement is always open to the public, instead of being irrevocably burned down at the end of every season.

Last year I took the chair at a Drama Conference sponsored by the Edinburgh Festival. In the course of it Joan Plowright said with some passion that subsidy meant, above all, the recognition that the artist had a right to fail. "Millions of pounds," she said, "are spent on the right of scientists to fail, and the creative artist should be granted the same right as the man who experiments with nuclear warfare." People sometimes fear that state subsidy may bring with it state control and censorship, and in totalitarian countries this has often been the case. The truth is that governments have two equally effective means of controlling their artists. One is by direct censorship. The other is more oblique but not less potent—it is censorship imposed by *withholding* subsidies, thereby enslaving the artist to the box office and forcing him, unless he is a genius, to turn out lovable, undisturbing after-dinner entertainments.

What can happen to a theatre without subsidy was vividly animated for me at the Edinburgh Conference. Ninety people attended it, speaking twenty-odd languages, and among them was a young American director who wanted to stage, on the last day of the conference, what is known as a "happening." He explained it to me thus: "You see, Ken, Broadway is like a jungle. If you want to experiment you have to go out into the streets." He wanted to use the conference audience in the following experimental way: "First of all, there'll be no chairs in the hall. Not one. Just a couple of thousand used automobile tires, lying around on the floor. In the middle of the auditorium there'll be four monumental towers of gasoline cans. At the exits there will be four men in black sitting on motorcycles with the motors idling ominously. I shall then invite the audience to build a mountain of tires in the center of the floor. Next, and simultaneously, the lowest and the

[79]

highest notes on the organ will be sounded, thereby creating a sense of unease. The cyclists, at this point, start to circle around the people building the mountain. The guys on the towers of gasoline cans will begin to strike them with hammers on the off-beat. The audience will then dismantle the mountain." I asked him where they would sit. "On the tires, where else?" But (I pointed out) they had paid money and booked seats with numbers. . . .

At length I persuaded him to stage the happening outside the hall in the courtyard, after the conference was over. I stood on a balcony and watched it with a group of Eastern European directors, people who worked in theatres that subsidized experiment and were not faced with the stark choice between commercialism and cut-price improvisation masquerading as art. One of them said he had begun to mistrust me when, some years ago, I expressed faith in Socialist theatre. "I thought you had become a Socialist realist," he said. "I did not know then," and he gestured toward the happening, "what you were up against." Looking down at the elaborate practical joke below, we felt like Louis XVI and his court with the revolutionary mob howling beneath. Except that this was not a genuine revolution; it was a gesture born of economic necessity. I learned afterward what the young American was trying to do. He explained that he wanted to restore a sense of ritual and participation to the act of playgoing. But it was ritual without content, a party game instead of a communal festivity, a private fantasy which cost nothing and was therefore responsible to no one. It was do-it-yourself art—the only alternative, in an entirely profit-based society, to commodity art, art considered as a salable product.

Subsidy is the missing link, the third force which can occupy and colonize the great intermediate area between minority theatre based on private whim and majority theatre based on private profits. This is precisely the area that the National Theatre exists to inhabit and develop; and our hope is that it will be the first, not of the few, but of the many, the beginning of a chain reaction that will set up a national grid of subsidized theatres in London and in every provincial center. And if subsidy in itself still offends you as a concept, recall that you and every one of us are subsidizing the commercial arts at this moment to a vast and growing extent. Who pays for the enormous advertising campaigns launched on behalf of pop movies, pop magazines, and pop records? No one but us, the consumers. Eventually it is always the consumer who pays; and there is an element of irrationality about the man who opposes state subsidy to the arts while at the same time defending to the death his right to pay inflated prices for those commercial products he has seen most heavily advertised.

In the British theatre as a whole, chaos still prevails. The notion that an ideal playhouse is a place where you can see a permanent company of first-rate actors appearing in a large and varied repertoire of first-rate plays is generally accepted; but the notion that such a playhouse must inevitably incur an enormous financial loss, even if it plays to capacity, is less widely embraced. The formation of the National Theatre company was a step toward sanity, toward placing the theatre on the same footing as art galleries and public libraries. The pioneers of the National Theatre movement—people such as Shaw, William Archer, and Harley Granville-Barker—confidently expected that their battle would be won in time for the tercentenary of Shakespeare's death. That was in 1916. Victory was delayed until last October, when the National Theatre presented its inaugural production just in time for the quatercentenary of Shakespeare's birth.

There are many other serious legitimate theatres in Britain which are supported to a certain extent by public funds. The National Theatre gets more money than any of the others; but I should like to emphasize that none of them gets enough. To support our first year's operations, we received a Treasury grant of £130,000—only £50,000 more than the sum allotted the year before to the Old Vic. And the Old Vic employed a much smaller company at much lower salaries, and presented a much shorter list of plays. To keep our standards as high as our output, we shall need more money soon. The same applies to our friendly rivals, the Royal Shakespeare Company. I would like them to be able to compete with us on equal terms, because artistic competition usually makes for better art, whereas commercial competition seldom makes anything but money. The National Theatre and the Royal Shakespeare Company should be able to live side by side in the same kind of relationship as that which exists between the Comédie Française and Jean-Louis Barrault's Théâtre de France.

The tap of public patronage is not exactly gushing, but at least it has been connected. To borrow a dictum beloved of American Negro leaders, "We ain't where we ought to be, and we ain't where we're going to be, but we sure ain't where we were." The National Theatre, as a company, exists: the great *de facto* hurdle has been surmounted. It has acquired a brilliant architect in Denys Lasdun, and before long its permanent home will begin to creep up on the south bank, mercifully obscuring at least part of the Shell penitentiary. What form the theatre will take is something on which I cannot pronounce; I am not a member of the Building Committee that is in charge of planning its shape. Anything I say here reflects personal bias, not official consensus. It is accepted that there should be two auditoriums; it is also accepted that if you try to cram more than a thousand people into a single auditorium, you are entering an area where audibility or visibility or both are sure to be imperfect. Neither on nor outside the Building Committee is there absolute agreement as to how deeply the stage should project into the auditorium—how far, you might say, it should put its tongue out at the audience—but it is generally felt that actors and spectators should seem to be in one room, without the separating guillotine of the proscenium frame. Beyond this common ground, all is doubt and guesswork.

Speaking for myself and not for the National Theatre, I have two cherished hopes. One concerns the relative sizes of the two projected playhouses. Tradition, based on continental models and Harley Granville-Barker's proposals, dictates that one should be large, reserved for the major classics, and the other small, devoted to experimental work. I believe this dichotomy to be artificial and archaic. It derives from the days when all reputable theatres had to be large in order to be commercial; and when plays of doubtful commercial value were forced into converted cellars, attics, or church halls that could be cheaply rented. According to this viewpoint, there are two separate kinds of theatre: majority theatre, performed for money, and minority theatre, performed for kicks. This division, originally imposed by economic necessity, tends to survive in the minds and attitudes of those who are planning a theatre from which economic necessity has been removed. Instead of a big house holding a thousand and a little one holding three hundred or so, I would therefore propose two theatres much closer in relative capacity, eight hundred, let us say, and six hundred. Otherwise we may tend to perpetuate the class-conscious notion that there is one kind of drama for the many and another kind, implicitly superior, for the few. Any theatrical experience that cannot be communicated to six hundred people at a sitting is not, on the face of it, the sort of experience that a National Theatre exists to provide. I would hope, of course, for a third auditorium, a workshop or studio devoted to far-out experiment, such as the Schiller Theatre has in West Berlin, but the priority, in my mind, rests with the other two.

Next there is the anguished question of how far the stage should jut out into the audience; and this is bound up with what we have just considered. The aim is to get as many people as possible as close as possible to the stage. Geometrically, this means that the larger the prospective audience, the more you have to push the acting area out into their midst. Reduce the audience, and at once you reduce the necessity of shoving out a peninsular stage, which even at its best imposes on the customers a number of dire deprivations, such as staring at an actor's rear view when most you need to look at his face and hear the words he is saying. The analogy one often hears drawn with the Elizabethan theatre is pathetically invalid; the reason why the Elizabethan stage projected into the audience was not artistic but climatic —the plays were performed by daylight and there was no other way of ensuring that the actors were visible. I have heard it speciously argued that a projecting stage adds "a third dimension" to acting. What a grotesque abuse of language! *All* live acting is in three dimensions, as opposed to screen and television acting, which has two; and I cannot understand how the ability to see one's fellow spectators behind the actors materially adds to the sculptural roundness of the experience. If we erected a few rows of seats behind the actors on the stage of the Old Vic, would it really make the productions more three-dimensional? The truth, I suspect, is that *proximity* creates the illusion of an extra dimension, and in a theatre of reasonable size, you don't need a tongue-shaped stage to achieve proximity. It exists, after an improvised fashion, at that brilliant conversion job, the Mermaid Theatre in Puddle Dock, where the edge of the stage is straight.

[83]

All of us at the National Theatre worry about architectural problems, whether or not it is our business to do so. We also fret over our immediate task, which is to assemble the best available actors and put them into a snowballing repertoire of the best available plays, ancient and modern, comic and tragic, native and foreign. But we have also stumbled across an additional problem. It has to do with re-education; slowly and patiently, we have had to set about re-educating actors, directors, playwrights, and audiences alike. You would be surprised how hard it is, in a society where "theatre" means "theatre for private profit," to explain to people that *this* theatre actually belongs to them, and is not in any way stirred by the need or desire to show a profit. I have had to point out to playwrights that in our *modus operandi* they must take the long-term, not the short-term view; although we cannot offer them the quick financial gains of a West End run, we can offer them instead a repertory run that might last for decades. The base on which our enterprise rests can be simply stated: we are not selling a product, we are providing a service. Success at the box office is no longer the only criterion. We would rather have a first-rate work playing to less than capacity than a third-rate one filling the house. Instead of fearing criticism, we can learn from it without rancor, since we do not depend, as the commercial theatre must, on rave reviews for survival.

So far we have opened six productions in the space of five months. On the whole, the critics have applauded and the public has flocked. I don't doubt that this is partly due to the patriotic euphoria that clusters around the launching of any great national venture, and we are sure to run into an iceberg or two before long. But we have not fulfilled the cynical prophecy that the National Theatre would be a plush-lined museum; the names of Laurence Olivier, John Dexter, and William Gaskill are not exactly renowned for reverent conventionality, and I am no conservative myself.

Equally, we have not established a "style" of our own. This is because we never intended to. Good repertory theatres fall into two main categories. One is the kind that is founded by a great director or playwright with a novel and often revolutionary approach to dramatic art. He creates a style for his own special purpose. Examples of this process would include Stanislavsky's Moscow Art Theatre, Bertolt Brecht's Berliner Ensemble, and Joan Littlewood's Theatre Workshop. The other category consists of theatres with a broader, less personal *raison d'être*, whose function, more basic though not more valuable, is simply to present to the public the widest possible selection of good plays from all periods and places. In this group you can place the Schiller Theatre in West Berlin, the Royal Dramatic Theatre in Stockholm, and the National Theatre in the Waterloo Road. Their aim is to present each play in the style appropriate to it—and that is an ambition by no means as modest as it sounds.

A year or so ago, I noticed that out of more than two dozen plays running in the West End, only three had been written before 1950. This is the kind of fantastic imbalance that the National Theatre exists to correct. By the end of the summer we shall have staged twelve plays, eight British, four foreign; nine by dead authors, three by living. Of these, roughly half will remain in next autumn's repertoire, some of them, hopefully, for periods of many years. In 1964–65 a dozen more productions have been chosen to join the list. Shakespeare is a necessity, though not in bulk; we plan to present *Much Ado About Nothing* and *King Lear* but we are content to leave the lion's share of the Bard to the Royal Shakespeare Company. To test the stamina of plays that were praised in the fairly recent past is part of National Theatre policy, hence our decision to revive Noel Coward's *Hay Fever*, directed by the author. Other productions in active preparation include Congreve's *Love for Love*, Strindberg's *Dance of Death*, *The Dutch Courtesan* by John Marston, Brecht's *Mother Courage* (which, apart from the Berliner Ensemble's short but cataclysmic visit in 1956, has never been professionally performed in London), Chekhov's *The Three Sisters*, Lope de Vega's *Fuente Ovejuna* (adapted by Alan Sillitoe), a play by John Osborne based on de Vega's *La Fianza Satisfecha* (a strange and startling moral fable), and two original scripts, *The Royal Hunt of the Sun* by Peter Shaffer, and *Dingo* by Charles Wood. The list is long and various, and only high subsidy makes it even conceivable.

You may ask whether the public wants the theatrical goods we have chosen for them and for which their taxes have paid. The answer is that it looks that way; up to last week the average attendance at the

Old Vic was not far short of ninety per cent. And who are these play-goers? Where do they come from and what do they want? We have some information on this subject, derived from a questionnaire that we appended to the program of *Andorra*. Ten per cent of the audience, to date, have filled it in and returned it; and you may like to read some of the results, bearing always in mind that the audience for a play like *Andorra* is likely to be younger and more experimentally inclined than the audience for an established classic.

The *Andorra* figures show that thirty-five per cent of the audience is either teaching or being taught. A further twenty-four per cent con-sists of clerical or other white-collar workers. Point three per cent (0.3%) are manual workers. The last figure is the most distressing, demonstrating as it does that live theatre is socially beyond the desires and financially beyond the means of working-class audiences. Some-thing must be done to remedy this, the obvious course being to reduce the prices of admission, which would involve either an increase of sub-sidy or a lowering of artistic standards. The former would clearly be preferable. Encouragingly, fifty-five per cent of the audience is thirty-five years old or younger, which implies that we are not tailoring our program to meet the demands of gerontophile nostalgia. Many of our spectators are addicts, obsessed with theatre to the point (in some cases) of mania. Thirty-seven per cent of them go to the theatre more than thirty times a year; and fifteen per cent more than fifty times. One realizes that the theatre is kept alive by a hard core of absolute fanatics. Nine per cent of the audience, paying more than seventy-five visits a year, buy far more tickets than the thirty per cent who come fifteen times or less.

Geographically, the figures reveal an overwhelming majority of National Theatre-goers in London and the home countries—eighty-nine per cent, as against a tiny minority from the rest of Britain and the world. Obviously, we must tour as much and as widely as we can if we are to deserve the epithet "National." Replying to a question about the plays they would most like to see added to the repertoire of the National Theatre, the audience voted for Ibsen, Shaw, Brecht, Mar-lowe, Wilde, O'Neill, and Jonson, in that descending order. Sixty per cent of them liked *Andorra*, with only twenty-two per cent of hostility

—not bad, considering that it was the first new play (and an awkward, foreign one at that) which the National Theatre had ever presented.

I have tried, in this headlong survey, to give some idea of the direction in which the National Theatre is moving. My conclusions, of course, are those of a navigator and not of a pilot. I once defined a critic as a man who knew the way but couldn't drive the car. As a back-seat driver at the National Theatre, I am putting that maxim to the test.

—Delivered before The Royal Society of Arts, March 18, 1964

Filling the Blank
by Sir Tyrone Guthrie

I HESITATE to say anything about repertory as a socioartistic experience, since I am not at all clear about what a socioartistic experience is. Perhaps, like M. Jourdain, who didn't know that he was speaking in prose, I am undergoing socioartistic experiences all the time, but unawares.

The most socioartistic feature of our theatre in Minnesota is, I should imagine, the fact that it was called into being by the public to fill what was regarded as a blank in the cultural life of the Twin Cities —Minneapolis and Saint Paul.

More than two and a half million dollars were raised by public subscription to build a new theatre. Nothing was raised to subsidize the goings-on which it should house. The theory was that if these goings-on were satisfactory they would, as the saying goes, wash their own faces.

I am not sure that this theory holds water. And I feel rather strongly that if the theatre is to give a decisive lead to public taste, it may be needful from time to time to ask for subvention. But I appreciate that too much money is far more paralyzing to artistic affairs than too little. Necessity, someone has observed, is the grandmother of invention. But in theatrical as in other affairs, Granny is not always the best person to be the boss.

The theatre is owned by one nonprofit, tax-exempt foundation and operated by another. In the fullness of time I should assume that these twain will merge into one. Those of us who work for these boards, whether in an administrative or artistic capacity, are merely paid hands. The operating board gives us a very free hand, but it accepts

[88]

responsibility for policy and budget and retains the right to dispense with our services at its own discretion.

A repertoire of four plays is presented by a professional company engaged on a seasonal basis. As soon as circumstances permit, we are anxious to have a nucleus of actors under considerably longer contracts. Only so, we believe, can any cohesion of style and any satisfactory tradition be achieved; and, more practically, only so can we revive successes of previous seasons with a substantial nucleus of the original cast.

The Twin Cities, like all other American cities, have for the past thirty or forty years had very little opportunity to see any professional theatre, other than occasional visits by touring companies and the performances of a lively professional stock company at the Old Log Theatre, a few miles beyond the city limits. In both cases, the plays presented have been chosen primarily for their commercial appeal. Consequently, the public as a whole cannot have such a sophisticated acquaintance with the art of drama as any interested person can acquire in Paris, Moscow, London, or even, if he really works at it, New York.

But unsophistication must not be confused with unintelligence.

We believe—and the belief has so far been amply justified by experience—that there exists in cities like Minneapolis and St. Paul a considerable public which is gravely dissatisfied with the condescension to "popular" taste made by the commercial theatre, movies, and television; a public which is prepared to meet considerable demands upon its intelligence and energy. We determined to attempt to rally such a public behind our enterprise.

Now you can proclaim that your policy is to present "serious" or "good" plays; but how can you define such plays? For management just to choose the plays which appeal to its own personal taste is apt to be a bit capricious. I, for instance, have a weakness for nineteenth-century farce, and for society melodramas with characters called by such names as Lord Maltravers and La Viscountess de Beaumanoire and strong situations where the Viscountess, producing a tiny jeweled revolver, says "Die, my Lord, like the dog that you are," and shoots my Lord in the stomach as the second act curtain falls. But few plays like this can be regarded as "good" or "serious"; and a program, in which

[89]

they formed a considerable element, could not, I feel convinced, be very socioartistic.

It seemed better to settle for plays which a consensus of educated opinion had, over several generations, agreed to regard as serious and good; which had, in fact, become classics.

Plays about native life in America written by natives can, with very, very few exceptions, and those mostly in the curio department, hardly be said to have existed before Eugene O'Neill. And O'Neill, flourishing in the third decade of this century—only just over a generation ago—has not had time to become A Classic. Therefore, a solely and severely classical program would have to omit all American plays.

This seemed a bad idea for several reasons. Americans very naturally want to see plays by their native writers and about their own environment. Equally naturally they resent the notion that any imported article—be it a play, a carpet, a suit of clothes, or a grand piano —must necessarily be superior to its homemade equivalent. Such a notion is always insulting and frequently false. Furthermore, between O'Neill and the present time there has come into being a considerable American drama. While no one can yet assess its power to survive, some of it has at least the potentiality of classical status. I should put Thornton Wilder at the head of the list, but reasonable claims could be made on behalf of Elmer Rice, Clifford Odets, Lillian Hellman, Arthur Miller, and Tennessee Williams. This list is not exhaustive.

We decided, therefore, to announce a program which should give as wide and diverse a view of classical drama as we could manage, and that juxtaposed to three classics, a fourth play would be included each season by an American author of potential classical status.

Of course such a program has inevitably been a target for criticism. One gentleman, whose financial support and influence might have been extremely valuable, withdrew both because our first season's program (*Hamlet*, translations of *L'Avare* and *Tri Sistri*, and *Death of a Salesman*) seemed to him hopelessly and pathetically "popular." He suggested that *Agamemnon* of Aeschylus was a "must" and that by way of something fluffy and relaxing, we might offer one of those side-splitting farces of Plautus. A more usual criticism was made of our omission of any new works, with reproachful comments that we were doing nothing to "encourage" contemporary writers.

Our reply to this is that nowhere in the world do contemporary writers receive more encouragement than in America, and nowhere are the dramatic classics of the world so seldom and, in general, so feebly produced.

It is our view that an intelligent contemporary author will feel considerably encouraged by a theatre which makes it possible for him to see a half-decent production of any of the plays on our list without his having to travel half across the world. The presentation of the classics, the exemplars of their art, is the second most important service which a theatrical management can render to playwrights. The most important, certainly, is to produce their plays. But half a hundred American managements are looking for new plays to produce; not half a dozen offer to young dramatists the necessary opportunity to get acquainted with the masterpieces of their predecessors.

It may be argued that, in general, theatrical managers are on the lookout for plays of commercial, rather than artistic, value. It may be so. But it is not my opinion, and I have some experience to back it, that the desks of producers, agents, or anyone else in the theatre, are stuffed with unproduced, neglected masterpieces. Moreover, we felt that at the outset of an extremely costly and financially uncertain project, we had no right to undertake obvious risks. A new play is necessarily more risky than a classic. The worth of a classic has been already proven; whereas no one really knows whether a new script, however effective on paper, will really "play" well. Besides, no sensible newspaper critic will come right out and say *Hamlet* or *The Three Sisters* is a bad play. They will pay at least lip service to a classic and concentrate their censure on its interpreters, whereas a new play draws their fire.

Incidentally, wouldn't it be fun to read notices by Howard Taubman or Walter Kerr, had they been able to attend the original performance of *Hamlet*? What a thrashing young Shakespeare would have had: sprawling, untidy, overblown, long-winded . . . What, if anything, does it all *mean*? . . . However, thanks to the experienced skill of Mr. Burbage, who has rarely been seen to greater advantage . . .

To conclude the defense of a classical program: our plan was to collect both an audience and a company of actors and then not to teach them, but to let them help one another to learn something more about the art and craft of play acting and playgoing, by experiment not with ephemeral trifles too light-weight to extend anyone's power of inter-pretation, but with a series of masterpieces.

Make no mistake: there is an art, or craft, of playgoing. Naturally everyone feels entitled, and rightly, to judge a play and to judge its ac-tors. Everyone has a similar right to judgments on painting, literature, music, theology, the theory of relativity, or whether the state of New Jersey should remain within the Union. Not everyone, however, has a right to expect that his judgment should be taken seriously.

It is a fallacy, accepted by almost all of us, that our own taste is good. "I don't know a thing about painting, but I do know what I like," say ninety-nine per cent of us. The statement does some credit to our honesty and also to our common sense, because, let's face it, there are no valid aesthetic standards other than the totally subjective. But it is rather meaningless to say that you know what you like and, in the same breath, to proclaim that you don't know a thing about art. In that case your likes and dislikes are of significance only to yourself and had better be treasured in silence.

Good taste is not inborn. It is acquired. And it is acquired in only one way: by experience. Experience becomes meaningful only when one experience can be compared with another. You cannot be a critic of drama if you know only one play; or of actors until you have seen enough performances and learned enough about the craft of acting to be able to distinguish not merely what you like from what you do not like, but easy from difficult, till you can have reasonable views about this or that style of acting in relation to this or that style of text. A man-ner of speech and behavior which would be quite appropriate in a play by Odets is not necessarily right in a play by Shakespeare. Styles ap-propriate for Shakespeare and Odets may neither be suitable in text by Bernard Shaw.

In general, judgments by the public, and indeed all too often by professional critics who ought to know better, seldom rise above "I like him," or "I hate her," purely subjective reactions to a particular personality.

[92]

It is not generally realized that an actor's skill, as opposed to his personality, can only be assessed when he is seen in a number of widely different roles. There is, for instance, almost no opportunity to assess the skill of most film stars. Joan Crawford and Cary Grant are very attractive and handsome people and have acquired a considerable technical skill in presenting to a camera the very limited portrait of themselves which is demanded by all the roles which they play. Their acting ability would only be revealed if they departed completely from the familiar stereotype and played other kinds of characters in varying kinds of dramatic style.

There is, surely, an analogy between the choice of repertoire for a theatre and that for a symphony program. No one can pretend to an educated musical taste until he is familiar with a considerable part of the classical repertoire—the symphonies of Mozart, Beethoven, Schubert, and Brahms, the work of Handel and Bach, and in opera, Mozart, Wagner, and Verdi. It is upon these that taste is formed. New work is judged in comparison with these, and in the light of the musical knowledge which acquaintance with the classics can alone bestow.

It is true that well-arranged symphony programs juxtapose new works with classics, and each throws light on the other. In the fullness of time our theatre may be able to do likewise. But do not forget that in a concert season several hundred works can be included; whereas we cannot in the foreseeable future achieve more than four, or possibly five, new productions in a season.

On Broadway a new piece can be type-cast from an enormous pool of available actors. In repertory it must be cast from an existing company—in our case, thirty-five to forty actors. On Broadway a successful play can run for hundreds of performances. In repertory the number is far more limited—forty-five is our present average; and, because the price of seats is considerably lower than Broadway prices, the author's percentage is apt to be considerably lower too.

On the other hand, if a repertory theatre has a faithful and intelligent following, the author's play has a better chance of being well received. An intelligent author cannot but reflect that his chances of a smash hit on Broadway are slim—for a serious play, one in twenty might be reasonable reckoning; and if it isn't a smash hit, his play will almost certainly be a smash flop and will, in that case, barely survive for eight performances.

On balance, however, I think few authors would choose a repertory to a Broadway showing. They would figure that a failure on Broadway need not necessarily preclude a subsequent production elsewhere; whereas it is almost unthinkable that any producer would risk the enormous expense of a Broadway production of a play which has failed to please in rep.

There is, I suppose, a third possibility, that new plays should be "tried out" by repertory theatres on behalf of Broadway producers. I cannot see, however, that this play would be likely to commend itself to repertory theatres either on artistic or commercial grounds.

Even if, as time goes on, an occasional new play is included, I hope that we shall, in general, stick to a classical policy. It cannot be overestimated how needful it is, if you want to find and hold an audience, to stick to a consistent and clearly defined policy.

The great commercial as well as artistic weakness of the English-speaking theatre has been that producers have tried all the time to appeal to an enormous, generalized mass public. More than fifty years ago this public forsook the theatre for the movies; and now the same public is forsaking the movies for television. The theatre now is to movies and television what the gourmet store is to the supermarket, or the custom tailor to the seller of mass-produced suits.

Obvious confusion would arise if a gourmet store were suddenly to exchange its stock with a branch of the A & P. But this is just what is happening all the time in the theatre. Serious plays, farces, musicals are all offered in the same houses by the same managements. In the hope that a gullible mass public will be attracted, all are advertised in a similar loud, screaming, vulgar style.

Surely in shopkeeping it is elementary that you try to associate your site, your staff, your promotion, and your merchandise with a particular group of customers; or, put another way round, you try to collect a group of customers who want your particular kind of merchandise, sold in your particular kind of way.

I do not see how a serious theatre can be brought into being unless

[94]

it consistently pursues a clearly identifiable and clearly stated policy. This policy must not be planned with the general mass of the public in mind. The general mass has shown clearly for hundreds of years that it has not the slightest use for a serious theatre, serious music, painting, or literature. The desire for these is felt by only a tiny minority of the public; and even then intermittently. Serious art, even when we admit that art is worth taking seriously—an admission which a majority of even a so-called civilized community is quite unprepared to admit— makes serious demands upon our energy. Most of us are lazy all the time and by middle age are quite incapable of serious effort of any kind, physical or mental; the rest of us are lazy most of the time and capable only of infrequent effort. Now and again we will make the effort to appreciate serious, and therefore difficult, works of art; most of the time we will content ourselves with what the magazines have to offer in the way of literature and visual art; for drama and music we rely on television.

Therefore, do you agree, if a serious theatre is realistically managed, it will not waste time and money trying to woo the great mass of the public? It will concentrate on trying to collect a much, much smaller but more serious and faithful following. Such a following will not be found in any one group of a community. Emphatically, it will not be exclusively the best off or even the best educated. Although numerically small, it will turn out to carry weight and influence out of all proportion to its size.

If some of your theatre's productions turn out to be extremely successful, you will have no need to proclaim this fact from the housetops. Word will spread automatically. There is nothing in the theatre which the Great Public values so highly as Success. If word gets around that such-and-such is A Great Success, people will crawl on their hands and knees over broken glass to buy tickets. They will not bother to ask what the play is about, or who wrote it, or who is acting in it. That is all of secondary interest. What they want is to associate themselves with something which is largely and loudly successful, with something which has Made The Grade, has Got Ahead, about which Everyone Is Talking; to associate themselves with an event which is publicly expressing one of their own important private aspirations. By aiming

[95]

your policy and promotion at the Faithful Few, you will not keep out the Fickle Many.

Since the following must, I think, be socioartistic, I should add that for three weeks at the beginning of both our seasons, and for a further week at the end of this season, we have played exclusively to high school students. They have proved a splendid audience, alert, polite, ready to laugh at what is amusing and marvelously still and concentrated when stillness and concentration are required. This year they came "prepared" by "kits" which gave information about the plays (*Henry V* and *Saint Joan*). These were written by qualified people (mostly members of the English department of the University of Minnesota) and edited by the theatre's publicity director. We feel that their usefulness has been proved and next year's kits will be somewhat more ambitious and comprehensive.

These school performances are offered at a price which involves the theatre in a small loss. It is felt that this is justified, partly in terms of public service, partly of self-interest, since youngsters who enjoy these performances will be the nucleus of our future audience.

We have no present plans for a school attached to the theatre. We prefer to work in close, though informal, alliance with the drama department of the University of Minnesota. Through the generosity of the McKnight Foundation, a certain number of graduates in drama from the University are annually awarded fellowships which enable them to take a postgraduate course with the drama department, followed by a season, in an apprentice capacity, with the theatre. These fellows are chosen jointly by the faculty of the drama department and the directors of the theatre. So far there has been a happy unanimity of choice; I see no reason why the scheme should not continue to the mutual gain of the fellows, the department, and the theatre.

During this coming winter a brief tour is being undertaken. An anthology program, entitled *The Platform*, will be presented, designed to be extremely mobile and to serve as a sort of introduction to the living theatre, not didactic, except in the sense that a salesman is didactic when he shows his wares to a new customer. The program will be directed by Douglas Campbell and acted by leading members of the theatre company. It will be in no way inferior to the productions given in our theatre, but will be attempting something different both in technique and intention. The tour has been booked by Midwestern universities, but the performances will be available to the public; the universities being, as it were, sponsors on behalf of their several communities.

In conclusion, let me tell how our project has been welcomed and supported by the public.

Before the first season over twenty-two thousand season tickets had been sold for each of the four plays in the twenty-week season: eighty-eight thousand admissions in all—a splendidly solid buttress against failure. We were aware that these season ticket holders must have been partly influenced by the novelty of the scheme—a handsome, brand-new building, for instance; and partly by a promotional drive initiated and carried through with immense verve and persistence by more than a thousand voluntary workers. It was all too possible that enthusiasm would fade away.

In fact, the audience grew very steadily as the season progressed, until for the last eight or ten weeks the problem was not so much how to fill the house as how to accommodate those who wanted to come.

When the holiday season began, visitors arrived in large numbers from all over the United States; there was also a pleasant trickle over the border from Canada. This was not only helpful to the box office, but very much so to our local prestige! It began to be noticed that Drama might be not only uplifting and inspiring and all that, but that its patrons could give quite a nice little nudge to the local economy.

The whole season played to eighty-four per cent of capacity of a house which holds 1,437 people. When the second season began, the number of season ticket holders was smaller than the previous year by a thousand or two, but the general advance booking was significantly larger. This trend had been foreseen and was not alarming. Many people found that the price reduction of season tickets was more than counterbalanced by the inconvenience of having to plan their theatre-going far in advance. As I write, there are still some nine weeks of the season to go. But unless some unexpected reverse occurs, the business of the second season will substantially exceed that of the first.

So much for quantity; what of quality?

We have been greatly impressed, though not at all surprised, by the alertness and freshness of the audience. The same qualities had been apparent at concerts in the Twin Cities, at lectures, in church, even at cocktail parties. These people are not blasé, and they most certainly are not inferior in intellectual quality to a metropolitan audience. I believe this is because the people who come know, in general if not quite precisely, the *kind* of entertainment which is going to be offered. They know that the plays are going to make considerable demands on their energy, and they are willing to accept this challenge.

In general they are younger than audiences in the West End of London or on Broadway. This is partly, I guess, because our prices are not so prohibitive and partly because of the demands made upon energy. There are, naturally, plenty of serious people; but the audience, when you look at it from above, is not, even at matinees, one troubled, blue-gray sea of permanent waves.

I hope too that we are, in a small way, helping to subvert the fine, all-American belief that art and culture are strictly for women, indeed for elderly women, nay more, for rich elderly women; that a manly man feels nothing but contempt for art and culture and must devote his superior physical strength, powers of concentration, and decision to *important* pursuits, like watching ball games on television.

I still haven't lived long enough in America to be able to size up an audience in terms of income, background, or occupation. I am forever mistaking Latin professors for construction workers. But I am assured by shrewd and experienced local observers that our theatre is not the haunt solely of eggheads. We cover, as they say, a very wide cross section. And I hope it will not sound unduly complacent if I confess to a thrill of socioartistic pride when Pillars of the Church laugh consumedly at Ben Jonson's most outrageous jokes, or when some Midwestern lady tycoon is seen to brush a tear from her metallic cheek as the hopes and youth of *The Three Sisters* fade away with the retreating strains of a military band.

The Valley to the Waterers
by Herbert Blau

W̲e̲ ̲h̲a̲v̲e̲ done a lot of plays in the last twelve years. That is our main achievement. Most of the plays that fill these thoughts we've done. When I worry, I am not casting stones. I worry about my own theatre first.

These thoughts will fill my own stage.

As the couples dance off at the end of Brecht's *Caucasian Chalk Circle*, the Story Teller comes forward and addresses the audience:

> But you, you who have listened to the Story of the Chalk Circle,
> Take note what men of old concluded:
> That what there is shall go to those who are good for it,
> Thus: the children to the motherly, that they prosper
> The carts to good drivers, that they are driven well
> And the valley to the waterers, that it bring forth fruit,

That is not the voice of abstract Necessity. It is an ethical voice, down to earth. He means that, in justice, the valley *should go* to the waterers. We know, in fact, it often doesn't; and Brecht's play has demonstrated, on behalf of the waterers, how capricious justice can really be. The action, brought to heel by the mad rogue Azdak, is wish fulfillment. The theatre by its nature promises nothing.

The burden falls upon you, you who have listened to the Story, and you may be ruffled by a hint toward revolution behind the wrinkled wisdom.

For all that, the men of old concluded well; and America, born of revolution, has in practice lived by promise and wish fulfillment. The valleys are customarily immense and, historically, the road to promise is

[99]

paved with contradictions. So it is with the idea of repertory. How long some of us in the theatre have clamored for it! I should like to examine some of the contradictions because it is characteristic of America that when we finally get what we want it is almost time to distrust it.

The valley has been watered and it has brought forth fruit in abundance. Repertory is one of them, and yet, and yet . . . why is that nagging *and yet* so much a part of the American consciousness? Or is it, as they are quick to say, just in my mind? All over the country one hears trumpets summoning the audience to Shakespeare. I don't know how they sound to other ears, but I can't help wondering if there's something wrong when all the trumpets sound alike.

And is it not habitual with us that we can gather in public places and still be essentially strangers? I have seen it happen in our theatres again and again. No wonder the sociologists speak of the Lonely Crowd. Descriptions like that are as abundant as the fruit. The *idea* of repertory is a challenge, I take it, to the promiscuous gregariousness of American life, congregation without harmony, the running away in public, the anonymity at High Noon, the fragmented identities, the spawning facelessness, and the callousness of perpetual estrangement which comes from the hard, odd, isolate strain beneath the geniality of our national character. Free as we are of Original Sin, there is no country more gratuitously guilty.

I read this morning that psychiatrists were relieved when well-known Americans cried openly after the assassination of President Kennedy. The psychiatrists wished such emotional release could occur more often as an exemplary purgative for secret hostilities, the moral constipation, the backlash of hate. In Genet's *The Balcony*, a quite un-American play which knows all about hate, they say, "All the scenarios end in Death." There is something in the American Heritage that always knew it. The conquest of New England ended in a witch hunt, and the settling of California included cannibalism at Donner Pass. The cultural center to be built in Washington was a computer's slow-moving dream until it became a memorial to our late President. And think how Freud's reality principle, that secret craving, thwarted with every successful retrieval of a space capsule, was satisfied beyond belief by the murder of Lee Oswald on television.

[100]

Danger winks on opportunity. In potential, repertory could translate democratic process to the stage, but we must remember that the New Repertory is an outgrowth of the New Affluence, with all its leveling benevolence and evasive moderation, against which we had last summer, at the Republican Convention, the fierce reflex of the New Nostalgia which we also saw on television; something frightened, protective, unforgiving, lethal when aroused, raking in all the chips, the mythomania of the Wild West, the American Dream, where all solutions, by dead reckoning, are simple.

Really, what were we to think of those demonstrations? The triggered hysteria, the bandwagons, the apotheosis of the Booster; or the interminable nominations without meaning to which nobody listens, the deprivation of true debate, the morality of the motel, the bowling alley and the used-car lot, the New Money, *après la guerre*, protecting its property; the Old Money limp as an old leek, the ignominiousness of the Good Loser whose dissent was as skin-deep as his career—the zealously staged cynicism of it all, party unity be damned. As the cynicism represents a mortification of political life, does not the forced Fun represent a deadening of the Spirit of Play?

Remember: our children were watching.

In the same year Columbus discovered America, Antonio de Nebrija gave Queen Isabella a copy of his *Castilian Grammar*, the first of any modern European tongue. "What is it for?" she asked. He said: "Language, your majesty, is the ideal weapon of empire." If we no longer believe in empire (and I'm not sure of that), we certainly do not believe in language. Or am I not to believe my ears at all? The debasement of language on the public scene is not irrelevant to the New Repertory because inherent in the art of drama is Eloquence. And I don't mean the unctuous afflatus that often passes for it. No wonder the American drama is retarded. When I heard that speech of concession, I could not help but remember the words of John Quincy Adams, an unpopular politician who defended America's interests against its inclinations: "Yet my choice is made, and, if I cannot hope to give satisfaction to my country, I am at least determined to have the approbation of my own reflections."

That is a dramatic voice. It should not be mistaken for the kind of voice that is liked by both sides even if it's dead wrong. It is the business of the New Repertory to revive that other voice and, as the poets say, purify the language of the tribe.

If theatre is the most direct, the most public of our arts, holding the mirror up to nature, there would seem to be two alternatives for the New Repertory: to become a symptom of the leveling or to expose it, with all its violent, self-mortifying, and hysterical latencies, as they become a travesty of the democratic process. This is not partisan politics. For me, a Theatre is a sort of moral Congress transcending the two-party system, or any system for that matter. It raises all the questions that politics can never answer. The drama specializes in extremism but is much too wise to recommend it. For on its tragic side, it is one long history of disaster; in comedy, the worst returns to laughter. All passion spent, the end is Communion, the ample grace of purified feeling; as when the valley has been watered and the fruit first comes forth.

An isomorph of the cultural explosion, repertory can become another commodity, well packaged in nice buildings, or it can explore the instinct in its own nature that prevails against the leavening drift of the New Leisure and the disintegrative forces in American life which, whether they explode on us or sneak up on us, deprive us each day of a measure of will, that negligible little tithe of identity that reduces will to nothing. One of the uses of repertory is to give us intelligence on these forces, to assert through every subversive encroachment on it the priority of the essentially human; to protect our private property.

I mean the only thing we really own, ourselves, our being, our fantasies, in the rhythm of their proper nature—their season. One node of that rhythm is the desire to find a home in the world outside your property. Repertory is an experience we've had only in fits and starts. One hesitates to go to the Soviet Union for contrast (and the contrasts are disappearing with the Thaw), but there are those stories about the Moscow Art Theatre, to which people used to return again and again to see the characters of Chekhov, as if they were visiting friends of the family. Repertory gives substance to that lovely word *season* in the communal sense. An ingathering. Up to now theatre in this country has been a scandalous example of our penchant for conspicuous waste. Think of all the talent that goes begging! Repertory is an extension of the War on Poverty. I mean that literally, professionally, and spiritually. A repertory company is a concert of talents. A man in his time plays many parts. He is not disfigured by long endurance of a single mask—or none at all. Yet, in the context of a permanent theatre, he is spared the breadline hypocrisy of the daily round, where one prepares a face to meet the faces that one meets, even if one doesn't respect them. If repertory gives security to the actor, a congenitally displaced person, it gives mooring to an audience which, the more it goes into the suburbs, the farther it goes from the village green, the town meeting, direct access to the agencies of Power, and that locus in society which is its constitutional right.

Indwelling in the concept of repertory is a restoration of a sense of history. By nature, repertory is a testament to recurrence, not mere repetition—the tawdriness of imitation, the paralysis of mere habit—but the return, the coming back, the living through of what was lived, the awakening to what has not. As a social experience, it gives something of the pleasure, and the assurance, of a refrain in a ballad. Repertory implies continuity, reliable presence, *a body of work*, permanence in change. This is especially significant in a country driven by principle to possession by incessant change, reckless about its past, and ill at ease with its ghosts, like Huck Finn confounded on the river by the floating body of his dead father.

Whatever is truly living comes back to itself in a tribute to its own worthiness. A repertoire is a harvest. The valley watered, we may reap together at full moon.

When the spooks walk abroad. A repertory theatre is an extravagance if there is not something lunatic about it. I mean adventurous, mantic, providing for Huck, as well as the King and the Duke. "Into the dangerous world I leapt," cries the Infant in a song by Blake. Then he got lost. We got a glimpse of him out the window on the bleak landscape of Beckett's *Endgame*. It is the theatre's mission to find him, for that Infant is the Spirit of Play.

Repertory begins at home.

In my garage, as I write, my son and daughter and a couple of their friends, in the tried and true tradition of free enterprise, are setting up a business for profit: they are developing a Spook House.

"Come and see the dummy!" my son cries, and I go to look and there is the Hanged Man spinning on a rafter, his chest dappled with stigmata. "We're gonna sell eyeballs," my son says. And his friend, a sinister teenager in flowing hair and jeans—Fata Morgana in pubescence—is laying out cloth as if for an altar. She says, "The main attraction's a sacrifice."

Total theatre.

"That's going to be a haunted mansion," my daughter says, "for the Mad Doctor." I wipe my glasses, squinnying through the dark. In an alcove, a ghoul floats out of a trunk (did it mean to giggle?); from the ceiling another sheet unfurls. Writ there in shuddering red: PEEPING TOM! DO NOT LOOK! But the eye is lured to a hole in the sheet and lo! behind that veil of Maya, a tiny death's head.

"What we really need," my son says, returning to the Work in Progress, "is some of that there electronic music, you know"—like me he talks with his hands—"eeeoup! pbuuhh! iiirrm! graaakk! braghhh! *pfoouuummmb!*" Releasing decibels from the tips of his fingers, his hands describe a mushroom. Spooks are real. His father's house has many mansions. All the scenarios end in death. The Spirit of Play knows what we're living for. (It is missing in those Shakespearian trumpets.)

The play is not the thing, however, only the passing shadow of it.

There! You Died was the title of a new play we did last year. Certain people wondered what it was about. The kids could explain. *Those are pearls that were his eyes.* "We'll make them of stones," Morgana says, raising a knife. Business is business, after all, and there's no telling how the kids will do. Meanwhile, they're building character. Let us hope that in Time's more mercenary attritions their histrionic ghouls will turn up the good ghost of a healthy profit; suffer a sea change into something rich and strange. We can play along by keeping out of their prophetic hair. A theatre is a Spook House before it becomes anything else.

I am not imagining things; I am speaking scientifically. Ask the anthropologists. This is what I read in the greatest drama: If our little life is rounded with a sleep, then a theatre is the place where the prophetic soul of the wide world may do its dreaming on things to come. *In* the wide world. The theatre begins when Mystery shows its phantom face in public. Revelation! If the soul is not illumined, if there is not enchantment, if the experience is not magical beyond Eloquence, if the skeletons remain in the closet, if passion is not aroused to fear and trembling (ready to giggle), whatever is spent—either in feigned passion or foundation grants—is bound to triviality. If there be profit in it, a theatre must send a shiver up the spine.

In the wide world, today, that's a real problem. As the subsidies come, we are running out of shivers. Or rather, we grow inured to them. ("Inside I'm blinking," says a character in another new play we did.) There are, it could be, stranger phantoms today than were dreamt of in the Eleusinian Mysteries. "Is the world as it was, man?" asks the madcap Lucio in *Measure for Measure*. "Which is the way? Is it sad, and few words? Or how? The trick of it?" "Still thus, and thus," says the Duke of Dark Corners, "still worse."

Since the Renaissance we've been studying a leak in the universe. The earth, say the learned astronomers, is a wasting star. Two world wars in this century have brought Mystery, Great Whore of Babylon, into the open, more shatteringly than was perhaps good for our spines. And the animated suspension of the Cold War has left us, with every flourish in the economy, pacified by dread. That's both foreign policy and existential fact. Overkill, God bless it!, is one of the biggest sponsors of the New Repertory.

We wondered at all this in *The Marriage of Mr. Mississippi* by Duerrenmatt. Other cultures have had their hangups, of course, but there has never been such a market for tranquilizers—and I don't only mean pills. We're bugged, we're tapped, we're tabulated, for our own benefit, they say. What we have been trying to do at The Actor's Workshop, which began shortly after Winston Churchill gave the Cold War its name, is to keep from getting cornered in *that* market.

It's not easy. And no particular spook is after us. If there is, our most virtuous enterprise helped to summon it. The Great Books, which the cultural explosion has strewn in spineless backs over the drugstores, give us warnings nevertheless. To wit: in the seventh circle of Dante's Hell, there comes up from the abyss "a shape like one returning through the sea from working loose an anchor run afoul." It is Geryon, "the beast that makes the whole world stink," on whose back Dante and his Guide must descend in further quest of the Beatific Vision. Geryon is the Monster of Fraud, reptile below, but his face is "innocent of every guile, benign and just in feature"; and it was the cord bound round Dante's waist like a belt that he yielded to the Guide to lure the monster from "the bottomless darkness of the pit."

Well, Dante made it, why not us? *Misericordia*. In our world, far more relative than his, plenty of guarantees are offered, but none of them is relative to this.

Take The Actor's Workshop: in the beginning, because we started from the ground up—no money, no real estate, no reputation—the major task (in keeping with the Cold War) was Survival: to build a company, to keep actors from running scared to New York (moral exhortation with middling success), to develop a subscription (the same), to balance the books. Actually, we began as a studio in a room; like other Americans, we had modest ambitions; we wanted to become a theatre in a theatre. So we lured the monster. The terror was always bankruptcy, and we had no deterrents except the questing inclination of personal will, to the degree it could collect itself in common action.

And the repertoire.

That was, for me, the locus of aspiration; a continuum of plays playing off against each other, the one examining the other in a spectrum of possibility, a circulating vision, a revolving lens on the deviously yawing course of a world that when it renounced the tranquilizers seemed to have nothing else and was like Captain Ahab "not so much bound to any haven ahead, as rushing from all havens astern." The repertoire, as my wife once said of a friend's novel, was "a clarifying glass"—in our case exposing new alluring confusions, like the spume of the White Whale. It dazzled our eyes, tested our courage and craft, made us laugh like hell.

There was the liturgical stasis of *Godot*; the murderous Epic trade of *Mother Courage*; the hieratic depravity of *The Maids*; O'Casey's *Cock-a-Doodle-Dandy*, now-you-see-it-now-you-don't, running your pants off; the chortling brainwash of *The Birthday Party*; "Thank God I'm normal, normal, normal," sang *The Entertainer* with acid in his mouth; there was *The Dance of Death*; and, in *King Lear*, "the thing itself," stripped to the marrow. If our productions were dark in choice and style, what we saw in them corresponded to what we saw around us, what the Pentagon called the Balance of Terror. *Volpone* began with a parade of skeletons, the Seven Deadly Sins, in honor of the Morality Play imbedded in it. "Scars have style," a lovely lady said in a play of my own.

Dark as it was, for those of us in our company and in our audience who could see things the same way, there was joy in it and a marvelous adventure. Sad to say, not everybody saw it the same way.

There was always controversy about our repertoire. And if there were those in the company who wished we played it safer, "normal, normal, normal," I might also report that controversy, contrary to myth, is *not* good box office. If our subscription, after all these years, isn't what subscriptions are at some of the new regional theatres before they even begin, it is because we lose as many subscribers through outrage each year as we pick up through approval. People always congratulate us for being in San Francisco, but that cosmopolitan city is built, we learned, on a hard rock of provincialism. So be it. In pursuit of the phantom, one doesn't ride on a bandwagon. "We crawl by inches," says Brecht's Galileo.

There are two honorable courses a repertory theatre may take. The first is to become a kind of museum or art gallery (I do not use the words pejoratively) and provide a permanent trust fund of important plays—one of the announced functions of the National Theatre in England; an aspect of this is to make available plays which have not been seen in the community, which service is being fulfilled by the new regional theatres here (few of which, including The Workshop, can manage to keep all its best plays in repertory indefinitely, because that is too expensive). The second course is to conceive a repertoire as I have described it, as a kind of Quest, even a Way of Life. The courses overlap depending on the people involved and the leadership of a theatre, and they do overlap at The Actor's Workshop. We have never really been consistent in the Quest because of a certain wariness about the service. Nor am I naïve about the degree of collective assent one is likely to get within a theatre to this conception of it—especially in what began as an unsanctioned operation out of nothing, and soon appeared committed, in plays and style, to Nothingness as a datum of existence.

Most people in the theatre are, to begin with, just there to do plays. If they happen to be in an environment where exceptional plays are done, they will do them ("I just want to act"). Partly this is due to the historical debility of their profession in this country; but I have seen too many people in the theatre who could tell better from worse choose worse. As for the Quest, most people are inclined to stay right where they are indefinitely, even if they don't know. That may seem every man's privilege, and it may seem presumptuous to ask that theatre people make choices they don't make with any more frequency in other professions, except that the theatre is an art and, as D. H. Lawrence has said, "The essential function of art is moral. Not aesthetic, not decorative, not pastime and recreation. But moral. The essential function of art is moral." He rubs it in because it is a morality which changes the blood.

I hold this truth to be self-evident: you may be very talented, but in our time you are not an artist if you are not willing to measure yourself against the abyss. The valley goes to the waterer.

The Spine of a character or a production (it is our term for Stanislavski's Superobjective) is at some crucial point inseparable from the Spine of one's whole being. If we *were*, however, to embark on a Quest together, what was to unify us? I said before that repertory implied continuity but, as Henry James remarked on his return to America, "The question for the particular case is but continuity of what? The basis of my individual hope had been that of the reign of the orange-grove; but what it proved, at the crisis I name, was positively that of the usurpation of the snowbank." One could have wished for a good white objective snowbank, but it was our destiny to create a theatre when all distinction had shaded into the uncrystallized gray of the Cold War, with dark powers gathering. The character of the period was nowhere better transcribed than in the nonobjective landscapes of the American painters. If Nothingness didn't unite us, politics surely didn't.

If we lacked the tyranny, we also lacked the cohesion of Ideology, as at the Berliner Ensemble.

Perhaps that accounted for my own particular commitment to the Quest. Though we wooed the community, I didn't want us to become a Civic Theatre, but a *Theatre*—with a point of view of its own, as dissident as we wished, as critical, as clarion. Because we were entertainers, there was no reason to be second-class citizens *in* our art. We are one and indivisible. (After years of inbred technique, artists and those who believe in art are anxious to reconcile the claim of personal responsibility with the obsessions of the secret life. We see it in the gravitation of the novel back to a social form and in the poetry readings; and for the first time in a long time artists who have disdained it, rightly so, I mean poets, painters, and musicians, are beginning to think of working in the theatre.) Again, I am speaking for those who responded to the adventure. Others went along despite their natural inclinations. If we approached things at loose ends, the great advantage of permanence in a repertory theatre is that it gives loose ends time to grow together, and when the Quest becomes a climate through the urgency of a few, nobody can wholly avoid it. But we must remain clarion.

Endurance pays off. Our most offbeat work gave us notoriety. Members of the company soon became connoisseurs of drama they had detested, the more it became apparent that some of these plays— by Brecht, by Beckett, by Genet, for instance—were becoming the vogue. Now that we've reached the point where the new daring plays we once did are in the Common Market, the smart money (*viz.*, David Merrick and Roger Stevens) is in there buying up the newer daring plays. Like our Cost-Plus stores, oddities from exotic places.

When people complained, however, about our avant-garde drama, what they failed to see then is what alarms many of them now—that these plays, these antidramas, cryptic and disaffiliate, off in the catacombs, were predicting total change in our social atmosphere. When they asked about these plays, "Can things really be that bad?" the plays kept saying, "Still worse." I've said before that the best commentary I know on our relations with Cuba is Jean Genet's *The Maids*. If one looked back over our repertoire, he could have predicted that change

[109]

in the political climate on which practically every liberal commentator blinked with dismay, and which appalled many of us on television. But let me emphasize, except for Brecht these were not political plays (and Mac's knife goes deeper); they were plays which cut below the surface of appearances to the psychic tremors of a world in stalemate. Drama is history coming. And the underground drama through which we explored looked on history with the jaundiced eye of Uncle Jimbilly in Katherine Anne Porter's story *The Witness*: ". . . someday somebody was going to get a mighty big surprise, and meanwhile everybody had better look out."

And there's more history coming. Uncle Jimbilly, a Jim Crow type, had seen the valley go everywhere but to the waterers. Was he predicting revolution? For the history that has suddenly come upon us is decidedly revolutionary, and the New Repertory, like it or not, is moving in the orbit of the Revolution. It is, indeed, a minor corollary of it. Like the civil rights movement, it has been long in coming, has been impeded by the same forces, and is subject to the same perils. Equivocation, gradualism, and stage fright.

But the winding sheet of history is ripped wide open. The spooks are in the jungles, in the rice paddies, and some, rising in the ghettoes, are already banging at our doors. The battle in Africa, in the underdeveloped countries of the Orient, in Harlem, and in the South is not simply one of economics and power structures, it is finally a battle for the Valley of the Shadow of Death, for the soul and the soul's right in any individual man to claim its psychic rights in the civil order of things, lest that disappear. No theatre developing today will mean anything tomorrow unless it is conscious of this transcendental battle, in which the dark powers in men, the powers of blackness, are seeking territorial rights, as the population explodes, in the swiftly diminishing geography of the human.

The Subject Is Not Roses, or The Grandeur and Misery of Repertory
by Harold Clurman

CHAMPIONS of the repertory system too often plead for or praise the advantages of this well-established method for the presentation of drama. I would rather they "blasted" those who deem it necessary to defend it. The kind of organization which has fostered the plays of such dramatists as Shakespeare, Ben Jonson, Molière, Racine, Ibsen, Haupt-mann, Chekhov, and Gorky needs no defense. The community which possesses no repertory theatre merits scorn. "What, you have no repertory company in your town or state? You are hardly a cultured folk." That should be the attitude!

It is nonetheless a fact that we have had very few repertory theatres in the past fifty years and the need for them has to be explained over and over again.

Even the exact meaning of a repertory company is often not under-stood. For example, the Group Theatre (1931–41) is frequently referred to as a repertory company. It wasn't. Its actors and directors constituted a permanent company—the same group of people united by a common artistic policy remained together for ten years producing a variety of plays. Though certain monetary arrangements were made to enable these people to adhere to the organization through the years, the plays were produced one by one with funds supplied by various, and nearly always new, backers, very much as plays are mounted in the so-called commercial theatre. Some plays—Kingsley's *Men in White*, Odets' *Golden Boy*, *et al.*—had profitable runs; others—Paul Green's *The House of Connolly*, William Saroyan's *My Heart's in the Highlands*—though generally admired, had comparatively short runs and were thus unprofitable.

Nor is the Actors Studio Theatre a repertory theatre. Most of its actors are chosen from members of the Actors Studio—a study group for professional actors—but their productions, though largely financed during its first season by the Ford Foundation, are set up on the commercial theatre basis. Through the presence and generosity of Paul Newman and Joanne Woodward, *Baby Want a Kiss* was financially successful, while other of the organization's productions—*Strange Interlude* and *The Three Sisters*—failed to make money.

How little understanding of the repertory theatre idea exists was brought to my attention with a special force when I heard Edward Albee, a thoughtful person as well as a talented dramatist, say that while he appreciated the benefits of the repertory system for actors (actors don't have to grow weary and stale by playing one part for months and years on end or go begging for parts after they have appeared in flops), he didn't see the benefit to playwrights.

It had to be pointed out to him that Chekhov was not an immediately successful playwright in Russia. This is not a reference to the fiasco of *The Seagull* when it was first produced "commercially" in St. Petersburg but also after it had been acclaimed at the Moscow Art Theatre. It was an artistic rather than a box-office success. Its incorporation in that famous theatre's repertoire made it possible with the passage of time for material success to match its prestige.

Perhaps examples closer to home may be given of the dangers inherent in our customary method of play production. O'Neill's *The Iceman Cometh*, well produced by the Theatre Guild under the author's supervision, was a box-office failure. If it had not been revived by José Quintero at the Circle-in-the-Square, it would have been known only to readers and to people in towns which have community or college theatres. The same holds true of Tennessee Williams' *Summer and Smoke*.

Any theatre buff can name at least a dozen plays produced within the past twenty-five years which failed to get the attention they deserved because of our boom-or-bust method of production, which makes each play a separate enterprise supported by nothing more than the immediate box-office response. Both playgoer and playwright suffer.

[112]

Still it is not so much the advantages of repertory which need emphasis now but its difficulty. To understand a phenomenon thoroughly, we must examine it in its negative as well as its positive aspects. (If one were conceivably capable of painting the pleasures of life to the newly born, one would be guilty of a crime if one omitted mention of its rigors!) Perhaps more light may be shed on the repertory idea by a less than utopian approach to its problems than by espousing its cause as an absolute good.

It is perfectly true that our theatregoing public is unaccustomed and therefore inhospitable to repertory. But habit is not unalterable. A novelty may become a norm. There was only a very small audience for ballet (a repertory operation) in this country before the advent of such organizations as the Ballet Russe and the New York City Ballet. It is not so much the public which has made us laggard in respect to repertory as the professionals themselves. They are often more rigidly conventional than others.

Deeply ingrained among us are two basic assumptions which not only impede the creation of repertory theatres but which also prevent any true understanding of the theatre's essential nature.

The first assumption is that the theatre's purpose is putting on "shows." The second is that the theatre's goal is profit. Where these two notions become dogma, progress in the theatre is not only retarded but, in such a society as ours today, very nearly impossible. It explains the desperate shrinkage of theatre production itself from 1927 to the present.

That we think of theatre as no more than a series of "shows" may be adduced from criticism—both lay and official—of productions in our repertory theatres. Dr. Guthrie in his book *A New Theatre* has made this point very well. The faults found in the production of *Hamlet* with which the Tyrone Guthrie Theatre in Minneapolis opened may all have been there but in view of the aims of that organization as a whole (that is, as a *Theatre*), they were for the most part misconceived and improperly stated. Guthrie's *Hamlet* was not simply another production of the play to be compared, let us say, with those in which John Gielgud or Maurice Evans appeared, but the first step in the formation of new theatre.

Certainly every individual production must be judged on its intrinsic qualities. But every offering in a true Theatre is not a discrete effort without antecedent meaning or further significance. Theatre bespeaks service to a particular community and each production is a partial testimony to the kind of service intended as a contribution to the community's life. The theatre's work represents a process of growth within the community. The audience is a conscious part of the community and, as long as it feels the theatre understands and expresses its needs, it will follow that theatre with the kind of allegiance that may be compared with the loyalty the good citizen brings to his government. Evidence for this may be read in theatres throughout Europe. In Germany, for example, there is one (municipal) repertory theatre in every city with a population of twenty-five thousand, while the larger centers often have several such theatres.

When Guthrie opened the theatre in Minneapolis, he did not imply that in George Grizzard he had discovered the greatest of all Hamlets. The production was meant to demonstrate the kind of theatre the new organization was to be: one which hoped to give vivid and robust interpretations of classic plays. In addition to Shakespeare's text, the production was intended to say, "This is a beginning; we hope to do more, to do better in time. Above all, we hope that the players and public which are to make this theatre will continue its life together for years."

The work of a theatre bespeaks a career, not a packaged display of wares for sale. A theatre is a conscience, a communion, a communication which through the marriage of its constituent parts (of which the audience is a vital element) matures through the progress of its collective life. A theatre in time evolves its particular physiognomy.

A Theatre—actors, dramatists, directors, designers, patrons—develops and must be given time to develop in a manner corresponding to the growth of an individual artist. Thomas Kyd and Christopher Marlowe, who preceded Shakespeare, were not his equal, and Shakespeare's *Henry VI*, *Love's Labour's Lost*, and *The Comedy of Errors* were not of the same stature as the work of his maturity: *Hamlet*, *Macbeth*, *Othello*, *King Lear*.

The reason why so acute a critic as Edgar Allan Poe could find so much to praise in Anna Mowatt's *Fashion* (1845), a play we now consider a quaint bit of flummery, was that he saw in it the promise of further developments; it stood for the best that our society could produce on the stage at that time. It was a comedy of American manners, a vein which needed exploration. Similarly William Dean Howells, who could appreciate Turgenev and Tolstoy, lauded James Herne's play *Margaret Fleming* (1890)—ludicrous today—for that too marked the impulse toward dramatic "realism" in our land. (It was not till 1920 that this impulse achieved significant form with Eugene O'Neill.) Laurence Olivier's presence in Behrman's *No Time for Comedy* in 1938 was less favorably noticed than were Katharine Cornell and Margalo Gillmore. The Olivier of *Romeo and Juliet* as done in New York in 1940 was certainly not yet the admired artist of today.

The British National Theatre could open its first season (1963–64) with impressive results, despite several failures, because its path was cleared by years of preparation afforded by such institutions as the Old Vic and the Royal Shakespeare Theatre at Stratford.

To judge the production of a repertory theatre as we do the ordinary single-shot show—hit or flop—is to bring to what for us is new territory the same sort of spirit and thinking as have become threadbare in the old. Many folk, loud in their complaints about Broadway's commercialism, come to the new theatres with the same casual air of the idle and indifferent playgoer who buys his tickets from a speculator for the privilege of attending a smash hit. The playgoer's mind is too often full of the bugs which infest neglected edifices. It would be a good thing for him to wash his brains.

The importance and positive contribution of the Repertory Theater of Lincoln Center's first season was that it marked the first stage of an *apprenticeship*. The word "apprenticeship" must be understood in a specific context. The directors, designers, and a good part of the acting company in this infant organization were people who have functioned successfully on Broadway, people who have repeatedly proved their ability to put on "good shows," but their conjunction as a permanent troupe under the still unusual circumstances of the repertory system made their first years together a period of learning.

Let us note a minor instance of the tasks faced by such a theatre. One of its first duties is to produce both contemporary and classic drama. On Broadway one can choose actors who are chiefly trained to do contemporary American plays. When classics are to be presented (a rare occurrence), a management will seek actors who presumably have had some association with such plays, which up to a few years ago meant mostly British actors. But an American repertory theatre rarely commands the means to employ a company large enough to include both kinds of actors. Very few American actors are prepared to do both types of plays.

The problem exists for the Tyrone Guthrie Theatre as well as for the Repertory Theater of Lincoln Center. In Dr. Guthrie's book he asserts that the actors chosen for his theatre must have daily exercise in speech and voice for at least five years before they achieve the ability to give full value to the language of classic drama. In the interim he is constrained, and willing, to produce Shakespeare, Ben Jonson, and the like while the actors are still novices in this regard.

Just as each production must have its own stylistic coherence, so a *Theatre*, if it is to play its proper role as an expression of a community's consciousness, must cultivate an organic character which is something more than a seasonal matter. Where the time element is overlooked, stage activity is condemned to diminishing returns. We have many talented writers and actors whose promise wanes at the point one expects it to flower. We are eager to enjoy the fruit, but we constantly neglect the tree.

Actors such as John Barrymore were as naturally gifted as any of their English counterparts. But with us such talent is blighted by the absence of support which can only be supplied by a permanent theatre. The waste of our talents will grow more marked in the future unless we develop the kind of theatres of which all of Europe now provides examples. Gielgud, Olivier, Redgrave, Richardson, Guinness, Scofield, Edith Evans, and Peggy Ashcroft could not have become the actors we know today if they had not spent a large part of their working time in the (now largely subsidized) British repertory theatres.

None of these theatres could subsist if they were expected to serve as business ventures: none of them, with hardly any exception, has ever been or can be profitable. I speak of *successful* theatres, well attended by audiences satisfied that they are performing their functions well.

We have all heard the argument that even though no library, museum, or symphony orchestra—no matter how well patronized—ever makes money, why then should a serious theatre be expected to do so. Still we are not convinced. Why not? Very few people sincerely interested in the theatre as something besides a gamble or a benevolent frivolity know what the actual work—the mechanics of play production—entails. It is about time people who profess devotion to the theatre began to investigate it. When a difficult enterprise is undertaken, perpetual dilettantism is nefarious.

A repertory theatre which presents three or four new productions a season (in the hope, it should be added, of retaining for as long as possible those which have particular and more or less enduring value for their audiences) must employ a large permanent company. Forty actors should be considered a minimum if the company is to deal satisfactorily with every play chosen. Several plays must always be in the process of preparation at all times, hopefully with adequate rehearsal time. In a great metropolis the theatre should stay open for at least forty weeks a year. If possible, as Kenneth Tynan says of the British National Theatre, it should never close.

The Repertory Theater of Lincoln Center has two-year contracts with only twenty-five actors. The British National Theatre lists sixty actors and most continental theatres a far greater number. While it is true that such actors cannot be paid at the rate of those employed in our commercial theatre, which rarely guarantees more than a two-week employment or at best a contract for the duration of the play's run, actors of a repertory company, if they are to possess respectable competence, must be paid enough to maintain themselves at a decent standard in good or bad box-office times. Otherwise the actors cannot reasonably be expected to remain at their posts. Sacrifice may be demanded but not slavery.

A considerable technical staff must always be on the job, as the changing and care of settings and costumes are a constant factor when as many as four or five plays are offered each week. (Space to store all the equipment should be made available in the theatre building.) The technical staff should not be haphazard but should become an integral part of the theatre's artistic contingent.

A reservoir of plays must be built. When one play proves unsatisfactory, the theatre should be in a position to replace it at once with another. Some of the best plays will not always prove the most popular. These must be sustained by those which are.

The condition which necessitates the closing after a week's run of certain plays not readily appreciated by a mass audience is harmful to both dramatist and public. Whatever one's criticism of a play such as Saul Bellow's *The Last Analysis*—it is at the moment of this writing the most recent example—there is no doubt in my mind that it deserved greater attention than the Broadway circumstances of its production allowed. We have already mentioned the classic case of Chekhov, the neglect of whose early plays might have deprived us of the masterpieces which followed. This trust in the eventual justification of support for the imperfect or "difficult" play—essential to the establishment of a theatre—demands an expenditure of funds which supporters of a theatre must regard as inevitable and necessary.

Since a repertory theatre, unlike the commercial manager, cannot be inactive until the "right" (good and, naturally, universally pleasing!) play miraculously appears, time must be spent to project future plays.

Writers are shaped by the theatre conditions of their community. The Broadway setup does not attract most of our finest writers. When such writers do approach the theatre, they willy-nilly regard it as a place for a great "killing." They are wary of repertory because the immediate revenue from a new play—it may possibly be given only three times a week—will not be nearly as great as from a smash hit given eight performances a week in the commercial theatre. A novelist is resigned to wait for success, but when he writes for the stage he prefers to "go for broke."

This makes the acquisition by repertory companies of certain outstanding new scripts, "properties" the profession calls them, a knotty task. In other words, many writers must be persuaded, or "tempted," to contribute their work to the repertory theatre not only through the inducements of a hypothetical cultural concern for the theatre but by the offer of some monetary compensation for the "sacrifice" they believe they are making in submitting their plays to a repertory theatre. It is no secret that most playwrights, particularly new ones, are convinced that their plays are all destined to achieve tumultuous triumph. Only experience may teach them that financial success in the theatre never has been the norm but the exception.

A repertory theatre, being a new thing with us, is expected to please everybody. A company of this kind which resolves to devote itself largely to plays of classic stamp displeases those who feel that what we most sorely need in our theatre is more American dramatists. Others find concentration on contemporary American plays parochial and disheartening because such new plays rarely measure up to the "highest standards" (they are not classics), and there are some who behave as if they cannot abide anything less than the first rate. (These are usually infrequent playgoers without much appetite for the theatre.) For some reason, a new repertory company, in New York particularly, is expected to satisfy both groups at the same time and, American fashion, right away. Certainly cities such as New York, Chicago, Los Angeles, Boston, *et al.*, should have several repertory theatres. It so happens that it has proved next to impossible to establish even one.

In this connection I must confess a personal bias. I believe since we possess very few "classics" of our own, one of the main goals of an *American* repertory theatre should be the development and production of native plays of serious intent and sound craftsmanship. We cannot thrive only on what others have created for us in the past any more than we can deprive ourselves of what our forbears from many lands have bequeathed. But though many may applaud this sentiment which has little to do with "patriotism," it is one thing to say this and quite another to find the means to do it. Talent, even genius, is not solely in God's hands. We must prepare the soil and learn how to conserve what may issue from it.

Room must be found for a "laboratory" or "studio" theatre, a small house in association with the larger where plays not requiring the panoply of large-scale production or the patronage of huge audiences can be presented along with the more technically ambitious plays which require a more spacious stage and more numerous spectators to survive. I am not speaking of what are called "experimental" plays. Such plays as Sartre's *No Exit*, Beckett's *Godot*, Pinter's *The Caretaker*,

Genet's *The Balcony*, Brecht-Weill's *The Threepenny Opera*, and Albee's *The Zoo Story* are not "experimental" except as Broadway ventures. They are, to say the least, plays which interest a considerable body of alert playgoers. They are plays most suitably housed in what the Europeans call a chamber theatre. In it new plays, particularly though not exclusively American plays, should be produced by both young and more practiced directors, by companies recruited from actors of the main house in addition to fresh talent not yet under long-term contract. The main enterprise without the more modest one will always be encumbered by the need to command a massive audience. A small theatre unattached to a larger body will suffer a kind of isolation which must needs give it the appearance of minor importance.

A training program is imperative for a repertory theatre which does not shop for actors, vying with agencies, television producers, and motion picture bids. The Old Vic some years ago ran a school which produced some of the best actors of the now resurgent British theatre: Joan Plowright, to name only one. Such schools have for a long time been a fixture of two of the best Moscow theatres. There is another school in Moscow supported by the state at which the instructors are the leading actors, directors, and technicians of the country.

A repertory theatre, it cannot be too often repeated, does not stand in the market awaiting the main chance. It must plan ahead for the gathering, training, and maintenance of all its diverse forces, for it is no theatre at all if it does not envisage its life in decades and generations. The Moscow Art Theatre, founded in 1898, has never ceased functioning since then. Its existence brought about and encouraged the formation of a number of entirely new theatres, several of them in aesthetic opposition to the parent organization.

All this, in addition to an educational program for the public (if possible for the unions, including Equity), costs money. That embattled idealist, Gordon Craig, in characteristic hyperbolic fashion once declared that he would not open his theatre unless he had the assurance of funds for ten years of preparatory work! The symbolic value of so extravagant a request is that it gives some indication of the complexity as well as the costliness of such a project. Craig wanted lovers of the theatre, trustees, and other would-be patrons to realize that the making of a theatre is no overnight job, no smug matter of issuing a manifesto and of collecting several thousand subscribers. To approximate the best work that has been done in this field takes time and money. The money required for such an endeavor is never an investment but a gift. Those who give must share the temper, the need, and to a considerable extent the understanding plus the information of those who receive.

We cannot hope for miracles. We are vouchsafed hardly any municipal or state aid for theatre in our country and no national subsidy. All the new organizations—whether in San Francisco, Washington, D.C., Houston, Minneapolis, or New York—are brave adventures proclaiming a dream in the midst of a vast public still incompletely aware of the stakes or apprised of the goal. We must not bemuse ourselves by supposing that any of these theatres are yet, or at the moment can possibly be, a Comédie Française, a Royal Shakespeare Company, a Moscow Art Theatre, a Berliner Ensemble. That lies far ahead. Shall we therefore accept the proposition that the richest country in the world and surely one of the most highly endowed with energy and creative capacities must lag behind the others in giving living testimony through the drama to its feelings, imagination, and thought?

A true Theatre is not an *objet d'art;* it is a world.

Lionel Abel

Author, *Metatheatre*; contributor, *Partisan Review, Commentary, The Nation, The New York Review*; formerly professor of Drama, Columbia and Rutgers Universities.

Herbert Blau

Comanaging director, The Actors Workshop, San Francisco; professor of English and World Literature, San Francisco State College; author, *The Impossible Theatre*.

Harold Clurman

Director; theatre critic, *The Nation*; author, *The Fervent Years, Lies Like Truth*; cofounder and managing director, Group Theatre; Chevalier, Legion of Honor; Honorary L.L.D., Bard College; Honorary D.F.A., Carnegie Institute of Technology; executive consultant, Repertory Theater of Lincoln Center.

Tyrone Guthrie

Artistic director, Minnesota Theatre Company, Minneapolis; former administrator, the Old Vic and Sadler's Wells; founding director, Stratford Shakespeare Festival; Chancellor, Queens University, Belfast; author, *A Life in the Theatre* and *A New Theatre*.

Barry Hyams

Director, public relations, Repertory Theater of Lincoln Center; theatre critic, *American Examiner*; producer, *Ulysses in Nighttown*.

Richard Meyer

Associate professor of Theatre at Grinnell College, spent a year with the Lincoln Center Repertory Company during its initial season at Washington Square. He and his wife Nancy are now at work on a book based upon his own intimate view of the story behind *After the Fall*.

[123]

Henri Peyre

Sterling Professor of French, Yale University; Chevalier and Officer, Legion of Honor; member, American Philosophical Society and American Academy of Arts and Letters; author, *The Contemporary French Novel*, *Observations on Life, Literature and Learning in America*.

Alan Pryce-Jones

Book critic, *New York Herald Tribune*; drama critic, *London Times, London Observer*; editor, *Times Literary Supplement*, 1948–1959.

May Swenson

Poet, *Another Animal, A Cage of Spines, To Mix with Time*; contributor, *The New Yorker, Accent, Hudson Review, Partisan Review, The Nation, Paris Review*.

Kenneth Tynan

Literary manager, British National Theatre; drama critic, *London Observer*; author, *He That Plays the King, Persona Grata, Bull Fever, Curtains*.

Photographs by Inge Morath
Printed by Clarke & Way, Inc.

The vehicle, a dark, bulletproof van, rolled into view. The driver let the siren *whoop!* one more time before turning into the parking area. People had to move back, and in the pushing and stumbling, Devlin and Gerrity were separated, Devlin farther from the door where the van was stopping. A big guy moved a half step sideways to block Devlin's line of sight completely. Devlin wondered what he was doing here anyway. Why had Levine called him? Devlin could hear the door of the van being unlocked—and suddenly everybody was silent. Out on the street a horn blew. It blew a second time.

Pop! A pause. *Pop! Pop!* People shouted: "Get the gun!" "Grab him!" "Son of a bitch!" And people shouted to learn what had happened. "Shot him," the replies tumbled back, over the pushing and shoving. "The suspect has been shot." "He killed him." "Who did?" "A guy in a yellow jacket."

Somebody yelled, "Sniper!" sending everybody down. . . .

DEVLIN

Roderick Thorp

FAWCETT GOLD MEDAL • NEW YORK

A Fawcett Gold Medal Book
Published by Ballantine Books
Copyright © 1992 by Roderick Thorp

All rights reserved under International and Pan-American Copyright Conventions. Published in the United States by Ballantine Books, a division of Random House, Inc., New York, and simultaneously in Canada by Random House of Canada Limited, Toronto.

Library of Congress Catalog Card Number: 92-90148

ISBN 0-449-14793-2

Manufactured in the United States of America

First Edition: August 1992

For
Michele
with love

NEW YORK CITY
MONDAY,
JUNE 30, 1986

4:22 P.M. . . .

As usual, the young woman reserved the room and
arrived a few minutes early. She stripped to her panties and
bra, then put her shoes on again before she lit a joint.

The shoes were the idea of the man she was waiting for.
She was growing increasingly uneasy with this business, and
so having to keep the shoes on, at least for the preliminaries,
was more than a little annoying. What really bothered her was
the increased riskiness of these meetings. Because of his
prominence, the man was being absolutely reckless, choosing
hotels for these special sessions. They had a perfectly safe way
of meeting at her apartment uptown, but this was something
he needed. He was fixated. They had a game in which the
impersonality of the hotel room was a part, a little ritual he
had to go through, step-by-step, touching a dozen ever more
desperate grace notes until he was ready for the jackpot.

The man's peculiarities were nothing new to the young
woman, or terribly unpleasant. She had had affairs with an
actor, a congressman, and a black football player—in that order, a bisexual, a sadist, and a searcher for the perfect fellatrix.
The current festivities always began exactly as the man had
written in a letter that had arrived unexpectedly at her apartment this past spring. The story of his sex life, all his damned
excuses and justifications, including who was doing what to
whom among his big deal friends. *Now that you have read
this, destroy it*—stuff like that, describing what he wanted her
to do. . . .

Their drama began when he asked her if she had destroyed
the letter. "Did you destroy the letter?" Now she had to hear

3

the question only once to be driven completely nuts. He wanted her angry, wanted to feel her rage. And rage was all right with her. She didn't lie to herself about her negative feelings about men, and she had more than enough experience to draw on to go thermonuclear, if that was what he wanted. Her father was an alcoholic suburban squire whose beatings had made a crippled, dependent old woman of her mother. Sometimes just recalling her father's smoothly shaven, booze-bloated puss was enough to propel the young woman to violence. . . .

"Did you destroy the letter?"

"Yes, I told you."

He had been here ten minutes, and she had been hoping it would start soon. Oh, it was a wonderful, wonderful cathartic experience. He was removing his shirt. The first minutes were always normal. How have you been? Did you have trouble getting here? Kisses. Feels. And now:

"You wouldn't lie to me, would you?"

"No, damn it! I've told you a hundred times—"

"Not that many."

She was twenty-seven, twenty years his junior. It was apparent this evening that he thought he could provoke her more by indulging in petty argument. Quibbling. So she waited. He thought she was stymied, and as he removed his shirt, he smiled. She kept waiting. This wasn't acting. It was a game, intense, exciting. Real. She had the belt in her hand; he had seen that she was ready. Maybe this time he wanted it quickly. She hoped so. She wanted the payoff, suddenly wanted it so much that she had to close her mind to it, dare not think of it.

Her bladder almost opened as she swung the belt. Done perfectly, only the buckle touched his skin, raising a welt like a curved V. He cried out, but did not turn around, hurrying to undress. She brought the buckle down across his back again. He howled. When he was naked, he crawled onto the bed and curled into a fetal position. She kept hitting him, flicking the buckle as deftly as she could. It was his fixation, but her effort was the secret that made it work. She had to hit him until she grunted, until heat radiated from her body, until her aching arm made her tighten her stroke. He was aware of what was happening to her—and she believed he took it as evidence of her willingness to join him in a personal hell she could never understand. Love! He saw it as love, for God's sake! Suddenly he reached for her, not looking at her, but clawing desperately to get her close to him so he could bury his face against her breasts. He had to tear at her underwear, too, never able to bring himself to look at her while he did it. Tearful and still in pain, he wanted to hide from her even as he pushed himself into her. He fucked her hard, as hard as he could, still crying, hiding. She held him around the neck so he couldn't show his face even if he wanted to, and as always, that roused him more—and her thrills began. They didn't last all that long, but sometimes her orgasm was as deep and intense as any she had ever known. And this was when he seemed, strangely, more vulnerable to her; as out of control as he was, this was when she liked him best. This was the time when his cock was hardest, thickest, when it plunged pistonlike in and out of her, relentless, when he was about to flood her with semen, that the mystery of his craziness served her, too, at last, when the thought of being able to beat him again thrilled her so much that she exploded into laughter, and came with him. . . .

Sleeping afterward was part of the purging of his self-hatred. Always, when he called to tell her to get a hotel room, he told her when he had to be gone again, and she calculated the time of the jolting wake-up call accordingly. But now something had awakened her before the operator rang. Daylight—it was still only afternoon. The young woman sat up and looked to the door to the hall, wondering if she had imagined the knob turning. Maybe she had dreamed it. The man was asleep, and she arranged herself in the crook of his body, her backside against his belly, her head on his bicep. Nothing to worry about. This wasn't simply a good hotel, but one of the world's greats—and the men she had seen in front of one of the other rooms when she'd arrived looked permanent, like security men or bodyguards. . . .

Safe. Safe with this sadly flawed, potentially great man. She did not like to think of how he dealt with the marks on his body in his wife's presence. His problem went back to his parents, of course, truly crazy people, the young woman surmised. Whatever the truth, she knew he shared his secret with no one but her. Anything else wasn't possible. She had kept the letter. He didn't know that. The way the world was going, the letter might be worth a fortune someday, and no one would—

There! Someone *was* at the door! The young woman sat up again, pulling the sheet up about her breasts, and watched the doorknob turn. . . .

5:04 P.M. . . .

"COME ON, DON'T HOLD BACK THIS TIME!"

"I want it to last!"

"*I* can't!" Eileen cried. She bucked her hips harder. "Come with me, baby! Let it go!"

Frank Devlin did, his lips finding her lips to muffle their cries. Little kids were playing on the sidewalk just one flight down. He loved this woman as he had never loved anyone before. In another moment, between breaths, he told her so, taking another moment to add, "You make me feel like a teenager again."

Eileen laughed. Grinning, she gently pulled the hair on the back of his head so she could look into his eyes. "You're just some kind of freak of nature. Will you ever act your age?"

Devlin thought of Satchel Paige's teaching—*How old would you be if you didn't know how old you was?*—but the telephone rang before he could voice it. "I stopped worrying about that eighteen months ago."

The telephone rang again, but neither of them moved. Devlin was off-duty today and meant to stay that way. The upcoming Liberty Weekend and unveiling of the statue meant nothing to him but overtime he didn't want or need. The telephone rang a third time.

Eileen said, "Thank God it didn't start two minutes ago. It would have ruined me rhythm."

"Count your blessings. Twenty years ago I was the kind of guy who'd have reached for it."

Now she had to speak over her own voice, as the announcement tape of her answering machine came on. The volume was up so they could hear who was calling. "And there was a time, to hear you tell it, when you could have talked on the telephone and done the other at the same time."

She was teasing him. He hadn't told her anything of the sort. But in fact he had done it, talked on the telephone while making love, a long time ago, before his separation from Maryellen Brennan. "Done the other" passed through his thoughts, too. Eileen had stopped using the universal four-letter term because her Irish accent made *fook* of it, which sounded so childlike to Devlin he couldn't help laughing. After all this time together they still laughed at each other like innocents. They were a miracle, she'd said once, and he believed it. The caller began to leave his message.

"This is Captain Dan Cummings, of the One-twelve. I'm looking for Detective Frank Devlin. It's kind of an emergency."

"Go ahead," Eileen said. He didn't move. "You never know," she said.

He reached to the night table and picked up the handset. "Hello."

"Devlin? You're *Frank* Devlin?"

The connection was lousy; the guy sounded like he was shouting in a tunnel. Devlin dialed down the volume on the answering machine, but that didn't help. "Do I know you, Captain?"

"Ah, no. No, you don't. Of course everybody knows *your*

name. People here have a special memory of you, and I need a certain kind of help—''

Eileen tapped him on the shoulder. If he was going to talk on the telephone, she wanted to untangle. He sighed. "I'm the right Devlin."

"I'm not your customer," Cummings said quickly. He sounded like an older guy. "It's, ah, my brother-in-law." He let the words hang in the ether a moment, and it made Devlin think that Cummings was making an admission of defeat. "He's I guess what you call a binge drinker. He'll be on the wagon for six months, and then he's gone for three, four days. He comes home filthy and sometimes with a little blood on him, too. Always broke. He just drinks until he's broke."

"And he's a cop, eh?"

"Not one of us, no," Cummings said. "He's some kind of cop over in Jersey. He wants a cop, and my sister remembered something I said about you, something I heard on the job. Just a minute." He was back before Devlin had reached his cigarettes. "Are you recording this?"

"Oh, yeah. The machine's running."

"Could you turn it off, please? And erase the tape?"

Devlin moved. He had never heard of Captain Cummings, and he hadn't heard anything warm or forgiving in his tone. Even in this circumstance, the man could turn out to be a real prick. Eileen's answering machine clicked twice quickly as it rewound and erased the tape. Eileen's bathroom door clicked, too, with her on the other side of it. Devlin would have liked another look at her. She was true black Irish, so Spanish-looking that all she needed was a pair of castanets. "Who gave you this number, by the way?"

"Your partner, John Lord."

Cummings was some salesman. On Devlin's day off, John usually told people to get another guy. "Go ahead."

"He's ready to go in now, but he wants you. She was working on him and mentioned you, and you're the one he wants. Will you do this? I think he's ready to face up to himself. I was on the phone with him this morning, and he couldn't stop wailin'.''

The brother-in-law was only drunk enough for a crying jag—but that was plenty drunk.

"Do they have a place for him?"

"Oh, yeah. She's been in touch with a group over there. It's all set up. But he wants to talk to you. I guess he thinks there's something you can tell him. I know this is asking a lot. Can she call and explain things to you?"

Devlin said sure and hung up. Any other week, he thought. Liberty Week had disrupted everything. Normally he was with Eileen every other night, but never Monday. On Monday nights Eileen visited her cousins in Bayside. On Monday nights, Devlin did the laundry, and while it was in the dryer, he walked up to Queens Boulevard to get straight with Major, his one-eyed bookmaker. This week Devlin was a winner. On Sunday he had taken Detroit in the first game, and the Mets and Houston, each for three units. This morning, he had noticed that Sid Fernandez was scheduled for tonight, and so he had gone for five units on the Mets. Major was good for the money—he was safer and more accurate than any bank. Devlin tapped on the bathroom door. "It's twelve-step work."

"Anything to give me a rest. Don't come in." The telephone started ringing again, and Devlin returned to the bedroom.

"If that's her, she's quick."

"A woman? What happened to Captain Dan Cummings, of the One-twelve?"

She had lowered her voice in an attempt to imitate the guy. Devlin was standing over the telephone when he heard the bathroom door open again. Over his shoulder, he said, "Cummings's sister, the client's wife."

"You have a handsome backside for a man your age," Eileen said. Too late he became aware of sucking in his gut, and she laughed loudly as she closed the bathroom door again. She knew exactly how to turn the tables on him; he never had a chance. He was still grinning when he said hello.

"Mr. Devlin?"

The woman had a really harsh, broad city accent. "I'm calling from Sussex County, not far from Route 80—"

The next few seconds flew by. Devlin hadn't thought of Sussex in years. He wondered how much time had passed since he had hung up on Cummings. It seemed like less than a minute, but it was hard to tell because Devlin had been having fun with Eileen. The sister must have been sitting by the telephone, waiting for Cummings to give her the okay. She said her husband was asleep.

"Your brother told me the circumstances, Mrs.—"

"Quinn. Irene Quinn. I know this is asking a lot. It was asking a lot of my brother." She started to tell the story again. Devlin was thinking that Sussex was a long way from the city when Eileen came out of the bathroom yawning and waving bye-bye. Frank Devlin was forty-three and far from a freak of nature. He had slept all afternoon. Eileen had taken the day off to be with him, but she had brought work home with her, attending to it while he slept. On the other hand, they had been in bed, mostly not sleeping, since Saturday night. After meeting Eileen O'Sullivan, getting horizontal with her was just about his only idea of a good time. *Thank God,* he thought. She saw him looking at her.

"If somebody needs you, go, because I'm going to sleep. Be back by eleven or forget it, because I'll be a ruin if you wake me after that."

"Fair enough; I'll go to my own place."

As if she had been listening to Eileen, too, Mrs. Quinn asked him where he was located.

"On Forty-eighth Street, in Sunnyside, Queens." He wanted to add, And if I'm not home by eleven, I'll be sleeping five and a half blocks away. Eileen's dark eyes were fixed on his. He really didn't want to go anywhere, but he would be unhappy with himself if he didn't help these people, and sometimes Eileen knew him better than he knew himself.

In seconds, Irene Quinn was giving directions. . . .

7:50 P.M. . . .

THE SETTING SUN WAS BLINDING. DEVLIN USED HIS HAND to shield his eyes while he eased his car onto the exit ramp that curved down to the right and disappeared under the trees. The sedan that had been behind him all the way from New York roared on by, toward Pennsylvania.

Route 80. Devlin had only a vague idea of where he was, gotten from a glance at a glove compartment map. EXIT 19, HACKETTSTOWN—ANDOVER, the signs said, confirming the directions Mrs. Quinn had given. Devlin might as well be in Nebraska or New South Wales. He had spent three summers in Sussex County back in the early fifties. The woman had said he would drive fifty or fifty-five miles from the George Washington Bridge. At this time of day, it had taken two hours. The traffic had been miserable, mostly trucks, the big ones, hammering dustily into the sundown.

In fact, Frank Devlin had not been outside the city of New York in almost a dozen years, and not so far into western New Jersey since 1960, the spring his cousin Alice married. Practically everything was different. Twenty-six years ago New Jersey had looked like an old abandoned car; now, Devlin thought, it looked like a *new* abandoned car.

Devlin had been seventeen years old in 1960. The wedding had been held not far from here, he had realized when Mrs. Quinn was dictating the way to her house. In the hours since, Devlin had been remembering summers a few miles to the north of where he was now, when Sussex County had been farms and upland forest—hillbilly country, his parents had called it.

11

Devlin was wise to memory: always, inevitably, an act of self-deception, events remembered wrong to make the re-memberer feel right. At Alice's wedding he had gotten drunk with his crazy uncle Buddy, the card-carrying Communist who was then becoming a yellow-eyed alcoholic. At the age of seventeen Frank Devlin had been able to pass for twenty-one, the legal drinking age in New Jersey in those years. More probably, the bartender hadn't given a damn. Not that it mattered. For all Devlin could remember, Alice's wedding had not been the first time he had gotten headbustingly bombed in the afternoon. He could still remember Buddy raving . . .

No, wait. Devlin wanted to figure it out. He had started college six months before, so Alice's wedding could not have been the first time he had gotten drunk in the daytime. He shook his head in amazement at his self-deception. It was still that painful to remember that he had taken his first steps into alcoholism at the age of sixteen. Not even seventeen. Devlin's father had already given up trying to control him—the truth was, his father hadn't tried very hard after years of nasty, even cruel bullying. *Your father is getting old,* Devlin's mother had said at the time. His mother had been his father's biggest victim. At sixteen, a know-it-all, Devlin had gloated over the idea that the fire in the old man's belly was finally going out. . . .

The directions indicated that at the foot of the ramp Devlin was to cut a hard right onto County Road 517. He had asked Mrs. Quinn if 517 went through Newton. No, she had said, it went to Sparta and after that she didn't know. Devlin had not thought of Newton in decades, part of an old world buried in his heart: Newton, Sparta, and the town of Sussex, the county seat, Branchville, Augusta, and Lafayette, whitewashed dusty places he had seen only in the summers, when insects buzzed in the relentless sunshine. Now the signs pointing to housing tracts, and others offering land for sale, showed that Sussex had become the far edge of The Big Town, impaled under developers' beady eyes. From what he could see, all Frank Devlin had learned in his youth about life outside New York City had ceased to exist—and he might have never have known it if not for the most remote of connections, an almost random arrow out of the universal darkness.

Three and a half miles on 517, the directions said, *and then three sharp rights around the lake*. The shadows cast by the thick foliage were so dark that Devlin had to turn on the headlights to read the tiny, TOYTOWN, U.S.A., street signs as he wound through the last three right turns. He couldn't get a good look at the lake. Lake Tranquility. Devlin knew nothing about Lake Tranquility, except that it was in Sussex County. What Devlin himself remembered was that Sussex was dotted with lakes—Owassa, Culver's, Paulinskill. Great fishing lakes, he had been taught in his teenage years, back when the men who had taught him fished at night so they wouldn't get caught by fish-and-game wardens. The fish went on the table or into the freezer, never to waste. The men had evolved a quiet, mysterious way to live, half off the land, so poor they had to be outside the law. Devlin supposed that many of them were ghosts now—or half-deaf old goofs, hardly the freebooting outlaws slugging out their Saturday nights at Poison Pete's, the ramshackle bar, bowling alley, and motel across the highway from the Culvermere Hotel, where city secretaries stole summer weekends with their soft, manicured bosses, unaware of the fierce, silent energy whirling outside. . . .

Probably no one in all of Lake Tranquility had ever heard anything of the area's old days. Lake Tranquility was another conventional, split-level suburb, the landscaping almost mature, with some of the lots butting onto a puddle too big to be called a pond. The numbers on the mailboxes indicated that Devlin was heading to a house with waterfront footage. Irene Quinn had the New York accent for life. Her brother, Cummings, had none of the accent, but Cummings had that N.Y.P.D. attitude-of-command crap in him. Devlin had heard it immediately in the way Cummings had tried to fix Devlin's identity.

Devlin knew about accents. In his early years in A.A., standing before groups everywhere in the Northeast from Maryland to Maine, responding to remarks about his own big-city speech, he had worked up a routine that had put people at ease with the way he seemed to mangle the language. Devlin had imitated five immigrants yelling at each other on a noisy Lower East Side street corner at the turn of the century—Irish, Italian, and Jewish, with German and Russian thrown in. In about a minute, with commentary, Devlin had boiled the accents down to the raw edge New Yorkers have in their speech today, and he finished by showing how the accent changed from borough, neighborhood to neighborhood, and one occupation to the next. A police sergeant never moved his lips when he talked and neither did a nun, but they didn't sound alike; a garment district worker didn't shout in the same way as an Aqueduct railbird. Devlin used to do this routine, reminding the audience that New York was *loud* and getting *louder*: the old street corner was not as loud as today's Fifth Avenue, for instance. Devlin's partner, John Lord, who had never seen the bit, thought there might be some truth to Devlin's theory, but Devlin didn't know or care. He had been manic for years after getting sober, speaking four and five times a week, proudly calculating the miles traveled. The whole period was something he had had to work through. Now Devlin thought— *hoped*—he was as different from the guy who had wanted to prove he was sober as that guy had hoped he was different from the jerk who had spent almost fifteen years trying to prove he could drink. Devlin's sense of humor had survived, but now it was dark, mordant, too cutting at times for squares. He rarely did celebrity voices anymore, Bogart, Cagney, or his own favorite, Randolph Scott singing "Take the A Train." Years ago, Devlin had been celebrated as a man who could mimic practically anybody. Early this year, when Queens Borough President Donnie Manes finally succeeded in killing himself, Devlin had shouted in the voice of Mayor Hamilton, "I won the pool! I won the pool!"—a crack lost on noncops, but a howl to the burned-out bulls for whom it had been intended. They knew that once a guy starts trying to kill himself, he usually doesn't stop until he's overwhelmed by success. *Every* old cop knew that the meter had started ticking on Manes weeks before he had actually done the job. And they didn't care, for it was a fitting end to a common, greedy little thief.

Devlin had changed. He knew it. He hadn't put a guy in the hospital for drying out since the early eighties. He couldn't remember the last time he had seen a New York City Department of Hospitals Flight Deck. No reason for pulling back, except maybe getting closer to the old man's age when the fire in his belly had begun to go out—but Devlin didn't think he was going downhill yet. He was in much better shape than his father had ever been, positively healthy except for the cigarette smoking. He had never been a heavy smoker, and now he was down to a half a pack or less per day. For the past eighteen months he had been exercising, starting with Eileen's mini-trampoline, then working his way through ten- and twenty-pound dumbbells. He walked three and four miles two or three times a week. Eileen had gotten him to give up red meat, and currently his cholesterol level was under a hundred and forty. John Lord was crazy about Eileen. "She's got you loving life again," he'd said. Devlin loved life more every day. He hadn't known it was possible to love life so much. . . .

A car was parked out on the street in front of the Lake Tranquility house, a faded orange Pontiac hardtop with the new, cheap-looking New York plate with the Statue of Liberty in the center. Devlin parked in front of the Pontiac and walked back, pulling on his blazer as he went. On the passenger seat of the Pontiac was a paper bag overflowing with groceries and a red and white airline ticket folder. The driveway was empty, flanked by a pair of ragged spruces. The driveway blacktop was cracked and lumpy, the yard unkempt and bare.

The city had been hot, but the air here was only warm, if not exactly mild. Bugs were singing everywhere. The house was sheathed in some kind of mustard-colored battenboard, trim and neat against the vivid summer twilight. Through a clear diamond-shaped window in the garage door Devlin could see a chrome luggage rack on the roof of a station wagon. He wondered if he was about to enter a house that smelled of wet diapers; he could be here for hours. Devlin pushed the button beside the front door, but didn't hear anything inside. A gust of warm, humid air came up as he pushed the button again. The door was opened by a big brunette in jeans and a Mr. Met

T-shirt. She was in her late twenties and her long hair looked as if it had not been combed today. Devlin had seen that before. He introduced himself. She let him step inside and then she locked the door. Mrs. Quinn. Irene. She had freckles, and was sheathed in the hot bloom of nervous perspiration. Like many another Irish-American woman in an emergency situation, she thought she had to speak quickly, through her teeth.

"He woke up a little while ago. I've never seen him so sick. I've seen him bad, but Jesus, not like this. The kids are with my sister. I had to get them out of here."

The hall was narrow, and Devlin eased himself past her. He felt comfortable with the situation now. His tension was gone, like that of an athlete whose game has begun. He caught a glimpse of the family room: sofas and end tables. No pictures on the walls. Devlin had seen that before, too. With the head of the household hitting alcoholic bottom, life drained out of the family so completely that no one had the moral resolve even to brighten the walls.

"Is somebody in there with him?"

"Mr. Lederer," she said, and repeated herself slowly so Devlin got the name right. "I missed his first name," she said. "I'm sorry. He's the one who made the arrangements for Tom. The place is only about twenty minutes from here, some kind of converted estate off 517."

Convenient. Devlin liked the Flight Deck route better, when it was possible. Although he knew from observation that not every drunk needed waking up in a city hospital alcoholic ward amid the scum of the earth to get him thinking hard about himself again, Devlin knew from experience that nothing beat the icy jolt of the stink of fifty men, unwashed, drooling, as much dead as alive, moaning their despair and pain, and the knowledge that you were one of them, and belonged in their midst. Devlin's sponsor had made sure of that. *Dandy*, Bill Ward had called him. *Mr. Snappy Dresser*. And worst of all, *Nightclub Devlin*. A smart-ass caption writer had come up with that in the *Daily News* in 1970. *Frank "Nightclub" Devlin*.

"Irene!"

A bellow. That would be Tom.

Mrs. Quinn led the way. Sometimes in these situations, for her own safety, the woman would tie the man to the bed. Devlin did not think that would be the case here. Mrs. Quinn was a strapping woman, as tall as Devlin, who was five-ten. Old Tom had had the weeps today, according to Cummings. So in spite of the raised voice, Tom might be really pretty docile. Lederer. If Lederer wasn't a cop, this could take longer. There were things cops could say to cops, in the presence of other cops, that couldn't be said in any other context. That applied to A.A., too.

Tom Quinn was sitting on the edge of the bed, nude except for a sheet over his skinny thighs, his head down, his sandy hair matted. In his mid-thirties, he looked emaciated and dehydrated. The place didn't smell sour, which was odd—usually a drunk in his shape only had to pass through a room to foul the air. Devlin realized he was smelling fresh paint, only a week or two old. That could explain the bare walls as well as anything else.

Lederer was a big guy about Devlin's age. He had the vein-blown, bulbous nose of a longtime heavy drinker. His suit was a brown pinstripe and the collar of his white shirt was wilted. Lederer extended a fleshy hand and said his first name was Bob. Tom looked up, his eyes red-rimmed and bloodshot. He hadn't shaved in four days.

"Who are you?" he asked weakly.

Devlin said his name. "How are you doing?"

"Fuck you," Tom snarled. "You're not him. You're too young. Shit, you look like you never had a drink in your fucking life!"

Devlin flashed his shield. As if its proximity made Tom lose his balance, he rocked on the edge of the bed. His head bobbed up and he gazed at Devlin blearily.

"Whatja do, have plastic surgery?"

"No, I got on the program," Devlin said. "If I hadn't, I'd be dead. If you don't wise up, you're going to die. When was the last time you went to a doctor? Do you know what that shit is doing to your blood pressure, kidneys, and liver? What about your brain, asshole, thousands of cells at a time? Is there enough left of it to remember the last time you had a real hard-on, and making love wasn't a desperate struggle to prove yourself?''

Tom rocked again as he looked away. "Fuck you double. Fuck you, *fuck* you!"

"Don't talk like a bad movie," Devlin said. "You should get down on your knees and thank God you still have a wife who cares enough to try to help you. Right now you're worthless and you know it, or we wouldn't be here—"

"Who are you bullshitting?" Tom slurred. "You're married to an heiress. Your brother-in-law is going to be senator. I used to see you in the newspapers, in the gossip columns—"

"My wife and I have been separated for fifteen years," Devlin said.

"Oh, another good Catholic," Tom said, and looked bleakly at his wife. His lips trembled and twisted.

Devlin knew what was coming. He wanted to put his fingers in his ears.

"Irene!"

"I'm here, baby," she cried.

An enabler. Mrs. Quinn was the daughter of an alcoholic, more than likely, trying to remake the movie of her childhood with her husband as the new star. *See, Daddy? I love you.* She wasn't digging her husband's grave—he was doing that job well enough—but she was holding his jacket while he swung the pick. If all that were true, Mrs. Quinn was competing with Mom without realizing that defining her life on her mother's terms made her a loser on the first jump out of the gate. Mrs. Quinn was as big a loser as her husband, and her refusal to admit it was part of the process that was destroying them both and passing the problem on to their children. This was one reason why Devlin's sense of humor sometimes turned merciless. Humanity's worst suffering was self-inflicted. Well, he hadn't come all the way out to Sussex to be reminded of the devil he had been wrestling for most of his life.

"You wanted to see me, Tom. What can I do for you?"

"Oh, man—" Tom clasped his hands between his thighs

and rocked even harder. He looked up again, the tears stream-
ing down his cheeks. "Can I have a drink? I need a drink, one
last drink before I go in."

Devlin glanced at Lederer, who appeared to be more interested in Devlin's tailoring than in Tom Quinn. Lederer wasn't
going for the liquor. Reaching into his hip pocket for the flask
Bill Ward had given him for this purpose, Devlin wondered
about Lederer, who he was, what he did. But Devlin knew
better than to ask, lest he hear Lederer's complete life story.
Devlin's mother would have called Lederer a drip. Devlin's
mother's vocabulary had stopped evolving sometime in the
fifties, but for the rest of her life she thought she was up-to-
date. Hep.

Unscrewing the top of the flask released the flowers-of-evil
smell of the bourbon inside. Through his tears Tom Quinn
flashed a sucker's smile, and in another moment he could be
heard chugalugging. Devlin exchanged glances with Mrs.
Quinn. By the expression on Lederer's face, he didn't know
what was going on. Maybe he was a dope as well as a drip.
All the more reason to treat the guy decently. Part of the program. Drunks didn't keep each other sober with disdain or
contempt. Gasping, Tom returned the flask.

"Were you like this?" he asked Devlin. "Really? Tell me
the truth, for Christ's sake."

"Worse in every way," Devlin answered, permitting himself to block momentarily the most vivid parts of the memory.

"Is that what happened to your marriage?"

"Yes and no. Yes, I was a son of a bitch. How about you,
Tom? Are you a son of a bitch?"

Tom's lip twisted again. Devlin had to backpedal. He didn't
want a lot of boohooing, he wanted a decision. No matter
what, he was going to see that Tom was put inside and given
a chance to dry out—but without a decision, Tom would be
out again before the end of the week, wandering from bottle
to bottle like a dog sniffing his way from tree to tree.

"How long did it take you to get straightened out?"

"I'll let you know when I get there, kid." Devlin took
Tom's clammy arm. "It's one day at a time, as I'm sure you've

heard before." He started to lift Tom to his feet. "Look at me. You've heard it before, haven't you?"

"Yes. One day—Ah, *fuck*! Who can live like that?"

"Everybody *does*, Tom, whether they know it or not." Tom was standing now with Devlin holding him mostly motionless. The towel fell to the floor, but Tom didn't care. Mrs. Quinn's eyes, wide, fixed on her husband's exposed, limp penis. As if frozen to her spot, she made no move to cover her husband— standing in front of the others drunk, naked, and nothing to brag about. Lederer got the towel and held it in front of Tom. Tom rocked heavily, his head turned away from Devlin; just as well: Devlin didn't want a noseful of Tom's moist, bourbon breath. "Tom, it's schmucks like us who don't want to face the fact that life is a one-day-at-a-time proposition. You're feeling sorry for yourself and you don't even know why anymore."

Tom nodded, but then abruptly he grew rigid. His hand came up to his throat, and he tried to swallow. Turning to Devlin, he stared, his eyes wide, surprised, as his larynx bobbed so suddenly that Devlin could hear it. Devlin knew what was happening, but he could not move out of the way without letting go of Tom, who could fall like a corpse and split his head open on the corner of a dresser or the edge of the bedframe. *No good deed goes unpunished*, Devlin thought ruefully. Tom's eyes opened wider, more astonished, as his tongue, curled like the tip of a fortune cookie, protruded from the center of his bulging cheeks, and then faster and more copiously than Devlin could have imagined, Tom vomited all over the blue blazer, white shirt, red tie, tan slacks, and shined shoes of Francis Xavier Devlin III, Detective Third Grade, Shield number 67842, New York Police Department.

11:21 P.M. . . .

"**D**EVLIN," THE MESSAGE TAPE BEGAN, "THIS IS SERgeant Mariano of the Chief of Detectives' office. Would you call in, please, as soon as possible? I'm going to give you the chief's private number. Under no circumstances are you to give it to anybody else." Devlin was ready with a pen when Mariano gave the number.

The answer machine was on the dresser in his bedroom. Devlin stopped the tape. Rewinding it when he had come in had taken almost a minute. Five or more calls, according to the indicator light. In the fifteen months he had had the machine, a gift from Eileen, it had never recorded so many; most of the time he was at Eileen's, and most of his friends knew it. Devlin, barefoot on his thick, brown carpet, a cup of decaffeinated coffee in hand, could not remember the last time he had been called by anyone from the Chief of Detectives' office. Years ago. A decade or more. He didn't know Mariano. Now the window air conditioner turned itself on and Devlin reached over and turned it off. If the department wanted him for more time this weekend than he had already been assigned, he was going to have to find a way to get out of it. He started the machine, and after a moment, Mariano's voice came on again. The message was the same, but the tone was a bit more urgent. Devlin wasn't being asked to work more overtime, that was clear. As he stopped the tape a second time, the telephone rang.

He couldn't let it go, or the machine would record over the messages he still hadn't heard. Devlin picked up and said hello. It was John Lord, his partner.

21

"I've been calling you every half hour since eight o'clock, Frank. Vito Mariano, in Harry Levine's office, called me twice before—"

"You know Mariano?"

"He was in the Two-six with me. You want to know about him?"

"Yeah." The Twenty-sixth Precinct was West Harlem, black and Hispanic, graffiti scarred and garbage strewn, where young rookies learned in their first tour that the rules were the same as prison: you went along, and as soon as somebody looked at you funny, you hurt him. The Two-six wasn't the toughest precinct in the city, but it had all the necessary elements.

"As I understood it, Vito had a rabbi in the Chief of Operations office," John said. "He wasn't any kind of a cop on the street and he couldn't wait to move up. People weren't supposed to see it, but I could."

In the N.Y.P.D., a rabbi was an older, highly placed cop who steered a favored youngster in the right directions. "Did Mariano play the game, or just mind his business?"

"I can only guess," John said. He was silent a moment. John, another second-generation cop, had come into the department with his father's reputation preceding him; his father had never even *seen* a nickel. Back in the sixties, until the life Devlin had been living had blown up in his face, *he* had played the game, like his father before him—although he had known nothing about his father's cheap chiseling until he had earned a shield of his own. Devlin's first beat had been in Central Harlem, and at the end of the first week, a sergeant he had never seen before motioned him over to a squad car and tucked an envelope into Devlin's breast pocket. Seventy-five bucks. From the numbers operation in the middle of the block, about which he had known nothing. In the thirteen years he had been sober, Devlin had not touched so much as an apple. Some people in the department thought that change in him, as much as anything, had stopped Devlin's career cold. Devlin was content to let them think what they wanted; when he had changed his life, he had changed it completely. He had started all over again dead broke, and when his father died, Devlin's own savings—and sports winnings—were above forty thousand dollars.

"Fuck it," Devlin said. "Tell me what Mariano said to you."

"He was looking for you. The second time he called, he wanted to know if I had any idea where you were. I said no. Monday's the night you don't see Eileen, right?"

"We changed it this week. I was with her today, but I had to run an errand." Devlin remembered that Cummings had gotten Eileen's telephone number from John—when? "Mariano's been calling here, too. I was listening to the messages when you called."

John said, "At eight o'clock Levine himself called me. That guy *never* moves his lips when he talks. Very calm. Told me to give a hand in putting you in touch with him."

Devlin knew Harry Levine the way John knew Mariano. Another guy who thought that the real action in the N.Y.P.D. was at Police Plaza—Centre Street, back then. Devlin had no more evidence on Levine than John had on Mariano, and because he had to guess, Devlin figured Levine had never touched anything. Never told anything, either, at least for much of his career. Once you were close to the top, it was no longer in your interest to turn your back on the misdeeds of brother officers. They weren't brothers anymore anyway, but children to be praised or punished.

"So you don't have a clue, either, to what this is about, except that they want me."

"Oh, they *do* want you," John said. "If you can tell me what it's about, I wish you would—"

"When I find out."

John hadn't finished. "—And if there's anything I can do to help, just say so."

Devlin felt a pang of alarm. "What makes you say a thing like that?"

"To be honest with you, Frank, it really does sound like one of those deals."

One of *what* deals? Nothing Devlin had done—or had *not* done—was worthy of the attention of the Chief of Detectives.

Devlin was pulling his weight on the Liberty Week project, clearing as many, or as few, Ninth Precinct burglaries, muggings, stabbings, shots fired, and domestic quarrels as ever—the real everyday life of a drug-and-booze–saturated district like the Lower East Side. Two weeks ago Devlin and John had had to use force to subdue a young black man obviously under the influence, swinging a Louisville Slugger at anyone who came near him. The confrontation had been an accident—Devlin and John had been in the next apartment, talking to a kid named Hector about a series of muggings of old ladies—when furniture crashed and a woman began screaming for the police.

With his battered girlfriend begging the two detectives not to shoot the guy, Devlin and John, who never drew their guns, were able to take him into custody. Sure, they had to use kitchen chairs like lion tamers to get the bat away from the bastard, and then had to punch it out with him for what might have been ten minutes before being able to cuff his wrists and ankles. When he wanted to bite, flopping around on the floor like a crazed lobster, the girlfriend got a balled-up pair of socks to shove in his mouth, and later, through the blood caking her teeth, she thanked the two for not hurting her sweetie more than they had. According to the hospital report, sweetie had sustained a broken nose, chipped teeth, cracked ribs—and according to no hospital report, just the partners' own tally—John Lord had skinned a knuckle and pulled a muscle in his back, and Frank Devlin had caught a fat lip. . . .

That had been two weeks ago, long enough for the guy or his girlfriend to decide to yell police brutality.

But Devlin didn't believe it. Such people didn't file complaints unless they'd been hypnotized by some media-shrewd rabble-rouser. Devlin called the number Mariano had left on the machine, and the telephone on the other end was picked up almost instantly.

"Yeah?"

"Frank Devlin, Mariano—" He stopped because Mariano muffled his mouthpiece and said something indistinct to a third party.

"Devlin, we've been looking for you all night. The chief wants to know how soon you can get down here."

"What for?"

"Ah, we're not going to discuss it over the phone," Mariano said. "In fact, *you're* not going to discuss this with anybody, know what I'm saying?"

"I've been speaking English a lot longer than you, kid. Figure it's going to take me at least twenty minutes to get downtown."

"You have a car, don't you?"

"Yeah, and it'll be in one piece when I get there." Devlin hung up. After Mariano had told him to be quiet, Devlin had been tempted to say something about Mariano and Levine calling John Lord. Was that being quiet? But that wouldn't have done John any good, and there was no sense in letting Mariano focus on what Devlin might know about him.

Advancing the message tape on Fast Forward so it wouldn't be erased by calls to come, Devlin heard one set of mouse squeaks in a higher register than the others. Eileen. She liked to leave gag messages. As much as he wanted to hear her voice, he didn't want to be distracted from his concentration on what he had just heard from Mariano.

Devlin was sure Harry Levine had been listening to Mariano's every word—and probably Devlin's, too, for that matter. *The chief wants to know* . . . Levine had heard that, no question about it. As Chief of Detectives, Harry Levine liked to think he wore a velvet glove. When instructing or chastising one of his detectives, he liked to lean back, smile, and chomp the dark, spitty end of a big, green cigar. Devlin's crack years ago—that Levine's breath smelled like cat shit—got back to him, and he called Devlin. "My wife agrees with your assessment of my breath, but she wants to sic Internal Affairs on us to find out how you know."

Levine had inherited that wonderfully resonant bass voice: his grandfather had been a cantor, and his great-grandfather before him. Devlin knew a lot about Levine. That branch of the Levine family went far back in the history of New York, with Levinskys buried in the oldest Jewish cemetery in the city, a tiny triangular plot not far from Police Plaza, its tarnished brass plaque shadowed by the dark, rough brick of the surrounding tenements, tilted pebble-garnished tombstones angled against the surrounding stiff, yellow weeds: Levensky, Levinski—uniform spelling did not begin until the nineteenth century, and the stones went back to the seventeenth. In those days, and until the late nineteenth century, when their overwhelming numbers more or less dissolved the issue, the Jews were as startling to New York's ruling English, Dutch, and Scots as the many nationalities of Arabs were to the Jews, Irish, and Italians who ran the city today, and the Blacks, Puerto Ricans, and Asians who, Devlin was certain, were going to run the city tomorrow.

Harry Levine had been the toughest kid in Brownsville. In uniform, he had averaged two good collars a day for two years, leaving his Irish superiors no choice but to put him in plainclothes. Later, as a homicide detective, he had been relentless, and sometimes a sleuth. Today his son was a show business lawyer in California, his daughter a doctor, he had five grandchildren, and his eighty-six-year-old mother still lived with his wife and him, as she had since the day of their marriage. Levine liked Devlin, but, because of the bad old days, didn't exactly trust him. *Possibly.* Devlin wasn't sure. With Levine, nobody, not even the commissioner, was *ever* sure.

Devlin rode up in the elevator alone, grabbing a few last drags on a cigarette before tamping it out on the heel of his shoe and pocketing the butt. *Now* he was nervous. Driving down on the Brooklyn-Queens Expressway, he had kept himself diverted by remembering the locations of potholes, weaving from lane to lane on the dark, usually heavily trafficked road. At one point, the speedometer needle of his ten-year-old Cadillac Seville had touched seventy-five. He hadn't tried to clear his head and imagine what Harry Levine could have on his mind. Sometimes, usually the worst possible times, Devlin knew, people reverted to childish processes, defensiveness, disappearing into themselves. . . .

The elevator door opened. Mariano, three feet from Devlin,

rocked on the balls of his feet and heaved an enormous sigh. His lips formed the words "Follow me," but Devlin heard nothing and didn't see Mariano's larynx move. Mariano had blue eyes, neatly cut hair, and a uniform that looked custom-tailored. He was a good-looking guy, one of those Italians who knew he was attractive to women, moving with the kind of swagger that said he was used to having his way. Devlin had been there—had believed essentially the same lies about himself. Nothing could touch Mariano, or so Mariano thought. There was a joke about Christ being Irish because He was in the building trades, out of work, and His mother thought He was God. Italians were different only in style. If Mariano really wanted to grow up, maybe he would have the luck to have his nose rubbed in himself before much more time passed. *Sour*, Devlin mentally labeled his own attitude. Maybe he should have listened to Eileen's message after all, he thought as Mariano opened the door to Levine's office.

Harry Levine was putting the telephone down. His hair was completely gray now. He was wearing a summer-weight, short-sleeved white shirt, even though he lived all but a few minutes each day in conditioned air. The cigar was out. He told Devlin to sit down and then dismissed Mariano with a thank you. Mariano's eyes darted suddenly; he was surprised to be excluded. He knew what was coming, and was just now seeing that his boss wanted to give Devlin—what? The *appearance* of privacy? Perhaps only the *temporary* appearance of privacy. Levine wanted to tell Devlin something known to Mariano, a sergeant. Maybe there were others who knew, all the way up to the rank of super chief. Why not above, too? A little insight into the situation had an oddly calming effect, Devlin realized. He saw, too, that he was staring at the lights of Brooklyn through Levine's two windows, Brooklyn and the bridge, red and white lights trickling sluggishly in all directions. The public parts of this building looked like what you expected to find in the Moscow subway, but this office was a bit better. On two walls Levine had pictures of himself with politicians and figures from show biz, like the owner of a nightclub. Upper-echelon New York cops saw themselves as celebrities, too;

Devlin himself had been on the same track before he had de-railed.

Devlin watched Mariano close the door. Levine relit his cigar. "You still A.A.?"

"You're always A.A.—if you're lucky," Devlin answered. The Quinns? Had something happened in New Jersey?

"How long? For you, I mean?"

"Thirteen years."

"That's wonderful . . . I guess. I don't know. I was married and had little kids before I was twenty-five years old. That's the truth, Devlin. I took myself as too busy to get into the kind of trouble you and a lot of other guys made for yourselves. I mean no offense, it's just the difference between us." He leaned back. "Do you know a man named Octavio Lopez?"

A little guy with a crater face, wispy goatee and mustache, and a navy blue beret. "He's a dope dealer on Fourth Street between B and C."

"The Ninth? The Lower East Side?"

"Alphabet City," Devlin corrected, being facetious. Real estate interests had dreamed up the new name for the area encompassing the lettered avenues, which was the same as calling cancer a freestyle cellular development. Levine snorted.

"He's your informer?"

Mariano knew this? Why? "Oh, yeah. Very small potatoes. I want him to work the kids, the young burglars. Octavio deals to them. I want him to keep his ears open, not ask questions. Sooner or later he'll help us on something worthwhile. In the meantime, he's good for small stuff and background. You know the game."

"He deals to burglars." Levine picked up a computer print-out. "He caught nine months on Riker's back in '81. Your collar."

"Receiving stolen goods. I got him again, in '83, possession of heroin, and when he realized he hadn't recognized me, he decided he needed help being a crook."

Levine grinned. "And you're working him for a big one. In the meantime you get small stuff."

"I'm working and waiting. Maybe he's too small. I don't know if he ever gets off Fourth Street."

Levine looked again at Octavio's rap sheet before tossing it back on his desk. "You don't know if he gets off Fourth Street."

"He's a dope dealer. I don't think he gets out of his flat that often."

Levine looked up at Devlin, one eyebrow raised. "When was the last time you saw Jack Brennan?"

"What?"

"Jack Brennan, the Democratic candidate for the Senate."

"And my brother-in-law . . . still. Are you kidding?"

"Humor me, Frank, please."

Now it was Frank. You never knew with Levine. Devlin decided to go for it: "The last time I saw Jack Brennan was on Thursday, September sixteenth, 1971, in the backyard of his father's house out in Jamaica Estates. It was about six-thirty in the evening." Devlin was looking directly at Levine, never believing he was addressing the point Levine wanted clarified, but falling deeper into the memory of what he was describing. It dialed into clearer focus so Devlin could see it, not in his mind, but before his eyes, like a movie, or worse, a dream he had had over and over, and was having again. Devlin could see the fading sunlight shining across Jack's shoulder as he turned away and brought his drink to his lips. "Lisa Wagner was there—she was starring in the revival of *Brigadoon* that year—and I remember thinking that she was going to be late for her curtain."

Devlin stopped, but Levine was staring, listening. He wanted to hear the rest of it. Devlin didn't need a prompter to feed him his next words. The images were too sharp, and, he realized again, somehow still fresh: Brennan snubbing him, the back turned for good. "I was so drunk I thought I was sober. I had just seen Jack's father. Their faggot English butler was at the door. He couldn't help smiling as he opened it for me, so I stopped and asked him if he thought something was funny. He didn't answer, but let his eyes move toward the front walk. This way to the egress."

Devlin had thought that at the moment, *This way to the egress*, fixing it in his memory forever. "The smile got wider, so I hit him. I brought one up off the floor and connected with his chin. My first thought was that it was a near miss, but he flew back against an antique table and the Chinese vase on it. The table and the vase disintegrated." Levine was smiling. "Nothing to be proud of," Devlin said. "Later, when I was on the program, I wrote him a letter of apology, offering to apologize in person, but I never received an answer. Let me go on. I stepped outside and saw the limo down at the curb that was going to take La Wagner to the theater. Maybe she had a police escort, maybe Jack wanted more before the curtain went up. This was before Jack knew Anita. I heard later that she was banging one of the producers, too. That's Wagner, not Anita." Anita was Jack's wife. "The last time I saw Jack Brennan, in person, was when he turned his back on me that afternoon, September sixteenth, 1971."

"What about when Joe Brennan died?" Levine asked. "You didn't go to his funeral?"

"Jim Brennan made a point of disinviting me."

"And you remember all this stuff from 1971 as well as you say because—"

"Because I'll remember that day, every minute of it, for the rest of my life." *But not tonight.*

Levine puffed on his cigar, sending a gallon of blue smoke writhing upward. "And, ah, when was the last time you saw Octavio Lopez?"

"Is this being recorded?"

"No, no. Just humor me. It's all right."

"I have to think," Devlin said. "Maybe I have it logged . . ."

"Just the best of your recollection, Frank."

He was trying to focus, get away from thoughts of the Brennans. Did Levine think he wanted to stall? "Now I remember. In the winter. This past winter. My partner, John Lord, was there. John and I ducked into the supermarket on First Avenue at the corner of Fifth Street to pick up an Italian bread, spiced ham, and store cheese to make hero sandwiches for lunch."

Levine allowed himself a silent chuckle. "You remember *that*?"

"This is easy. I was telling John how I used to eat lunch in the school yard at Junior High School 125 in Queens, for twenty-three cents—fifteen cents for the sandwich, eight cents for the soda—how I could remember the taste of the sandwich and washing it down with a twelve-ounce Pepsi because Pepsi was the most for the money. This was before John was born. He wanted to try it. Because we're different generations and like each other, we've made a point of trying to understand where we're coming from. Anyway, it was a very cold day, too cold for that kind of food. Octavio was waiting at the checkout, which surprised me. He really should have been at home. Guys like him—junkies—always feel the cold worse than the rest of us. I had nothing to say to him, but he followed us back into the store. He wanted to bullshit. I asked him what he knew about the rapist who's been working the neighborhood for the past year. He said that the guy was probably coming in from outside, meaning Octavio didn't know squat."

"That rapist is still running around, isn't he?"

"Yeah. He's not out of control, either. Figuring the rapes we don't hear about, he hits about once every six weeks or so."

Levine sighed. "Well, here's the reason we called you down: Octavio Lopez shot and killed Jack Brennan in a room up in the Waldorf Towers at five o'clock this afternoon. He also shot and killed one Jane Milburn, twenty-seven years old, a researcher for *Time* magazine. The victims were in bed together. Brennan was due downstairs in the main ballroom at eight-thirty for a thousand-dollar-a-plate dinner. He was shaving it close, don't you think?"

Devlin wanted a cigarette. There had been a minor news item about Jack Brennan on the radio tonight, but Devlin's mind suddenly couldn't get past the butt in his jacket pocket, and when he brought it to his lips, his hand was shaking. Levine's eyes were on him. *Take a good look,* Devlin thought. He got the cigarette lit and took a long, deep drag. What he really wanted, he knew, was a drink—but that was normal for him, even at this late date. He'd settle for coffee. He was just as well off with nothing at all, he told himself. He continued to resist a flood of thoughts about the Brennans, about Maryellen, about her father in a wheelchair the past seven years, about Octavio Lopez— *Octavio Lopez?* Devlin said, "On the radio I heard that Jack missed the dinner because of a stomach upset."

"A head upset, too. Lopez emptied a .38 police special into both of them before the private guards of a visiting Arab prince down the hall rushed in and disarmed him. According to their preliminary statements, Lopez was just standing over the bodies, glassy-eyed. We're running blood tests on him now."

"If you didn't get a lawyer's consent, he might walk."

"Lopez was too shot up with something to notice what we were doing. We don't want evidence anyway. Commissioner Torres wants information. That story you heard on the radio came from upstairs. You know our commissioner. While I was in his office, Mayor Hamilton called three times." Levine's mouth twisted. "You know our mayor, too."

Devlin nodded. Police Commissioner Norberto Torres was a whorehound who had stocked Police Plaza with many of the city's star cocksuckers, and Mayor Hamilton was found in the company of women for political purposes only. The two had a lot to fear from a political sex scandal. Mildly Devlin asked, "Do you want to know where I was at the time?"

"Standard question," Levine said evenly. "I was going to get around to it."

Devlin told him he had been in bed with his girlfriend, then had left before six to drive to Sussex County.

"Well, that you can prove," Levine said. "Right now, Hamilton and Torres want to keep this quiet for as long as they can. Can you believe it? I heard Torres say something to Hamilton about a half billion in business and thirty-three million in sales taxes because of this Liberty deal. What kind of minds do they have?" He sighed. "But, with so many people getting away with so much these days, I shouldn't be surprised by anything they do." Now he raised an eyebrow. "You appreciate my position, Devlin, don't you?"

Levine was saying that he knew he had been set up to have the can tied to his tail; and that, if necessary, he'd lay the problem off on someone else. Devlin said, "I appreciate it completely."

"I want you to tell me everything you know about this Lopez character."

"No problem."

Levine stood up and reached for his jacket. "And I want you to tell me everything you know about the Brennans. No-holds-barred." He glanced at his watch; Devlin figured the time at close to midnight. "Come with me. You know as well as I do that old Jim Brennan has more skeletons in his closet than a whole medical school, and that his sons weren't any different. I want to hear it all, no matter how old, how secondhand. Right now the New York Police Department is about as effective as a high school marching band, but if people think this is the time to take advantage of us, to make *use* of us, so they can get away with murder, they're dead wrong. I want to go up to the Medical Examiner's office, where they're holding the bodies. Apparently Jack Brennan had more sexual problems than lack of time. Jesus." Levine stopped at the door and raised his fist as if to punch a hole in it, but then he let his arm drop to his side. "Ah, these motherfuckers! If they're pulling anything, I'm going to pound it so far up their asses they're going to look like the balloons in the Thanksgiving Day Parade!"

Devlin had never heard Levine curse before, but he was too busy thinking of other things for the word to register with any more violence than a distant squeal of brakes. Devlin knew nothing about Jack Brennan having sexual "problems." And Devlin had already told Levine most of what he knew about Octavio Lopez. A bombed-out freak like Lopez couldn't travel from the Lower East Side to the Waldorf-Astoria—three miles? not much farther—any more than he could dance *Swan Lake*. *Glassy-eyed*: all right, chosen by person or persons unknown, but of all the dirtballs in town, why him? And a .38 police special. Harry Levine opened the door and held it, his eyes on Devlin's as Devlin passed through.

Now Devlin remembered a news item on the car radio last night mentioning Jack Brennan. *Yes!* About Brennan being unable to attend the cardinal's dinner at the Waldorf-Astoria "due to stomach upset." Years ago Devlin had taught "bad clams" to Jack Brennan. " 'Bad clams' is the best excuse for otherwise unexplainable disappearances," Devlin had told the Brennan brothers one particularly rowdy night.

He had stayed away from all the Brennans, their activities and associates, just as he had been told to do by old Jim Brennan fifteen years ago. Having been eighty-sixed by old man Brennan had turned out to be the best thing that had ever happened to Frank Devlin. John Lord had been Devlin's partner for years without ever asking about the Brennans. As young as he was, John was acutely sensitive to other people's privacy, and before Devlin met Eileen, he had seemed to want to be left to himself. In 1984 an article appeared in the *Times* about Jack Brennan's political ambitions, with a review of the family history, and Devlin found John reading it.

"Any questions?"

"I don't think so," John said. "You're probably better off without them."

"Oh, I know I am," Devlin responded.

He didn't feel a twinge about the newspapers, radio, and television being full of Jack Brennan's shoo-in Democratic candidacy for the U.S. Senate. On the other hand, contending with the emotional impact of the media was easier than a face-to-face confrontation in his real life, even with an asshole like Tom Quinn in New Jersey earlier this evening. Devlin's last contact with the Brennans had been eight years ago, when Joe Brennan, once Devlin's best friend, had drowned. Devlin had wanted to go to the funeral, but then the word had come down from old Jim, ever Devlin's nemesis, to stay away—*stay the hell away*, was how one of Brennan's assistants had phrased it on the telephone. Not even the death of a son had been an occasion for Jim Brennan to ease up. . . .

Devlin had heard last night's news broadcast at 10:30, crossing the Jersey Meadows at eighty miles per hour, figuring it would be just his luck to get pulled over—Quinn had left Devlin feeling queasy and unhappy. He had had a conversation about Jack Brennan last Friday morning. Devlin was one of the guys in A.A. the church called on when a priest had a problem, and Father Steve Loncaric was one of Devlin's "boys"—five years sober. Loncaric was currently attempting to do the biggest favor Devlin had ever asked of anybody in his life.

"Frank! Can you have lunch with me this afternoon?"

"Pass, Steve. I've got to be at Police Plaza for a meeting on South American pickpockets."

"Tuesday, then," Loncaric said. "I'm busy Monday, and this has to be fast. We're going to get some questions from Rome on your annulment petition, and you know the cardinal takes his pastoral duties seriously. He'll want to meet with you before he signs you off. You know what his schedule is like. If he gets a cancellation, he wants to move things up. I'm hoping to get you in to see him sooner rather than later, and you need to be briefed."

The prospect of meeting the cardinal made Devlin nervous, but he couldn't argue. What the cardinal wanted to do was judge Devlin, exactly what Christians were forbidden to do. But you couldn't debate theology with a cardinal, especially when the old bastard held your future in his fist. At the age of forty-three Devlin thought he was capable of sitting obediently like a schoolboy in front of a desiccated old bozo asking the most intimate questions. Devlin would be able to deal with his anger. At twenty, thirty, maybe even thirty-five, Devlin would have wanted to slap His Eminence around like a suspect.

"Tuesday," Devlin said to Loncaric. "South Street Seaport, at that joint where the carrots look like Lucille Ball's hair."

"Angel hair julienne," Loncaric said. "Uh, you know the cardinal is going to be sitting next to Jack Brennan at his Liberty Dinner at the Waldorf Monday night. Their chitchat might impact negatively on your personal timetable, whatever that might be. I've been thinking that it's in Jack Brennan's interest to let the annulment slide until after the election. Purely a political thing—nothing personal at all. Brennan might even expect you to understand that. Some of our beloved laity object to annulments, you know. They think annulments go to the rich, like the medieval sale of indulgences."

The beloved laity was right, but Devlin couldn't say that to Steve Loncaric. Devlin's bank account was ten grand lighter since he had begun the long walk to Rome to dissolve his marriage. "Those people don't know the difference between an annulment and a divorce."

"With no grounds for annulments themselves, they don't *want* to know," Loncaric said. "It isn't going to help Jack Brennan in the voting booth if they think the Brennans are getting special treatment from Holy Mother Bingo."

With Devlin and perhaps a few others, Loncaric could be as irreverent as the most ratchet-mouthed lapsed Catholic, which was what Devlin had been before he had fallen in love with Eileen O'Sullivan and started to have thoughts about getting an annulment from Maryellen Brennan. "So what are you telling me?"

"What I'm telling you," Loncaric said, "is to stay light-hearted. You'll live longer."

"I'm forty-three," Devlin protested. "My meter's running."

"What am I saying? See that your taxi's going to the airport, and live one hell of a long time. Do you know what you're asking of God? A second life, nothing more or less than that. I'll see you tomorrow."

"God bless you, too," Devlin muttered, thinking that Loncaric was cuffing him around for not addressing *Eileen's* concern: having a child of her own. Devlin wanted it for her, but if it didn't happen, all his wanting wouldn't lift her pain for a split second.

No, it was going to happen. He would do whatever it took.

Sure. The same guy who had almost forgotten his lunch date tomorrow.

TUESDAY, JULY 1

12:14 A.M. . . .

THEY WERE HEADED TO FIRST AVENUE AND THIRTIETH Street, the Bellevue complex. Levine drove the big, rattling, unmarked police sedan up East Broadway to Allen Street, north on Allen until Allen became First Avenue, and then on uptown.

At this hour the stores were closed, the folding metal gates drawn over and locked, but people still crowded the sidewalks, purplish-gray under the arc lamps, stepping over and around the litter and, here and there, someone sleeping on the sidewalk. This wasn't the worst of lower Manhattan: a few blocks to the west was the Bowery with its alcoholic bums. The same distance east, the free-fire zones of slum and housing projects where, amid the burned-out cars and overflowing garbage cans, one could score crack, smack, coke, speed, angel dust, designer drugs, and probably a whole lot of addictive crap Devlin had never heard of. During the three years after his father's death, struggling with depression, Devlin had seen this as one of its causes. The Lower East Side had not been as bad twenty and thirty years ago. Devlin was old enough to remember the pushcarts and the Sunday bargain shopping on Clinton and Rivington streets, the choice of a dozen Kosher delis where the juicy sandwiches were so thick you couldn't get your mouth around them, the sound of thousands of voices in scores of languages, dialects, and accents.

It was all but gone now. One clinical definition of depression said that the victim believed he had no effect on his environment. Devlin had been in that state of mind from the age of thirty-eight to forty-one, and now he could remember looking at this desolation and thinking of how bad it was, how much worse it had become, during his lifetime. He had not really taken care of his parents, he had only eased their dying. An evil chewing in his gut had accompanied that notion, and now, as he thought about the Brennans, about both Jack and Joe being dead, the wild great promise of twenty-five years ago plowed under like just another cheap idea, Devlin could feel it again hot in his belly, drawing the warmth from his extremities until he actually felt cold and sick. Maybe it was the reappearance of death, or his awareness of its reappearance, Devlin's awareness of the losses in his life, all of it fitting together in his gut again, what he had promised himself he would never feel again.

Jack for senator: Jack had been five years older than Devlin, but at the time Devlin had known him, Jack had been a lightweight in street smarts. Old Jim was a tougher son of a bitch than either of his boys, but not the kind of conscientious, nose-to-the-grindstone father who would teach his sons how to turn themselves into political powerhouses. But Jack Brennan had learned something somewhere. In fifteen years, Jack Brennan might have picked up a lot more than even perhaps his father could have taught him. Right now New York Democratic party morality was at an all-time low, lower than a roach in Chinatown, where the cellars went three levels down to black, dripping bedrock. The greed slime covered practically everybody: the late, unlamented Donnie Manes, suicided Borough President of Queens; his fat friend Geoffrey Lindenauer; Meade Esposito, party boss of Brooklyn, whose contacts and connections made doing business in that part of the city without him impossible; Stanley Friedman, his counterpart in the Bronx; guys in Staten Island milking a Navy contract; congressmen, judges, their sons and daughters—all of them, one way or the other, caught with their dukes in the tambourine. These people hadn't stolen millions from the people of New York, they had stolen billions, and now that some of them were heading to jail, they were tripping over themselves in the rush to rat on one another. Jack Brennan must have cut his deals, or he wouldn't have been made the Democratic senatorial candidate.

There *was* no other possibility: in New York, Jimmy Carter–style straight arrows were lucky if they were allowed to teach high school history on a substitute basis. In South Ozone Park, yet. A bellyache? Devlin had no way of knowing that he would ever hear the truth, but the way things worked in New York *and* the N.Y.P.D., the story would probably filter down, snake along the grapevine, until Frank Devlin, formerly "Nightclub" Devlin, soon-to-be ex-Brennan in-law (he prayed to God), heard it all.

"You're going to see the body," Levine said. "Welts all over it. Beside the bed was a woman's belt, a thin leather one. The dress the girl must have been wearing—it was on a chair, the only dress in the room—had a belt of the same material still in the loops. So the whipping, if that's what it was, was planned in advance."

Devlin knew as much as the next cop about bondage and discipline. Some powerful men accustomed to ordering people around and being waited on were not happy unless they submitted to an equal and opposite degradation—being spanked, tied up, urinated upon, or worse, the polite words for which were found only in twenty-pound dictionaries. None of it had ever deeply aroused Devlin's intellectual curiosity, and so he assumed he had no idea how an individual psyche made a connection between pain, suffering, and degradation, and the pleasure and completeness of lovemaking. Had Jack Brennan ever given a sign that his personal circuits were wired funny? The Frank Devlin of fifteen and twenty years ago, "Nightclub" Devlin, had had little way of telling. Too young, too inexperienced, in addition to being a drunk. If a powerful man had secret feelings of unworthiness or inadequacy, just the knowledge he had to deal with them secretly—*ultra*secretly, with a woman found for the purpose—would cause him to shift his public behavior even further from what he feared might be discovered about him. Maybe. Jack Brennan hadn't been anything like a public tyrant. Quieter than his younger brother Joe, Jack had been the family grind, the good student, the one who could be counted on to tend to details and paperwork. . . .

Harry Levine said, "Tell me about Joe Brennan. All I remember now is reading that he died."

Again, Devlin wasn't sure he believed Levine. "Joe Brennan drowned," he said. "Out at the family place in Southampton. Joe liked to swim before breakfast. He was a powerful swimmer—everybody knew that. It was July eighth, 1978. Mrs. Brennan—Charlotte, Joe's mother—heard him go out at about seven-thirty. Usually he was inside again in forty minutes, but by eight-twenty, when he hadn't returned, she roused the household and they went down to the water's edge to look for him. Everybody knew he'd swim straight out for a quarter mile or so, then come back. It took them only a couple of minutes to find him. He was floating in the surf, facedown. Charlotte was the first to spot him and she knew right away. Everybody else did, too. Jim got rid of the Southampton place before the year was out, and the following spring he had his stroke."

"How do you know so much about the drowning?"

"What wasn't in the papers was told to me over the telephone by the flunky who relayed Jim Brennan's message to stay away from the funeral. Another example, possibly the last, of old Jim's thoroughness in getting everything exactly the way he wanted it."

"What kind of a woman is Mrs. Brennan? It was no secret that Jim Brennan cut a swath through this town thirty and forty years ago."

Devlin wanted to think about his answer. He had been dating Maryellen Brennan three weeks when he heard for the first time of Jim Brennan's swordsmanship, from Devlin's own old man, as he belched and farted through his nightly quart of brew. Brennan, Devlin's old man said, liked to wave his dick around—he wasn't above using his money and influence to get the women he wanted. Devlin could remember seeing through the old man's self-righteousness to the envy beneath. To Levine, Devlin said, "Because old Jim was so blatant, people have always assumed Charlotte knew everything better, in greater detail, than anybody else, and her silence about it was part of her breeding, culture, religion, and style. Charlotte has always been *relentlessly* classy.''

"I don't understand the religion thing," Levine said. "To tell you the truth, I don't know that much about Catholicism."

"It's not Catholicism as much as the Irish view of it," Devlin said. He was thinking of his father again, how he had distanced himself from Devlin's mother's side of the family, including the branch in Sussex County, even Devlin's cousin Alice, a teenager at the time. *Holier than thou,* Devlin's uncle Buddy, his mother's brother, had said. "Charlotte is an Irish type. She wraps herself in her religion. Because she goes through the motions, she's justified in everything she does, like putting up with her husband's philandering. If she suffers—and I don't know that she does—then she's also relieved, even proud, because she believes God will be good to her for having never quit going through the motions, no matter what He's thrown at her. That's the type, what I grew up with."

"There are Jewish types, too," Levine said.

"I know. Charlotte supports the arts, she's active in the charities, she even stands up straight. She's a good *example*. She was born with the proverbial silver spoon, convent schools, Manhattanville College of the Sacred Heart, and she's spent her whole life thinking she's been putting something back into the world. The woman has a shell around her you couldn't penetrate with an Exocet missile. The shell has been up so long I'm not sure there's anyone inside. She knows how she's supposed to behave in any and all circumstances, and she never fails herself. But don't misunderstand: Jim Brennan is an Irish type, too. He started with nothing and got lucky. He believes she's everything he really wants for himself. I don't mean she's an ornament in his life, because it's more. Maybe he once hoped some of what she is would rub off on him. She added class to his image of power broker and wheeler-dealer. The Brennans are lace-curtain. That's what we call them. In their case, because of their millions, it's lace-curtain raised to the ten-thousandth power."

"All from a few bus lines in Queens," Harry Levine said.

"Just about all the bus lines in Queens and most of Brooklyn. I don't see how this is helping you."

"I don't take Jack Brennan's murder to be politically motivated. Not politics *per se*." Levine chewed on his unlit cigar. "Give me credit for being on this case a few hours longer than you have. The marks on Jack Brennan's body tell more than his own story. If the people who put Octavio Lopez up to killing Brennan only wanted to take him out of the race for the Senate, all they had to do was confront him with evidence of his private behavior and threaten to go public. If they knew Brennan was in the Waldorf Towers, they knew about the sadomasochism, too."

Devlin said, "They wanted the disgrace. A little more than murder."

"There you go,"Levine said. "Not necessarily or completely politics, but something else, and maybe going back in time. All I'm trying to do now is get as much of a lay of the land as I can. The timing of this thing, the instructions I've gotten from the commissioner—and Hamilton. Mr. New York. That little prick. I'm confiding in you, for Christ's sake—I don't *like* it. It *scares* me. The press may be kicking the mayor's ass all over the city, but Torres as the first Latino commissioner is still untouchable. Where does that leave me? I don't have to report crimes to the press, but suppose the press decides to turn on me for not reporting the murder of the Democratic candidate for the Senate? How do I cover my ass on a deal like this? Is it possible? On the other hand, maybe it's being assumed that I'm going to try. I have been on this case longer than you, Devlin, but I can't help thinking that some people have been on it a whole lot longer than me."

Devlin stayed silent as the M.E.'s building came into view. Commissioner Torres, with Hamilton behind him, wanted the murder kept quiet. It had taken them by surprise. The mode and timing of the killing was supposed to mean something. *Sending a message*, the old mob guys used to call it.

Levine said, "So the Brennans are lace-curtain, eh? What type are you?"

"Shanty."

"What's the difference?"

"My uncle Buddy used to say that lace-curtain Irish don't fart in the presence of clergy."

As they entered the autopsy room, the smell of rotting corpses wrapped around them. Devlin hated dead-body calls. He was glad his family was done with funerals—his family was *done*, period. Jack and the girl were on adjoining metal slabs, naked. She was pretty, but patches of her were purple. She had been shot in the left eye. Her teeth were bloody, too. The back of her head was a mass of matted hair, bits of skull, and bloodcoated lumps of brain. Death as instantaneous as it was possible to get, as in *Lights Out*.

Seven other detectives were in the room, all Levine's boys. Devlin knew most of them—one, he thought, from A.A. No doctors. One attendant.

"Why aren't these bodies being processed?" Levine asked him."

"All I was told," said the attendant, "was that if you wanted more information, you'd have to talk to the M.E."

Devlin brought himself to look at Jack Brennan. He had been shot three times, in the right breast, the left shoulder, and below the right eye. His eyes were glaring, gleaming dully through partly opened lids. Dried blood caked his open mouth. Devlin didn't recognize him as the young man he had known twenty years ago, just as the thicker, older man claiming the same identity as a political candidate on television. The body was marked with more than two dozen V-shaped welts, some of them open cuts beaded with bubbles of dried blood. The cardinal had all but endorsed this man. The mayor *had* endorsed him. What had they known about Jack Brennan's private jollies? The way New York worked, certainly a lot more than the average subway-riding working stiff would believe.

A guy named Gerrity stepped out of the crowd toward a corner. Levine followed, and when Devlin hesitated, Levine motioned him forward. "I want you to stay close to me."

Gerrity had smooth, flushed cheeks and red hair that was

fading to white. Devlin remembered reading in one of the department publications that Gerrity had been a detective for twenty-five years. "Get this," Gerrity said, "I got this from a friend down in City Hall. Hamilton's there now, Mr. New York, in his office. He's having a little trouble understanding the concept of a chain of evidence. He's worried most about the pictures of the bodies getting in the *Post* before the week is out. How's that for a fucking mayor, worrying like a hostess about pecker tracks on the living room sofa? He wants to make sure the party goes well."

Levine stared. "You're kidding me, aren't you?"

"I wish I were."

Levine bit down on the cigar. "Well, tell them to process the goddamned bodies! Time is of the essence. I want to know about entry angles. How did this Octavio character get in the room?"

"It seems he had a key," Gerrity said. "One of the Arab bodyguards finally remembered that he saw a key in the lock, and that he took it out and put it on the round table by the door."

"That's where it was when I got there," Levine said. "Good. I just don't want any questions about the facts. Now what about the lights? Those two people were in bed. Who put the lights on?"

"The Arabs are clear on that. They came in and found Lopez standing over the bed. The drapes were drawn and the room was dark. They turned the lights on."

"Where are the bodyguards now?"

"Back at the Waldorf. They have diplomatic immunity. Who knows, maybe they're diplomats. Their sultan or whatever he is has seven women with him. His boys wanted to get back to the Towers to protect him. Nothing can protect a man trying to fuck seven broads at once. They don't think much of us, either. Isn't that a kick in the ass? Twenty years ago these guys were sucking camel dick and glad to get a nice one."

"Where's Octavio Lopez?"

"In the prison ward next door. We won't have any trouble

with the blood sample. The doctors say they would have done it anyway, run the same tests.''

''I want him in maximum security as soon as possible,'' Levine said. ''We can't have any screwups. Does everybody understand that?''

''Oh, sure.''

''Let's get it moving,'' Levine said. ''Nobody's sleeping tonight.'' Gerrity nodded and shouldered past them. Levine turned to Devlin, whose imagination, for a moment, allowed him to see a sleepless night fading into the brightness of dawn on the Brooklyn-Queens Expressway, heading home. He could see Brooklyn silhouetted against the pale yellow sunrise, steeples, asphalt roofing, and aluminum siding covering the decaying walls. Devlin shivered. Levine said, ''The mayor and the chief called the Brennan household. Did you know they have around-the-clock nurses?''

''Old Jim has been in a wheelchair for seven years, and Charlotte must be getting frail,'' Devlin said. ''The last time I saw her was on television last spring, at a flower show at a church in Brooklyn. She seemed to be moving at a stately pace. It made me think she had invented a way of concealing the fact that she really was slowing down.''

''Is she capable of that?''

''It's her idea of normal,'' Devlin said.

''Now, you see, that helps. The mayor wanted to consult with the nurse on the best way of telling them. This was early in the evening, at Gracie Mansion. Mrs. Brennan picked up the telephone. She recognized the mayor's voice. She started asking questions, and quickly enough figured it out for herself. 'He's dead,' she said. Very quietly. The mayor couldn't say anything. He waited for her to ask *how?*—you know, what happened—but she never did. She said, 'I want to have a doctor present when Jim is told.' That's all. She put the telephone down, and then after a moment the people with the mayor— let's just say I have all this on good authority—could hear Mrs. Brennan tell the nurse to take the call in the kitchen. Her voice was flat. The nurse picked up and she and the mayor discussed the situation, but the other line was never disconnected. Mrs.

Brennan could have been listening. Later, when the Mayor replayed a tape of the conversation, somebody noticed that Mrs. Brennan never called the mayor by name or title. Someone else in the room with her might never have known who was on the other end of the line. Also, how quietly she said, 'He's dead.' It's possible someone else in the room wouldn't have heard her. Question: Could old Jim have been in the room while she was learning of the death of their son? Could she have concealed her reaction from him?''

''She's good at it, sure, if that's what you mean,'' Devlin said, ''and if his wheelchair was facing away, he wouldn't have seen any more than the mayor did. Since the stroke, Jim Brennan hasn't been able to turn his head.''

''How do you know that?''

''When he had the stroke, I talked to a doctor I knew, an A.A. guy. He said the stroke was just too massive for there to be any chance of recovery. 'Lucky to be alive—or maybe not,' was the way he put it.''

Devlin realized he was staring at Levine. Even with Jack Brennan running for the Senate, Harry Levine didn't know enough about the Brennans to be close to the truth about old Jim's condition, in spite of the fact that he hadn't been seen in public in seven years. For Devlin, that spoke volumes about what remained of the Brennan power. If the Brennans didn't want the truth known, they could suppress it from people as important and centrally located as Harry Levine. Devlin didn't envy Levine. It took cold blood to put a spy in the boss's office. Devlin had seen Brennan's cold-bloodedness for years. Cold-bloodedness was no way to be remembered. ''Nightclub'' Devlin was bad enough.

''Now I'm ready to see Octavio Lopez,'' Levine said.

Gerrity joined them for the trek over to the other building, and Devlin was thankful that Gerrity didn't want to make small talk. A chasm was opening under the feet of an awful lot of people, and Devlin wanted to get an idea of where he might wind up. On the bottom, probably, under Levine, Commissioner Torres, Mayor Hamilton, maybe even the cardinal. Levine wasn't going to get any help from the two men he had to answer to. It was time for Devlin to think hard about that.

As everyone in New York now understood, Norman Hamilton would have cut a deal with the devil himself to become mayor of the city of New York. Why Hamilton had wanted the office so badly was anybody's guess, because no mayor had ever advanced to higher state or national office, and the city had been running downhill for years. Not since John Lindsay in the sixties had a candidate tried so hard to do the New York equivalent of wrapping himself in the flag. Just as Lindsay had decided that New York was "Fun City,"—Hamilton had campaigned as "Mr. New York," seeming to laugh along with the street-smart New Yorkers who were laughing at him. He was an independently wealthy Park Avenue bachelor, Jewish on his mother's side, which was politically useful, wired to Wall Street, which was even more so, and well connected to the city's nearly all-powerful developers, which was most important of all. In their turns the Irish had had Jimmy Walker and Bill O'Dwyer, the Italians La Guardia and Impellitteri. As one *Village Voice* columnist had written, it was now the turn of the Jews, and Hamilton was the city's most presentable *haimisch* male, a New York Robert Redford. Hamilton was good-looking, just fifty, still yellow-haired. During his first campaign, the stories about his lifelong coolness toward women had had no trouble making the newspapers. It wasn't that he hadn't been able to find Miss Right, he had joked, it was just that there were so many of them. That had stifled enough of the talk; he remained hostesses' number-one extra man at dinner tables all over the Upper East Side. As a campaigner, Hamilton had played the fool as much as any other candidate for mayor in the city's history, stopping for food at every groaning board from Nathan's Famous in Coney Island, to the mafia *ristorantes* of Little Italy, to the glitzy outdoor cafes of newly upscale Columbus Avenue. In the first campaign and the flush days at the start of his first term, Hamilton had looked and sounded like a presidential candidate, but by the time of the next Democratic convention, the surrounding presidential talk had stopped. Too many bad things had happened in the city, Hamilton had put his foot in his mouth too many times. He was holding his first and last elective office, and everybody knew it.

Still, he remained cheerful, relentlessly cheerful. Devlin and others, including some editorial writers, could see the true mirthlessness behind Hamilton's eyes. As a clown who could let his joke go only so far, Hamilton was perfect for a city whose government had become completely unaccountable to its citizens, a city that was a quadriplegic on life support, alive by definition only. Thanks mostly to Lindsay, who had run for mayor back in the sixties first as a Republican, then for reelection as a "fusion" candidate, there was no two-party system in the city anymore. The Democrats held all the major elective offices in the city, but more important, all the appointive offices, from judges and commissioners—all the way down to the municipal court bailiffs—were in the hands of the five county party leaders. To become mayor, Norman Hamilton had had to secure the leaders' support, acquiesce to their greed, and now thievery and malfeasance were being uncovered in nearly every city department, commission, bureau, and courtroom. According to the evidence unearthed so far, the only city organization passed over by the plundering politicians was the Fire Department.

For police commissioner, Hamilton had appointed Norberto Torres, whose previous experience had been with the Transit Police, and not very high up, either. As politics, it was a masterstroke, co-opting those black and Puerto Rican leaders who otherwise would have attacked Hamilton at the slightest hint of police discrimination. Hamilton could always claim that he was moving as quickly as possible on the only permanent solution to the problem. Who was to say he wasn't?

But as a result, as all cops knew, the department was burdened with hundreds of women too small and light for the frequent hand-to-hand combat with quarreling spouses and belligerent drunks the job required. The revised literacy requirements were so low that many new patrolmen couldn't write a report, and more than a few new sergeants couldn't read them. Some officers were disobeying orders because they considered them racially motivated, and others were wearing shields solely to prey on dope dealers, because they were dope dealers themselves—as they had been before joining the force. One story the department wanted hushed up had to do with the longtime officer's resignation the day after his partner's gun belt fell down around her ankles in the middle of a hot pursuit.

Norberto Torres's biographical handout ran some ten pages of public relations' obfuscation: reading it, one learned Torres's birthplace (Ponce), his alma mater (St. John's), his wife's maiden name, and the ages of his children, but one still did not know the man. Flackery only confirmed the general feeling that behind Torres's dead eyes was not so much a personality as a collection of appetites, wants, and desires. Like so many successful modern men, Torres seemed to live for the perks. The police commissioner of the city of New York was an alcoholic whorehound. He was frequently drunk on duty at his desk, and more than once television news had shown him intoxicated in public—without comment. Always without comment. The situation was too delicate. Torres was untouchable, the first *Rican* to have climbed so high. Hamilton had co-opted the media as well as the city's minority leadership. No one wanted to call attention even to Torres's failure to appear at the scene of the murder of a policeman, or his disappearance for two days, during which there occurred a fatal arson fire in the Bedford-Stuyvesant section of Brooklyn and the quintuple machete murder of five Bahamian dope dealers in Harlem.

During his no-shows, Torres was having a woman perform fellatio upon him. No secret. On the contrary, he bragged about it. Torres went about that part of his private life with an arrogance so vast it had to celebrate itself. In addition to a wife, Torres had a full-time mistress, another part-timer in the department who had the only other key to his private elevator, and several women on call elsewhere in Police Plaza, the kind who could not conceal their special connection to the commissioner. Morale low? Some old-timers wanted to spit when the principal players walked by.

Devlin, the recovering alcoholic, knew what was in Torres's heart. Torres only believed he had gotten lucky—he knew he was empty inside. He would be more guarded about indulging his pleasures otherwise. Hamilton was another story. Devlin was sure that Hamilton was a profoundly sick man. Absolutely everything was fodder for his ambition, including his own sexuality. Most of the city needed no proof that the mayor was a homosexual, but Norman Hamilton and all his people kept insisting he wasn't. Over the years, free-lance spies had gathered other rumors, and now, with more and more of Hamilton's cronies and allies going belly-up in almost-weekly scandals, the common threads wove a tapestry different only in style from those Hollywood fall-of-Rome epics of the fifties. At the center of the New York City version, instead of Nero making music while the city burned around him, was a desperately sad little creature who had sold the city so he could be its mayor. Devlin took Norman Hamilton to be another example of that certain kind of American personality that wants to self-destruct before the greatest number of people. Richard Nixon had done it, and so had John Belushi. *Here I am as I really am—destroy me.* But if Hamilton was going to follow the pattern, he was going to fight like hell, kick, scratch, and bite, if necessary, to postpone his exposure. He didn't want the murders in the Waldorf Towers turning into a political sex scandal. Levine was supposed to clean it up as quickly as he could. Levine had played fair with Devlin in the questioning about Lopez and Jack Brennan. Devlin could consider himself lucky. With another guy, Devlin might even be in custody.

1:07 A.M. . . .

TWO UNIFORMED OFFICERS STOOD AT LOPEZ'S DOOR, AND as Devlin, Gerrity, and Levine approached, a plainclothesman Devlin didn't know stepped out of the room. A young, skinny Irishman with curly hair down the back of his neck. His collar was open and a twenty-year-old knitted string tie was pulled up to it. "Good," he told Levine, glancing at Devlin. "Downstairs they said you were on the way up. The *Daily News* is onto it. I just got the call from downtown. Some night guy called your office to confirm, blah, blah—"

"Mariano? What did Mariano say?"

"He directed the guy to public relations. How do you think it got out?"

"Anybody at the Waldorf could have called it in," Levine said. "A lot of old-timers still think the newspapers pass out fives and tens the way the gossip columnists used to do. You don't remember that, but Devlin does. Excuse me. Frank Devlin, Kevin McQuaid."

They shook hands. "How are you?"

"Whattaya say?" McQuaid turned back to Levine, too quickly for Devlin to believe it. Devlin had been watching McQuaid's eyes taking in Devlin. If Devlin had had to say what McQuaid was really thinking, it would be, *Who is this guy? Is he someone I'm supposed to pay attention to?* By looking away now, McQuaid was indulging in a little gamesmanship. He wanted to see if Devlin was going to pay attention to *him*. Devlin's age and experience allowed him to do something young McQuaid wasn't capable of: Devlin made himself opaque. Glancing at Devlin again, McQuaid said, "Anyway,

53

Mariano wanted you to know that the *News* night guy said he was looking for *corroboration*. He wasn't checking a rumor, Mariano says, he's working from a confirmed sighting. It's just a matter of time before the guy starts calling hospitals. He's probably doing it now.''

"We'll see.'' Levine gestured toward the door. "Anything new in there?''

"He hasn't said a word. The doctors still don't know jack shit about what he's on. My seat-of-the-pants opinion, which is the only one of any value around here, is that The Joker is coming down off whatever he was shot up with, and he's going to crash with one very big bang. He's just starting, but that's my considered opinion.'' He held up three fingers. "Scout's honor. We've started calling him The Joker because of that nutty smile.''

Levine eyed him. "Do you think he'll start saying something?''

McQuaid shrugged. Devlin couldn't remember Lopez ever sporting a particular kind of smile. *On* something? What Devlin was remembering of Lopez was the weakest of individuals, as likely to be led into buying a trampoline franchise as into a dope deal. He wanted to be hip. Fragile souls, Eileen called such types. Lopez in the supermarket when Devlin was evoking for John Foy Lord a childhood memory of cheap, tasty lunches. Lopez the time before that? *Sure* . . .

Last fall, on one of those brilliant October days with the sun so warm that for a few afternoon hours you were actually overdressed in a jacket and sleeveless sweater, then shivering against the cold shortly after dark. Devlin had several such memories of last October: Eileen, pasta, racing home to her apartment. He could have seen Lopez on the afternoon of one of those nights. John would have been there, in Lopez's ground floor, cold-water flat, the detectives eyeballing the ribbed rubber enema tube that ran around the gas meter in the kitchen. Lopez spun a tale of a *Rican* boy and a black girl, a true New York love story. . . .

Two junkies. He was also a thief. She was on welfare, her three kids in foster homes. When she became pregnant again, she decided she wanted to keep the baby—which meant concealing her pregnancy from the welfare caseworker, who would have moved to place that child, too, after its birth, in foster care. Keeping the baby was what the boyfriend wanted. *Junkies in love,* Lopez said, *know what I mean?*

The baby was born addicted. A couple of weeks in the hospital was all she would have needed, Lopez told Devlin and Lord confidently; a couple of weeks was all a baby needed to cry junk out of its system. But then the doctors and nurses wanted the mother to have her blood tested. The baby had AIDS, Lopez said, and now the lovebird parents wanted to kill each other. Lopez thought the woman would be willing to talk to the police about her boyfriend's burglaries and car stereo thefts. John Lord asked if the mother had had the blood test.

"Oh, no, man," Lopez said. "Neither one of them. They be sleeping with other people now, too. I don't think I would have a blood test." He smiled. "Man, who'd want to know?"

All you needed to know about Lopez, Devlin told himself as he remembered that last crooked smile, *a patriotic citizen of the end of the world.* . . .

Lopez was sitting on the bed, the upper half of the mattress cranked up behind his back, his ankle manacled to the white-enameled, curved iron pipe at the foot of the bed. Four other guys were in the room, two in pressed blue uniforms, two in wash-and-wear green. An I.V. ran into Lopez's left forearm. Lopez looked at Devlin, seemed not surprised to see him, then let his eyes go to Levine. Same expression, the corners of Lopez's mouth turned up, his eyelids a third of the way down. His eyes looked out of focus, or just uncaring. Goofy.

"What do you think?" Levine asked.

"He's been this way since the Arabs grabbed him. Too long for a shot of heroin."

"Cocaine and Quaaludes would do this," Devlin said. "But coke would have worn off by now."

" 'Ludes and speed," McQuaid said, rocking on his heels, his hands in his pockets. He grinned at Devlin. "It's been a long time since I've seen any 'ludes. You old guys must have them all. He could go this long on speed, and Quaaludes would do more than make a rubber chicken out of him. You're char-broiled over mesquite, right, Joker?'' he asked Lopez. ''Right now you could fuck a Buick, couldn't you?''

Lopez blinked dreamily.

''Octavio,'' Devlin said, ''make life easy for everybody and start telling us about this.''

No reaction. Lopez was looking at one of the doctors. Levine motioned Devlin and McQuaid outside, then pulled the door closed behind them.

''What would you tell a guy to make him behave like that?'' Levine whispered. ''I mean, clam up. I know he's high. I can see that.''

''He didn't have to be told anything,'' Devlin said. ''As long as he carries on like this, nothing bad will ever happen to him again. Room and board the rest of his life.''

''Fuck that,'' McQuaid said. ''As soon as he comes down from that shit he's on, he'll be crying, screaming, yelling, shouting—and singing his fucking head off.''

''I believe you,'' Levine said.

''I'm not sure,'' Devlin said. ''I know Lopez, and when he's in control of himself, he's sly and devious. I've never seen him this way before.'' He glanced to McQuaid. ''And trust me on this: I *have* seen him high.''

McQuaid couldn't help laughing. ''*I* believe *you.*''

''There was nothing in his flat,'' Levine said. ''I've had four men in there since eight-thirty, and the last I heard from them, they told me the place had been cleaned out—no dope, no paraphernalia, nothing on paper. After so many years behind a desk, Devlin, I don't claim for a moment to know as much as you do about a donkey like Lopez, but I do know that guys like him never take care of their business so well.''

''All right,'' McQuaid said, ''people cleaned up the place so nothing would lead back to them.''

''We're going to have to talk to everybody Lopez knew,'' Levine said. ''And we're starting from scratch. We don't know who his friends are. Devlin, you'd better have good logs.''

''Literary masterpieces.'' Now there was something *he* wanted to know. ''How did you identify Lopez?''

"He had I.D.," Levine said.

McQuaid said, "A wallet. The blue cloth thing with the Velcro closure. Social security card. He had a driver's license. Can you imagine him on the road?"

"To where?" Devlin asked.

"I have a list of the stuff in the wallet," McQuaid said. "It's a whole lot of nothing in particular, but I'll read it off to you if you want."

Devlin flashed on Jack Brennan downstairs. Brennan often had been less than the best possible friend, but Devlin had liked him enough to have told him: *Yes, I like you.* Maybe, Devlin thought, he might remember that drunken night, too, as well as he remembered September 16, 1971. He said, "Give me your card. I'm supposed to be helping you—and more as a witness than a fellow officer."

"No shit?" McQuaid asked. "How is that?"

"I'm married to the victim's sister."

"Oh, hey, I'm sorry."

Devlin shook his head. "I haven't seen any of them in fifteen years."

McQuaid twisted his mouth. "I'm only a kid. I didn't know I was signing up for an oral history project."

Levine glanced at Devlin with an expression that Devlin took as a request for forgiveness. For the first time Devlin glimpsed the consequences of Jack Brennan's death on the annulment petition. He was going to have to ask Loncaric to put on the brakes. It was important to behave correctly. He had to find an appropriate way to express his sympathy to the Brennans. *And* Maryellen. All Devlin knew about her now was that she was teaching grade school in Minnesota. He had drunk his way to sunrise on September 16, 1971, not knowing that it would be the last day he would ever set eyes on her.

"I don't want you leaving Lopez for a moment," Levine told McQuaid. "If you're right about him starting to talk as he comes down, you'll get a commendation."

"Not if he talks a lotta crap," McQuaid said.

Shaking his head, Levine turned to Devlin. "I'm going back downstairs to make sure all the right questions get asked."

"That's how you really feel about us," McQuaid said. "You think we can't do shit."

"I'm ambivalent about you," Levine answered, deadpan. He turned to Devlin. "Take a pass on downstairs. You might as well get your rest, because I want you on call from here on out. For all we know, there's something stuck in that head of yours that's going to be just what we need. I'll have someone take you back downtown to your car."

Devlin nodded. He didn't want to see Jack Brennan's autopsy. *Octavio Lopez!* It might be an hour before Devlin got home. He wasn't looking forward to trying to sleep, but that was exactly what he was going to have to do.

"Nice meeting you," McQuaid said. "Take it easy."

"Yeah," Devlin said, "easy does it."

Repeating the A.A. line reminded him of wasting his time this evening with the Quinns in New Jersey. *Shit.*

Devlin lived in his parents' old rent-controlled apartment, where he had grown up, after years of living elsewhere. His mother had died young, after three ever-more debilitating strokes. Sixty-four years old. Devlin moved back home when it became obvious that his father was temperamentally unfit to care for her. He'd known his parents' marriage hadn't been happy; what hadn't occurred to him was that they had gotten worse with each other while he had lived away, bickering, sulking, carping—grim, hateful stuff. Had Devlin lived in a dream? His mother's slurred speech made her almost unintelligible, and her frustration unleashed resentment that had been building for years.

Her death, when it came, surprised and crushed him. She'd gone into the hospital the week before, having been unable to hold down her food, but insisting, as well as she'd been able, that she felt all right. Stomach cancer, a tumor the size of a football—a doctor told Devlin that she must have felt it. His father was with her at the end, and Devlin knew that something passed between them, but the old man didn't want to talk about it . . . at first. But he started falling apart, and one night, bleary on vodka, he talked, confessed, sobbed, his final questions a plea for absolution. Her last words to him, whispered, croaked in the heat of her oxygen tent: *I hate you.* "She didn't mean it, did she, son? It was the stroke talking, don't you think? She never said anything like that about me to you, did she?"

Devlin said no, but inside he was thinking that she had been so unhappy that she had allowed herself to die. Maybe the old man sensed something in his son, because his own decline accelerated. Devlin's friends told him that he was justified in putting the old man in a home, but Devlin never seriously thought of it, even when the apartment stank of beer and old age, when the old man's nurses quit, one after another, because of his foul-mouthed ingratitude. The old man hobbled on, ever more feeble and confused, then incontinent, until he fell down a flight of stairs in the autumn of 1981. Devlin slipped into a depression that didn't lift until after his father's estate was settled almost three years later—two years ago. Some people thought Devlin had had a tough, heartbreaking life. Devlin's mind hadn't worked that way since the day he'd met Eileen. She said they were lovers who had become best friends, but he didn't care about the definitions. He was desperately in love with her. He considered himself a man who had come through, who was still learning, glad to be awake and alive, a happy man. And thanks as much to the strongbox under the old man's bed as his life insurance, and a rent that was still under three hundred dollars a month, Devlin considered himself relatively wealthy, too. . . .

Devlin was closing the front door when Eileen called from the bedroom, "I thought you wouldn't be able to resist me."

Now he saw that the bedroom light was on. "I'm sorry," he answered. "I was going to get into bed beside you as quietly as I could."

She was sitting up. "I woke up at eleven and turned on the news, and I've been awake ever since. I'm sorry. I'm sorry for him, I'm sorry for you."

They kissed. "I'm supposed to see Steve Loncaric tomorrow."

"We'll do what needs doing."

He realized that she didn't know about Octavio Lopez. Not a thing. Devlin had never mentioned the man. There was no need to tell her tonight. The connection might not mean anything anyway. But she was looking at him in that way that told him she knew he was holding something back. He kissed her neck. "We don't have to talk, do we?"

Eileen held him. "You have another plan?"

"Like what?"

"A fook." She pinched his cheek. "Ah, now look at that grin. You're easy, you know. I could make you forget a nuclear war."

"The way you pronounce that word—"

"Of course! I did it on purpose, just to watch you turn to mush. Or somethin'." Now she grabbed his belt buckle and pulled him toward her.

4:26 P.M. . . .

SOFT TIME, HE REALIZED AS THE DREAM UNFOLDED pleasantly. His cousin Alice. The Sussex County of the early fifties, when Devlin passed from innocence to young manhood. Convicts called dreams like this *soft time*. A good dream of sultry summer nights with all the windows of the car rolled down, roadside brush slapping at the old clamshell fenders. . . .

A '37 Oldsmobile . . .

And much later, his cousin Alice, pretty on her wedding day and laughing at his stupidity: *"Are you always going to be an asshole about women?"*

Now the dream turned dark and frightening. He and Alice

were indoors, in a house full of voices. The table between them, a kitchen table, round, oak, was covered with coffee cups and open baker's boxes. A house full of voices, a bad dream, threatening, even evil, and then from a great distance, Eileen's voice . . .

"Frank! Come on, darlin', wake up!"

He opened his eyes and the dream disappeared in a thousand tiny fragments.

"Are you all right, then?"

"Yes." He sat up, not awake yet, and looked at the clock. Almost five. The death of Jack Brennan was descending into his consciousness with the speed and silence of a rock dropped off a bridge. He had a very long schedule today and there was no point in putting it off. Another of Eileen's teachings: When you wake up in the morning, get out of bed and get busy—you'll feel better and probably live longer. When Devlin asked her where she had gotten such stuff, she'd answered, "That last one from George Burns, who's certainly in a position to know."

The woman was full of surprises.

"Well?"

"All right, I'll bite."

"Am I going to hear about your dream, or what?"

He grinned. He couldn't remember the dream at all, but then, in an eye blink, he remembered what the dream was *about*: Sussex.

"I may have dreamed of the first girl I made love with."

"What do you mean, *may* have?"

"I don't remember," Devlin said.

"You'd make a great criminal, not remembering this and *may have* that. What was the slut's name? This was in the country where you whiled away the summers of your youth."

"Having fun?" He was dressing.

"Pamela," she said. "My God, why would I remember a name I never expected to hear again in my life? On second thought, keep your dream to yourself, thank you very much. And don't go contemplatin' Pamela and her massive mammaries."

"I never said anything about the size of Pamela's mammaries . . ."

"You didn't have to. It's a phase."

"It wasn't a phase for me."

"Really?" She smiled. "It was for me. Size, size, size. I couldn't look at a stallion without getting all slippery. Now go. Have a nice day." She feigned a yawn. "Think of me now and then. Go, I said. And leave the money on the dresser."

"Don't I always?"

"Only because lifelong habits are hard to break."

With a smile, he kissed her again, and she rolled over to go back to sleep.

At his own apartment, he could hear his telephone ringing even before the elevator door opened. The answering machine would field the call, but someone calling at his hour had something important in mind. It wouldn't be Eileen: she knew how long it took to get from her apartment to this. Besides, only a death in the family could rouse her before seven on a workday.

Four rings. That kicked in the answering machine. He grabbed the kitchen extension. "Hold on, I'm here," he said over his own voice on the announcement tape.

"Devlin, this is Lieutenant Nelson in Levine's office. Octavio Lopez is scheduled to arrive at the Tombs at six-thirty, and the chief wants you there."

"Well, he said to consider myself on call."

"Six-thirty, the Tombs."

"I heard—"

Nelson was gone. Devlin hung up and went on to the bedroom. The answer machine was recycling. It had recorded Nelson's call. The machine blinked three times quickly between pauses. Two people had called him in the middle of the night, when he had been downtown with Levine, or later, at Eileen's. Normally nobody called him after ten o'clock. Now he probably had to rewind, fast forward, then stop and listen through the whole damned tape, from yesterday evening and all those calls from Mariano, in order to be sure he had heard everything. The new technology. Devlin told people he had given up trying to understand advances in electronics somewhere between the introduction of stereo sound and the passing away of black-and-white TV. He punched the Rewind button.

In fact, there had been two calls from women last night, before he had gone downtown to see Levine. The first had been Eileen: "Almost eleven o'clock and no you. If I told you I changed me mind, would you think I was rubbing it in? I hope not. I'm sittin' here thinkin' how nice it would be, and it's just so much sweet torture. I think I'll watch the news. I love you."

The second call was from a woman who didn't identify herself. After the beep, she said, "I . . . yes . . . no," and hung up. Devlin wasn't sure he didn't recognize the voice. It *sounded* familiar, but no name or face leaped up from memory.

I . . . yes . . . no.

Devlin wanted to play it again, but he wanted to hear the late calls, too. He ran through the last of the calls before his arrival home from New Jersey. More calls from Mariano, another from John Lord. A patch of blank tape where Devlin had advanced it more than far enough to preserve the preceding messages.

And then Eileen again. "It's after one, so maybe you're asleep and safe. I hope so. I suppose you've heard the news. We'll talk tomorrow."

Another beep: "This is Roger Burke at the *Daily News*. Would you call me, please, as soon as possible." He gave his number.

And finally Nelson.

Devlin went back to the kitchen to crank up the coffee maker. Normally he liked to stick to a routine: two cups of coffee, maybe some raisin toast, and go. This morning he would pass on the raisin toast and have breakfast downtown. He wasn't calling any *Daily News* guy. Rule one: Don't talk to the press. *Never* talk to the press. It made becoming a famous cop a harder job, but back in the days when Devlin took himself to be on his way to becoming a famous cop, he knew he hadn't done it by talking to the press. No, he had done it by marrying into a rich and powerful family. Old Jim had always thought Devlin had been cashing in. No again: for a brief few years, Devlin had been in charge.

Devlin didn't think of his dream again until he was on the Williamsburg Bridge, stopping and starting in the framework of girders over the middle of the river. All he could remember was the subject. He and Maryellen must have been newlyweds when he saw his cousin Alice for the last time. He realized he had to fix a whole lot of half-forgotten life clearly in his mind again. He didn't meet Maryellen until the summer of 1966. Five years from beginning to end—forever at the time. After forty, five years was nothing, a twinkling.

Through the angles of steel the morning sky was a wonderful cloudless blue: it was like being inside a diamond. He switched on the radio for some news.

The dream was gone from his thoughts before he knew it.

6:27 A.M. . . .

HE WAS TRYING TO FIGURE SOME SLACK IN HIS SCHEDule. From four to twelve this evening he would be working Times Square, tonight's only likely target for pickpockets, purse snatchers, and the new bicycle thieves. News announcers on radio stations from one end of the dial to the other were nattering like back-fence gossips over the assassination of Jack Brennan and a woman not his wife in a room in the Waldorf Towers. The announcers were saying "last night" for the time of the killings to conceal how late they were on the story. Things hadn't begun to heat up yet, but by nightfall, Devlin knew, the city would be in a frenzy. A media event in New

York had a natural history as much fun to watch as a pennant race, and this one promised to be a doozy. Devlin was hoping he might be able to catch a nap in the late morning. He would get the most out of it, too, if he went easy on the coffee. Before the day was over, he'd hear again from the *News*, from the *Post* three or four times, and maybe even a talk show or two. He didn't want to be interfered with while out on the streets, and he hoped nobody would wander so far from the central issue, Jack Brennan's death, as to bother Eileen. Devlin wondered if he should call her and warn her. *No.*

As Devlin headed on foot from Centre Street into the Tombs's parking area, the first person he recognized was Gerrity, the puffy-looking detective who had been in the M.E.'s building uptown last night.

"Were you able to get any sleep?" Gerrity asked.

"That guy Nelson called me too soon. I thought I'd see Harry Levine here."

"He's down in his office."

Now Devlin saw someone else he recognized—but not the canary-yellow sports jacket he was wearing, more than a little bright for this crowd. Devlin didn't know where he knew the guy, or when. A lot of years had passed, Devlin was sure of that. He kept trying to see the guy as much younger than he was now. The guy was on the other side of the lane the cops were forming. An Italian—or was he Jewish? Had Devlin known him in the sixties? *That* long ago?

"Anybody ever escape from here? I can't remember."

"I don't remember, either," Gerrity said. "God, how I hate the inside of this building! All the fight goes right out of me."

Devlin couldn't help laughing. Up the street, a siren howled.

"That's them," Gerrity said.

"I wonder if Lopez started talking. This thing would go a lot easier if he did."

"I don't know a thing about it," Gerrity said. "I've been down here since three o'clock."

The vehicle, a dark, bulletproof van, rolled into view. The driver let the siren *whoop!* one more time before turning into the parking area. People had to move back, and in the pushing

and stumbling, Devlin and Gerrity were separated, Devlin farther from the door where the van was stopping. A big guy
moved a half step sideways to block Devlin's line of sight
completely. Devlin wondered what he was doing here anyway.
Why had Levine called him? Devlin could hear the door of the
van being unlocked—and suddenly everybody was silent. Out
on the street a horn blew. It blew a second time.

Pop! A pause. *Pop! Pop!* People shouted: "Get the gun!"
"Grab him!" "Son of a bitch!" And people shouted to learn
what had happened. "Shot him," the replies tumbled back,
over the pushing and shoving. "The suspect has been shot."
"He killed him." "Who did?" "A guy in a yellow jacket."

Devlin wheeled to Gerrity, eight feet away, about to say, *I
know him,* but he stopped because of the look on Gerrity's
face—stopped, he hoped, before Gerrity could read more.
Something was going through Gerrity's mind. For a split second, Gerrity seemed to be asking, *Who?*

Somebody yelled, "Sniper!" sending everybody down.
"Inside!" came a shout, followed by a disgusted, *"No
sniper!"* getting everybody up again—and pushing inside.
"We have the new suspect in custody," somebody called.
Lopez's body was carried into the building, blood in the middle of his chest. "Who saw anything? Make sure we know
who you are."

What Devlin had seen was the killer's arrival. *Anybody else
notice?* Devlin wasn't going to count on it. "How many shots
did you hear?" a guy asked him.

"Three. One and then two."

"I thought I heard four."

"Somebody must have seen it," Devlin said, to silence him.
"Somebody was standing there." Three shots, not four. How
did the guy get four?

"Relax," another guy said. "It's all on videotape." *Who
is the guy in the yellow jacket?* Devlin knew something about
him, but it was distant, out of focus. And what was on Gerrity's mind? *Who?* Devlin hadn't *said* anything to Gerrity about
Mr. Yellow Jacket. Devlin's nerves were unraveling like an
old man's polyester slacks. Maybe Lopez getting shot twenty

feet away was ninety percent of Devlin's problem, but that didn't change the fact that in his nervousness he was starting to go a little haywire. Focusing on Gerrity, for example. Gerrity was at the entrance, not looking in Devlin's direction. Devlin tried to close the distance.

Inside, the cops' voices rang off the walls. Devlin moved up beside Gerrity.

Gerrity drew a breath. "You didn't see the shooting from where you were, did you?"

"I didn't even see Lopez get out of the van. What I did see was when the other guy arrived, the shooter."

"I know you saw that," Gerrity said. "Your eyes were all over him."

Devlin kept quiet. One thing he was sure of: the yellow-jacketed man had given no sign of recognizing *him*. Maybe there wasn't a way to connect them if Devlin didn't volunteer the information. "You were going to ask me something."

"Wait a minute." Gerrity rubbed his chin. "Oh, yeah. How about that? I'd forgotten what it was. You must have seen something on my face. Yeah. What was the name of that guy who called you? You said a name."

"Nelson."

"Never heard of him. He called you too early? Nelson?"

Devlin was on the street again by a quarter to eight. A third guy remembered the yellow jacket appearing just a minute or two before the arrival of the van. Important stuff. The shooter's name was Antonucci, and he was saying he had acted alone. People were arguing the question of whether it was even possible for Antonucci to have acted alone. When had he learned of the Brennan killing? How? How had he learned of Lopez's transfer from Bellevue? "That's the kicker," one cop said, "because it opens a whole new can of worms."

Right. Devlin never mentioned having seen something familiar about Antonucci. He had known Brennan and Lopez, and that was enough. He wasn't so nervous now, but he wasn't all right, either—another, deeper kind of nervousness was filling him, like a tide rushing into a grotto.

From an outdoor telephone, near the parking lot where he had put the car, Devlin called John Lord at the Ninth Precinct. John told him that Lopez's murder had made the 7:30 news. "And now I find out that you were on the scene—a witness. And you're already tied into both ends of the original murder. Maybe we ought to talk about this. Maybe we ought to meet somewhere."

"Is that what you think?"

"Let's just say I'm wondering."

Devlin felt his stomach tightening; it was casting a vote for John. John *believed* something enough to take it seriously. And John hadn't been told that Devlin thought he knew Antonucci. Devlin was connected to three of the four principals in the case. The only one he didn't know was the murdered girl, Jane Milburn. "I'll meet you in that bacon-and-egg joint around the corner on Second Avenue. I'm leaving now."

And Gerrity! Gerrity had said he had never heard of Nelson, and then he'd asked again to confirm what Devlin had said originally about Nelson. Why? What had been on Gerrity's mind? Devlin had volunteered Nelson's name. If Gerrity had never heard of him, why the curiosity? Gerrity was suspicious? What was he suspicious *of*?

One step at a time. Devlin was going to have to keep his head clear of speculative scenarios, his scenarios were usually not only speculative, they were self-destructive. He had Nelson on tape, period.

He had to test his memory. A lot was going to be asked of it in the next hours. He was going to have to remember the details of unpleasant and painful events, some made worse by the happy, even gaudy moments preceding them. . . .

Like everything that had ever happened between Maryellen Brennan and him . . .

The question his cousin Alice really had asked was, "Come on, you're not going to be one of those guys who's *always* an asshole about women, are you?"

Emphasis on the always.

He was remembering, all right—a '37 Oldsmobile, sum-

mers in Sussex, Pamela, years and years before the only time
Maryellen and Alice ever met. When?

Fresh out of the Army and the Police Academy, young Frank
Devlin had no trouble finding women. He was a good-looking
guy, gaining confidence with every experience. Women were
everywhere, eager and attractive, intoxicated with opportunity. After three months in Central Harlem, he was moved,
put in plainclothes, and assigned to street narcotics—the lowest level, busting people for selling reefers and carrying hy-
podermics—but he didn't have to tell that to the women he was
meeting. In the early sixties, people liked cops, and narcotics
were still a mystery. So what if he was telling God's truth when
he murmured to a woman, "There really isn't a whole lot to
talk about?" On the infrequent nights he arrived home at din-
nertime, the conversation was never about where he had been
the night before, or the night before that.

Sometimes the old man wanted Devlin to talk about what
he was doing, and Devlin could see that his father needed the
connection through him to police work. No garbage about
being New York's Finest. They talked—away from Devlin's
mother—about being on the pad. The old man had never been
in plainclothes. As for taking money, he said, he had learned
never to initiate anything, never to make trouble for himself.
"You never know who the players are," he said late one night.
"Even when I was in Traffic, I was careful about the folded
tens and twenties in with license and registration . . . who I
took them from, I mean." Devlin already knew these conversations made his father feel important. He would keep talking
as long as Devlin was willing to listen. And so the old man
said, "You never know who you're dealing with and what he's
liable to do, because human beings will do anything, anytime,
anyplace—all they need is a reason."

Learning to be a detective and read people's faces, Devlin
was beginning to see how his real feelings for his father poured
out of his eyes. Devlin's mother dealt with her son's private
life in her own style. One night, during a television commer-

cial, she said, "Look, son, if you're taking violin lessons, it's all right with us if you practice at home."

A year later, outside the Copa, a Mafia capo's daughter dismissed the chauffeur by saying, "It's okay, Carmine, he's a cop!" Devlin woke up the next morning in a motel in Fort Lee with fresh, white snow on the ground outside. The brightness of the snow whacked his hangover so hard, his memory whited out, and for almost a minute, staggering back from the window, he could not remember his name. Later, Devlin heard, the girl's father beat her up in an attempt to get the name of the cop who had made a laughing-stock of his family and reputation. Devlin had to go back to the Copa—he had been in there so much in the previous half year that his absence would be noticed and, possibly, connected to law enforcement's latest, and friendliest, assault on organized crime.

Devlin was seeing others. Always—whether he had known the woman for years, since high school, or she was an eighteen-year-old talked into a quick, post-shift trip upstairs—Devlin played as hard and recklessly as he dared. If women wanted to bullshit themselves into believing they were falling in love, that was not his problem. At a crowded party Devlin picked up a girl across the room by using sign language. When they met at the door, she put her finger to her lips. The silence lasted hours, enough time for the mystery to give way to a vision of a night-long ordeal with a demanding, insensitive compulsive who didn't smell very good. It happened before; such nights were only the luck of the draw.

"Look—" he started.

"Get out!" she shrieked.

Which was what Devlin did, as quickly as possible. Half-way down the stairs, he realized that her silent movie had been written so it would always end the same way, with her screaming for him to get out. If he had waited until tomorrow morn-ing, her response would have been the same. She had interrupted him that quickly. She was crazy; one step away from being locked up.

On the following Monday, his next night off, he was in Joe

King's German-American Rathskeller on Third Avenue. The G-A had catered to an affluent college crowd for years. At the bar, in the midst of a dozen people, sat a blue-eyed honey-blonde in a shoulderless black cocktail dress. She saw him at the same time he saw her; when their eyes met, they didn't turn away. Sign language again, cutting through the noise. He wanted to go over to her and talk. She gazed off as if thinking about it, turned away—and then looked over her shoulder at him and smiled. Vivid, beautiful eyes, a wonderful smile, and freckles on her shoulders.

She was a little drunk. He had had only a couple of beers at P.J. Clarke's, and he was still all right.

"I don't do this," she said, looking straight in front of her. "I don't pick up men in bars."

"Well, figuring the age you're starting, you were never a contender to go the distance."

"Think you got it made, huh?"

She had a bright, chirrupy voice. "I don't think like that. Are you ready?"

"Huh? Oh." She peered into her glass. "No."

"Gotcha," he said. When he looked at her again, she was blushing. She reached for her drink; as the glass touched her lips, she lost the capacity to resist the desire to look at him. He was waiting—he loved watching women go through these gyrations—and he laughed at her.

"Oh, boy." She swallowed. "One of those nights, huh? What are you, some kind of a salesman? Garment district, that's it. What kind of Buick do you drive?"

He was driving a '53 Mercury two-door, hardtop, green and cream, a beautiful green and cream interior, an absolutely wonderful car. Automatic. He didn't bother to answer her question. He wanted to stare at the stray hairs curling up at the nape of her neck. He loved necks. She watched him studying her. Straight lips, a wide mouth. Her turn to laugh. Lovely teeth. The eye contact continued. When it got as intense as this, Devlin, who was drunk so often, tried to remember to be bold. Now, because he was sober, he was timid.

"So? Are you going to answer me? What do you do for a living?"

"I'm a cop," he murmured.

"Bullshit."

He opened his jacket. Her eyes widened and her hand came up toward the gun before she saw what she was doing. He took her hand and put it against the gun before letting go. A couple of her friends were staring at them now, but Devlin kept his eyes on hers.

"Who are those people?"

"Leftovers from a cocktail party. I'm free to go." She looked down at the floor. "Yes, I did say that, I guess."

"How many drinks have you had?"

"This is my fourth. I just broke up with my boyfriend. He said I had too many problems. I could tell you stories about him." Her eyes turned up to his. He took her arm. "Don't you even want to know my name first? You really are a cop, aren't you? I don't want to get hurt."

He showed her his shield. He wanted to tell her he didn't want to hear her life story, but for all he knew, she was loaded enough to get nasty on him. "You're going to have the time of your life," he said.

"I believe it. Let's go someplace nice. My name is Mary-ellen Brennan, by the way."

8:42 A.M. . . .

HE CALLED EILEEN AT HOME. "I HAVE A MINUTE, I thought I'd spend it with you."

"The news said there was another shootin' . . ."

"Let's talk about something else," he said.

"That sounds fair enough," she said. "All right, I meant to ask you, what took you so long to get to my place last night, when it was clear in me voice in the message I left that I was lonely and distracted?"

In Ireland, she'd told him long ago, "distracted" could be taken to mean clawing-the-walls horniness. "As a matter of fact, I was downtown on official police business. And I'll be working until midnight tonight."

"You haven't remembered that dream yet, either, I'm sure. Too busy thinking about the pneumatic Lady Pamela. You're not at the station. Where are you?"

"In a phone booth in a restaurant on Second Avenue. John is meeting me here, so we can go over some things without being interrupted."

"Are you all right?"

"So far, so good." One of their jokes. "So far, so good," was what the man falling from the Empire State Building kept saying. Now Devlin saw John at the front of the restaurant. "Our minute's up. I love you."

"All right, 'bye."

Devlin caught John's eye and waved him toward a window table. The Lower East Side was filling with yuppies, blending in with the hippies left over from the sixties, and this earthed-out, natural-wood coffee shop on Second Avenue had become a meeting place for both crowds. John fit in, a merry, rosy-cheeked young Irishman, his yellow hair always needing cutting. His ties were loose, his jackets and slacks mismatched. He didn't give a shit. Devlin had been a long time coming to understand that about John's generation. They could be up to their butts in mutual funds and second mortgages on second houses, but as long as they held back on the clothing, some-how turning themselves into walking emblems of disdain, they could believe in their hearts that they were not really part of society's game. Merely playing *at* it. Devlin loved John, but he believed that about him. John was a terrific cop, but Devlin almost expected to answer the telephone one morning to hear John say he was turning in his gun and shield for a saffron robe in a monastery in Nepal.

They were finished with their eggs when Devlin got to the shooting of Lopez. Now, for the first time, Devlin told someone that the shooter, Antonucci, had looked familiar to him. John put down his coffee cup.

"I just can't place him," Devlin explained.

"That's nearly perfect," John said.

"I don't follow you."

"Perfect would have been if you couldn't remember him at all, and you could still be tied to him. Suppose you were at a hotel the same time he was? There might be 'evidence' you met at the ballpark. Where were you at the time Jack Brennan and this Jane Milburn were killed?"

"With Eileen. Cummings called just after five."

John frowned. "Cummings. You keep saying that name as if I'm supposed to know it."

"He said you gave him Eileen's number."

"No, not me. Not recently. Cummings? Then you went to New Jersey?"

"Right."

"Let's check that out. Cummings." He stood up. "Give me the change you have, I'm going to make some calls."

Devlin motioned to the waitress for more coffee. "I should have brought in a newspaper."

"I don't think you're going to be nonchalanting this for much longer."

"That's not what I'm doing, kid. I'm trying to stay sane. While you're making the calls, I'm going to think of something else, like tonight's card at the Meadowlands."

He was still saying the words when he remembered again his cousin Alice had been in his dream last night. He had thought of her earlier this morning, too. *Are you always going to be an asshole about women?* The business between Maryellen and him had never been resolved, only abandoned. He had forced himself to stop thinking about her when he'd realized his torment wasn't going to end any other way.

As John returned to the table, he peeled a couple of bills from his roll, dropped them on the table, picked up the check, and motioned Devlin toward the door. "Outside," he said quietly at the cash register. "One call was all I needed to make, and I'll tell you about it outside."

Devlin waited at the curb. John was out of the restaurant almost at once. He took Devlin by the elbow and strode up the side street toward the Bowery, away from the precinct station. He covered his mouth with his knuckles. "No Cummings," he said. "They never heard of him. Nobody by that name *ever* at One-twelve. You sure of everything you told me?"

Devlin had to catch his breath. "Cummings. Tom and Irene Quinn. Lake Tranquility, New Jersey. And another guy." He shook his head. "Oh, no. I'm going to remember it." The block lifted: Lederer. Bob. "Bob Lederer." Devlin's stomach felt on fire. "The car parked outside was a faded orange Pontiac with a New York Statue of Liberty plate. On the front seat was one of those airline folders they put the tickets in." He remembered the colors. "TWA."

"Any writing on it? Were the blanks filled in?"

Devlin shook his head. There was still Lake Tranquility and the Quinns, a house and real people. And Nelson, whether Gerrity had ever heard of him or not. Devlin had Nelson on tape, solid evidence. "I want to see how many faded orange Pontiacs have Liberty plates."

John said, "You want to run down Antonucci."

Devlin was looking around. "Assume I'm being set up. Is Levine part of it?"

"You'll find out soon enough. It doesn't make much sense. Why would he bother? To pay back a favor? Where's the evidence Harry Levine owes that kind of favor?" John grinned. "And even if he is in on it, the surveillance you'll be under won't be just window dressing. All concerned are going to have to give a good account of their time. I'm willing to bet you still have a few hours before they connect you with Antonucci. After that, it's anybody's guess. In the meantime, I'm going to try to get a line on him. If I'm lucky, I might be able to make the connection before anybody else does. Who knows, maybe you'll remember on your own."

Devlin lit a cigarette and flicked the match into the gutter.

"You've reminded me of the things on Levine's mind last night. He wants to get through this *without* problems."

"Spoken like a true civil servant," John said. "Good luck to him. Are you going to check on Lake Tranquility?"

"I want to think a little more about that. What's the point of making a trail that might point Levine in the wrong direction? Why would I go up to Sussex again if I wasn't worried about it? Suppose it's simply this: A guy said he was a cop because it was the only way he could get his brother-in-law into the program. My car is around on Second Avenue. There's something back home I want to get my hands on." Devlin didn't want anything happening to the Nelson tape. He turned back toward Second Avenue and caught the morning sun in his eyes. The day was going to be splendid. "How do I fit into this? Why would I want to strike out at Jack Brennan or anyone else? I want to get *married*! Wouldn't I *want* to keep my nose clean?"

"Oh, she called. Eileen."

"Yeah, I know. When I just spoke to her, she knew I wasn't at the station."

"She asked me how you were taking it. I told her I thought you were all right. You had a call from another woman. She wouldn't leave her name. She said she'd get back to you."

Déjà vu. A woman had called him last night before he had come home from New Jersey. There had been something as familiar about her voice as there had been about Antonucci's face. Devlin could almost hear her voice now. Three words. Now he remembered he had *her* on tape, too.

"What'll I tell people if they ask about you?"

"Tell them you haven't seen me," Devlin said. "That's the easiest way."

Now Island-bound BQE traffic was bumper-to-bumper from the Brooklyn end of the Williamsburg Bridge to Newtown Creek. Devlin was trying not to jump out of his skin. He was getting plenty of input. Over the radio WCBS was reporting the shooting death of the alleged Brennan assassin, Octavio Lopez, outside the Tombs early this morning, by Bobby Antonucci of Brooklyn. Knocked off the air by this latest development was the sidebar on Jane Milburn, last night's other victim, a Vassar girl from Upper Saddle River, New Jersey, an affluent community of one-acre estates. Neighbors there said . . .

Radio, or for that matter, television, didn't use tabloid words like "love nest" and "tryst"—the *Post* this morning had referred to Milburn as "Brennan's youthful bedmate"—but behind the radio announcer's careful language and trained, measured tones was a breathlessness that hardly concealed common school yard curiosity. According to WCBS, Anita Brennan was in seclusion and not available for comment. And a spokesperson for Brennan's parents indicated they would have nothing to say. Devlin thought people were going to remember how public the Brennans had been in the aftermath of Joe's death, and maybe some people were going to conclude that the years and tragedies had worn the Brennans down to weakness and maybe even, at last, a little humility.

The bold headlines of the early morning editions had been relatively restrained compared to the screaming banners hitting the streets at this hour. Devlin had all four papers, the *Times*, *News*, *Post*, and *Newsday*, on the seat beside him, and as the traffic crept forward, he turned pages, tossing them neatly on the floor when he was done. He thought he was managing his panic quite nicely, thank you. The *Post* had the last picture of Jack Brennan alive, taken yesterday afternoon at his campaign headquarters with the normal collection of semibeautiful volunteer workers—one plump brunette in the second row was caught with her eyes closed. The *Times* had a complete obituary, with Jack Brennan's genealogy back to his maternal great-grandfather working as a laborer on the construction of the then privately owned Interborough Rapid Transit Company. Possibly only the *Times* would print the old, full name of the I.R.T. branch of the New York subway system. The lower two-thirds of *Newsday*'s front page was simply a formal color photograph of Jack, his blue eyes gazing intently into the camera, his fine sandy hair brushed carefully

into place. Dark blue suit, blue shirt, medium blue silk tie
with little yellow sea horses floating across. The drop behind
him was a pale blue satin. Devlin guessed that this was the
picture that would have appeared next fall on the telephone
poles across the state. BRENNAN MURDERED was the headline.
For all the time Devlin had known him, right up to September 16, 1971, Jack Brennan had been interested only in the
seduction of beautiful women, the more famous, the better.
Would he have been alive today if he had stayed a lightweight?
Through Devlin's mind flashed a picture of Jack running his
hand up a girl's leg at a nightclub. Elmo's, The Blue Angel—
it could have been any one of a dozen places. With Jack, the
girl would have been his date. With Joe, it would have been
Jack's date. With Devlin, when he'd had enough to drink, it
could have been anybody's date. . . .

You were not a nice guy, Devlin.

He flipped through the *News* as he rode up to his third-floor
apartment in the building's dingy, vandal-proofed elevator—
the original polished mahogany walls were covered with a
wallboard as grim as it was hard: someone's penknife had been
able to make only the thinnest scratches in the stuff. The *News*
had four pages on the Brennan killing, including a sidebar on
the Brennan family history, another on Joe's death, and a
third—the first complete story, if you wanted to believe a word
of it—on Jane Milburn. According to the girl with whom Milburn shared an Upper West Side apartment, a fashion editor
for *Cosmopolitan* magazine, Milburn had met Jack Brennan
last fall, at a private fund-raiser Anita Brennan had not attended.

Jack called Milburn the following week, and by the end of
January, when the two were able to sneak a weekend at St.
Croix, they were having an out-and-out affair. . . .

La roommate's story accounted for everything but the welts
on Jack Brennan's body, and that his killers—the people who
had operated Lopez—had known exactly where Brennan would
be late yesterday afternoon. And for that matter, what he would

be doing, or more accurately, *who would be doing it to him*. . . .

Devlin had left lights on, and the coffee maker. He had done that before, letting two cups of fluid cook down to a crusty mass in the bottom of the glass pot. A twenty-minute cleaning chore. Not this time. He turned the power off and emptied the pot, promising himself to clean it before he left, when the glass would be cool to the touch.

As he turned from the stove, he saw a piece of notepaper, creamy yellow, folded, on the carpet a foot inside the front door. He had missed it when he had come in. It *was* a note, too; advertising didn't look like this. Devlin put on his reading glasses as he headed into the bedroom, where the morning sun still slanted in through the venetian blinds.

The answering machine light was blinking. A call had come in since he had left this morning. He read the note.

Frank:
Call me from an outside location after 5 P.M.
                                    Marcia Feldman

No telephone number.

He didn't know any Marcia Feldman.

The handwriting was a woman's, a clear, graceful script—in ink. Ink. The note had been written with a fountain pen—and now Devlin knew who had written it. He hadn't remembered *Marcia Feldman*, and at this moment, he couldn't be sure if he ever would have. But he knew a woman who collected fountain pens. He had known her for over thirty years, and she was now an assistant district attorney for Queens County. Her name was Liz Becker Weinstein. Liz Becker, to Devlin. She wanted to talk to him urgently enough to have walked from her apartment to slip a note under his door. She knew enough about something to keep from signing her name. It had been her voice on the tape last night, Devlin realized now. Maybe she had been the one who had called him at the Ninth Precinct this morning. Certainly. But what did she want to tell him? What did she know, and how did she know it?

"Oh, boy," Devlin murmured. He slid the lever on the answering machine that rewound the message tape. It stopped after only a moment.

That was wrong. Not how Devlin had left it, he was absolutely sure. Nelson's message had been at the end of a series of incoming calls, and in order to save it, Devlin had left the tape advanced to a point *after* the Nelson message. This latest call this morning, the single flash Devlin had seen, would have followed all those other messages, including Nelson's and this rewinding would have taken longer than it had.

Devlin slid the lever so the message tape would play. "Major, here, Devlin. What the hell are you doing, trying to kill me? Let me know before two P.M. if you're going to do anything about tonight, because I have to go to the V.A. about my fucking blood pressure."

The Mets must have won; Devlin had forgotten all about taking them yesterday morning. The machine beeped, signaling the end of the message, and then the tape hissed evenly. Devlin couldn't even hear voices not fully erased from previous cyclings. He opened the machine to look at the message cassette. It seemed the same—what he remembered, if he remembered anything at all. He didn't know. Had he looked at the damned thing since he had set it up? The tape was all but fully rewound. Devlin slid the lever and saw the tape back up to the beginning as quickly as before, almost instantly.

He couldn't whistle his way past this any longer! Someone had come in here since he had left this morning. Someone had been here before Liz Becker pushed her note under the door. Until now Devlin had felt this, if at all, only in the distance— no panic that he was handling well enough to congratulate himself for. Now that it was close enough for Devlin to shrink from the heat of its breath, Devlin's pulse raced. He could feel his blood pressure rising in his teeth.

He wanted to sit down. He was tied to Brennan, Lopez, and Antonucci. He had been sent out of town right after Brennan's murder, minutes after, then drawn in to witness Lopez's murder by Antonucci—and while that had been happening, someone had come in here to remove the only evidence, however thin and faint, that anyone but Devlin was responsible for his actions over the past twenty-four hours. Less than eighteen hours, actually. No Cummings. What about the Quinns? Involved in this was someone who knew Devlin well enough to proceed with everything else in the plan on the basis of a call to Devlin from the nonexistent Captain Cummings. The last eighteen hours were only what Devlin could see. The plotting went back—how far? Months?

Involving at least one person who knew him better, perhaps, than he knew himself.

Very few people knew him at all, he was thinking, when he suddenly asked himself about Liz Becker. Liz Becker, for instance, for *example*: did she *remember* him so well? How many Liz Beckers were there in his life, people who had come and gone? People now in the middle distance?

And who among them hated him so much, considered him so low, as to position him in the middle of Jack Brennan's killing? And for what purpose? Devlin was nothing to anyone outside of his own immediate circle; he didn't even think like "Nightclub" Devlin anymore. He had been a different man for years. When he had gone to A.A., he had thought he was happily turning himself into a nobody. No. He hadn't known it at the time, not the way he knew it now, but he had been turning himself into a human being, the one he was today.

While he ran hot water into the coffeepot, Devlin went through the sports pages of the *Daily News*. If he had won money, he owed himself the pleasure of learning how, no matter how much trouble he had concentrating on it. Mets over the Cards, 7–0, behind the seven-hit pitching of Bob Ojeda. Bob Ojeda? Sid Fernandez was supposed to have started. Devlin wouldn't have bet on Bob Ojeda. Devlin tried to keep reading. How much did Major owe him? Fourteen hundred. Major could handle it. If Devlin's telephone was being tapped, his relationship with Major was no surprise—or big deal—to the people wearing the earphones. Somebody among them thought he knew Devlin better than he knew himself, maybe even presuming to know where his breaking point might be, the moment when he would reach for a drink. . . .

Oh no, not that way. Not that way at all. "Fuck you, whoever you are," he said aloud.

The time was already twenty to twelve. He was supposed to meet Steve Loncaric at the South Street Seaport. Devlin still wasn't sure of the meeting time. He almost wanted to take the answering machine tape, too. A wireman could tell him if the tape had ever been recorded, then erased. Devlin was sure this was a new tape, but only electronic analysis would settle the question. *Why? Why him? Why him now?*

There was more to come—had to be. Someone was going to be able to make the link between Antonucci and himself. He had not met Antonucci at the time he had known the Brennan family, he was clear on that much. Mugs like Antonucci never got close to the Brennans. Antonucci was . . . *what* to Devlin? And Lopez? It could be argued that Devlin had had Lopez completely under his thumb. Devlin could have been supplying Lopez with drugs. Someone was making it look *easy!*

Devlin was supposed to work this evening. Eileen expected to see him afterward. Lunch with Loncaric. Devlin's real life seemed so far away now, he thought he was looking at it through the wrong end of a telescope. *Wait a minute.* Whoever had him in his sights knew this about him, too. Devlin was going to have to get control of himself. He was going to have to manage his energy and concentration—*and* start anticipating. More *was* coming. He hadn't told John Lord about the Nelson tape. Now he would. And about Liz Becker, too. Liz Becker *Weinstein.*

Devlin was headed back to Manhattan twenty minutes later. The day was an absolute sparkler, the air clean, the clouds moving quickly. He was still taking stock of himself, methodically, carefully. He had had horrible feelings before, and he didn't have to prod his memory to pinpoint when. After his experience with the Brennans. After his parents' deaths. He could remember his first adult nightmare: 1957, the beginning of his great Pamela adventure. What Devlin could remember too well was the awful feeling of the bottom dropping out, nothing being the same, of suddenly not knowing anything.

In July 1957, Devlin boarded the bus for Sussex County hoping he would find ways to find girls, to be with girls, to get his hands on girls, without his stepcousin, Everett, hanging around talking about six-guns and catfish.

But Ev had grown, too. He had a girlfriend, Cindi, confidentially, the highest praise for her: "She sure can squeeze the snot out of a chicken's neck." Ev considered himself in love, a man. Devlin would have laughed out loud if he had been getting any sex himself. Ev was getting more than Devlin, too, a hillbilly in hog heaven.

Devlin's cousin Alice had a new friend, too, Pamela, who was only a month older than Devlin, fat-assed, blue-eyed, blond-haired, and a bit of a scandal; according to Ev, rumor had it that she was not a virgin. Devlin wanted experience, and he started hanging on Pamela, as Ev said, laughing, "Like spit on a hurricane fence." Even Alice thought Devlin was funny.

Pamela was sweet, maybe a little dumb. She liked to lean back when kissed; if you wanted to diddle her, too, that was fine. Devlin learned how to excite and satisfy her, but he couldn't get her to touch him the way Cindi was grabbing young Everett. Ev told Devlin not to let her get away with it, and Devlin, growing angrier, agreed.

On the Saturday night of the Labor Day Weekend, Devlin got Pamela alone and drunk in the backseat of the '37 Olds. He was wild to be initiated into the mystery of sex, ready to sacrifice everything of himself for the first time ever. He was ashamed of what it said about him, but he was not going to stop. Pamela needed more booze—she didn't need more convincing than that. Soon they were "howling like puppies," as Ev told him later. . . .

Devlin had horrified himself. He needed St. Theresa's communion to purge his bone-rattling guilt. He was too ashamed to tell her what he felt so he told her nothing at all. He didn't write to her, and soon her letters stopped coming. . . .

The following spring, 1958, Cousin Alice got married. The marriage was necessary, according to the morals of the time, because the bride was pregnant.

On the appointed late spring Saturday, the Devlins and Uncle Buddy headed into New Jersey in a borrowed car. The old man didn't like Buddy, and Buddy didn't like him, either, but the two could be quiet about it as long as both were sober. The old man planned to stay that way, and not really because he was driving a borrowed car. Everybody knew the real reason: sobriety and grim near silence was how he showed his contempt for all his in-laws. No one was fooled, and Buddy wasn't silent about it. "Your father is a lace-curtain asshole," he once said to Devlin. "I don't know how your mother puts up with him."

He took a wrong turn, and in the forty-five minutes they wandered around the bare March countryside, Buddy produced a pint bottle and had himself a snort. Bourbon was Buddy's drink. After Buddy had a second shot, Devlin reached for the little bottle automatically. His eyebrow arched, Buddy passed it over. The old man said nothing, if he noticed at all, and in another few minutes, he had them back to the place where he had gone wrong. In the backseat, that called for another round to celebrate. Devlin thought it was going to be a good day.

The bride and her entourage stood huddled outside the church in the brisk, sunny air when the Devlin car rolled up. Alice was enormous and, by the look of her, even crying, as happy as she had been saying on the telephone. Devlin stood back from the hugging and kissing until she saw him. Alice reached for him, planting a wet kiss on his lips. Her belly against his felt like a basketball.

"I'm so glad you made it. We waited as long as we could."

"Come *on*," somebody whined, "it's cold out here."

Devlin recognized Pamela's voice. He turned. They were face-to-face, and even though she must have seen him first, she seemed as startled as he was. She'd changed—gotten heavier. Her face was round and ruddy, and her hair, done up for the wedding, looked thicker, stronger, and in spite of the primping, somehow wilder. She had put on a *lot* of weight, he decided. He tried to say hello, but it came out a stammer. Her lip curled, and as she turned to break the eye contact, she did something that froze Devlin, something so extraordinary that it riveted itself instantly on Devlin's memory, and for all time. He knew that at once, and that whatever she had intended, she had done more, and by overshooting, revealed herself. On the spot he thought that it was one of the lessons of his life, that people could show themselves more than they wanted, if they didn't think first and be on guard.

She growled like a dog.

The Devlins entered the church, Buddy disappearing again. When he slid into the pew, the smell of bourbon around him was that much stronger. Halfway through the service, Buddy muttered something about Alice's belly. Devlin didn't hear his words, but his mother did, and she leaned in her son's direction.

"Get my brother out of here before I kill him." When Devlin hesitated, she said, "Go. Get him out before he ruins everything."

"Anything to get out of this whorehouse," Buddy seethed, and turned toward the aisle.

Out in the sunshine, Devlin grabbed Buddy's arm. "What did you mean back there?"

"Fucking bitches," Buddy yelled. "The one standing there so proud of her daughter, the daughter thinking the whole travesty is perfectly acceptable, wearing white with her gut halfway to Cleveland, the bridesmaid's somewhere in Akron . . ."

There it was again, Devlin's gut turning to ice. He was counting months as quickly as he could, comparing Pamela's shape with Alice's. Alice had told him she was racing to the altar. If her baby was due in the next month, it had been conceived in early summer . . . Pamela could have become pregnant—when? She had growled like a dog, hadn't she? Devlin's mind raced down corridors it had never known before. During the winter his guilt had withered, and he had had sex with two other girls, and he loved his freedom and prospects.

The reception was a big country buffet and a 45 rpm record

player loaded with records by Vic Damone, Eddie Fisher, Patti Page, Tony Bennett, and Hank Williams, who made the New York City contingent writhe. Alice wanted to dance every dance, and when she got Devlin on the floor, she wanted to know what had happened to him during the ceremony.

He motioned to their uncle Buddy, who was now in a corner, unconscious, seated, his head resting against the rough plaster wall.

"Who baby-sat who?" she asked. "Dance, asshole. If that jerk I just married sees me rubbing bellies with every man in the room, maybe he'll realize he still has to pay attention to me."

Her stomach made Devlin feel a jolt of fear for her. Women *died* in childbirth. Fewer and fewer of them, but it did happen. He was terribly uncomfortable now, and she told him that he was dancing like a wooden soldier.

"Pamela, uh, look, uh . . ."

Alice laughed at him. "I was wondering if you were going to say anything. That's what she got for Christmas last year, and she doesn't know who gave it to her."

Devlin stopped dancing. He felt like a man gripping the bayonet stuck in his chest to keep from falling down dead. Alice's eyes widened. "You thought—?" She laughed again. "Oh, no; oh, no. She was wise to you. You didn't even send her a Christmas card. So, she said to hell with you. I don't blame her, except she was stupid and got nailed." Alice saw he was taking it badly. "Come on, you're not going to be one of those guys who's *always* an asshole about women, are you?"

He didn't know if he answered her or not. Years went by before he allowed his thoughts to pass over the moment again.

Alice's mother died, and two years later, Alice's husband beat her up and put her in the hospital. After the divorce she married a fat guy who bit his fingernails and thought he could be rich if only he had start-up capital. He didn't like Devlin's clothes, New York City, or the memories Devlin and Alice shared. Alice had six more babies, and then she and the fat guy migrated to rural Florida. Years later Devlin's mother learned the rest of Alice's story through the Monahan family grapevine, but she didn't tell her son until he was clear of the Brennans and clean and sober. . . .

Are you always going to be an asshole about women?

The truth was that being thrown out by Brennan had plunged him to the bottom, and then to A.A., but he had never even thought of hitting the booze when his parents died. Never. And this was not life, the force of nature. Someone was after him. Devlin thought again of last night's dream; the images suddenly jumped into his consciousness. He remembered how the dream had turned sour and dark. He and Alice had been sitting at a kitchen table covered with cake boxes and coffee cups. . . .

He had no trouble remembering now.

It had been the last time he saw Alice, in the fall of 1968, in Sussex. Maryellen had been there. She hadn't wanted to make the trip. They were people she didn't know, she'd said; never mind that Alice was his family, or that his presence in Sussex was a sacred duty.

Alice's seven-year-old daughter had died in a school bus accident, one of five very unlucky children. *Funerals all over town,* one farmer said.

Devlin had gotten the news from his mother, too sick herself to make the trip. No point in asking his father. The family had already disintegrated by then; Devlin's aunt, Alice's mother, was long dead, and Buddy had become a drunken derelict who appeared, bleary and ripe, only at odd moments. And by then Devlin had developed a warm sentimentality about those already distant summers with Alice, young Ev, and Pamela, riding around in the Oldsmobile. . . .

Maryellen, in her mink, was uncomfortable among the country poor, but she went with Devlin from the funeral home back to Alice's place without argument. It must have been after ten o'clock when they settled in the kitchen, Alice, her fat guy second husband, Maryellen, Devlin, Alice's neighbors, three or four women, cake on the table, coffee on the stove, beer in the refrigerator, some of the neighbors' husbands in the living room in front of an old black-and-white television console. The air was layered blue with cigarette smoke. Alice looked like an old woman; there was nothing left of the teenager Devlin had known. What struck Devlin was how *grateful* Alice was for his presence.

The neighbors were impressed with him, a fancy-dressed, big-time New York City detective. When he told them, gently, that his cousin Alice remembered him when, he created an opportunity for her to let go a little, and she seized the moment, started talking, reminiscing. . . .

Remember young Ev and his girlfriend working away at him? *What was her name?* Alice started to laugh; Devlin had forgotten how earthy she could be. "That girl, when she gets old, she's going to have bursitis of the elbow and not know why!"

The women shrieked with laughter. Alice wasn't finished. She remembered Pamela's behavior with other boys when Devlin wasn't around. Devlin found himself ready to laugh at that, even in Maryellen's reserved, almost stony presence. Alice wanted everybody laughing, and almost willfully, maybe even deliberately, Maryellen wouldn't relax. The neighbors had tears coming down their cheeks. Alice wanted to hear jokes, Devlin started telling them, mixing in funny stories about their parents and Buddy and young Ev, things he hadn't thought of in years, the beer parties at Culver's Lake, more jokes. One of the women got her husband to come in and listen, and then the other men came in, too. They had lame hillbilly jokes they wanted to tell, but in a few minutes they saw it was Alice's time. She wanted her cousin from the city to make her laugh, the only person in the room who had known her when a night like this was beyond all imagining, when night itself held only promise, adventure, and what in their youth they had believed was dangerous romance. All that wonder and joy had come to this woe, Devlin was thinking, and if this was the bitter truth of life, it was also very funny. Alice had gone full circle inside herself tonight, and before the visit grew overlong, Devlin rose to leave. Then she cried, but briefly, and while still laughing.

The drive back to the city that night was quiet. Now Devlin remembered wondering if Maryellen had been cowed by the power of the emotions involved in a life she had dismissed as beneath her. Probably not. What had Alice thought of Maryellen? Devlin had seen. Even in her grief, Alice had not been able to keep herself from taking odd moments to study the grim, ice-cold Maryellen. It wasn't that Alice had disliked Maryellen so much as she had felt sorry for her cousin.

Always the asshole.

Some dream. He could have expected a dream of Sussex after last night's fool's errand to Lake Tranquility, and he could have expected a bad dream after learning of Jack Brennan's murder. But what Devlin had dreamed of was the death of a child. At thirty-eight, Eileen had no time to waste, and while her father was alive, she didn't want to marry outside the church, not if there were a chance that she could. . . .

It might have been the same nightmare without any killings. If Jack Brennan had lived through his appointment at the Waldorf Towers, a little later at dinner he would have sat, welts and all, near the cardinal—who might just have remembered later, when reviewing Devlin's annulment petition, the resurrection of Irish power in the city. What did a Frank Devlin and his petition mean in the scheme of *those* things? Now the cardinal was going to remember something else. The Brennans had always been big contributors to the church. Three months from now, the cardinal could decide that the Brennans had suffered enough. Three months? Try six months. Would Devlin have to wait six months before bringing up the subject again? That brought them to next year. What else could Devlin have dreamed of but a dead baby?

Eileen would be thinking of all this soon enough. He didn't know what he was going to say to her. This wasn't simply battle damage, it was heartbreaking defeat. Some dream. The child he had begun to believe would be born was probably already dead. No good to protest any injustice, that the hopeful father-to-be was a relatively innocent victim, not quite as innocent as Cousin Alice, for instance, dead herself now at least a dozen years. The news had come through the Monahan family grapevine, and Devlin's mother had hesitated for months, almost a year, before telling him, she was so afraid it would knock him off the wagon.

Alice had not done well with her fat guy second husband in Florida. He had not traveled well. Antagonizing the locals led to unemployability, which in turn led to rage, and Alice finally blamed herself. "I pick drunken losers," she wrote to a Monahan woman who talked regularly to Devlin's mother. "Something was going to happen," Devlin's mother was told. Finally Alice lit out, taking the youngest child, a girl, all she felt she would be able to support, farther south, to Miami, where she moved in with another woman and got a job as a cocktail waitress. In her last letter, she wrote, "They let me wear dark stockings to hide my varicose veins." She wasn't thirty-five years old. A month later a pain in the lower back was diagnosed as a kidney infection, but it got worse, and a trip to the hospital led to the discovery of a cancer that had probably started in her uterus and had metastasized into her liver and lungs. Alice lived one more month, not time enough to write another letter. The letter informing the family that she was gone was written by the roommate, whom Alice had entrusted, the roommate said, with her baby girl. . . .

Devlin's mother had been right. A dozen years ago, Alice's death fresh in his mind, thinking of her, or life itself, had made Devlin feel doomed and meaningless. Would anyone ever know that Alice had lived at all? Where was the redemption in such squalid, pointless suffering? Cancer? Devlin had read that women got cervical cancer when their men didn't keep themselves clean. Was Devlin's cousin dead because a fat guy had been too lazy to wash his dick?

Devlin knew he was going to have difficulty sitting through lunch. For all he knew, he wasn't going to get to the entree without some kid from Harry Levine's office laying a hand on his shoulder, saying, Keep your hands where I can see them, Devlin.

No Cummings. The Nelson tape had been stolen out of his apartment.

He was going to have to wake up!

12:46 P.M. . . .

DEVLIN PULLED INTO A PARKING LOT SIX BLOCKS FROM South Street and walked the rest of the way to the Seaport, wondering if he should be grateful for having even found a place to park. He had forgotten about the traffic—and the tourists. Under normal summer lunch-hour conditions, the streets of lower Manhattan were mobbed with short-sleeved office workers. Shuffled among them today were cellulited women in shorts and T-shirts, men in shorts and adjustable caps, kids with balloons, kids eating, kids squinting in the sun, more kids than Devlin had ever seen before in this part of town. A fair number of the dads, moms, and kids had festooned themselves with Liberty clothing and trinkets, mostly green polyurethane Lady Liberty tiaras. Sprays of green spikes waggled everywhere in the surging flood of bobbing heads. All these clowns were going to be in the city until Friday, the night of the big fireworks show. By then, all would be covered with Liberty memorabilia—someone somewhere had gotten the idea that this junk would have value someday, if you only held on to it long enough.

New York had a big, bad reputation with the rest of America and this was the reason why: New Yorkers loved to skin Americans. Tall ships, world's fairs—every ten years or so, the city staged an extravaganza that shook hundreds of millions from American pockets. An out-of-town lady Devlin once dated accused him of having a ''New York mind'' and he supposed now that this was what she had meant. But it was not his problem: if the Ozzies and Harriets of America wanted to hate New York for costing them so much, it was really only because

91

of the dancing green polyurethane Lady Liberty tiaras; how dumb did you have to be, to buy a thing like that? And then *wear* it? Better to hate New York than admit it had fucked your ass again.

Steve Loncaric was wearing his collar. He made a show of looking at his watch as Devlin was led by the maitre d' to their outdoor table. "You had another fifteen minutes. I was beginning to wonder if there had been a late-breaking development that I hadn't heard on the radio, or seen on television. Or read in the newspaper. I'm sorry about Jack Brennan. And for you. How are you doing? Are you all right?"

"It's still sinking in." Devlin sat down. A nice breeze swept up off the water. Loncaric was drinking Saratoga Vichy. Devlin asked for iced coffee. "What time was I due?"

"Noon."

Devlin winced. He used to show up forty-five minutes late for lunch when he was on a bender and trying to conceal it.

"We're going to have to play this by ear," Loncaric said. "Happily, His Eminence was aware of your petition before last night. I won't know until the time comes when I can approach him again. He'll be in Rome in October, maybe into November. That's what you're looking at, Frank. You can't rush him on a thing like this. He's very sensitive to doing things properly. I can hear him say that this is no time to burden old people like the Brennans. He might even say *poor* old people."

"I thought of that." Devlin was looking out at the big sailing ships tied to the south side of the pier. Tourists clambered over the varnished carcasses as disrespectful as insects. Loncaric didn't have to know anything about Devlin's connections to last night's and this morning's murders. What was the point? For all Devlin knew, everyone he saw would be called as a witness. He pointed to the collar. "What are you doing in that getup?"

"From here, I'm going up to Washington Heights for the funeral of an eighty-eight-year-old nun. The old biddy had the habit for seven decades, since before our entry into World War

One. She saw a lot of changes. She saw them at a distance, but she saw them.''

The waiter brought the menus. Devlin knew what he wanted, cold poached salmon with dill sauce. Loncaric was the gastronomic adventurer. When Devlin found something he liked, he stayed with it until his dining companions started making fun of him. After the waiter had gone, it was Loncaric's turn to look out toward the river. He was a little guy, five-seven or so, and would have looked younger than his age, thirty-seven, but for his receding hairline and the puffiness of permanent exhaustion under his eyes. Devlin took him to be a driven man, but Devlin didn't know what Loncaric was driven to, or from. At least he was sober. Aside from a desire to be in the center of the action, Loncaric didn't seem to believe much in anything. He rarely discussed God, faith, religion, ritual, or prayer, and when he did, he seemed embarrassed. By Loncaric's vaguely amused expression now, Devlin could see he had nothing so intangible or subjective on his mind. ''You might as well know the worst of it, Frank. The cardinal and Jack Brennan had done a deal to stay off each other's turf after the election—not embroil each other on the abortion issue, and so forth. You have the idea. You can imagine what His Eminence thinks of the City Hall crowd and all the funny, *non-Catholic* characters floating around the mayor. It's a far cry from the old days . . . when St. Pat's was quite properly called The Powerhouse. Having Jack Brennan in the Senate was going to restore the old balance, as it were. The cardinal was all but rubbing his hands with glee. What you might as well know is that His Eminence is now mightily pissed. He said that something funny was going on up at the Waldorf Towers, that one of his 'boys' in Harry Levine's office tipped him off that our almost-next senator was into S and M. Is that right?''

Devlin grinned. ''You mean, is that what they call it?''

''Don't fuck with me, Frank.

Levine had a spy in the mayor's office; the cardinal had a spy in Levine's office. Who spied on the cardinal? The Russians, most likely. *And who spied on Frank Devlin?*

He said, "Even if I knew something, I couldn't tell you. You know that. Assuming I did know something and could tell you, what good would the information do you?"

"Don't give me that. Brennan was being systematically beaten by the girl."

Devlin stared at him.

"This could have been very painful to His Eminence," Loncaric said, "and no pun intended. Just the sort of thing a political opponent would have loved to use, oh, a week before the election. Even privately, to make Brennan fold, it would have been hideously embarrassing. By election day the cardinal would have been out to here for Brennan, singing his praises from the pulpit. It was in the works. In the future we're going to have to be a lot more careful and thorough."

Devlin shook his head. "The cardinal did a deal with Brennan. What did he think he was dealing *with*?"

"Then you do know something!"

"No more than you. The *deal* was corrupt. Corrupt deals are not made by saints."

"The cardinal happens to be the personal representative of the Vicar of Christ," Loncaric said, unable to smother his mirth.

"So was Francis Cardinal Spellman, and try to stop the rumors about him being a homosexual."

Loncaric laughed. "Rumors? How discreet! Sometimes I think I liked you better before you fell in love and started worrying about God and other things that don't concern you." He laughed again. "What shit. What have you said to Eileen?"

"Nothing. We decided not to talk about it."

"Nothing like facing reality. What *are* you going to say?"

"I don't know yet. Any more than she's read in the papers, she doesn't want to know. Not interested in what the horses do off the track, is her way of putting it. Unlike some priests I know. Aside from the probable delay—"

"All but certain," Loncaric corrected.

Devlin's frustration boiled up and he wanted to bring his fist down on the table. Instead, he took a deep breath and sighed. The damned question rose up before him still one more time: *Why would someone want to implicate him in Jack Brennan's murder?* Loncaric's eyes went up. The maitre d'.

"Mr. Devlin?"

"Yes?"

"Mr. Lord on the telephone. He says it's urgent."

"Excuse me," Devlin said. On the way to the front of the restaurant, the maitre d' said, "You'll have to take it at the reservations desk. We're not really equipped for incoming calls."

"I won't tie up the line for long."

"Thank you."

As he took the desk handset, Devlin saw a pay telephone on the wall in the corridor to the restrooms. "Do you want me to call you back? I can't talk here."

"Maybe you'd better. I'm at my desk."

"How'd you describe me to the maitre d'?"

"Light brown hair, some, gray-blue eyes, beige sports jacket, brown slacks, white shirt, brown tie. And maybe sitting with a priest."

"Smart-ass. I'll call you right back."

Devlin had plenty of change. John picked up on the first ring.

"I'll talk," he said, "you listen. There's no Nelson in Levine's office. No such person. I called New Jersey Bell. They told me a telephone at the Lake Tranquility address was disconnected four months ago. I called local real estate agencies and asked if the property was listed. Eventually I got to the broker of record. He confessed. The house you went to in Lake Tranquility has been on the market for the last four months, empty because of an executive's transfer. With the owner out of town, the broker figured he could take two grand under the table for a one-month rental from a guy named Lederer."

"When did this happen?"

"Early last week. Don't worry, I got everything he knows. He really thought I was after him for grabbing the two grand. Scared to death. Lederer walked in off the street and paid cash. The broker hinted that he thought Lederer was a dope dealer. All he remembered about Lederer himself was that he was middle-aged and had a big nose.

"The broker doesn't know anything about a couple named Tom and Irene Quinn. He never went around to the property because he figured he was being paid to stay away. You still don't remember anything about the place you took Quinn, do you?"

"Not a prayer. It was quite a trick, following another car's taillights while I had my head up my ass."

"I'm glad your spirits are up, because we have the first information on Antonucci. He's your age—actually, forty-four. And from your neck of the woods . . . Well, close: Astoria. He has a very long sheet, mostly robbery of one kind or another, including car theft, muggings, and trying to do the safe of a discount store out on the Island. Eighteen months for that. The rest are various assaults. Quick with his fists—even now, at his age. Antonucci is five-five and weighs a hundred and thirty-five pounds. I guess he has some kind of little-guy complex. Nothing connected with dope. If there's a way to tie him to Lopez, that isn't the route."

"No, the route is me. I know him from somewhere. How did you get all this stuff?"

"I have a friend in the know. Don't worry about it. Anyway, he says the story on Antonucci is that he's too dumb to be in the mob, but they use him."

"*He* thinks he's in the mob," Devlin said. "What else did your friend say? He knows who your partner is."

"Coincidence. That's the word they're using down there. Understand, they have *not* tied you to Antonucci."

"Yet," Devlin said absently. He was thinking of the Quinns, and the lengths they had gone to trick him. *No*: Tom Quinn had been really sick, as if he had drunk too much too quickly. What sort of person goes *that* far with a charade? *Ah, an easy one at last.* Devlin was going to have to think his way through every minute of it. He remembered a black sedan following him all the way from the George Washington Bridge—seeing if he got to the correct destination? What was bothering him now was something in John's voice when he had first mentioned Antonucci. Devlin said, "What were you thinking when you said Antonucci came from my neck of the woods?"

"To tell you the truth, what passed through my mind as I heard all this stuff about Antonucci is that you could have gone to the same high school, but you didn't."

"Where did he go?"

"Long Island City. You went to Bryant, right?"

"Wrong. I went to Long Island City. Where the hell did you get the idea that I went to Bryant?"

"Sunnyside is in the Bryant district, isn't it?"

"Across the street from me. For Christ's sake, Antonucci is forty-four? I *must* have gone to high school with him, but I can't remember. My mind's a blank."

"Relax," John said. "The way I got the information, Antonucci *attended* Long Island City High School. Even in those days, there must have been guys who weren't in high school long enough to find their lockers—"

"There were those guys," Devlin finished, "and with his sheet, Antonucci must have been one of them. And I'm an absolute blank. Jesus! I have a yearbook at home, but if you're right about Antonucci, he isn't in it. Only seniors, people who were expected to graduate. For God's sake, John, what the hell is going on?"

"You're being fitted for something, my friend, by person or persons unknown, for reason or reasons unknown."

"Why would I do anything to Jack Brennan? Loncaric just told me my annulment petition is shelved until late winter."

"You ought to think about taking this back to Harry Levine. Levine being involved in what's being done to you makes no sense at all. I think you can trust him."

Devlin told John about the Nelson recording. "I'd have to tell Levine about that, too. Levine would have to ask why I'm drawing attention to myself. Nuttier things have happened, like that L.A. cop who planted the bomb during the '84 Olympics because he wanted to be a hero."

"Frank—"

"I'll think about telling him."

"Okay. Just stop thinking crazy, okay? What you just said

is crazy. It has no reference to you. I'll tell Levine myself how I dug up this stuff about Lederer and the Quinns. That real estate man has my name and shield number. There's no reason for me to be anything but completely up front with everybody all the way around. That goes for you, too.''

"Do you have time to call Long Island City High School?" Devlin asked.

"Thanks. I'll butt out when you want me to, but I'd rather butt in. I'm going to identify myself to those people, too. You have to make a record. What was just done to your answering machine says that whoever is setting you up has wheels still in motion. Think about talking to Harry Levine ASAP.''

Without responding, Devlin said good-bye and hung up.

Whatever Loncaric saw in Devlin's eyes caused him to half rise out of his seat. The fish had been served. "I went ahead without you,'' Loncaric said, "but before I started, I worried about your dish getting cold. Then I remembered that it was *cold* poached salmon, so I worried about it getting warm. You look like shit. We clergy worry about our effectiveness ministering to our flock.''

"I can't tell you a thing," Devlin said. He remembered that before John's call they had been talking about Eileen's reaction to the consequences of Brennan's murder. "If you want to know what will be on Eileen's mind, I know she's going to ask me if I've tried to get in touch with Maryellen, and if not, why not? Eileen is one of those people who wants to stay in touch with everybody they've ever met, no matter what has passed between them.''

"And that makes you uncomfortable because it's more than you've ever asked of yourself. Your life would be much more manageable if you had stayed in touch.''

"You know as well as I do that I had no choice about Maryellen.''

"Her father just made it easy for you," Loncaric said, going at his food.

"All right, but even now I have trouble looking at the person I was with Maryellen. I'm ashamed. I'm *still* ashamed.''

Loncaric put down his fork. "I'm sorry. I don't know why I said what I did. I've heard enough about Jim Brennan from others to know what kind of pressure you were under. Well, maybe I don't know. But I have an idea."

You don't know anything about Jim Brennan, Devlin thought, but stayed silent. Perhaps Loncaric was thinking he had struck a nerve, or that Devlin was contemplating the depth of Loncaric's insight. Nothing like that, but Devlin was content to let Loncaric think what he liked. With his mind's eye, Devlin was looking again at the information John had dug up about the Lake Tranquility place. Maybe, finally, the real estate agent would testify that a guy named Lederer had rented the place. The real estate agent's testimony meant nothing in itself, but it was a piece of the puzzle. But Devlin could have hired Lederer to create a story John Lord's detective work only seemed to corroborate. All Devlin's protests about a tape of a guy identifying himself as Nelson meant nothing, either. Zilch. What remained true was that Devlin had been Jack Brennan's brother-in-law, had run his assassin Octavio Lopez as an informer, and had attended high school with the man who had shot Lopez. That much remained true.

And, in John's phrase, wheels were still in motion.

For a few moments after he said good-bye to Steve Loncaric, Devlin was disoriented. He could not remember where he had parked his car. He was trying to remember another lot, another day, and for a split second, he forgot the rest of the day's agenda. Now it unfolded before him: Major had asked him to call before two—too late for that now. And Liz Becker, after five, from an outside phone. By then Devlin would be working Times Square. . . .

2:51 P.M. . . .

SIX BLOCKS. WALKING IN THE SUNSHINE THROUGH THE crowds, Devlin had his jacket open. He wanted to take it off, but he was wearing his piece on his belt, where it would be seen. His shirt was soaked with sweat front and back, slapping cold against his skin with the shifting of his body. He was only too aware of the time. He had things to do at his desk and wanted to have another word with John before getting up to Times Square before four o'clock. Because of the time, it was beginning to look like he would have to go straight uptown, without stopping at Fifth Street.

As soon as he turned the corner and the parking lot came into view, Devlin could see something wrong with his car. The Seville was sitting back on one haunch like an old dog. Flat tire.

"Shit!"

People turned. Devlin hurried across the street as the lot attendant saw him coming; *he* knew the tire was flat. Devlin caught up with the attendant as the kid took another customer's ticket.

"Hey! What happened to my car?"

"Don't ask me. I have to get this other guy's."

"Hey, I'm a cop! I'm talking to you!"

"I don't care if you're Lee fucking Iacocca, man! Read your contract!"

The other customer turned away, grinning. The attendant meant the disclaimer on Devlin's ticket, the self-determined, limit-of-liability notice printed in type only teenagers and birds of prey could read. It was nonsense as law, but that sort of

100

thinking wasn't going to get Devlin on the road, either. He didn't have time to change a tire. He couldn't leave a key and his triple-A card with the attendant. Devlin yelled to him, "I'm going to have to let the car sit for a couple of hours!"

The attendant answered without turning around. "That's up to you!"

Devlin's moment of panic was passing. He had to figure a way to get a key to Sal, his mechanic, and hope that Sal could fix the tire quickly. But that and the other telephone calls would have to wait; Devlin had no time to spare. He wasn't far from the Broadway-Nassau station of the Eighth Avenue line. Was that the best way to go? Devlin rarely used the subway anymore; the filth, graffiti, and derelicts reminded him so vividly of his depression of a few years ago that his skin prickled. The *heebie-jeebies*, his parents' generation had called the sensation. Devlin had heard Jim Brennan use the phrase during one of his evening lecture-reminiscences. Devlin could remember that moment, his sudden wondering about the origin of the phrase, and why it was rooted so deeply in the minds of those who had grown up with the century. Old Jim had been not only healthier back in the early sixties, he had been more powerful, physically strong, still tough enough to kick the shit out of any of the three young men listening to him, good enough, probably, to take them all on and leave them hurting, if not unconscious. Jim talked out of the side of his mouth in the style of the now-gone New York. He was one of the thousands of his time who liked to say he was off the streets and proud of it. What made Jim Brennan different from the rest was that he usually said it in black tie, in a leather wing-back chair, a brandy snifter in one hand, a genuine Cuban cigar in the other.

For all Devlin knew, he remembered those lecture-reminiscences and all the rest of what happened to him with the Brennans as well as he remembered September 16, 1971. Levine said he might want to know everything. It would take weeks to tell, maybe months, and Devlin could sense a reluctance to subject himself to that experience that was much,

much stronger than his reluctance to ride the A train up to Thirty-fourth Street.

The hottest time of day. The food vendors, crowds, and the dense traffic raised the temperature and humidity even more, spicing the air with whiffs and reeks of humanity and its works, familiar, intimate, repulsive, enchanting. Cities stank. In Tokyo people wore face masks. Decades ago, New York overwhelmed its citizens with the smells of leather tanning, coffee roasting, fat rendering, and God-knew-what nineteenth-century technology.

As Devlin headed down the subway stairs, he thought again of Levine's request to stand by: he hadn't let Levine's people know his whereabouts since early this morning, when he'd checked out of the Tombs. If John's information was correct, they weren't interested in Frank Devlin—which was exactly the kind of story Devlin himself would give out while an investigation was in progress. *They were checking everything!*

The air underground was even hotter and wetter than the laundry steam sloshing around on the streets above. A train was pulling into the station, brakes shrieking. At the token booth Devlin flashed his shield, moving quickly. The train's doors were open, people pushing in. Devlin picked up his pace through the moving crowd, easily replicating maneuvers he had learned as a kid. The Subway Samba amazed tourists; hundreds of people rushing in all directions, in a very small space, without ever hitting one another. They knew how to do it. The ones who didn't probably were pickpockets.

The train's doors closed, then popped open again, making Devlin hesitate, then move once more. The doors started to close a second time when he was ten feet from the train, near enough for him to get inside if he kept going. Somebody kicked his right ankle as he was bringing his foot forward so that his instep looped around the back of his left leg. Devlin went down and forward hard, on one knee, yelling, plunging headfirst toward the train as the doors locked shut. Devlin had to throw his hands flat onto the concrete platform to brake his momentum. The train began to roll out of the station. Devlin could feel the concrete abrading the skin from his hands, but he dug in, *tried* to keep from barreling headfirst into the moving train. People were yelling, or was it him alone? If he raised his hands to protect his head, he would hit the train. He grabbed the wooden rub rail at the edge of the platform and held on and pulled his head into his shoulders. Three inches, four at most, between the rub rail and the train, less between the top of his head and the metal plates flashing by.

Somebody grabbed him. People pulled him up, looking quickly into his eyes. He felt like the last guy in a school yard game of Crack the Whip. Blood was beading up in the grime ground into his palms. *Kicked.* He looked around, past the faces of the crowd around him. No one was looking back over his shoulder at Devlin. If the kick at his ankle had been deliberate, the attacker had learned the trick in grammar school.

"You want to sit down?"

"No, I'm all right." He was going to have to clean up and change clothes. His pants were torn, the shoulder seam of the jacket split. His knee was scraped, too, and he had felt something in his back he knew wouldn't begin to hurt until the end of the week.

First he had to get uptown and show his face—and the rest of him. Any other time, he would be told to go home. In any other circumstance, he would do it. If Levine really suspected him of being involved in Brennan's assassination, the story of Devlin's accident would get to him almost instantly. Devlin wanted to be on the record. John was right about that. There was nothing to hide.

Devlin was shaking, his heart rate up, sweat running unpleasantly down the backs of his legs. The pain began to tune up, not so much like a section of violins as a set of fingernails across a blackboard. People had moved away, replaced by newcomers who gave him a wary once-over before averting their eyes. His ankle throbbed. *Kicked!* No doubt about it. What Devlin couldn't decide was the question of intent. It could have been an accident, someone not watching where he was going. No one had been looking back at Devlin in the moment after he had been pulled to his feet. And no one near him now seemed to be feigning lack of interest in him.

He had returned to the parking lot to find his tire flat, and then minutes later he had taken a near catastrophic fall on the subway platform. Was his thinking too paranoiac? Had somebody anticipated he would take the subway, or had he simply presented that somebody with an early opportunity?

To do what? Kill him?

Why would anybody want to kill *him*? The platform began to shake as another train approached. Devlin could feel the strength draining from him, as if he might not stand up long enough to get inside the car. *Was anybody watching him? Was he presenting another opportunity?*

The train rolled in. Devlin was thinking that he could have gone in any direction from the parking lot. All anybody would have had to do was follow him. . . .

Wheels still in motion: Devlin to New Jersey, unalibied Devlin to the Tombs, summoned by a man who didn't exist. Why not Devlin dead? Maybe the plot didn't work unless Devlin was dead.

On the other hand, if someone wanted to neutralize him, scaring him into immobility was probably the best way short of murder to do it.

And while Devlin was playing mind games with himself, the someone or something infiltrating his life, decade by decade, year by year, down to the days and minutes, every breath he took, like some kind of horror movie, was going to pass through the very molecules of Devlin's existence. Mind games: they wanted him to doubt himself, wonder what was wrong with him, until finally he was telling himself that in his sleep he was creeping through backyards and poisoning kittens' milk so that children could find them dead.

When the train passed out of the station, Devlin studied the people on the platform for little signs of interest in him. Nothing. No one.

He was beginning to hurt all over.

6:37 P.M. . . .

FROM HIS POSITION FACING THE STATUE OF FATHER DUFFY of the Fighting Sixty-ninth in the center of Times Square, Devlin surveyed the crowd. Every fifty feet, it seemed, strolled a pair of uniformed officers, male, female, black, white, all young, in nearly all shapes and sizes, most out of condition, a few improperly dressed: maybe they fooled the yokels, but not anyone who knew what a big city cop was supposed to look and act like.

No matter, Devlin thought, with a smile. *He* was on the job. He was looking for what professional gamblers called the "tells," little signs that gave away what people really had on their minds. Nothing was so obvious as a facial tic, or a fluttering of the hands; more possibly a barely audible deep breath, a slight movement of the eyes, interested, maybe wary, searching for opportunity. Psychologists observed patients for clues to the real inner life, salesmen kept one eye on buyers, and closer to home for Devlin, customs agents matched incoming travelers against memorized checklists of giveaway behavior. A street crimes specialist watched loiterers, people who watched the passing crowd, others who seemed too consciously purposeful as they went about their business, strollers staying close to others they didn't seem to know—partners: while one distracted the mark, the other lifted his wallet.

With the victims carrying credit cards, picking pockets had become enormous international business. Brokers had cash ready for cards that could be Air Expressed anywhere in the world in a day and a half. The credit-card companies wrote off the losses against their colossal profits, but taxes paid for the added police work, whatever it's worth. This was one of the reasons why Devlin had told Eileen a long time ago he could take his job or leave it. Collaring a pickpocket still meant nothing. The best pickpockets these days were Colombians, often teenagers. With their connections to the money of the drug trade, they simply made bail and skipped the jurisdiction. Or maybe not . . . How could you find them in today's ghettoes? So what did police work mean? Throwing career thieves off the top of the Empire State Building wouldn't accomplish anything, either. Crime was as much a factor of the human equation as blue eyes. As in every other endeavor, a new generation was coming up fast, more skilled, sophisticated, and merciless. Modern communication had turned crime into sport, with records made to be broken. Sometimes the job was fun all over again for Devlin when a suspect's bladder-spilling collapse reminded him what a deep, down-and-dirty thrill arresting someone could be; but more often it was like this evening, uncomfortable, slow, routine, with the deadliest enemy, boredom, settling on the brain as suffocatingly heavy as volcanic ash. Devlin could see it glazing the eyes of the young plainclothesmen moving slowly against the crowds under the movie marquees surrounding the intersection of Seventh Avenue and Broadway. Devlin wasn't feeling the boredom. The bright summer evening was uncomfortable, slow and routine for Devlin, but something else was crawling up his spine: he was remembering what that grammar school kicking-of-the-ankle had been called. With the Seville down on one rim, why hadn't he thought of it earlier? Did someone have a macabre sense of humor? On the staircase of Junior High School 125, when one kid kicked another's ankle so that falling down was inevitable, it was called a *Flat Tire*.

Devlin was wearing a borrowed pair of trousers. The split seam in the shoulder of the jacket wasn't as bad as he'd thought. A four-inch gauze pad covered his knee. All the scrapes had been washed with antiseptic. They hurt, and he could sense that he had pulled a couple of different muscles, but he wasn't stiffening up, not yet. All his exercising might make a difference in how he felt tomorrow. No question in the minds of his fellow officers about the authenticity of his accident. Maybe fifty guys had seen him this afternoon, and more than half of them had gritted their teeth, sucked air, or winced. He'd probably see fifty more before the night was out. . . .

If he lasted. He was coming back again and again to the thought that something was in motion, he was a little cog in a very big machine. Never mind why. He was the connection to three men, two of them dead. If Devlin were dead, too, the connection could be twisted into anything. But so what? The important thing was *not to die*.

After he had cleaned himself up in the locker room in Manhattan South, Devlin had been able to grab fifteen minutes at a telephone. Still too early for Liz Becker—she had skidded far down Devlin's priority list, anyway.

No Sal, either. According to Sal's resident illegal alien, a kid from Bolivia, Sal was up at Bronxville Radiator—"Bronkvil Rayiayor" to the kid. Devlin was able to get the kid to write down his name, the location of the car, and a telephone number where Sal could get more information if he wanted it. Eileen's number. It was possible that the kid didn't understand Devlin and was only saying he did. Devlin was thinking of the Seville in an unattended lot in deserted downtown: the Midnight Raiders could have it stripped down to its body shell by dawn. Then he told the whole story all over again to Eileen's answering machine.

And now Devlin was suddenly asking himself if he could be sure she would be safe even in her own place. Did he know what was going on? No. Did he know which of the sitting ducks—Brennan, Lopez, Antonucci, himself—was the next target?

And now, coming down Seventh Avenue, behind a guy in an eye patch walking a dog the size of a golf cart, Devlin saw a face he recognized, a man he had watched change and age for the past twenty-five years. Clarence "Bingo" Malone. From Harlem, lean and good-looking in his youth back in the early sixties. A pimp, rolling in dough, he loved to thump his girls, white girls, who worked the midtown hotels day and night. The smack he used to keep his girls' brains on hold finally rose up and grabbed him. By the middle seventies Malone was a heavy-duty dealer and looked it, haggard and thin. The girls were gone—with heroin, a lot of guys don't need girls, and Malone was one of them. In and out of Lexington after that, years up the chimney, finding his way downtown and back into Devlin's life. Devlin remembered. 1980, one of Devlin's unhappy years, when he was looking after his father. And wasting time with Liz Becker.

Malone was called "Bingo" because he liked to say the word so much. Looking at him now, as bad as he was, Devlin had no doubt that "Bingo!" still punctuated his every sentence. It had in 1980, on a gray winter afternoon when Malone caught sight of Devlin walking through Tompkins Square Park. A bitterly cold day: Devlin's ears rang with it, as brittle as a pair of brass bells.

"Hey, Devlin, my man! Here you down among the downtrodden! Bingo! How the mighty have fallen! What happened to the Toast of Broadway?"

Only then did Devlin place the verbal tic with the man's name. Thinner than ever, in old war-surplus khakis, shivering against the wind, spittle drying in the corner of his mouth, Malone went on. "You fucker, you know you did me! Look at you lookin' at me! Goddamn! Well, look where doin' me got *you*! You're no better off than I am, fucker, and I can see it in your motherfuckin' eyes."

"Yeah. I know," Devlin said, moving on toward Avenue A, "I ruined your life."

Devlin could remember what he'd thought that day: *You beat one girl too many.* No remorse in 1980, no remorse today, watching Malone in rags, panhandling, tugging at sleeves. He was a few years younger than Devlin, and lucky to have lived this long. Murder was the leading cause of death among young black males, and for a long time, early in his manhood, Malone had made an awful lot of people want to kill him. Women he hit, for the most part, ripped-off and beaten Johns, cornball victims of the Murphy game, their knuckles sore from pounding on doors for girls who weren't on the other side, drunks Malone mugged, and other targets of opportunity—Malone had nothing but contempt for them all. When Devlin gave him a warning, Malone told Devlin to fuck off. Then Malone beat a girl from Wisconsin—Devlin remembered that much about her, and that she was big, maybe five feet ten, not pretty, not smart. Malone broke her arm, three ribs, her jaw, cheekbone, and nose, knocked out five teeth, and left her eyeball hanging half out of the socket. Devlin saw that. Homely to start with, she was going to wind up looking like an old prizefighter. She wouldn't say Malone did it, but other girls did, and other pimps couldn't stop yakking about it. According to Devlin's informants, Malone all but crowed in his glory, as if he had changed the course of history with his will alone, teaching that bitch a lesson, ushering in a new era in human relations, one in which Clarence "Bingo" Malone would be free to do whatever he wanted to anybody. Eventually he would *kill* somebody.

So Devlin framed him.

September 1970. Devlin picked the lock of Malone's apartment, slit a small hole in the top of the lining of Malone's alpaca coat, and planted enough smack to certify Malone as a dealer, and then withdrew. In November Devlin spotted Malone's lavender Cadillac pulled over to the curb at the corner of Seventh Avenue at Fiftieth Street, outside the old Roxy Theater, and pulled Malone and the alpaca coat out from behind the wheel. Devlin's partner searched the coat.

"Oh man!" Malone yelled. He was wise at once, knew who had done him, if not how. Devlin stayed away from the courtroom when Malone came up for sentencing; as it was, Malone cursed Devlin as he was led away. That didn't bother Devlin. The sight of him might have left Malone with an even more bitter memory, bad enough to make him snap—as if two years in Attica would not be bitter enough.

Oh man!

Devlin could hear it still. And here was Malone, fighting the tide of the crowd on Seventh Avenue, hopping around on shoes taped to his feet, mooching spare change. Had Devlin kept him from becoming president? The question of right and wrong intersected in Devlin's brain with his memory of that Wisconsin apple-knocker's busted mug and Devlin's certain knowledge that Malone had done it. One beating too many. Devlin had no problem understanding the impact of the Malones of the world: they caused nothing but pain, which was as close to a definition of pure evil as Devlin could get. In not much more time Malone would have been the perpetrator of a murder—or the victim. All these years later, it was, in fact, a statistical miracle that he hadn't become one or the other anyway. Devlin had been drinking in those days, too, and it had surely affected his judgement. Maybe Clarence ''Bingo'' Malone should have thought of such things before laying bare that girl's facial bones with his fists.

Oh man!

Sure, Devlin thought, *make me care.*

''Boy, are *you* daydreaming!''

John. Devlin blinked. John Lord was leaning across the front seat of his old Dodge sedan, looking up at Devlin through the passenger-side window. Devlin had been so lost in thought that he hadn't seen John's car roll up in front of him.

''I'm going to park here.'' John gathered up some paper bags from the car floor. ''Every time I want sushi, you want corned beef. I hate going into Katz's. Those bars on the windows do nothing for my appetite.''

They began to use the roof of the car as a dinner table. ''What did you get for yourself?''

''Lox.''

''Jewish sushi.''

''That's why I got it. I hope it satisfies the craving. I owe Lee Mistretta. At six o'clock it was my turn, and he took the squawk.''

''Has he said anything to you about Brennan or Lopez?''

''He asked me what you thought. I told him we hadn't had a chance to talk. The squawk was another rape. Same guy. An old lady, sodomy and fellatio.''

''We owe Lee big.'' Devlin's stomach rolled, and he put the sandwich down.

John grinned. ''How is it?''

''You have to ask for lean,'' Devlin said. ''All this fat on here, I'm going to get too much cholesterol and take a heart attack.''

" 'Take a heart attack,' " John mimicked. "Bug off. You had me going until you said that.''

"Don't tell me about little old ladies getting their butts reamed while I'm trying to eat.''

"How have you been today?''

Devlin shrugged, still chewing. "My brain is working better. The Quinns were professional actors who may have never worked together before. Only an actor would drink enough to make himself sick just to add realism to the part. But that's what Tom Quinn, whatever-his-real-name, did. And when his towel fell down, exposing his penis, she stared. She'd never seen it before. Wives don't stare at their husbands, not like that.''

"Right. After a while they look only to make you feel good.''

John had never been married. Women really did look, Devlin was thinking, you just had to catch them at it. With Eileen, Devlin always acted as if he never saw her do it. "I have a thought about Lederer, too, and that plane ticket in his car.''

Devlin could see John growing wary in spite of himself. Devlin said, "I think Lederer is a professional hitter. If I were running a deal like this and wanted to get Frank Devlin out of touch and without a believable alibi, I'd get two eager-to-please dummies to put on a show, and then I'd park them where they couldn't tell anybody about it.''

John smiled. "A bare-knuckle scenario, I must say.''

"Jack Brennan and Octavio Lopez have already written their reviews. I think the Quinns, whoever they are, will turn up dead, probably unidentifiable. If you're right and things are still in motion, then I have to move fast. If your friend in Levine's office can keep his eye on D.B. calls—well, let me put it this way: If he finds a pair of corpses matching the Quinns' description, I won't have to go through all the actors' directories looking for them. What you got from that real estate broker says that Lederer did everything himself, including hire the Quinns. All I need is corroboration that those people were in that house when I got there. Circumstantial evidence, testimony from anyone that one or the other had an unusual job, one time only, in New Jersey, will do it. Lederer ought to show up on FBI crime-flow charts. Even if we do lay hands on him, it won't mean much, because he won't talk. But that helps me, too. All I have to do is show that there is a conspiracy against me—that, and stay alive."

With a paper napkin John dabbed a bit of cream cheese from the corner of his mouth. "It occurred to me that the deal might work better with you dead. You want to be careful."

Devlin didn't want to tell him about tripping in the subway. Instead, Devlin said that his car was stuck downtown with a flat tire. John sucked at his teeth.

"That's just perfect," he said. "You get the tire fixed, slide behind the wheel, turn the key, instant Cuisinart. You have that mechanic, Sal, don't you? Have him go over it, inside and out, before you try to move it an *inch*."

"Does that make sense?" Devlin demanded. "What would that prove, besides that there *was* a conspiracy, and that I was just one of the victims?"

"No," John said. "The same reasoning you've applied to the Quinns will be applied to you—one small piece of the puzzle. You did your job, whatever it was, and met with the traditional Mafia layoff."

"Mafia?" Devlin repeated.

"All right, CIA. Whatever. You know as well as I do that if you're going to create a chain of evidence, you'd better build in a link weak enough to be broken. Lee Harvey Oswald might have been that link. You know what I think of that civilian in the Iran hostage deal. The Quinns had to go if, as you say, they were actors. If they lived to see you get it, or see you turn up in the newspapers and on television, talking to us and the press might have opened career doors for them. People dumb enough to take a job like that in the first place? *Try* to keep them quiet."

"All right, Sherlock, how does killing me make sense?"

John smiled. "A bureaucrat's dream. What a mystery! What the hell were you up to? Suppose all the corpses are accounted for. Even so, there isn't enough of a trail, enough living witnesses, for the real story to emerge.''

"So whoever was responsible for explaining it all would just make up a story to fit the available facts. The can would be tied to my tail.''

"Your *dead* tail," John corrected. "Now let me tell you about Antonucci. What year did you graduate high school?''

"1960.''

"Antonucci graduated with you. He was in your class every step of the way. He didn't drop out.''

The shock was like a concussive wave. Devlin could hear his voice rising. "Why didn't I remember him?''

"You *did*! You remembered his face. You *knew* him. What do you expect of yourself after twenty-five years?''

"More.''

"Are you saying you accept my point?''

Devlin stared off at nothing, trying to ignore John's Jesuit-trained logic-chopping. Devlin was thinking instead of how he had chosen to see that time of his life so long ago: innocent, even irrelevant. Why Antonucci? What was the point of going so far back in Devlin's past? And how? How did they, whoever they were, learn so much about him?

"Antonucci's supposed to have mob connections.''

"My buddy in Levine's office fed me a little of that," John said. "Antonucci's connections are with the very bottom rung of Johnny Gotti's ladder. His last real job was as a car-parker at that restaurant on the West Side where they'll cover your license plate while you're inside—a real cultural breakthrough, that, right up there with television evangelism. Have you heard anything I've said?''

"You were talking shit," Devlin said quietly, even though his thoughts had drifted elsewhere. "The joint to which you refer is mob-owned, as you know, and they're covering the license plates just to bust balls, just like they keep insisting they're legitimate businessmen. But you're right, I was thinking of something Levine said last night. He wanted me to focus on what I knew about the Brennans. That maybe something in the back of my head somewhere would shed some light on

Jack's killing. I was just trying to take the idea one step further—into the area Levine still doesn't know about, presumably, which is how tightly wired to this I really am. Suppose I've been made part of it because someone knows something in my head puts me in the middle? Someone thinks I *know* something? My God!''

"When are you going to talk to Levine?''

Devlin suddenly thought of Eileen. If the situation was as bad—threatening—as he was beginning to believe, he owed it to her to involve Levine. *Yes.*

"I have to call Levine myself. For all I know, Levine knows everything about Antonucci—and more—and is using your friend and you to feed me the kind of stuff to make me come in and talk about it. Levine is that good.''

He looked around. The lights of the theater marquees and the billboards made the fading daylight high overhead seem far away. Baseball scores scooted across the lighted strip around the New York *Newsday* building—less the upgrades inside and out, the old *Times* building. Devlin had forgotten to call Major. He knew he was trying to forget Liz Becker. He didn't like the woman, had no respect for her. But he wanted to touch base with Sal. And he *had* to call the Brennans! And now he wanted to make an appointment with Harry Levine.

Remembering. Doing his homework for Harry Levine . . .

"So you know about Hadley.''

"Yeah, I know about Hadley,'' Devlin said. He and the Brennan brothers were in an old workingman's bar under the el on Jamaica Avenue, just a few blocks from Gertz's Department Store, on a Saturday afternoon in the heat of summer, the Yankees on television, Yogi Berra at the plate. Devlin had known Maryellen for six weeks, and this was his first time in the company of her brothers, Jack and Joe.

Devlin figured they wanted to size him up, and he had gotten an idea about them from Maryellen. She saw her older brothers as tough, savvy guys. Devlin quickly saw for himself that they weren't. Older than he was, too, they were simply big, pushy Irish brats who were used to getting what they wanted. Bullies. Hadley was the guy who had just dumped Maryellen when Devlin ran into her in Joe King's G-A. Too many problems, Maryellen had reported Hadley had said. Devlin was wondering now if Hadley had meant these two in addition to all the others, including Hadley himself.

The Brennan brothers and Devlin were getting drunk on beer. They had called him around noon to come out to the Jamaica Estates place and say hello. Maryellen and their mother were in Manhattan for shopping, lunch, and more shopping, and their big-deal old man, the famous big-city fixer Jim Brennan, had flown to Washington for a private Saturday meeting with the Secretary of Commerce.

So Devlin drove out in his jewellike Mercury hardtop. Six weeks with Maryellen Brennan had been action-packed. After their second date, he realized as he drove home, he could have written the script in advance, especially her dialogue explaining why she wouldn't let him near her: *Last week was a mistake. I was drunk and upset.* He had been through it before with two other women he had taken to bed on first acquaintance. They always wanted him to know they were not that kind of girl. He had to laugh at the logical impossibility: what kind of girl did it, if not the kind who already had? Maryellen was as vehement on the second date as she had been passionate on the first. Irritating about it, too, aggravating, until after a while he got the idea that she wanted to convince him the week before had been *his* fault. Catholic craziness, she-craziness, mixed with sweet talk and touchings just too provocative; he was wise to her, he decided. Parked outside the Jamaica Estates house—his first glimpses, for he had met Maryellen in town—he opened his pants and brought her head down on him, her struggling giving way quickly to an astonishing expertise. After a moment, he was pumping himself furiously into her mouth. And then she held him warm in her lips. The girl was a champion. A star.

But then she began to sob. She wrenched away from him and curled up against the car door, wracked by heaving wails he had never heard from a human being before. He put his hand on her shoulder—she screamed. Frightened, even beginning to worry about his career—(What had he done to her? What would she *say* he had done?)—he withdrew, smoking a cigarette to quiet his nerves as she slowly unwound, shook silently, floundered for a handkerchief.

"There's something wrong with you," he said.

"And nothing wrong with you, I suppose."

"I didn't say that . . ."

"Well?"

He was ready to set her straight when she turned suddenly, as if to get a better look at him, sneered, and quickly got out of the car. He watched her march up the drive, his mind going back to an earlier experience, a name he couldn't remember. . . .

Pamela, growling at him outside the church before Alice's wedding. Well, he hadn't needed that, and he didn't need this, either. He slammed the car into gear and screeched the tires as he drove away. He knew there would be no quick calming down. Twenty minutes later, on Queens Boulevard, he could not shake the memory of her violent sobbing, and so he cursed her, aloud, at the top of his lungs. What was the matter with her? He was done, finished. He wasn't going to call her anymore.

She called him the following Wednesday, her third call of the evening, his mother said. Maryellen was sorry, she had thought it over, there had been things on her mind she shouldn't have taken out on him. She wanted to talk. She wanted to see him.

And from the soft purr in her voice, she wanted to give him another shot at her, too. He decided to be the tough guy. Seeing her did not mean he had to lose control, did it? By the end of the conversation, she was whimpering again, murmuring that she was eager to see him, couldn't wait for Saturday night. *Bullshit,* he thought. She was up to something, but so what? He wasn't going to lose control of the situation, was he?

Maryellen stood him up, spending that weekend in bed with Hadley, as she reported the next time Devlin saw her, the following Tuesday, outside the East Forty-second Street Automat where she intercepted him. She was sporting a black eye the size of a peach—not even sunglasses could conceal it. She had told Hadley about Devlin, and Hadley had popped her. Now Devlin wanted to pop her for standing him up to spend the weekend in bed with Hadley. Devlin told her, and she burst into tears. Again. He wanted to get away from her. What he didn't understand, she said, was that she told Hadley about him because she knew she had made a mistake. *More bullshit,* he thought at once: how many times had she made the mistake with Hadley before telling him? How many times *Friday night?*

Devlin didn't get around to asking *her* that question until two weeks later, and when Maryellen laughed at it, he laughed, too. They were in bed, exhausted. By then, he wasn't sure if he cared about what she had done or was doing or would do. He was seeing other women. She didn't know it, or wasn't going to let on. There was no doubt now that she liked him, and he liked *that.* Maryellen was a beautiful girl, curvy, with wonderful hips. But she was vain, too: she worried constantly about getting fat, like a grandmother now dead, and she liked to look at herself, even in bed, raising one leg and then the other, examining their curves. She didn't think he knew what she was doing, but he was taking it in, all of it. She was uninhibited, often outrageous—but then moody, dependent at times, even clinging. She had an explosive, violent temper. She *screamed*, her face red with rage. He was beginning to understand that she had to cry after such episodes; once, she cried for two hours. He timed her, but that was the depth of his involvement. He deliberately kept himself distant from her emotionally, drawing back more with every outburst. She knew it. He could see that in her eyes. But she was merciless— or wanted to be.

"You're not the biggest guy I've ever been with, you know."

He laughed in her face. He didn't want her to see that her coarseness stung. Tears came to her eyes. Tears of shame, she said.

He had had moments with rich girls in the past, but he had always known that he wasn't going to be around for long. With Maryellen Brennan, he was beginning to wonder. Accom-

modating her idiosyncrasies could open big-time doors for
Frank Devlin. He had been seeing Jim Brennan's name in the
papers since childhood—Brennan, the multimillionaire party
power broker, wheeler-dealer, opportunist, influence peddler,
fixer, and even world-class crook. Maybe Devlin's father was
right about Jim Brennan, seducer of scores of women over the
decades, but the fact was that he was the only man in the
borough of Queens who could guarantee you an audience with
the Pope. In six weeks, Devlin had actually spoken to Jim
Brennan only once. Brennan was in black tie, on the front
walk of his Jamaica Estates place, stepping toward a waiting
limousine as Devlin arrived to pick up Maryellen. Brennan
paused, a fat cigar clenched tightly in his teeth.

"Who the fuck are you?"

"I the fuck am Frank Devlin."

Brennan eyed him for a long time and then got into the limo.

Devlin waited to hear about that, but never did. He still
wasn't sure old Brennan, obviously a very tough guy, had a
sense of humor, and in the absence of evidence either way,
Devlin decided not to press the matter. He'd be more respectful next time around. As an only child he had always been
curious about how larger families organized themselves, and
what he found unusual about the Brennans was the absence
of chaos and confusion. Everyone had a part to play, and if
Maryellen was an example, each played it perfectly. With her
beautiful eyes and hands, Maryellen was the little princess. If
Devlin cursed in front of others, she glared at him. When the
conversation turned to the harsher realities—his work, for instance—another subject had to be brought up lest her delicate
stomach be made upset. But that new subject could not be sex.
With others present, and sometimes, inexplicably, when they
were alone, she acted as if she knew nothing about sex. When
he tried to kid her about it, she started shouting. She didn't
want to be mortified, she yelled. He thought she was joking,
tried to tickle her out of it, and she screamed for ten minutes.
Like a child. *Screamed.*

If Maryellen was the princess, her mother the self-possessed mother superior, and Joe and Jack the goofy, energetic pups, then old Jim was bigger than a king, a kind of god in his own right. The rest of the family teased him and laughed at him behind his back, but Devlin thought he recognized cowed behavior when he saw it. Brennan ruled his roost. He had the voice for it, the chesty growl of an old street animal. Even when he was asking only for more iced tea, he sounded as if he were running down the assignments in a bank heist. Everyone deferred to him. The iced tea appeared in his hand, the English butler lit the fat Cuban cigar, the barber, manicurist, and masseur always arrived early. Brennan's laugh could be heard all over the house, and Devlin could imitate it perfectly. Devlin had Brennan's act down pat. Brennan was six feet two, two hundred and twenty pounds, and wore silk shirts, pajamas, and underwear. Sensitive skin, Devlin was told. Devlin's father said that Jim Brennan had a hundred custom-tailored suits. After six weeks in Brennan's house and shadow, Devlin thought the estimate low by two-thirds. All the Brennans, king, mother superior, the pups, and the princess, lived in unashamed luxury. Devlin had never seen anything like it. He had never *imagined* anything like it. He puzzled through Maryellen's mercurial behavior, trying to make sense of it, calculating the quality and intensity of the unhappiness and pain concomitant with knowing her at all. He wasn't sure where brothers Jack and Joe would place in his catalogue of woes, but he guessed that their position would be somewhere between the butler's postnasal drip and Maryellen's own unpredictable episodes of humorlessness. Did Devlin know about Hadley? The Brennan brothers weren't sounding Devlin out on their father's instruction—old Jim was much too subtle and well-connected for that—but toying with their sister's new friend, they thought, the way a cat played with a bloody mouse shivering in terminal shock.

They thought.

Now, on the gray television screen above the end of the dreary bar, the Detroit pitcher made a mistake, threw one low and inside and, as anybody who had been following the Yankees for the past fourteen years figured at once, Berra golfed it into the stadium's short right-field porch.

In the bar, guys cheered.

Devlin was just drunk enough to think he was waiting for an opportunity to show the Brennan brothers that he could handle them *and* Hadley—and, for that matter, Maryellen, too. Their money made them think they were better than he was. Sunnyside, one year in City College, and the N.Y.P.D. were inferior, second-rate—*low class*. Devlin had never seen himself in these terms before, and he disliked it so much his skin itched.

Jack and Joe had their backs to Devlin as they watched Yogi motor around the bases. Devlin dropped his cigarette into Joe's beer. Joe picked up the glass without looking, brought it to his lips, noticed the butt at last, and almost jumped off his stool. He laughed, his shoulders shaking. He turned to Devlin, whose eyes were now fixed on the television set. Joe picked the soggy butt out of the beer and wiped it on the sleeve of Devlin's seersucker jacket, then turned back to the game.

Devlin poured his beer over Joe's head.

Joe scrambled off the stool, backing away, glass in hand, as beer poured out of his sandy hair. Jack, wondering why he had been splashed on the back of the neck, saw that Devlin was to blame and loyally tossed his beer in Devlin's face. Jack didn't think this was funny; he didn't get the joke. Joe laughed at him, then doused him, laughing louder. The bartender came running up.

"Three more," Devlin said, deadpan.

Joe laughed for two minutes. Ten minutes later, he laughed all over again. Devlin had them. At seven o'clock all three called Maryellen to tell her where they were. This way she couldn't say she was being stood up, Devlin explained to his new best friends.

He never learned how they got out of the bar, or how his Mercury, not a scratch on it, got into the Brennan driveway. Devlin awakened in the dark of the following morning in a Brennan guest room, made his way down the hall to Maryellen's room where he found her asleep, nude, with her hand between her legs—not even she knew the best of her secrets. She didn't resist him. When daylight entered the room, she was on top of him, playing a game of trying to make him cry out. He had already realized he had found her drunk. Secrets— the princess kept a fifth of gin in her room.

On Labor Day they were in Southampton, Devlin in a guest room. Old Brennan was in a great mood, and if he was still ill at ease with Devlin, he was trying to be friendly. Apparently Brennan always reserved this weekend for his family, another Brennan Tradition. Devlin marveled at how seriously they took themselves, even when they were trying to have fun. Dinner Saturday night had to be in the town's most expensive and fancy restaurant, the men in ties, the women splendidly turned out, their hair done that afternoon. The Brennan boys had dates, Park Avenue debutantes whose talk, mostly with Mrs. Brennan, was of openings and shows. Jack was banging the blonde, and Joe was banging the blonde and brunette. Everybody would be in separate guest rooms later, of course. Devlin had a bottle. Maryellen had said that the beach house, as they called it, had walls too thin for midnight visiting. Another of her moods—the week before, she had given him a blowjob on the Grand Central Parkway at fifty miles an hour.

Tomorrow would be Mass, a big family breakfast, a family day on the beach, an early family dinner, and a family movie in the living room. Next day would be the traditional family barbecue. Maryellen's conversation in the previous weeks about Labor Day had given Devlin fair warning: plenty of clothes. It was all a grand show they were putting on for one another. Jack and Joe behaved altogether differently around their father, stiffening up and deepening their voices. They were lawyers, Jack in private practice, Joe an assistant in the Queens County D.A.'s office. Jack was almost thirty, Joe three or four years younger.

Devlin had hoped to get a moment alone with Maryellen sometime during the weekend, but no. Definitely not. The more he made love to her, the more he wanted to. He realized what was happening between them, and he was determined not to let it make a monkey of him again. She was too emotional for him to think about surrendering to her; it was going to have to be the other way around . . . But Devlin wasn't sure he wanted that, either. There was a fury in the excitement she boiled up in him that made what other women did entertaining, but always flawed, like the dancing of nightclub chorus girls. He wanted her, but he was sure he couldn't trust her behavior for long. For that matter, he wasn't sure he could trust himself. He *was* still running after other women; he was angry with *her* too much; and he was thinking—couldn't help thinking— that he didn't really want to change his mind. He didn't have to pay attention to it; he was still having too much fun.

Maryellen didn't have to be in town until the following weekend, while Devlin had to be on duty at 8 A.M. on Tuesday. Using the excuse of wanting to stay out of the worst of the traffic, Devlin was able to hang around until Monday midnight, when Maryellen walked out to the car with him. He opened the passenger-side door, but she didn't get in, staring at him.

"What's the matter?"

"I feel funny right now. I had a good time. I just feel kind of flat about us tonight."

"What are you telling me?"

"I don't know."

"Do you know how many times you've pulled this crap?"

She winced. "I don't want to have an argument with you."

He slammed the car door and moved around to the driver's side. "I'm getting out of here before you put yourself in orbit. Don't call me again until you decide to act like a human being."

He left her weeping. The next night he was in bed with one of his regulars, who was beginning to wonder what had happened to him.

Maryellen called the night after that, contrite and pleading, breathless to see him again.

He was beginning to see that it figured. Joe and Jack didn't take Maryellen seriously, that was clear. She was years younger than them, a girl, too often unreasonable. Devlin's interest in her fascinated them. He was beginning to see that they imagined him to be some kind of original, self-invented man, at heart a rebel, things they had never had the nerve to be. So they studied him. What was it he knew? He certainly thought he knew something about women. He really did seem to have the handle to Maryellen, didn't he? Devlin thought it was funny, and in the moods he was in, he felt impelled to be ever more outrageous. One night when he was with the Brennan brothers in Toots Shor's, three girls he knew from a show that had closed the previous spring came up to say hello. The girls were having a sort of reunion. After dinner they were going to walk over to the Music Hall and pretend they were tourists.

They were on pills. It was clear at once that Joe and the little blonde in the middle wouldn't mind a change of plans, and that Jack and the big redhead were envious enough of the other two to wonder if they could find consolation in each other. Although Devlin had laid all three girls, the little brunette was a particular friend, very hip, up to conspiracy. He invited the girls to join them for dinner, and murmured to the little brunette that the Brennans weren't supposed to know how well he knew *her*. She said right, and on the way to the table reached back and squeezed his dick.

After a few minutes at the table, the girls excused themselves to update each other and gobble more pills. Devlin thought he had a little additional edge if he didn't bother to tell the Brennans about the pills. Let them wonder why the girls were giddier and giddier; if they tried to keep pace on booze, they'd wind up asleep in a doorway. Devlin still didn't have an idea how he was going to get away from the Brennans so he could get the little brunette alone. He was far enough into the evening to have decided he wanted that.

She crossed him up. Returning to the table, the little brunette took the seat opposite him. The other girls, following the usual boy-girl, boy-girl seating arrangement, placed themselves on either side of him. The brunette never looked at him—none of them did. On both sides, the other two played kneesies and made random grabs at his crotch under the table. They had worked this out in the bathroom. It was clear enough to Devlin that the little brunette was playing a similar game with both of the Brennans, while the other two girls worked them from the other sides. The Brennans took little notice of him; they had three beautiful women talking to them under the table, as it were. Devlin had not forgotten the pills, or that the Brennan boys would want to keep as happy as the girls—they were going to bag all of them, weren't they? The little brunette stuck to her game plan, signaling her friends with her eyes, Devlin saw. Crazy stuff, near misses under the table, went on for over an hour. By the end of the meal the Brennans were so drunk and so focused, however blurrily, on the women, they did not see the two flanking Devlin working on him together, not looking at him, pouring a hundred percent of their above table attention on the two brothers. But for everything the Brennans were missing, they had never been involved in anything like this before. Devlin knew it, but whatever "edge" he may have had was long gone, washed down with double Scotches.

After dinner everything went much faster, a cab ride down to the Commodore, raucous laughter in the hallway upstairs, more hilarity, the flash of bodies. Devlin awakened in the morning after ten, everybody else still unconscious. He wasn't on duty until four, giving him time enough to get himself together, but that didn't matter: when the Brennans came to their senses, they would run him out of their family on a rail, tarred and feathered. . . .

Joe Brennan found him on a stakeout in Spanish Harlem before midnight. "Nice friends you have. We're going to see them again this weekend. Do you want in, or do you have a date for Saturday night?"

Meaning, with his sister Maryellen.

"Who are you?"
"I don't understand the question."
Jim Brennan shifted in his chair behind the desk in his sanctum sanctorum, the library. Another Cuban cigar—Kennedy's boycott meant nothing to him. ("Fuck Kennedy's boycott, look what it got him.") Devlin knew now that Brennan

felt laws were only an inconvenience, when he didn't want to obey them.

Devlin had been out to a movie with Maryellen. At the door the butler mumbled something to her, and she turned to Devlin, her sudden alarm collapsing into heavy submission and defeat. "My father wants to see you," she whispered conspiratorially. "I'll call you tomorrow."

Brennan was in shirtsleeves, his collar open, his tie undone. According to Gabe Pressman on the local news, Brennan had testified that morning at a New York City Board of Estimate hearing on the impact of low-cost, high-rise Title One housing in Rockaway Beach. Title One housing was a politician's license to steal, Devlin knew, all the deals done and players satisfied long before the first public hearing. Brennan had come down in favor of the project, banging his palm on the table. If Devlin understood who Jim Brennan really was, his appearance this morning at the B. of E. had been on the order of a holy blessing. Brennan owned or controlled every bus line servicing the Rockaways, he was a member of nearly every commission, board, and charity in the city, and nobody, presumably, knew the situation down there better. It was wonderful window dressing. The public was being shown that Brennan's private interests were involved. Hilarious nonsense: His skim off the top of the public money when the project went through would amount to ten times his profits from the bus lines for all the years the project would stand. Devlin was getting the Brennan story: he had come up off the streets, using his fists. Big fists they were, too. He had developed his father-in-law's little jitney line serving North Beach, where La Guardia Airport was located now, into a true feudal duchy with hundreds of buses serving neighborhoods from the East River to the middle of Nassau, and from Long Island Sound to the Atlantic Ocean. You did not do business anywhere on Long Island without the imprimatur of Jim Brennan.

"What do you mean, who am I?" Devlin asked. "I'm a cop." The air undulated with webs of smoke. "I went to City College—"

"I know all that shit," Brennan said, looking vaguely

pained. "You're porking my daughter. Do you want me to tell you about the little party at the Commodore you set up for my sons?"

Devlin wanted to smile. "Give me a goddamned break. I *knew* those girls . . . They saw me with Jack and Joe."

Brennan had had him under surveillance? Devlin remembered very quickly what Brennan's operatives would have seen. "Those girls didn't pay any attention to me—"

"Don't give me that!" Brennan roared. "Do you think I was born yesterday? You set it up on the way to the table. When those bimbos came out of the ladies' room higher than kites, their game plan was to zero in on Jack and Joe."

"That's right, and if your spies stuck around at the Commodore, they would have seen that I was the first one out the next morning. Everybody got carried away. The girls were out for a good time. I don't even know if any of them have been in touch with your sons. They haven't been in touch with me."

Jim Brennan leaned forward. "I've been seeing young sons of bitches like you come and go all my life. You fuckers always burn yourselves out. In the meantime you learn how to get around a little, women go for you for a while, maybe you even get mentioned in the gossip columns. For every cop who's ever married a rich young girl—actress, heiress, whatever—a thousand must have tried. Booze is going to get you first. You've got all the makings of a first-class lush. Who the hell are you? Never mind the badge—"

"Shield."

"Oh, you fucking moron! Look at yourself! You're *boiling* mad. As if you can even figure out what's happening to you." Brennan jabbed a finger at Devlin. "You're a smart-assed, snot-nosed flash in the pan, a gutless punk! The booze gives you away. There's nothing inside you. You're not tough enough. You're a loser. Do you think any of that poor-Irish-kid-from-Sunnyside shit cuts ice with me? Right now you have a certain influence around this house. People find you attractive. That will pass."

He stood up and walked to the door, indicating that Devlin was to leave. "It will pass because of you." Devlin rose.

Brennan opened the door. He clapped Devlin on the back. "The older I get, kid, the more I realize how much patience really is a virtue. I don't have to do anything to get you out of my life. You'll fuck your own ass. Do you know how I know? Because of one question you can't answer, Devlin, and that's Who are you?" Brennan moved close enough for Devlin to feel the heat of his cigar breath as he whispered through wet lips, *"Who are you?"*

The following morning, Maryellen telephoned to ask what her father had said to him. Devlin told her. Quickly, breathlessly, she tried to assure him that her father had just thrown a tantrum, it wasn't important, he hadn't said a word to her. For his part, Devlin enjoyed hearing her squirm and struggle. She wanted to see him that night. She wanted to fuck his brains out and suck his dick. He couldn't help smiling. Her father wasn't going to interfere, she said. *Who are you?* Brennan had answered the question himself. Devlin was the guy who was porking Brennan's daughter.

Devlin acted hurt, even though he had a date with another girl tonight. Having a reason for a little distance between Maryellen and him made getting it a lot easier. *Who are you?* Whatever the laughter he would wring out of the situation, the old man's question still burned—seared. Devlin was going to see Maryellen again, but he was not exactly the same inside. He wasn't fooling himself now about his position in the Brennan family. He was trying to tell himself that he was not sure he had ever cared. He saw a red light as big as the moon in front of the Brennans. Something was wrong with all of them, and if he proceeded, it was with the devil's arm around his shoulder.

But in the middle of the week Joe Brennan called Devlin to make a date for lunch. He wanted to discuss business—law enforcement business. Devlin was highly regarded by Joe's contacts, a smart young cop who was getting a handle on the way things worked in New York. "My own experience attests to that." He laughed. "You know, I'm not just parked out here in the Queens D.A.'s office, Frank. I've had some ideas for a long time and, to be absolutely truthful, I haven't discussed them with you because I didn't think you had what I was looking for. Well, appearances are deceiving. Maybe you do know something about life that I don't. Do you remember how Tom Dewey got to be governor?''

"Sure, he went after Murder, Incorporated, organized crime's executioners.''

"I want to do something like that.''

The following week, Maryellen told Devlin she was pregnant and wanted an abortion. He arranged it.

WEDNESDAY, JULY 2

12:22 A.M. . . .

FROM OUT OF THE PARKING LOT STRODE A UNIFORMED officer in a plastic, visored helmet and wearing what looked like a very thick nylon vest. Kevlar. Bulletproof. Cadillac fender-proof, too, one imagined. The parking lot was as bright as a ballpark lit for a night game: the bomb squad's trucks came equipped with that kind of candle power. From inside Harry Levine's sedan, Devlin saw other Darth Vader look-alikes quickly release the pneumatic jacks under the Seville, which bounced on the pavement. Harry Levine lowered the electric window next to him.

"Well?"

"Nothing," said the vested officer. "Clean as a whistle."

"What about that tire that you changed?"

"Cut. Slashed. A broken bottle could have done it."

"Nah. He wouldn't have noticed a flat like that right away? He wouldn't have seen it when he was getting out of the car? Give me a break." Levine closed the window and turned to Devlin. John Lord and Kevin McQuaid, Levine's man, were in the backseat. Devlin didn't have to be told McQuaid was John's connection in Levine's office. "Devlin, it looks like if they took a shot at you, they did it down in the subway station. You were kicked as you ran for the train, you say?"

"That's the way it felt."

"Why didn't you mention this to me?" John asked.

"I thought of it later." *Right,* Devlin told himself. Levine had come up from Police Plaza to Times Square in the middle of the evening for the chance to talk to Devlin alone. Devlin thought of the subway incident after Levine told him that tele-

131

phone company records showed calls from Devlin's apartment to the numbers of both Antonucci and Octavio Lopez.

Earlier, while Devlin had been on the telephone with Levine, Lord had been talking to his contact in Levine's office, and apparently Levine heard Lord's version, too, before meeting Devlin at Times Square. What Levine knew was that Devlin had come in with his story, more or less confirmed by John Lord, *before* being told that Levine's office had found trouble in the telephone records. Levine had already checked the times of some of the calls made from Devlin's number—all times department logs showed Devlin on duty. This evening, John's notes corroborated the official documents. Devlin had been working when someone had been using his telephone. For Levine, it didn't look like anything but a ham-handed frame. Somebody had been breaking into Devlin's apartment for more than six months. Levine was sure the telephone records were going to connect to a mile-wide trail leading to the perpetrators.

Devlin saw another problem: while Levine was in charge of the case, he still had to report to Norberto Torres and, through him, without doubt, to the mayor, who would weigh the evidence on the basis of personal political considerations. If personal political considerations dictated, the mayor would play sleuth and decide that Frank Devlin *had* to have cooperated with the conspirators in some way, at some time, and order Devlin taken into custody. Certainly Devlin in custody was less effective in his own behalf than Devlin at large, and maybe that was all the conspirators desired. Just the same, Devlin could see that the evidence required Levine to take some action; doing nothing could be construed even as an attempt to *suppress* evidence. Levine was thinking along the same lines, it seemed.

"How do I put a tail on you that isn't going to be seen as going through the motions, or a way of telling you to lay off, or to keep your distance from people?"

"I'm cooperating fully with the investigation," Devlin said.

"Not much of an argument if you're guilty of something and cooperation is the way to avoid exposure. Do you see what I'm saying? Damned if I do, damned if I don't."

"Me, too," Devlin said. "Suppose you decide now to let me go. If you're overruled later, there won't be that much heat."

"That's what you think," Levine said quietly. "And sometimes listening to other people's tantrums is all the heat I can take. But you want me to let you go, eh? Do you mind telling me what you're going to do?"

"Well, if the perps do want to take a poke at me, I want to be available, if not exactly completely accessible. I have my own ideas about the New Jersey angle. I want to take another look at my life, not the long view you meant last night, but maybe back over the time you think people have been working this scam."

Levine nodded, as if buying Devlin's reasons . . . but you never could tell with Levine. You couldn't tell with Devlin, either, in this matter. Devlin wanted to check something else, something he had forgotten during his first conversation with Levine on Times Square, and which he was holding back now.

He had talked to Eileen just minutes before Levine's arrival. She told him that a young man, a Latino, had come to her door to get the spare set of keys for Devlin's car. Devlin and Sal had done this before, exactly this way. Eileen knew Devlin trusted Sal completely. Eileen had given the young man the key to Devlin's apartment, where he could find the spare car keys. That's what Devlin had forgotten to tell Levine earlier.

And that's what Devlin was deliberately keeping from Levine and the others now. The Seville showed no evidence that Sal or his Bolivian minion had come anywhere near it. On Devlin's arrival downtown, a moment had passed before he realized that the tire hadn't been changed—and then it was an explosion inside him. All Devlin knew was that someone had stopped at Eileen's and picked up his apartment keys. Anyone who knew the Seville was disabled wasn't interested in cleaning out Devlin's apartment. The tire was changed now because Harry Levine had told the bomb disposal squad to do it.

"I won't have to see anybody until ten o'clock tomorrow," Levine said. "You have until then, barring further developments, and after that, maybe you get no warning." He turned in the seat so he could see the two cops behind him. "You get

this? If you two young monks want to save our church, St.
Frank here isn't the guy to fight the crusade over.''

"Fuck you," McQuaid said cheerfully. "That's funny, coming from an Arab like you. I think Devlin's guilty as original
fucking sin. I wouldn't piss in his cuffs to keep him from blowing
away with the wind." McQuaid used the back of the front seat
to pull himself forward to get closer to Devlin. "I'm not kidding,
you old piece of shit. I think you set this up because Jack Brennan
owed you something that he was going to pay back after he was
in the Senate, something you didn't want to collect. You haven't
convinced me of a fucking thing, and I'm going to continue to
develop evidence no matter who has to eat it.''

"I don't agree with his opinion, Frank," John said calmly.
His tone contained a message that Devlin had already deci-
phered: McQuaid was an excitable guy.

Devlin said, "I think the two birds who played the roles of
the Quinns are going to turn up dead. That could be in Jersey
. . . anywhere. You have their descriptions. I've told you everything I know about Lederer. If anything comes in that
vaguely matches what I've told you, at the least check it out."

McQuaid snorted. "What you meant to say was, let *you*
know it. I won't interfere with you. Those phone calls from
your place are accounted for by someone working *with* you,
someone you left in your apartment after you went to work.
What's the big deal? What's so tough about that?"

"Kevin," John said, "I was in the man's company every day
when all this was supposed to have taken place. It won't wash."

"We'll see," McQuaid said, watching Devlin. A movement
of Levine's eyes told Devlin to get out of the car.

"I'll be in touch," Devlin said.

Devlin stepped out and walked up the empty, echoing street
to the parking lot. The bomb squad was packing up to leave.
The rear seat of the car was still pulled out of its moorings.
No point in thinking about the rest of the mess. Sal was going
to get a lesson in what happens to a car suspected of seques-
tering an explosive device.

"Next time, call triple A," somebody yelled. Devlin flashed
his shield. The way the guy said, "Oh!" told Devlin they

hadn't known it was a cop's car. Would they have gone easier on it? The keys could be seen in the ignition. The contents of the glove box were on the floor in front of the passenger seat. What else had they done? Devlin decided he was going to have to have Sal check the engine mounts.

He hadn't reached Liz Becker in two tries: Liz was a night owl who much preferred the Italian restaurants on Queens Boulevard around Borough Hall to going home. He had already called the Brennan residence, leaving a message with some temporary factotum. When he'd asked about Maryellen, the young woman didn't know who he was talking about. Devlin wanted to check his apartment before he did anything else. He had told Eileen to keep her door double-locked. He would let himself in.

With the car rattling like a pickup truck full of skate keys, Devlin took only twenty minutes to get to Sunnyside. He had lost track of the number of trips back and forth he had made today. He double-parked in front of his apartment building and retrieved his mail before going upstairs, trying to settle down inside himself.

Wait a minute! Wake up! Suppose somebody was inside the apartment? Was Devlin supposed to draw his gun now? Suppose the somebody was Sal, having been delayed, or his Bolivian kid, ditto, or even Eileen, checking to see that only his car keys had been taken? Devlin almost cursed aloud, but then remembered that someone might hear him. A wrong someone . . . *Shit!* This was not the time or the place for him to prove he was more than a paper-target marksman!

For the first time in years—the first time ever, off-duty—he entered an apartment with his gun drawn.

Nobody. The place was empty. And nothing had been taken, not even the car keys. On the answering machine, almost a dozen messages, most of them from the *News*, *Post*, and Channel 11: *Please call. Please call.* He nearly missed the one real call. "Major here, Devlin. Call me." Major—how far Devlin was from his real life. The man had called him this morning, and Devlin had forgotten all about it. The clock said the time was just after two. He called Eileen anyway.

And woke her up. "What?"

"It's me. Are you all right?"

"Waitin' for you. What is it? What's wrong?"

"What time tonight did that guy come around for the car keys?"

"Before eight, why?"

"It looks like he never got here. I have the car fixed—that's not the problem. I'm coming right up there."

He hung up. He put together a complete change of clothes, shirt, underwear, socks—everything. He had half his clothes at her place, but suddenly he felt he had to demonstrate to himself that he was in charge of his life, that he would have clean underwear in the morning. His mother would be laughing out loud. Was his head spinning? At least he was thinking that he didn't want Eileen to see the scrapes on his hands and knees. That could wait. He would undress in the dark tonight. . . .

At the beginning of the day, when he'd gotten the first idea about the trouble he was in, Devlin had thought about booze, about the absolute necessity for keeping straight in his mind why he would reach for booze in a situation like this. *At the first sign of stress,* the commercials said. Now he was thinking of the long-term, heavy consequences of this sort of bone-twisting nightmare. From his apartment to Eileen's was a gauntlet of Irish saloons that could only remind him of what he had done to himself in the past. He wasn't interested in having a drink now, not at all. He knew exactly what steps he would have to take to get him in front of a bottle as big and bright as a box office: he would have to begin to worry about who was doing this to him and why, grieve over it, worry about what was coming next and what the consequences of that would be, closing his mind to everything in his life but what was wrong with it. The thing that was wrong, that could grow and finally overwhelm him—what did it have to be? How big? Only as big as the awareness that his enemies, whoever they were, *thought* he had a weakness. . . .

All ancient history—*that's* what he had to remember, and not just to stay sober, either. The people who were working against him didn't know the man he was today. A.A. had gotten Devlin sober, everybody knew that. Devlin had continued to change, grow, and develop. *That* was what somebody out there didn't understand about Frank Devlin today: he had the depth and perspective to stay on top of his life.

His *normal* life. Devlin wanted to remember that.

Liz Becker—Liz Becker *Weinstein*—lived only a couple of blocks from Devlin's apartment, at Fiftieth Avenue at Forty-fourth Street, one of the last spots in Sunnyside where mature trees stood at the curbside; Saint Theresa's R.C. Church across the street probably had something to do with that. It was possible that Liz could be awake at this hour. From behind the wheel of his car, it took him a moment to find her window, and to see that she was still up.

And then, as he watched, the light went out. He hadn't forgotten that she wanted him to call her from a safe telephone. Eileen's wasn't; he had learned that today. Liz was on her way to bed, if his memory of her nightly routine had any validity. He'd have to go to a bar to call her, and by then she might be asleep. He didn't want trouble. Even in this situation, she might slam the telephone down. No matter what, he was going to have to wait another day to find out what she wanted to tell him. Both Joe and Jack Brennan had done tours in the Queens County District Attorney's office, but they had been gone for years before Liz's arrival. So what did she know? Why had she gone out of her way to slip a note under his door? She did know one thing: that people really were listening to him. That was enough. *Oh, yes.*

He double-parked the car, locked it, and entered the building. The vestibule smelled of urine and the brass cover of the intercom was torn loose on the right side. Half the nameplates were missing. As a kid Devlin had gone from one building like this to another, in costume, on Thanksgiving morning, begging for pennies. Memory: his index finger reached out toward the bell labeled WEINSTEIN. He had not been here in more than five years, and somehow he remembered. He pressed a second time.

"Who is it?"

"Frank Devlin, Liz."

She hesitated. "What college did you go to?"

"CCNY, for one year."

He heard the buzzer that signaled the unlocking of the inner door.

She didn't unlock the door until she'd eyed him carefully through the peephole. "At this hour, I don't know whether I'm glad you got my message or not, Frank." Her eyes went up and down. "You look well."

"Thank you." She didn't. She was in a bathrobe, of course, and her hair was undone. She looked smaller and more round-shouldered than he remembered, as well as more gray. He had gray hair, too, but he wanted to think that he had not aged so badly. *Insane!* He knew that he did not care for this woman, or even want to be in her company, but he also told himself that he did not wish her ill. So why was he gloating? Death did not call only on those who seemed older. Maybe it was just his too human way of dealing with his own fear. He stepped into the apartment, which smelled almost suffocatingly of cats and their shit. "A couple of things happened today that made me want to find out why you wanted me to call you on a safe line."

"Let me close the door. To tell you the truth, Frank, for the past several days I've been worried like hell about you. What the fuck is going on?"

The apartment was unchanged in the years since he had seen it last, the walls dirtier, the furniture even more threadbare. Some of the stuff in here went back to the forties, or even earlier, and the paint job could be twenty years old. She just didn't care. In his life Devlin had met a lot of people who were like her in that regard. A cat jumped off the couch and trotted quickly into the bedroom. "Tell me what you know."

"Figured . . . I knew I'd have to tell you first. Do you want some coffee?"

"Decaf." How old was she now, forty? Forty-one? He'd known her first as the younger sister of a kid in his grammar school class. After Jim Brennan threw him out of the rich life,

Devlin found her working as a public defender in Manhattan Criminal Court. Still under thirty, idealistic, trim, straight, and full of ambition, she told him he'd been a hero to her since childhood, even more after he'd become part of the Brennan clan. He was still in his downspin, and maybe it was all very romantic to her, but somehow something ignited between them. He was still thinking of Maryellen every day, sick over her, determined to prove something to himself. In the end the booze made him nasty, abusive, maybe even sadistic, and Liz left him, hung up on him when he called, threatened to get a restraining order if he didn't leave her alone. When he saw her again, almost a decade later, after his mother was dead and his father was in a tailspin of his own, Liz had been married and divorced. Devlin saw a panic in her and thought he owed her something from their previous go-around. Wrong on both counts. In 1979, '80, and '81 he saw something that had been hidden before, undeveloped, ugly, unstable. Whether he wanted to admit it or not, he and Liz had shared their lives perhaps as best as they had been able. A drunk and a screwball, out of sync with each other. Until he read her note this morning, Devlin had assumed he was never going to see this woman again. Done . . . Finished . . . And looking at her, he knew that that was still in the bottom of his heart, truly—that, and his sad dread, which he felt to be akin to walking into a funeral parlor to view the corpse of a friend.

"I had a call about you last week from the FBI. They wanted to know what I knew about you."

"When was this?"

"Thursday. I think they believed what I said. God knows where they got my name. When did we go out, 1980?"

She knew better. He decided to ignore her. "Details, kid. What kind of questions did they ask you?"

"Boy, that's cold."

He sighed. "I don't mean to be. I have a lot on my mind."

"The feds wanted me to tell them about you. They wanted to know how we met. Since we live in the same neighborhood and, except for intervals, always have, I told them more or less the truth, that I had known you since grade school. I didn't tell them about anything between us before 1980. That earlier stuff is something else.''

''Why did you do that?''

''I don't know. What difference does it make? I told them you made no secret to me about being A.A., that I'd never seen you take a drink, and that fairly frequently you helped other people. They asked me if you were a secretive person, and I said no more than the next cop.

''Then they asked about Joe Brennan. They wanted to know if you had ever mentioned Joe's death. I remembered what you told me back when we were seeing each other. I told the FBI that you knew what you did because you called the Brennans after Joe's death, and the person who talked to you gave you the story.''

She hadn't told them about their connection in the early seventies because he'd been a drunk and that cast her in a poor light. He knew all her tricks—how easily he remembered! She put the decaf down on the table in front of him, and he pretended to sip at it. The FBI had wanted to know if Devlin had some kind of inordinate interest in the Brennans six years ago, almost ten years after the finish. Maybe they knew something he didn't know.

''Anything else?''

''They asked me when I'd seen you last. I told them the truth, four years ago.''

''When was that?''

''On Greenpoint Avenue, across the street from Kingdom Hall, formerly the Bliss Theater.''

''I don't remember that at all.''

''You're getting old, Devlin.''

''I guess so.'' He stood up, taking his cup and saucer with him. The cup was still full. ''Have you heard from the feds since last Thursday?''

''No, but on Monday, before Jack Brennan was shot, one of the men in my office who knows you and I dated came in while I was at my desk and closed the door behind him—and asked what I knew about what Brennan was going to do when he got into the Senate. I said I wasn't aware I was on the inside. Right, so he told the story he wanted to tell in the first place. Brennan was going to kick off the campaign with the promise to introduce a series of anticrime bills that would make organized crime an international issue, among other things. Naturally it sounded familiar—what you told me years ago about Joe Brennan clicked into my mind a moment before this guy in my office asked me if you could be on some 'secret team' that Jack Brennan had put together over the years. So there—there you are. That's the story, Jerry.''

She was still saying that—the television commercial had stopped running almost fifteen years ago. Devlin's realization about his mother's speech mannerisms had come when his mother had been the same age as Liz was now. Rubbing his eyes, he said, ''For what it's worth, I've had nothing to do with the Brennans for fifteen years. You put the note under my door because you thought my phone was tapped?''

''Was that too self-serving for you?''

She still wanted to fight. Once she'd started fighting with him in '80 and '81, nothing had stopped her, telephones slammed down, doorbells not answered. The torment had dragged on for months. Now, as if the years had not passed, he reminded himself to go slow. ''I'm grateful for all this information. All I'm doing is absorbing it aloud. After the FBI and Monday's conversation with your colleague, in your professional opinion, you thought a tap was likely.''

''Not unlikely.'' She laughed.

''Spoken like a real lawyer.''

''So? All this notwithstanding, how are you?''

''I'm well. Tired right now. I have to go. Thanks for opening the door. And the decaf.''

''You're very defensive. Is it because of what's happening? Or because of me?''

''Right the first time. I don't know anything about Jack Brennan's murder. I found it waiting for me when I came home last night.'' On the answering machine. FBI tap or not, somebody had broken into his apartment this morning and stolen the message tape. He had to start worrying about whether these people were going to let him live. He swallowed. "Maybe we ought to catch up with each other. How are *you*, for Christ's sake? How are you doing?"

"I'm all right. My mother has diabetes. I just hope she doesn't have too many complications before she runs out of gas completely. There's nobody really special in my life—you know, a couple of things that didn't last long. I'm beyond mellow, Devlin. I just don't give a shit anymore. New people bore me. I went to a shrink for a while, but he didn't help. I don't really want to change my life, anyway. I've got a couple of old regulars, good friends . . ."

She trailed off, perhaps because she remembered using the same language to describe her life back in 1979—and again in '81, at the start of their last reconciliation. He put his cup on the table. "Walk me to the door. Call the FBI and tell them I called you and said that I want you to know I'm not involved."

"Why would you do that? Why would you call me?"

"Tell them that's what you asked me, and I said that I re-membered how interested you were in the Brennans and that I knew—"

"Oh, that makes you look guilty as hell, Devlin. Out of the clear blue?"

He saw that he didn't really mean any of it. He was just trying to close the conversation and get the hell out of there. "Do whatever you want. I'd like to get their reaction now, after the killing. They talked to you *before*, and that I don't understand."

She rubbed his arm in a familiar way. "Go home. You'll feel better in the morning."

"Thanks again."

He heard the locks turn behind him and found the elevator waiting where he had left it. What could he believe? Even five years ago, she had been so concerned with her career and reputation that she had thought twice about the people she had coffee with. *Go home.* Did that mean someone would be com-ing for him? Maybe he *was* tired. Heading the other way up Fiftieth Avenue, he burned rubber on the asphalt. Liz must have heard it. In the confusion between them, what did she think it meant?

Eileen opened the door before Devlin could remove his key from the lock. She pulled him by the sleeve quickly over the threshold. Their lips brushed and he could smell a new perfume on her soft, slender neck, another new perfume, sweet, mild, and clear.

"No British patrols out there," he said.

"Don't be smart." She locked the door again. Her light cotton gown was unbuttoned, and she was nude underneath. "Are you all right?"

"I feel like I'm a hundred years old."

"You look only seventy-five. Inside. Get undressed, brush your teeth, and into bed. The weather says it's going to rain tomorrow, and gettin' wet is all you need after a day like this." She pushed him toward the bedroom, pausing along the way to extinguish lights. "You were terrible to live with when you had the flu last November."

He looked at her. She had overdone the teasing. She turned away, hiding her eyes, but he could see the color coming to her cheeks. *Only foolin'*, she usually said at this point, but now she was quiet.

She raised her eyes to him. They were filling with tears. "At half eleven I turned off the news, and fears I thought I'd put behind me came up again. I realized I was waiting for the ground to thump, as it does when a bomb goes off, or the little *pop pop* of pistol shots in the next street. I won't let you down, I'm just sayin'—"

"I know, it was the last thing I was worried about." He told her about the bomb squad searching his car. And about falling in the subway station. And finally about what Levine had found on Devlin's telephone bills, and what Cummings's call here Monday evening said about the privacy, or lack of it, on her line. "Tell me you'll be careful," he said.

"Yes, I will. And you have no idea what this is about?"

"None. Just that it's been in the works—"

"Don't bother to tell me. I'll be careful. Come to bed. Can you forget about this awhile? All that worries me is how you're dealin' with this. You wouldn't hurt a fly. I worry about that as well."

''You're different? We're a pair to draw to, we are. On the other hand, I don't like being fucked with. I'm still in too much shock to feel angry.''

''I was having the same thoughts this afternoon. I thought, If someone's having us on, I'm going to haul him before God.''

''Loncaric wants six more months,'' Devlin said.

''I thought it would be somethin' like that. My father is just going to have to accept our situation. I'll write him a letter. I'll telephone him first and tell him it's coming. I wanted to please him, but he'll have to be realistic. More and more, I want to have a child. I don't want to live the rest of me life without one. My father won't withhold himself. I won't let him.''

A moment later, when Devlin came out of the bathroom, Eileen sat up in the bed and reached for him. He pulled her close and buried his face in her shoulder, thinking that she was always ahead of him. He wanted to tell her, but she was already kissing his ear, tickling him deliberately.

''You have to pay attention, or this doesn't work.''

He laughed, and she giggled when he kissed her, lying back again and pulling him down on top of her. Their minds were working alike. She arched her back, languid as a cat, and ran her hand up through his hair. Being together was only as real as they wanted it to be. He stroked her ribs, she turned her dark eyes up to his, and stroked his cheek with her fingertips. ''I love you, you know,'' she said.

He loved *her*. On the night they met, they sat in her kitchen talking over coffee until four A.M. He told her the story of his life more honestly than he had ever tried before. He liked her and wanted to see her again, but after more than two years of womanlessness, he wasn't sure he could function. He told her that, too.

''Well, if it's any comfort to you,'' she answered, ''I've already decided to be faithful to you. But it's not for you that I'm doin' it, it's for me. I have to do what's right for me. Do you understand I'm a changed person, too? I left Ireland because I saw that I couldn't be happy there, with all its hatred and divisiveness. I can't live with things stirred up all the time, and I'm not talking about bombs going off at the end of the street. With your Maryellen and that Liz Becker, from what you've told me, I hope you've gotten your lifetime's supply of uproar.''

He was staring at her, wondering what he had done to deserve a living, breathing miracle like her.

''Well? Can you say it? That you've had enough?'' He grinned like a kid. He could feel decades lifting from his shoulders.

''Yes.''

6:25 A.M. . . .

WHEN HE AWAKENED, HE FOUND LIZ BECKER IN HIS thoughts. The telephone . . . He had it by the third ring. He could hear Eileen in the shower.

''Hello.''

''Alley oop,'' John Lord said. ''Rise and shine. I just talked to Kevin McQuaid. He isn't so sure that you were involved in the Brennan killing anymore.''

''That's what he tells you.''

''No, there's a reason for a change of mind. He thinks they have the Quinns. Small-caliber holes in their heads. Their bodies were found a couple of hours ago out on New York Boulevard, near Kennedy Airport, in the kind of car you saw parked outside the Lake Tranquility address. Orange Pontiac. No identification on the bodies, but a TWA airline ticket envelope like the one you described was under the seat. Kevin would like you to come in and positively identify them.''

''I'd like Levine to tell me that.''

''Kevin and I had that conversation, too. Levine isn't due

to meet Torres until ten o'clock. You can be in and out of the morgue long before. Kevin gave me his word, Frank. I'm valuable to him.''

The bathroom door opened and Eileen, in a bra and half-slip, made coffee-sipping motions. Devlin was supposed to have made the coffee. He was also supposed to have squeezed the oranges and scrambled the eggs. He put his hand over the mouthpiece and whispered, ''John. I haven't started breakfast yet.'' As she reached around to pinch his nose, he grabbed her fingers, love-bit them, and pulled her into his lap.

''Am I interrupting anything?'' John asked.

''The lady wants her coffee and I've been talking to you.''

''Don't give me that. I woke you up.''

Eileen whispered, ''Will you have some toast? Do you have time to eat?''

''Sure. John, you heard. I'll see you on Fifth Street.''

''No, I'll see you up at Bellevue. I want to be there when you see Kevin.''

''What for?'' Devlin let Eileen slip out of his arms.

''I'm looking out for you, schmuck. I want Kevin to see how important you are to me.''

''I thought I wasn't a suspect . . .''

''In Kevin's book, *everybody's* a suspect. He told me once that he'd frisk the Pope for silverware. When I asked him why, he said he knew what was in his own heart. Kevin's on duty all the time.''

''As long as he doesn't discover the idea that relief is just a swallow away.''

''Four packs a day,'' John said. ''Cigarettes are already rotting Kevin's gums.'' John hung up.

Eileen came into the bathroom while Devlin was still drying himself.

''You must be moanin' inside with scrapes as deep as those.''

''All that's bothering me physically is that I haven't had a chance to do my exercises since Sunday.''

''Missing a day or two won't hurt you. Are you going to drive me into the city?''

''Do you want to go in so early?''

"I want to call me father. It'll be teatime over there. People asked a lot of questions yesterday, and I didn't get any work done. My boss wanted to know if you had been working with Jack Brennan. Can you believe it?"

The same story Liz Becker had told him. Eileen's boss was a corporate attorney just back from a business trip to China. Eileen made close to fifty thousand a year, more than Devlin. "Tell him I haven't had any contact with any of the Brennans in fifteen years."

"I know that. He heard some story at lunch—"

"That's what I want to know. Where did he have lunch? And with whom?"

"The Four Seasons. With other lawyers." A-list gossip. Where did the alleged top people pick up such stuff? Everybody loved mystery and intrigue; everybody would stretch disbelief for a really juicy rumor. Who had the ears of high-living corporate lawyers? Norberto Torres liked to be seen at the Four Seasons. The story was wonderful propaganda, hinting of mystery and ancient plots.

"Do pass along what I said, okay?"

"Yes," she said. "I'll tell him to straighten out his mates, too. People can be very childish in these matters. I've seen it before."

"Your mind is working on this."

"Oh, yes. It won't do any good simply to react without thinking."

Now he remembered the young Hispanic who had showed up here last night. "Eileen, there are wheels still turning here, to paraphrase John. It may be necessary for both of us to avoid familiar haunts for a while. I know you'd prefer to stay at the cousin's in Bayside, but you might be safer at John's place."

"What about you?"

"Me, too."

"And you want to leave it like that? You're not going to tell me more?"

"I don't know that I have any more to tell, except for childish rumors."

"Let me think about it. I don't want John giving up his bed for us unless we have good reason."

He thought of her waiting for bombs at the end of the street, or pistol shots in the next street over. It was unimaginable to him, but the fact was that she had lived it for many, many years before quitting and deciding to carve out her own life—with Frank Devlin, as it had turned out. Her presence honored him; her conduct just now had only given him another reason to think of it.

Devlin knew the shortcuts down to the Fifty-ninth Street Bridge, Fiftieth Avenue down past Vandam Street, picking up the upper ramp on the Thompson Avenue Bridge. The sky looked like it was building up to a day-long rain. The harder, the better, as far as Devlin was concerned; anything to keep the suckers indoors.

The upper ramp exited north of the bridge, on a west-bound street. Eileen's office was in midtown. Devlin headed down Park, made one round-the-block loop, and let her out in front of her office. Almost two hours early. Any other day, Devlin would park the car, put his "Police" card on the dashboard, and have breakfast with her. There was no place in her office where they could make love—in the morning. One evening he tagged her on a desk, like a kid. She laughed about it for weeks afterward.

"I'm sorry . . ." he said suddenly.

"I can see how unhappy you are. We will get through this—*we*. Do you hear me?"

"Of course. I was thinking of something else: John's place. Maybe you ought to go up there after work tonight."

"I'll need fresh clothes."

"Make a list, we'll get them for you."

"That does seem to get the unhappiness out of your eyes. All right, I'll do it." She kissed him. "We'll talk later."

He looked unhappy? *Threatened* was really the word. Why chained dogs go wild when approached. He wanted to keep Eileen as far from this as he could. "Look, I do want you to be careful."

"I will be, I promise." She put her arm around his neck and kissed him again.

At Bellevue, Kevin McQuaid and John were waiting for him in the vestibule. "The shit we had to go through to get these stiffs over here," McQuaid said, leading the way inside. "I don't want anybody in Queens touching this case. The whole fucking borough is rotten from the top to the bottom, and I don't trust anybody out there."

Behind McQuaid's back, John smiled. They were approaching Gerrity, standing at a desk, talking on the telephone. He gave Devlin a nod.

"This was a mob hit," McQuaid said, walking quickly. "Small-caliber weapon fired from behind the head. Devlin, yesterday you described a guy, a car, *and* an airline ticket. If he ran that show for you out in Jersey, we're going to have one hell of a fucking time finding out who hired him. Perfect. Seamless."

Gerrity caught up with them. "That was the chief," he said to McQuaid. "Let's go take a look at the bodies and then I'll tell you what he said."

They still had the Quinns in the hall, clothed, on their backs. His eyes were open, peaceful—and stupid. Her head was turned toward the wall.

"Is that him?" McQuaid asked.

"That's him," Devlin said.

"How about her?"

Devlin took Mrs. Quinn's head by the jawbone and turned it to him. "This is her. Shit. I can find that clinic we took him to, I'm sure I can."

"That won't be necessary, Frank," Gerrity said. He looked to McQuaid. "The chief is completely satisfied about Devlin. He wants us to let him in on what else we know."

"What's the point of that?" McQuaid asked.

"The chief has the idea that Devlin knows something that he doesn't think is important. Or he needs his memory stimulated."

McQuaid curled his lip. "At his age, more than his memory."

"Start," Gerrity said to him.

"All right." He turned to Devlin. "Lopez talked. To me, here, before we took him down to the Tombs. He was high and trying to be cute, but he was cracking. He was beginning to think he had to buy time. He said cops put him up to it. I asked him what cops, and he said, 'Cops.' That don't help you, Devlin. He was your snitch, and as soon as he said that much, he was killed, and you were present. Will you excuse me if I don't personally let you off the hook?"

"You've made your point, Kevin," John said evenly.

"Lopez was *my* prisoner!"

"Right," Gerrity muttered.

McQuaid pointed at Devlin. "And you knew Antonucci in high school . . ."

"I didn't know him. I couldn't place him even after I was told his name. He looked familiar, that's all. I don't remember ever having anything to do with the guy."

"Tell him the other thing," Gerrity said.

"Brennan had set up his fall campaign. He was going to promise to get tough on organized crime. He was going to pick up where his brother Joe left off. His brother Joe never got any farther than the Queens D.A.'s office, did he? So what did that mean?"

"Maybe Jack Brennan was going to make his brother out to be a martyr. Their father is tough enough to pull that kind of thing. I don't know about Jack from my own experience, but given what I saw Monday night, I wouldn't put anything past him."

"What do you mean by that?" McQuaid demanded.

"The marks on his body, for Christ's sake! Did *that* give him his thrill? Maybe getting beaten was screwed up in Jack's mind with his brother's death. I don't have any way of knowing. I haven't had any contact with these people since 1971."

McQuaid rocked on his heels, his chin drawn into his neck. He looked like a rooster. Devlin was wondering if what he had just heard from Eileen about her boss, and what Liz had told him last night, had any connection to this stuff about Brennan's campaign. People got things mixed up all the time. It was when the wrong people got things mixed up that trouble started. Had that happened? Devlin had to talk to Sal about last night. What else? Who else did he want to talk to?

McQuaid let out a deep breath. "All right. Shit." He shook his head. "Devlin, you stay in touch. If you can't keep your dick out of a wringer, send us a postcard from the track."

"You're working too hard," Devlin said, and turned away.

It had started to rain. Devlin motioned John to his car. The overcast had turned the daylight into nightfall; lights gleamed across the wet pavement everywhere. John winced when he saw the interior of the car.

"A certifiable mess. Any real damage?"

"I don't give a shit. I just don't want to leave my socks with my feet still in them. Look, you're amused by your friend McQuaid. I'm not."

"I want to see what else he has on Lopez and Antonucci. Details, especially on Antonucci. Antonucci had a real life. Your telephone records show calls to a real telephone, in a real apartment."

"It's been torn to pieces by now."

"I'm going to see what I can do," John said.

"Ask about the girl, too. Jane Milburn. She had a roommate, Susan Michaels. This conspiracy goes back a long way. Maybe Milburn said something to the roommate that means more to me than it would to McQuaid."

"Are you buying that idea now?"

Devlin was thinking again of Liz's story and what Eileen had told him about her boss. "Many years ago, Joe Brennan and I had a series of conversations about going after the Mafia. At that age, we were in love with the sound of our own voices. Jack sat in on a couple of those sessions—drinking sessions, really. Drinking and chasing girls."

"You were married to their sister at the time, weren't you?"

"If I wasn't, I was about to be. I tell myself I was a different person. I was. I remember almost nothing about those conversations with Joe, and by the time he started to make *his* political move, in the seventies, I hadn't had any contact with the Brennans for years. I've got to check a few things. If you have to go out, leave a number where I can reach you. I'm going to ask you to put Eileen and me up for a couple of days.''

"No problem." John looked like he was having trouble digesting what he had just learned about his older partner's past. Was it such a surprise? If so, maybe Devlin had grown up a little. But talking with Joe Brennan twenty years ago about smashing crime, for God's sake! Who would think that important? Was it even possible?

Devlin took John around the corner to his old Dodge Dart and then headed uptown. He had to make some more calls. Another item that had fallen away with the collapse of New York's standard of living: telephone booths, with seats, lights, and real doors. Near Fortieth Street he found a coffee shop with the telephone in the window, where he could watch his double-parked car.

Sal's line was busy. The time was now 9:15. The rain came down steadily, a dark all-day rain, no doubt about it. But at last he had an idea. His car had stalled a lane of traffic all the way back across the intersection behind it. People could wait. Sal liked to tell a customer exactly what was wrong with his car even when the customer obviously didn't understand a word Sal was saying. On impulse, Devlin called Eileen.

"What is it? Are you all right?"

"Sure. I just wanted to hear your voice."

"Well, you wanted it, now you can listen carefully. It says in the paper that the funeral's at St. Pat's tomorrow. A private burial in the New Calvary. Donations go to the New York Foundling Home instead of flowers. How much are you going to send?"

"I called last night and left a message."

"How much are you going to send?"

"How much am I going to send?" he repeated.

"Yes. Are you going to write a letter to your wife and tell her how sorry you are?"

"I did last time. I never heard from her."

"I know, you told me. All the more reason to try again."

One of those rare occasions when a letter was delivered overnight. Jim Brennan intercepted the letter: when Devlin called, Brennan's man was ready with the language to tell him to stay away. Devlin's A.A. sponsor, Bill Ward, was dead, and Devlin went to three and four meetings a day for weeks until he slipped into the rhythm, again, of one step at a time. Now Devlin realized he had forgotten how close he had come to a slip that time.

Eileen said, "I'll probably go to Mass this noon, so don't be surprised if I'm late gettin' back."

Eileen prayed for the sick and dying. She visited them, too. And wept later. Part of life, she said. Once Devlin saw that Eileen's attention to what she thought was right in the eyes of God actually made her feel good, he tried to see it in terms of Eastern systems of thought, which worked because their practitioners believed them deeply. Devlin now took Eileen's way to be as valid as Buddha's, and he knew from experience that if she told him to donate to orphans, it would make him happy, no matter what he believed at the moment.

"Thanks," he said.

"What for?"

"Your understanding, for one thing."

"And being too busy to worry about, for another. I have to work." She was gone.

Devlin tried Sal's number again, and this time the line was clear. Out on First Avenue, a patrol car, lights boiling, rolled up behind the Seville. A young black cop got out from behind the wheel and took a quick look around, then ducked back into the car again. Sal's phone rang for the third time. A fourth. A horn blew twice, maybe the patrol car's. Devlin put his shield up against the coffee shop window, but the distance and the rain made it impossible for the young cop to see. Devlin drifted . . . What was rattling in the back of his mind? He waved his shield to one of the three young women waiting for coffee to go.

"When a guy answers, tell him to hold on. Police business."

Her teeth showed, and she wanted to back away. Devlin wrapped her fingers around the handset.

"If this works out, you'll get a commendation, I promise you."

She glanced at her friend. Devlin was out the door, into the rain, running to the patrol car. The young cop rolled down his window. He saw the shield.

"That's really a terrible place to park, man."

"The Brennan case. I'll be out of here after this next phone call."

"Get out of the traffic first." He hit the siren a *whoop*! and pulled away. In the coffee shop, the girl was still holding the handset. Devlin could hear the continued ringing as he got close.

"No answer."

"Thanks." Devlin hung up, suddenly remembering Major. Major had called him again last night. Major picked up on the first ring, and Devlin identified himself.

"Gotta talk to you," Major said. "You know that new Greek joint on the north side of Queens Boulevard? On the other side of Forty-third from the Center Theater? Can you meet me? I sit in the back, in the last booth."

Devlin hesitated. Major had never done this before. Because Devlin never asked Major about his business, and vice versa, their conversation rarely exceeded the depth of passing the time of day. Never *gotta talk*. Never. "When?"

"Eleven o'clock. But you have to be on time. I have a business to run."

Devlin hung up slowly as a horn blew again. Traffic was lined up halfway to the next block. The horn blew another time, again triggering—a memory? Not that of the young cop a few minutes ago. Not even an image, actually. Devlin had to get going. He pumped another quarter into the wall box and dialed Levine's direct wire.

"Chief's line."

"This is Frank Devlin—"

"He just left, Devlin. Ten minutes ago. He and the commissioner are walking over to City Hall."

"Who am I talking to?"

"Vito Mariano."

Devlin waited, but Mariano wasn't going to say more. Another guy who considered Devlin a suspect? Now Devlin remembered what John Lord had said about Mariano's ambition—and, maybe, connections. *Innocent until proven guilty. Sure,* Devlin thought, *starring James Stewart.* "Do you have a way of reaching him over there?"

"Oh, yeah."

A perfect secretary—even Eileen would be impressed. Devlin looked at his watch again: not quite a quarter to ten. Levine had left his office at about nine-thirty to pick up the commissioner for a ten o'clock meeting with the mayor. Did that leave time to go over things before they faced Hamilton? Devlin could feel his curiosity rising; in his youth, curiosity had ruled his life. "How long do you think the meeting with the mayor will last?"

"Meetings with the mayor rarely last forty-five minutes," Mariano said.

Devlin remembered hearing that long ago. The mayor's attention wandered like a schoolboy's, and because he was the mayor, he didn't mind letting people know. He celebrated himself, only half facetiously offering himself as a political Leonardo, capable of curing AIDS with a daydream. Devlin realized that it was time to get moving. "Tell the chief I'll get back to him before noon."

Outside, traffic was tied up across three lanes. Behind the wheel, Devlin wiped rain from his eyelids, remembering that he was pointed north only because he had been looking for a damned telephone in the first place. A horn blew, and Devlin thought of the experience he'd just had in the coffee shop, that he'd wanted to tell himself something, something that was now even more out of reach. . . .

On the other side of the Fifty-ninth Street Bridge, at Queens Plaza, Devlin pulled into the old Q39 bus stop and went into the Dublin House to make another telephone call. Susan Michaels, Jane Milburn's roommate, was on Manhattan's Upper West Side—and certainly sick and tired of talking to police. Still another detective calling now might even raise her suspicions. How did Devlin feel? The humidity was making him sweat. After three rings, a young woman said hello.

"Susan Michaels?"

"Yes."

He was using an Irish accent. "My name is Michael Finn, and I'm a reporter for the *National Enquirer.* You know why I'm calling. I'll try to make it easy for you—"

"You don't know how much I've talked in the past thirty-six hours, Mr. Finn," she said. "I've got to go out to New Jersey this afternoon and I'm already late for the office. I really don't know what I can tell you . . .."

"And that's exactly the point, Miss Michaels," Devlin said smoothly. He hadn't pulled a stunt like this in years. "At the *Enquirer* we've learned that people often don't realize the importance of what they know, and need a little direction to bring it out."

"The police said the same thing yesterday."

"I'm not surprised." Devlin had only paraphrased what Levine had told him Monday night. "We consult the same authorities on interviewing. What I want to do is make a time when we can get together. And another thing: Even though the police must have searched your roommate's belongings, they may have missed something the *Enquirer* will pay you for—"

"I'm not interested in money," she said.

"On a story like this, we'll pay up to twenty-five thousand dollars."

"Oh."

"Oh, indeed! And if you stop and think, the police didn't search the whole apartment. As for what you can tell us, we can protect you."

"Let me have your telephone number. I want to think about this. She said things to me. I mean, she's dead, what difference would it make if the world found out she had an attitude?"

"Not the slightest."

"Right. You're nobody's fool, Mr. Finn. Maybe we can talk. Will you people pay me for just a straight interview?"

"I'll see what can be done." He gave her his home telephone number, thinking he didn't care if the message was intercepted, but then he thought again, quickly. "If you get my answering machine, which doesn't give my name, use the name Gail. We operate in a very crazy world."

"There's only one reality, and we all have to live in it," she said. "I'll talk to you later."

Devlin went out into the rain as a train rolled around the curve of the el toward Court Square. Susan Michaels was going to be one disappointed yuppie princess when she found out there wasn't going to be an *Enquirer* check at the end of her newly blooming rainbow. Devlin wanted to talk to Anita Brennan, too. He had never met the woman, and only God knew what she had heard about him over the years. Water poured from the car's rain gutter onto his knee as he slid behind the wheel. Could he trace Antonucci into his Gotti connections at this point? Probably not. Devlin knew people connected to Gotti, but he had not spoken to them in years. Probably they wouldn't want to talk to him. Antonucci's connections to them were thin, Octavio Lopez's nonexistent. The Quinns had gotten the classic kiss-off, their bodies left in a time-honored gangster dumping ground. That identified Lederer clearly enough. He could have covered his trail completely, but what connected Lederer to the case was only Devlin himself. No, there was the real estate man, who had rented Lederer the Lake Tranquility house, but a guy like him probably would develop brain damage when he saw what kind of people he was dealing with. In that context, the whole thing did make more sense with Devlin dead. Why not an accident on the subway? Why wasn't he dead already? Everything else had been so carefully choreographed that a misadventure made a certain ironic sense.

Why were things beginning to point to the grandiose conversations of three semiambitious young men, sipping the patriarch's cognac in a room large enough for them to play catch with a tennis ball? They had done that once, Devlin remembered clearly enough, but he couldn't remember another specific thing. For months, Joe had talked about the vulnerability of organized crime to the conspiracy statutes, that it would be easy enough to develop evidence, but Devlin could remember no more than that. He might have been bored. Or daydreaming about an intrigue. More likely, contemplating Maryellen's latest atrocity. Certainly he had been drunk. Perhaps not as drunk on those nights as some others, but drunk nevertheless. *No euphemisms*, Bill Ward had taught him. Drunk. Drunk is drunk. *Drunk!*

Heading up Queens Boulevard, still almost a half an hour early for his appointment with Major, Devlin felt a different kind of anxiety crawling into his belly, one he recognized so quickly that he shivered with the recognition: Liz. Their long and painful ending in 1981 had had the two of them hoping to the last minutes that they could work back to what had been a luminous, joyous beginning. Rebeginning. Devlin had lied to himself about her, he knew now. He had wanted love in his life just that much. He hadn't been able to face it, pursuing their early golden moments like a junkie chasing the dragon of the first wonderful high. Devlin knew that Liz had loved him probably as much, in her own way, as truly, as any woman ever had loved him. But Liz had no control over herself, never having been forced to look into her behavior as he had had to confront and accept his alcoholism. He'd told her as much as he had about the Brennans because of her badgering curiosity. With him, in too many ways, Liz Becker had been a dynamo of need, overpowering in her weakness. Even though he had known her for decades, it was not until his first days and nights alone again with her that he had seen how much like Maryellen she was. 1979. Older then, sober, Devlin had thought he could handle it.

As things turned out, the answer was, *No*.

11:03 A.M. . . .

T HE NEW GREEK JOINT WAS DECORATED IN BLOND WOOD-grain Formica and a wallpaper featuring giant tropical leaves. On a day like today, even with the hearty $4.95 Businessman's

Special steaming the windows, the place felt like a tree house for grownups where, if you listened creatively, the clink of flatware on the heavy china could sound like raindrops jarring a childhood dream. Today's Businessman's Special was pot roast with horseradish, beets, and mashed potatoes, and Devlin was almost tempted. Pot roast had been a staple of the Greek joints of Queens since Devlin had been a child. No Major, but that was okay. The law aside, a bookmaker was a much more important person in a New York neighborhood than a cop who only lived there and didn't cover the territory.

Inside himself, Devlin was gliding through a patch of smooth water, resisting interpreting events or the possibly imagined tone in Vito Mariano's voice. Devlin thought he remembered Major saying he sat in a booth in the rear, where a booth was empty, but Devlin chose to wait in the front of the restaurant near the window. If he took the booth now, the counterman would probably try to shoo him, forcing Devlin to say loud enough for others to hear: I'm waiting for Major. Major wouldn't like that; in fact, Major might even think Devlin was losing his grip.

With his palm Devlin wiped the window to watch for Major, and saw him right away, ten feet from the door and moving as fast as he could. With one-eyed guys Devlin always forgot which eye was real—*not* the one that looked normal, but the one that bulged out and constantly scanned the room like something from a science fiction movie. *That* was the real eye—and the one with which Major signaled Devlin to follow him to the back. Major was a big man, almost sixty, with a shock of gray-white hair; rain poured off his lightweight coat as he stomped to the rear.

The counterman shot an interested glance at Devlin, then relaxed when Major gave him a sign. "Coffee?" he asked. Devlin nodded. The counterman knew what Major wanted.

Major sat with his back to the rear wall, so he could watch the door. "Put your hand under the table. Reach. All right, put that in your pocket. It's all there, fourteen units."

Devlin had let it slip his mind. "Thanks. Why did you want to talk to me?"

Major sat back while the waitress put down two coffee cups.

"Can I get you boys anything else?"

Major shook her off. Devlin tried to avoid watching Major's real eye watching the waitress get her distance, but that was what Devlin did, and when Major leaned forward to talk, Devlin leaned, too, zooming in on the eye.

"Only because I know you so long," Major said. "Don't bring me into this crap you're in. Ever. I want to do you a favor, but you have to keep me out."

"Of course."

"This is serious."

"You have my word."

"Let me tell you about my business," Major said. "For all I know, even you don't know how it works. What I got here is like a franchise. When Cuomo said there's no Mafia, I almost broke a rib. Anyway, people want to get to me, they just have to ask. Six months ago, two guys came in here to ask me about you. Under the circumstances—who they were—I told them what I knew."

"Who were they?"

"From Brooklyn. Perfect gentlemen. They called in advance. They wanted me to tell them about you, how you bet, what I knew about your life. Hell, what I know wouldn't be hard to find out from a lot of people, Frank, people you don't even notice. Neighbors. Okay? I'm giving you the whole thing. These guys wanted to know all this stuff. Because they were so straight, and they weren't asking dangerous questions, I asked them if you had done anything. One of them had his hands flat on the table, and he just raised the tip of his index finger, like this, and said, 'I have no way of knowing. I was just told to do what I'm doing.' Okay. I believed him . . . you know, his tone. It was the kind of thing I didn't think I had to mention to you—that is, until yesterday morning."

"I appreciate what you're doing for me. How do you know they were from Brooklyn?"

"I said they called in advance. I couldn't talk to them and they left a number. I always save numbers—you never know, right?" Now he smiled goofily, his good eye wandering. "It's out in the car, under the el. I realized I left it there before I got halfway across the street, but I didn't want to go back in the rain. Brooklyn. I know all the exchanges. That one's in Bensonhurst, Flatbush, around there.''

"And how do you make them for being the real thing?"

"Oh, who they said put them onto me. You don't get to know his name. Knowing his name wouldn't do you any good. Take my word for it. It's a complicated business. Anyway, when I looked in the papers yesterday and saw your name—well, those guys didn't mention Brennan, and I had to ask myself if maybe it was significant by omission. You know, in retrospect.''

Devlin got it. *Conspicuous* by omission. "What did they look like? What do you remember?"

"Well-dressed. Manicured. This was last winter. I remember expensive overcoats. A black Eldo. Chances are, the guy they reported to reported to somebody else. That's the way things work. Nobody ever knows the whole story.''

This could be a real break. Time to play cop. "Get that phone number. I'm going to need it."

Major smiled. "In a minute. I want to get the chill out.'' He sipped his coffee.

"Now.''

Major didn't like it, sitting back for a moment and glaring, but then Devlin caught a movement in his brow—Major was realizing that Devlin was serious enough to forget their long friendship and turn himself into just another tough guy behind a shield. Devlin couldn't remember a time he had played tough with a pal. The taste was very unpleasant. But this was not a time for him to dwell on unpleasantnesses. People were trying to frame him, maybe trying to kill him, and he dared not cut *anybody* any slack.

Major stepped through the door, drawing his head down into his collar as he forced himself into the rain. Devlin had a couple of minutes, enough for him to use the telephone. He still had to talk to Sal. And Harry Levine would be back from the meeting with the mayor and Torres.

Devlin had to move quickly to get to the telephone before a woman coming in from outside reached it first. He thought of producing the shield and telling her he was on police business, but he—and Major—didn't need the attention. She muttered something and moved toward the counter. Sal's line rang. Devlin wiped the window again for something to do. With Sal you had to wait. Sometimes Sal was up to his elbows in a car's umbilicals and it took him eleven rings to wipe the grease from his hands. Even so, Sal's telephone was the color of the bilge in a Nigerian tanker.

Devlin was thinking about Lederer again. Lederer hadn't so much paid the Quinns the respect their position as saps deserved, or made the mistake of assuming that Devlin would not be around to be able to identify them, as simply had been lazy—lazy, nothing else, about wrapping up a loose end. As of last night, Brennan, his girlfriend, and their killer were dead; all, or more likely, almost all, of his employers' objectives had been gained, the links from the crimes back to their perpetrators broken—No, not all: there *was* Antonucci. Antonucci in custody. Antonucci was standing up, a man among men. What marvelous stuff he must have been told to make him put the steel of heroes in his spine! Now Sal picked up.

"Frank Devlin, Sal." The traffic lights on Queens Boulevard changed and cars began to stop. At least Major wasn't going to be out in the rain any longer than necessary. "What happened last night?"

"Oh, I'm sorry, Mr. Devlin. I ran too late up in the Bronx. Did you get my message? Do you still need me?"

"What do you mean, message? I didn't get any message."

"I called your place this morning."

"The kid came around and got the key last night."

"Your car key?"

"Come on, Sal." Major came into view, walking quickly under the stone aggregate structure of the el. Above him, a rain-soaked train rumbled toward the city, random cars livid with graffiti. The traffic rolled again and a truck blocked Devlin's view of Major. "Your kid came around to my girlfriend's place last night and picked up the key to my apartment."

"The hell! Just a minute." The mouthpiece on the other end was suddenly muffled. Outside in the rain, a white Lincoln turned under the el, the driver looking through his open window, back toward the restaurant. An expensive car with all the goodies, including a cellular telephone. U-turn. Sal came back. "Mr. Devlin? Jesus says he didn't go to your girlfriend's place last night. Look, is she saying he got wise with her?"

"No, no." Whoever had come to Eileen's door had not wanted access to Devlin's apartment. Somebody had gotten that months ago. So what had been accomplished?

Somebody had visually identified Eileen.

The white Lincoln was stopped under the el on Forty-fifth Street, U-turn completed, the driver still looking this way, squinting, the slanting rain pelting him in the face. Major was heading back to the Forty-third Street intersection, the piece of paper bearing the telephone number where Devlin could see it between thumb and forefinger of Major's right hand. Two guys looking for a parking spot so they can have lunch. An old guy is running an errand. And last night someone eye-balled Eileen—for what? Somebody wanted to *see* her?

Devlin had to get to her! And to John Lord, or Levine! "Sal, you're absolutely certain of this kid?"

"Oh, yeah, Mr. Devlin."

Now the white Lincoln burst through the red light and turned onto Queens Boulevard, its rear end fishtailing on the slick black asphalt. The driver gunned the car down the inside lane across Forty-fourth Street. As the car passed the restaurant, Devlin could see the passenger leaning across the driver toward the open window. Half a block in front of them, Major stepped up to the curb.

"Mr. Devlin?" Sal asked.

Devlin let the telephone drop as the Lincoln slowed as it approached Major. Devlin's mouth was hanging open. He knew it; he could feel the first surge of adrenaline roaring through his body.

"Hey!" he yelled.

He could feel people in the restaurant turn toward him. The Lincoln was in front of Major, at a crawl, as Devlin hit the sidewalk, skidding, almost losing his balance. An Asian couple was standing beside Major, looking toward the city.

"Hey!"

Major turned around just as a hole appeared in his cheek and blood flew out of the back of his head. Now the sound of the shots, two, *three*, of them. Somebody screamed as Major fell backward like a sack of cement, his head bouncing on the pavement. The Lincoln was already across the intersection, changing lanes to gain even more ground. Devlin hadn't seen a single number on the license plate.

He wasn't sure he had even thought of drawing his gun.

And he was better off for it, he thought at once. People were running across the boulevard as traffic immediately backed up and horns blew. The Asian woman was screaming. Devlin had been seen sitting with Major. This was not the time to be detained for questioning, not with Eileen unprotected. Why would anybody want her, except to get to him? Devlin moved with the gathering crowd, through the snarled traffic, toward Major's body, thinking of the telephone number now, the piece of paper that was his only lead to anything. Jane Milburn's roommate wasn't going to be able to unravel much even if Devlin was able to make his way back to Manhattan to see her. If Eileen was safe. Every cop in the city was going to be looking for him if someone tied him to *this* killing.

But he wasn't tied to it yet, and wouldn't be, if he just kept right on hoofing past the ten or so people gathering around Major and the shrieking Asian woman. From three car-lengths away Devlin could see that Major was more than a mess. Devlin could feel his blood thudding in his eardrums. In this rain, Major's piece of paper would not be far from the body. Devlin looked over his shoulder. People were coming out of the restaurant—but they were pouring out of other places, too. It was not going to be difficult to disappear in this confusion, if he kept his wits about him. Traffic in all directions was stopped, and horns were shrieking. All Devlin was sure of was that he was going to get the hell away from here and alert *somebody* about Eileen.

As he pushed through the last knot of people around Major, Devlin saw at once that Major's hand still clutched the piece of paper. In Major's left cheek was a hole the size of a dime.

Major's eyelashes fluttered under the gentle pummeling of raindrops. Somebody turned to Devlin. "You a doctor?"

"Yeah," Devlin said, averting his eyes a little. "Let me through."

He stood over the body. The rain was flooding Major's chest wounds and spreading diluted blood on his raincoat. Blood haloed out darkly from the back of his head across the concrete sidewalk. Maybe Major was still alive, but he certainly didn't look it. The shapeless bits of material, like soft cheese, floating in the scum on the pavement, were pieces of Major's brain.

"Are you going to give him mouth-to-mouth?"

Devlin got down on his haunches and picked up Major's wrist as if to take his pulse. He had his own fingers on the piece of paper when he heard the voice again.

"Are you going to give him mouth-to-mouth?"

Devlin palmed the paper as he rose and turned around. He was shaking so badly that he gripped the paper tighter to direct and dissipate some of his energy. The guy who had asked the question was in his forties, pear-shaped, unshaven, and balding, the kind of *shlub* that had been haunting New York neighborhoods all of Devlin's life.

"With that hole in the back of his head, mouth-to-mouth would only make him sound like a fucking tuba." He pushed past the guy and headed toward his car, which was parked on the south side of the boulevard.

"Hey, where are you going?"

"I'm going to call for emergency medical backup. He looks like he's beyond their equipment, but there's always a chance." Devlin wondered how his imagination was coming up with such stuff. A moment ago he had thought he was looking at two guys wanting to have lunch and an old guy trying to get back into a restaurant out in the rain. Now everything was crazy, but somehow Devlin was keeping pace. His car was on the south side of the boulevard, in front of the Chinese—or was it Korean?—joint that once had been Gildea's Bar and Grill. The one thing in view that remained the same from Devlin's youth was the Mobil station. Even the White Castle hamburger stand was larger. And big old Sunnyside

Garden, where the first televised wrestling had originated, had been torn down for a Burger King.

"Hey! Where the hell are you going?"

The *shlub* was pursuing him! Devlin wanted to move faster, but that would give him away. The guy grabbed at Devlin's sleeve, but Devlin pulled loose, still moving. Traffic on the south side was beginning to roll again, and Devlin was still half a block from his car.

"Hey! Wait a minute!" The guy grabbed him solidly now. "You screwed around with him back there! You're not a doctor!"

Devlin stepped in toward the guy and at the same time hooked his ankle. As the guy went buttdown on the wet asphalt, Devlin produced his shield. The guy's eyes went from the shield to Devlin, who pocketed the shield quickly and pointed to the guy, pointed to him while backing away—like a lion tamer in an animal act on the *Ed Sullivan Show*. And the guy sat still, staring at the pointed finger with the same dumb, big-eyed expression of an intimidated animal.

"FBI," Devlin said. "Got it? FBI."

The guy's lips almost formed the words. Good enough. A lot of people couldn't tell the difference between one law enforcement badge and another, and even if the guy became suspicious again, what he'd tell police was that Devlin had said FBI. It might buy time. Devlin didn't know if Major had been killed in front of his eyes as an artful touch or a matter of expediency. *An artful touch?*

He had to get Eileen to safety!

11:49 A.M. . . .

"**L**ORD."

"John, it's Frank. Look, I just tried Eileen. She took an early lunch—"

"Is this your neighbor we're talking about, Mr. Osborne? What about him?"

"What? Oh." Devlin was at an outdoor telephone under the el on Roosevelt Avenue at Sixty-first Street. Sal's repair shop was a couple of blocks away. And John Lord, at his own desk on Fifth Street, couldn't say aloud that he was talking to his partner. "You're talking to cops. They're looking for me."

"Of course, that's important, Mr. Osborne," John said. "Three-twenty-three East Fourth Street. That's an apartment house, so I have to know the floor, if you can tell."

John was making Mr. Osborne sound dumb enough to take a long time figuring out which floor. Devlin said, "Somebody just murdered my bookmaker in front of my eyes, and I'm concerned enough about Eileen to call you because you're closer to her than I am. Freer to move, too, even under your present circumstances."

"That helps. What *kind* of funny smell? Pleasant? Unpleasant? The Lower East Side is all about funny smells, Mr. Osborne."

"I don't think you can string it out any longer than this without them getting suspicious, John. Eileen is my first priority. See what you can do—please. I can't help myself in custody. What made me think that this wasn't going to get worse? Your telephones will be tapped after this. Mine's no good. Eileen's, too. *Don't* stick your neck out."

167

"I don't think your neighbor is dead, Mr. Osborne. A corpse doesn't smell 'kind of nice.' A corpse smells terrible. That's why we bury them. Thanks for calling."

And he hung up quickly, as if someone was moving to take the handset from him.

Maybe.

Devlin hurried back to the car, thinking that he was probably still a step or two ahead of Levine's people. Obviously Levine had lost his argument with the mayor and the commissioner, and so Devlin was to be today's headline. At the latest, tomorrow's.

He had an idea already, but first he had to get his car off the street.

1:22 P.M. . . .

SWEAT RAN INTO HIS EYES. DEVLIN WAS DRIVING SAL'S loaner, a 1964 Falcon with standard shift. The car was uncomfortable and clumsy, bulbous, with imprecise, toylike controls. The windshield was steaming up, not responding to the defroster, and the vent window allowed the rain to splash in on Devlin's lap. He had had to get out of Sal's garage, and as of two minutes ago, Father Steve Loncaric had not called back to say he was with Eileen or that the police were on their way to her office to take over.

Devlin was on his way to Susan Michael's apartment. She wasn't home, which was the way Devlin wanted it. Her interest in doing business with the supermarket press was all Devlin needed to believe she was wondering if she might actually have something to sell, something half remembered, something *tangible*. Devlin knew too much about the level of police science skills in the New York Police Department to imagine that detectives searching the apartment had gotten everything. He had heard of one young plainclothesman at a murder scene picking up the telephone before it had been dusted for prints. Another guy who liked to take his own pictures of corpses—a common enough perversion among cops—found one he couldn't photograph because of an overturned chair, so he righted the chair, took his picture, then turned the chair over again. The existence of a photograph that contradicted the official evidence came to the attention of the prosecutor at a late night dinner during the trial and the Heimlich maneuver was required to save his life.

Devlin took the Queensboro Bridge back into Manhattan. No toll-takers, nobody eyeballing him. The radio wasn't mentioning his name, but of course that didn't mean anything. If anybody listening to John Lord talking on the telephone had gotten wise to the identity of the caller, he might have been able to conceal his reaction even from John. And if that were the case, Devlin was going to have to be careful around John, too. *Jesus.* At least Devlin had the fourteen hundred Major had owed him. He was thinking he'd save it for a lawyer when he thought again about having to be careful around someone as close to him as John. If Devlin *really* couldn't trust John Lord, he'd be better off spending the money on a psychiatrist.

He had the Falcon's old AM radio turned to WCBS. The FBI had entered the Brennan case because the candidate's civil rights had been violated. Sure, Devlin thought, what had been on their minds in Liz Becker's office last week? With the N.Y.P.D. looking for Devlin, Liz was going to get an interesting response from the federals if she gave them Devlin's message. Not when, *if.* Devlin had seen early with Liz that she reminded him of Maryellen in many ways, and what he still did not understand about himself was why he had decided that she would be right for him anyway. In his time with Liz he had thought he had decoded all her gestures and intonations—so he could sort through the truth and lies like a grocer going over a basket of peaches—but when it was over, when he was so sick of her he couldn't even look at her, what buried it was the thought that he couldn't allow himself to believe anything she had ever said to him. *A liar.* If he talked to her again, he was going to have to listen very carefully to what she said. *Yes.* Devlin didn't believe he would have trouble remembering. . . .

Susan Michaels's apartment was on West Eighty-third, half-way between West End and Riverside Drive. From what she had said to Devlin, she didn't seem like the sort of young woman who would be scared out of a good apartment by the murder of a roommate. It might be a while, though, before she found some-one willing to rent the room of a murdered girl.

It was a pretty good building, too, the Turkish-bath tilework of the lobby relatively free of chips and cracks and the kind of grime that covered Sal's Falcon. Devlin pushed intercom but-tons until someone responded.

"Exterminator!"

The buzzer sounded and Devlin went in. Fourth floor. This part of town had been up, down, and back up again in Devlin's lifetime. You could find a spectacularly beautiful apartment behind the most dreary, paint-encrusted door. In the elevator Devlin tried to straighten his clothing, which was weighted with sweat. He wasn't going to pick the lock on Michaels's apartment door, he was going to use one of his passkeys. Dev-lin had been carrying passkeys since his first days as a cop—some of them had been his father's. "We had a guy break his fucking leg kicking in a door," the old man used to growl. "What's the point of that?"

The living room windows offered a broad view southward, the river a gray slab fading under gloomy veils of rain that looked painted on the air, sooty strokes that sagged even as Devlin drew his eyes away and closed the door. The place, darkened now, had been given a good working over, and Susan Michaels had not gotten around to even a few first steps to putting the place right, like closing doors and drawers. Books were in disarray on the shelves, clothing heaped over the back of the couch. In the kitchen, food covered every surface, cereal boxes crushed, jars and bottles opened and left that way. Open cupboards displayed appliances and serving bowls that were obviously out of place. Not so bad, Devlin was thinking. A really thorough police search could reduce an ex-con middle-weight contender to a sobbing heap, begging the cops to stop. The stove could be pulled out from the wall, for instance. This one had not, and the dust and grease of sixty or seventy years of all kinds of cooking was a wonderful place to hide photographs, or even a few documents.

No. The scraped palms of his hands didn't like the sharp metal edges of the back of the stove, but worse, his chest muscles, for all their recently developed strength, didn't like wrestling with a near immovable object.

In all, this search had been a good one. Someone had preceded Devlin through the freezer, ripping into the packages to be sure they really did contain peas, mixed vegetables, and Mrs. Paul's Frozen Fish Filets. The garbage had been emptied into the sink, and a serving spoon nearby looked as if it had been used to paw through the chicken bones and pizza crusts. Returning to the living room, Devlin had to half leap over a pile of LPs splashed behind the sofa. The pictures on the walls of the hall were askew, and the bedroom doorways facing each other gave glimpses of more chaos inside. In the right-hand room the mattress was square with the innerspring; Devlin took the other room to be Jane Milburn's.

Devlin snapped on the light and stepped over a pillow and a night table drawer into a pink, high-ceilinged cubicle that, at first glance, looked waist deep in clothing, bed linen, books, bottles, jars, slashed stuffed animals, and a few old, large pieces of furniture, a bedroom set in good condition, possibly a family heirloom. A few magazines were scattered about the mess like tomato slices garnishing a dinner salad, but Devlin could see no papers or personal books, like diaries, journals, or calendars. Levine's people had all of it. Many young women kept records of their escapades, and if Jane Milburn had been one of those diarists, Levine now had a record, bout-by-bout, of her affair with Jack Brennan. For Devlin, the idea was startlingly spooky. He remembered reading in the *Times's* announcements column that Jack had married Anita Walton Brokaw of New York, Newport, and Palm Beach, a graduate of Goucher college, working for Assisi Galleries on the East

Side—pretty fancy, for the son of an Irish mug who had put together his empire with his fists. 1975 or '76—Devlin could remember the new Mrs. Jack Brennan from her wedding photograph, a tall, slim, angular, startled-looking blond society type. Devlin remembered thinking at the time that she looked both opaque and uninteresting. Did that mean something now? At the time of his death, Jack Brennan had been into kinky sex. Why would the Jack Brennan Devlin remembered marry a sex problem so he could go out and develop one of his own? What Devlin remembered of Jack was that he was normal, maybe a little slow on the uptake, and that he was just as nuts about getting laid as his brother and brother-in-law.

Devlin supposed the search team had looked under the night tables. He grinned. He didn't know which old bull had taught him to do that, back at the start of his plainclothes career, but he did remember a time when the teaching came back to him, inappropriately, and his laughter had made his head ache, and that had made him only laugh louder. . . .

Drunk with Maryellen one summer weekend out at the Southampton place, the two of them alone. He was trying to live through his hangover on Sunday afternoon when he turned his head on the pillow, to the night table beside him, and suddenly wondered how he knew the table had been built in Chicago. Then a brain cell flickered: at some time during the night before—he had no way of knowing when—he had had his head under the table, face up, his eyes focused on the red label glued on the wood under the tabletop. How had he done it? He didn't know, and started to laugh. Maryellen had been in the same shape. . . .

And that had been one of their *happy* nights, Devlin thought as he got up from his hands and knees after checking the underside of the night table in Jane Milburn's room. He had to wipe his hands of the dust from the Milburn wall-to-wall. Knees, too, gently over yesterday's scrapes. Would the knowledge that Jane Milburn had not been especially clean sharpen the anguish of the former Anita Walton Brokaw? Was there a Milburn diary? The skin on the back of Devlin's neck crawled. Jack Brennan's most intimate behavior had occurred here. In the fifteen years since they had seen each other, Jack Brennan, like Devlin, seemed to have turned one hundred and eighty degrees. Devlin moved around the bed to the closet with care, almost convincing himself he could hear the passion of corpses. A sheet covered a table in the corner. The closet was empty, except for a few wire hangers and a clutter of shoes. Nothing on the shelf. Devlin stepped in, turned around, and checked the doorframe. Nothing at all.

He pulled the sheet off the table. Not a table, he saw, but a sewing machine. Devlin remembered his mother's, with a start-stop lever she operated with her knee. You opened the machine like a book, unfolding the top. What happened after that? You had to do something else to get the machine itself up and ready to sew. There was a trick to that part, he remembered; his mother had reached in and done—what? Forty years later, he still didn't know.

More to the point, how had the search team coped? Most automobile-oriented males couldn't operate dishwashers, washing machines, dryers—and sewing machines. Devlin wanted to try his luck. His skin was still crawling, and he didn't think it took much imagination to understand why. He was in a murdered young woman's bedroom remembering his mother, and wondering what had happened to his brother-in-law, and trying not to worry about his girlfriend. Was that just another day in the life?

With the top unfolded, Devlin put his fingers in the obvious handhold and lifted. Something heavy rose a quarter of an inch and stopped. This was what Devlin remembered of his mother's machine. How was it different from remembering a red label from Chicago under a night table? Devlin couldn't remember how he had learned this, so how had he retained what he had learned? Now something made him reach down in front and—No, the front was a door, that was what he was remembering. Of course, where would a woman put her knees? If the search team was as inept as Devlin, a sewing machine was a very secure place to hide something like an audiocassette. Why not? A latch. He pressed and lifted from the top. Up came the sewing machine, hefty, cumbersome, an old black metal casting with a bright steel wheel on the side.

Sew what?

He had been hoping for a miracle. He had no reason to believe there was anything to search for. It was like looking for secret messages in the frozen fish filets.

Moving the sewing machine had lifted a corner of the wall-to-wall carpet. Devlin knew about that stuff, too, but knew how he knew it: one college summer he'd worked as an apprentice to a floor mechanic. Tackless installation of wall-to-wall carpeting was part of the trade, along with putting down linoleum and tiles of all kinds. Once down, carpeting wasn't supposed to come up unless you *pulled* it up—casual moving of furniture wouldn't do it. Devlin moved the sewing machine and lifted the carpet some more.

It came up easily. When it was installed properly, carpeting was stretched out from the center of the room, over little hooks rising out of strips nailed to the floor around the sides of the room. You got the carpet up by stretching it outward again. This had been lifted, but not reinstalled properly. The padding was rotted, hardly more than a pancake of dust. Devlin kept lifting.

And under the padding, flashing white where the padding was crumbled, almost four feet from the corner of the room, was a piece of paper. Devlin reached. An envelope. In the warmth and humidity, bits of padding wanted to stick to his fingertips. The envelope was fat, covered with fragments of carpet padding the length of shaved whiskers that did not blow or wipe off. Nothing written on the outside of the envelope. Devlin moved around toward the hall. No point in putting things back the way they had been, not when the letter Devlin was unfolding was handwritten on legal-size yellow foolscap, and addressed, *"Dear Jane,"* and signed, after five pages, *"Your loving Jack."*

Sure! Let Levine's people come back and see that things had been disturbed! Devlin hoped he had a bargaining chip even if it wouldn't mean much to whoever had killed Major and the others. Devlin still didn't have any evidence that all the killings had been done by the same person or persons anyway.

But he wasn't going to find that evidence here. He had to get moving again. He wanted to talk to Loncaric and John Lord. He wanted a name and address to go with Major's saved phone number in Brooklyn.

From the living room window he looked down into the street just as a patrol car turned from West End Avenue. He waited, watching. The car stopped in front of the building. Uniformed officers got out of both front doors and hustled through the rain to the entrance. Quickly Devlin got moving.

In the hall, he closed the apartment door carefully, quietly, and wiped the knob with his handkerchief. The elevator jolted into life, going down. Devlin took the stairs down, slower.

The elevator reached the lobby when he arrived at the third floor. Devlin listened to the elevator start up again, then continued down the stairs, slowing more as he reached the lobby. It was empty—no tricks. Devlin was seeing how he had to develop alertness until it was in every thought. The people after him could get lucky, he could turn a corner and walk into Norberto Torres. What else could Devlin do but try to stay alert? He crossed the lobby, eyes on the car outside. Why were they here? Had someone spoken of a letter?

As he opened the door to the sidewalk, Devlin caught a movement in the backseat of the patrol car. Time to act natural, the hardest thing in the world to do. Turning toward West End, he made sure his eyes seemed to take in the car, but not the guy in plainclothes sitting in the back. Devlin didn't know him. This was a specific errand, no doubt about it, but not about a letter. All kinds of gold shields would be crowding around, if that were the case. If they had been here yesterday, the two who had gone upstairs would notice that the carpet had been taken up. Devlin pulled his head down and strode vigorously up the street, away from the direction the car was pointed.

In the Falcon, while the windshield defogger roared, he opened the letter.

March 13, 1986

Dear Jane,

In the past several weeks, as you've been aware, an

issue has come up between us, one I'm certain has disturbed and confused you, all the more because we haven't really been able to discuss it. I've said things, I know, but they could not have made much sense to you. I'm sure of that because I could see it in your eyes. If my handwriting is difficult to read, it is because my hand is shaking so badly. We've been seeing each other a little over five months. I knew as soon as you looked at me that you wanted to get involved. I've told you how skillful you've been in drawing and holding my interest. I sometimes forget that, as young as you are, you aren't inexperienced. Is that so strange for me to say, after all my insistent curiosity?

Devlin wanted to get going. For all he knew, Levine's people were onto the car switch and were looking for this one. Devlin wasn't much interested in Jack's "confession," if that's what the letter was. Jack had wanted something of Milburn, and Jack had gotten it. Devlin used a different approach on Eileen when he wanted to talk her into something good. He did it with a smile—but then, his idea of something good was nothing like what had been on Jack Brennan's mind.

But twenty years ago the two men had occupied pretty much the same space. In the time since, he had grown in one direction, Jack Brennan another. When he'd known Jack, Devlin had wanted adventure with Maryellen more or less at the center of it. Years later, it took him eighteen months to get into his thick head that Maryellen was gone, his party over. Liz Becker blazed through his life, then abandoned him because of his drinking. If he had grown in a different direction from Jack Brennan, he didn't want to take any special credit for it. If he hadn't grown somehow, he would have died.

Devlin drove down Broadway, wipers clacking, defogger blasting, vent window dripping rain onto his left knee. At Lincoln Center, traffic backed up, and when the skinny, dark-haired driver of the cab next to the Falcon opened his *Post*, Devlin reached for Jack Brennan's letter.

. . . after all my insistent curiosity? Even now as I write this I am in a state of the most incredible, delicious, unbearable tension.

Behind him a horn blew. *Fuck off,* Devlin thought, stepping on the gas. Jack's maundering was irritating the hell out of him. Wasn't the search for illicit thrills something you outgrew? By the age of forty-seven a man ought to know when he's kidding himself. . . .

Suddenly Devlin wasn't so sure he could pass his own test. Traffic stopped again, leaving him with a view of new apartment and office buildings of the kind of gigantic proportions he could remember from the comic books of his childhood. A generation raised on visions of space travel, buildings that reduced people to the size of ants, and a steady rat-tat-tat of violence had turned them all into commonplaces. Devlin knew he was kidding himself if he thought the words in Jack Brennan's letter wouldn't have him drooling into his sock if they had been written by a woman instead of a man. *That* would have his attention, even if, for instance, the woman were Jane Milburn with all Devlin knew about her. *Sure,* he thought, letting himself smile, *a woman would have made it different.* ''I could have told you that for nothing,'' Eileen would have said, using one of her favorite expressions.

He was south of the garment district, near Gramercy Park, when he was able to pull over and stop the noise of the windshield wipers. No matter what the letter did to Devlin's nervous system, the fact was that it had worked on Milburn—and given her the really bright idea of hiding the letter well. That meant something, too, and if what Devlin was about to read didn't justify Milburn's behavior, he might just have to look for the thing or event that did.

Now he had no trouble finding his place.

. . . Even now as I write this I am in a state of the most incredible, delicious, unbearable tension. I think about the things you've told me and wonder about what you really know . . . You see, I've been struggling for some time to take you into my confidence. I'm not sure that this effort will be successful. It's not that I don't trust you. The question is, am I brave enough to reveal to anyone what I know is my deepest, darkest secret? And it is not merely a secret, oh, no; it is also my shame, pleasure, and treasure—I *hope*! I mean what I say about shame. It adds to my pleasure to know I must make myself completely vulnerable to you. If I knew why I was riveted to this, like a hypnotized chicken with eyes glued to a pebble, I think I would have the key to free the world.

My brother Joe had this. At the end of his life, Joe was obsessively interested in watching couples making love. What he said, what he told himself, was that he liked three-ways, but because I watched him watching me, I knew the truth. He looked like there was some part of it he didn't understand.

This was news to Devlin. The two or three times he and the Brennan brothers had gotten into free-for-alls, it had been for the purpose of passing the girls around—or so Devlin had thought. Would he be able to remember something else if he tried? Those nights had been too many years ago, and he had been drunk continuously throughout. He didn't like what he was feeling now about Jack and Joe Brennan. They hadn't been much when he'd met them, and if Jack was telling the truth about his brother as well as himself, they hadn't been much afterward, either. Something inside them had deteriorated and given way. What was the letter itself but evidence that its author was evolving for the worse? Devlin didn't like what he was feeling at all. It was like remembering the worst of being a lush. If Devlin didn't keep reading, the emotion would sweep him into the awful memories of raging at his father, being thrown out of gin mills, stealing from his mother. . . .

I've never told you about my own previous experiences, but given what you've learned about me in these months, I don't believe you're terribly surprised. There's much, much more, but you aren't a woman interested in gossip or provocative conversation. What I liked about you the afternoon we met was the way you told me—with your eyes, to be sure—that you were going to "take charge." And as I told you later, you more than fulfilled your promise. The way you used your strength that first night ignited my imagination. Does that explain why we've been so violent together, so angry, combative, belligerent? I wanted it. The heat of your rage has left me breathless and tingling. The punching, biting, and scratching—haven't you seen the pattern? Remember the night we had our first "real" argument? You said I was looking for trouble. I was. You even accused me of enjoying myself. I couldn't let you know how aroused I was becoming. Later, as you exhausted yourself in your fury, I had to be careful approaching you. I was afraid you would see the direct connection between your desperation, for that's what it had become by then, and my *excitement*!

Oh, my darling, you have been honest with me about the intensity of your response. Can you be honest about your true lack of surprise at my behavior? You were ready for me when I entered you, as angry as you had been. I have never hammered a woman so hard and so long. You *shrieked*! Afterward, you said you had never heard a man roar before. I didn't even know I was doing it. Beyond the beyond, you said. You were so disappointed the next time we saw each other. You expected me to tear your clothes off in eager passion, like a college boy imitating a movie star. As you've been learning ever since, *I don't work that way!*

You'd be surprised how many importantly placed people there are who are different. It goes with the need for power. In my lifetime we've had one mayor who used call girls, another who propositioned every woman he met, and one who was caught sucking off a teenager in a subway men's room. That last was our current Mayor

Hamilton—and his police commissioner was the arresting officer. Hamilton made the mistake of confiding in his lawyer, a politically ambitious man who passed on the information to my father.

I've spent years thinking about my situation, to state the obvious. We Brennan children were spanked, Joe particularly viciously by our father, but then we were rebellious, nasty, stubborn, and willful children. Joe and I had sexual experiences together, and we had our moments with Maryellen separately and together. I think . . .

Devlin groaned. This was new to him, too. He was going to have to get the letter copied and the copy deposited in a safe place. A dead man's gossip to his mistress wasn't evidence in and of itself, but it pointed toward what Devlin needed to protect himself from the mayor and his stooge commissioner. In all the years he had known the Brennans, it had never occurred to him that the brothers and sister had explored their sexual curiosity with one another. Apparently an only child remained ignorant for life about such things. In the fifteen years since he had seen Maryellen, he had had many moments when he had thought that he had never known her, that she had never allowed him to know her, and now he was thinking it again. Filed in his memory was a montage of images of Maryellen, the kind a drunk trots out to excuse a toot, her husky, barking laugh, for instance, or vivid blue eyes looking into his. Devlin could not remember all the occasions he had been in the company of the three of them, the conversation so smooth, polished, and rapid-fire, so *cool*. Never a hint. How had they handled it inside? Devlin had been in the first or second grade when he'd first realized that he had no idea how brothers and sisters got along with one another. The Brennans had only reacquainted him with one of the great mysteries of his life. Memory wasn't tricking him now. Jack, Joe, and Maryellen Brennan had been brothers and sister in the same ways he had observed in other families all of his life. The Brennans had been a little wilder about it, a little more extreme; in light of their father's celebrated lustiness, Devlin really had no reason to be surprised by revelations of their childhood sexuality. The Brennans hadn't been conventional people, but they *had* been a family. Now he saw just how much he had been avoiding remembering them as they had been, and why: the hold Maryellen had had on him . . .

The rain was coming down harder, drumming heavily on the car roof. Devlin wanted to get moving again. His next step was to check out Major's Brooklyn telephone number, and he might be doing himself a favor if he deferred calling the telephone company until he was actually in Brooklyn. John had confirmed to him that police were looking for him. Devlin had to proceed on the assumption that all agencies that cooperated routinely with the police, like the telephone company, banks, and other government departments, had already been notified to report any inquiry from Detective Frank Devlin. Devlin would have a few minutes more lead time getting to the address that went with Major's telephone number if he called the telephone company in the area of the number's prefix. That is, as long as police weren't already waiting there for Devlin.

Devlin would have to have a street map ready, too. *Yeah, right.* His street map was in the glove box of the Seville.

And there was also the possibility that police were already at the address developing other evidence, and Devlin would walk into them *accidentally.*

He drove west before heading south again, then pulled over and lit a cigarette before reading again. He was getting that haunted-house feeling, as if he were stepping into a crime scene.

. . . I think none of it hurt us. In fact, given the way my father conducted his affairs so openly in front of us all— Joe and I realized what he was doing with women when we were ten and thirteen respectively—I wouldn't be surprised if some shrink came to the conclusion that our own activities kept us diverted from the sordid truth about our beloved daddy.

I had the misfortune to marry badly. All of Anita's public and private virtues do not make up for her inability to be intimate. I discussed this with you. When you said,

''It sounds as if she makes love warily,'' I thought that I was in the presence of a woman who is truly wise. In any event, I don't know if marriage to Anita made me worse than I would have been, but I do know that my realization that the marriage, irrevocable as it was, was to be a failure, triggered the process that led to the revelation of my obsession in all its power and glory.

The rest, another two and a half pages, had been written at another time, and by the look of the handwriting, somehow more spiky, words crammed together, as many as fifteen per line, Jack was under very heavy internal pressure during the writing. Devlin was getting the haunted-house effect good now, his skin crawling, palms itching. *I don't work that way!* What the hell was wrong with acting like a college boy imitating a movie star? Devlin did it all the time, if Jack was talking about sending the lady flowers, taking her to the places she wanted to go, and otherwise giving her reason to smile.

Sure. Devlin folded the letter and looked out the steamy windshield for a bar, coffee shop, or newsstand. In the middle of the block was a Chinese restaurant, just as good.

The place was empty. The telephone was in the rear, on the wall between the doors to the toilet.

The woman who picked up Eileen's line said she hadn't seen Eileen since morning. Devlin recognized the woman's voice. She had gotten things wrong before. Devlin called John Lord, who picked up in the middle of the first ring.

''Ginzboig?'' Devlin asked in a thick Yiddish accent.

''No, he isn't here, Marvin,'' John said quickly, ''but neither is anybody else. The guys who were questioning me lit out about fifteen minutes ago, when word came down from on high that someone broke into Jane Milburn's apartment. I just talked to Kevin McQuaid, and now I have to talk to you. Do you remember Mike's Eclectic Bar, on Christopher Street?''

Mike's Eclectic Bar was John's name for it. The name on the window suggested some place exotic, the customers called it ''The Dungeon,'' and it was John's idea of a safe place for them to meet, because anyone seeing you there had to explain what *he* was doing in the place. "I'll see you in fifteen minutes," Devlin said.

He was early. Parked in a bus stop, he resumed reading.

I have been trying to make you want to hurt me. That "insistent curiosity" of mine—what's your reaction? You've even yelled, screamed at me to shut up. I wanted to go further, to see how angry I could make you, but I was afraid you would quit on me completely. Now I am going to take you that final step. I've seen that you have it in you. You will find at the end of this letter exactly how I am going to torment you, and I will, and you will grow angry enough to do anything to make me stop.

And then you will hit me.

You will be out of control, and you will hit me again and again. You will use a belt so you don't hurt yourself. You will hit me as hard as you can, and even though you will never have to go so far, proceed on the assumption that you are going to keep hitting me until your strength gives out. But, as I say, that will never happen. Why?

At the beginning of this I write that I was in an unbearable state of excitement. That was some hours ago. Since then I have had a couple of drinks and taken one of your Black Beauties. I am in more control now. So what will happen to keep you from spending all your strength?

You will experience a part of me I myself have seen only once, in Brussels where I attended an international law enforcement conference. Go ahead, laugh. In the hotel bar I fell into a conversation with a young German couple. She was dark-haired and dark-eyed, very pretty and vivacious. He did most of the talking, one of those extremely polished, urbane Europeans, while she supplied the heat— higher and higher, as the conversation became more and more provocative. We went into the hotel dining room for dinner. She sat on one side of me, he on the other. She started by rubbing her leg against mine. After more drinks, she started to feel me up under the table. When I saw that

that was all right with him, I began to enjoy the party. I have never been so excited in my life! He was talking about some people having special needs. Their timing was perfect. She wanted eye contact with me, vivacious and warm except when she would ''hint'' under the table as to her own special need, and then her eyes showed an intense seriousness, a promise; she was squeezing the head of my cock, squeezing it hard. She wanted me looking at her, so for all I knew, he could see what she was doing. At that exact moment, when I was feeling the most intense pleasure, pleasure that was painful, I heard him ask, ''Do you want to fuck my wife, you naughty boy?'' Her eyes stated the exact terms of the deal, and I had to have it, and her. At that point he got up and left the table and went back into the bar.

Upstairs, she beat me with a belt. All I can tell you is that I became aroused as I had never been before, and that when I could no longer stand the excitement or the pain, I overpowered her and took her, had her as violently as I have ever had anybody. The result—her response— was overwhelming, quite beyond your understanding (that is, of course, *if* you've told the truth about being more responsive with me than with the others). The woman lost all control of herself. Later, when she tried to cross the room, her knees buckled so that she fell hard against the wall. That was when she was coming to me for one last kiss good-bye.

Her husband wasn't in the bar downstairs, and over the years I've wondered if he wasn't in the adjoining room, listening. He got his pleasure out of it somehow; he wasn't the kind of man who would have catered to his wife's special needs.

Now that you've read this, destroy it. You understand the situation and what is expected of you. I'm completely vulnerable to you and will want you to convince me that the letter doesn't exist anymore. Obviously you will not be successful if I choose not to believe you. If ''insistent curiosity'' inflamed you, doubting and disbelief will drive you to violence—all the more because you know the truth about my behavior. I'll bet you haven't destroyed the pages you've already read. Why haven't you? What are you waiting for?

So you see. Now it has to be this way. Take the next step, and destroy this letter, do you understand? Or is it all too complicated for you, because you're a dumb fucking cunt with no imagination, like all the rest?

I'll feel your anger yet,
Jack

John's car pulled up behind Devlin's. Devlin slipped the letter under the seat of the Falcon and hurried into "Mike's Eclectic." A guy in the middle of the bar was in the last stages of AIDS, blotches of Karposi's Sarcoma blackening his face and arms. John led Devlin to the little restaurant in the rear. After telling the waiter that he and Devlin wanted only coffee, he stayed silent until the waiter left, and then he said, "Harry Levine went home this morning in the middle of the meeting with his bosses. Didn't like what they wanted to do about you."

"Went home?"

"Exactly. Home. 'I'm going home to Forest Hills,' he said, 'and you two can go fuck yourselves.' That's the quote I got from Kevin, whose account I have to believe . . . I'll tell you why in a moment. The mayor and Torres want you taken into custody ASAP because of the negative publicity otherwise, you follow?"

"Yes."

The coffee arrived. John waited again. "All right, now let me tell you why I have to believe Kevin. Torres has put him in charge of delivering you. I'll be honest, this surprises me—there's more to Kevin than meets the eye. Apparently he has been working his connections in the commissioner's office. He sees this as some kind of career opportunity."

"Swell."

"Kevin sounded gleeful. *That's* why I believed him."

Devlin heaved a sigh, letting the air hiss through his teeth. "I'm concerned about Eileen."

"I called her myself at lunchtime. She was at her desk. She says we're all bunking together tonight. I should make you sleep on the couch." John eyed him. "You're withholding."

He told John about the guy coming to Eileen's door. "So not only is her line tapped," Devlin said, "but she was identified, and I don't believe it was done for no reason."

"Obviously. Do you want me to tell Kevin? The least he can do is see if it was the FBI—whatever. You want it in the record."

"Let me think. Have you heard anything about Major?"

"Nothing. You saw it?"

"From a hundred and fifty feet. A white Lincoln. Two guys." Devlin watched Mr. Karposi's Sarcoma shuffle toward the men's room. He was in terrible pain. Devlin shuddered. He had problems? "The driver had dark receding hair and slightly puffy cheeks. Thirty-eight or forty. Dark eyes. I didn't get any part of the license plate."

"Are you going to turn yourself in?"

"No. I have a better chance out here. But Eileen doesn't, and tell Kevin I said so. You're right, let's get it in the record."

"Okay. There are some other things. One story being circulated—and checked out—is that Jack Brennan was going after the mob, and that somehow you were tied into his plans."

"Nonsense."

"Of course. I've been with you night and day for two and a half years. When? When did you do this?" John cleared his throat. "The other thing, which is not being checked out, is that old Jim Brennan was an *extremely* tough customer in his young manhood, and that at the time a lot of people thought he was involved with the heaviest hitters of the period. This was the thirties."

"Who told you this?"

John smiled. "My father. I asked him for details. He said that a lot of people who were usually well informed thought Jim Brennan was a very dirty guy. Capable of anything."

Devlin stood up and put three dollars on the table. "You have to know the history of the bus business in this city to understand how people of the time would think that. No apologies for the old man, but it was very rough. And a long time ago. Anybody left alive from those days is in the same shape as Brennan." Devlin was trying to keep his eyes off Mr. Karposi's Sarcoma as he returned from the men's room. The man knew he was all but dead. What did he think? What did he feel?

"The point my father was trying to make was that he wouldn't be surprised if Joe Brennan was murdered, too."

"Joe Brennan *drowned*."

"Yeah, and he was a terrific swimmer, too. Something to think about."

"I'll get back to you later."

"Be safe," John said, moving in front of Devlin in the bar. Mr. Karposi's Sarcoma impaled them with his stare in the yellowed mirror as he remounted his stool. Instinctively Devlin looked away. The guy was angry; he had heard them. Saying what? He had not been able to hear the fear of death in their voices. *That's right,* Devlin thought, as he stepped out into the rain again. The guy had heard only life—life-*loving*.

That thought made Devlin want to be more alert and wary.

At the Battery traffic backed up briefly and Devlin found himself looking across the bay toward Liberty Island, where the still-shrouded Statue of Liberty awaited another unveiling. He thought he remembered that the statue had been scrubbed in the forties, after the war. No hoopla then, no drawing attention to the fact that the statue's relatively soft copper skin was almost as thin as a quarter. Knowing how easy it would be to turn the old girl into a baker's rack was all the encouragement a lot of weirdos needed to go at her with an Uzi—or even a cannon. The politicians lining up to take their bows might find more fireworks than were being advertised. In the mood he was in, with everything that was gnawing at him, including the revelations in Jack Brennan's letter to Jane Milburn, Devlin thought they deserved whatever happened to them.

Devlin didn't want to picture Joe and Jack being sexual with Maryellen. If Jack had really believed that it had been good for all of them, he had been as self-deluded as he had been sexually disordered. Jack had been six years Maryellen's senior, a huge difference during childhood and adolescence. Was it any wonder Maryellen's behavior had been so profoundly erratic?

In eight years, it had never occurred to Devlin that Joe Brennan had been murdered. But if John Lord's father was right, and if Jack had been killed by the same people, then a conspiracy against Frank Devlin made no sense at all. But suppose it did, in a way Devlin couldn't see? If somebody could wait eight years between one killing and the next, how far back could a vendetta go? What in fact *did* Devlin know about Jim Brennan?

4:26 P.M. . . .

A WOMAN ANSWERED THE TELEPHONE. IN RESPONSE TO recent events in her life, her "Hello" sounded as if her head were going on a chopping block. She seemed resigned to it, too, sick of living. Devlin was calling from the back of a kosher deli in Bensonhurst, near the neighborhood in which the telephone on Major's slip of paper was located.

"May I speak to Mrs. Anita Brennan, please? I realize that this is a bad, awkward time to call, but—"

"I'm Anita Brennan."

He drew a breath. "This is Frank Devlin, Mrs. Brennan, the brother-in-law you never met."

"The FBI questioned me yesterday about you. They wanted to know if Jack had spoken of working with you . . ."

"He couldn't have."

"I know, that's what I told them. Please." She stopped. In the silence he realized that she was exhausted, unable even to try to keep up with events. "Look, Mr. Devlin, I knew Jack really wasn't a serious man. He was running for the Senate because he didn't know what else to do with his life, and his polltakers told him he could win. He had no more business being in politics than he had being in the Waldorf Towers . . .''

Devlin had to take a chance. He phrased his next question to draw her out. "Then you knew about Jane Milburn."

"I knew he was having some kind of affair, yes. He had many liaisons and affairs. He was the kind of man who loved intrigue. He couldn't conceal his involvements. I wasn't married to him long when I learned that."

"Do you mind telling me how?"

She coughed. "I was married before—outside the church, of course—and went into this marriage knowing—" She stopped again. "I hate that old bastard."

"Who?"

"Our father-in-law. Who else? I realized a long time ago that I couldn't believe a word out of his mouth where you were concerned. I thought I hated his son, too—I'm speaking of Jack—but dead is dead. No one ever really hates the dead. I was saying, I went into the marriage knowing somewhat more about men than he probably supposed. When his behavior became inexplicable, I hired a private detective. That was after less than a year."

Devlin could hear too much tension; he had to be very careful with her. "If you'd been married before, why did you tolerate what he was doing?"

She sighed. "You've been away from the Brennans a long time, Mr. Devlin. As you must see at this point, your wife isn't the only crazy member of the family. Charlotte wanted a senator, no matter what it cost; Jim has made the payments all these years; and their son kept his part of the bargain by not interfering with *my* life. I travel—"

"What do you mean, Jim has made the payments? I thought he was totally incapacitated."

She laughed. "You really have been away. The last time I made the mistake of being alone with him, he told me what he'd do to me if we had real privacy. His son's wife. This, years and years after he told me that the deal we made cut me out of the will. I'm sorry, Mr. Devlin, but I don't know who killed Jack. I used to hear Jack and his father arguing, but it was always behind closed doors, when Charlotte wasn't around. I don't know what more I can tell you. I want to get off the telephone now.''

Devlin said thank you and good-bye and put the handset on its cradle. Had he been away from the Brennans? He had been trying to be straight with himself for so long, he had forgotten what a manipulator Jim Brennan really was. Payments! The sexual overture was no surprise to Devlin. Maryellen had told him stories of her father seducing, or raping, her girlfriends. At times Devlin had not believed her—not the only crazy one in the family, but definitely in the running for craziest of all.

None of this got Devlin closer to unraveling his immediate problems. He dialed Steve Loncaric, who picked up on the first ring.

"It's me, Steve, Frank. I want to ask you about a story circulating about Jack Brennan and me . . .''

"Take it easy," Loncaric said. "You sound tighter than a tick.''

"I saw a man murdered today.''

"Frank, listen to me. People are worried about you.''

"The man was a friend of mine.''

"You're not getting the point, Frank. I'm worried about the way you *sound*. You may be my sponsor, but I never have thought you were invincible. You know what I'm talking about.''

"You're talking about booze, and you knew better than to beat around the bush about it. Going on a bender is absolutely the last thing on my mind—'' Devlin stopped. Two uniformed officers, a black woman and and apple-cheeked white man, came into the restaurant. They had come on duty at four o'clock and were taking a break forty minutes later. They moved to the counter. It took both of them to pick up a couple of sandwiches? Who was monitoring the radio?

"Frank? Are you all right?''

"Yeah, Steve. Look, I'm going to have to call you back.''

"Where are you? What are you doing?''

"I'm in Brooklyn. I have to get going.''

"Frank—"

Devlin hung up. He was better off staying where he was until the two cops left the place. He couldn't be sure that the department didn't have his picture in every precinct house in the city. He didn't know if these two birds could find water if they fell out of a boat, but he had a fair idea of what would happen if he misstepped and wound up in custody. Devlin turned his back to the take-out counter, dropped a quarter in the telephone, dialed 411, identified himself, and told the effeminate-sounding young man on the other end the information he needed. In the mirror on the back wall Devlin saw that he had a clear view of the entire restaurant and a good portion of the street outside. The apple-cheeked cop gave his order to the counterman as the information operator spoke up again.

"Detective? That telephone is listed under the name Robert Antonucci, and the address is 2492 Coney Island Avenue. That's Sheepshead Bay, not Coney Island, but not exactly the high-rent district, either."

Devlin disconnected with a fingertip, continuing to hold the handset to his ear. Bobby Antonucci. Octavio Lopez's vividly dressed killer didn't fit Major's description of either of the men who had interviewed him last winter. Devlin focused again on the dynamic duo at the take-out counter. The woman was talking now. All that connected Major's interviewers and Bobby Antonucci at this point was Devlin's own say-so. In fact, if Devlin were picked up now, with Antonucci's telephone number in Major's handwriting and Antonucci's address in his own, as well as a letter to Jane Milburn from Jack Brennan, half the potential jurors in the city would want to put him *under* Sing Sing.

Outside, a black Plymouth rolled by, slow because of the rain. Devlin couldn't bet that it wasn't an unmarked car. The female cop turned his way. Anything he did might seem reactive and call her attention to him. He moved his lips and fished in his pocket for another quarter. She looked away. The bathrooms were in the front, not near the kitchen, which was to his left. Almost all restaurant kitchens had rear doors. But Devlin would have to cross the line of sight of the counterman, who would want to know what Devlin was up to.

Devlin called Eileen's office. Busy. It had never been busy before. How many lines did that office have? Loncaric could hear something in his voice? Devlin could feel it crawling up his spine. If he wasn't careful, he was going to do something to get himself collared right here and now by these kiddie cops and their playmates. Devlin had to keep his back turned to the take-out counter, not be curious about what was happening behind him.

Devlin dialed Eileen's office again. Still busy. He hung up, waited for his quarter, put it back in the slot, and dialed the weather forecast. Something to listen to.

After another five minutes, Devlin's peripheral vision picked up the reflection of blue uniforms moving toward the door. Had the cops paid? Devlin almost wanted to identify himself to the counterman and ask.

He wanted to try Eileen again, but now he couldn't remember what he had wanted to say.

The rain was letting up, but not enough to allow him to turn off the old Falcon's wipers. They had two speeds, loud and louder. The radio still had nothing on Major's killing. Devlin was heading down Ocean Parkway, trying to guess where to turn left so he could get a glimpse of Antonucci's apartment. For all anybody knew, Antonucci himself had never set foot in the place.

At least, Devlin thought, he was getting a dumb-cop, by-the-numbers satisfaction in gathering evidence. And it wasn't even good evidence, only arguable, supportive of his case. After the conversation with Anita Brennan, he didn't enjoy the idea of putting Jack's letter in the spotlight, introducing it as an exhibit in a trial, but Devlin wasn't holding on to it *not* to turn it over to his lawyer. Showing that the victims weren't nice people was part of any defense attorney's game plan. Devlin could see just how much he did not want to be a victim himself. If he kept moving, working, he would continue to convert his rising anger into energy. The one thing he did not want to do was brood. *Stew*, his mother used to say.

A good defense lawyer would find a graphologist to confirm

that the telephone number had been written by Major. But then what? Only Devlin's word about two wise guys paying Major a call—hearsay. More likely, the prosecution might argue, Major had been part of the larger conspiracy that involved double crossing and murder, and that Devlin had led Major's killers to him.

What about telephone company records of Antonucci's bills, a record of all calls outside the immediate area? If the wise guys had told Major to call them there, for what other purposes had people used that telephone? Wasn't this the same telephone called from Devlin's apartment when he wasn't there? Telephone records showed the times of calls, too. More than just providing new leads, the records themselves would illuminate the chain of events.

As he rolled slowly across Coney Island Avenue, Devlin took long looks in both directions and saw a patrol car parked in front of a four-story sandstone structure. If his colleagues were waiting for him to turn up here, parking a blue-and-white out front was not the way to do it. No, the Antonucci apartment was under study, perhaps made more intense because of the break-in at Milburn's place. Devlin almost allowed himself a smile.

This once comfortable part of Brooklyn was as run-down and dirty as the rest of the city. Devlin pulled over and heard his stomach growl. He hadn't eaten since morning; he'd forgotten about it. Was that a good sign or bad? Devlin caught himself: Bill Ward, his A.A. sponsor, would have skewered him. "You're not taking care of yourself, giving you an excuse to feel sorry for yourself. That's the beginning of stinking thinking, and let me be the first to tell you."

The radio grabbed Devlin's attention like a baling hook: "—the gangland-style shooting death of a longtime bookmaker on Queens Boulevard, in Sunnyside, this afternoon. Eyewitnesses say two men in a late-model white Lincoln sedan fired several shots in the crowded intersection before speeding off. Police are also questioning a witness who reported a man who identified himself as a federal agent before fleeing the scene. Also in Queens, attorneys for alleged bagman for Donald Manes—"

Federal agent. If the report had said FBI, the station's telephone would be ringing right now. Any negative reference to

the FBI was the same as blasphemy to the Bureau, and if it
detected a pattern to the station's negativity, life would become
difficult, doing business impossible. The CIA was no better,
and just as effective. Unveiling a refurbished Statue of Liberty
was an emptier gesture than Devlin wanted to contemplate.
He turned off the radio, then the ignition. He wanted to know
more about the guys in the white Lincoln, who may or may
not have been the same guys who had questioned Major about
Devlin last winter. *Those* guys may have been truthful with
Major when they'd said they had no way of knowing why people were interested in Devlin. It could be that they had heard
the story Liz Becker had passed on, the fragment of gossip
heard by Eileen's boss, that Devlin had been working for Jack
Brennan. . . .

Devlin had to talk to Eileen. He looked in both directions
for a telephone; it didn't matter which way he walked. He
didn't need to go near Antonucci's apartment for what he
wanted to do there.

Outdoor booths a block south had been vandalized. When
he reached a luncheonette a block and a half farther on, his
clothes were heavy with rain. His stomach growled again. The
old woman behind the counter looked Vietnamese. She
squinted at him before he spoke, as if bracing to grapple with
the English language.

"I'd like a bacon, lettuce, and tomato sandwich, please."

"Oh, BLT."

"Yeah. And change for the telephone. I have to make some
calls."

"You want me bring sandwich to you?"

He was thinking of his idea for getting more information
from the cops in Antonucci's apartment. Who knew where
ideas came from? This one, fully formed, had arrived before
his eyes as suddenly as a hummingbird. At home, John Lord
picked up on the first ring.

"It's me, John. What's happening?"

"Things are under control. I talked with Eileen in her office
twenty minutes ago, and she told me she was going to pick up
some things before coming up here. That's as good as it can

be. I asked her if she wanted to wait for me to pick her up, but she said no. I guess she wanted to do her shopping in private.''

That wasn't it. Eileen would buy panty hose in front of the Pope if she had to. She had decided that special efforts were unnecessary—*fussing*, she called such efforts, and she had no patience with them.

''If Levine's successor on this case—What's his name? That punk! Damn it!''

''Kevin McQuaid,'' John said gently, not patronizingly.

''Anyway, if he and his people are looking for me—''

''They are. Look, you're tired and you know it. I just talked to Kevin. He told me that they went citywide on you with the four-to-twelve. Every cop in the five boroughs is looking for you. Start thinking about this, as tired as you are. The more tired you get, the more likely you are to get careless or make a mistake. Suppose you go up against some kid who misreads a gesture?''

''That's farfetched.''

''That's exactly the way it happens, Frank! Do you think you're going to be able to bail yourself out on this thing? You're stalling for time, hoping for a break. You should come in before more people get hurt.''

''I haven't hurt a soul, John.''

''Why was that bookmaker killed?''

''Major would have been killed if he had been talking to *you*! He was talking to a shield!''

''Ah, but you're the special shield who's been fitted with a frame so tight you can't say cheese.''

''People think I know something. Harry Levine thought I knew something. That's why he wanted me out on the street.''

''That's not exactly true, and a non sequitur besides,'' John said. ''I was there. Harry Levine saw the evidence against you as unpersuasive. He might still think so, but with another man killed, he'd want you off the street, and you know it.''

''I'll think about what you said. Thanks. I'm really all right.'' He hung up and waited for the operator to call back with the additional charges.

''You want over there still, or over here?''

The old lady was talking about the BLT. She was an Asian learning English with a Brooklyn accent. If Devlin could listen to her for ten minutes, he'd have her voice down cold.

And that was how he was going to scam the cops at the Antonucci apartment.

The BLT was served with a pickle and a little paper cup of coleslaw. In the months he was getting sober, Devlin had focused consciously on the small joys of life like a monk saying his prayers, clearing his mind so that the memory, then the reality, of the pleasure of, say, a piece of Bickford's apple pie, could return to him. Bickford's was history now, but in Devlin's mind to this moment, the restaurant chain had served the best apple pie in the history of the world.

Sobering up, he had walked around Sunnyside, visiting places where he had played as a child, some of which he had not seen since World War II. He had seen the school, J.H.S. 125, when he had taken Maryellen on a tour of his old haunts. By then someone had settled with spray paint a score with a teacher Devlin could remembering hating, and the spray paint was still there, twenty-five years later: VOORHEES SUCKS. Years later, when Devlin called it to Eileen's attention, she said it was funny, just how a tyrannical teacher should be remembered. When Maryellen had seen it, she had reacted in the opposite way, angry and even hurt for the hapless Voorhees. ''You can't help it if you're that way,'' Maryellen had said. ''That's exactly the point.''

Yes.

He heard a siren coming this way fast. The trick was not keeping his eyes off the window, but off the old lady. The sound had made her lean back and watch out of the corner of her eye; if she felt the need to be seen minding her own business, she could do it instantly. A war refugee's cunning. She would see Devlin's eyes if they shifted to her, and maybe she would regard his interest as suspicious. In her position, Devlin would: he had no legitimate reason to be interested in her reaction to the police. As the car flashed by, the boiling red lights bright in the rainy late afternoon shadow, Devlin let himself take some notice of it. The old woman saw, and when he brought his head around again, she was ready for his comment.

"All the time, these days," he said.

"I don't go out at night no more," the old woman said. "Too dangerous. Makes me crazy."

Devlin was curious about the police. "You never know," he said as he got up from the stool. "You can't be too careful, know what I mean?" He thought the rain on the window would make it difficult for him to see what was happening. Not at all. "See? It's just up the next block. *Two* cars, and here comes a third." They had the Falcon— *how*? How had they learned of it?

The *shlub* at the scene of Major's murder had seen Devlin drive off in the Seville. No. The people who had heard Devlin leave the message concerning Sal on Eileen's machine and had sent the young Latino to Eileen's door last night must have figured out that Devlin had gone to Sal's for another car. When they found the Seville, Sal had had to tell them what Devlin was driving. In Devlin's mind, the question of who had tapped Eileen's telephone was settled: cops. Federal cops, most likely, or even, given the story that was circulating about Devlin and Jack Brennan, some kind of federal-local task force.

Your tax dollars at work.

Devlin looked around quickly. Maybe somebody up the block would have the sense to feel the Falcon's hood. It was still hot—and maybe somebody would deduce, like a real detective, that Frank Devlin was not far away. Then what? In the same situation, Devlin would look for the man on the street, heading away. They weren't going to look for him in a luncheonette, but that didn't mean they couldn't get lucky and find him when they were stopping here for an egg cream. He'd do himself a favor by staying away from the window. And hiding Jack Brennan's letter. He turned to the old woman. "I can't see what it is from here, but at least I know to take another way home."

She nodded and turned her back to him. Something else entered Devlin's mind: as soon as somebody thought of it, the cops up the street would see that the cops in Antonucci's apartment knew that Devlin's car had been found less than a mile away. So Devlin had to get his plan working. He took the half sandwich over to the telephone, even though he wasn't going to be able to eat while he was talking. From the booth he couldn't see anything of the street. He called the Antonucci number. It was picked up quickly, and a cop said, "Yeah?"

"Kevin McQuaid," Devlin said through his teeth. "Who am I talking to?"

"Detective Anthony Corella. What can I do for you?"

"We now have reason to believe that Frank Devlin is on his way to Brooklyn, maybe to your location. I want to make sure that we have all the names developed from those telephone records."

"The Hoboken cops finally got to look in the apartment over there and it looks like it belonged to that actor who took the hit out by the airport, what's his name, Matthews—"

"Fuck the corpses," Devlin said as McQuaid. "We're trying to come up with some names of living conspirators here. Do you have anybody east of the Hudson? What the hell, I'll settle for east of the Mississippi."

"We thought what we got yesterday was working out," Corella whined.

"That was yesterday," Devlin said quickly. "Today they all talked to their lawyers. What about those local numbers that weren't called much? What are you getting on them? For instance, we want to know if anyone used Antonucci's telephone to talk to that bookmaker in Queens." Trying not to use too heavy an accent, Devlin gave Corella Major's whole name and telephone number. "Go back as far as you can. I'll wait."

"Just a minute."

Devlin waited, wondering if cops were going to walk through the door while he was holding a receiver to his ear. If he filled his face with a half sandwich, he might look so natural that they'd pass over him. A desperate notion, it showed him only how risky he knew his predicament really was. He wanted to check out the old woman. She was watching him. He waggled his fingers and drew a small, dry smile. Corella came back on the line.

''Yeah, we got a call to that number. Queens, right? One call in January, two minutes long. January is as far back as we can go. We've been working on that call to the liquor store on Twenty-first Avenue in Paterson. In New Jersey. We've got something, too, we think.''

Was something important about New Jersey to these guys? ''Let's hear it,'' Devlin said in McQuaid's voice.

''This call was in February, before eight o'clock on a Sunday morning,'' Corella said eagerly. ''That part of Paterson is an old Italian neighborhood, still one of the places the new immigrants settle while they learn the language and figure out what's going on. After Charlie Lucky organized the mob, Paterson was home base for one of the first dons, Vittorio Di-Bennedetti, formerly of Brooklyn—''

Devlin stayed in character. ''Why are you bothering me with this prehistoric Sicilian vespers shit?''

''The guy's still alive, kid. Eighty-eight years old. His house is right around the corner from the liquor store, the one on Twenty-first Avenue. The guy who owns it says the store is closed Sundays. He has a kind of part-time manager who has a key, and we're going to talk to him tomorrow.''

''Who is he?''

''A neighborhood guy. The owner already talked to him. The part-time manager thought he was doing a cranky old man a favor, opening the store for him, but then the phone rang, and the other guy with the old man told the manager to get lost. I'm reading from my notebook now. 'Going to the front of the store wasn't good enough for him. I had to wait outside.' ''

''Whose quote is that?''

''That's the owner quoting the manager.''

''Make sure *that's* written down. Call all those people and tell them to keep their fucking mouths shut.''

''I already did. The owner told me that the manager said that if he didn't have his parents to take care of, he'd be on the next nonstop to California. He definitely does not like the position he's been put in.''

''He shouldn't do people favors. Anything else?''

"That's it," Corella said. "I think DiBennedetti and company made a big mistake there."

"They did us a fucking favor. Let the FBI spend two million dollars to learn that some imported hitter called his uncle Vic. It could be that simple. Frank Devlin is the key to this thing. *He* knows."

"Tell me about it," Corella said. "We're turning up even more stuff about him like we sent in after lunch, stuff that goes back thirty years."

Devlin froze. "Well, there you go," he said as McQuaid, and hung up.

And turned around to see the old woman staring at him as if hypnotized. She had heard him speaking in two completely different voices. He winked and bit into his sandwich. She gave a nervous little smile and nodded timidly. She was frightened, all right. He'd said something about the FBI. If she suspected he was a cop, she was wondering about the things he had said earlier. The understanding that he was some kind of tough guy was in her eyes. Given where she came from and what she might have seen there, that was enough. Flashing his shield would probably be overkill. He got up onto the wobbly stool again. "Good coffee," Devlin said in his own voice. "Let me have another cup."

The old lady withdrew to the little back room. Did she have another phone back there? He couldn't take the chance, but the wobbly stool gave him an idea—a memory. As a child he had spun on stools like these, and one day he had wanted to see how they worked. The padded top lifted off. The pedestal was hollow. Now Devlin moved quickly and quietly, folding Jack Brennan's letter in half lengthwise. This seat lifted easily, and the letter slid into the hollow pedestal, wedging itself at the top. Nothing to it. Devlin called good night, left a dollar tip, and headed for the door.

He turned up the cross street, out of view of the crowd of cops gathered around the Falcon. When he was past the building line, he quickened his pace. Something made him look back: the old lady was coming out of the luncheonette. She saw him looking at her and started running toward the Falcon.

Devlin ran the other way, as hard as he had run in years, his feet hitting the ground heavily. He turned again at the next corner. He had a few seconds, he thought, while the old woman told her story. Where was the subway around here? He was in a short block and would reach the next corner in only another few seconds. His lungs didn't like this much. Trying to hide was stupid; all he needed was one old busybody or little kid to see him, and cops would be thicker than the roaches on West End Avenue. He wanted to think. What was he going to do if he got out of here? Would Harry Levine be willing to talk to him? There were subway stations nearby, but the transit police were probably looking for him, too. The Brennan-owned buses would be a different story.

Where was a goddamned bus stop?

A taxi turned the corner, its off-duty light on. Devlin pulled out his shield and showed it—and then barely got out of the way as the driver stepped on the gas. *"Motherfucker!"* Devlin yelled. *New York!* Another car approached from halfway up the next block. The driver waved to Devlin, who kept his shield where the driver could see it.

The guy came to a stop beside Devlin and opened the passenger door for him. "I saw that. Do you want to go after him?"

Devlin got in and reached for the seat belt. "Nah, you don't want to spend two weeks in front of the Taxi Commission. Besides, I've got bigger problems than that guy."

The guy's eyes widened. "Can you talk about them?"

"What the fuck, it's probably going to be on the six o'clock news. Some son of a bitch stole my car."

The driver stifled a giggle. He believed it completely.

7:28 P.M. . . .

WHERE FLATBUSH AVENUE BECAME MARINE PARKWAY, the bus picked up speed and the standees, twenty of them clinging to bright metal pipes, lurched to the rear. The setting sun poked through the lifting clouds and filled the right side of the bus with orange light—and enough heat to poach the multiracial crowd. Devlin had found a messy copy of this morning's *Times* and was systematically letting his eyes pass over every word of page B5, all Liberty Week stories, from the honoring of prominent immigrants to the surplus collected by the Liberty-Ellis Island Committee. Devlin was in Brennan country. This was a Brennan bus, and it had just passed Brennan-backed housing projects on the way out onto the rank, humid mirror of Jamaica Bay. Courting Maryellen Brennan had meant a lot of trips to Rockaway, Devlin's next destination. In those days, Maryellen had been curious about life's sleazy side, provided Devlin took responsibility for what they saw and did, and she took control of how they dealt with it later. In New Jersey it was burlesque; in the Village, gay bars; in Rockaway it was going from one Irish dance hall to the next, getting blotto on beer and looking for trouble. It hadn't taken him long to realize that she had wanted so much to see a brawl that she was capable of trying to get him into one. . . .

Another hot night: he caught her flirting over his shoulder on a dance floor and walked away to let her contend with the goon alone. Twenty minutes later, she came running up to their car, where he had been waiting, having second thoughts about what he had done. "Do you know what he said to me? Do you have any idea what you put in that man's mind?" He didn't believe her, but stayed silent, leaning against the car's fender, letting her run her course. A guy came along. Devlin wouldn't have recognized him, but Maryellen pulled close. As he passed, the guy raised his hand to fend Devlin off. "No trouble, brother. I'm just on my way to my hotel." He kept going, but Maryellen held on. When he was thirty feet away, near the corner, he called, "Get yourself a new girl, fella!"

"Keep your mouth shut!"

The guy rubbed the base of his spine with his index finger. "Nice little starter button she has back here."

A mole. The guy couldn't have found it without exploring carefully. Devlin's stomach churned. Maryellen wrenched free. "He *grabbed* me!"

He got in the car. She had to tap on the window to get him to open her door. She wanted to fight, and he didn't. He was thinking about the guy's advice. The trouble was, the wedding date had been set. The whole world knew they were getting married.

He was becoming a part of the great Brennan saga.

In New York, everyone knew some part of the story of the Brennan rise to wealth and power. In the twenties and thirties, before La Guardia became mayor, the buses feeding New York's subway system were operated by free-lance owner-drivers who fought one another with their fists for passengers who paid five cents a ride. Because of the Depression, people facing starvation, the violence sometimes escalated to sabotage, arson, and gunplay. In Queens, the most successful of the bare-knuckle entrepreneurs was a man named Brady, a widower who operated six buses in Jackson Heights and Astoria. One of his drivers was a big boy from Brooklyn named Jim Brennan, who became his boss's pride and joy one winter morning by putting a competitor temporarily out of business with one punch through the guy's new, laminated safety-glass windshield. The punch busted Brennan's hand, and when the guy got out of the bus, Brennan had to fight him with his left hand only. The night of Devlin's wedding to Maryellen, one of Brennan's oldest advisors remembered the fight clearly enough to regale Devlin and the Brennan pups with an account of it.

"The old man's left was as good as his right, and he was

pissed at the guy for even thinking he could set foot out of that bus. Brennan blocked the guy's first punch, a right, so easily, completely, that the guy's jaw dropped—and that's where Brennan hit him, without a hitch, coming out of the block with a smooth, almost nonchalant chop downward. You could hear the bone break down the street, somebody said. That's when the old man smiled. You don't mess with Jim Brennan, not now, not then, not ever. You could see that the guy's jaw was broken, it hung down off his face like a bag of dimes. The old man broke his nose next. He was fighting with one hand, remember, his left hand. The guy pulled his arms up to protect his face, and Bill hit the guy in the belly so hard he came right up off the pavement, doubled over, finished. He hit the ground like a dead animal. Later the guy spent a month in the hospital with internal bleeding. He never would say who did it, even though the story was all over the city.''

None of the Brennans, children or parents, ever talked to Devlin about the courtship of Jim Brennan and Charlotte Brady. One time—and one time only—Jim Brennan spoke of his affection for Charlotte's father, saying that Brady ''had opened the first door, figuratively and literally,'' leading Devlin to the conclusion that Brady had brought his star driver home for dinner one night, a beginning that Devlin reckoned must have been stormy, given what the principals must have been like in their youth. By 1966, thirty years later, the story of the Brennan family was carved on the consciousness of the entire city. The gossip columnists, Sunday magazine articles, and political reporters had gotten it mostly right. Of course they never explained why Charlotte put up with her husband's flagrant adulteries, affairs, and womanizing. Devlin never was so secure in the family that he felt free to play detective, so the deepening of his understanding of the Brennans and their story was osmotic, when it didn't come in spine-shivering bursts of revelation. . . .

The widower Brady died of a sudden heart attack within a year of Jim Brennan's marriage to Charlotte, and that effectively gave the bus lines not to his daughter, a pregnant eighteen-year-old, but to her husband. From the beginning of their life together,

Devlin saw, all the money and power was Brennan's. If Devlin read between the lines correctly, whenever Charlotte needed that big lesson pounded home, Brennan did it. Maybe with his left hand, but more likely, if Devlin understood Brennan correctly, with his right, or even both fists.

After he took over Brady's lines, Brennan's fists made the streets hopelessly unsafe for his competitors, and when their incomes fell, he picked up the paper on their equipment. Bankers were interested only in what they saw in their books, which told them Brennan's increasing dominance of the market made him a better and better risk. New York in the Depression wasn't all breadlines and apple vendors, it was also burlesque, rent parties, blind pigs, numbers, and slots. In this climate Brennan was laundering the nickels and pennies from the illegal slot machines and numbers games, getting professional help to enforce control of his bus lines, which were now running all over Queens. When Brennan bought new buses, he brought his own salesmen to the deal, and they kicked the commission back to Brennan. Why not? It was a buyer's market, cluttered with manufacturers struggling to stay alive.

By the end of the decade, Jim Brennan was a power in Queens Democratic politics. La Guardia's antics, Brennan told Devlin and the pups, made him see the wisdom of participating in the political process. As mayor, La Guardia drove burlesque out of New York, closed down the slots, drove the numbers into the ghettoes—and asserted the city's right to franchise the buses that ran on its streets. Brennan had to win again from the city what he had already wrested from the competition, and in the end only his assets, including the best-connected lawyers he could buy, put him in business under the new system. "Too close a call for me," Brennan expansively told the three young men one night. "I lost a sweet thing when the slots went. They had to go sooner or later, but if I'd known then what I know now, it would have been later rather than sooner."

By the end of the war, Brennan had control of the last unbuilt lots in Jackson Heights, acres of them. The leases, deeds, and other paperwork filled two rooms of filing cabinets, he recounted gleefully. When the G.I.s came home, his congress-

men and senators pushed through legislation for veterans'
housing. Through boardmen and bagmen, Brennan's land became the site of thousands of metal quonset-hut apartments
from whence the ex-G.I.s took Brennan's buses to the subway
that carried them to their jobs in Manhattan. When the last of
the huts was bulldozed away, seven or eight years later, Brennan was a landmark on the city's political landscape, his wife
noted for her religious and charity work, and his growing children famous in the Sunday magazines for being rich, smart,
good-looking, and not the least ashamed of any of it.

Could some secret business have been going on while Devlin
had been in the Brennan family? Devlin thought not. If old Jim
had been up to something unacceptable even for a political power
broker, it would have made itself known to Devlin at the time.
Brennan bragged about bribery the way he bragged about bimbos. He was making millions out of the redevelopment of the
Rockaways, working his Washington connections with dazzling
finesse. He took his women down there, too, although Devlin
only occasionally heard about them directly. Brennan talked to
Joe and Jack as if they were drinking buddies, and in turn they
talked to Maryellen as if she were another brother. Once, in an
argument, she told Devlin, by then her husband, that he could
not possibly be as virile as her father.

But by then Devlin knew that Maryellen would say anything
if she thought his attention was drifting away from her . . . In
another tantrum, after a morning quickie, she clenched her
fists and cried that she didn't want to be fucked all day.

At that point Devlin was telling himself that he was beginning to learn how to control her. The trick was in not losing
his temper—and this time he held on to it because he was able
to read her body language, the bowed head, averted eyes—and
heard, in the very softness of her voice, that something ugly
was coming. Without another word, he walked out of the house
and went to work. When she called to find out what had happened to him, he kept his voice flat, dead calm. It made her
nervous, he had learned, and made her open up, even tell the
truth for a little while, for a change.

And then she would beg him not to give up on her. She

would change, she promised—she *could*, with his help. "Please don't throw me back!" She'd want sex then, too. After he'd known her six months, he believed that she was going through a process that was more than simply an attempt to manipulate him. "Love me good," she would plead. "Love me *good*!" She was more excited at those times, needing to be held. She would whisper she loved him, and in the sense that he knew something was wrong with her, he believed it.

Even after the attention-getting became atrocious, after she'd told him that he wasn't the best she'd ever had in bed, after she'd announced she wasn't sure she could be faithful for life, he held hope—what he told himself was hope. His ego was at stake: he told himself he could solve her problems. They'd been married two years and he'd never really stopped salving his ego with other women, he might not have ever been truly, completely sober, but he *still* held that stupid, vain hope. The hardest part about remembering now was his shame and guilt. Thinking about that period of his life, Devlin wanted to race on to the last atrocity, the third abortion. He had wanted that child. . . .

The simple truth was that he shouldn't have been there in the first place, and he had known it all along!

Devlin hadn't been in Rockaway in more than twenty years, and he almost didn't recognize the place, from the higher skyline to the changed storefronts on 116th Street, and the bleak rather than inviting glimpses of the boardwalk. Hotels and bars that had been landmarks a quarter-century ago had disappeared without a trace. Devlin had to find a telephone with privacy. He wasn't surprised to find himself thinking about Maryellen again. After he broke up with Liz the second time, he had thought hard about contacting Maryellen—then, as now, all he knew was that she had resettled in Minnesota, far enough from New York. Even in 1981, the wound of the separation was still raw. Maybe he could even think of her that way again now, this evening, but he wasn't going to give himself the chance. . . .

Tomorrow was Jack's funeral, there would be more cops around than folding chairs, but if Devlin wanted to see Maryellen, she would be there. After fifteen years, he might not even recognize her. That was the truth. He had not recognized Liz in 1979, less than seven years after their first affair.

Rockaway had changed only on the outside. All four saloons he tried were mobbed, the crowds older and fatter than he remembered, but as reactionary Irish as ever, two of the places displaying Reagan's picture along with the usual flags and shamrocks. Finally Devlin found a telephone that wasn't surrounded by reveling drunks, in a candy store near Rockaway Beach Boulevard. He called John, who picked up immediately.

"Dial Eileen's number," he said. "She changed the announcement tape—by remote control, I guess. What she has to say is for you."

"Let me get back to you." Devlin hung up and fished in his pocket for more change. A newspaper truck went by, and the driver threw a bundle of papers onto the sidewalk. The old man behind the counter came out to get them. The search for Devlin would be citywide by this shift. Kevin McQuaid would have been able to describe what Devlin was wearing. Eileen's telephone rang four times before the answering machine kicked in.

"This phone probably has more taps than Gregory Hines, and I have only thirty seconds to get this said, but I'm goin' to Macy's before I go on to your friend's. I was questioned all afternoon and I'm just fed up. I hope we can talk—" The beep sounded.

A coded message. Devlin wanted to think about what she was doing, but not here. Rockaway was a peninsula only three or four blocks wide. If he were spotted, it would be easy to seal him off and then tighten the perimeter until they had him. The old man cut the string on the newspapers and put them on the bench under the magazines, then took one for himself. *Shopping at Macy's* was the clue. A long time ago, talking about police work, he had told her that the best way to lose someone following her was to go someplace crowded with people, like Macy's. So she thought she was being followed, and she was going to lose the tail before she went to John's place.

Devlin's next stop was Forest Hills. He wanted to call Paterson. It was almost nine o'clock now. He hadn't forgotten the fourteen hundred Major had paid him. No subway—he had to stay away from people. The old man behind the counter spread the newspaper, a tabloid, almost certainly the *Post*, out on the glass counter. Devlin called John again.

"If your line isn't tapped now, it will be soon. Tell Eileen I'll call her there later. Briefly."

"I wish you'd turn yourself in, Frank."

"You had to get that on the record."

"No, Frank, I mean it. You're spinning your wheels. What you need is a lawyer who eats his young, and nothing less."

"My lawyer is going to love having the prosecution present the tape of this conversation as evidence."

John laughed. "Don't hire a lawyer with children."

Before he left the telephone booth, Devlin got some change ready for a paper. The old man was getting a guy some cigarettes. Devlin moved quickly, keeping his head turned away from the old man, scooping up a *Post*, and dropping the change on the counter in the same motion. Devlin's picture covered two-thirds of the front page. There was no way to tell what the old man had seen. Devlin could only keep on going.

9:24 P.M. . . .

DEVLIN HAD THE DRIVER PULL OVER NEAR ONE OF THE kiosks of the IND 71st Avenue-Continental Avenue station on Queens Boulevard, and then he gave him enough change and small bills to keep him in place counting and able to witness Devlin's descent into the subway. Devlin was not just trying to throw people off his trail. Harry Levine lived five blocks from here; Levine's place was Devlin's ultimate destination.

Levine needed protection, too. The people who had tapped Eileen's telephone could have a van full of eavesdropping equipment parked outside Levine's house right now.

Devlin had visited the house ten years ago, working the One-twelve when Levine had been second-in-command in Narcotics downtown. A weekend meeting, three or four guys. Devlin couldn't remember the case, just the house itself, second from the corner in one of the last tree-shaded neighborhoods in the city. A nice house that was now probably sixty years old, old-fashioned, with smallish rooms furnished comfortably in an old-fashioned way. By now Levine probably had the place paid for; he was all set to roll the capital gain into a retirement condo. Safe and sane. Slow and steady. Only a coronary—or cancer—could pull the rug out from under him.

Up on Queens Boulevard again, Devlin found a candy store with an old-style, folding-door telephone booth in the back. Paterson was in the 201 area code. Information had a listing for a V. DiBennedetti on East Twenty-fifth Street. Devlin lit a cigarette before dialing, and then he let the telephone ring. Mafia don or otherwise, an old man was slow getting to the telephone.

"Yeah?"

It was him, DiBennedetti himself. "This is Frank Devlin calling, and I want to know why you and your people are fucking with me."

"What? Who is this?"

Devlin said his name again. "Detective, N.Y.P.D. I'm being framed for the Brennan and Octavio Lopez murders, and the evidence points to you and your friends."

"What are you talking about? Are you crazy?"

"I'm talking about a call from Bobby Antonucci's apartment in Brooklyn to a telephone in your neighborhood one Sunday morning last February. You were there to take that call. It's enough to subpoena your wrinkled old ass into court, which I will do if this thing gets that far."

"Who are you threatening, you crazy son of a bitch? Don't call here. Don't ask for more trouble than you already got, you punk—"

That was enough of an admission—and the old man was

beginning to blow. Lovely. Terrific. "You got my name right? *Devlin? Frank Devlin?*"

"Yeah, I got your name—"

"Good. Now fuck yourself, fuck your mother the school yard cocksucker, and if you still have any relatives in Palermo, Sicily, fuck them, too. If you know their address." Grinning, Devlin hung up. On his way out of the store, he folded his *Post* carefully. With a newspaper under his arm, Devlin would look like he belonged in the neighborhood, another working stiff on his way home after staying late at the office.

Being careful added another twenty minutes to getting to Levine's house. No one around, no van, no guys sitting in cars. But now it was after ten o'clock. The lights lit on Levine's ground floor might be only a chief of detectives' idea of a crime deterrent while his family slept upstairs. Devlin had wanted old DiBennedetti pissed off—pissed off enough to give himself away, as he had done—but a pissed-off Harry Levine might just slap handcuffs on Frank Devlin.

Devlin went up the short concrete walk and pressed the bell. Chimes sounded within, and then Harry Levine asked, "Who is it?"

"Frank Devlin."

The lock was turned quickly. When the door opened, a cloud of cigar smoke blew out. Harry Levine was grinning. "Schmuck, you got my message."

" 'I'm going home to Forest Hills,' " Devlin said.

"Come in, come in." He gave Devlin room in the small foyer. In the living room, two women were watching television. "I figured I could count on Kevin quoting me verbatim even when I can't count on him for anything else." Levine shook his head. "Can you believe it? You don't know anything about a guy until you wave an opportunity under his nose. What Kevin is doing only tells you what the department is really turning into, a dumping ground for yuppie wannabees. He's still picking up food with his fingers. But apparently Kevin thinks he's smarter than I am. I'd like to see his face right now. Let's go into the kitchen. Do you know my wife? Frank Devlin, Naomi, the detective you saw on the news this evening."

Mrs. Levine was petite, black-haired, with pale skin and eyes, a very pretty woman. "You've changed since those pictures were taken. You call me Norma, Mr. Devlin."

"Nobody calls her Naomi but me," Levine said proudly. "Say hello to my mother." A wisp of an old woman in an armchair nodded. Devlin nodded back. "They're watching *Dynasty*. Reruns. They saw this stuff last fall—"

"Be quiet, Harry," his wife said pleasantly.

He beamed. "Have you eaten? We have some nice chicken, cheesecake, you name it. Wonderful cheesecake. Tell me what you've been doing. Where've you been today?"

Passing into the tiny, knickknack-filled kitchen, Devlin said mildly, "You're a different man at home."

"I should be, don't you think? Relax, you're safe. You're sure you weren't followed?"

Devlin nodded.

"They tried to push me too far today. The mayor and that guy. The commissioner." Levine imitated the mayor. " 'We're not *asking* you to do this, Chief! We're *telling* you!' They wanted me to wreck a man's life for political expediency. They want things tidy by the weekend. A collar. They want to show America that they're on the job. Never mind you. *Fuck* you. Let me get you some coffee. Decaf."

Levine turned on the gas under the kettle. "They know the case against you won't stick. 'By all accounts, Detective Devlin is not a nice man.' The mayor of the city of New York actually said that to justify what he's doing to you. You're all over the television news—"

Devlin waved the newspaper at him. "It's my fifteen minutes."

"They've gone public not just because you're proving to be embarrassingly hard to find. They don't want the press digging into Brennan's death. Or life. Jack Brennan is only an embarrassment to them now. So they would have us believe."

"Why did you want to see me?"

Levine had measured out the instant coffee and now he was watching the kettle. "Let me do this first, then I can sit down." The kettle started rumbling. "You shouldn't boil the water when you make coffee. That's too hot." Delicately he stirred the contents of the cups, then brought them to the table. "Milk? Sugar?"

"Milk. Please."

He poured the milk for Devlin. "Is that enough? Stir it."

"It's fine."

Levine put the container on the table and slid into the chair opposite Devlin. "We talked to Brennan's campaign manager, Marlene Santana. The night of May fifth, Brennan's campaign headquarters was broken into, the files rifled, some of them stolen. Brennan had a lot of confidential material in one cabinet that only Santana and a few others had access to. That included the antimob material he was going to use in the fall, the kind of legislation he was going to propose. Who knows? Maybe he only wanted to have something on paper in case somebody asked. Who knows what these bastard politicians really mean anymore? Anyway, that file was taken, and so was yours."

"Mine? Why did he have a file on me?"

Levine raised a hand to quiet him as his attention was drawn to the door.

"It's time for Mom's toddy," Norma Levine said. "She just remembered that she didn't like the clothes on this show. Go ahead, I won't disturb you. Mr. Devlin, we're pushing cheese-cake tonight."

"No, thanks. Your husband has already asked me."

"That I know. If we listened to him, we'd all weigh four hundred pounds."

"I thought you weren't going to disturb us," Levine said.

"I'm not disturbing you. Do you look disturbed?" She had already filled a tall glass with ice. Now she poured a healthy shot of Scotch over the cubes. "It helps Mom sleep, Mr. Devlin," she said as she took the milk from her husband. "She's been sleeping alone for thirty-seven years, so she's entitled."

"I think so."

"We have harmony. She wishes you well. So do I. Harry tells me your life is nice now."

"It was."

"Everything works out for the best. You'll see."

"Thank you."

"I tell her everything," Levine said belatedly. He looked up. "Are you going to bed now, too?"

"I'm going to watch this handsome Irishman on the news. When you come upstairs, you'll tell me everything from here and now. Right, Mr. Devlin?"

"As it should be."

She kissed her husband on the forehead. "I'll see you later."

Levine waited for her to get out of the room. "Why did Brennan have a file on you? Marlene Santana doesn't know, and neither does the one other person who remembers seeing it. That was his secretary, one of those women with a perfect office mind. She told Gerrity she thought she had done all the filing in that particular cabinet, but that she couldn't remember that folder. When she saw it, she told Gerrity that she thought, 'I don't remember filing that one.' "

"What was in it?"

"She doesn't know. She didn't look in it. Confidential file and she didn't put it there, so she figured she wasn't supposed to look. That's the bad news. The good news is that Marlene Santana did."

"And?"

"Old stuff," she said. "Some yellowed sheets with old-fashioned typewriting about your private life. Copies of confidential N.Y.P.D. documents. A couple of sealed envelopes with nothing written on the outside. Santana didn't open them, of course."

"And this was stolen?"

"Do you have any idea what might have been in those envelopes?"

"No, I don't."

"After the robbery, after the secretary went through the files and made an inventory, she remembered the Frank Devlin file. She told Marlene Santana that it was missing, and Santana told Gerrity that when she mentioned it to Jack Brennan, he didn't know what she was talking about. He didn't know anything about a file on you."

"No witnesses to that conversation," Devlin said. He was thinking of Jack Brennan's letter to Jane Milburn.

"No, but the two women have the same recollection of their own conversation. Now let's see what the testimony points to—''

"That the file was planted so it would be stolen. One bad guy is using others to get at me.''

"One *enemy*,'' Levine corrected. "But you say you don't have an enemy like that.''

"I don't think I'm at the center of it,'' Devlin said. "If somebody hates me that much, why doesn't he just kill me and get it over with? Did you send someone around to Eileen's apartment last night to pick up my car key? Really to identify her?''

"Car key? No.'' Levine stopped lighting his cigar to look Devlin in the eye. "Last night? Does my office know about this?''

"I told my partner to tell Kevin McQuaid.''

"Should I check? McQuaid thinks I'm coaching him from the sidelines, the little son of a bitch. He's got another think coming.''

"Wouldn't McQuaid wonder how you have the information?''

Levine curled his lip. "Nobody who has ever worked for me wonders how I have information. Let's not fuck with each other, Devlin. No one in my office had any instructions to go near your girlfriend last night. What we were developing at the Antonucci apartment—and picking up from informants— points to certain members of the Gambino family in Brooklyn. At the time of Brennan's killing, seven of them were out in Babylon, Long Island, in one of their well-established hangouts, eating bay scallops and linguini with garlic and oil. They drank Fazi-Battaglia verdicchio. They did everything but have their picture taken together. These are the same guys who brag they don't kill innocent people. Their idea of innocent doesn't include anybody they think might know something, like that couple out at Lake Tranquillity, or Janice Drake, the comedian's wife, who had nothing more on her mind than giving little Augie Pisano a blowjob as soon as they dropped off the guy who killed them. Remember that one out by La Guardia? The two of them shot in the head in little Augie's Cadillac?''

"That was before I came on. Why are you doing this?"

"I'm angry, for Christ's sake! Hamilton and Torres have wanted to get rid of me since they took over. Never mind the years I've served this city. Torres knows as well as I do that a case against you won't stick, but by the time you've been dragged through the courts and the media, your reputation will be ruined. And your life. The two of them wanted a cop to do that to another cop." He sucked air through his teeth. "Now listen: We've talked to people who were in the Brennans' lives back when you were married to their daughter. I know you're still legally married to her, but I'm talking about the time you were living together. Underneath the carefully managed facade, the real Brennan life-style sounds like a fucking zoo."

"Tell me about it. I was one of the animals."

"That you were. You were all animals. But it also sounds as if you left with Jim Brennan hating your guts."

"Brennan has no quarrel with me. He gave me my marching orders and I followed them. When we had that last conversation, he told me I'd have no trouble with him if I—" Devlin choked. Stopped.

"Obeyed his marching orders. You already said it." Levine was looking into his eyes again. "Does it still get to you? After all these years, just talking about it, not even telling the story, you're getting rattled. He must have done some job on you."

Devlin had himself together again. "Tell me about Vittorio DiBennedetti."

Levine's eyebrows shot up. "Where did you get his name?"

"I got lucky."

"Kevin told me somebody broke into Jane Milburn's apartment and pulled up the carpet in her room. Did you find something good?"

"I have to hit the road," Devlin said. "It's getting late."

"Don't give me that. I'll take you anywhere you want to go. If you're spotted, I'll just say you surrendered to me and I'm taking you in. No assistance required, thank you, good night, and good-bye. You're safer with me than with anybody else in the city."

"Why did you ask where I got DiBennedetti's name?"

"He's related to two of the men who were in Babylon Monday night. Father of one, uncle of another. Now do you want to tell me how you got his name? You're onto something."

"Maybe you won't think so." Devlin shifted to Kevin McQuaid's voice. "I got it from Detective Anthony Corella, who was working Bobby Antonucci's apartment."

Levine couldn't suppress his mirth. "Now I really would like to see Kevin's face. Why did Corella tell you that?"

"This McQuaid asked him if he had anything new on the telephone calls from the apartment." Devlin told Levine what Corella had developed out of the Sunday morning call to the liquor store in Paterson. The neighborhood guy who had opened the store for DiBennedetti last January might wind up buried under Jimmy Hoffa. Devlin had to figure out something for that man. *No good deed goes unpunished.* Devlin realized he had thought that about himself recently, and now he remembered: after Tom Quinn had vomited on him. Method acting. The world's a stage.

And remembering that made Devlin remember something else, something that intrigued him.

Levine said, "I didn't hear about the DiBennedetti connection before I took my walk on Hamilton and Torres. The old man took the call outside his house? Does he think his line is being tapped? When Kevin calls here again, I'm going to tell him to see what New Jersey and Washington are up to, if anything. Even so, what was so important to the old fart? Guys his age spend their winters indoors. They don't want to take chances catching the flu. And for a man like him, who knows he's going to hell, it had to be pretty important."

"What do you know about him?"

"He's always had close ties to the Gambinos. Last summer I saw a photograph of John Gotti listening to him respectfully at a wedding. I'm going to tell Kevin to ask some questions of the New York Organized Crime Task Force."

"Maybe you can find out who went to Eileen's door."

"It sounds like an FBI trick. The guys who built your frame have had months to I.D. your girlfriend. We'll see. You were right not to telephone me before you came here. If Torres hasn't tapped my line already, he will soon. I want you to stay in touch. The longer you're free, the better chance we have of breaking this thing. That's what I believe. I'd love to shove this up Hamilton's ass along with everything else that's been up there. They might find Judge Crater, for God's sake. Can we be truthful with each other? Can you agree to that?''

"I have to protect myself. Do you want to take me into Manhattan? I'll tell you about my last day with the Brennans.''

"All right, that's good enough.'' Levine got up. "I have to tell my wife that I'm going out. Finish your coffee.''

Devlin did, and not because Harry Levine thought it was good for him. Devlin was not in the mood to wander around the living room, thinking about the happiness in this household. He and Eileen had harmony, too. If this had been a normal night for them, they would be asleep already.

Levine returned wearing a light windbreaker. "Naomi's up there laughing because she remembered you were the one with the crack about my breath.''

"The cardinal has a spy in your office.''

"I know about him. The cardinal I can handle. Come on, I don't want to be out all night.''

"I remembered something else,'' Devlin said. "Just before Antonucci shot Lopez, I heard a horn blow. Twice.''

"Good remembering. We have it all on tape. As a matter of fact, we think that the tape tells us something. The horn blows when the picture shows Lopez beginning to emerge from the van. The picture was on a half a dozen screens inside the Tombs. Two were allegedly unmonitored at the time. Both of those sets are within reach of telephones. If—if—somebody on the inside wanted to tell Antonucci that Lopez was ready for killing, a word to a guy in a car with a cellular telephone would start the process. A guy at one of those screens had the best view of all of Lopez. The horn set Antonucci in motion. We *think*.'' He led Devlin into the garage. "We have the number of guys who could have done it down to forty-three.''

"The car used in Major's killing today had a cellular telephone.''

Levine eyed him. "Yeah, you have to stay free.''

* * *

The rain had stopped and the streets had dried to black semigloss, but here and there on Queens Boulevard potholes filled with rain flashed under the wheels. This was Harry Levine's own car, a Peugeot with one-sweep wipers that Levine operated with an intensity that bordered on mania. Out of the house, Levine was turning into the chief of detectives again. When Devlin said that the last two weeks with Maryellen fifteen years ago were mostly a blur, Levine snapped that that sounded like bullshit.

"We were on a bender," Devlin explained. "And not the first one. This started the week after Labor Day. Maryellen and I had taken a place out on the North Shore, figuring that with the reduced rates we might also get peace and quiet. We needed that, because our problems were getting worse and worse."

"What problems?"

"Booze. She was speeding. She'd smoked a lot of hash that summer. I didn't know whether I was drunk or sober. The way we dealt with each other would have turned us into nervous wrecks anyway. She would do things to enrage me, and I never knew where the hurt was coming from next. I did a lot of yelling and breaking things. In addition to all our other problems, we were snake-bit. Nothing worked right. The place we rented had a view to the west, and the setting sun poured in at the hottest time of day. We went out for lunch and little flying bugs attacked her sandwich so relentlessly we had to abandon the table. She'd put on so much weight that she'd taken to wearing a nightgown from the bathroom to the bed, then taking it off once she was under the sheets. I was supposed to pay no attention. She was miserable with herself, and that didn't make me less jumpy. More than anything else in those days, I was jumpy. I was falling apart."

At Sixty-third Drive the traffic light stopped them and a patrol car crossed their bow.

"Is this car known?"

"Nah," Levine said. "When I'm in this car I don't want to be known. You're talking about the week after Labor Day. What does this have to do with two weeks later?"

"It was like watching a plane crash. You can see it coming, there's nothing you can do about it, and then for a long time afterward you're dogged by the agony of the moment. I'd just made detective, working out of Manhattan North. You remember my boss, a good guy—"

"Yeah, what's-his-name. I know who you mean."

"Let me get on with it. Saturday afternoon. There were kids playing on the rocks below our balcony. I was talking about my boss, I don't know why, and suddenly she said she'd seen him before the holiday. I asked her when. At least a week had passed. How long would it take your wife to tell you she'd seen your boss?"

"From the time she got in the door, a minute and thirty seconds. She'd say, 'I gotta pee, then I got something to tell you.' "

"Right. But the way Maryellen did things, I figured I was supposed to drag it out of her. It was one of her little games to keep the attention focused on her. I asked her, 'What did you talk about?'

" 'You, mostly.'

" 'What did you say?'

" 'Nothing bad about you, Frank. Don't worry about it.' "

Levine laughed aloud. "What a *lulu*!" He caught himself. "You're a lot older and wiser now, I hope."

"I was in love with her. The good times were perfect. *Seemed* perfect. I kept hoping we'd find our way through. Not this time. I'd caught her in so many lies that I couldn't be sure that she hadn't pulled another damned stunt with Sid Levitt. That's his name. Eileen says the first thing that goes is the memory. So I asked Maryellen again and got the same answer. When I asked her a third time, I got, 'I don't want to talk about it anymore. It's not important.' I even tried to live with that, but as I say, she'd already done too many other things."

"Finish the story."

"That Saturday, when we should have been watching the sunset, I couldn't help coming back to what she might have said to Levitt. With her track record, she might have even gone out of her way to plant a lie. I told her I couldn't live with what she had told me. She said that if I didn't like it, I could get out. It wasn't her father's money that had paid for the place, it was mine. We lived on my income, had a nice apartment in Flushing, and unless she wanted something special, my salary paid the bills. For a two-hundred-dollar dress, she went to her father, who had always given her everything she wanted.''

"The only sure way to ruin a child for life," Levine said.

"She always had plenty of spending money from him, too. He would give her a thousand at a crack. In any event, the place on the shore had been paid for with money I'd earned, and she was trying to throw me out of it. So I threw her out. I pushed her out the door. She had the money for a motel, I knew, so I figured I was free to get even more drunk than I was. I did, and passed out. It was dark when I woke up, and I expected the place to be empty, but she was asleep in the second bedroom. She knew me. She'd waited until I'd knocked myself out.''

"She crawled back, but not far enough to give you the satisfaction.''

"Whatever. I still had it in my mind that she'd tried to throw me out of a place I'd paid for. I pulled her out of bed, dragged her by the hair across the floor, opened the door, and literally kicked her butt out. She said, 'You'll regret this the rest of your life.' ''

"How about her? Do you think she could have meant that?''

Devlin shook his head. "I didn't see her for the next two days, but she called me at home Monday night, saying she wanted to come back. She'd already done that so many times, I'd lost count. The beginning of the last disaster. I was sick . . .''

"From what?''

"The booze. You really don't know. Nothing will stop a real drunk from drinking except the threat of death itself. We were scheduled to spend the weekend of the eighteenth in Jamaica Estates.''

"The whole weekend?''

"The house was big enough. Charlotte liked to have everybody together. She'd told Maryellen that she wanted us to set an example for the boys, when they married. Everybody could be just as close as ever. I doubt—'' He stopped, thinking of Jack

Brennan's letter lodged in the pedestal of the stool in the lunch-eonette, and its revelation of sex among brothers and sister.

"You doubt what?"

Devlin was ready with a believable lie. "I doubt if Charlotte had any idea of what the future held. So we went. Early. I had more vacation days. We went out on Wednesday. The fifteenth. Maryellen was always able to smile her way publicly through anything we were going through privately, and this visit was to be no exception. She wanted to say that we'd had a wonderful time out on the Island. I was sick enough to be nasty and keep her wondering if I would perform as ordered. On Wednesday night I just started drinking, pissed as hell with her. I didn't sleep, didn't even try to go to bed. My recollection—for what it's worth—is that Jack and Joe set about the same pace. In the morning I was brooding again about what she could have told Levitt."

"Did you ever find out?"

"I already knew. It was stupid and pathetic, and explained perfectly why she wouldn't tell me. She told Levitt that we were planning to have a family."

"What was she doing, springing a surprise on you?"

"No. She'd already had three abortions. I'd stopped talking about having children after the last one, a year and a half before. I'd seen Levitt on Monday. When I told him I was having terminal marital problems, he was stunned. She hadn't simply told him that we were planning to have children. She'd spent an hour elaborating on it, telling him how much in love we were, more in love than ever. She knew we were in terrible shape with each other when she spoke to him. I thought about it a long time afterward. She had no need to say anything at all to him, of course, but that was the one thing she could say that left her in a favorable light with him . . . no matter which way our marriage went. That was later. On that last trip to Jamaica Estates, it was still sinking in. She didn't know what Levitt had told me. I wasn't going to tell her, either. I started Thursday sleepless, hung over and with her latest whopper very much on my mind. Having a hangover means you're still drunk, just on the downside, with your motor functions and judgement still impaired. I decided I was going to stay in the room all day. Maryellen was beside herself. I'd never shown any of our real life to her parents. 'Tell them I'm sick,' I said. 'Tell them anything you want.' I was in that frame of mind, still drinking, thinking I was pacing myself, telling myself that I was right next to being sober. She came up once, in the morning. 'As far as they're concerned downstairs, I'm looking in on you, the way a good wife should,' she said. 'What I really want to know is how long you intend to maintain this reign of terror.' ''

Levine chuckled. ''Maybe you were still drunk, but at least you weren't pussywhipped anymore.''

''There was more to my behavior in those years than that,'' Devlin said. They were approaching Sunnyside. ''Living with a drunk is never a day at the beach.''

''You live near here, don't you?''

''Three blocks south of the boulevard.''

''Tell me where to turn. I want to drive by and see if anything is happening. You can keep talking.''

''I don't want to get picked up.''

''You won't, I told you. What's the matter, you don't believe a cop?''

''Cops are pricks,'' Devlin said. ''Ask them. I decided at three o'clock to go downstairs, which meant that I got there at four-thirty. I thought I was sober, but I was stiff, my eyelids at half-mast, my gait a cross between John Wayne's and Robert Mitchum's, or maybe both at the same time.'' He'd gone straight to the bar, he remembered. ''Joe was out, Maryellen elsewhere in the house, and everybody else was dead quiet. I didn't get the idea.''

''The other night you mentioned an actress.''

''Lisa Wagner. She was there with Jack. Charlotte was there. And Jim. Jack and Wagner went out into the backyard, and Charlotte went upstairs.'' Devlin heaved a huge, shuddering sigh. ''Turn left. When you get to Forty-eighth Avenue, turn right. I was standing at the French doors, watching Jack and his ladyfriend outside. I was beginning to feel uneasy as well as sick, but I still didn't have a clue to what was going on.

When the hairs on the back of my neck were straight up, Jim Brennan said, 'Okay, fuckhead, into the library.' ''

"Did he usually talk to you that way?"

"He did a couple of times. Once when he thought I'd organized an orgy for his sons—I hadn't—and another time when Maryellen ran home after one of our arguments. He was wise to me, he said, and he was just waiting for me to fall on my face. Those were his words both times."

"Why?"

"He considered me a drunk—and a nobody who didn't love his daughter. He was two for three. I loved her more than I knew."

Levine made the right turn and allowed the car to roll the short block to Devlin's apartment house. Outside the building, a four-door sedan was double-parked. Levine pulled up behind it. A rental, by the sticker on the rear bumper. Devlin turned his eyes upward. The windows on the third floor were dark. The scene was so still, it looked like a photograph of itself. Devlin was about to say he wanted to finish his story when a middle-aged woman with the beginnings of a dowager's hump emerged from the building entrance and walked quickly past their car. Levine spoke just as Devlin felt a shock of recognition.

"I know that woman," Levine said.

Devlin watched her cross the street: she was headed home. "You know her as Liz Weinstein. She's in the Queens D.A.'s office."

"How do you know her?"

"I've known her since she was seven years old. I went to junior high with her brother."

"I hear more than that in your voice. She looks ten years older than you. What is she doing here?"

"Probably leaving a note for me," Devlin said. "The FBI questioned her last week about my connection to Jack Brennan, and she got around to telling me about it yesterday morning. I asked her to pass along the message that I hadn't seen Jack Brennan or heard from him since 1971. I asked her to tell me how they reacted."

"Let's get that note." Levine turned the engine off and set

the brake. He shoved a snub-nosed .38 in his jacket pocket. "It's a hell of a thing when you need a backup to enter your own home, but in this case, you do."

"We'll take the stairs," Devlin said.

The halls were empty. The mailbox contained nothing but bills and junk. Upstairs, Devlin eased the door open slowly. Liz's note was on the foyer floor. The interior of the apartment was dark. With Levine covering him, Devlin stepped in and turned on a light. What he saw on the wall, from the ceiling to the floor, gave him a moment of mortal terror. Blood, still sticky. He did not want to see the rest of the place. "It looks like a massacre happened here," Levine said, going ahead. "I guess they had a special at the slaughterhouse." He picked up the note. " 'Call me.' That's all it says. Why didn't she call you? You have an answering machine."

"She's afraid I'm being bugged. Liz doesn't take any career risks."

The place was wrecked, blood spattered everywhere, some of it wet, the couch and love seat slashed, books spilled from their shelves, drapes pulled down from the windows, linings ripped out. In the bedroom, the answering machine light glowed steadily—five messages or more. The second bedroom that Devlin used as an office had been rifled. Levine called him from the bathroom.

"Just in case the idea eluded you."

In the bloody sink was a heart the size of a football. On the mirror, in blood, were two words: LAY OFF!

Devlin told Levine he had called Vittorio DiBennedetti less than two hours ago. "Some of the blood is still wet. I have to assume that they're acting that fast. I can't take the chance of looking at it any other way."

"You were tripped in the subway and your tire was flattened. Love taps. Your bookmaker was murdered today because he was talking to you—oh, I know all about it. Now you've been told to keep away. Loud and clear. The next message is going to be louder still, but you may not hear it, because it will be the shot that kills you."

"They wanted me alive," Devlin said.

"And framed."

"Alive and framed," Devlin repeated. "I don't see how it makes sense. What's the point of it? Let's get out of here."

Levine started out. Devlin stopped in the bedroom and took the message tape out of the recorder and put it in his pocket. Levine watched him from the hall. "Finish what you were telling me about Brennan."

Devlin stayed silent until they were in the elevator. "We're not going to Manhattan. I want to find out what Liz Weinstein has to say."

"I'll drop you off," Levine said. "If she doesn't take any career risks, she doesn't want to see me."

"All right: Brennan. He wanted to talk to me in the library. He turned the lock on the door. He had never done that before. I still thought I was only going to get a lecture on making a pain in the ass of myself, but then he took the glass from my hand. 'You've already had your last guzzle of Brennan booze.' I made a little move to take it back, and he saw it. 'Look at you. Life as you've known it for the past five years is over. You're on your way out the door, and you're such a lush you can't think of anything but more liquor.' It started like that, and went on for a long time. I couldn't possibly repeat it for you word-for-word." They were outside now, headed for the double-parked Peugeot. The rental car was gone. "He had a laundry list of grievances. Complaints. Some of it had obviously originated with Maryellen, but just as much must have started with Charlotte . . . That woman didn't like me, really did not like me. One thing was something I'd said at dinner three years before. Maryellen's reduced standard of living without anything else to show for it was another. It went on and on."

Levine started the car, and Devlin gave him directions that would take them to Eileen's house. He wanted to hear the answering machine tape. Levine asked, "How are you supposed to have something to show for a reduced standard of living?"

"I understood what he meant," Devlin said. "I *was* a bad guy. I was an alcoholic when I met Maryellen."

"She didn't help you," Levine said.

"One of the reasons I've stayed sober since is that I've accepted responsibility for what I did while I was drinking. Brennan got hotter and hotter. For a while I was able to insulate myself from the things he was saying, but he kept at it. I've never seen such a rage before or since, and he was still building. I was helpless. He knew things about me I thought no one could know."

"What kind of things?"

"How I was conducting myself outside the marriage, mostly. I don't want to go into that, if you don't mind. He knew about my family, my background. I've always assumed he'd hired private detectives . . . ."

"And you're wondering how anyone could have found Antonucci and Octavio Lopez? Come on, Devlin, this is what we've been looking for! You still want to know who framed you?"

"No, Jim Brennan is helpless. Even if he weren't, he wouldn't kill his only surviving son. He loved both of them. He was proud of them. They were his young heroes—that's what he called them. What did you just tell me about the Gambino connection?"

Levine turned onto Forty-eighth Street. "All right, finish. I have other things to tell you."

Devlin kept his eyes straight ahead. "The cursing stopped, and then he said, 'So you're out. Out of the house, out of our lives, out of my daughter's life so that you'll never see her again! Never, do you understand me? *Never!* If I ever see you again, if any member of my family ever sees you, or hears from you, or you attempt to communicate with Maryellen in any way, I will hurt you.' He leaned in, and even though the last thing he said came through his teeth, the spit kept flying out of his mouth. He was shaking with rage, as if he were having a seizure. His face was almost purple. He said, 'You'll be worthless to Maryellen. If you don't stay away from her, I will have your dick cut off. All that will be left of your sex life is the desire. *Now get the fuck out of here!*' And then he spat in my face. Three times. It took me that long to get away from him. You can stop in the middle of the block."

Levine was silent. Maybe he was thinking that Devlin had

taken the story too far, but Devlin knew what he had omitted, or glossed over: why he had sat there and taken Brennan's abuse until the spitting started. A drunk's weepy cowardice. Devlin had known it at the time, deep inside himself, that he was at the climax of five years of disgracing himself. He'd known it and done nothing, frozen not by the force of Brennan's monstrous rage, but his own craven hope that somehow he would be allowed, finally, to continue his mad waltz with Maryellen.

Devlin had to keep his head clear. He had to remember that he had been over all this again and again in the years afterward, as he put himself back together piece by piece, slowly, with the help of Bill Ward and a dozen other guys for whom 12-Step work was the joy of their lives—and the salvation of Devlin's. Devlin had to remind himself that the years between September 1971 and the present had been years of sacrifice, struggle and, through A.A., service to others. He was a different person today. *I am*—he almost said it aloud.

Levine said, "And you don't think Brennan is the cause of your trouble?"

"Why did he wait fifteen years? And even if he did, he would have needed advance knowledge of his son's murder—his only remaining son. No. Absolutely not."

Levine stopped under a streetlight in the middle of the block. "What I'm going to tell you stays between us—don't even tell your girlfriend. Donald Manes wasn't the only casualty in the mess here in Queens, and if he hadn't killed himself, he probably would have been murdered. The people who shot down Paul Castellano outside Sparks Steak House last December wanted it public—an old-fashioned gangland execution, just as the newspapers called it. Another message, and sent to a hell of a lot of people. Castellano was killed not because of any goddamned dope-dealing but because the conviction of the judge out here for bribery threatened not only to expose the mob's hold on the Queens judicial system, but the alliance the mob has with politicians in every borough in the city. The alliance is holding, even though Manes is dead and Stanley Friedman is as good as convicted. Donald Manes understood himself perfectly when he put a knife in his own heart. Stealing is the major business of the government of the city of New York today. That convicted judge hasn't talked and never will, no matter how much time he serves, because if he says word one, it will be his last. As strong as the mob has been in the past, it's stronger than ever today, and it means to stay that way. This is really why the mayor and the commissioner want you brought in. Any revelation at all is likely to open a larger can of worms. You start running your mouth about Brennan and DiBennedetti, the press will tie in Johnny Gotti and the rest of the Gambino family, and then the Brooklyn politicians. Domino effect? No end to it. The mayor would be running for his life. He can't even think about you talking to anybody. *Anybody.*"

Devlin was staring ahead again. "I didn't help my situation when I called DiBennedetti. There's a guy in Paterson I jeopardized, too. He opened a liquor store so DiBennedetti could take a special telephone call. It won't take a rocket scientist to figure out that the guy talked to the police."

"I'll take care of it. I know that this is the street where your girlfriend lives, not that Weinstein dame. I suppose you want to hear that answering machine tape. If there's anything on it, let me know. Stay in touch. Devlin, you've got the cops, the' mob, and maybe what's left of the most powerful political family in the city after you. You don't have the reflexes and eyesight of a young man, *and* you're exhausted. When was the last time you used your weapon in the line of duty?"

Devlin was getting out of the car. "I never have. Thanks for your help."

Levine shook his head. "You may need more than I've been able to give you."

11:22 P.M. . . .

HE COULDN'T REMEMBER THE LAST TIME HE HAD BEEN in Eileen's apartment without her, and he felt like a ghost, outside himself. He went straight to the bedroom and replaced her message tape with his own, rewound it, and pushed the play button. The first message was from Eileen, essentially the same as the one she had put on her own announcement tape. There were two from the guy from the *News* whose earier call Devlin had not returned. Two from a young woman who identified herself as a producer on *Live at Five*, the local NBC magazine show. And then the last, a male voice as flat and monotonous as death itself: "You made a mistake talking to my father. Faster than you can imagine, we're gonna hunt down who you love best in the whole world, and then we're gonna kill her."

Devlin headed out, turning both locks after him. Another of the few advantages to being a drunk was knowing where all the public telephones were. There was a bar on the northwest corner of Forty-seventh Street and Forty-eighth Avenue, practically right around the corner. Devlin wasn't as sure now as he had been in Levine's company that it had been the FBI that had identified Eileen the other evening. And that would mean that the wrong people would be able to hear Devlin calling John's number to warn Eileen. They could have that white Lincoln rolling even faster than they had this morning. Morning: Devlin had been going nonstop for fifteen or sixteen hours. And contrary to what Levine had said, he was not exhausted. If anything, Devlin was getting still another wind. He had change ready for the telephone before he entered the bar.

John picked up on the second ring. "It's me. On my answering machine was a clear threat to Eileen's life. Brooklyn-based wise guys. It's my own fault. I called their daddy and cursed their grandmother. Don't open the door until you see uniforms and I.D.s."

"She's sitting right here, Frank," John said calmly. "Want to say hello?"

"I certainly do."

He heard the handset being moved. "Hello? How's your ugly old self?"

"Like horseshit, as my mother used to say, all over town. Were you being followed earlier this evening?"

"I certainly was!"

"Describe him for me."

"Oh, he was FBI."

"How do you know that?"

"He was better dressed than your lot, and certainly better dressed than you, you old sod. He was fair, and had smooth skin, not so much like an Englishman as a Scandanavian, or even a German. The Hitler Youth Bureau of Investigation. He wasn't much good at follerin', either. At first I thought he was a sex criminal, he was so obvious. I wanted to go up and tell him to lay off, but then I thought maybe he was being obvious to scare me, and *that* scared me. Sorry. Tell me about yourself."

"I've been busy. I won't be able to talk for long. In addition to all that, you've been threatened. By the other side. Until those people are taken off the board, you should take every conceivable precaution. I just told John. He knows what to do."

"Whatever you say. I saw the news about Major on the television. John and I were just talking about it. Oh, I really am so worried about you, all my foolish jokes aside."

"*Don't* worry about me. I'll call you again when I have the chance."

"Do you want to talk to John again?"

"Yes." A gloomy, balding young guy sat at the bar, a beer, a pack of cigarettes, and a pile of bills in front of him. He thought he had problems? His problem was that he was sitting in a bar, drinking, smoking, and wasting his life. *There's noth-ing worse than a reformed drunk, Devlin.*

John said hello. "Call Levine," Devlin said. "He's in the Queens directory. Give him another ten minutes to get home. Tell him what I told you about the threat. He'll tell you what to do next."

"You really are full of surprises, old man. The whole de-partment's looking for you, and you're with the chief of detec-tives, exactly where nobody thought to look. Willie Nelson says something about choosing old age and treachery, every time. I thought Levine had taken himself out of it."

"Stick with old age and treachery, kid. I've never seen any-one work a case harder. Given what Hamilton and Torres are trying to pull, Levine is right where he can do the most good. I'll call you later."

Devlin headed straight down Forty-seventh Street to Fiftieth Avenue. From there it was only three short blocks to Liz's place. He wasn't blaming himself for having stirred up the Di-Bennedetti family. The old man had given himself away with his remark about Devlin being in enough trouble. And if his son and nephew were upset with Devlin, why weren't they going after *him*? Now, after Major's death? They didn't know he had witnessed it—that was it. Of course. They hadn't understood the meaning of Major's trip out of the restaurant and back again. Devlin wasn't sure he could identify the one man in the car he saw clearly, the driver. He'd seen only the shooter's profile as he turned to point the gun through the driver's door.

He was still two blocks from Liz's house when he realized he was seeing something. . . . What? It was like stepping into one of those what's-wrong-with-this-picture? puzzles. There was another double-parked car outside Liz's building. . . . No, not *another* car, Devlin realized, the *same* car! The same rental sedan that had been double-parked outside his own place. Had somebody seen Liz at his place? *Somebody?*

"Liz!"

He ran. Someone had followed her from his place! If he yelled again, would she hear him? *"Liz!"* Beyond the vesti-bule, the door to the inner hall was locked. Devlin pressed

Liz's button. No answer. He went outside again to see if her lights were on. Yes. Now, as he approached the front door of the building, it opened. Devlin was six feet from the man coming out. It was Lederer, and he was wet from his hands to the elbows with blood.

"You!"

Lederer rushed him. Devlin brought up his knee, but Lederer turned away to protect himself. The collision drove Devlin back against the fender of a car. Lederer kept coming. Devlin hit him with both fists, getting only the left past Lederer's upraised arms. Lederer punched at Devlin's groin. Devlin got his thigh up, but the punch hurt there. Lederer knew how to fight. Devlin was going to have to kill him. Lederer got him around the waist. Devlin punched down with his right fist. He couldn't feel any effect. Devlin's clothing kept him from getting his gun. Lederer bit him on the arm as Devlin punched him in the face, straightening up just in time to get kneed in the balls—hard enough to be lifted off the ground. As much as he could, Devlin rode with it. *He'll be able to kill me!* Devlin came down clawing for his gun as the pain curled him into a ball. He fired once as Lederer moved to kick him again. Devlin didn't think he'd hit him, but Lederer turned and ran anyway. Devlin was trying to keep from blacking out, trying to get himself up and moving. Lederer got in the car and started it as Devlin keeled over backward. He thought he was up again at once, but the car was already screeching away.

Liz!

Devlin hobbled into the vestibule again, broke the window on the inner door, and reached in to turn the knob on the inside. The elevator was still on the first floor. Devlin had to remember the floor of Liz's apartment before he could push a button. He was still gasping. When the elevator door opened again, he lost his balance stepping into the hall and smacked against the opposite wall. Liz's door was open, and light from inside slashed across the hall. He saw blood on the inside wall before he pushed the door open the rest of the way. Blood all over the apartment, in sprays, not splashes, on the walls, the ceilings, but most of it on the carpet, almost a trail back to the bedroom.

"Liz!"

He thought he was hearing something. He called her again. His pain made him hold his groin as he crossed the living room. She was sprawled on her back on her bed, her hand to her throat, covered with blood. Lederer had slit her throat and left her to run through the apartment pumping out her blood like a Sunday chicken. She was still alive. Trashing Devlin's place, Lederer had heard the elevator ascending, watched through the peephole as she slipped the note under the door, and had thought she was Eileen. He had taken the stairs to follow her after he had seen Devlin and Levine get out of the Peugeot. It had been that close.

Devlin took her in his arms, and she clutched at him, her eyes on his. The slash was four inches wide, through her windpipe. The blood wasn't pumping hard now. She knew what was happening and had stopped fighting it, profoundly unhappy and afraid, more and more second by second. "I'm sorry, baby," he cried. She looked at him angrily. He shook his head, but then she nodded, indicating, Yes, you! She was tagging him with it. And she was right; she wouldn't be dying if he had told her to butt out instead of encouraging her to run errands for him. Had she thought they could get back together again? He knew she had felt something for him, if only a sense of what they had lost. His pity overflowed. "I love you," he whispered. He knew he was telling the truth. At the end of her life she was putting herself in the rest of his for good.

He had never seen anybody die before.

He held her closer. Her bloody hand came toward him, and then her eyes stopped moving. He wanted to think he was seeing a little more, another moment, but she was dead weight. He put her down on her back on the bed.

And stood up. He had to get out of here. He was covered with her blood. He wouldn't get very far looking like this.

An old woman was in the hall, one hand tentatively up to her lips. She turned and ran into her apartment as Devlin hurried to the elevator. He had to get to his apartment and change clothes. Silently—maybe the electronic bugs wouldn't pick him up. Lederer! The Quinns had died in the orange Pontiac. Had that been their car? Devlin was thinking of the airline ticket on the seat. Lederer was not a New Yorker, if Devlin remembered his mid-American accent correctly. Now he was driving a rental car. Lederer had rented the Quinns' house. The scam in Lake Tranquility had required an import, somebody never to be seen again. Devlin had seen Lederer twice now. Was that enough for Lederer? He'd just killed Devlin's girlfriend, hadn't he?

Devlin was able to stay off the street by using the courtyard of the Celtic Apartments to get to Forty-eighth Avenue, a route he'd taken many times in his boyhood. No sirens. Yet.

THURSDAY, JULY 3 . . .

12:31 A.M. . . .

DEVLIN GRABBED SOME ITEMS FROM THE BATHROOM, then took fresh clothing up to the roof and changed there. He would be able to hear police coming to the building—and the roof wouldn't be their first destination, giving him the chance to go down the back fire escape. The bloody clothing would be found no matter where he stashed it, so he had to take it with him. That meant going back into the apartment for a bag. He couldn't help believing that the police were just minutes behind him. Certainly they would be tapping his partner's telephone now. At this hour Devlin had only one move anyway, and after that, he was going to get a lawyer. In the orange Pontiac when the Quinns had been found had been the airline ticket folder. Devlin remembered that. TWA's colors: Devlin remembered that, too. Devlin was thinking that if he were Lederer, he was deciding he'd seen enough of Devlin. And he'd activate the open ticket he'd been carrying around for days, maybe weeks. It was such a long shot it should be taken off the board, but it was the only shot Devlin had at this hour. All he had to do was pick the right airport.

He was in and out of the apartment again in less than a minute. He headed down Forty-eighth Avenue to Fortieth Street, the next street that would let him walk against the traffic. No one was going to roll up behind him. Less than two blocks ahead, on Queens Boulevard, was the Flushing elevated line, with connections to both airports, but what Devlin was hoping for was a metered taxi. He figured he'd have to call for a gypsy and wait for him. A blue-and-white charged up the boulevard, lights boiling. No siren. That would be for

239

Liz, the first of many. All the officers in those cars had just eyeballed Devlin's picture, and Liz's identity, when it was learned, would have some of them wondering about a connection to him, and maybe wondering about a connection to that bookmaker killed up on Queens Boulevard, too. The arresting officer would get a commendation for sure. The farther away from Devlin a fellow officer was, the easier it would be for him to capitalize on the luck of spotting a cop supposedly gone sour—or nuts.

Liz's face was in front of Devlin's eyes. He sensed that it would be easy for him to lapse into shock even now. Lederer had thought he was doing Devlin's girlfriend. It *could* have been Eileen. Devlin wanted to focus on that: strangely, it was the easiest escape from the fact that the actual victim had been just as innocent. *Dead is dead,* he thought. *No one ever really hates the dead.*

Another blue-and-white came along while he was standing on Queens Boulevard, waiting for the light to change, and he saw two more cars turn into Forty-fourth Street from the other direction. At least Liz was in official hands now. What was going to happen to her diabetic mother? And just as quickly as he'd asked himself the question, Devlin decided that it was his business to find out what happened to Liz's mother.

An empty metered taxi was coming—and behind it, still another blue-and-white, its boiling lights starting the instant he saw it. Had they spotted him? Had he already started to flag the taxi? He had to raise his hand again, he saw that, and that the blue-and-white was close enough for one of the cops inside to pick up a false gesture. The taxi began to brake. Devlin had to keep his eyes off the blue-and-white, off the two men sitting in the front seat, another in the back. *Stop looking!* At the last second, the blue-and-white swerved around the taxi, barely missing it. Now Devlin stared. The police car had come within inches of an accident that would have nailed him—because the driver *wasn't* paying attention. Devlin got into the taxi.

''Where to?'' the driver asked. He was a young black guy,

and he had a folded copy of the *Post* on the front seat beside him. Devlin's picture was face down.

"The airport."

"Which one?"

"Kennedy."

After he lowered the flag on the meter, the driver punched the steering wheel once, hard, and cursed through his teeth. Devlin sat back. At a traffic light the driver could idly turn the paper over and match the picture on the front page to the man sitting behind him. Being trapped with a driver who didn't want to go to the airport was bad enough under normal conditions; if he matched Devlin to the newspaper photograph, he might come after him with a tire iron.

They were in Elmhurst when the driver said, "Look, man, I don't really want to go to the airport."

"Take me to Forest Hills, where I can catch a bus."

"How about Woodhaven Boulevard? There you can catch the train to Forest Hills."

Devlin didn't answer; if he gave in too quickly, the driver could become suspicious. As the driver looked in the mirror, Devlin turned his eyes to the sidewalk outside. He put his hand up to block the driver's view of his face. "Split the difference," Devlin said. "Rego Park."

The driver laughed. "Ah, fuck, I'll take you to Forest Hills. 'Split the difference.' That's hot!"

Devlin had to discourage the guy's attention. He moved away from the lights from the passing stores and kept his face turned to the shadow. The driver looked in the mirror another time, turned to the road in front of him, then suddenly back again, locking eyes with Devlin.

"Hey, I know you."

Devlin sat back, reaching for the door handle.

"Yeah. You're the guy on Channel Seven who reviews the movies. Some job you got. Do you ever get to meet any of those movie stars? The women, I mean?"

"Oh, sure." Devlin let out a sigh in spite of himself. "Most of them are all right, but a few are pretty crazy."

"Oh, yeah? Tell me about a crazy one."

He swung onto the Long Island Expressway. He had forgotten about not wanting to go to the airport. Devlin leaned forward. "Let me have your paper there. I want to check the price of a stock. Then I'll tell you all the stories you want to hear about the celebrities I've known."

"What's your name, man?"

Devlin didn't answer. Who was the driver confusing him with? Devlin didn't watch television anymore. He opened the paper and folded the front page back on itself.

"Come on, man, what's your name?"

"I'm going to let you suffer," Devlin said amiably.

"Come on, man, I'm not kidding you! Tell me your fucking name!"

"I don't want to tell you my fucking name."

"Oh, no," the driver seethed. "I'm not puttin' up with any of that shit! Gonna get you the fuck out of my cab like *now*!" He pulled over to the right lane, blowing the horn. Devlin took out his shield and his gun, then pulled the guy back by the collar to see them. "Take a good look. Do you know my name now?" Too subtle for the driver. Devlin pushed the barrel of the gun into the guy's neck. He was wild-eyed with terror. "You just take me to the airport, or you'll be in trouble the rest of your life."

The driver squirmed as he stepped on the gas again and moved to the middle lane. "Fuck, why didn't you say you was a cop in the first place?"

"Just shut up," Devlin said. If Devlin took the newspaper, and had a little luck, the driver might never report the incident. He was going to know that Devlin's destination was the TWA terminal. Devlin simply didn't know JFK well enough to get out at another terminal and walk the rest of the way. They were in the airport, Devlin following the color-coded signs, before the driver spoke again. Devlin cut him off. "TWA. And if I ever see your ass again, I'm going to set it on fire."

At the terminal, Devlin got out of the cab with the newspaper under his arm. He had the fare and a good enough tip ready. The driver said, "Let me have my paper."

"Get another one."

"None of that shit, man. Don't take my fuckin' paper!"

Devlin leaned in. "I *need* this paper! Don't interfere with an officer!"

The driver moved away. "You really are one ugly mother-fucker, do you know that? Did anybody ever tell you?" The driver gunned the taxi out into traffic again. He blew his horn a couple of times, changed lanes, and then disappeared from view.

Devlin entered the building in a purposeful manner. Even if there weren't any N.Y.P.D. bulls on the premises, there was bound to be a Port Authority plainclothesman who might have seen his picture, or a private TWA flatfoot whose attention would be attracted to a hesitation or false gesture. Only two clerks were working the check-in counter. Fewer than a hundred people were in view. Lederer would have had to clean up. He had a room somewhere, probably not far from here— a subculture of anonymity surrounded airports. Who would understand it better than Lederer? A quick shower, a change of clothes, gathering up the incriminating evidence, checking the room one more time for anything that might have been left behind. Lederer probably had a pocketful of fully operational credit cards bearing a half a dozen names. He had made a lifelong study of killing people for money. And Devlin had made a lifelong study of people like Lederer, trying to figure out how their minds worked. Criminals weren't like the rest of the population. Their minds were more primitive, evaluating everything in terms of threats and opportunities. Where was Lederer? How had he perceived tonight's events? Devlin spotted a plainclothesman, a young black man with a newspaper folded under his arm. He was sitting in a passenger waiting area, smoking, his eyes working the crowd. Devlin continued toward a combination coffee shop–bar, keeping his eyes focused on his destination. If the plainclothesman had been alerted to Devlin, he hadn't adjusted for a change in clothing. The coffee shop would give Devlin a view of the plainclothesman and the entrance to the building beyond. A television screen showed that the next flight, to Paris, was leaving in fifty minutes. Lederer was not going to Paris. Lederer was not a Paris kind of guy.

Devlin ordered a small container of coffee and moved to a table in the back of the coffee shop. In a few minutes the plainclothesman got up and moved to the other side of the waiting room. All he could see of Devlin was the profile of a guy reading the *Post*. Hours had passed since his last cigarette, Devlin realized. He wondered if he could turn his mind away from them for a little while longer—a hell of a thing to think about, under the circumstances. The plainclothesman opened his paper, another *Post*. Weren't there any other newspapers in town? For all Devlin knew, the morning papers—the *News*, anyway—had bigger, newer pictures of him. He felt somebody pull up to the table behind him.

"You are one smart motherfucker, aren't you?"

Devlin didn't turn around. He knew Lederer's voice.

"I want you to get up and walk toward the front entrance."

"What are you going to do, take me for a ride?"

"Don't fuck around, Devlin. You could be dead in a heartbeat. No point in killing a cop. Besides, certain people would be very mad at me if I dusted you."

"Old DiBennedetti, you mean?"

"Shut up. Just walk."

The plainclothesman was looking the other way. To get to the entrance, Devlin was going to have to walk right past him. Lederer had a gun, no doubt about that; all he had to do was leave it in a toilet before he boarded his plane. "Tell me about DiBennedetti," Devlin said.

"I told you to shut up. Get moving. This could get *real* ugly if you don't listen to me. See that woman over there? If I kill you here, I kill her, too."

Devlin got up. He had to figure this right. The plainclothesman might not even be close to being a real cop, like a security guard, completely untrained. He had been easy enough to make. Devlin wasn't sure he had seen the guy take a single precaution against being spotted. Devlin couldn't be sure that Lederer hadn't made the guy, too. Devlin moved forward, noticing that Lederer stayed back far enough to keep Devlin from getting a good look at him. "Why is DiBennedetti framing me?"

"For making it personal."

"What?"

"You made it personal. You and the Brennans."

"It's bullshit. I never heard of Vittorio DiBennedetti before this afternoon."

Lederer gave him a little push. The plainclothesman saw it. He tried to act as if he wasn't suddenly alert, but he wasn't fooling Devlin. Lederer said, "I'm only telling you what was told to me. There's no fucking point in arguing with me about it."

The plainclothesman saw that Devlin was trying to make eye contact. Devlin gave a little jerk of the head. The guy's eyebrows moved. Devlin didn't know what Lederer was looking at. They were twenty feet from the plainclothesman. "I don't see how those people put me in the center of it. I haven't seen any of the Brennans, including my wife, for more than a decade. Why does DiBennedetti want me alive?"

They were passing the plainclothesman. He had his face in his newspaper. If Lederer had seen his eyebrows go up, the guy was just calling more attention to himself. Beyond the row of plastic chairs was an information booth, empty now.

"Hold it right there!"

The plainclothesman. Devlin dived for the information booth. Lederer turned with his gun drawn, catching the plainclothesman with his hand still inside his jacket. Lederer's gun boomed, a hole appeared in the plainclothesman's wrist, and he started to sag. He had a look of unhappy surprise that said he knew he was dead. People screamed. Lederer fired a second time, and the man fell. Devlin had his gun out. Lederer turned and Devlin fired, yelling, *"Son of a bitch!"* The first shot hit Lederer in the neck, and Devlin felt a bubble of glee. He stood up and shot twice more, hitting Lederer in the chest. Lederer tried to get his gun up, but Devlin fired again, from a distance of only six or eight feet, aiming for Lederer's face. The bullet hit Lederer in the corner of his left eye, and he fell back. People were still running. Devlin got out his shield. "Police! Police!" He pocketed Lederer's gun, a .45 automatic, then patted down Lederer's jacket. A .45? Not the gun that had been used to kill the Quinns. The check-in clerks were standing, staring. "Call for assistance," Devlin yelled at them as he found the keys to the rental car. The little chain carried a tag bearing the license number. He moved toward the entrance. The clerks still had not moved. "I'm going after the other perpetrator! Call the police!"

Outside, Devlin put his gun away and headed toward the nearest parking lot. He'd be all right in Lederer's car until Lederer was identified and his last moves backtracked. Maybe. Devlin started shaking. DiBennedetti thought *Devlin* had made it personal? Wonderful: a career criminal had decided that Devlin was his enemy. So what was the point of letting him live? Or going after Eileen to punish him? There was only one way for Devlin to find out. He had to stay free. There would be plenty of time later to consult a lawyer, the aftermath of this might see him in court for years. This was the time of day for him to travel. If he paid cash for a motel room, he might get some sleep, too. All he had to do was clear his mind of everything on it, and not worry about cops—or the Di-Bennedetti family—breaking into the room while he was asleep.

4:46 A.M. . . .

HE COULD SEE HIS OWN PATTERN NOW, DRAWING INTO the comfort of zero-horizon darkness and the warmth of old memory. Some scientist two centuries from now will be able to relate it to primordial animal behavior under similar threatening circumstances. He was in a motel room in New Jersey, on his back with his eyes closed. His mother wasn't far from the surface of his thoughts. He was thinking about Liz, and his late cousin Alice, and of Eileen so frightened for him earlier tonight. Women's lives ruled, wrecked, and possibly destroyed by men. Devlin would never have met Eileen if not for the trouble in Ireland. Some psychologists insisted that the world would be no better off if it were ruled by women. All Devlin could see was that in this world there was no way to know, no vision or technology capable of lifting the clamp of male warmaking, and the effects of winning and losing, from the hearts and souls of women.

Devlin was trying to rest, and in those moments when he realized it was impossible, he forced his thoughts back to old Jim Brennan—Devlin aware that he was running to the refuge of himself as cop, avenger, warrior, away from life's nightmare rising up around him from every side.

Liz. Liz and the Brennans, Liz buying eagerly into her piece of the nightmare, giddily telling him a story her mother had passed on to her about old Jim Brennan, this one from back at the start of World War II, or shortly before it, when Brennan and his whole generation were younger than Devlin was now— or Liz *had been*. His horror and grief for her gave him a sad, strange perspective of the passage of the generations from youth through adulthood to old age. When were adults not railing against the primal terrors of childhood? When were the old not pathetic replications of themselves as children, surrendering at last to those same terrors? Liz's mother's story was about a girlfriend modeling in the garment district before the war, a woman who could not have been thirty at the time, perhaps barely twenty-five, not a woman in Devlin's eyes so much as a girl. . . .

One of Jim Brennan's girlfriends. By the time Devlin heard the story, he knew that what Maryellen had told him about her father seducing and raping her girlfriends had been a bit more than attention-getting or neurosis. The model had met him at a cocktail party, and that night, at her apartment, he made it clear that it would be easier for her to yield to him than struggle. Whatever the truth, she was left ready for more, and when he called again, repeatedly, at all hours, she acquiesced, drawn in as much by her curiosity about him as her appetite for the excitement of having sex in the front seat of a car or the backseat of a taxi, against a wall or out on the terrace of a penthouse. He wasn't generous or even especially kind, but she was young and a certain amount of roughhouse spiced the experience. But she was a model; dark circles, the unfashionable kind, began to appear under her eyes, and she broke it off. . . .

Until two years later, the height of the war. By then she belonged to a senator, and when she saw Brennan in a crowded, noisy Washington restaurant, she tried to avoid him. A few minutes later she looked up to see him standing in front of her. He said hello to her senator, calling him by his first name, and then said hello to her. The senator lapsed into silence, and the model had no trouble at all identifying who was the more important of the two men. A busboy told the senator that he had a telephone call, and the senator quickly excused himself. Brennan sat down beside her and, according to the story, immediately put his hand up her skirt. No panty hose in those days, and as a model she was too slim for a girdle. His fingers worked inside her.

"You're spending the night with me," he was supposed to have said.

All she could do was stare at him. Two tables away sat a Supreme Court justice and a member of Roosevelt's cabinet, who smiled and waved when he saw Brennan, who smiled, but did not wave back. In another few minutes the busboy returned with a note for her that expressed the senator's regrets; he had been called to an emergency subcommittee meeting.

Brennan wasn't smiling. He had a suite in a hotel around the corner, and she didn't get out of there until two o'clock the next day. He hardly spoke, and never smiled. What he had taken a month to do to her in their last go-around he was able to accomplish easily in a single night. A part of it was very painful, and she bled for a long time afterward. She thought they would be seeing each other again, but no, she never heard from him again. She never heard from her senator, either, and when she returned to New York to get her old modeling job back, it was no longer available. She spent the war working in a magneto assembly plant in Brooklyn, where she met the man she eventually married, without ever mentioning Jim Brennan, whom she held responsible for the downward turns her life had taken. She never knew how, or why. She told Liz's mother she felt as if she had been buried alive.

On the bed in the motel room in New Jersey, Devlin struggled to remind himself that this was at the heart of Liz's lifelong curiosity about the Brennans, and her curiosity about the events of the past several days. Devlin struggled to remind himself, but logically enough, the idea wouldn't stick. He let his mind wander, and soon he was drifting in and out of consciousness. . . .

10:46 A.M. . . .

As soon as he awakened Devlin was moving, sitting up in the unfamiliar bed. The voice he heard was his own, crying out in alarm. He saw that he was all right, alone in the room. Devlin peered through the venetian blinds at the traffic sweeping by on Route 4. It was a nice day, overcast but pleasant. He showered and dressed quickly, feeling his stomach grumble. By now John's home telephone surely was being monitored, but Devlin dialed it anyway. It rang nine times before Devlin hung up again. Now he called John's Ninth Precinct number.

"She's still there, Frank," John said. "We have a signal: I ring twice, hang up, and call again. And then she doesn't talk.

I talked to Levine last night. As of then, he still had complete confidence in you. Told me to make sure Eileen was safe and not discuss her whereabouts with anyone but you. He called this morning, less than half an hour ago. You were positively identified as the man who survived the shoot-out at the airport. They haven't publicly connected you to Liz Weinstein yet, but they do know you were at that apartment. Apparently they're covering up the exact details. I brought up the subject of you turning yourself in. He said that if you wanted, he would call some lawyers. You'll need the best in the city. He said that.''

"Lederer slit her throat. He thought she was Eileen."

"Turn yourself in, Frank . . .''

"There's more to this than I can tell you now. And you know I can't talk long. Please tell Eileen that I'm all right.''

"Of course.''

Devlin hung up. Now he was going to have to get some distance from the motel before he could stop to eat. Liz and that plainclothesman would be alive if Devlin had taken John's advice when he had first offered it. Devlin drew his breath and tried to slow himself down. It was pointless to look for other people to blame for any of this. He wanted to be free, able to eat when he was hungry, not marched to a commissary with a thousand other men. In his position, other people would be doing the same thing, and there was no shame in being tough about it.

He missed what the map had showed to be the exit closest to DiBennedetti's place, and then spent twenty minutes sorting through Paterson's numbered streets and avenues—and getting lost and turned around until he was in front of a courthouse with so classical a set of columns and frieze on top that it looked like something out of a movie set. Definitely not DiBennedetti's place. A cop who looked like a bouncer in a whorehouse stocked with ugly women gave him directions that led past a little waterfall, then some old red brick buildings that looked nineteenth century. The cop's directions seemed right, the turns where they were supposed to be, the street numbers counting off as satisfyingly as an office clock marching toward quitting time. Out of the downtown area, Paterson looked settled and comfortable with itself, like a couple married long enough to have a second refrigerator in the garage. Ninety-five percent of the buildings were covered with aluminum siding. The siding made for so many horizontal lines that the whole place looked like it had been drawn on the looseleaf paper in a schoolboy's notebook.

Devlin ran the same pattern past DiBennedetti's street that he had tried yesterday afternoon in Brooklyn. Two-story houses lined both sides of a tree-shaded block where there was plenty of curbside parking, like Sunnyside forty years ago. On a workday most cars were elsewhere. Devlin made the turn for a drive-by. The numbers on the houses were easy to see. Devlin couldn't go too slowly, or a second time around, lest some self-appointed street-watcher take him for a burglar.

In the middle of the block was an opening in the trees, and a shallow lot that was in fact a manicured lawn dotted with garden sculptures and a pair of concrete birdbaths. In the rear was a bright, freshly painted trellis heavy with tiny, pearlescent grapes. The house next door seemed to wear its aluminum siding more as a disguise than weather protection or insulation. DiBennedetti wanted anonymity? The three-story house was too big for that, too well-maintained. It took this style of life to the tenth power.

The driveway was on the far side, and as the rental car's forward motion revealed it to him, Devlin froze. The white Lincoln was backing toward the street. On impulse, suddenly feeling the most intense rage, thinking of Major, Liz, and the Quinns, and the plainclothesman, Devlin stepped on the gas and cut the wheel hard, holding on to it tightly. The impact lifted the rental's rear end clear into the air, but the seat belt held. Devlin saw the two heads in the front seat of the Lincoln snap like balloons on strings. Devlin struggled to get Lederer's gun out of his belt. The other two guys were still stunned, only beginning to move. Devlin was out of the car, gun drawn. What was he supposed to do? He couldn't bring them in without getting busted himself. He couldn't bring them in at all from New Jersey—he wasn't a cop here. The driver was climbing out.

"Hands up! Up where I can see them!" As the other guy opened the far door, Devlin slammed the driver against the side of the car. "Tell him! Tell him I'll blow your fucking brains out!"

"It's him, for Christ's sake!" the driver shouted. "Don't do anything! He's crazy!"

Wide-eyed, the other guy raised his hands. The driver was the same one who had been behind the wheel yesterday. Devlin patted him down quickly, watching the other as he did it. No gun, but not a good search, either. Devlin glanced back at the house. Nothing. He could feel the blood pounding in his ears.

"You can't do this," the driver growled.

Devlin hit him, clubbing the side of his head with such force that he startled himself. The guy hit the pavement as if dead. The other guy went for the Lincoln's glove compartment. Devlin poked the gun through the open door and fired. The compartment door folded like a beer can and the guy yelled, backed up, and began to wet his pants. Devlin's own bladder opened a bit. *Swell*, he thought. His eyes still on the guy, Devlin pulled the mangled door open. A .25 revolver, a ladies' gun. Now Devlin's hands were full. With his little finger Devlin pulled the Lincoln's ring of keys from the ignition. "Around the front of the car. Come on, where I can see you." He backed up so he could get the front door in his field of vision. "All right, pick him up."

The guy bent halfway. "Aw, look at the size of him. I can't do it alone."

"I don't give a shit. Get him on his feet."

"He's bleedin'. You hurt him bad."

"Up!"

A woman yelled from across the street, "I'm gonna call the cops!"

Devlin didn't look around. "I *am* a cop!"

"I can see the blood!" she answered. "That ain't right. I'm callin'!"

He looked around. She wasn't in sight, doing her yelling

from any one of a dozen windows. When Devlin looked back, the guy was breaking into a grin.

"You were just talking about me," Devlin said.

"We decided you're nuts, and I don't mind telling you."

"I don't want to be fucked with!"

"You're an asshole." He glanced at the little revolver. "You don't know how you're making it worse—"

Devlin brought the butt of Lederer's .45 down on the bridge of the guy's nose, flattening it like an eggshell, the bone crunching almost audibly. The guy fell backward with a whimper, eyes rolling as he lost consciousness. Devlin pulled fat wallets from the jackets of the two men, then stepped toward the rental, the front of which was deeply harelipped. Was there some other trouble he could cause? As he backed up, he committed the Lincoln's license plate number to memory. The wallets contained dozens of credit cards. He had their names, he could identify the car and driver in Major's murder. If he lived.

He had come out here to talk to DiBennedetti, and if necessary, squeeze out of the old man what he knew about Jack Brennan's murder. Mobsters from Brooklyn, a connection to a man who was almost ninety. They said Devlin had made it personal, he and the Brennans. What did that mean? If he got through this, he was going to have to build a completely new life, a new identity. There would be no annulment. These people had known so many other things about him, they must have known he was petitioning Rome. Notorious figures didn't get annulments, and now, thanks finally to the *Post*, among others, Devlin was a notorious figure. In that way these guys had hurt Eileen before he had cursed their old man. He was not sorry about what he had done to them now. It even felt good. *Sick*.

Ten minutes to twelve. He wanted to regroup, get himself together. A reaction was setting in. Jack Brennan had been buried this morning in Calvery Cemetery in Sunnyside, and this was the first that Devlin had thought of it. He had probably fractured the driver's skull. His own head was spinning. Eileen, Major, the rooftops of his childhood offering a look at the funeral that probably marked the wrecking of what was left of his life.

Time to check into another motel, one that allowed him to park the car where it wouldn't be seen.

12:27 P.M. . . .

HE TOOK THE TURNPIKE DOWN TO THE APPROACH TO the Lincoln Tunnel, and then pulled off when he saw a six-story motel that looked back over the Meadowlands. He was feeling a little nauseous, his skin clammy with cold sweat. Maybe he hadn't come as close to dying today as he had last night, but his body was telling him something about what it expected in the future. The DiBennedetti family was that kind of angry now. Because of his call to the old man last night, they had concluded he was crazy. Had their earlier information on him led them to believe that he was going to submit passively to being framed and having his life destroyed?

He got a room on the fourth floor with a view of the parking lot, and he was barely inside when his stomach started heaving. Devlin had not had his head in a toilet in thirteen years. As a child he'd wanted to know what caused the roar of a flushing toilet, and his mother had told him, "Blitzen the whale." This wasn't the time to be remembering such things—why was it happening? His stomach heaved again, and involuntarily he yelled, bellowed, as his empty gut kept seizing. He knew what came next. It was as if he had been on a three-week bender. Sweats. Chills. Weakness. In the old days, when he was hung over and still drinking, hours passed before his strength returned. He was in better shape now, and knew how to put himself right.

He was still thinking about the DiBennedettis having so much misinformation about him. It gave him an edge, strengthened his resolve. Killing those two in Paterson wouldn't have helped—that was a kid's solution. In his old age his father had said he was grateful that he had never had to kill anybody. By then Devlin had come to terms with the reasons why he had become a cop, and it had warmed him to hear the old man express his own feelings about killing. Too late for that now, even if he didn't feel any remorse about Lederer. He had always wondered how people could kill and not feel remorse. Now he knew. Lederer had been human garbage. If you were going to kill and get away with it, you had to know that about your victim. Not feel or believe. *Know.*

If Devlin had come close to killing again today, it had been when he had conked the driver of the Lincoln. Rizzo, James Rizzo, according to his driver's license. The credit cards were in five different names. The other guy was George Gentile, with an even richer assortment of cards. Both guys were in their late thirties. They'd been kids when Devlin had made plainclothes. Why had he bothered with police work? Maybe it was time to retire—as if Devlin had another alternative now.

He cleaned up and got out of his clothes and eyeballed the car in the lot below. It was in a corner, its battered front end tight against a wall so it could not be seen. Devlin turned on the television set. A notice laminated to the top said the motel had a satellite dish, and listed scores of channels available. Local news wouldn't start until five o'clock. With the set tuned to *Headline News Service* and the sound turned very low, Devlin called John Lord.

"I was hoping you'd get back to me sooner than this," John said. "I called Eileen at my place right after we hung up to give her your message, and she didn't answer. I went straight up there, siren blasting, and she's gone. No sign of a struggle, but the kitchen looked like she left in a hurry. I know that's not like her . . ."

"What do you mean, she left in a hurry?"

"Breakfast dishes still on the table. I take Eileen to be the sort of woman who cleans up after herself."

"Yes, she is. Did you call Kevin McQuaid?"

"He wasn't available, but Vito Mariano was. He said he didn't know a thing about Eileen. I called her job, just to be sure. She didn't call in, which she told me she was going to do. That would have been at ten o'clock, so we have a pretty good idea when she left my apartment. Early. There's more, just as bad. The FBI is looking for you now, too, in connection with Liz Weinstein's death. Apparently she had a confidante in her office, and told that person she had seen you on Tuesday night. A neighbor positively places you at the scene last night. You're in all the papers this morning, and on television, too, according to three guys here."

Devlin cursed. "Take this down and put it to use in case I get unlucky." He read the names and addresses on the driver's licenses. "Rizzo drove the Lincoln yesterday on Queens Boulevard. Don't ask me how I got the information. I have to go."

He disconnected and dialed Eileen's office. The television screen showed St. Patrick's Cathedral from a neighboring high rise, zooming in on the front steps as a gleaming coffin was borne down by six somber men in black suits and gray gloves. A woman veiled in black, obviously Anita Brennan, followed. The telephone in Eileen's office rang once and the squeaky-voiced receptionist answered. Watching a ravaged Jim Brennan rolling out of the cathedral, in an electric wheelchair, Devlin asked to speak to Eileen. Charlotte stepped into view beside Brennan, looking angry as much as grieving. The receptionist spoke as Devlin leaned forward in the expectation of seeing Maryellen step out into the sunshine. "She didn't come in today, Mr. Devlin." The picture went to a young man in a blazer holding a microphone.

"Did she call in?"

"No, she didn't. Is something wrong?"

Devlin paused. "Uh, no. Everything's fine. Thanks. Thanks for your help."

"The reason I ask is, you're the fourth person to call about her today."

"Fourth? Did the others identify themselves?"

''No, but to tell you the truth, a couple of them didn't sound too nice.''

''Thanks. I wanted to know that. Thanks a lot.''

''Uh-huh. Good-bye.''

Nobody seemed to want to say You're welcome, anymore, as if it were demeaning instead of gracious. Devlin sat back. He wanted to stay in control of himself. Mariani was no George Washington, but Devlin couldn't proceed on the assumption that he had lied to John. Three other calls to Eileen's office? John accounted for one of them. There were three candidates for the other two: the FBI, Levine's office, and the DiBennedetti family. That Devlin has sensed nothing from Gentile and Rizzo about Eileen was irrelevant. How many wise guys had been at that dinner out on Long Island the other night? But could they have learned that Lederer was dead, or that he had gotten the wrong woman, in the time before Devlin's arrival in Paterson? What had been on the morning news? If the DiBennedettis had somehow learned that Eileen was at John's apartment, she was already dead.

No. All that had been out of order at John's apartment had been the breakfast dishes. No signs of forced entry, no resistance on her part. Someone had rung the bell and talked her into opening the door. Because of her experience in Ireland, Eileen was as savvy as anyone. She must have seen N.Y.P.D. shields or federal identifications. Devlin had to stop worrying.

Now the television set showed the tall ships in New York Harbor. In his mind Devlin replayed the scene at St. Patrick's: no Maryellen—or Maryellen so slow following her parents that she had been edited out. Which? After so much time, what did Devlin know of her behavior? His memory seemed clear enough, but was it accurate? Devlin called Eileen's number and entered the two-digit code that replayed her messages. Kevin McQuaid identified himself.

''I was one of the detectives who questioned you yesterday, Miss O'Sullivan. Please call the Chief of Detectives' office at your earliest convenience.'' He gave the number, and then the machine signaled no more messages.

Devlin dialed the number. Vito Mariano answered. Devlin asked for Kevin McQuaid.

"Who's calling?"

"Frank Devlin."

"Jesus. Hold on."

Another extension was picked up. "Hello, asshole. Tired of playing Willie Sutton?"

"You're too young to remember Willie Sutton."

"I'm too young to remember you, you old turd," Kevin McQuaid said. "Are you going to turn yourself in like the mayor asked you in a very nice way, or do we have to track you down and shoot you like the fucking dog in the street that you are?"

"Where is Eileen?"

"John Lord got told not once, but twice, the second time not two minutes ago by me, that this office doesn't know squat about your girlfriend's whereabouts. Hold on . . . don't hang up." Devlin heard him say to someone else, "Really? *They* want him *too*?" McQuaid said to Devlin, "So now you're wanted in Jersey for assault with a deadly weapon, maybe attempted murder. One guy has a concussion—"

"That guy also has an eyewitness who puts him behind the wheel of the car driven in the killing yesterday in Queens."

"You left the scene, nitwit. A defense attorney is going to make shit soup of your testimony, especially after what you did today. Are you having a nervous breakdown, or what? What the hell were you doing in Paterson? How did you get DiBennedetti's name?"

Devlin did McQuaid's voice. "There's this punk in the Chief of Detective's office who's on this case . . ."

"I don't sound like that!"

"Ask the guys working Antonucci's apartment. *Now*: Why did you call Eileen? Why do you want her to call you?"

"Confidential police business—"

Devlin hung up. On the television screen, an old hillbilly crooner was displaying his upper plate and nostril hairs while titles of songs Devlin had never heard of slid upward in front of him. Devlin switched to CNN. On the screen

was the temporary stage on Governor's Island. Devlin turned
the volume up.

". . . thousand Elvis impersonators. Elsewhere in New
York, at famous St. Patrick's Cathedral, family, friends, and
political leaders mourned the death of senatorial candidate Jack
Brennan . . ."

The screen showed the tape he had just seen on the other
channel. Devlin's neighborhood of Sunnyside was one of the
many, many New York areas that did not receive cable.
The only reason most of the city didn't have cable was that the
politicians wanted larger bribes than even cash-fat cable op-
erators were willing to pay. By the look of this, they deserved
each other. Maybe America deserved them both. Now the shot
of Jim Brennan being wheeled out onto the steps. ". . . the
widow of the slain candidate, followed by his parents." No
mention of Maryellen. None.

Devlin was remembering how Kevin McQuaid had told him
that he didn't know what had happened to Eileen. All cops
were good actors. Kevin had to suspect that Eileen knew
something of Devlin's whereabouts and activities. If she were
in custody, it was not illegal procedure for him to lie about it
to Devlin or anyone who might be loyal to him, like John Lord.
Devlin dialed John again.

"I want to ask you something about Kevin McQuaid—"

John cut him off. "I just got off the phone with your friend,
Father Loncaric. He wants you to call him. It's important, he
said. I want to talk to you, too. It may be that Loncaric has
the same thing on his mind. It's time for you to come on in.
You're not guilty of anything, and anybody with a brain cell
working knows that."

"That's not so now." He told John what he had done in
Paterson. "Going there in the first place wasn't the brightest
move I've ever made, but I wanted to stir things up. Now I
can see some eager beaver prosecutor saying I coldcocked
those guys only to foul his case against them for Major's murder. I ran from the scene yesterday. I can hear Mr. Eager
Beaver asking a jury why I ran if I wasn't guilty of something.
When I was with Major yesterday afternoon, I still thought I

was acting under Harry Levine's directive. I thought I could do myself some good. At this late date I can't even prove I was in Sussex County Monday night. The FBI knows that Jack Brennan's campaign headquarters once contained confidential files with my name on them, and that when somebody broke into that office, those files were taken. I was trussed up and ready for roasting long before I was aware of anything moving against me.''

"Time to come in, Frank. Really.''

"Why are you pushing it?''

"By your own admission, you're making things worse for yourself.''

"The mayor and Torres have a lot to keep covered up, too! You know the city stinks from top to bottom!''

"I'm not going to get into an argument with you,'' John said calmly. "You know you're not going to be allowed to walk away from what you did in Paterson. If one side doesn't get you, the other will. Our side *will* protect you from their side, which will kill you.''

"Ah, shit.'' Devlin closed his eyes. "What about Eileen?''

"Call Loncaric.''

"Did he say something about her?''

"No, he said it was important. Look, Frank, no matter what, *come in.*''

"Not while Eileen could be in trouble.''

He hung up and went to the window to check on his view of the car. A police cruiser was rolling down the street, beyond the parking lot, away from the rental car. Devlin had arrived at the window just seconds too late to know if the police had spotted the car. The cruiser turned the corner and disappeared behind the building. Devlin couldn't take chances, not in this jurisdiction. Being a New York cop cut no ice in New Jersey. If he were caught, he'd be booked and jailed until bail could be set, and without any real property, he might not be able to find a bondsman to cover him. He started dressing as he reached for the telephone again. He dialed 4.

"Front desk.''

"Hello down theyah. Ah'm upstayuhs heah on the thud floah

and mah lady saw the po-lice goin' ovah this lil ol' cah out in the pahkin' lot. Is theyah gonna be a shoot-out o' somethin'? Should we stay in owah room?''

"The police just pulled up in front now. Do you want me to ask them?''

"No, thass quaht aw rat.'' Devlin hung up and grabbed his shoes, socks, pants, and jacket. If he'd known the desk clerk was going to be so loose-lipped, he wouldn't have bothered to struggle through an Alabama accent. He didn't finish dressing until he was between the second and third floors on the fire stairs. Unless these cops were completely stupid, they would learn from the desk clerk that Devlin was on the fourth floor, and then they would call for backup. He had to be considered armed and dangerous. For the next few minutes, Lederer's car would be unattended—maybe. Devlin had the keys. He also had two guns, but in all likelihood, the cops didn't know about the second. The .25 was small enough to fit inside Devlin's sock. The wise guys wouldn't have volunteered to the Paterson police that they had been carrying a gun in their glove compartment. They had probably explained the bullet hole as more of Devlin's craziness.

The fire door opened onto the side street. The car was only about a half a block away. If Devlin had calculated the time correctly, and if these cops were doing their jobs properly, they were in their cruiser. Was Devlin supposed to run? He was walking so fast he was breaking into a trot. Good enough.

The air in the car was oven-hot. His eyes on the outside rearview mirror, Devlin started the engine. He wasn't going to be able to take the car through the tunnel. All he wanted to do was get a mile or so distance, near a bus stop. Another problem: the Port Authority Bus Terminal. It was crawling with cops, many of them in plainclothes, and they were almost certainly on the lookout for him.

Devlin rolled out of the lot as quickly as possible without drawing attention to himself, turned up the hill toward the tunnel, and mashed the accelerator. As he reached the crest, six blocks away, the rearview mirror showed the police cruiser nosing around the corner. Devlin kept the pedal to the floor.

He couldn't take any kind of a chance, even checking if they had spotted him. They would see in the next two seconds that the car was gone. Devlin's palms were so wet with sweat they were slipping off the steering wheel. Psychiatrists said that criminals *liked* this. They liked living on the edge, getting as close to the edge as possible.

"Assholes!" he shouted. *"Assholes!"*

The Hudson Tubes—they were called PATH now. After the war, when he was still in grade school, his aunt and cousins lived in Irvington, beyond Newark. The Devlins had made the trip by public transportation. Focusing on that experience, Devlin suddenly remembered the dank smell of the tubes, like nothing he had encountered before or since. *Journal Square* popped into his mind: the hub of Jersey City. A PATH stop was there or nearby, and in just minutes he would be back in Manhattan—but far downtown, near the World Trade Center and all the Liberty hullaballoo. Not the worst thing: it was easier to hide in a crowd, easier to move around. His only added problem might be finding a telephone. He had to call Steve Loncaric. And he wanted to talk to Vittorio Di-Bennedetti.

Now more than ever.

4:12 P.M. . . .

"STEVE, IT'S FRANK DEVLIN. WHAT'S ON YOUR MIND?"

"Eileen is safe. She's here. I could have told your partner that, but I thought maybe his telephone was being tapped."

"Good thinking. Let me talk to her."

"She's lying down—asleep on the couch in the office upstairs."

"What made her leave John's apartment?"

"A telephone call. She had a signal with John. The phone rang twice, stopped, started again, and when she picked up, no one spoke. Someone was checking to see if she was there. It was all she needed. She came here, very rattled. This is the one place they wouldn't dare violate."

"Steve, the cops are looking for me everywhere. The mayor and the commissioner are behind it. The mob killed Jack Brennan. There's some suspicion that they killed Joe eight years ago."

"What does that have to do with you?"

"That's the part I don't know yet," Devlin said. "Some files in Jack Brennan's office had my name on them, they were stolen during a break-in, and that's where they got the idea that I was involved, I *think*. They could have killed me at anytime, but haven't yet. I made things worse for myself today, but given the story of my life, that shouldn't surprise anybody."

"What did you do?"

"I cracked a couple of heads. Forgive me, Father, but I don't think I've sinned. If I don't learn anything new in the next couple of hours, I'm going to get the hell out of town. I'm going to wait until dark before I come for Eileen."

"What time?" Loncaric asked.

"Figure nine o'clock. The streets are full of uniformed cops. Did you see Maryellen at Jack's funeral?"

"I didn't attend, Frank."

"Why not?"

"I was on other business for His Eminence."

Loncaric's tone had turned flat—cold? Devlin said, "Nine o'clock," and hung up. Almost five hours to kill. The more time Devlin spent in this place, a bar with a pizza and pasta menu, the better off he would be. He called DiBennedetti. No answer.

The waitress told him the scampi was the best thing on the menu, shrimp on a bed of linguini, in a sauce made with the real Italian green olive oil. He'd want extra bread to sop up the last of it, she said. He told her he wanted extra garlic, too, but no wine in the sauce.

She didn't look up from her pad. "Coffee?"

"Yes."

He kept his eyes on the television set over the bar. More Liberty celebration coverage: tall ships, the battleship *Iowa*, thousands of pleasure craft of all shapes and sizes, forty thousand of them expected tomorrow, lists of street and tunnel closings, warnings that tomorrow night's fireworks were going to be heard from Brooklyn to New Jersey.

Eileen had spent years trying to get into this country, and now the man who loved her probably was going to have to get the hell out. Devlin had to stay free one more day, until the banks opened tomorrow morning. His father's little green box had contained over twenty-seven thousand dollars—now in his son's safety-deposit box. His insurance and Devlin's savings brought the total to almost eighty thousand. Jail was no place for a cop, particularly one with Mafia enemies.

DiBennedetti. An old man, an evil old man. Joe Brennan had decided to go after organized crime and had died. Jack was about to announce he was going after organized crime, and *he* had died. Not surprising, especially if their father had run with tough guys in his youth. That was personal, all right. The old rule about not bothering the innocent, including family, existed because guys like DiBennedetti didn't want it done to them. The new Colombian gangsters didn't observe such niceties; when they wanted to teach a man a lesson, they strangled his child, raped his babysitter, and left his wife with a salami shoved down her throat.

At 7:30 Devlin tried DiBennedetti again. This time the telephone was picked up after the third ring.

"So you decided today that I'm crazy—"

"And then you proved it, stupid son of a bitch!" the old man roared. "You want to die? For guys like you—"

"You wanted me to live," Devlin said.

"Why didn't you mind your own fucking business?"

"You were framing me. You killed my friend of twenty-five years right in front of my eyes. That *isn't* my business?"

"Come on! You were going to walk and you knew it. Nobody believed it for a moment."

"You got that from Vito Mariano in Harry Levine's office," Devlin said, "or you gave it to him. Thanks. Now let's talk about your evidence on Mayor Hamilton . . ."

"You're so fucking stupid I can't believe it. We had all the stuff there is years ago. We own him. We've *always* owned him. We run New York. We ran it when I was a kid. The only time we ever took a step backward was when that little prick La Guardia was in there. Stupid son of a bitch, not even seeing your bookmaker friend get it taught you anything. He couldn't keep his mouth shut. Now it's you not only shooting off your mouth, you break my nephew's nose. You tell me how we're supposed to let you get away with that?"

"You tell me why you roped me into your bullshit in the first place!"

"Ask your wife," DiBennedetti said, and hung up.

Devlin was gasping, dizzy. He returned to the booth and waved the waitress over and motioned for still more coffee. He didn't want to try to talk. He was supposed to ask Maryellen? A woman he hadn't seen in fifteen years? If what he had seen on television was a glimpse of reality, Maryellen hadn't been at the funeral. What had Anita Brennan said about her? *Yes.* Suddenly Devlin thought not of Maryellen, but of Liz Becker. How long had she been married, in the mid-seventies, between her two affairs with Devlin? Four months?

"Oh, God. Oh, my God." Devlin pushed change into the telephone. Anita Brennan said hello, and he identified himself.

"I have to locate Maryellen. My life may depend on it."

"Let me get the telephone number for you." She put the handset down, and a moment later he heard her talking to someone else. Silence, then other voices, distant, murmuring. Finally Anita Brennan said, "Some friends have come by, Mr.

Devlin. I've never needed people more. The Brennans own this house, and they've ordered me out of it in thirty days.''

"And you're out of the will.''

"Out from under Jim Brennan's thumb, too, I'm happy to say. Oh, I will be so happy to see him die. He was in his wheelchair today for the benefit of a sympathetic public. Can you believe it? His son's corpse is lying in front of him and he's playing the crowd. Your ears should have been burning this afternoon. He threw one of his fits, and you were among all the people he blamed for every bad thing that has ever happened to him in his life.''

"I thought he was an invalid.''

"That's what he wants you to think. You and everybody else. He thinks people care. At his age. I've kept away from the both of them. They're relentless. They chartered a yacht months ago to see tomorrow night's fireworks, and by God they're going to be on it. I was, too, until the sudden change in my status this week. Charlotte told me that I was a living painful reminder. Would I kindly fuck off? Not those words, not from her mouth, but you get the idea. If you want to see Maryellen, call the following number after nine A.M. tomorrow. It will do you no good to call earlier.'' The number was in the 914 area, in New York State, north of the city.

"What is it, some kind of business?''

"You'll find out,'' Anita Brennan said.

"The yacht the Brennans chartered tomorrow—you wouldn't happen to remember the name of it, would you?''

"The *Seadancer*, a sixty-foot motor yacht. Let me go now, please. I know you have your troubles, but you know I have mine.''

"Yes, I do know, and I'm sorry. I appreciate your help.''

"Good-bye, Mr. Devlin.''

8:53 P.M. . . .

HE HAD THE GYPSY CABDRIVER TAKE SIXTH AVENUE north to Herald Square, then Thirty-fourth Street east to Park Avenue, and then north again. Devlin wanted to be sure Steve Loncaric's line hadn't been tapped, and cops weren't waiting for him outside.

At Fifty-second and Park Devlin had the driver stop. The sidewalks were nicely crowded—no green Styrofoam tiaras here. No cops, either. Devlin took his time crossing the north-bound side of the avenue, allowing himself to get nailed at the dividing island by the red light. He couldn't be too obvious about looking for people looking for him. There was no better way to be found. The light changed again and Devlin kept going, part of the herd.

He would be reaching Madison Avenue north of the diocesan offices. Traffic ran northbound, he would be walking south. He hated living like this, aware of all his weaknesses, jumping from every shadow, fighting to keep his head clear. Anyone who wanted to live this way *was* an asshole, a serious mental problem who deserved a swift, sure criminal justice system, hard time, and maybe even the kinds of punishments that were meted out in the Arab world.

At this hour he had to ring the bell and wait for the buzzer to unlock the door. He had been doing it for years before meeting Steve Loncaric, who had been an ugly, belligerent drunk like so many of his predecessors here and colleagues all over. Behind closed doors and drunk, the clergy sometimes tended to forget unconditional love in favor of throwing their fists.

The buzzer sounded and Devlin entered and climbed the stairs. Originally this four-story mansion had been the private residence of a single family; now it projected fully the solidity of the church that claimed to be built on a rock.

Steve was at the top of the polished wooden stairs alone, looking pale and grim. He turned and went into his office. Devlin followed, expecting to see Eileen rising from the green leather club chair. Instead, the door was slammed shut behind him. Steve moved behind his desk, his lower lip trembling. A pistol hammer clicked behind Devlin's ear, and Kevin McQuaid, sucking on a toothpick, stepped out of the corner. He grinned.

"Gotcha, dickhead. Don't move. Raise your hands slowly."

Devlin sighed. "Why did you do this, Steve?"

He wasn't looking at Devlin. "I *agreed* to it because you're not doing anybody any good, especially yourself. Eileen is in terrible trouble because of this."

McQuaid took Devlin's service revolver. "Offered the choice between voluntary departure and prosecution," he said, "she chose the next available flight to London, at midnight tomorrow."

"Prosecution? For what?"

"Aiding and abetting. Conspiracy." He grinned. "Want to see what's behind door number three?"

Devlin looked again at Loncaric. "You *knew* about this?"

"No. No, I didn't."

He was lying, Devlin sensed at once. Kevin rattled his handcuffs. "Turn around, old-timer."

"I've got bursitis, give me a break."

"What the hell," he said, and locked Devlin's wrists together in front of him. "Anything else? Want me to light a cigarette for you? How about a blindfold?"

"You have it all wrong, kid."

"Maybe I do, but I still have my career—and my girl. When you get out of the can, you're going to find Ireland very geographically undesirable for dating."

"Shut up," Loncaric said.

"You've got your career, too," Kevin answered. "And your

girl.'' He pumped his fist. ''So stop the bullshit and let me get him out of here.''

''The cardinal wanted this, Frank . . .''

''Forget it, Steve.'' He paused for effect. ''Just pour yourself a drink and forget all about it.'' He regretted the remark at once. Kevin pushed him toward the door.

Downstairs, Gerrity was waiting, his wilted shirt collar curled up like a potato chip. ''I'm sorry, Devlin. You can see the position we're in.''

''Yeah, one step up in the food chain. Don't worry about it.''

Kevin said, ''The car's around the corner. You don't mind the short walk wearing those things, do you?''

''Whatever you say. You're getting pretty tight with Norberto Torres. You saw your opportunity and you took it. You don't give a fuck about the facts or other people's lives. You're in the middle of wrecking mine, and what haunts you is that you don't understand it, you haven't a clue. You're just another careerist punk not old enough or mature enough to understand what can happen between two people and how precious it is.''

Kevin smiled. ''What are you trying to do, geezer, piss me off? You want me to hit you upside the head? Give you a cause to claim brutality?''

''Why don't you shut up?'' Gerrity asked. ''You, too, Devlin.''

The car was a black Plymouth plainwrap. Kevin opened the back door and motioned Devlin in. Gerrity got behind the wheel—a break. Devlin wanted to push the situation a little further. He had to get Kevin angry enough to keep his eyes front. It was going to take time, but not much—a few minutes. Gerrity turned the car south on Park.

''Kevin, I think this stunt is going to cost you John Lord for life. It's a hell of a price to pay to ingratiate yourself with Hamilton and Torres.''

Kevin was staring straight ahead. Devlin reached for the .25. ''Well, you're a lovely couple,'' he said as Groucho Marx, ''but now it's time to play *You Bet Your Life*.'' He rammed the barrel of the little pistol into the back of Kevin's neck. ''How do you like it, small balls? Do anything funny with the car, or Gerrity makes a play, the gun goes off and your life disappears faster than a fart in a hurricane. Gerrity, ease the car over to the right-hand curb and get out. Leave your gun. Very carefully, please. I *will* kill him.''

''You're crazy,'' Gerrity said. ''You'll regret this the rest of your life.''

''Do as he says!'' Kevin screamed. The tension in his neck told it all. ''Do it, you stupid son of a bitch!''

Gerrity was reaching with his fingertips into his shoulder holster. ''How stupid are *you*? You searched him. You wanted the collar? You got it.'' He turned slowly and dropped the gun on the rear floor. ''Okay?''

''Yeah. Get out and head up the side street. Stay where I can see you.''

Gerrity opened the door. ''Do yourself a favor, Devlin, and don't kill the little son of a bitch. If you come out of this clean on everything else, I'll go to bat for you.''

Kevin looked at him. ''You fuck. You'd sell your mother to save your own ass.''

''If I kill him, it will be for what he's done to Eileen's life. Might as well, I can't dance. Get out and start walking toward Fifth.''

Gerrity did it. When he was a hundred feet away, Devlin prodded Kevin. ''Drive. Work us over to the left lane and then make a left turn. Where do you have Eileen?''

''Forget it, she's downtown. You can't get near her.''

''Nobody is going to back you up on this. You're holding her incommunicado, a violation of her constitutional rights.''

''She's not a citizen!''

Devlin almost laughed at his stupidity. ''You're in very deep shit.''

''No deeper than you, you old turd, for a long time to come.''

''Just drive,'' Devlin said. He was making and changing plans with every passing minute. He'd thought he was going to dump Kevin in Manhattan before taking the car over the Fifty-ninth Street Bridge to the one place in the city he was sure would be safe for him for the night. Now he was thinking that it would be wiser to hold on to Kevin. Not as a hostage, but in a precautionary move. At First Avenue Devlin told Kevin to turn uptown. "We're taking the upper deck to Queens."

"Fuck *Queens!*"

"As a matter of fact, I want to show you where I got laid when I was in high school."

On Thompson Avenue, a quarter-mile west of the bridge over the railroad yard, Devlin had Kevin make a right turn, and then, two very long blocks south, another right onto Forty-eighth Avenue. They were in the middle of Long Island City's factory district, a square mile of bleak, dark buildings, rail spurs, and recessed loading bays. When Devlin had tried to show Eileen the bay where he had come with a girl from Dr. Gall's American History class, and could not find it, Eileen said, "With so many other places to park, why do you want to fool around lookin' for a particular one? I've been waitin' a long time to do it the American way, and I'm in America now, so let's not waste any more time about it." Now Devlin had another thought about Eileen, and filed it for development later. When he saw a deep and empty loading bay off one of the side streets, he instructed Kevin to turn in, kill the lights, switch off the engine, and remove the ignition key.

"Get out slowly and keep your hands where I can see them. You're getting such a big break from me that it might make even a weasel like you think twice." He realized that saying more might invite Kevin to fight, or run for it. "Open the trunk. Leave the key in the lock." He stepped back from Kevin. "Put the guns, yours and mine, on the ground, take off your jacket, and get in the trunk."

"I'm going to suffocate."

"You're worth more to me alive." He waited until Kevin was cowering in the fetal position on the floor of the trunk, then quickly scooped up the jacket and one of the .38s. "Get yourself a new jacket." The handcuffs made wrapping the jacket around the barrel of the gun difficult and maybe a little dangerous, but Devlin was able to fire the gun through the trunk lid. The report was not as sharp as it might have been. "Now be a good boy in there." He threw the jacket in the trunk, closed the lid, and removed the key. If he worked fast, he could make the short trip east, a bit more than a mile up Forty-eighth Avenue, to Sunnyside and his apartment, for the things he would need tomorrow, including fresh clothing and toilet gear. He started the car to get the air-conditioning going.

Getting Kevin's key into the lock of the handcuffs was a lot more difficult than wrapping the jacket around the revolver. Four guns now. Devlin thought of his father's relief over not ever having had to kill anyone. The only reason Devlin hadn't shot anyone before last night was a lack of opportunity. Now he was in a position that did not allow him to think more than a few minutes into the future without feeling terror, and he knew it was because he would not hesitate to use the guns again if he had to. He had stepped into another world.

FRIDAY, JULY 4 . . .

4:27 A.M. . . .

T HE WHITE PLYMOUTH RELIANT CAME AROUND THE corner the third time and then Devlin was in it with Eileen, whisking them through the Midtown Tunnel back to Queens. Devlin knew he was dreaming; perhaps the knowledge itself made the dream something less than soft time, because it wasn't. Not a nightmare, either, not yet. Enough of Devlin's consciousness still flickered to let him know he was sleeping, his body contorted on the seat of a car, Kevin's car, in the factory district in Long Island City. The factories became the firetraps of Alphabet City. Devlin expected to see Octavio Lopez, but then he didn't, remembering that Lopez had holes in him, put there in high school, Long Island City High School.

The dream carried Devlin into the next dingy room, where Maryellen stood waiting, fragrant, happy, smiling, reaching out to him. *Ask your wife!* This was to be one of the perfect times, he thought gratefully, as her smooth, plump arms enfolded him. *Love me good,* she whispered. He still loved her smell. He was astonished at how vulnerable he remained after all this time, how much this part of him missed and wanted her. Eileen was a million miles in the future, existing only in the knowledge that this was a dream, that the arms and blue eyes and sweet-smelling, honey-colored hair were rising from the mystery inside himself, below the surface, where footsteps thumped and doorjambs rattled, shook! Devlin was trying to be rational, looking over his shoulder at Eileen behind him in that other room. Eileen loved parties And here was Maryellen again, needful again, as if twenty years had never happened, in the original sunny morning of their youth. His lips pressed

275

on her thin, firm lips, as always. They were in her room, the hinged windows swung inward, holding the curtains apart. He had forgotten nothing. When things were perfect between them, Maryellen wanted to be held, the two of them face-to-face, their lips brushing, her deep blue eyes fixed lovingly on his. That she was so close to him again had him terribly aroused, so erect the skin of his penis felt stretched taut. When she was heavy, the weight in her hips and thighs, he made love to her with her on her back, him on his side beside her, their legs in a tangle; but what she liked better, when she was slim enough, was for him to get on top, her legs high in the air. She liked to pat his back lightly and sigh, loving the sound of herself, taking even that pleasure self-indulgently, Devlin remembered. He loved licking her, did it often, just so she would slip beneath the covers to have him thrust in her mouth. He was the best lover she'd ever had, she said when they were perfect; but even in bed, when something went wrong, her anger would flare, anger always just below the surface . . . .

He was running again, through garbage-strewn alleys. Cans tumbled over with a roar. He kept reaching for his gun, but it wasn't there. . . .

Devlin awoke in the dark, sore, with an erection, remembering the dream, focusing on where he was: the loading bay he had found last night. It took a moment to sit up, and then get out of the car. While he was urinating he thought of Kevin in the trunk and *his* needs, and laughed. Let Kevin lie in his own stink awhile. Devlin wanted breakfast, and then he had to figure where to stash this car for the next four and a half hours so it wouldn't be seen. He had to find a place to eat at this hour that wasn't likely to be frequented by cops. No tuna fish sandwich takeout for Kevin. If Eileen had to go back to Ireland, even temporarily, then Kevin could go hungry for as long as Devlin could arrange it.

Now he remembered a place for breakfast and for "hiding" the car: a diner on Fifty-eighth Street, south of the cemetery and the expressway, in an industrial area of Maspeth that had been developed only in the last twenty years. No one ever was on foot there. Devlin got out of the car and slapped on the trunk lid. "Hey, I'm going to breakfast soon! You can lie there pissing your pants and thinking about all that food, or you can tell me you're going to be a good boy and call your goons to let my girlfriend take a walk."

"Fuck you," came the muffled reply.

"You're in for a long day," Devlin said, and slapped the lid again.

First light. From an outdoor booth in Queens Plaza he called John Lord at home. "Hey, John, this is Kevin."

"I don't want to talk to you. I heard enough last night."

"No, this is the *real* Kevin, not the guy who imitated my voice the other day."

Devlin enjoyed the sudden silence. "Oh, *that* Kevin," John said. "I'm glad you're all right. How can I help you?"

"I'd like to have a private conversation with you. Over the phone will be okay. I just want to be sure it's really private, you hear what I'm saying?"

"Can you wait until seven-fifteen?"

"I'll call back then."

"Exactly," John said, and said good-bye.

Time to return to the loading bay.

The sun was above the horizon, and traffic outside the diner was picking up. He was working through breakfast, ordering courses one at a time, turning the meal into a Chinese banquet. Juice. Pancakes. Bacon and eggs. Paging through the newspapers between every mouthful. The statue had been unveiled, the torch lit, and new citizens from all over the world sworn in.

At 7:15 he called John, who gave him a telephone number and asked for ten minutes more. Devlin went back to the counter and ordered a wedge of apple pie to hold his place at the counter. He would be here after his conversation with John. The bank wouldn't open for hours more.

Devlin had taken two forkfuls of pie when it was time to call John again.

"The guy behind the counter here has me made for a cop," John said. "A candy store. My second trip in half an hour. I had to wait for the place to open so I could get the number of the pay phone." He drew a breath. "Kevin called me last night to say he'd spent yesterday lying to me and wrecking your life and doing the same to Eileen's. Not to mention lousing himself up with the rest of the department's blue eyes in the process. He thought he saw an opportunity. I guess he was wrong. As of eight-thirty last night, he had you bagged and tagged. What happened? What did you do with him?"

"He's waiting in the car."

"Seriously?" John gave a short laugh in spite of himself. "On the other hand, it's kidnapping now."

"It's *been* kidnapping—that's what Kevin has done to Eileen. He says she's going back to Ireland at midnight. I want to know she's safe . . ."

"Frank, I can tell you what he told me last night. She's in a hotel he's used before to hide witnesses. I don't know where that is—I'd certainly tell you. She's with two guys he brought down from the Bronx for the job of getting you. He told me a long time ago that they're good guys."

"How can he tell?"

"No argument from me on that score," John said. "Take it for what it's worth. They're *cops*." He paused. "Assume that they're not crazy. Can you do that?"

Devlin realized that they would be asking themselves the same thing about him. "All right," he said. "There're a couple of things you can do, if you're willing." Devlin pinpointed the location of Jack Brennan's letter. "Get hold of Harry Levine. He'll know what to do with it. I think it's all the protection I need from the mayor and Torres." He told John about talking with DiBennedetti last night. Devlin said, "I know he's twisting my crank, and I know why—really. He knows where Maryellen is."

"Let us handle it." Devlin was ready with another idea. John listened, obviously unhappy, but not arguing. Devlin had thought it out very carefully. The only ass hanging out was Devlin's own; what he did decided if he would live. When Devlin finished, John said, "I'll be there. I'll do everything I can."

9:30 A.M. . . .

WHEN HE CAME OUT OF THE BANK, DEVLIN CHECKED on the Plymouth, parked under the el on Queens Boulevard, before ducking into a candy story to call the 914 number Anita Brennan had given him. He'd already called Sal, who'd said he would take care of the car. No trouble in the bank, if one thought signing seventy thousand dollars in traveler's checks was no problem. He'd been asked why he was withdrawing his money. *Moving,* he'd answered truthfully.

He pushed the buttons to connect him with somewhere up-state, nervousness suddenly a hot ball in his belly. Ringing. At last it was picked up.

"Ann Elizabeth," a woman said.

"Excuse me? My name is Frank Devlin and I'm calling from New York City. I'd like to speak to Maryellen Brennan Devlin, if that's possible."

"Mr. Devlin, I've been reading about your troubles this week in the newspapers—or rather, *deducing* your troubles from what I was reading." She spoke in an even tone, controlled but not strained. "I was wondering if you'd call—"

"I was *told* to call. By an old Mafia don who said my wife would explain why he was framing me."

"I don't think she would know why he's doing that to you." A pause. "Yes, I do see what he means," she said gently.

"She can come to the telephone, but Mr. Devlin, the best thing would be for you to come here. Can you do that? It's Dutchess County. Not far from Hyde Park."

"Can we have confidentiality? Let's not kid around. People are looking for me."

Another pause. "I know that, Mr. Devlin. You'll be safe. No one will know you're here."

Devlin hesitated. DiBennedetti—if Devlin understood that old man, a professional killer would be waiting at the front door. "All right," he said.

"I'll tell Maryellen to expect you after lunch. That way, you and I will have time for a little chat. It's necessary." She said good-bye.

His stomach churned. It was a long mile between suspicion and reality, between what Liz Becker had said about herself, and how he thought it might apply to Maryellen. Francis Xavier Devlin III didn't really want to imagine what his Maryellen could be like, after all this time.

11:43 A.M. . . .

THE PLYMOUTH HAD BEEN BUILT FOR DRIVING AROUND town and on arrow-straight interstates, not for the curving roller coaster of the Taconic Parkway. Kevin was letting Devlin know he was still alive, kicking and yelling. Devlin was looking for an exit, not any exit, and not the exit Ann Elizabeth had given him. The parkway was slicing through Clarence E. Fahnestock State Park, in Putnam County, the featured amenity of which seemed to be the entry sign Devlin had passed minutes ago.

Thirteen hours in the trunk would have Kevin almost permanently stiffened, if not docile. The legal holiday was Monday, not today, and maybe the park was as empty as it looked from the road.

Another exit from the parkway appeared, this one on the left, across the southbound lanes. No point in going farther. Devlin swung the big car over into the intersection, waited for a station wagon to pass, and shot across and up the hill.

He got out a set of handcuffs. A mile up the two-lane blacktop, a dirt road forked to the right. Devlin took it, rolled past some deserted tables and benches and fieldstone barbecues and then down into a little hollow where the picnic area was out of view. He turned the car around and put the gear selector in Park. Outside, he pounded smartly on the trunk lid.

"Rise and shine!"

Kevin groaned. Devlin drew his gun, unlocked the lid, and let it rise, sunshine pouring into the cavity. Kevin tried to cover his eyes. Devlin slapped one cuff on Kevin's wrist. The car was equipped with a space-saver spare. Good enough. Devlin pulled Kevin out of the trunk. Kevin's cramped legs were as worthless as an infant's, and he pitched forward onto the dirt, raising a cloud of dust. Quickly Devlin spun the butterfly nut retaining the spare, hefted the spare up to the lid, and swung it onto the squirming, crawling Kevin. Then Devlin threw the three confiscated guns in the trunk. He was going to stop before he reached Dutchess County to hide them well, especially the .25. Devlin had figured it out last night, after he'd realized how he'd changed the game when he'd attacked Rizzo and Gentile.

"I have to slow you down, asshole."

"Just give me a drink of water," Kevin gasped.

"All I can do is piss on you," Devlin said, as he locked the other cuff to the spare wheel. "Don't tempt me."

"Where am I?"

"Up the creek. I want you to think again about what you're doing to my girlfriend. If you want to change your mind—"

"It's too late to change yours, son of a bitch," Kevin gasped. "Kidnapping! *Kidnapping!*"

Devlin pinched his cheek like a baby's. "If you're not back

in town by midnight, I'll tell people how to find you. You won't die. Adios, muchacho.''

In another minute Devlin was going back past the picnic tables and barbecues. Dragging the tire with him, it might take the crippled Kevin an hour to get that far.

12:34 P.M. . . .

THE REAL COUNTRY. NARROW ROADS, WIRE FENCES ON both sides, fields beyond, neatly stitched rows of vegetables stretching to lines of trees a quarter of a mile away, dark green hills in the distance. No one was following him. Small clouds, like torn fragments of cloth, whiter than he ever saw in the city, seemed to strain upward for higher, darker blue. Little towns and barns, estates, signs pointing to Poughkeepsie, Dutchess County, just north of the city. For twenty years he had allowed himself to think that Maryellen had been teaching grade school in the Middle West. What had been the matter with him? Why hadn't he been able to face facts? For the hell of it, he took his hand off the steering wheel and tried to hold it still in the air. He couldn't.

The road turned downhill, through a rural high-rent district. Stone walls and trimmed hedges replaced barbed-wire fences. Acres of lawn instead of fields. The river came into view, a barge toiling northward. In the distance, the Catskill Mountains rolled away in the darkest green, until they almost met a line of lowering clouds, just a ribbon of pale blue between. Devlin had never seen this before, and after today and tonight, he might not ever be allowed another chance. He didn't care, and didn't find the feeling odd. Hillcrest Road. In a few minutes more he would know what Maryellen had made of herself, where life had taken her. . . .

The curving drive led to a low brick building with a multiarched main entrance. Devlin parked in the empty blacktop lot opposite. When he got out of the car, a slim, handsome woman of forty in a trim gray summer suit stepped out of the shadow and approached him. No one else was around. Her fading brown hair was tied back in a bun and she wore no makeup. When she drew near, she extended her hand. Devlin took it.

"Hello, Sister," he said.

"Hello, Mr. Devlin," she answered, with a smile. "You're not surprised?"

She had light blue, almost gray eyes. "It wasn't difficult. *Sister* Ann Elizabeth. How long has Maryellen been here?"

"She's been our paying guest, with a couple of intervals, for almost fourteen years."

"She's not a nun?"

She wrinkled her nose. "We children of the sixties discourage that word. No. I've known Maryellen—Brennan, we call her here—for eight years, or since I returned from completing my clinical work." She shielded her eyes with her hand. "Look at the view. Those clouds on the horizon mean it's going to rain tomorrow. But you're here on about as nice a day as we ever have. Have you had lunch? I can have something brought around to my office while we talk."

"I've had a very big breakfast," he said.

Ann Elizabeth gestured toward the entrance. "Let's go in, then. Usually guests sign our register, but I'm going to walk you by. We have our own little office politics here. Originally we were a teaching order, but in the fifties we expanded into other services."

"Mental health," Devlin said.

"Maryellen told me once that you think with your skin— that you were a much better cop than you realized." She let him open the heavy wooden door. The comment about him was pure Maryellen, another way to keep herself in the spotlight: he knew how good a cop he was, and she knew it, too.

A nun at a desk glanced up at him, then went back to her writing. "You don't look like you're drinking."

"I celebrated my thirteenth anniversary in February. You're Maryellen's psychologist?"

"More or less."

Everything about this place was heavy, unembellished, built to last centuries. When he was young, he used to wonder about women like Ann Elizabeth; now he knew they had their reasons. *Life is a bitch, and then you die.* Why couldn't he ever believe it, when it was so obviously true?

In her tiny office, the telephone was ringing. She picked up and motioned to Devlin to sit down in the club chair facing the desk. Behind her were a pair of framed diplomas, a B.A. from Loyola Marymount, whatever that was, and a Ph.D. from the University of Wisconsin, dated 1972. Devlin looked at the B.A. again. It had been awarded to Veronica Koontz.

She said into the telephone, "The point of all this is, the question you have to ask yourself, is the relationship worth your pain and suffering? That's right, you're in a tailspin together. You're facing that head-on, a big step. Now what? Is it worth it? Time to deal, lady. Whose problem is it?" She turned in her swivel chair to the window and its view of an enclosed garden beyond. After a moment, she giggled. Swinging back, she said, *"Now* you're talking. Call me anytime. I'm proud of you and I love you." When the telephone was cradled, she said to Devlin, "I get involved."

"Veronica Koontz."

She waved to the diploma. "That was only recently put up there, part of my own self-acceptance. My mother says that when I asked her to send it to me, she sat down and cried for an hour. For joy. My mother has her own problems, but I've led her a merry chase around a very big circle, the way coyotes do with a dog they're trying to exhaust and kill. That metaphor, when I finally saw the truth of it, turned me one hundred and eighty degrees as a human being. Loyola Marymount is in Los Angeles, and when I was growing up, in La Mirada, we knew all aboutcoyotes.'' She clapped her hands. ''Thirteen years sober, huh? I hope you're proud of yourself.''

''Not, too—that doesn't help.

''Maryellen *is* eager to see you, just as I thought. She was able to get an appointment with her hairdresser this morning, and she drove off in an absolutely euphoric high. She's still up there.''

''I remember.''

''There's much more to her now than what you remember, Mr. Devlin.''

''Frank.''

''Thank you. Frank. She has never, ever, experienced the straight and level flight that many people are on naturally, and the rest of us aspire to.''

He shifted in the chair.

''I was told she'd gone to Minneapolis.''

''Minneapolis? Whatever for?''

''To teach. She has a certificate. I think I had to believe it for my own sake. I didn't want to question. I had to work to close my mind to her for my own sake. To use your phrase, we had been in a tailspin together. It took me a long time to realize that. We didn't have a relationship based on understanding, respect, and consensus.''

Ann Elizabeth smiled. ''You have that now.''

''Yes, I do.''

''I'm happy for you. You seem like a man who's taken charge of his life. You seem at peace with yourself.''

''Not what you were told to expect, eh?''

''Maryellen will say anything about anybody, anytime, anywhere, you know that. Are you at peace with yourself?''

''Yes. But now this—what you've been reading about in the papers.''

''Accept the things you cannot change.''

''I can change it,'' he said. ''I'm not lying to myself. I can. It's why I'm here.''

''I'm not playing games with you, Frank. This is serious. I want to feel that you're not here to test yourself, no matter what you may think about Mafia dons and your life being in danger. The way your relationship with Maryellen ended left a lot of questions unanswered. Are you getting this? The way she tells it, whether you like it or not, Maryellen Brennan was the great passion of your life.''

"You can see I don't like it. Passion isn't all there is to love. She liked life action-packed. I did, too, at that age. What went on between us added to the intensity of our sexuality. I was always chasing her—or cheating on her,'' he corrected. "Or drunk. *And* drunk.''

"I wasn't finished. It happened to you because you didn't know there are people like her in the world. You fell in love with someone who is charming when she wants to be, unstoppable when she wants to be, and constitutionally incapable of feeling remorse. You were primed for her, whoever you are, whoever you were. After you left, she started deteriorating.''

Who are you? He slumped back. "You mean she's insane.''

"That word had no meaning. She's not *insane* now, not having an episode. She's eager to see you. She had her hair done. I know she's going to be charming. You know it, too. Stop and think: do you really want to put yourself through this?''

"How did she get here?''

"According to the records, her father and mother brought her when she was in what turned out to be a very long episode. She was disassociating, manic. It lasted until she wore herself out and ground to a stop. That's the pattern she's followed since. When things haven't gone her way, this behavior surfaces and takes control. When she reaches physical exhaustion, she returns to something closer to the middle ground. I called her our guest. Her parents pay—plenty—and she's free to come and go. Twice she's attempted to make it on the outside, and both experiences led to setbacks. The second time, she returned voluntarily. She knows she's better off here than anyplace else, including her parents' home. For all their money, the Brennans are profoundly ignorant people. Jim Brennan once said to my predecessor that he felt sorry for Maryellen in her childhood because she was a girl and couldn't have the life he wanted for her.

"Maryellen is functional now—not perfect. She has her own apartment, which she manages quite nicely. She may talk about the woman downstairs. As you'll see, there is no downstairs. If you point that out to her, she'll ignore you. The 'woman downstairs' is someone Maryellen can point her finger at, an imaginary scapegoat. The other thing you'll see is that she's chosen to behave as if she were decades younger than her actual age, which is forty-four. She may range anywhere from fifteen to twenty-five. This morning she was a very happy young woman."

"You like her."

"I love her. She makes choices, I said."

"I'm still her husband," Devlin said. "What would happen if I tried to have her declared incompetent?"

"She would choose a behavior that would fool the most talented psychiatrists, and the case would be thrown out of court." Ann Elizabeth stood up and switched on her answering machine. "That's an opinion, but I've seen it in others. As one of them told me, 'I acted sane.' "

Devlin was on his feet. "Are you going to be with us?"

"No, she doesn't want that. But I won't be far away."

"What does she know of her brother's death?"

Out in the hall, Ann Elizabeth locked the door behind them. "Everything. Maryellen watches television, listens to the radio. She cried on Tuesday, spoke to her mother. On Wednesday she was depressed, but on Thursday she seemed to have put it out of her mind. Joe's death, on the other hand, triggered an episode that was short, but very fierce. From what I saw, she loved Joe very, very much. She was closer to him in age, and that alone can mean a very special feeling."

At this moment he didn't want to think about Jack's letter and its revelations about the Brennans' childhood sexuality. "I know. How does she feel about me?"

"As I told you, Maryellen can *say* anything about anybody. It's all for effect. Everything is for effect; it doesn't have any value on its own. Over the years, I've heard everything about you. That's how I know about your alcoholism. We go out here." Ann Elizabeth opened a door on another, larger, tree-shaded garden. In one corner was the only single-story stucco building in the convent, new, but conforming in style with the rest. Devlin felt a deep stab of apprehension. "The Brennans paid for it," Ann Elizabeth said. "It will revert to us eventually—not soon, I hope."

"I'm glad you're in her life," he said. He was devastated. Fourteen years!

"We're friends. She has a whole life up here. She does needlepoint, gives to charity, and goes out at night. She is part of our community. When I catch her in a lie, as I did today, I have to let it go. When confronted, she simply changes the subject."

"I remember that. What lie did you catch her in today?"

"You. Wednesday, when she was depressed, she said for the fortieth time that she had made up her mind never to see you again. Ah, here's my sister now."

The wooden door in the center of the building opened, and Maryellen emerged—or rather, his eyes told him, a woman who could have been Maryellen's mother. She didn't look like Charlotte—never had—but an older variation of the young woman Frank Devlin had known twenty years ago. She was staring at him as he was staring at her. She was heavier, much heavier, weighing maybe as much as two hundred pounds, very wide through the hips, her face rounder, fuller, her eyelids puffy. The same honey-blond hair, maybe dyed now. Her eyes had a sadness that looked permanent. She smiled and came toward him, her firm, chubby arms reaching out. She used to worry about her upper arms "flapping in the breeze." She wanted to hug him; he didn't want her to. He saw Ann Elizabeth nod to him. Woodenly, even coldly, he put his arms around Maryellen, realizing at once how much he had been afraid to admit he had never stopped wanting this, the part of him that ruled his dreams, defying reason and experience, weeping like a pregnant widow for what might have been. He shuddered, and she felt it.

"Oh, Frank. I've missed you so much."

He almost wanted to believe. He *knew* better, but that didn't change what he felt. *Like alcohol*, he thought. *Yes, exactly.*

Ann Elizabeth had just spoken of a metaphor that had changed her life, and now he understood. Just as he couldn't take that first drink, he couldn't let his guard down with Maryellen.

"Let me look at you," he said, disentangling himself. She was wearing an expensive, perfectly cut glen plaid suit the same tone of gray as Ann Elizabeth's uniform. "You look nice." Maryellen's eyes were filling up. He pointed to their clothing. "Plain and fancy."

Maryellen laughed. "When they finally got out of those horrible old habits, they decided to dress like Aeroflot stewardesses." When he didn't laugh—because he didn't want to relax—she looked quickly to Ann Elizabeth, then back to him again. "It's *her* joke!"

"It is, Frank."

He saw Maryellen form his name with her lips, as if she thought Ann Elizabeth's using his first name suggested a deeper intimacy. Sexual? He didn't want to believe anyone's mind worked that way, and when he saw it, he saw his complicity in Maryellen's power over him. Like alcohol. He had made his one-hundred-and-eighty-degree turn. "Come on, give me another hug," he said. This time she buried her face in his chest, reached for Ann Elizabeth's hand, then turned and hugged her, and stepped back.

"I made some coffee. And found some apple pie. It's not as good as Bickford's, but it *is* the best in Duchess County."

She remembered. Between fifteen and twenty-five years old? She seemed like nineteen to him, around the time they were beginning to play their game in earnest. "Good. I eat a lot of apple pie these days."

"I'm going back to my office," Ann Elizabeth said. "Have a nice visit."

Maryellen was holding his hand, smiling, her blue eyes bright. "Let's go inside. You look *wonderful*! For all I knew, you could have been a potbellied bald guy. You're still a cop. I can see that you don't drink anymore."

He stepped into the middle of the room as she closed the door. Lovely: a love seat, a leather chair and some wooden bookcases, a fireplace in the corner, a true dining room beyond. Windows on all sides. "The two bedrooms are in back," she said. "The whole place is going to be another set of offices when I'm out of here." She approached him. "What did she tell you? Did she say I was crazy?"

He took her arms from around his neck. "She said you were doing well. You're a guest. You have your own life."

She pulled her fists to her bosom and gave him a little-girl look. "What did she say about that?"

"That's it: you have your own life. So do I. It took me a long time, but I finally have something together that I want to preserve." He wanted to add, *and cherish.* "Now your brother has been murdered, and more than you can see in the papers, I'm being fitted for the collar. I know enough of the who, what, when, and where. What I don't know is *why?* An eighty-eight-year-old mafioso in New Jersey told me to ask you."

She laughed out loud. "I thought *I* was crazy! Oh, come, let's have some coffee and apple pie. It took all that to get you to come find me, huh?"

"Maryellen—"

She shook his arm. "It's a joke." She wanted him to sit facing the little kitchen, the place *could* be converted into a set of offices later. She was going to sit on his right, showing him her best side. She had done the same thing fifteen and twenty years ago. After she had served the pie and poured the coffee, she sat down and said, "You have another girl. What's she like?"

"Irish. Wise. Joyous."

"Where did she go to school?"

"Londonderry."

"Oh. One of *those* Irish!" The same perky, musical voice. She was the Maryellen he'd fallen for, charming, sometimes suggestive. She patted his hand. "Good for you. I have my adventures, too. Right now it's the man who owns the carpet store. Before him was the son of the movie theater owner. All safe. They don't want to get involved. Meeting on a regular basis is just fine. I keep my life in compartments. Click, click, click, like mail slots. It's better that way."

"Married?"

"The current one is. I don't care about that. He takes me

places.'' She narrowed her eyes. "It's not how big it is, but how hard!''

"Let's talk about the Mafia.''

Her head tilted back and she laughed again. "I don't know anything about the Mafia. I've been here.'' Her eyes sparkled. "Really. My life is very carefully defined. I don't go east past Millerton, south past Poughkeepsie. Really, Frank, I don't know what that man had in mind.''

"You know about the annulment proceedings,'' he said.

"Oh, yes. Better to pretend it never happened. It never *should* have happened. I remember. We had good times, though, too. *You* must never forget that.''

"I remember a lot of drunken brawls. Whether it was a sex brawl or just a plain brawl, it was drunken. I'm sober now.''

"I still drink. Socially. There's nothing in the house. I never cared about drinking. You taught me that.''

"You drank before you met me.''

"I mean *drinking*, as in making a career of it! It would have been different without the drinking. It would be different now. Wouldn't it?''

He stared. He remembered a fight about drinking and telling her he had found booze in her room before they were married. Had she forgotten that? Did she think he had? Her anger had blazed up, then vanished, like the flash of a firecracker. It was gone now. Her facial expression said that all he had to do was take her into the bedroom. *All effect,* Ann Elizabeth had said. Functional? New York had fifty thousand dimestore lawyers who could get her chewing the witness stand in five minutes. Devlin asked himself if thinking that was only a back-door way of beginning to believe all of her bullshit. How could *this* woman "act sane"? The Brennans were ignorant? They knew her, from the childhood tantrums on. Maybe Ann Elizabeth knew about that much and more, and had a different definition of *functional.* The woman Devlin was looking at could brush her teeth and *maybe* remember to feed the cat, but she was still the same woman who could not help stirring up trouble: told that he had a girlfriend, she had instantly turned seductive. "No, I don't think it would be any different.''

"You love me! You do! Admit it!"

"Look, when we broke up years ago, I had to pound it into my *head* first. I had my adventures, too, but that's all they were, for a long, long time. I finally healed. I want to stay that way."

"You didn't answer my question."

"Do you want yes or no, or the truth?"

"I want to suck your dick. And you want me to, too." She laughed. "Look at you, scared to death I'm going to rape you. Remember all those times I sucked your dick? 'Look, Ma, no hands!' Remember that one?"

"Stop."

"I have a list," she said.

"What?"

"A list. Of all the men I've fucked. You're number twenty-two."

He didn't answer.

"Twenty-two!" She leaned toward him again. "Do you know what the woman downstairs did?" she asked, her voice suddenly quick and bright again. "She fucked five different men on five consecutive nights!"

"What did you tell me that for?"

Maryellen looked down. "I don't know," she whispered. "I don't know what other people feel and think. I really don't."

"Don't worry about it." What Devlin was thinking was that there was something Ann Elizabeth didn't know: Devlin was a *key* to Maryellen. He didn't have to do anything to set her off—his *presence* was too much for her. Vittorio DiBennedetti knew this, too. Who could have communicated it to Di-Bennedetti? Someone in Jack Brennan's office? DiBennedetti knew that Maryellen Brennan was nuts—*incompetent*, if properly provoked, whether the law said so or not.

"Do you know why it ended?"

"Why, Maryellen?"

"I told Daddy I was attracted to another man. I was just so tired of you and our fighting. I didn't think he'd do what he did. I thought you would come back. It took *me* a long time to realize you weren't coming back."

"Your father said he'd maim me. He spat in my face."

Her head snapped up, her eyes glaring. "You're a liar!" she shouted. "My father is a great man!"

"I told the truth."

She looked away. When she turned back again, she was crying. Tears streamed down her face. Her pain was real—it couldn't be otherwise. Functional? Devlin could believe she was this way with everyone eventually. All it took was intimacy. A history together.

"I didn't want our visit to be bad," she cried. "I wanted it to be nice."

"All right, it will be." He hadn't touched his pie. She watched him start to eat, and then she spoke his thoughts exactly.

"You're looking at me as if I poisoned the pie."

"That's the way you're looking at me." He wanted to laugh. What he had said had made him seem childish. How had it happened?

She lowered her eyelids, turning up the heat and gently parodying herself at the same time. "The most expressive eyes since the young Barbara Bel Geddes, you used to say."

"You've remembered a lot."

"No, I haven't, actually. I really don't remember much of anything. Just *things*, you know? . . ." She reached for his hand. "We can hold hands, can't we?"

He really didn't want to, but he didn't want to deal with the trouble following saying no. He remembered that well enough. She would go off on a tangent, then come back to the issue, nasty about it. She said, "Do you know, before I came here, I seduced my high school boyfriend. I looked him up. He was married, too. His dick was too big. Want to do it? We can see if we were doing it right."

"I think I'd better go."

"No!" Maryellen got up. "Wait. I have something to show you. Don't go. Don't embarrass me in front of Ann Elizabeth. You've been here only a few minutes." She ran back to the bedroom. He asked himself if he should step outside anyway. It was almost two o'clock. They could continue to talk. Where was the embarrassment? Being where other people could see the real her always took Maryellen down a notch. She returned cuddling a stuffed bear. Under her arm was a slim, leather-bound book. "It was stupid, telling you about the list. You're one of the people—Sometimes I hear your voice, you know. I know it isn't you. But I hear you." She glanced at the bear. "This is my baby. Best kind of baby to have—I can leave him alone whenever I want to go out and fuck." She hugged it with the affection some people have for pets. "Not going to grow up and kick the shit out of me for it, either. I'm going to get it someday, I know. I'm going to have to answer." Now she looked at Devlin. "See, that's an example."

"Of what?"

"What I said before."

"I'm sorry, I don't understand."

She growled in exasperation. "*You!* You've been getting me to say things I didn't want to, that I didn't want you to know. Or anybody. You're getting me to tell my deepest secrets." Tears came to her eyes again. "Do you hate me? I didn't want you to know the truth about me. Ann Elizabeth didn't ask me if you could come up. I would have wanted to think about it awhile. Ann Elizabeth certainly has her own problems. Why did she do this?"

"What problems?"

Maryellen turned away, as she used to do when she wanted to lie. The anger had come and gone again, this time like lightning on the horizon. "For God's sake, Frank, Ann Elizabeth is a lesbian! Don't tell me you didn't get it!"

"I didn't think about it. It's not my business."

"Ho! Ho! I remember you when! Come on, sit down. Let's have a nice time." The bear under her arm, she opened the book. "This is my journal. I want to read something from it to you. Don't make me say bad things—promise?"

"Yes."

She took his hand. "Will you kiss me? Will you kiss me nice?"

"When we say good-bye."

"She told you I was crazy, I know she did. If she hadn't done that, all this would have been different."

He sat down. "Let it go. Read."

No, she wanted to hold his hand and look into his eyes, and, he knew, if he moved closer to her, she would start fondling him under the table. He remembered every bit of this, back when she was supposedly sane, when it never occurred to him that she was crazy. Just rich. Spoiled. "Remember the time you met me at the airport and I got off the plane all flushed and sweaty?" No, he didn't, but he gave her no sign. He listened. She patted his hand. "You don't remember, but I do. You didn't say anything, but your eyes were all over me. You wanted to know what happened. Oh, look at you! I have you. You love me. I can see it."

"Tell me what happened." He didn't remember when she had traveled alone by airplane. Maybe she wasn't talking about him, but somebody else.

"On the plane I got so excited about you, I had to go to the bathroom and play with myself." She seemed pleased with his reaction—he was stunned. "You always believed what I said about not being able to play with myself. What a fool you were!" She stopped, her eyes welling up. "You're making me say bad things again. That wasn't even true."

"I'm not doing a thing, Maryellen."

She put the book in her lap. "I want to get out of here," she cried. "I hate New York!"

"That's up to you." She was completely out of control now, tears pouring down her cheeks. He bolted up. "Let me get a breath of air," he said. When she tried to hold his arm, he pulled free. "Just a cigarette. I haven't had one since I got here." The truth was that he had forgotten all about cigarettes, hadn't had one since before daybreak.

She ran after him. "Oh, Frank—"

When he opened the door, Ann Elizabeth and two of her colleagues were standing on the other side. Maryellen saw them. She stepped back, sobbing and snuffling.

"It's all right, Maryellen," Ann Elizabeth said as she entered. "Everything is fine."

"Let me read this! Please!"

Devlin couldn't move. The nuns weren't blaming him. They

weren't blaming anybody. They just wanted to edge a little closer to Maryellen. She was looking at him as she opened the book. "Are you ready?"

He smiled. "Sure."

Dear Frank,
   I have never stopped thinking about you, dreaming of you, remembering the wonderful times we had together. I know we can solve our problems if we work at them. I just won't be blamed for the mistakes I made in the past. I want to have nights in front of a fire somewhere, a good movie on TV or Django Reinhardt records on the phonograph. I want to marry you again, Frank. I want to suck your cock and lick your ass. . . ."

How sad.
"Maryellen," Ann Elizabeth whispered.

Maryellen turned to her, cold, her eyes narrowed. She dropped the book. She bared her lower teeth. Devlin's cop alarms started ringing, but in this context, this setting, he wasn't hearing clearly. He knew it. He didn't move fast enough. With a crisp left hook, Maryellen punched Ann Elizabeth in the face, nearly knocking one of the other sisters flying. They were on her, grabbing her arms almost as quickly as she subsided and stood still. Ann Elizabeth had been spun around and doubled over. She came up holding her eye. "Is she all right?"

"Yes," one of the others said. "She wants to cry now."

"Back to my office, Mr. Devlin . . . Frank."

He moved. In front of the house, a breeze caused the tops of the trees to sway. His hands shook. Cigarette time. *No. Not over her.* He could hear Ann Elizabeth speaking gently to Maryellen, then giving instructions to the others. She wanted to tend to her eye, she said.

Coming out, Ann Elizabeth didn't break stride on her way to her office. "Come on. Getting kayoed adds to the day's tension. She does throw a good punch, though, doesn't she? Her father taught her how to do it. I'm going to have some shiner. Here."

In their five years together, Maryellen had never told Devlin that her father had taught her how to punch. What did that mean, if anything? Devlin opened the door to the main building. "You've had this happen before."

"Oh, yes, but not often. Really. This is only the third time in eight years. Once she broke a couple of ribs—mine, not hers. Another time she came after me with a butcher knife. I had to hide in a bathroom. Don't go looking for anyone to blame for this. I'm the one with the black eye. Maybe God's trying to tell me something. Certainly was quick enough about delivering the message. I thought she was going to be able to handle this. *Really* thought she could. I thought it would be good for her. Everything I told you is true. She has a life of her own."

"She told me a bit about it."

They were at her office. Ann Elizabeth waited until she had unlocked the door before answering. "It's a real life." She was using a tissue to cleanse the tears and mucus from her eye. "To you it may seem completely pointless, but it's what she can handle. We're happy that she's able to accomplish as much as she does, which is a lot of good around here. She's a hard worker when she has a good day."

"You need ice on that eye. How would a gangster, an old, *old* gangster, know that she was going to behave like that?"

"I don't have any idea. Let me show you our kitchen. It's the only place where I'm going to find any ice." She had to lock the door again. "My patients' files. All kinds of people pass through these halls."

"Who else has this effect on her?"

"Oh, always the current boyfriend, especially before the end of the relationship. Her parents, but they haven't been here—and Maryellen hasn't been home—in years. Me, if I mishandle her as I did today."

"Her parents," Devlin said.

Ann Elizabeth nodded, probably wondering why he was pressing the point. Her eye was going to be a beaut. She asked, "Do you have any other questions? Maybe you don't want to see the kitchen after all."

"How long is it going to take her to calm down?"

"She was calm when I left her."

"I don't need to be lied to."

"Frank! Maryellen has a *date* tonight!"

He caught his mouth hanging open. And he'd just thought he was cured. After a few minutes, a part of him had believed everything Maryellen was saying. He shook his head. That was how it had been years ago: round and round. All she had ever wanted was attention and control. It never went anywhere. *Completely pointless.* Then: *Always the current boyfriend.* Devlin laughed out loud.

"I've been trying to get an annulment."

"I know. You won't—not with this Pope. Yours is exactly the situation that fits the phrase, 'in sickness and in health.' You get to bear the biggest cross and set the best example. Marriage is very important to His Holiness. I know you have trouble relating that to your real life, but if you were in his position, where would you start to restore decency and dignity to the world?"

She smiled, even as her eye was closing up. "It's just that the human heart doesn't play by his rules. I mean your wife. Maryellen. I've been accused of harboring a homewrecker. She loves married men, sees them as a challenge. Mother Superior calls her a bitch on wheels. Maryellen had another abortion in the seventies—we had her fixed then, by a Jewish doctor—and she blamed the mess on somebody else. For anybody studying it, her life is a bad dream. For her, life is a nightmare. Is she responsible for the pain she causes when she can't control the pain she feels? She feels the pain over and over. It never goes away. She does what she needs to do and finds the justification afterward. If we don't know what causes a personality like hers, how can we know how to deal with it? Don't ask where the truth lies with her. She tells you. It's *all* true, at the time she says it. Five minutes later, the truth is something else. We're not supposed to notice when a story keeps changing. She's given me fifteen reasons why she didn't want children, even that her mother told her she wasn't good enough."

"Her mother may have said it. I'm looking at your eye. Tend to it instead of wasting time over her. You're trying to make sense of life? So am I. And she has a date tonight."

Ann Elizabeth smiled. "Nothing is going to keep her home. I made a note to that effect in my journal Tuesday afternoon."

"While she's on her date, her parents will be on a yacht, watching the fireworks."

Ann Elizabeth winced. "I think I will tend to my eye. Thank you for coming. Good luck in your quest."

2:58 P.M. . . .

Y OU WERE PRIMED FOR HER. . . .

The nun at the desk eyed him again as he passed. Opening the door to the parking lot, he expected to see a car full of DiBennedetti hoods waiting for him, but there was no one, just the grand vista he had enjoyed before he had gone inside for his very last look in his life at Maryellen Brennan. A waste of a human soul. Intellectually he knew he was not responsible for what had happened to her, but he *felt* something else. Wrong, and as crazy as she was. And just as wrong was the idea that she had any control over her behavior. She didn't, and *he* had to accept the things he could not change.

He sat in the car awhile. He expected to pick up a tail as soon as he rolled out of here. If DiBennedetti knew Maryellen was shithouse nuts, he probably had an informant here in the convent. John Lord hadn't liked Devlin's plan, but he had agreed that it was probably the only one that would work. This was another cigarette opportunity, the last one Devlin might get for hours—or worse, for the rest of his life—but he still didn't want to smoke. He didn't know why. What had been desire was now almost revulsion, and consciously he had done nothing to bring about the change.

He sat back. He didn't want to think of Maryellen, but her face rose up, fourteen years on her own personal treadmill, obviously worse, much worse, *episodes*. . . .

He yelled out loud. He saw Maryellen flashing from perky, to enraged, to the verge of tears, images of her as she was, and he still wanted to believe something. *Who are you?* Devlin had made the connections back to Maryellen through Liz Becker. Mrs. Weinstein by virtue of four months of marriage. On the telephone this week she'd said she'd been in therapy and it hadn't done her any good. *Who are you?* When he hadn't understood the Brennans, he had chalked it up to his own inexperience, indefinitely deferring judgement on the whole self-satisfied mob, including himself. Of course he hadn't wanted understandings, hadn't wanted to make judgements. *Don't bother me with facts, I'm too busy reaching for what I want.*

Devlin was closer now to anything he might have wanted back in the sixties, but he felt no special sense of irony. Contrary to what Maryellen's father may have imagined, Devlin had never given the Brennan money that much thought. In due time, he'd expected his Brennan connections would open doors in the N.Y.P.D., that's all. . . .

The doors that could open now were the doors to the Brennan vault itself. What did Devlin have to do? Outlive Jim and Charlotte, then hire that lawyer who ate his children. The whole deal might cost Devlin no more than the first twenty-five-cent call to the lawyer. In fact, unless he signed documents stating otherwise, Devlin stood to inherit control of the entire fortune, as Brennan himself had done so many years ago.

Devlin had always known he could get something, if he wanted to press a case. Five figures minimum. Brennan was old, Joe was dead. Devlin was a loose end that could be tied up with—how much? A hundred grand? Fifty, easy. Cash. The lowest possible offer if Devlin walked in off the street. Never mind the maiming threat. Brennan was too old, too damned much time had passed, even if he wasn't the invalid the world had been told. But Devlin had given up that kind of thinking when he had resolved to get sober and stay that way. Only a guy like Jim Brennan wouldn't believe it. A guy like Jim Brennan never could find selflessness, or decency, or a sense of fair play motivating anybody. . . .

The frame never was supposed to fit. After all the bullshit, Devlin was supposed to have walked.

Ask your wife.

If DiBennedetti and company had wanted to twist a knife, Brennan was the perfect target for a double cross. Had he seen Jack's death coming? Maybe he'd known Joe's death had been murder. How far back did a deal like this go? How old was DiBennedetti?

Devlin wanted to see Eileen. He had never thought of an alternative to life in New York because it had never been forced upon him, but now alternatives were parading across his imagination like models in a fashion show. He would think about Maryellen later. If he had learned anything in forty-three years about the workings of his mind, he had learned that he would think of Maryellen later. This time would be different. As pitiable as she was, he felt no pity for her at all.

He didn't think he would ever feel anything for her again.

The tail, an Olds 98, swung in close behind him when he turned off Hillcrest Road. Only twenty or thirty feet behind him, Devlin could see two men in the front seat and one in the back. Devlin stepped on the gas. He wanted them to catch him, but he couldn't be obvious about it. In the rearview mirror he could see the front seat passenger talking on a cellular telephone. Was there a second car? That would make getting caught a lot easier. He put the gas pedal to the floor, and the Plymouth lurched ahead. This two-lane road was mostly straight for about five miles before it reached the Taconic Parkway, Devlin remembered. The Olds, back a bit, seemed to be maintaining its distance. Devlin had to conclude that there was a second car somewhere in front of him. He was doing almost seventy, about the limit for the car on a crowned, undulating road. His heart was pounding. If he had misunderstood these guys, he would be dead in only a few more minutes. The fear made him feel sick to his stomach. The Plymouth reached the top of a rise—and at the end of a quarter-mile straight, the white Lincoln was turned across the road to block both lanes. Devlin took his foot off the gas pedal and let the Plymouth coast as the occupants of the Lincoln got out and moved around behind the vehicle. One had a rifle or shotgun. If Devlin was right, what he couldn't do was defend himself. He continued to let the car coast.

The Oldsmobile fell back. In his rearview mirror Devlin could see the front passenger still talking on the telephone. Six of them altogether. If he stopped the Plymouth out of pistol and shotgun range of the Lincoln, maybe the Olds would follow suit. If they didn't want him alive, he might be able to force them to keep their distance until he was able to stumble onto the standoff.

Devlin stopped the Plymouth in the middle of the road, the nose facing the Lincoln, the tail pointed toward the Olds. Behind the Lincoln, a guy was talking on a cellular telephone. He said something to the guy with the rifle—A rifle: using the hood as a rest, the guy took aim at the Plymouth. Devlin ducked below the dashboard. He didn't hear the shot. The Plymouth pitched forward, down and to the right. The tire. Now the Plymouth lurched to the rear. Devlin was being shot at in stereo—but they *did* want him alive.

"Come on out, Devlin! We can make it real unhappy for you!"

A bullhorn; they knew exactly what they were doing. Now Devlin heard a shot, and bits of glass fell on the back of his neck. They were going to shoot out the windows, make him cower in the foot well. He had told John that he would try to stay with this car when he returned to the city. Glass started flying everywhere, the rearview mirror spinning into the backseat. Devlin heard fluid pouring on the pavement. They wanted to burn him out? All things considered, an excellent idea. He pushed in the cigarette lighter. More shots and the roof buckled. He'd have to palm the lighter in the hand that held his gun—*His* gun. The lighter popped out.

"Hey! I want to give up!" He blew the horn. "I quit! Let me get out of here!"

"Keep your hands where we can see them!"

Devlin pushed open the passenger door. They were still behind their cars protecting themselves from their own gun-fire. He had to do the unexpected, keep them off-balance a moment more. The lighter burned his palm.

"Chuck the gun! Do it now!"

Gas was flowing toward the side of the road. Devlin tossed the gun and the lighter together into the wetness. Fire boiled up at once. Devlin had to act surprised, even if it meant getting a little singed. Flames erupted from under the rear of the car. Now Devlin moved, running toward the Lincoln. The gas tank exploded with a roar, sending Devlin flying forward. For a moment everything went orange. A piece of sheet metal flew past him and landed on the road with a clatter. Devlin had his arms up in front of his face as he landed in the weeds on his stomach, hard, and felt the wind go out of him. The world was green again briefly, Devlin could smell the earth and the weeds, and then things went black.

The motion of the car awakened him. He thought of keeping his eyes closed, but then he heard someone say he was awake, and so he sat up. The backseat of the Lincoln, where he was not alone. Outside, the hills were steeper than in Dutchess; more cluttered with buildings, too.

"Where are we?"

"On 9W. We're avoiding tollbooths. You snore, do you know that?"

Devlin didn't answer. Route 9W was on the western side of the Hudson. The dashboard clock indicated twenty after four—less than eight hours to midnight, when Kevin's men were going to put Eileen on the plane. The Lincoln was headed south, apparently toward Paterson. Devlin would arouse suspicion if he asked about the Plymouth. He sat up, allowing the change in his position to make him aware of what was in his pockets. Everything seemed to be in place, which told him something about the haste with which they must have departed the scene of the ambush. Of course.

Thank God!

5:06 P.M. . . .

THIS TIME THE NEATLY TRIMMED DRIVEWAY WAS EMPTY. The driver wheeled the Lincoln in and drew even with the front walk. The Olds parked at the curb so that the view from the street of the walk was blocked. Everybody but Devlin and the guy sitting next to him got out of the cars. Three entered the house, one stayed at the curb, looking left and right. Devlin's seatmate watched for a sign from the driver of the Lincoln, who was waiting for the guy at the curb. He turned to the driver and nodded. The driver tapped the window with his key. Devlin shuddered. The guy beside him smiled.

"You should be scared, shithead." He got out. "Slide across. Don't try that other door, it's got a child lock."

Devlin moved. He had never been so frightened in his life.

The front door was open, but the room inside was dark. The venetian blinds had not changed position since yesterday.

"Go," the driver said.

An old man appeared in the doorway. He was short, squat, sturdy. He had no hair, not even eyebrows. He had no teeth, either, no teeth and no neck. Just a crisp, white shirt with a head on top. His lips worked, and drool appeared on his chin. A smile, Devlin realized. "Look at this fuckhead," the old man mouthed to no one Devlin could see. "Smart. Piece of shit. Come in."

Devlin climbed the stairs. A hand emerged from the darkness and grabbed him by the necktie. He was clubbed on the side of the head with something heavy and sharp. Devlin went with the direction of the blow, rolled with it, but the hand wrapped in his tie held, spun him around, and set him up for the gun butt flashing down on the bridge of his nose.

It was like peering over a pile of snow. For a moment he felt no pain, had no knowledge of where he was—and then he realized. His nose felt like a five-pound lump of lead. He could feel wetness under the snow cone in the middle of his face.

"Don't get up," a guy said. "There's no point."

Devlin brought his hand up to his face carefully. Tape and gauze—a big pile of gauze. They had broken his nose and thrown a patch on it. His pockets were empty. They had his passport and wallet. "You followed the trail the way a chicken follows feed. Now let me make this simple. Tell us the location of the little gun you took yesterday from the Lincoln and you walk. You and Rizzo got the same nose. We never wanted you dead. Your life is fucked and that's enough. It's going to take you years to get out of this trouble. Maybe you'll even do time—and inside, you'll probably have to kill somebody to keep from getting turned into a girl. Brennan knows now that we aren't going to kill you. We got the message to him yesterday morning, at St. Pat's during the funeral. Beautiful. In spite of your involvement with his boys' anticrime bullshit, letting you live is a better way of twisting his dick. Fuck him. Hell was made for guys like him."

Some sales pitch. Devlin remembered Harry Levine saying that old DiBennedetti knew he was going to hell. They wanted the little gun that Devlin had taken from the glove compartment—he had been right about that. Setting Kevin's Plymouth on fire had kept them from searching for it. Devlin knew exactly where the gun was, in the trunk, inside a metal toolbox, under a pile of old wrenches and screwdrivers. Fire would not have touched the gun, and the rust that follows automobile fires was not going to louse up the necessary ballistics tests. Not even putting the car through a crusher would foul the gun as evidence. "Let me sit up."

"Sure." The guy took Devlin's hand and pulled. A living room. On the windows and door were the venetian blinds he had seen from outside. The light in the sky was fading. What time was it? Sitting up made Devlin's nose feel heavier. He could feel something crunching inside. His throat was dry. Now the nose burned. They had made the mistake of their lives, leaving the .25 in the Lincoln. The little gun tied them to Lederer and all the killings. Since it had fallen into Devlin's hands, the .25 had been the only thing on their minds. All he had to do was tell them its location and he'd walk? Sure. Next week he was going to star on Broadway. "You don't care about Lederer."

The guy smiled. "That was the beauty part. You saved us money. He never got his last payment."

Maybe they thought Lederer was a fair trade for Liz Weinstein, Major, the TWA plainclothesman, and the two actors who had played the Quinns. Rizzo entered the room, his face crisscrossed with tape. He lunged at Devlin. "You're the luckiest guy alive, you motherfucker! If it was up to me, you'd be dead already. I'd be wishing I could kill you again. It's going to take three operations to fix this fucking thing. Three!" He whacked Devlin on the side of the head.

"Don't," somebody said. "You're going to start him bleeding again. Who knows if he can take it?"

"He can take it."

"Do you *know*?"

A young guy with red hair. Their little drama wasn't missing a beat. Good guy-bad guy. Cop stuff. They were almost *too* good at it.

On the couch next to the guy with red hair was old DiBennedetti, his eyes tiny and piglike, stuck in his hairless head like raisins imbedded in a mound of dough. Five guys were in the room now, Rizzo, the guy who had told him that they had wanted him to live, and another guy sitting in an armchair in the corner. His hair was thinning and he watched Devlin intently. The nose felt like an anchor. Devlin had to be careful.

"Brennan don't want you to get your hands on his fucking money," DiBennedetti said. "It's his worst nightmare. You'll go for it, we know you. Free money, right? Nothing would suit him better than to see you get an annulment, but it ain't gonna happen. He sent his own guy to Rome back in the early seventies. Months ago he called the convent to tell them to watch out for you, to tell him if you showed up. We're not the only ones who've been watching you. You got a nice girlfriend there. Lovely woman.''

I'm lucky she's alive, you son of a bitch. "Did you tap his calls?"

The old man leaned back, blinking. "What the fuck is wrong with you? We could kill you anytime, and you're still asking questions!" He looked at the others. "Can you believe this guy?" Suddenly, as if he had leaped across the room, he was inches from Devlin's face. "You and his fucking kids were going after us! Who the hell did you think you were? Who the hell did you think you were dealing with?"

"Jim Brennan planted that stuff in Jack's office," Devlin said.

"Bullshit! What for?"

"So you would go after me. He's just evil enough to think I wanted his money in spite of my interest in another woman. You just said it yourself. He wanted you to do his dirty work for him."

"You don't know nothin'. You can't. He doesn't want anybody to know what an evil motherfucker he is. He doesn't even want himself to know." DiBennedetti's little eyes bulged. "But don't you bullshit me about him framing you! That file had everything you've been doing with the Brennan task force for the past sixteen years, the secret trips to Washington, the stuff from the N.Y.P.D. you fed to the Brennan brothers— everything. It had your whole fucking life, even shit about where you spent your summers as a kid. What it didn't have is why Brennan sent his kids and you against us, and that's because it was the one thing he couldn't tell you." He studied Devlin, but then suddenly waggled a finger. "You *aged*! You got gray hair!"

Rizzo said, "Why are we wasting our time? All he's got to do is tell us where that gun is."

The old man waggled the finger at Devlin again. "See?

That's all." He stood up straight, looking down at Devlin. "It's a straight deal."

"I was listening. This goes back twenty years?"

"Double. More than that. It goes back before *you* were born."

Devlin struggled against showing emotion. He decided to play his card. "The gun is in Manhattan. At an apartment."

"And you'll tell us there?"

"I'll take somebody there."

"What *is* this?" Rizzo demanded. The red-haired guy waved him off.

"The man *knows*. We're makin' sense to him. He hands over the gun and goes free. We are *not* going to kill a cop! It's absolutely unnecessary." He rubbed his brow. "It's a fuckin' rule, for Christ's sake."

The rest of them looked at one another and laughed. Couldn't they see they weren't fooling him? "Right," said one. "Now how do we get them to stop killin' us?"

"That's another rule," the red-haired guy said. "When the cops kill us, they give themselves a medal." Everybody laughed again.

"You caused Joe Brennan's death," Devlin said to the old man.

Vittorio DiBennedetti moved closer again, searching Devlin's eyes as if there were enough left of his own to reveal something beyond shape, color, and size. "Why do you want to know? What's the point?"

"There isn't any. As soon as I show you where the gun is, I'm headed to Kennedy and the midnight flight to London. You searched me. That's what the passport's all about."

The old man gave him a toothless smile. "And the traveler's checks. We noticed the traveler's checks. Makes you wonder how a cop puts together so much money."

Devlin sat up. "Did you notice eleven grand in cash?"

DiBennedetti shook his head. "No. Nobody noticed that." The others smiled. He patted Devlin on the shoulder. "Be grateful you're alive with your traveler's checks. You want me

to tell you about this, eh? How we got frogmen to hold the
jerk under? A drowning is quick, quicker than you think.''

"I want to hear this thing that goes back so many years,"
Devlin said. "I thought you said the Brennan boys were killed
because they were planning to go after organized crime . . ."

"That's a joke. You can't hurt us that way, we're too big,
too tough. Nah! That had nothing to do with it. Nah, nah."
He looked at Devlin. "I tell you this, you tell us where the
gun is?"

"I'll take you to where the gun is."

"Whatever," the old man said, and laughed. He sounded
like a jungle bird, an ugly one. "First I'll tell you how we
killed Joe Brennan, then I'll tell you why."

Devlin had been as crazy as this.

Maybe he hadn't sat around planning how to drown a guy
in the ocean outside his own house, but as a cop, a young man
about town, a member of the Brennan family, Devlin had lived
for years as close as this to the violent heart of the city, guys
who had been shot, chorus girls who had poisoned themselves, people who had died for no reason at all, except maybe
being on the wrong street corner on the wrong afternoon. Devlin had been this crazy, wanting to hear how people died.
Maybe his eyes had lit up like this old man's. . . .

Maryellen remembered him when. *Ho, ho*, she had said. He
remembered himself. Yes, *this* crazy. Old man DiBennedetti had
maybe months to live, yet he remained obsessed with events of
fifty years ago. He was still laughing over suckering Devlin into
going to Maryellen's convent. Brennan had been like this, and
in their separate ways, so had his kids. A nest of them, Ann
Elizabeth had said. A nest of what? You saw them everywhere.
What had attracted Maryellen to him? What had been so great
about Devlin? *Who are you?*

What had Brennan feared?

A young American on the make?

"When I came over here from the other side," DiBennedetti
said dreamily, with a faint smile, "before the war, I moved in
with my father's cousin, Bruno Ippolito."

Bruno was in his sixties, with four daughters and a son, Vinnie, who was younger than DiBennedetti, but as tough and streetwise as they came. Vinnie Ippolito was going to be a big success in his father's organization. His father's fear was that Vinnie was too eager, not smart enough about people, too trusting.

"You're not a father, so you don't know how a father feels about his son. It's special. I don't know how Vinnie knew Brennan. I was closer to him than his father, but that was because we were both young, single guys." The old man swallowed. "I didn't know Brennan from a hill of shit! Vinnie came to me with Brennan's deal because he knew his father would never go for it, but Brennan was offering five hundred dollars, which was a lot of money in those days. You could buy a new car for that much.

"I'm telling you, I didn't know Brennan from a hill of shit. Vinnie was my connection to the deal. Brennan was driving a bus in Queens for a guy named Brady and had just married Brady's daughter. She had made the mistake of getting on Brennan's bus one night at the end of the line. He slipped it to her, nice Catholic girl, a virgin. She kept her mouth shut about what he did even though she wasn't exactly a volunteer, if you know what I mean. Back then, what choice did she have? She knew her father thought the world of Brennan. Anyway, Brennan saw his opportunity. After the marriage, all he had to do was get rid of Brady. So Brennan went to Vinnie, and Vinnie came to me. Vinnie knew his father would never go for a deal like that. I gave Vinnie the stuff that Brennan had to get Brady to drink, and I told him what to tell Brennan about how to use it. It gives a guy a heart attack. I was trying to do the kid a favor. If Vinnie hadn't kept telling me how it was going, I might have forgotten about it, with enough time."

Devlin thought he knew what was coming. What interested him was the reaction of the other men listening to DiBennedetti. They knew this story. They were eager to get the little gun. Still, they were being respectful, not simply acting it. The old man might be crazy, but he was still in pain over Vinnie Ippolito, and the pain was important to them all.

"Vinnie told me that the stuff worked, but then, a little later, he said that Brennan was acting funny, like he decided he couldn't trust Vinnie no more. I told Vinnie to stay away, and he said he would, but that was only to shut me up. One night Vinnie didn't come home, and the next morning the cops found him in an alley, beat to death. I saw the body. Did you ever see a guy who got beat to death?"

Devlin said yes.

"His head was all lumps. I never saw skin so many colors like that. A thing like that is a sin. A sin. I knew right away who did it, but I had to keep my mouth shut. Vinnie was his father's pride and joy, maybe even what he lived for. I should have known better than to let him go ahead with Brennan. Old man Ippolito was the guy who took care of me, and look how I repaid him. Vinnie's death broke his fuckin' heart."

"Come on, Vic, take it easy," the red-haired guy said.

The old man nodded. "Ippolito had his own ways of finding out what happened, and they worked. He never said anything to me about being involved, but he knew. I know he knew because of how he asked me to take care of it . . ."

"Wait until Brennan was a father."

"No!" the old man roared. "Better! Better! Wait until Brennan couldn't be a father *again*! Take *his* son away from him forever!"

"Brennan had two sons."

"And Bruno Ippolito lived to see that! It made him sick to his stomach!"

Twenty to seven. Sonny, the one with the thinning hair, was going to take Devlin where he wanted to go. The red-haired guy said, "You said the gun was in Manhattan?"

Devlin was being helped to his feet. The red-haired guy wanted an intersection. They wanted to cruise by in another car first and make sure it was safe before letting Devlin near. "The Upper West Side," Devlin said. "Yuppieville."

He wasn't supposed to see them exchange glances, but he did. Now he had to act as if he hadn't. He had to be very, very careful. He couldn't act too believing, couldn't act as if he knew he was only playing for time, praying for a miracle. He couldn't talk too much. No one in his right mind, behind a nose like his, would want to talk much. He had called something vivid to their minds. A mile of trendy restaurants and clothing shops on Columbus Avenue, the sidewalks filled with women. And tonight, the first night of a holiday weekend? It even made sense. A lot of stand-up citizens lived in that neighborhood, people a guy like Devlin would know, and with whom he might even stash a gun.

At the door, the old man stepped forward. "I know I can count on you. We're even. Good luck to you. Enjoy London. You can cash a traveler's check at the airport."

A hair overdone, Devlin thought. In a mirror he could see that his shirt and jacket were a giant bloodstain. He *had* lost a lot of blood. If he was bleeding now, it wasn't much. But he couldn't think about that, either. The old man had overdone it because he liked death games so much. It had taken Devlin a few minutes to figure it out. The old man had told the story of Joe's death because he'd thought he had been looking at a man about to die, the perfect audience. The old man's eyes had given Devlin all the clues. Constantly searching Devlin's, trying to read Devlin's mind. *What does he know? What is it like?* Dying tormented Vittorio DiBennedetti. He had thought about it too long, in too many ways. Devlin hadn't shown anything— on target, he thought, for a man who had it in the back of his mind that maybe he really was only playing for a few more minutes of being alive.

The Lincoln had been turned around. Sonny preceded him down the stairs. He was built like a small tank. "It'll be dark soon. Your nose won't show so much." From across the roof of the car, he asked, "What street?"

Give a little more. "Columbus Avenue."

Sonny got in and started the car. He buckled up. "You, too. They stop you for this shit now."

As soon as Devlin was secure, Sonny pushed his release button. "I gotta get something."

Devlin sat still. He was supposed to believe that he and Sonny were going into the city alone. Sonny was in the house telling the others that the street was Columbus Avenue. Maybe somebody was already thinking that Devlin was playing his string for every minute he could get. These guys were tough, but they weren't geniuses. Being stupid had gotten them into this trouble in the first place and they knew it. They were going to have to settle for the second car following Devlin and Sonny, not going ahead to check things out. It wouldn't do them any good if they went ahead, anyway. They wouldn't see anything. And with them following the Lincoln, Devlin knew exactly where they were. And that was what was important.

7:08 P.M. . . .

THE TRAFFIC WAS HEAVY, BUT MOVED SMOOTHLY UNTIL they reached the long grade up to the top of the Palisades. Then it was bumper-to-bumper, moving a car-length with every surge.

Devlin said, "Pull into the emergency lane and pass all this shit."

"What?"

"You worried about getting a ticket? I still have my shield. Nobody's going to recognize me with this over my face."

"Not a chance. I don't want to deal with cops. Besides, they'll see us from the tollbooths. We get up there, they're going to want to know what's going on."

"My *nose* is what's going on. I'll show them my shield. I don't want to miss that fucking plane!"

"You won't. Lots of time."

Devlin wanted Sonny distracted. A second car, almost certainly the Olds, was behind them. Devlin wanted to be positive about the identity of the vehicle, but he couldn't be seen looking in the side mirror, much less turning around. Back on Route 80, Sonny had made a couple of maneuvers for the purpose of lining up a second car. Devlin had to keep working on Sonny. There were only so many options with a guy like him. Devlin scratched his right ear. Sonny *was* tough—obviously he was the designated hitter. Even if Devlin waited until they were on the bridge before taking him on, it might take Devlin so long to have any effect that the guys in the second car might arrive before he was done. Guys. Two—one to keep the other company. Devlin figured the red-haired guy and the one who had helped Devlin sit up. Not Rizzo. Rizzo was too emotional, not one hundred percent, a liability.

It took another fifteen minutes to reach the tollbooths, and then traffic moved again, slowly. Devlin was trying to keep his head clear, but it was difficult not to think of all the dead—*and* Jim Brennan. From the upper deck Devlin could see the Manhattan skyline, brighter than usual, but not otherwise different. Traffic on the West Side Drive wasn't moving at all. Not even inches. "Take Broadway," Devlin said.

"You really want to get there, don't you?"

'It's going to be nine o'clock before we're done. You see what's happening. I can hit one bottleneck, maybe two, but if I get caught in something like that, I'm dead."

Sonny was quiet. "Yeah, I see what you mean."

Perfect. Devlin scratched his ear again. When it was time to change lanes, Devlin looked behind them as Sonny cut the wheel. The Olds—no mistake.

He was about to find out how good a cop John Lord really was. Harry Levine, too, if he'd jumped for the bait of Jack Brennan's letter to his girlfriend. They were looking for Kevin's Plymouth plainwrap; they had it in their minds. Devlin had said he was going to *try* to stay with Kevin's car. A lot had happened to Devlin in the time since his last conversation with John. For all he knew, John was in jail and Harry Levine was in the next cell.

No, Devlin thought, *John would do better than that.* Harry Levine was even more able. *Look on the bright side,* Eileen would say, using another Irish expression Americans thought was their own. . . .

7:54 P.M. . . .

HE WAS BEING CAREFUL. AT NINETY-SIXTH STREET HE told Sonny to turn left, and then on Columbus he said to turn right. The sky was medium purple; all the streetlights were on. "Stay in the left-hand lane. It's between Eighty-seventh and Eighty-sixth, or Eighty-sixth and Eighty-fifth. I've already caught myself getting the numbers backward, but I'll recognize the building."

"Whose apartment is it?"

"My girlfriend's girlfriend. Won't she be surprised to see me?"

"You hittin' on her?"

"No, I meant the nose. Actually I'm just hoping somebody's there." *More than you know.* Devlin wanted to keep him entertained. "Yeah, I hit on her once. Some women are like that. They have to know what their girlfriend is getting. This one was very slick. I didn't tip to her at all until she saw her shot and took it." *Eighty-eighth Street.* He had to start looking for people on the sidewalk. "You ever have one like that?"

"I like a little one," Sonny said. "The little ones are the best, especially the first time you get 'em alone. Just wave it at 'em. They can't take their eyes off it. They're all so full of shit. They never want anybody to know what they're doin' in private."

Eighty-seventh Street. "Start taking it easy," Devlin said. Columbus was crowded with pedestrians. He powered the window down.

"What did you do that for?"

"I can see better. Wait a few years, Sonny. All kinds of weird shit starts happening to you." *If you live that long.* Devlin wanted to get caught at the light, wanted the Lincoln to be first in line. He still didn't see any plainclothes cops. "Take your time. Wait. No, that isn't it."

The light turned yellow. "Are you shittin' me?"

"No, the building on the next block looks just like this one here. Calm down." The light turned red. Sonny had another twenty feet to roll. "Nobody wants this finished more than I do." Devlin was scratching his ear when they reached the building line, jerking his thumb back behind him.

"What the fuck are you doing?" Immediately Sonny's eyes were drawn to what was going on outside.

"Behind us!" Devlin yelled. "The black Olds!" As he went for Sonny, he saw John Lord toss his topcoat aside, revealing a sawed-off shotgun. People started screaming. Sonny was going for his gun. With both hands, Devlin pushed the gun against the driver's door. John was yelling something. Sonny's gun fired. Outside, an explosion, an ear-ringing boom that left Devlin all but deafened. Sonny was trying to get his left hand around to push on Devlin's nose. Through the cotton in his ears Devlin heard more screaming. Another boom, this one a few feet farther away than the first.

The screaming went on. Sonny's hand was free to get at Devlin's nose. Devlin had to keep both hands locked on the gun. It fired a second time. Devlin pushed Sonny's finger back hard against the trigger guard.

"Get your head down, Frank," John said calmly, suddenly close. Devlin did it, holding tight.

"Kill this son of a bitch!"

"No problem. Get your head lower. *All right, you, drop the gun!*"

Sonny yelled, struggled against Devlin; it was pure panic. John's shotgun went off like a cannon on a battleship.

Behind the Lincoln, in the windshield of the Olds Regency four-door, were two holes the size of basketballs, and in the front seat, head-shot, dead, were the red-haired guy and the other one. Not Rizzo. Maybe next time. The red-haired guy had his hand inside his jacket. The other one had one hand in his lap with the palm up. Blue-and-whites had arrived immediately. John had had to tell Devlin to display his shield. John's hand seemed welded to the shotgun. This was the arrangement Devlin had made with John this morning. DiBennedetti and Company had expected him in Dutchess County this afternoon. Devlin had expected to get them to this intersection between 7:30 and 8:30 this evening. The shotgun had been John's idea. Or maybe somebody else's, Devlin thought. People were staring at him, pointing. He was bleeding again. The intersection had filled with blue-and-whites almost instantly. More cars were nosing in. A gold shield pushed through the crowd. The eyebrows went up when he saw Devlin.

"Henderson, Manhattan North. You all right?"

"Yeah. Look, we got things to do . . ."

"Did you talk to the chief?" John asked him.

Henderson gave a cop's tight grin. "*He* talked to *me*."

"All right," John said. "I identified myself to these two back here as a police officer when I heard a gunshot, apparently from this other car. I saw the two here go for weapons. I fired one round at each. There was another shot from the front car. I went to the aid of my partner, who was hand-to-hand with the third perp. I ordered that man to drop his weapon. He resisted. I fired one round at him." John thrust the shotgun at Henderson. "It bears my mark. Tag it and bag it. My partner and I need a ride to the Seventy-second Street Marina." When Henderson didn't move, John let his eyes roam the crowd. "Like right now," he said quietly.

Henderson looked at Devlin. "You don't want to get to a hospital?"

Devlin was testing the gauze for sogginess. "I have to see Brennan," he told John. He felt a chill. Was it shock?

"I have the files you wanted. They're at the Seventy-second Street Marina—on the launch." To Henderson, John said, "He's a big boy. Check it out with the chief's office, if you want. Just get us the car!" He turned to Devlin. "That's some mess where your nose used to be. You're right about Harry Levine. When I told him about the letter, he reacted like a kid. 'I'm going to the office,' he said. 'You answer to me.' You had to love it. He told me to bring the shotgun.'' John was peering at Devlin's nose. ''I like what you said this morning about where you would be sitting when you rolled up. If you weren't driving, you had no slack. When I saw you in the passenger seat—and that bandage—I went to red alert. Instantly.''

Another chill. Devlin was beginning to realize how very close he had come to dying. They could have killed him in Dutchess or Paterson if they had felt lucky about finding the gun. Devlin pushed through to the Lincoln. Sonny's head rested against the windowsill, his hair sparkling with blue-white fragments of the door window. Sonny had been a split second from not dying, and now he looked like that had been his last thought. Devlin said, ''Up in Dutchess County somewhere is Kevin's shot-up, burned-out Plymouth. In the toolbox in the trunk is a .25-caliber revolver that was used to kill the man and woman found on New York Boulevard in Queens Wednesday morning.'' A blue-and-white let out a whoop. ''I got the gun in Paterson yesterday.'' He turned to John. ''What about Eileen?''

''I'll tell you in the car. Come on.'' Henderson took the gun. ''You played right into their insanity,'' John said. ''You stuck your head in the lion's mouth. You did some job just getting here alive.''

''I out-acted them.'' He climbed into the backseat. When John closed the door after him, Devlin said, ''Sonny's gun went off because I was grabbing it. It was one of those things.''

''He shouldn't have pulled the gun in the first place. I don't know why the other two went for their guns. I had them, absolutely had them. Sonny? Was that his name?'' Now the siren sounded.

Devlin said, ''When you came back, he couldn't let go of the gun because I wouldn't let go of him.''

John pointed toward the siren and pulled on his earlobe. He was going to wait before he spoke again. John would argue that if you wanted to play cops and robbers, you became one or the other. Sonny had played into the insanity of the police. Devlin looked at his watch: 8:30. Three and a half hours to midnight. The fireworks were scheduled to start at 9:30, but already, so far uptown, people with folding chairs and coolers were trooping riverward. Devlin realized he was on the wrong side of the window; he felt he was on the outside looking in. He needed a little more strength. They turned into Seventy-second and the driver killed the siren. Firecrackers were going off everywhere.

"Eileen—"

"She's still with Kevin's people, and fine, according to them." He leaned forward. "Did anybody clock all that back there?"

"Four point two seconds," the driver said. "They played the tape over the radio twice already."

John unwrapped a stick of gum. What the hell did he care about the time the shooting had taken? What did he know about Eileen that he wasn't telling? They rocked from side to side as the driver wove across the Broadway intersection, using the siren to shoo pedestrians. "We've got problems," John said quietly. "Kevin got back to town this afternoon. He wants to hurt you for what you did to him, and Eileen is the only way he can do it. I want to wait until we're out of the car before discussing it. Try to take it easy, Frank, please."

8:34 P.M. . . .

THEY NEEDED THE SIREN AGAIN ON SEVENTY-SECOND Street, and were over on the other side of the double line for half a block. Thousands of people lined the sidewalks, all kinds of things under their arms, some even wearing green polyurethane Liberty tiaras. At Riverside Drive Devlin could see crowds in the gloom of the park and moving up the drive, heading to higher ground. The air shook with the rumble of celebration. A rocket hissed skyward. With another tap of the siren, the blue-and-white went under the West Side Highway and out to the edge of the water. The sky was dark purple, the Jersey side still boldly silhouetted, even though it seemed that every electric light over there was turned on. No *Seadancer* in the near distance—nothing sixty feet long. A police launch was tied to one of the docks, lights boiling. When they were out of the car, John said, "We don't have until midnight, we have until eleven o'clock. That's when Kevin's men call him to find out if they should put Eileen on the plane. If Kevin doesn't get what he's looking for, he's going to let Eileen go to London. He has to hang tough. That's what Harry Levine says. He's claiming he acted under Torres's authority. If he doesn't get immunity for what looks like a kidnapping charge, he's got to make it look like he thought he was doing the right thing . . . After all, you will have to do some answering yourself. Eileen could be out of the country for months, even a year. That's Kevin's idea of making trouble for you."

"Do you know where they're keeping her?"

"Not yet. Since they're not giving themselves much leeway, she can't be far from the airport."

Devlin didn't answer. Two guys ran the launch. They turned on the searchlight and cast off, drifting out and downriver, toward a ghostly fog of tiny lights floating just above the water. Devlin couldn't remember how many thousands of ships had been expected, but all had their lights on now. In seconds the air was cooler and quieter, the street-corner fireworks distant, fading. The dampness soothed him, even though Devlin's stomach was tying itself into a tighter knot. How many people had died this week?

"Harry Levine was back in his office at eleven o'clock," John said. "Eileen's paperwork got done yesterday; it's in offices all over the city. Harry had a deal with the mayor and Torres that included Eileen until Kevin undid it. Kevin has something on Torres. My guess is that he went to a meeting wearing a wire, and Torres said something indiscreet. Figures."

"Kevin has something on Torres, Torres has something on Hamilton." Devlin shuddered, and made his nose hurt. "The hip bone's connected to the thigh bone."

"And Brennan's connected to the mayor," John said. "Harry's hoping you'll get Brennan to spill his guts a little."

Devlin closed his eyes. All he had hoped this afternoon was to get something out of old DiBennedetti that he would use to get Brennan to leave Eileen and him alone. Now he wasn't sure he was going to be able to do that. Brennan hated him that much, Brennan was that powerful, and he was crazier than anybody had imagined, crazier than Devlin had ever thought crazy to mean.

John lifted one of the seats to get at a storage compartment. "Here are the files on Brennan and DiBennedetti, everything you asked for. The two old men have only one thing in common: Brooklyn. That's all. Jim Brennan was born in Brooklyn, and Vittorio DiBennedetti spent his youth and young manhood there. Different neighborhoods. There's no record that they ever met. Look for yourself."

"I don't have my reading glasses. We'll have nothing on Brennan without a wire. I was wondering how you made a tape of the shoot-out, four point two seconds. You're wearing a wire."

John smiled. "Broadcasts to a recorder down below. There was another in a blue-and-white off Columbus Avenue. I'll show you how it works."

The sounds of the city disappeared under the urgent burble of the engine of the launch. Devlin was thinking of Eileen in a hotel near the airport. He knew how the decision had been made today not to search for her—and who had made it. Budget. Liberty Week priorities. Liberty Week politics. With those factors in mind, Harry Levine had chosen not to send as few as four men—two teams—to canvass two dozen hotels. When Kevin surfaced again, any chance to correct the mistake was gone. Devlin had to accept it. He had to keep his mind clear. What more could happen? What more could crazy people do? If any part of what Vittorio DiBennedetti had told him was true, maybe all he had to do was lean on Brennan, and the rest—Hamilton, Torres, and finally even Kevin—would tumble. In fifteen years, and especially in the last two with Eileen, Devlin had made himself more free of their common madness than he had realized. Maryellen was all the proof he needed. This afternoon, Maryellen had been a gaudy, even obscene, caricature of herself—as always, almost in focus, almost whole, but unable to take that last step into real commitment as a person. And still playing it to the hilt, still mooching for patience. In the past, his failure with her had tantalized him. Now he knew he had no idea of what kind of person she would be, if any at all, if the raging inside her ever stopped. And the raging hadn't eased, it was worse. She dreamed of romance while she decayed into incompetence. A part of her knew, just as another part wanted him back.

And another didn't at all.

Devlin remembered Bingo Malone.

He felt the damp air again and smiled. *Bingo!*

Whatever it takes!

Yes. He almost said it aloud. They were coming out to the middle of the river. On the instrument panel was a radar screen, but the special transponder the police had fitted to the *Seadancer* hadn't shown up yet. Harry Levine had been on the telephone with the captain of the yacht; there wouldn't be any problems.

The launch passed a tall sailing ship, the hull bright with new paint. Blond teenagers with heavy accents hooted and yelled, "Copper! Copper!" Maybe they thought they were in an American movie. Maybe they knew America better than America knew itself—certainly better than it wanted to. The old man aboard the *Seadancer* had long ago proclaimed himself one of America's favorite sons, his family one of America's first. Had anyone ever mounted an effective argument against him? Devlin thought of holding Liz in his arms at the moment of her death.

"We have the transponder blip," said the man at the wheel.

"How far away?"

"The whole five miles on the screen. We don't want to push too hard. You don't know what's floating in the water tonight."

* * *

They kept on, into a shadowy forest of masts and spars, bending and swinging on the heaving river. The searchlight picked up mist and banks of firecracker smoke. The water was full of debris, candy wrappers, wooden crates, bottles. Sometimes a bit of music could be heard from a nearby boat, or people's voices, but for no more than an eerie second or two. In the intense white light of the searchlight, the water was a lusterless green, foamy in spots with a mustard-colored froth. A garbage bag, full and neatly tied, floated by. The launch passed the twin towers of the World Trade Center. The sky was black. The launch swung away, toward New Jersey.

The Statue of Liberty came into view, floodlit against the night sky, brilliant. Spotless, after the months of work. Gleaming. Devlin was focusing on Jim Brennan. The man had changed and aged, but not as much as he wanted people to think, according to his daughter-in-law Anita. Devlin wanted to blame him for Maryellen, but really knew better. When everything else was stripped away, Maryellen loved herself as she was. Maybe her father had helped, given her a nudge, but he had done that with everybody. If Brennan thought he was getting less than one hundred percent, he hounded people. Or they were gone. Maryellen was only a case in point. Of course there were more appropriate facilities for her, better professional care. But this way, she was out of sight, not an embarrassment. . . .

I'm being realistic.

Devlin could hear Brennan saying it.

If there was any truth to DiBennedetti's story, even a grain, Jim Brennan's whole life was a work of evil, and Brennan himself never had been far from knowing it. If DiBennedetti had not lied, most of the time the knowledge had breathed down Brennan's neck, worse than DiBennedetti's fear of death. . . .

The blip showed that the *Seadancer* was as close to the statue as the authorities were permitting ships to get. The man at the screen said, "The *Seadancer* won't be hard to pick out in this parking lot. One of the new Italian jobs, a helicopter pad on the top deck. Probably has a hot tub, too."

Not far away, a string of firecrackers went off. Light from the statue fanned out behind the *Seadancer*, three decks of futurism in white plastic. The bridge leaned forward at the same sharp angle as the bow. A radar dome crowned the bridge like the peak of a dictator's cap. Jim Brennan wanted people to believe he was looking forward to the twenty-first century? Or was this the way he wanted to be observed, as close to 2001 as one could get this year, and by enjoying it, pronouncing himself its first master? The launch slowed.

"The Brennans don't expect us," John said. "At least, that's what I was told."

"We'll see," Devlin said. "Brennan can make you think he has eyes in the back of his head." *Right*: Brennan could make you think he could see around corners.

One of the crewmen tapped a horn and waited. The captain came out on the deck and directed them toward a boarding ladder. He was a burly young guy who looked uncomfortable in a uniform. The two detectives climbed the ladder. On deck, John asked, "How's it going?"

"It's just the two of them," the captain said. "There's food for forty in the galley. They didn't tell us they'd canceled all the invitations. It's typical of them. They've chartered before. They had a light dinner. She's been out on the fantail since, while he stayed in the salon. I saw him on the telephone. He has a portable cellular, nothing to do with our equipment. How do you want to work this?"

"Tell him the police are here, that's all."

The captain nodded and turned away. Devlin drew a breath. He was more nervous than he'd been this afternoon, walking through the convent with Ann Elizabeth to his meeting with Maryellen. Round and round, just like the old days.

"Just play him along, see what you can get out of him," John said. "Harry is doing everything he can to locate Eileen."

"Yeah, I know."

The captain reappeared. "He's feeling playful—mean. He can get downright abusive, so don't be surprised at anything he says. And be careful there, that door will feel heavy because of the air-conditioning."

John went first, grappling with the door. He held it for Devlin.

White plastic on the outside, teak paneling within. Thickly padded royal blue carpeting silenced their steps. The air was icy, motionless as death. From behind the top molding of the walls indirect lighting sprayed softly across the ceiling. At the other end of the salon, a plush, L-shaped settee faced sliding glass doors leading out onto the fantail. The whole back wall was glass, and beyond it, brilliant, so big Devlin couldn't see all of her upraised arm, was the Statue of Liberty.

The settee was covered in pale blue silk. Opposite was a curved bar with three stools. Between, Jim Brennan sat in his electric wheelchair, facing the statue. Most of the fantail beyond him was in darkness, except for a six-foot, illuminated pale turquoise hole in the deck. A hot tub.

"Good evening, gentlemen! Pour yourselves a drink! As you can see, the bar has everything." Brennan moved a toggle switch and wheeled around with a *whirr*. "Come over here so I can see you—and your shields. News about my son, have you?"

His speech wasn't slurred, but his voice wasn't what it had been. It was more gravelly now, higher, weaker, and not so distinct. His lower lip quavered, he bit down on it.

"Yes and no," John said. He was in front. Now Brennan wanted to see the identification cards, too. He looked up at Devlin and slowly, perhaps too slowly to be really convincing, he allowed himself a small grin.

"That's some nose you've got there . . ."

"Frank Devlin, Jim. We know each other."

Brennan rubbed his chin with his knuckle, staring.

"Fifteen years," Devlin said.

The old man looked away, his lip curling. Now Devlin saw that his jaw trembled. "I hate the sight of you."

"That's what I want to talk to you about."

Brennan tried to give a bit of a crooked grin. Somebody had tipped him. He'd expected them. He looked gaunt, with vertical lines in his face and neck Devlin hadn't seen that last night in the library. The hair was white, the little that was left, unkempt, and his eyes were older, angrier, quicker, more impatient than ever. Devlin was remembering that Brennan had spat in his face and gotten away with it.

"You piece of shit," Brennan said. He rotated toward John. "Well, now. Given your partner's business, and the play he's been getting in the papers the last couple of days, there isn't much reason for you to be here, except as a witness. Maybe you're even wearing a wire. Either way, you're out. I've always cooperated with the police and I'm cooperating now, but you don't have a warrant or probable cause and until you do, I'm boss here. So get the fuck out. The galley's behind the bridge. Fill your face there. Get a drink. Have a good time! I'm only sorry that my hospitality is so limited, that I can't offer you a woman to go with the food and the booze. But it isn't that kind of a cruise, if you know what I mean."

John looked pained. For Devlin, the old man's behavior seemed studied, thought out in advance.

"On the other hand, we do have an Indonesian crew, all very pretty boys, if you care for that sort of thing."

John hesitated. Devlin would tell him later that Brennan was playing a game with them.

"This is one of his better moods," Devlin said.

"All right." John backed away. "I'm going to look for a spot to watch the fireworks."

"Get a drink!" Brennan yelled. "Go on!"

John waved him off as he went through the door.

"I didn't think you'd have the nerve," Brennan said to Devlin. He bit his lip again.

"The hell you didn't."

"Well, you haven't got much goddamned time," Brennan said. "The show goes on in fifteen minutes, and Charlotte expects me out there with her at the start, at least. Maybe the finish, too. I can't get chilled anymore."

The air was warmer outside, who was he kidding? "You were expecting us."

"Oh, for Christ's sake. Yes. Of course. Get yourself a drink, I mean it."

"No, thanks."

"Accept my hospitality! Have a drink! What the hell is wrong with you?"

"I don't want a drink, Jim."

He glanced quickly toward the fantail. "The least you could do is sit down. Jesus, you're giving me a stiff neck. Over there, where I can see you." Brennan waved a hand toward the settee and steered the wheelchair to the bar. On the wall was a panel of switches and rheostats. Reaching up, Brennan lit the room brightly. Eyes bulging with effort and anger, he used the bar to pull himself out of the chair. It took him a moment to square his shoulders and straighten his back. He was two inches shorter and thirty pounds lighter than he had been fifteen years ago. His teeth were clenched in triumph.

"There," he said. "Rheumatoid arthritis. I live with pain every day of my life. If you won't have a drink, I will. I'm not supposed to, but fuck it. I'll see what Charlotte wants." He started toward the glass doors leading to the fantail, walking slowly but not shuffling. The reflections on the glass from inside the room made the statue look ghostly. He stopped and turned around, and pointed to the chair with a surprisingly shaky hand. "You see, I do need the wheelchair. A woman who this week stopped being a member of this family once accused me of feeling sorry for myself. The fucking bitch was dead wrong. I *despise* self-pity."

There was a rush of air as Brennan slid the glass door open and stepped out. "Charlotte!" he called loudly. "What do you want to drink?" He left the door open, and the room began to warm up. He went around the hot tub, into the shadow, to one of the high-backed deck chairs facing the statue. *"I said, 'What do you want to drink?'"*

As Brennan leaned over the chair, Devlin looked away. His parents had shown him enough of old couples' wrangling, and he didn't want to have to deal with Charlotte unless he had to. At the forward end of the salon was a graceful white pedestal dining table with twelve delicate chairs upholstered in the blue silk that covered the settee. Whatever the dining set was made of, it gleamed like polished marble. One of the new Italian jobs, the police launch crewman had called it. It *was* like being in the twenty-first century, but so what? Devlin got up to take another look around. If it wasn't fixed in place, the table was worthless in a real sea. The chairs would bounce around like dice in a cup. . . .

"Bolted to a crossmember," Brennan said, closing the door. He glanced back to the fantail. "The table's part of the ship. The chairs are fixed to the deck."

"What do you get out of this?"

Brennan hesitated uncomprehendingly. He looked like he wanted to look around behind him. Now he nodded. "I see what you mean. I believe in the good life, all the bells and whistles. 'Living well is the best revenge.' "

"Against whom?"

"Ha! *Now* I get it! You're a changed man." He spoke the words slowly, savoring them. "You *shithead*!" He poured a Johnnie Walker Black Label for Charlotte. Devlin remembered: Johnnie Walker Black was the only Scotch that didn't give her a headache. It was also one of the most expensive blends. Her Catholic piety did not preclude drinking the good stuff. "I told you what would happen to you if you saw my daughter again."

"That's stupid. It was always stupid, but it sounds ten times worse coming from a man your age."

Brennan eyed him, shook his head as if in disbelief, then turned to take the drink outside. Charlotte had never had more than two drinks in an evening, not enough to give a canary a hangover. She just wanted to be known for drinking the best. Brennan leaned over the chair again to talk to her. Devlin heard murmuring.

You were primed for her, whoever you were. Devlin thought he understood Ann Elizabeth's remark better now. Maryellen had come wrapped in money, power, and the good life. The son of a mediocre, beer-swilling street cop had known too well that he had missed the brass ring only because of an accident of birth. But why *not* him? Devlin could remember his rage over being one of America's millions of born losers. . . .

Along with a certain eagerness to be an asshole about women.

The door closed again. "Sit down, sit down," Brennan said. "I didn't tell her you were here. I don't think she'd recognize you anyway—definitely not with that thing over your nose. You're a little thicker, fuller in the face. Your hair is graying. At least you've kept it." Brennan stood at the bar. Again, he seemed studied, self-conscious. His hand shook as he reached for his drink. "A bit of moving around is good for me. You're not one of those reformed drunks, are you? There's nothing worse than a man who lies to himself about his vices."

He wanted to give speeches? Devlin had to ignore him. "Who let you know I was coming?"

Brennan laughed. "Aside from my spy at my daughter's residence? Torres—the police commissioner. Who did you think I'd deal with? He's kept me informed right along. So has the mayor."

Devlin was watching him carefully. "As of Tuesday morning, the mayor thought you were a drooling moron locked in that wheelchair."

Brennan paused, clutching his drink. Maybe he wasn't used to words like "drooling moron" being applied to him. "It's been useful to let people think that. After the stroke, I didn't know how much better I was going to get. I'm ninety percent now. I spent two years in the chair. It gave me a chance to think, reorganize my life, assume a different kind of role. I deal with only a few top people. We have an election coming up that we can win for a change. We have just the boy. You wait and see. I had my lawyers tell the mayor on Tuesday that we wanted to be kept informed."

He brought his glass to his lips again, his hand shaking so much Devlin could hear the ice tinkling in the glass. "On Wednesday, when Hamilton told our people about the trouble with this Jewboy, Levine, he did it in a way that was too reminiscent of the positions he took at the beginning of his administration—about who was going to steal what, when, and where. The mayor is a ridiculous man who won't have any kind of constituency in the next election. Even if he manages to hold on to his job until then, he's ruined, and everybody but a deaf Burmese monk on retreat with his thumb up his ass knows it.''

Brennan shifted his weight from one foot to the other and sighed deeply, blinking. As cool as it was in this room, his forehead gleamed with perspiration. ''I have a masseur come in three times a week. It helps. Norberto Torres will have a real constituency in the future. We want to make friends. We want to start delivering to him, so he will deliver for us. He came out to the house Wednesday night.''

He drew a deep breath, allowing his eyes to wander. When he began again, he spoke faster than before. Devlin wondered if he was even interested in what he was saying, he was going so fast. ''By then I was sure you were in on killing my son. You had been recruited for the ultimate purpose of taking the fall, but you knew what you were doing. You were active in the plot. I'm still not completely convinced about what you did or did not know. This morning we were presented with another situation. The new official view is that you're innocent.''

Devlin didn't believe any of it, but he didn't want to call Brennan on it. He wanted to remember Liz dying, the awful slash across her throat. ''If that's what you want to call it.''

''New people in charge of the investigation. All right, Levine again. Then the commissioner called this afternoon to say that your criminal assault of his man Kevin McQuaid, ah, *queered* the deal of which your exoneration was a part. I'm going to sit down again. This shit makes me tired. *You* make me tired.'' Brennan lowered himself into the chair slowly. ''Did you know wheelchairs are a racket? This thing cost over two grand.'' He rattled the arm angrily. ''Flimsy piece of sht. There's nothing to it. This McQuaid wanted to press criminal charges *and* sue you. The little prick wants to be paid off. You deserve him.''

''You and I have other business to settle.''

''Well, when you decide to face reality, I'll give you the telephone number of your girlfriend's hotel room.''

Devlin's heart jumped. ''You slick son of a bitch.''

Brennan's eyes and mouth were open wide in a wild grin. ''Goddamned right! I got that turdlet to cough up the telephone number when nobody else could get him off the dime about *criminal* charges! I know how good I am!''

Outside, the sky flashed, followed by a deep, thudding boom. The *Seadancer* shuddered. Brennan was on his feet with real quickness. Devlin looked away, in case Brennan wanted to see if Devlin had noticed his sudden remission of symptoms. What was he so nervous about? What else did he have on his mind? Devlin knew him; even more important, his cop alarms were going off, the way they had this afternoon—before Maryellen had thrown her right cross. Another flash, another boom. ''That's it,'' Brennan said. ''I have to go outside now.'' He reached into his breast pocket. ''Here's the goddamned telephone number anyway. The telephone is in that suitcase. Extend the antenna.''

The explosions and bursts of color and light tumbled over one another. Devlin opened the suitcase in the expectation of finding more buttons and switches than on the dashboard of a fighter plane. No: only about thirty. In the darkness, he found *Ant.* easily enough, but then discovered that *On* probably meant *Off* and *Talk* meant a dial tone so he could push buttons. He pushed, carefully reading the hotel room telephone number digit by digit. A guy answered.

''This is the mayor's office,'' Devlin said. He waited a moment, his eyes on the dim image of Brennan standing next to Charlotte's chair. It looked like he was holding her hand. Devlin had considered doing the voice of Mayor Hamilton himself, but realized it would be a mistake. ''I want to confirm what Kevin McQuaid has been telling us about the condition of the O'Sullivan woman. Put her on the telephone.''

''Uh—''

''Put her on the telephone *now*!''

The mouthpiece was covered; Devlin heard a muffled voice. Outside, a series of flashes, then a cannonade of explosions.

''Hello?'' It was another guy.

''This is the mayor's assistant, Arnie Greene,'' Devlin said. ''I want you to put Eileen O'Sullivan on the telephone *immediately*!''

"I'm sorry, Mr. Greene, we have orders not to discuss the situation with anybody over the telephone."

"What's your name and shield number?"

"The department can give you that."

Devlin had to be careful. For his piece of mind, all he needed to hear was her voice. He didn't know these characters; they could be crazier with ambition than Kevin. Trying to keep his voice from showing his anxiety, Devlin said, "All right, we're going to play it your way. In the next few minutes, however, you want to think things through again, because you don't want your fellow officers to get the idea that you're going into business for yourselves." Devlin waited. Silence. "And of course if anything happens to that girl . . ."

"We're only following orders, sir." The guy hung up.

Devlin put the telephone away and walked to the glass door. Brennan had known how Kevin's men would respond. Nothing was beyond him. The *Seadancer* was under a canopy of bursting rockets. The explosions came from every direction, silhouetting a strange, jagged horizon. Devlin slid the door open just as a monstrous white flash filled the sky. The concussion that followed made his nose hurt.

"We gave a good account of ourselves," Brennan was saying to Charlotte. "The dream didn't exactly come true for us, but they'll remember that we were here. The mark we made turned out to be only our own effort. That's what we'll be known for, that we tried. That's *our* mark. We made something out of nothing, kid, and don't you forget it." He leaned over and kissed her. The glass on the table was almost empty. Maybe Charlotte had changed. She certainly had a lot to forget. Brennan pointed Devlin inside. Devlin could smell Charlotte's Scotch on Brennan's breath as he passed.

"Close the door," Brennan said.

Devlin pointed to the telephone. "Was that your idea of a joke? It isn't going to change anything."

"You don't hold all the cards," Brennan said, with a satisfied smile.

Devlin had to take control. Given a chance, Brennan could

blow smoke up Devlin's ass for hours—days. "I want to talk to you about Vittorio DiBennedetti," Devlin said.

"Who?" The explosions were muffled now, but they could be disruptive, if Brennan wanted them to be.

"I'm not going to go over—"

"No, say the name," Brennan snapped irritably. "I didn't get it." He pulled his ear. "Vittorio Di—what?"

Maybe he didn't know it, but this was a suspect's worst trick. "DiBennedetti," Devlin said.

Brennan repeated it. "No. Sorry."

"He thought I was going to die, so he explained how he's connected to you. He told me he hired two frogmen to hold your son Joe under water until he drowned."

Brennan jumped. "He *told* you that?"

"I said, DiBennedetti thought I was going to die."

Brennan studied him. Did Devlin see curiosity—or did Brennan perceive a threat? "Did he *want* you dead?"

"He had no choice. I tied a gun used to kill two people on New York Boulevard to DiBennedetti's nephew. It's a long story."

"But you're alive!" Brennan exclaimed. "DiBennedetti thought you'd be dead!"

Brennan knew DiBennedetti, no doubt about it. "Lighter eleven grand, too."

"Fuck your eleven grand. What did this—*DiBennedetti* tell you about Joe?"

Now the hitch in his voice. This was acting: he was trying to back away from the name. Too late. Devlin had him tight. Time to turn the screw. "They planned it for months. The swimmers were Italian, over for the job and then home again. Their boat was a mile east of your place. They swam the rest of the way, staying a quarter to a half mile offshore. They had to wait twenty minutes for Joe to get out there. Two very strong guys. Joe didn't see them. He wasn't looking for anybody out in the ocean. They went under and waited for him to come by over them. When he passed, doing the crawl, they grabbed his ankles and allowed themselves to sink like dead weight. He fought. They were wearing wet suits. He couldn't grab them so it hurt. Before he quit struggling, Joe was pounding on their tanks. They watched his face. DiBennedetti wanted a report on that.'' The best part of telling the story, as far as Di-Bennedetti had been concerned, Devlin remembered, the look on Joe's face with water rushing into his lungs.

Brennan gritted his teeth. He looked gray—drained. *Good*.

"You knew," Devlin said.

"What?"

"You knew in advance. You were told."

"Is this what DiBennedetti said? When? When was this, when I got told?"

"A long time ago. And several times more, over the years. DiBennedetti would call you every couple of years. Maybe he'd let it go five years, so you'd think he forgot. There was nothing you could do about it. He was as powerful as you, with the same powerful friends. Besides, you'd have to tell somebody why he was after you."

"Shit. All shit. I don't want my wife upset by this crap, do you understand? She's suffered enough for a hundred women— a thousand." Now he didn't look toward the fantail as he had before. What was going on between Charlotte and him?

Devlin said, "You planted the stuff about me in Jack's files. You started the stories about Jack, Joe, and me working to-gether." Outside, the sky flashed with the brightest fusillade so far, and the noise hammered down more terrifying than thunder. "Given Maryellen's condition, I would have been a conspiracy suspect no matter how Jack was killed, or by whom—that is, if *I* lived. You were hoping DiBennedetti would conclude that I was part of his problem and kill me too. But he liked the idea of leaving me alive, just to screw you up. I'm *your* problem. You decided you didn't want me around when you saw that Maryellen was going to be your sole heiress. All I have to do now is hire the right lawyer to assert my claim to control of your estate."

"I don't have to kill anybody," Brennan said. "I have an army of lawyers to make sure you never got a dime."

"All the lawyers in the world won't stop me from pulling your life down around your ears and shoving it up your ass. Your whole life! Levine's got the original of a letter Jack wrote to his girlfriend, but I have a copy. One hell of a letter about the depravity of the Brennan household, among many other things.''

''You're lying!''

''Try me.''

''What do you want?''

''You don't want the world knowing that your so-called 'good life' has nothing inside it.''

''What do you want?''

Devlin looked out toward the darkness of the fantail. ''Some people are going to think that for the last fifteen years you've denied your daughter the proper care—''

Brennan was on his feet, his eyes darting aft. ''Come on, damn it, you saw Maryellen.'' His voice quavered. ''Some days she doesn't know what sex she is. Tell me what you want. How much? A million? Two?''

''Where did you get all that stuff on me?'' Devlin demanded. ''Who told you so much about my life?''

''Oh, no. I had a file on you, but that was years ago. You had an uncle, Monahan, Buddy Monahan, who showed up at my office after he'd seen in the newspapers that you'd hooked the brass ring. I know all about you and your family, down to your country cousin pregnant on her wedding day. Shanty Irish. Shanty Irish.'' Brennan's teeth were clenched. This was the Brennan of old, Brennan the unforgiving, the unstoppable, the merciless. ''Stinko drunk, human piece of shit on his last legs, as full of hate as any man I've ever seen, hate for his family, hate for you—As far as he was concerned, you were just a little bastard who got lucky. Get the idea?''

''You sent people out to find him . . . more likely, somebody to pump him for information about me,'' Devlin said. ''For all I know, you killed him, too.'' Yes, that was true, too. Devlin suddenly believed it with all his heart. He could feel his anger leaping out of control. ''You wanted to know who I was. I remember you asking the question.''

''I *knew* who you were!'' Brennan roared. ''You were the male bimbo humping my daughter and everything else that moved, the guy who'd crawled out of the worst kind of Irish shit and thought he'd caught a lifetime free ride. Mr. Lucky, the golden tit in his mouth.''

"You thought I was the guy who was going to take it all away from you! You thought I was the guy who was going to do to you what you did to the man whose daughter you raped and stole! You poisoned him and stole his business! Then you beat the life out of the man who helped you do it. Vittorio DiBennedetti never worried about you going to the authorities for protection because he knew you didn't want anybody looking into that part of your life." Rockets went off directly overhead, red, white, and blue. Brennan seemed to jump with surprise. He blinked at Devlin, who said, "Among the papers left behind at Antonucci's apartment were some about me that had been stolen from Jack's office. We'll be able to tie them to you."

"You're going to punish *her*!" Brennan roared. "What do you think the newspapers are going to print? Who in all the world would that hurt most? My wife is seventy-six years old. Are you going to let that woman read in the newspaper that her whole life was a fraud perpetrated by her husband? That I stole her trust? That she might as well not have lived?" More explosions made his face shimmer suddenly, intensely. He was *scared*. "That I *used* her? It's a *lie*! It's *all* lies! When Jack and Joe were talking years ago about taking on the crime families, I warned them that these were dangerous people. You were around. You may have even heard me, if you weren't too drunk to remember." Several ear-rattling bangs went off. Brennan kept talking, but for a moment Devlin couldn't hear. ". . . Maryellen, too. Leave them their dreams."

"Dreams? What dreams? An old woman's of dead sons? Or a woman so confused that not only doesn't she know what sex she is—I'll take her father's word for that—she doesn't know what she wants, doesn't know what she's saying, or even that she's saying it. You know that. You've *seen* it."

"Transient psychotic episodes, they're called. That's enough—"

"No. This afternoon, when your daughter punched a nun,

I thought I saw someone as ill, mentally, as it was possible to get. But then I met DiBennedetti, feeding on revenge, consumed by his fear of death—by comparison, Maryellen is only a victim. And compared to you, DiBennedetti, as evil as he is, is only a dabbler. Do you really want to talk about stolen lives? Your wife, sons, your daughter! You sacrificed all those lives for your own!''

"All right. That's it," Brennan said. He slumped down into the wheelchair. "I've had enough of you. You get the fuck out!''

Devlin went to the door and opened it. John was on the other side, listening to a hand-held radio. He whispered, *"Eileen,"* and gave a thumbs-up sign.

Devlin grinned. "Come on in." To Brennan, he said, "Jim, be sensible. We've got what DiBennedetti told me about you and the Ippolitos. Women working in Jack's campaign headquarters can testify that they never handled any files on me, and one will say that Jack knew nothing about those files. Then there's what you said here about using Buddy Monahan to obtain information on me. You can insist that you didn't plant the evidence, but that doesn't mean a jury will believe you. You had it wrong when you threw John out because you thought he was wearing a wire.'' Devlin tapped his own lapel. "It's right here. Everything you said is on tape out on the police launch.''

Brennan pounded the arm of the wheelchair. "I knew that! Do you think I was born yesterday? Whether you think so or not, you're going to have a tough time in court. You,'' Brennan said to John, "go see if my wife wants another drink. She's in the tall chair.''

John eyed Devlin. Obviously Brennan wanted John out of there, if only for one more moment. At the door, John said, "Frank, let me give you the details about that telephone number he gave you. It's a hotel room out by the airport, just as we thought. We'll have Eileen in a few minutes.''

Brennan smirked and looked at Devlin as John closed the door behind him. "All's well that ends well, eh? You've got your little girlfriend back, what more do you care about? I suppose I owe you an apology or congratulations, maybe both. You really are a changed man. I wouldn't have said it was possible. I'm still not completely convinced here.'' He tapped his heart. ''Excuse me, that's where *you* have a transmitter.''

He was up to something, all right. What was the word the captain had used? *Playful.* Devlin detached the bug from his jacket. ''I don't think we need it anymore.''

Brennan saw through the ruse. The transmitter remained operational. He was still smiling when John slid the glass door open again. Brennan turned to him.

''Frank,'' John said, ''this woman is dead.''

''Suicide,'' Brennan said. ''She talked about it this afternoon. I didn't think for a minute—''

Devlin stared at Brennan. ''Suicide?'' The old man had no trouble meeting his gaze. ''Suicide?'' Devlin repeated. ''Who do you think you're kidding?''

Brennan didn't answer.

''You didn't miss a beat! You were waiting to say it!''

Brennan looked away.

''You set this up! Everything that happened here was a show to convince us she was alive! Talking to her, bringing her drinks . . . *'Go see if my wife wants another drink,'* he mimicked. ''She was dead when we got here, wasn't she? No wonder you were so damned frightened!''

Brennan turned to him, eyes narrowed. ''Do you *mind*? Junior, here, just told me my wife died.''

At the last moment his eyes betrayed him, because Devlin saw them dart toward the transmitter. He wanted to be on the record. Something turned over in Devlin's mind. ''You were afraid DiBennedetti's story about you, her father, and the Ippolitos would come out, and not because there would be evidence after all these years that would convict you of murder, or that people would have believed DiBennedetti.'' Devlin pointed toward the corpse facing the ghostly statue beyond. What was he thinking of? For a split second, the story of Brennan with the garment district model so many years ago. ''*She* would have believed! Charlotte would have believed DiBennedetti as no one else could, because his story explained every bad thing that has ever happened to her, including her daughter's insanity. *It's you!* You never loved her. You never loved anybody. Once you went after her, that woman out there never drew another free breath. You even decided when she'd stop breathing. *Monster* only begins to describe you!''

Brennan pushed himself out of the chair, his teeth bared. He jabbed a finger toward the transmitter. Devlin knew what was coming next, but Brennan was still too fast for him. Brennan spat in Devlin's face. John grabbed Brennan, but Devlin moved faster.

That's one time too often, motherfucker. Devlin was ready now. Bingo Malone! Oh, yes! Brennan had it coming like no one else in the world! Devlin waved John off, grabbed the old man by the throat, pushed him back hard against the wall, and pinned him there. With Devlin's hand against his windpipe, Brennan couldn't make a sound. Devlin had to be quick, before the old man suffocated. In Brennan's voice, he said, "That's it, pull that wire loose so it doesn't work. You want to hear? I'll tell you one time, you little chickenshit. I used the same poison on her that I used on her father, and there isn't a goddamned thing you can do about it, to trace it, anything." Brennan's eyes bulged. He clawed at Devlin's hand. In Brennan's voice, Devlin said, "Fuck yourself. I'll kill you, too, if I get the chance." Devlin let go of Brennan's throat, and as Brennan gasped, Devlin dropped the transmitter onto the carpet and ground it beneath his heel. John was smiling in spite of himself. Brennan filled his lungs. Devlin said, "You had me right twenty years ago. I was the guy who was going to take everything away from you. No matter what you did, whatever choices you made, it was all for nothing. History is going to know you as a man who let his sons be killed. I did it to you, and I'm as happy about it as anything I've ever done."

Brennan let out a screech, grabbed a paring knife from the bar, and lunged for Devlin, who raised his hand defensively. The blade went through the flesh of Devlin's palm and emerged near the back of the wrist. Brennan tried to pull it free again, John on his back, Devlin clawing his face. The two detectives wrestled the old man into the wheelchair and John cuffed Brennan's wrist to an armrest. Brennan grinned—insane. No, now they saw. He was up again, the armrest sliding easily out of its mounts, suddenly a weapon raised over Devlin's head. John had it, and pulled the old man back down again. Devlin found his handcuffs in his jacket pocket, covering them almost instantly with his own blood. John took the cuffs, pulled Brennan's other arm down to a wheel and locked him to it. Brennan swung the metal wheelchair arm at John now, cutting his head, knocking him back, blood splashing. Devlin yelled, "No more! No more!" He rushed the wheelchair toward the fantail, where the fireworks were still exploding overhead. Devlin opened the door. John clung to hang on. All three men were yelling. Devlin didn't care. Brennan saw what he was going to do, and tried to plant his feet in the carpet. Out in the warm air, Devlin pushed John back inside, and dragged and pushed the wheelchair to the rail. Charlotte Brennan's dead eyes stared past their struggle. Devlin felt John tearing at him, yelling for him to stop. Brennan swung the metal arm back, yelling, too—but Devlin was yelling loudest, shrieking, screaming. He levered Brennan up onto the top rail, perhaps thirty inches above the deck, where he teetered, silhouetted against a barrage of exploding rockets, John grabbing for him, Devlin pitting his weight in the other direction. Brennan went down toward the water headfirst, screaming until he went in, the electric motor shorting out with a sudden, fierce hiss. When Devlin turned around, his bloody partner was staring at him in disbelief.

"Two hundred and fifty pounds," John said. "Brennan and that wheelchair must have weighed two hundred and fifty pounds."

Devlin applied pressure to his wrist. He looked John in the eye. "I did everything I could to stop him, and I know you did, too."

John took his time answering, glancing at Charlotte Brennan and then at the black, boiling water below. "You're right," he said. "We recorded his confession and then he attacked us. Murder and suicide. Why don't you call Eileen while I get us some first aid?"

John pointed toward the cellular telephone and began to make his way forward. By now, Jim Brennan was learning what it was

like to drown, like his son Joe. Devlin wished his mind could
stop there, and he would never have to give the matter another
thought. He wanted to believe that all he had to do was collect
himself, stop thinking of the past. *No*, he almost said aloud,
down through the days and nights. He could call Eileen now.
Enough time had passed for Levine's people to arrive at the
airport motel.

Devlin drew a breath. Years ago, when Brennan had asked,
Who are you? he had been afraid that Devlin was becoming
the man most like Brennan himself. At the time, there had
been nothing inside Devlin, as Brennan had said. Just anger.
Brennan had not changed from that day to this; if anything,
the passage of time had allowed him to hone his skills at be-
traying those who loved or trusted him. His emptiness had
made him powerful, but never satisfied. Devlin knew he would
never sort it out, never get a clear understanding of what had
driven Brennan—himself, that part of him that had burned so
intensely in his youth. He had escaped, painfully, even reluc-
tantly, but with his life.

The telephone on the other end rang four times before it
was picked up, before Eileen said hello.

"It's me," he said. "For a while there I was afraid I'd never
hear your voice again."

"Well, I'm going home now," she said. "Wake me when
you come in."

Devlin felt his tears coming and he tried to hold them
back, tried to stifle a sob, but couldn't. It sounded like a
death cry. Eileen gasped in astonishment and that made his
tears come. He cried out loud, like a child.

About the Author

5-3-76

PILGRIMAGE

PILGRIMAGE

AN IMAGE OF
MEDIAEVAL RELIGION

Jonathan Sumption

ROWMAN AND LITTLEFIELD
Totowa, New Jersey

First published in the United States 1975
by ROWMAN AND LITTLEFIELD, Totowa, N. J.

© 1975, *Jonathan Sumption*

ISBN 0-87471-677-2

Printed in the United States of America

TO MY FRIENDS

CONTENTS

ILLUSTRATIONS

PLATES

between Pages 192 *and* 193

MAPS

PREFACE

I began by imagining (perhaps all historians do) that the subject of this book could be neatly confined between two convenient dates, like a row of disintegrating French paperbacks between two bookends. 1050 to 1250 was the period I had in mind. In fact, religious history cannot be divided into digestible slabs in this convenient fashion. Mediaeval Christianity inherited certain ideas from the classical past and bequeathed others to the modern world. The spiritual ideals of St. Bernard's day are incomprehensible when divorced from their origins, and misleading without some account of the process of distortion and decay which ultimately overcame them. Even the Reformation is not as decisive a break as one would suppose.

So, as it stands, the book is an attempt to draw a thin line through a very long period of history. In an age of academic specialization this approach has advantages and disadvantages. It does make it possible to present a reasonably coherent picture of mediaeval spiritual life as a whole, through the medium of an important and, I believe, representative part of it. So much for the advantages; now the disadvantages, of which the chief is that I may often have indulged in broad generalizations which lack of space has prevented me from justifying at length. I wish it were possible to write about the middle ages as Keith Thomas has recently done about the sixteenth and seventeenth centuries. But the evidence does not exist. The search for origins and consequences in mediaeval history is bound to be fruitless. Finality is an illusion. The conclusions drawn here must be regarded as my own impressions buttressed by examples which I consider representative. For every example, a counter-example could easily be cited. I have tried to avoid a tone of bold confidence, but there are no doubt places where the reader should insert a mental 'probably' at the beginning of a sentence.

One major omission should be mentioned. I have concentrated heavily on France and on the cultural world of which France was the centre – England, northern Spain, central and southern Italy. Germany has not been entirely ignored, but major sanctuaries like

Cologne and Aachen have not received the attention they deserve. There are a number of reasons for this, amongst them the extreme sparseness of the evidence before the fifteenth century. But I cannot deny that self-indulgence has been an important factor. I love France. German history bores me. There is, moreover, a homogeneity about the French cultural world which makes it possible to speak of it as a whole. Germany and central Europe are in some respects exceptional and ought to be considered separately. This is already a long book. I had no desire to make it longer.

I owe a very considerable debt to the President and fellows of Magdalen College, Oxford, for the leisure and agreeable surroundings which I have enjoyed there both as an undergraduate and as a fellow. I have benefited enormously from conversations with my old tutor, Karl Leyser, more, perhaps, than he realizes. Dr. Hugh Sinclair and Dr. David Robson have helped me out with some medical matters in chapter five. The staff of at least a dozen libraries in this country and in France and Italy have been unfailingly helpful, none more so than the staff of the Bodleian Library, who staggered daily to seat U.219 bowed down beneath the weight of ancient folios. My greatest debt is to my wife, and the fact that this is a common experience among authors will not prevent me from saying so.

J.P.C.S.
Greenwich, 1974

INTRODUCTION

The world which the mediaeval pilgrim left behind him was a small and exclusive community. The geographic and social facts of life made it oppressive and isolated and, except in the vicinity of major towns and truck roads, the chief qualities of human life were its monotonous regularity and the rule of overpowering conventions. Existence, for the great majority, meant rural existence. Towns were few and small, and separated themselves from the country by moats of legal privilege. Villages asserted their independence and marked out their territory with rows of stakes and crosses. Even where migration occurred, it was not allowed to disturb the placid conventions of rural life. English villages of the thirteenth century were forbidden to receive strangers, and were held collectively responsible for crimes committed in their midst. Townsmen were enjoined to watch for strangers and lock their gates at sunset.

Nowhere was the closeness of these communities more apparent than in their religious life. 'What is a parish?', asked the thirteenth-century canonist Henry of Susa; 'it is a place with well-defined frontiers whose inhabitants belong to a single church.' The parishioner 'belonged' in a very real sense to his church, and lived his whole life under its shadow. There, and there alone, he was baptized and married, attended Sunday Mass, paid his tithe and offerings, and there he was buried when he died. The statutes of the church constantly reminded him of the fact. No one may receive the sacraments in any church but his own. 'On no account admit to confession any person from another parish.' 'No stranger is to be allowed burial or marriage in the parish church.' A thirteenth-century archbishop of Bordeaux excommunicated 'all strangers who have abandoned their own parish churches which they ought to be attending, . . . for the parish priest should be able to see the face of every member of his flock.' Pierre de Collemieu, archbishop of Rouen, required parish priests to keep a list of their parishioners, and to eject any strangers whom they found in their churches on Sundays except for noblemen and beggars. It was not unknown for those who died outside their own parishes to be exhumed and brought back to their own churchyards.

The Lateran council of 1215 reinforced this dependence on the parish by making every layman confess his sins at least once a year to his parish priest, and to no one else. Only bona fide travellers and those in danger of death were permitted to confess to a strange priest, while those clergy who had no parishes were forbidden to hear confessions at all. The right of the mendicant orders to hear them was hotly resisted by the secular clergy as an intrusion upon their prerogatives, and was only tardily recognized by the papacy. Confession, the most personal act of piety which the ordinary man performed, was far from being the anonymous ceremony found in the modern Roman Catholic Church. It is true that the actual words spoken were inaudible, but the sacrament itself was held in public, 'openly, and not in some private place, especially in the case of women', as the synod of Nîmes ordained in 1284. Moreover the parish priest was expected to probe for further, undeclared, sins, and to inflict a lengthy cross-examination on the penitent. Several handbooks for priests were available in which useful and pertinent questions were set out for this purpose.

Dignity and privacy were not concepts dear to the hearts of mediaeval men, who conducted their communal lives on the unspoken assumption that the sins of one were the business of all. This was particularly true of breaches of sexual morality. In a small village near Bonneval in the Loire valley, the repentance of a prostitute at the end of the twelfth century was an event of public importance. Most of the inhabitants gathered in the street to debate whether she should go immediately to the nearest priest in Bonneval, or await his arrival for Mass on the following day. They decided to wait. In the morning they accompanied the sinner in a body to the church and, all speaking at once, recited her history to the priest. After a short homily, the priest confessed her in the presence of the villagers and sentenced her to an annual pilgrimage to Chartres. Then he absolved her amid scenes of emotion and jubilation. In the records of episcopal visitations it is clear that the majority of witnesses regarded eavesdropping and peeping through windows as a duty. When bishop Trefnant of Hereford visited his diocese in 1397, most of the laymen who appeared before him were accused by their neighbours of adultery, bigamy, quarrelling with their wives, denying conjugal rights to their husbands, and other matters which would now be regarded as private. A similar picture emerges from the records of a provincial society in France. When a Poitevin peasant-woman, Clémente Gaboreau, failed to appear in church one Sunday in 1387, her fellow parishioners recalled that she had often been seen entering and leaving the house of one Guillaume Achale and immediately suspected the worst. It was common knowledge in the village of Asnois (Poitou) that the wife of Pierre Vigoureux was the mistress of the parish priest. Jean Bourdeau, carpenter of Courlay (Poitou) was completely unaware that his wife was unfaithful to him, until several peeping-Toms told him so, whereupon he killed her with a sickle. The fifteenth-century author of a manual for parish priests no doubt had such incidents in mind when he warned his readers against 'all that standeth or hearkeneth by nights under walls, doors, or windows, for to spy touching evil.'

The popularity of the mendicant friars and of local holy hermits, was undoubtedly due in part to the fact that they offered an escape from the stifling framework of parish life. Pilgrimage offered another escape. A surprisingly large number of pilgrims seem to have left their homes solely in order to deny their parish priest his monopoly over their spiritual welfare. Contemporary churchmen frequently accused them of seeking to confess to a strange priest or to avoid the moral censure which they deserved. In one extreme case a lady of London, on learning that she was dying, had herself carried in a litter to Canterbury in order to avoid the payment of a five shilling burial fee to her parish priest. At the end of the fifteenth century a writer castigating the excessive devotion of the populace to pilgrimages reflected that their principal motives were 'curiosity to see new places and experience new things, impatience of the servant with his master, of children with their parents, or wives with their husbands.'

The twelfth-century chronicler Orderic Vitalis describes the dreadful fate of a priest who went with his mistress on a pilgrimage to St.-Gilles, in order to avoid the opprobrium of his family and friends. But many of the penitential pilgrims who filled the great shrines no doubt honestly felt that they would never live down their obsessions of guilt so long as they remained at home. St. Hugh of Lincoln once met a man in Rochester who admitted that he had led an evil life in his youth, 'until, unable to endure my shame and hating the scene of my destruction, I secretly left my mother's house and the city where I had been born, . . . and wandered I knew not whither.' Paul Walther, a German Franciscan who visited the Holy Land in 1481, confessed before his departure that he had not lived up to the requirements of the Franciscan rule 'and therefore I have resolved to go away to a place where the German language is unknown, and there I shall exorcize my sins from my wretched body.'

The Reality of Evil

The peculiar intensity of mediaeval piety had as many causes as it had symptoms. But pre-eminent among them was a view of the natural world as a chaos in which the perpetual intervention of God was the only guiding law. God appeared to control the entire natural world from moment to moment. He was the direct and immediate cause of everything that happened, from the most trivial to the most vital incidents of human life. Indeed it was not until the eighteenth century that men were prepared to concede to nature any power of her own, or to attribute the workings of the natural world to anything other than divine intervention. In these circumstances, men were inclined to feel that their lives were directed by irresistible forces. Since they could not control them, the only remedies available were supplication, and the performance of pious acts considered likely to propitiate them.

The reactions of men when faced with what they conceived to be overpowering supernatural forces, changed remarkably little in a thousand years of Christian history. At the end of the sixth century Gregory of Tours collected eight books of the miracles of the saints, every page of which demonstrates that the most normal incidents of daily life were interpreted as signs of divine favour or disfavour, provoking displays of general jubilation or incalculable terror. Simple men were terrified of the dark, sometimes to the point of insanity. Thunder storms brought panic to whole communities and drove them to take refuge round the altars of the saints. A flash of lightning created havoc in a small village, 'the people all fearing that the punishment of God was about to descend on them wherever they might try to escape.' Terrible cries were heard during an eclipse of the moon. Since all such phenomena sprang not from natural causes but from the direct action of God, it followed that the will of God could be discerned in them if only men knew how. To the people of Paris, a red sky at night three times in succession was a certain presage of war. A partial eclipse of the sun foretold disaster in the Auvergne. The heavens themselves blazed forth the death of princes.

These attitudes are not peculiar to the sixth century. They are found throughout the mediaeval period, and indeed afterwards. Unreasonable fear of the dark was one of the popular superstitions condemned by the eleventh-century canonist Burchard of Worms; 'many men dare not leave their houses before dawn, saying that . . . evil spirits have more power to harm them before cock-crow than afterwards.' Guibert of Nogent used to keep the lamp as close to his bed as possible in order to ward off demons. Shortly after the death of Robert the Pious, king of France, in 1031, it was recorded that the event had been presaged by three years of epidemics, famines, and 'prodigies'. In the fourteenth century it was still generally accepted that natural calamities were the just punishments inflicted

by God on sinners. This was, for example, the moral drawn from
the hurricane which struck southern England in January 1362, up-
rooting the fruit trees and destroying the harvest. In *Piers Plowman*
Reason preached before the King and

> *. . . proved that this pestilence were for pure sin,*
> *And the south west wind on Saturday at even*
> *Was pertlich for pure pride and for no point else.*

The same notion that a conflict of irresistible forces governed
individual lives gave a desperate, almost frenzied quality to the
religious life of the later middle ages. Jean de Meung, one of the
authors of the *Roman de la Rose* attributed this belief to most of his
contemporaries, though he does not seem to have subscribed to it
himself. Because of it, he observed, men attached excessive importance to trivial events. Of this attitude was born the conviction that
they had been set upon by demons. Sick men were driven to panic,
sometimes to hysteria. Sorcery, necromancy, conjuring of spirits,
visions of Heaven and Hell, were all, in the poet's view, products of
the same aberration.

Ordinary men could not regard evil as an abstract force; to them
it was real, visible, and tangible, capable of inflicting actual physical
damage. A crude pantheistic view of nature suggested to them that
the physical world harboured malignant powers hostile to men. A
gust of wind might be the breath of Satan. Gregory of Tours once
met a woman of the Limousin who believed that her child had been
struck blind because she failed to make the sign of the cross when the
wind blew up. Even at the end of the fifteenth century a gust of
wind which blew open the doors of an abbey near Dunkirk was
enough to strike panic in the hearts of the inmates. The friars of one
Dominican convent of northern Germany habitually went about in
pairs for fear of the Devil, who had broken all the windows of their
church. According to St. Bruno, the founder of the Carthusian
order, devils, the incarnation of all evil, moved in the air and in the
dust that floated in every stream of light; 'a breath of wind, a turbu-
lence in the air, the gust that blows men to the ground and harms
their crops, these are the whistlings of the Devil.' The whole atmosphere, thought Ivo of Chartres, was filled with the spirit of evil,
ubiquitous, all-knowing, powerful, spying out the inner thoughts
and weaknesses of men. Anything which inspired fear might be
evil, and thus the daily accidents of life suddenly took on a sinister
import.

In some of the oldest writings of the Church the Devil takes the
form of wild animals. He appears to St. Martin, for example, as a
bull. According to Sulpicius Severus, St. Martin 'could see the

Devil with his own eyes however cleverly he might disguise himself'. Peter the Venerable, the scholarly twelfth-century abbot of Cluny, collected a large number of stories illustrating the various forms in which the Devil assaulted sinners – a spider, a vulture in the sky, a bear seen in the forest near Cluny, a black pig found in the chapter house at Norwich, and a thousand other frightening creatures. Savage dogs occupied a sinister place in the mediaeval imagination. Walter, a monk of Durham in the twelfth century, was attacked by the Devil in the form of a huge black hound, while Guibert of Nogent's mother believed that lesser devils appeared as packs of small dogs to terrify children.

The Devil's most sinister form was that of a deformed, distorted human being, the horrifying figure so familiar from the sculptures of the Romanesque churches of France, or from Flemish paintings of the fifteenth century. This vision of the Devil makes its first appearance in the writings of the desert monks of the third and fourth centuries and particularly in one of the most influential saints' lives ever written, the *Life of St. Anthony* by Athanasius. During his twenty years in the desert, St. Anthony was said to have suffered temptations which are clearly modelled on those of Christ. He was perpetually conscious that 'the air around him was full of evil spirits'. The Devil frightened him at night, aroused carnal desires in him, tempted him to return to the comforts of civilization, and even struck him blows. The Devil commonly appeared to St. Anthony as a 'little black boy, his appearance matching his mind, with flashing eyes and fiery breath, and horns on his head, half-man, half-ass'. This is probably why the Devil is so often described by mediaeval writers as a negro or 'Ethopian'. It is also the origin of the idea that the Devil was a being, almost human, possessed of human cunning and human malice. In his biography of St. Benedict, Gregory the Great describes the temptations of his hero in terms borrowed from the *Life of St. Anthony* while the same conventions are observed more than five centuries later by Peter the Venerable. When the Devil visited the sick-bed of a monk of Cluny who had experienced fleeting doubts about the doctrine of the real presence, he was 'like a small black Ethopian, horribly deformed, with horns coming out of his ears and fire from his mouth as if he was about to eat the very flesh of the sick monk'.

It was very widely believed that dreams were a direct revelation of the supernatural world. A deepening sense of guilt about real or imaginary sins frequently resulted in nightmares in which all the sinister fantasies found in the writings of Peter the Venerable seemed to become reality. In the 1170s the daughter of a knight called Sewal had a recurrent nightmare in which she was attacked by devils in the form of vicious black dogs; she was convinced that her dream had actually happened, and was taken by her parents to St.-Léonard de Noblat, near Limoges, and then to Canterbury in the hope of a cure. A boy aged fifteen from the Cluniac priory of Pontefract dreamed that demons were trying to strangle him, and he too was taken to Canterbury. Nor did such nightmares afflict only the sensitive and the simple. Stephen of Hoyland, a knight and a man of some substance, suffered from the same nocturnal terrors for thirty years before a visit to Canterbury brought him peace of mind. In a window of the south-west transept of the cathedral, he is shown lying awake at night with a devil at the foot of his bed and another at the head.

In popular thinking, the Devil's organization and methods were a reflection of God's. He too had his twelve apostles of evil, his rites, and his Church. Just as God lived in the righteous, so the Devil 'possessed' the sinful. Sin physically delivered the sinner into the Devil's hands. 'In sign', explains a fifteenth-century preacher, 'that of them that are like hogs in gluttony, the fiends have power to dwell in them and to drench them in the sea of Hell.' 'Possession' of this sort was physical as well as spiritual. Hysteria, however caused, was a symptom of possession, and doubtless it was often in practice caused by intense guilt. Romanus, a monk of St.-Evroul in the eleventh century, was an incorrigible kleptomaniac who frequently had to be rebuked by the abbot for petty thefts in the monastery.

> 'One night as he lay in bed, a demon set upon him and horribly tormented him. Hearing his hideous shrieks the monks rushed to his aid and by shaking him and sprinkling him with holy water, they finally succeeded in freeing him from the devil who possessed him. When he came to himself he recognized that the devil had gained this power over him through the thefts that he had committed.'

The idea of devils 'possessing' the sexually unchaste is particularly common in monastic writing, and the sculpted figure of 'Luxuria' abetted by a demon is found in many monastic churches of the eleventh and twelfth centuries. In the nave of the abbey of Vézelay there is a terrifying capital showing Woman the seductress leading a young man to despair and ultimately to suicide, while a similar capital in Autun cathedral shows a young man tempted by a naked woman and thereupon being grasped from behind by a devil.

The Approach of Death

The sense of constant menace which these malignant forces aroused was heightened by a preoccupation with death verging on the obsessional. The brevity of human life and the imminence of death were commonplaces of mediaeval preaching for, as Chaucer's parson observed, the majority of conversions to the pious life were probably due to the fear of damnation: 'the . . . cause that oghte moeve a man to contrition is drede of the daye of dome and of the horrible peynes of hell.'

The celebrated thirteenth-century preacher Jacques de Vitry one day encountered a man who asserted that a single word had turned him to God. He had asked himself whether the souls of the damned could be freed from torment after a thousand years. He answered in his mind: 'no.' If after a hundred thousand years: 'no.' If after a thousand thousand: 'no.' 'And pondering these things he saw how transitory life was, and thus a single word, "no", converted him to God.' The sermons of mediaeval preachers are full of such 'conversions'. A loose-living student of Bologna was reformed when a Dominican told him how hard would be the beds in Hell. Caesarius of Heisterbach knew of several who were converted by hearing great preachers. Another was reformed by the sight of a funeral service, while sudden illness and imminent death were responsible for countless conversions. 'Indeed', Caesarius concluded, 'the occasions of conversion are innumerable.' But not all such conversions are edifying tales in sermons. Many people undoubtedly experienced genuine transformations during which they regarded themselves as beginning a new life, as entering an elite order for whose members the chances of salvation were infinitely greater. In the early Church, Christians were frequently not baptized until they had resolved to live the most perfect possible life. St. Augustine was not baptized until the age of thirty-three, and he spoke of it then as his 'conversion'. Bede and Gregory the Great both used the word 'conversion' to mean entry into the monastic life. Indeed the 'conversion' of saints was the classic stock-in-trade of mediaeval hagiographers from the time of St. Athanasius onwards. The same pattern – worldliness, conversion, sanctity – is repeated in biographies of St. Martin, St. Benedict, St. Dunstan, Odo of Cluny, Bernard of Clairvaux and countless others who attracted the admiration of their contemporaries.

From the notion of the converted elite was born the belief that the overwhelming majority of men were damned. This tradition was strong in the early Church and, indeed, it was natural in a minority religion suffering abuse and persecution. But it survived to become a corner-stone of the moral teaching of the mediaeval Church, a recurring feature of the sermons of revivalist preachers and the visions of mystics. St. Bernard had little doubt that there were 'few, very few who will be saved', while Berthold of Regensburg, the

great German preacher of the thirteenth century, assured his
audiences that less than one in a thousand of them would ascend to
Paradise. 'If we believed', wrote the fifteenth-century Dominican
John Herolt, 'that one man only out of the entire human race, was
doomed to perdition, would not every man be afraid lest he himself
should be that one? . . . How much more then does he have cause to
fear, when God himself has said that "many are called but few are
chosen." '

In 1091 a parish priest of Normandy reported an extraordinary
vision to the bishop of Lisieux. As he was returning from his rounds
one winter's night he seemed to hear the tramp of a great army in
the distance. At first he assumed that it was the army of the notorious
Robert de Bellême, engaged in some private war. But then a great
ghostly defile appeared in the moonlight and marched past him,
well-known murderers, noble ladies on horse-back, thieves, prelates,
judges, and knights. All were being escorted to Hell by squads of
negroid demons. Amongst them were men of great repute in their
lifetimes, some of whom had seemed to be holy men. Hugh, bishop
of Lisieux was amongst them, as were the abbots of St.-Evroul and
St.-Wandrille 'and many others whose names I forget, for man's eye
is frequently deceived but God sees them to the very marrow.'

It is difficult to decide how far this uninviting philosophy commanded general acceptance, for the denunciations of preachers are
not always a true reflection of mediaeval religious life. As the
preachers themselves readily admitted, their words often fell on deaf
ears, and there is no doubt that the later mediaeval period, for which
surviving sermon material is richest, was also a period of notable
popular worldliness. The prior of Holy Trinity, London reported
in 1200 that 'many believe neither in good nor in bad angels, nor in
life or death or any other spiritual things which they cannot see with
their own eyes.' There were scoffers, complained Vincent of Beauvais, who openly laughed at graphic representations of Hell.
Berthold of Regensburg devoted a whole sermon to the refutation
of those sceptics who argued that the soul must become insensitive
to the pains of Hell if they are indeed of infinite duration. Belief in
a merciful God was even, occasionally, regarded as evidence of
heresy. An Albigensian who appeared before the Inquisition of
Languedoc declared that if he could lay his hands on that God who
saved but one out of a thousand of the creatures he created, he would
tear him to pieces and spit in his face. Most people, however, were
not inclined to criticize official doctrines, and they continued to provide audiences for mendicant preachers. Margery Kempe, the visionary of King's Lynn at the beginning of the fifteenth century, had
originally refused to believe that most men were damned 'and when

Our Lord showed her any that should be damned she had great
pain; she would not hear of it . . . and put it out of her mind as much
as she might.' But the Lord was displeased at this aberration and
punished her until she came to accept the orthodox doctrine.

Mediaeval men were familiar with a number of detailed descriptions of Hell. The picture of Hell was repeatedly presented to them
by imaginative preachers like master Richard Alkerton, who declared in 1406, in a sermon delivered in London, that the damned
would be

> 'boiled in fire and brimstone without end. Venomous worms
> . . . shall gnaw all their members unceasingly, and the worm of
> conscience shall gnaw the soul. . . . Now ye shall have ever-
> lasting bitterness. . . . This fire that tormenteth you shall never
> be quenched, and they that tormenteth you shall never be
> weary neither die.'

The scenes carved on the west fronts at Conques or Bourges find
their counterpart in the hand-books of preachers. The *Pricke of
Conscience*, one of the most popular of these manuals, draws a
picture of Hell with intense dramatic power: the hideous din, the
shrieks of the tortured, the 'raumping of devils, the dyngyng and
dysching' of their glowing hammers, and the closely packed mass of
humanity swaying this way and that in the infernal oven, each
fighting and scratching at his neighbour's face like a grinning mad-
man, or ripping off his own flesh with indescribable passion. A good
many of these descriptions originated in visions, or in the accounts
of those who claimed to have descended bodily into Hell. In the
time of Bede, a Northumbrian who claimed to have returned to life
described it as an ever-deepening pit where sinners suffered extremes
of cold and heat, their cries drowned by the harsh laughter of
demons. 'Do you know who all these souls are?' asked his guide:
'they are the souls who failed to confess and atone for their sins until
they were dying.' Amongst seventh-century writers it seems to have
been agreed that the torments of Hell consisted of alternating extremes of heat and cold. The hermit Guthlac saw it as 'sulphurous
eddies of flames mixed with freezing hail', a mental image which
remained common throughout the middle ages. Even Shakespeare's
Claudio feared

> *To bathe in fiery floods or to reside*
> *In thrilling region of thick ribbed ice*
> (*Measure for Measure* III. i)

Educated men may not always have believed these tales of bodily
descents into Hell, though Bede and Gregory the Great certainly

did. But the descriptions of Hell which were based on them re-flected notions held more or less consistently by every generation. Guibert of Nogent's mother, after the death of her husband, 'saw by a wonderful dispensation of God in frequent visions the clearest possible images of the pains he was enduring in Purgatory.' A ser-vant of Ludwig, landgrave of Thuringia, claimed that he had been permitted a glimpse into Hell, where he had been able to watch the torments of his former master. Such accounts were received every-where with considerable interest. When, for example, a monk of Eynsham experienced an unusually vivid dream of Purgatory in 1196, the bishop of Lincoln instructed a detailed record to be made of it for the edification of his diocesans.

Profound pessimism was one of the principal characteristics of mediaeval religion. At a popular level it bred a fatalism in which the resort to rituals with the object of expiating sin, becomes somewhat easier to understand. The salvation of an individual man was nothing less than a miracle, to be sought of God through the inter-cession of the saints. In a powerful sermon on damnation, Berthold of Regensburg asserted that the salvation of a sinner was 'one of the greatest miracles that ever God does. That is why we sing in the Mass "*Mirabilis Deus in sanctis suis*", God is wonderful in his saints.' The relics of the saints, repeated a theologian of the twelfth century, were the means whereby the faithful might resist the power of evil in the world. They gave health to the bodies of men and absolution to their souls: 'the body of Elijah give life to the dead and remove death's sting from the living.'

CHAPTER II

THE CULT OF RELICS

The cult of the saints was the counterpoint of the fear of evil. Just as men tended to associate evil with objects familiar to them, so they attempted to give a human quality to the forces of good. This habit of mind was already common in the west at the beginning of the fifth century, when the Frankish collector Victricius of Rouen portrayed the saints as an army of auxiliaries in the cosmic battle against evil: 'see, a great host of saints comes to us. . . . Victory is certain when we fight along side such allies with Christ for our general.'

The veneration of the relics of the saints is attested by unimpeachable evidence as early as the second century, and it is probably even older than that. In a letter written in about A.D. 156 to the church of Philomelium, the Christians of Smyrna described the martyrdom of bishop Polycarp, who had been burned to death shortly before. From this it appears that the Christians 'took up his bones which are more valuable than refined gold and laid them in a suitable place where, the Lord willing, . . . we may gather together in gladness and celebrate the anniversary of his martyrdom.' During the most violent of all the persecutions, that of Diocletian (303–11), relics of the martyrs were eagerly collected by their followers. After the death of St. Vincent the onlookers dipped their clothes in his blood, and when seven brothers were martyred at Samosata in 308, a number of noble ladies bribed the guards to let them wash the bodies with sponges and collect drops of the blood.

The cult of relics was criticized from its inception by purists who regarded it as pagan. Amongst the earliest critics was the Gallic priest Vigilantius whose opinions are known to us from the denunciations hurled at him by St. Jerome. Vigilantius condemned the veneration of all inanimate objects such as the bodies of the saints, and especially the bodies of St. Peter and St. Paul in Rome. In reply, Jerome stated the classic Christian justification of such cults, that the relics were not worshipped in themselves, but were an aid to the veneration of martyrs of undoubted holiness whose lives were a model to later generations.

'We do not worship their relics any more than we do the sun or the moon, the angels, archangels, or seraphims. We honour them in honour of He whose faith they witnessed. We honour the Master by means of the servants.'

Ideas not unlike those of Vigilantius were advanced in the fifth century by the Pelagian heretics and by a number of individuals of varying orthodoxy. Many of the greatest thinkers of the patristic period concerned themselves with elaborating the theoretical basis of the cult of relics. In the first place, they argued, relics were the earthly reminders of holy men, who deserved at least as much respect as the inhabitants of the later Roman Empire commonly accorded to their own ancestors. Moreover they were, in the words of St. Augustine, 'temples of the faith' whom Christians should venerate in order to 'associate themselves with the merits of the martyrs that they may secure their intercession by prayer'. In Augustine's view the cult of the martyrs was no different from the cult of holy men still alive – both were a proper model for other Christians. Following Augustine, a later writer asserted that 'we revere the relics of the martyrs with the same respect as we accord to holy men now living; but perhaps we honour them more because we can be confident of their efficacy, for they have already fought the battle and won it.'

Popular piety went far beyond this modest account of the cult of relics, and certain theologians, particularly in the east, were inclined to accord intrinsic powers to the relics of the saints. Cyprian of Carthage defended the veneration of relics in themselves and even of objects touched by the martyrs. The chains they wore, for example, should be honoured for they have honoured the feet of the martyrs and led them to a glorious death. St. Cyril of Jerusalem also went further than Augustine in allowing the bodies of the saints some intrinsic power to work miracles. Even though the soul had left the body, the body was still venerable 'on account of the virtuous soul that once inhabited it. For it is well known that such external objects as handkerchiefs and aprons have cured the sick after touching the martyr's body; how much more then will the body itself heal them.'

The early Church then, produced a weak and a strong defence of the cult of relics, and elements of both appear in every major apologist of the middle ages. In the middle of the thirteenth century, Thomas Aquinas summarized all the various opinions canvassed in his own day and concluded that relics should be venerated for three reasons. First, they are the physical reminders of the saints and 'he who loves some one reveres the things that they leave behind them.' By means of their relics we retain a personal friendship with the saints. Secondly, adds the *doctor angelicus*, bodily relics enjoy a certain intrinsic merit, not as mere objects but on account of their connections with the soul of the saint. The Holy Spirit worked mainly through their souls (which are in Heaven), but also through their bodies, which may be venerated on earth. Thus these bodies are sanctified by God – a fact which distinguishes them from the holy images venerated in the Greek Church. Thirdly, by working miracles at their tombs God has plainly demonstrated that He wishes them to be venerated. 'We ought therefore to hold them in the deepest possible veneration as limbs of God, as children and friends of God, and as intercessors on our behalf.'

The Objects of Veneration

Most of the relics venerated by the early Christians were not bodily relics but simple mementoes, objects that had been in contact with the saint or his shrine. Pilgrims brought pieces of cloth or paper to the shrine, which they retained as private relics of the saint. Cyril of Jerusalem had remarked that handkerchiefs and aprons worked miracles after touching the bodies of the martyrs. The shrouds of popes were customarily divided amongst the people of Rome, until the practice was abolished by Gregory I. In the eyes of ordinary men these *brandea*, as they were called, enjoyed as much esteem as the body itself and occasionally even more. Indeed, a remarkable account of the tomb of St. Peter by Gregory of Tours suggests that quite literal notions prevailed as to the manner in which such *brandea* became impregnated with holiness.

'He who wishes to pray before the tomb', writes Gregory, 'opens the barrier that surrounds it and puts his head through a small opening in the shrine. There he prays for all his needs and, so long as his requests are just, his prayers will be granted. Should he wish to bring back a relic from the tomb, he carefully weighs a piece of cloth which he then hangs inside the tomb. Then he prays ardently and, if his faith is sufficient, the cloth, once removed from the tomb, will be found to be so full of divine grace that it will be much heavier than before. Thus will he know that his prayers have been granted.'

It is difficult to imagine that these recommendations were ever put to any practical test, but they tell us much about the frame of mind of an intelligent man who could accept such stories without question.

Pieces of tombs, oil from the lamps that burned before them, dust from the ground around them, found their way into the most distinguished relic collections of the west. While on a pilgrimage to the

shrine of St. Julian of Brioude, Gregory of Tours broke off a piece
of the tomb and placed it in the basilica at Tours, where it shortly
worked miracles. Dust from tombs, particularly from the Holy
Sepulchre, was venerated from the earliest times. A funerary table
of the fourth century, now in the Louvre, bears an inscription which
declares that it once contained 'dust from the land of our redemption', and Augustine observes that miracles were commonly worked
by such dust. Worshippers at the tomb of St. Theodore 'believed
that merely to touch the body was a blessing of indescribable holiness, and if anyone can carry off any of the dust that has settled on
the martyr's tomb he counts himself fortunate indeed.' Relics of this
sort were often enclosed in little reliquaries that hung from a chain
around the owner's neck. Gregory the Great, for example, used to
wear a small crucifix containing filings from the chains of St. Peter
and the gridiron of St. Lawrence. St. Jerome compared such charms
to the phylacteries carried in their robes by the scribes and pharisees,
and the practice attracted disapproval in certain quarters throughout
the succeeding centuries. The acts of the council of Braca in 675
reveal that the Spanish bishops of that period were in the habit of
wearing the relics of their churches around their necks, which the
council characterized as a 'detestable presumption'. Similar observations were made six centuries later by Thomas Aquinas, but the
practice showed no signs of abating. St. Hugh of Lincoln, an insatiable collector, carried about with him 'innumerable relics of saints
of both sexes' in a small silver casket which he later presented to the
Grande Chartreuse; a tooth of St. Benedict, presented to him by the
monks of Fleury, was set into his ring.

Although *brandea* could not compete with the bodily relics of the
saints which increasingly became available after the seventh century,
their popularity never altogether waned and the practice of collecting them survived into relatively modern times. An acquaintance of
Guibert of Nogent, who accidentally swallowed a toad, was saved
from death by the application of dust from the tomb of St. Marcel.
Similar miracles are attributed to many other saints. Rocks from the
seashore at Mont-St.-Michel were collected by pilgrims in the
eleventh century and even used to consecrate churches. As late as the
fifteenth century the Dominican Felix Faber took with him to the
Holy Land a bag of jewels belonging to friends who had asked him
to press them against any relics which he might inspect en route. His
well-travelled contemporary, Joos van Ghistele, brought various
gems which had been in contact with the relics of the Magi at
Cologne in the belief that, should he discover the land of the legend-
ary Prester John, they would make an acceptable gift to that poten-
tate.

Most of the saints whose relics were venerated in the fourth century were martyrs of the last and most terrible of the persecutions. But a succession of spectacular discoveries (or 'inventions') at the end of the fourth century and the beginning of the fifth dramatically increased the number of distinguished relics available. The floodgates were opened by the discovery of two quite unknown saints called Gervaise and Proteus in the basilica of Milan by St. Ambrose in 386. As he was dedicating the basilica in the presence of a large crowd, Ambrose dug in the ground beneath him and uncovered two unidentified bodies which were spontaneously gathered up by the crowd and venerated as the relics of saints and martyrs. The timing of this event was particularly opportune, for the Arian empress Justina was even then attempting to expel Ambrose from his bishopric. We cannot rule out the possibility that the invention was elaborately contrived for immediate political ends. There can, however, be no doubt of the enormous impact which the discovery made on contemporaries. St. Augustine, who was in Milan at the time, constantly refers to it, and the cult of the two saints enjoyed immediate popularity throughout the Christian world. The result seems to have been to make Christians more credulous in accepting the fabrications of visionaries or charlatans. Two unknown saints, Vitalis and Agricola, were unearthed in rather similar circumstances in Florence in 390. In the same year two monks claimed to have found the head of John the Baptist in the ruins of Herod's palace in Jerusalem. Even more celebrated than the invention of St. Gervaise and St. Proteus, was the discovery of the body of St. Stephen, the first Christian martyr, in 415. A certain Lucian, priest of Caphargamala in Palestine, experienced a revelation in which Gamaliel, the enlightened pharisee mentioned in the Acts of the Apostles, informed him that he had translated Stephen's body to Caphargamala. The relics were immediately located and portions of them distributed to churches in north Africa and the eastern Mediterranean. Some of them remained at Caphargamala, while the bulk of them were translated to Jerusalem. But fragments found their way to Uzalis, Calama, Minorca and Ancona amongst other places. St. Augustine acquired some for his church at Hippo, which became the object of an important north African pilgrimage.

The common feature of most of these discoveries was that they were alleged to have been inspired by visions or dreams. The belief in dreams as a revelation of the supernatural world is one of the commonest features of primitive religions. St. Augustine, for example, had no doubt that God spoke to men in visions, and his critical powers appear to have been suspended whenever other men's dreams were reported to him. Throughout the middle ages, dreams were cited to authenticate more or less bogus relics. Thus, for example, Moses' rod, whose discovery at Sens created a sensation at the beginning of the eleventh century. When the Provencal hermit Peter Bartholomew discovered the Holy Lance at Antioch during the first crusade his story was doubted by Adhémar, bishop of Le Puy, but it was enthusiastically accepted by the rank and file of the army. In some hagiographical works it is even suggested that it was sinful to ignore instructions conveyed in dreams, and indeed in the fourteenth century, Jean de Meung found that an exaggerated respect for them was almost universal amongst his contemporaries.

In doubting the authenticity of the Holy Lance of Antioch, Adhémar was probably fairly typical of educated churchmen of his day. He may perhaps have remembered another Holy Lance at Constantinople whose claims were rather more ancient. The absence of rational criteria for assessing the authenticity of relics bred a dangerous anarchy in which several churches might lay claim to the same relic, each discovered by revelation and each equally believed. Thus at least two heads of John the Baptist were venerated in the fifth century, and in the eleventh century they were both to be found in Constantinople, while a third head had made its appearance at St.-Jean d'Angely in central France. For such reasons the Church endeavoured at an early stage to stem the tide of dreams and visions. A north African council as early as 401 had occasion to denounce 'inane revelations which men suppose themselves to have received in their sleep'. Even Augustine, usually credulous in such matters, advised caution. Although the multiplicity of relics does not seem to have disturbed the populace, intelligent churchmen were aware that it discredited the cult of certain saints. For as Guibert of Nogent pointed out:

'Some say they have such and such a relic and others loudly assert that they have it. The citizens of Constantinople claim the head of John the Baptist while the monks of St.-Jean d'Angely confidently believe that they have it. Now what could be more absurd than to suppose that this great saint had two heads. Let us therefore take this matter seriously and admit that one of them is wrong.'

It was Guibert's opinion that all doubts about the authenticity of relics were due to the partition and translation of bodies. 'All the evils of contention over relics would be avoided if we permitted the saints to enjoy the repose of a proper and immutable burial place.' In fact, the early Church had originally refused to countenance either the partition or the translation of bodies. The burial of the dead was governed by strict rules of Roman municipal law. In the

Theodosian code, it was absolutely forbidden to disturb the dead even if it was only by moving the coffin a few feet. But at the time the code was published these precepts had already been abandoned, notably by the emperors themselves. The co-emperor Gallus translated the relics of St. Babylas to a disreputable suburb of Antioch shortly after 351, while the reign of Constantius (351–61) saw a series of spectacular translations to the great church of the Apostles in Constantinople. Magnificent displays signalled the arrival in the city of St. Phocas, St. Paul the confessor, John the Baptist, the prophet Samuel and a host of minor martyrs. Thus it was that the capital of the Byzantine empire, which had begun its life with no relics at all, possessed by the end of the fifth century the world's finest collection. These developments attracted unfavourable comment in the west where the dead remained inviolable until the seventh century. The popes repeatedly refused to allow the emperors to translate relics from Rome to Constantinople. A request for the bodies of St. Peter, St. Paul and St. Lawrence, was rejected by pope Hormisdas in 519 on the ground that Roman custom would not allow it. Gregory the Great refused a request for the head of St. Lawrence in 594, pointing out that 'it was not the custom in Rome to permit any one so much as to touch the relics of the saints'; those who had recently opened the tomb of St. Lawrence by mistake had all died within ten days.

Similar considerations applied *a fortiori* to the dismemberment of bodies. But this too was ultimately permitted in both east and west. This development, the source of most of the abuses of the mediaeval period, was readily justified by eastern theologians. Theodoret of Cyrus proclaimed that 'in the divided body the grace survives undivided and the fragments, however small, have the same efficacy as the whole body.' Victricius, bishop of Rouen, himself an enthusiastic collector of relics, uttered the same opinion at the beginning of the fifth century. In the Latin Church, however, dismemberment continued to be regarded with distaste. Gregory of Tours once met a Syrian merchant who was offering a detached finger bone for sale, 'though not, I think, with the approval of the martyr'. When bodies were dismembered, efforts were sometimes made to secure the saint's approval; the priest whom St. Radegonde sent to collect some relics of St. Mammas reported that on his approach a finger had detached itself from the body of its own accord.

The practice of fasting and praying before removing a relic was a survival of these ancient prejudices. Gregory of Tours reported that three bishops fasted for three days before opening a casket containing the blood of John the Baptist. Similar austerities were considered advisable in much later periods. When the Bohemians captured

Gnesen in 1039 they were prevented by divine intervention from removing the body of St. Adalbert until they had fasted for three days, renounced polygamy, and promulgated effective laws against murder and rape. The elaborate precautions taken by abbot Samson of Bury before opening the tomb of St. Edmund are recorded by his biographer Jocelyn of Brakeland. The rebuilding of the abbey church had made it necessary to move the coffin and Samson, accompanied by a chosen few, flagellated himself and dressed in white robes before proceeding to lift the lid of the coffin. Even then Samson did not dare unwrap the saint's winding sheet but cradled his head in his arms and said: 'Glorious martyr St. Edmund, . . . condemn me not to perdition for this my boldness that I, a miserable sinner, now touch thee. Thou knowest my devotion and my good intent.'

Two factors combined to create an unprecedented demand for relics, however dubious the source. The first was the growing feeling that relics were necessary for the consecration of churches. Relics must have been used for the consecration of Roman churches as early as the fourth century, for on the famous occasion of the invention of the relics of St. Gervaise and St. Proteus, the crowd shouted 'consecrate it in the Roman manner', to which Ambrose answered 'I will if I find relics.' Similarly Gregory the Great sent to Augustine and his fellow-missionaries in England 'all things needed for the worship of the church, namely sacred vessels, altar linen, ornaments, priestly vestments, and relics of the holy apostles and martyrs.' In 787 the second council of Nicaea insisted on the use of relics in the consecration of new churches and decreed that any churches which had been consecrated without them should acquire some as soon as possible. The conversion of northern France, England, and Germany brought into the Christian fold nations with few indigenous martyrs, who were obliged to acquire their relics abroad. In practice they usually acquired them in Rome, and the eighth and ninth centuries saw an unprecedented series of translations and partitions of the relics of Rome for the benefit of her newly converted daughters.

The second factor, which was of far greater long term importance, was the accumulation of enormous private collections of relics by connoisseurs at least as avid as the wealthy art collectors of post-Renaissance Europe. The earliest and most successful of these were the emperors of Byzantium whose collection, built up over five centuries, was dramatically dispersed across the face of western Europe when the fourth Crusade took Constantinople in 1204. This extraordinarily large and varied collection was lodged partly in the churches of the city, and partly in the various royal palaces. It was a constant source of wonder to Latins who passed through on their way to the Holy Land. When Amaury, king of Jerusalem, visited the emperor Manuel Comnenus in 1171 he was taken aback by the rich display of silks, jewels, and reliquaries in the imperial chapels. Surviving lists demonstrate that most princes of western Europe at all times expended a great deal of money and energy in enlarging their collections. Charlemagne and the German emperors accumulated an astonishing collection of relics at Aachen, many of which had come by more or less devious routes from Constantinople. Henry I of England sent emissaries to acquire relics in Constantinople, and he appears to have given much of his substantial collection to Reading abbey. Louis IX of France endowed the Sainte Chapelle with the crown of thorns, a portion of the true Cross, a piece of the Holy Lance, and fragments of the purple cloak of Christ, all of which had been sold or given to him by the bankrupt Latin emperor of Constantinople.

The unrestrained popular enthusiasm which greeted each new accession of the Byzantine collection demonstrates that relics were regarded as a proper object of national pride. On occasions the emperors were prepared to forgo significant political advantages in order to acquire an important relic. In 944, for example, the army of the emperor Romanus Lecapenus, at the climax of its triumphal campaign in Asia Minor, spared Edessa and released two hundred captives in return for the celebrated portrait of Christ which was preserved there. This attitude to relics explains much of the frenzied acquisitiveness of Latin rulers and their subjects throughout our period. Relics were the guarantors of political prestige and spiritual authority. William of Malmesbury described Cologne as 'the metropolitan city of Germany . . . with the patronage of the saints'. France, declared a French monk of the eleventh century, was 'like the treasure-house of the Lord' on account of the priceless relics that were to be found there. A sermon of Walter Suffield, bishop of Norwich, was largely devoted to the proposition that England was exalted above other nations by its collections of relics. The occasion was the translation in 1244 of a vase of the blood of Christ to Westminster abbey together with 'numerous sealed documents attesting its authenticity'. In the course of his speech, the bishop recalled that Louis IX of France had recently acquired a fragment of the True Cross.

'But we must consider not the nature of matter but the causes thereof. Now it is true that the Cross is a very holy relic but it is holy only because it came into contact with the precious blood of Christ. The holiness of the Cross derives from the blood whereas the holiness of the blood in no way derives from the Cross. It therefore follows that England, which possesses the blood of Christ, rejoices in a greater treasure than France, which has no more than the Cross.'

Not only a nation but a region, a city, or an individual, acquired new status when it obtained a valuable relic. To a powerful collector, the body of a saint might quite literally be worth more than gold or silver. So much was admitted by Fernando count of Carrion who, when collecting his debts from the emir of Cordova in 1047, rejected all the bullion that he was offered: 'of gold and silver I have enough already; give me the body of St. Zoyl.'

The Sale and Theft of Relics

So long as even an august churchman like Gregory of Tours was satisfied with *brandea*, few problems arose. But as soon as they began to insist on bodily relics the demand rapidly outstripped the supply and a nefarious trade in relics sprang up which provided a constant source of indignation among satirists and reformers from the fourth century to the sixteenth. When the eastern Church abandoned its objections to the translation of relics, the itinerant salesman came into his own. St. Augustine complains of wandering relic-hawkers dressed as monks at the beginning of the fifth century, while Gregory of Tours mentions with distaste the activities of Syrian merchants in France.

By the ninth century there was a large market for relics in the newly founded abbeys of northern Europe, which was supplied by highly professional relic merchants. In the 820s a Roman deacon called Deusdona is known to have travelled to Aix in order to sell relics looted from the Roman catacombs to churchmen at the court of Louis the Pious. Hilduin, abbot of St.-Medard of Soissons, and Einhard, the biographer of Charlemagne, were among his clients, 'and by this means', we are told, 'he succeeded in supplementing his low income.' In the eleventh and twelfth centuries the sale of relics was practised on an alarming scale and active measures were taken to discourage it. Emma, Canute's queen, bought several relics of doubtful authenticity. The bishop of Benevento sold her the arm of St. Bartholomew in 1017, having come to England for the express purpose of finding a buyer. During her exile in Rouen after 1016 she bought several bones of St. Ouen, at the thought of which William of Malmesbury blanched when describing it a century later, even though his own monastery proved to be the ultimate beneficiary. The trade in relics reached epidemic proportions after the sack of Constantinople in 1204, when the market was inundated with objects whose authenticity was impossible to prove. The fourth Lateran council condemned the traffic as sacrilege and simony but this did not prevent Jean d'Alluye, for example, from selling a piece of the True Cross to the abbey of La Boissière for 533 *livres tournois*. Nor did it deter Baldwin, the impecunious Latin emperor of Constantinople, from pawning the crown of thorns to the Venetians for 13,075 *livres* in order to mount a campaign against the Bulgars.

Few relic merchants had satisfactory credentials and fewer still could explain the origin of their wares. For this reason, the more important collectors preferred to steal relics than to buy them. Many of the greatest pilgrimage churches in Europe, including St. Benedict at Fleury, St. Foy at Conques, St. Nicholas of Bari and St. Mark in Venice, owed their prosperity to some pious theft. Einhard, friend of Charlemagne and founder of the abbey of Seligenstadt, had no compunction about stealing the bodies of Marcellinus and Peter from the Roman catacombs; his servant prised open the tomb with his own hands. Pilgrims were constantly attempting to steal relics, and as early as 385 armed deacons surrounded the True Cross at Jerusalem in order to prevent pilgrims from kissing it and taking a splinter away in their teeth. Fulk Nerra count of Anjou was alleged to have obtained a splinter in this way when he visited Jerusalem at the beginning of the eleventh century, and at Bury St. Edmunds, pilgrims to the shrine of the martyr king had to be prevented from biting off pieces of the gilt.

It is clear that contemporaries did not consider it possible to have any property in the body of a saint, and accordingly the customary canons of ethical behaviour did not apply to relics. This attitude is found in Greek hagiography very early but it does not make its appearance in the west until the seventh century or later. One of the earliest attempts to give moral justification to an audacious theft is found in the official account of the translation of the bodies of St. Benedict and St. Scholastica from Monte Cassino to Fleury. This event occurred at the end of the seventh century after the devastation of the abbey of Monte Cassino by the Lombards. According to the oldest account a French priest visited the ruins and, finding the tomb of the two saints in the midst of the desolation, placed them in a casket and carried them off to France. The body of St. Benedict was laid in the recently founded abbey of Fleury on the Loire, while his sister was taken to Le Mans. The official account by Adrevald, a monk of Fleury, was not composed until two centuries later, and it is full of apocryphal details designed to prove that God and St. Benedict had brought the translation about. Here we learn that abbot Mummolus was advised in a vision of the desolate state of Monte Cassino, while a similar vision was vouchsafed to the clergy of Le Mans. Two parties of clergy made their way to Monte Cassino, where a divine revelation led them to the tomb. Further miracles saved them from pursuit by the Romans and Lombards by causing night suddenly to descend. As soon as they had reached the Loire valley a man blind from birth was healed and a constant succession of miracles began which had not ceased in the writer's own day. In this account we have all the elements of the classic mediaeval justification for the theft of relics, which remained for several centuries the 'stock-in-trade of hagiographical writers: neglect of the saint in his former resting-place; revelation of his whereabouts to the thieves; divine assistance in accomplishing the theft; constant miracles on their return.

One of the more remarkable thefts justified according to this formula was the translation of St. Nicholas to Bari in 1087. St. Nicholas was a bishop of Myra on the Lycian coast of Asia Minor, who was believed (on no very sound basis) to have been martyred during the persecution of Diocletian. His body had been preserved at Myra for several centuries, but recurrent raids by Arab pirates had depopulated the region, and after the collapse of Byzantine power at Manzikert in 1071 the city was almost entirely deserted by its inhabitants. In the spring of 1087, several merchants of Bari met on a trading mission to Antioch and resolved to remove the saint to their native city. They completed their business as quickly as possible, purchased some crowbars and sailed to Myra. Forty-seven men, heavily armed and carrying the crowbars, knocked at the door of the monastery of St. Nicholas and asked to be admitted to pray at the shrine. Their prayer completed, they turned on the monks and demanded to know where the martyr lay, declaring that the pope himself had ordered them to remove the body 'on the express instructions of St. Nicholas who had appeared to him in a dream.' After threatening the monks with a naked sword, they located the body, disinterred it, and removed it to Bari where spectacular miracles immediately occurred.

The author of this account plainly believed that the theft was a pious act and that the end justified the means 'for as it is written in scripture, *bona est fraus quae nemini nocet*' – there is no harm in deceit if no one is injured. The fundamental argument of the author, an Italian Greek called Nicephorus, is that St. Nicholas demanded proper veneration and this the partially depopulated city of Myra was no longer able to give him. Bari on the other hand was at the height of its prosperity in the eleventh century, and its citizens were particularly devoted to St. Nicholas. According to Nicephorus the thieves replied to the protests of the citizens of Myra with the argument: 'We too are worshippers of Almighty God, so why distress yourselves? You have had the precious body of St. Nicholas for 775 years and St. Nicholas has now decided to bestow his favours on another place. . . . The city of Bari deserves him.' Thus it was that the distribution of relics could be changed in accordance with a new balance of power and prosperity among nations. The thieves further argued that if St. Nicholas had desired to remain in Myra he would have intervened miraculously to prevent his removal. 'Do you suppose', asked the monks of Myra, 'that St. Nicholas will permit you to take him away?' And Nicephorus reports that when St. Nicholas offered no resistance the monks cried out 'with lamentable wails', realizing that it was their punishment for deserting the shrine when the Turks had attacked the city some years before. 'We left him alone in the town and now he is leaving us to the mercy of the Turks. . . . It is clear that we are unworthy of so great a saint.' Then, when the thieves picked up the relics, they exuded a miraculous odour 'and everyone rejoiced for thus they knew that St. Nicholas consented to his translation.'

The view that the saint had a mind of his own to decide where he wished to be venerated amounted to a real conviction which was no doubt sincerely held by the thieves who translated St. Nicholas to Bari. According to Adrevald of Fleury (the story is certainly apocryphal), St. Benedict intervened to prevent Pippin from restoring his relics to the monks of Monte Cassino: 'The holy saint will only permit himself to be moved of his own free will', the abbot of Fleury is supposed to have said, '. . . and if it is indeed his wish, on account of our sins, to leave France and return to his native country, then there is nothing we can do to prevent him.' One of the commonest stories found in mediaeval miracle collections relates that a body remained rooted to the spot as soon as impious hands tried to move it without the saint's consent. A single example will stand in lieu of many. In 1053 Garcia, king of Navarre, resolved to move the body of St. Millan, an obscure Spanish saint of the sixth century, from Cogolla to Nájera where he had recently built a church in honour of the Blessed Virgin. A powerful deputation led by several bishops was sent to Cogolla for this purpose. The monks were unable to resist and the sequel might have been like the story of St. Nicholas of Myra. 'But God, the consoler of the troubled, had otherwise disposed. As soon as the party set out on the road with the coffin and entered the valley, the coffin suddenly refused to move an inch further and became so heavy that the bearers had to lay it down.' Garcia resigned himself to respecting the wishes of the saint and built an oratory on the spot where the miracle had occurred. The author of the twelfth-century *Guide for Pilgrims to Santiago* believed that such incidents were regular occurrences, and repeated a legend to the effect that four saints, St. James himself, St. Martin of Tours, St. Leonard, and St. Gilles had resisted all attempts to move them, even by the king of France.

August churchmen of saintly reputation are known to have shared the view that the sanctity of property did not extend to relics, that one was entitled to whatever one could get by fair means or foul. St. Hugh of Lincoln, then staying as a guest at the abbey of Fécamp, was permitted to see the arm of St. Mary Magdalene, which was tightly wrapped in cloth bandages that the monks had never dared to open. In spite of the furious protests of the surrounding monks he took out a knife, cut open the wrapping, and tried to break a piece off. On finding it too hard he bit at a finger with his teeth, 'first with his incisors and finally with his molars', and by this means broke off two fragments which he handed to his biographer for safe-keeping. Turning to the abbot, Hugh remarked: 'If a little while ago I handled the sacred body of the Lord with my fingers in spite of my unworthiness, and partook of it with my lips and my teeth, why should I not treat the bones of the saints in the same way . . . and without profanity acquire them whenever I can.' So long as St. Hugh's attitude prevailed it is no surprise to learn that churches with valuable relics took elaborate precautions against theft. The Lateran Council of 1215 instructed that relics were not to be exposed except in a reliquary, and a provincial synod in Bordeaux in 1255 forbade the removal of relics from their reliquaries in any circumstances whatever. Whenever the relics of St. Cuthbert were exposed at Durham, a group of monks was appointed to stand guard over them all night. Four armed men stood guard day and night in Chartres cathedral in the fourteenth century. When the Spanish traveller Pero Tafur visited the Lateran basilica in Rome in 1437, he found the portrait of Christ by St. Luke perpetually guarded by four men with iron maces.

False Relics

Acquisitiveness on this scale created a demand which could only be satisfied by fraud. It was acknowledged by most contemporaries that wicked men did sometimes fabricate relics, and some quite celebrated relics were regarded with intense suspicion. When Henry III of England solemnly received a vase of Christ's blood from the representatives of the crusading orders in 1247, 'certain hesitant and incredulous persons' in the crowd ventured to express doubts about its authenticity. The prior of the Hospitallers of Clerkenwell demanded to know whether these scoffers were accusing the military orders of fraud, but the objections still continued unabated. 'How can any of the Lord's blood exist on earth', insisted the doubters, 'when the Saviour was bodily resurrected on the third day?' Nor were they silenced until Robert Grosseteste delivered an angry oration proving its authenticity with arguments drawn from Scripture and natural reason.

Guibert of Nogent observed that in many cases the pressures of popular belief prevented any non-conformist from voicing his doubts. He vividly recalled attending a harangue in which a relic-monger was advertizing his wares in Laon. He was holding up before the appreciative crowd a little box which, he said, contained a piece of the very bread which Our Lord chewed at the Last Supper. Then, seeing Guibert in the audience, he pointed him out and exclaimed: 'there is a distinguished man, famous for his learning. He will confirm that I am telling the truth.' To his eternal shame, Guibert was frightened and simply blushed and held his peace. Contemporaries do not seem to have been greatly disturbed by such incidents. It was generally agreed that it was no sin to honour the relics of one saint under the honest impression that it was another, and even Guibert of Nogent was of the opinion that a man who in good faith revered as a holy relic something which was not, might nevertheless enjoy some merit in God's eyes. A story told by the German Cistercian Caesarius of Heisterbach suggests that God even worked miracles through false relics venerated in ignorance.

The problem caused embarrassment only when two churches claimed to possess the same relic. This commonly occurred when a church had lost its relics by theft, fraud, or force; it would then claim that the wrong relics had been taken in error. The confusion which followed was, in a sense, the penalty which the thief had to pay for his success. In some cases the thief does appear to have taken the wrong relic. Odo of Bayeux, for example, who bought the relics of St. Exupéry from a venal sacristan of Corbeil, was given the body of a peasant of the same name. Fulbert, bishop of Cambrai, practised a similar fraud in the tenth century when the emperor Otto I demanded the relics of two canonized bishops of Cambrai in order to enrich the city of Magdeburg. Fulbert gave him the bodies of two ordinary priests together with a few trappings from the graves of the saints. At the end of the eleventh century the monks of Monte Cassino claimed to have discovered the body of St. Benedict beneath the rubble during the rebuilding of their church, and the controversy which then erupted was still raging fiercely in the nineteenth century. The achievement of the Barians in acquiring the relics of St. Nicholas was so spectacular that others inevitable tried to deflect some of the glory to themselves. In every part of Europe churches announced that they had obtained part of the body of St.

Nicholas. A monk of Angers made off with the arm of the saint, which had been detached from the rest of the body and sheathed with silver for use in blessing crowds. But he was unable to escape to France and the relic ultimately came into the possession of the abbey of the Trinity at Venosa. Within a few months the abbot of Angers nevertheless announced that the attempt had in fact succeeded and the arm was in his church. The sailors who had brought the body from Myra gave it out that they had retained the saint's teeth and fragments of his tomb; a Norman pilgrim bought some of them in 1092 and gave them to the church of St. Peter at Noron. The Venetians claimed that the Barians had left half of the body behind at Myra, which they solemnly translated to Venice in 1099. Almost every successful pilgrimage provoked competition from imposters. The much-visited shrines on the routes to Santiago all had determined rivals who provoked the indignation of the author of the *Guide for Pilgrims to Santiago*. The church of St.-Léonard de Noblat was afflicted with a rival body set up by the monks of Corbigny, who attributed all St. Leonard's miracles to their own relics. St. Gilles was claimed by at least four churches in addition to the celebrated Provençal monastery which bore his name: 'Shame upon the Hungarians for claiming part of his body. Curses upon the monks of Chamalières who imagine that they have the whole body. The same to the people of St.-Seine who boast of his head, and to the Normans who actually display a body purporting to be his. For it is quite impossible that a single particle of the holy body could ever have left its hallowed tomb.'

Such impostures usually made little or no impression on the flow of pilgrims to old-established shrines. But there were exceptions, of which the most interesting is perhaps the pilgrimage to the shrine of St. Mary Magdalene. During the eleventh century the belief arose that Mary Magdalene was buried in the abbey church of Vézelay, which consequently grew from an impoverished religious backwater in an isolated corner of Burgundy into a powerful and wealthy monastery. The monks encouraged this improbable belief and put about a legend designed to explain how the body came to be there. According to this story Mary expiated her sins after Christ's death by taking ship for France and exiling herself in the Provençal desert. When she died she was buried in what is now the town of St.-Maximin la Sainte-Baume, until in the middle of the eighth century the place was deserted by its inhabitants and the saint's remains transferred to Vézelay. Such was the legend which was commonly received in the eleventh and twelfth centuries. But the great age of Vézelay ended at the beginning of the thirteenth century. The days when Vézelay had seen the launching of the second crusade and the departure of the third were no more. Disputes within the monastery, constant warfare with the counts of Nevers and the citizens of the *bourg*, and heavy papal taxes had eroded the abbey's wealth. In 1279 the monks of St.-Maximin took advantage of the troubles of Vézelay and turned the Burgundian legend to their own use. On 9 December they announced that they had discovered the body of the Magdalene in their crypt. A 'suave odour' emitting from the sarcophagus and an authoritative inscription permitted no doubt as to its authenticity and it was immediately put about that the monks of Vézelay had taken the wrong body in the eighth century. Charles of Salerno, count of Provence, was only too pleased to promote a major pilgrimage within his dominions and five months later he presided over a splendid ceremony at which the newly found relics were displayed to a gathering of princes and ecclesiastical dignitaries. St.-Maximin seems to have been accepted immediately as the true resting place of the Magdalene, and Vézelay entirely forgotten. Boniface VIII proclaimed several indulgences in favour of the Provençal shrine, and large numbers of pilgrims hastened to take advantage of them. So matters rested until the cult of Mary Magdalene sank into obscurity during the later middle ages, and pilgrims ceased to care where the penitent of Judaea was buried.

Disputes such as these have a somewhat unreal appearance, for in almost every case neither relic would survive modern critical scrutiny. Procedures for verifying the authenticity of relics consisted rather in a dramatic assertion of belief than a scientific examination of the evidence. When, in the mid eleventh century, the monks of St. Emmeran at Regensburg raised pretentions to possess the body of St. Denis the Areopagite, the reaction of the abbot of St.-Denis near Paris was to open the shrine of the abbey church in the presence of a crowd of bishops, abbots, and noblemen, including several members of the royal family, and to declare with great solemnity that its contents were authentic. The claim of St.-Denis to the body of the martyr was constantly disputed by other churches, and the monks invariably replied with imposing ceremonies at which their own relics were publicly displayed. In 1186 the canons of the church of St. Stephen in Paris 'discovered' the head of St. Denis is their own church. The monks of the royal abbey were outraged, and when their complaints fell on deaf ears they separated the head from the body and exposed it in a separate reliquary for a whole year. It may be assumed that before the relics were publicly displayed they were surreptitiously examined to ensure that all was well. Indeed, when abbot Suger failed to take this elementary precaution before the ceremonial opening of a reliquary, he was rebuked by his monks, who declared that 'it would have been better for the reputation of the abbey if we had secretly ascertained in advance whether the description on the labels was true.'

Despite the elaborate stage management of these proceedings the populace took a passionate interest in them, and seems to have been readily convinced. Any suggestion that a relic of note was false or had been stolen provoked intense public concern. The object of the ceremonies was therefore to create an atmosphere of popular enthusiasm in which the doubts of individuals would be silenced. In 1162, for example, a rumour spread in Paris that the head of St. Genevieve, the city's patron saint, was missing from its reliquary in the church dedicated to her. Within hours riotous mobs had gathered at the church. Louis VII threatened to have the canons of St. Genevieve flogged and expelled from their posts, while the archbishop of Sens announced his intention of holding a solemn examination of the relics. On the appointed day the king and the royal family, together with civil and ecclesiastical dignitaries, watched from a specially erected stand as the archbishop and his suffragans opened the reliquary and pulled out the head intact. This was immediately accepted by the crowd as proof, and the prior of St. Genevieve led them in a spontaneous rendering of the *Te Deum*. Some of the officiating bishops were, however, disturbed at this unexpected change in the protocol of the ceremony, and remained unconvinced of the relic's authenticity. Manasses, bishop of Orléans, demanded to know who had given them permission to sing, and pointed out that the head in the reliquary might not be that of St. Genevieve, but a substitute placed there by the monks. The prior offered to prove the authenticity of the head by carrying it over a bed of burning coals, but his faith was not put to the test. The bishop's objections were drowned by the singing and the archbishop of Sens peremptorily ordered him to be silent. The prior's biographer remarks with satisfaction that Manasses was shortly afterwards ejected from his diocese and struck down by the Lord in condign punishment for his presumption. But the truth is less dramatic. The bishop survived for twenty-five years in his see and died peacefully in his bed at an advanced age.

A miracle constituted certain proof of the authenticity of a relic and a common method of testing relics was to provoke one. In the 830s Erchanbert, bishop of Friesing, ordered the clergy of his diocese to fast for three days when doubts had arisen about a relic of St. Felix; 'and by this means we hope that we will become worthy of a sign from Almighty God indicating whether the Devil has been deceiving us.' According to a Canterbury legend, four Norman monks once offered some bones of St. Ouen to King Edgar, promising to prove them genuine by provoking miracles. 'We can prove it in any manner you suggest by casting them in the fire, for example, and withdrawing them unharmed. And if no such miracle occurs then we will admit that the relics are false and that we are outrageous liars deserving of all the penalties of the law.' Ultimately it was agreed that a leper should be brought in and touched with one of the bones, and when the leper was immediately healed 'the whole company fell on their knees in thankgiving for the merits of St. Ouen.' The story has no historical basis, but it is eloquent of the frame of mind of its twelfth-century author.

Casting relics in the fire was the simplest method of provoking a miracle and was widely practised, particularly in the early mediaeval period. In 979 Egbert, bishop of Trier, doubting the authenticity of the body of St. Celsus, broke off a finger joint and threw it into a brazier of burning coals, where it remained unharmed throughout the canon of the Mass. The monks of Monte Cassino, who possessed a piece of the cloth with which Christ washed the feet of the disciples, placed it in a red hot crucible where 'it changed to the colour of fire but as soon as it was removed from the coals it reverted to its original appearance.' A great crowd gathered to watch Meinwerk, bishop of Paderborn, putting St. Felix to the ordeal of fire. Again, when the townsmen of Clermont-en-Beauvaisis entertained doubts about the arm of St. Arnoul they cast it in the fire and it immediately jumped out again. Crude tests of this sort were generally applied when large numbers of relics were suspected. In the sixth century, for example, numerous churches were recovered from the Arian heretics and converted to Catholic use. They were usually found to contain relics of unknown provenance, and the second council of Saragossa officially sanctioned the use of fire to test them. A variety of methods were employed after the Norman conquest of England to test relics of the unknown saints venerated by the Anglo-Saxons. Indeed, the constant attempt to provoke miracles was by no means peculiar to the middle ages. Anna Gonzaga, dowager countess palatine of the Rhine, who died in 1685, left to the abbey of St. Germain a piece of the True Cross 'que j'atteste avoir veue dans les flammes sans bruler.'

CHAPTER III

THE SAINTS AND
THEIR RELICS

Heretics and Cynics

Individual relics might be discredited, minor abuses exposed, but opposition to the cult of relics as such was extremely rare. The same pressures of mass belief which enabled spurious relics to be venerated as genuine without exciting protest, applied *a fortiori* to stifle objections to a practice which was so basic to mediaeval religious life.

Levity and popular irreverence in the face of the saints there sometimes was. But even this was limited by the overpowering conventions of religious life of which the most powerful was that the saints, being possessed of a will of their own, mercilessly chastised those who mocked them. Gerald of Wales, in pointing out the extreme devotion of the Welsh to relics, explained that 'owing to a certain occult power granted to all relics by God, and owing to the special vindictiveness of Welsh saints, those who despise them are usually punished.' Cautionary tales describing these punishments can be found in almost every surviving collection of miracle stories. Out of the 139 stories by five different authors in the *Miracles of St. Benedict*, approximately half deal with the fate of those who scoffed at the saint, ignored his feast day, invaded the lands of his abbey, and so on. William of Malmesbury remembered from his childhood how a boy who laughed at a cortège of monks bearing the relics of St. Aldhelm was thereupon tortured by demons. Some courtiers who scoffed at the body of St. Evroul were forthwith struck dead by a thunderbolt. The man who spoke slightingly of St. Emmeram found that his tongue adhered to his palate, while the woman who 'raising her clothing displayed her posterior to the saint, behaviour which God on no account allows to pass unpunished' was afflicted with hideous ulcers. Contempt for the relics of the saints was regularly visited with dumbness, bodily distortion, disease, madness, and death.

If educated men ever expressed criticisms of the cult of relics, their opinions have rarely survived. The mediaeval Church vigorously suppressed heterodox writings and until the later middle ages the views of non-conformists are generally known only through the writings of their opponents. From this source we know that there existed in the fourth and fifth centuries a substantial body of opinion which totally rejected the cult of relics. It is also clear that opposition to the veneration of relics was characteristic of many heresies. The iconoclastic disputes which engulfed the Greek Church in the eighth century affected relics as well as icons. Constantine V, the second of the iconoclastic emperors, conducted a vigorous campaign against relics held by the monasteries of the capital. The iconoclastic position on images and relics was condemned by the council of Nicaea in 787, but it found several sympathizers in the west, particularly among the Franks. Claudius, bishop of Turin, denounced all pilgrimages to the relics of the saints and broke or burnt crosses venerated in his diocese; he was regarded by his contemporaries as a heretic and vigorously condemned by a synod at Paris in 825. In Spain, objections to the cult of relics emanated from the numerous groups of monophysites and manichaeans who had fled from their persecutors in the east. The council of Cordova in 839 was greatly concerned with the activities of a group called 'acephalites' whose errors included the rejection of the veneration of relics. But until the fourteenth century these opinions never attained any importance in the west. Such disputes as did occur were usually pale reflections of controversies in the eastern Church, and these had themselves been silenced by the end of the ninth century. With a single exception, orthodox writers rarely considered the spiritual basis of the cult of relics and never criticized it.

The single exception is Guibert of Nogent, whose writings constitute a remarkable corpus of evidence for almost every aspect of the religious life of his day. Guibert, who died in about 1125, was the abbot of Nogent-sous-Coucy near Laon. He was a prolific writer whose works included an autobiography with unusually introspective details, a treatise in honour of the Virgin, a number of Biblical commentaries, and a history of the first Crusade. He also wrote a treatise *On the Relics of the Saints* in which he examined some of the relics venerated in his own day in the most acid and critical tone. Guibert applied to relics the critical standards developed by Christian scholarship in connection with Biblical exegesis, and he concluded that many of them were wholly unreasonable and based on insecure historical foundations. This, together with his passionate nationalism and fascinating prejudices, has procured for him the unanimous acclaim of historians, one of whom has indeed compared him to Calvin, Rabelais, and Voltaire.

The historian of popular religion owes much to Guibert's book, but to contemporaries it passed entirely unnoticed. It survives in only one manuscript which, moreover, came from Guibert's own abbey of Nogent, and it is never referred to by other mediaeval writers. Although it surveys the whole field of popular religion, its purpose was limited to exposing a particular relic, a milk-tooth of Christ preserved at the abbey of St. Médard at Soissons. The monks of St. Médard had, it seems, issued a pamphlet advertizing the miracles of the tooth. Guibert had no difficulty in demolishing this booklet without straying from the line of strict theological orthodoxy. The Christian's hopes of salvation depended on the doctrine of the resurrection, which could not be completely true if a single particle of Christ's earthly body remained on earth. The only true relic of Christ was therefore the Eucharist which contained Him altogether and was incompatible with the existence of any other relics. To these conventional theological arguments, Guibert added historical ones. Since Christ would not have appeared particularly remarkable to his contemporaries until the beginning of his ministry, no one would have troubled to collect relics of his childhood. Guibert was not impressed by the miracles claimed for the tooth. There was no evidence to connect them with this relic rather than another. Indeed, God might work miracles through the relics of notorious sinners as easily as through the bodies of the saints. In the course of his argument Guibert warms to his subject and mentions other relics of doubtful authenticity. The two heads of John the Baptist and the two bodies of St. Firmin are the object of some scathing comments. The milk of the Virgin preserved in a crystal vase at Laon is condemned as an imposture. The absurdities of several contemporary collections are exposed.

Guibert had no objection to the cult of relics as such. His own abbey of Nogent claimed to possess pieces of the rope which bound Christ to the whipping post and of the scourges that struck his body, together with fragments of the crown of thorns, a portion of the True Cross, and a few shreds of the tunic of the Virgin. In his autobiography, Guibert defends the authenticity of these objects with the most improbable of stories. Guibert was in fact very selective in the relics which he attacked, and we cannot rule out the possibility that he was motivated by some unknown quarrel with those who possessed them. He defended, for example, the authenticity of the Holy Lance of Antioch which his contemporary, Fulcher of Chartres, had questioned. Indeed, in the treatise on relics Guibert asserted that the veneration of genuine relics was wholly justifiable: 'that which is connected with the divine is itself divine, and nothing can be more closely connected with the divine than God's saints who are of one body with him.' Guibert's quarrel was against the lax standards which his contemporaries applied when assessing the authenticity of relics. In the first place many popular saints did not exist, and of others nothing whatever was known. The Church was beginning to apply stringent tests before recognizing a saint. It had, for example, refused to proclaim the bodily assumption of the Virgin on account of the lack of evidence, a commendable reserve, abandoned in the twentieth century. The populace, however, was satisfied with miracles reported by ignorant men or visions vouchsafed to hermits. The Church might refuse to sanction doubtful cults, but it was in no position to resist them, for by permitting the translation and dismemberment of bodies it had allowed the destruction of the only conclusive evidence.

The basis of Guibert's views on relics was his devotion to the inner and spiritual life. In his other works he stresses the value of preaching and confession and of all spiritual exercises which held up a mirror to the faithful in which they might see their inward souls. He sought to create an 'inward world where nothing is either high or low or localized, where there is neither time nor place.' By contrast, in the world which he actually saw around him, popular piety was based on the wholly accidental location of the relics of the saints.

The Body of Christ

The excesses of which Guibert complained were largely a popular phenomenon. The official doctrines of the Church, created in the earliest centuries of its existence and formalized by the thirteenth-century schoolmen, never made any direct impact on popular piety. Orthodox theology was purveyed to ordinary people by a lengthy and indirect route and was considerably distorted in the process. Such religious education as the populace received was based on the teaching of ritual formulae and above all on stories, or *exempla*, from the lives and miracles of the saints. All these had the effect of greatly simplifying doctrinal issues and often unintentionally encouraged heterodox notions. In particular they encouraged uneducated men to look on the mysteries of the faith in a somewhat literal and pictorial fashion. Religious thought, in Johann Huizinga's brilliant phrase, 'crystallized into images'.

The transformation of the bread and wine at the consecration into the body and blood of Christ was constantly misunderstood, and as early as the fifth century stories were current in which the host literally turned to flesh and the wine to blood. A tenth-century writer related that Gregory the Great once settled the doubts of a woman who had confessed to him that she was unable to understand how God could be really present in the Eucharist. He told her that she would see the mystery with her own eyes and thereupon transformed the host into flesh on the altar before her, 'and all who saw it were overcome with the love of God and faith in the ortho- dox doctrine.' Guibert of Nogent reported that the figure of a small boy had been seen in the host in a small town near Soissons, and a similar miracle is described by Peter the Venerable. Jacques de Vitry tells of a woman who kept the host in her mouth for later use and found that it turned to flesh and adhered to her palate so that she could not speak. In the fourteenth and fifteenth centuries such stories multiplied prodigiously, and at a popular level they appear to have been accepted as a normal incident of daily life. The *Pupilla Oculi*, an English manual for ordinary parish priests, warns its readers of the possibility of such occurrences, as also does the *Summa Angelica*, an Italian production of the fifteenth century. In the Netherlands it was considered inadvisable to cut the host lest the body of Christ be damaged. George Carter, a servant of the abbey of Sawtrey who was examined for heresy in 1525, asserted that the host had a special band around it to prevent the blood from dripping out and that this notion was universally received amongst his acquaintances. The bishop's chancellor 'moved him otherwise to believe'.

In the later middle ages the doctrine of the immaculate conception and the mystery of the Trinity were literally portrayed in statues and popular devotional pictures. These were not usually works of art and few of them have survived, but several contemporaries have left descriptions of them. The dukes of Burgundy, for example, pos- sessed a small gold statuette of the Virgin, whose body could be opened to reveal the Trinity inside. Jean Gerson saw another in the Carmelite convent in Paris and was horrified, not, it seems, because of the crudeness of this literal image of the miracle, but because of the heresy of representing all three persons of the Trinity as the fruit of the Blessed Virgin. Many churches in southern France and Spain had scenes of the Visitation carved in wood, in which the abdomen of both the Virgin and St. Elizabeth were open, revealing Christ and John the Baptist within. Some had little mechanisms whereby the stomachs might be opened and closed at will.

The relics of Christ's body afford the clearest example of the dis- tortion of orthodox theology by popular imagination. The official position on such relics was that the doctrine of the resurrection was incompatible with the existence on earth of any bodily relics of the Saviour. On this ground Guibert of Nogent denounced the tooth of Christ at Soissons as a fabrication, and Thomas Aquinas ex- pressed doubts about the blood of Christ venerated at Bruges. The relics of Christ preserved at Rome caused some embarrassment to

Innocent III: 'What shall we say', he asked, 'of the foreskin or umbilical cord which were severed from His body at birth? Were they too resurrected? . . . Perhaps it is better to leave the resolution of such problems to God.' In the course of the late mediaeval period these theological scruples were slowly overcome in response to the strong popular demand for relics of the Lord. The earliest class of relics to achieve theological respectability included those which were separated from the Lord's body during his lifetime. Such, for example, were his foreskin, umbilical cord, and conceivably the milk-tooth conserved at Soissons. The umbilical cord, and foreskin were already preserved in the Lateran basilica in the eleventh century, and the official explanation of their origin was that they had been spirited from Jerusalem by an angel and presented to Charlemagne at Aachen, whence they had been brought to Rome by Charles the Bald. These relics were seen in the Lateran by generations of pilgrims but were clearly regarded with some misgivings by the Popes. At the end of the fourteenth century the Swedish visionary St. Bridget enjoyed a revelation in which the Virgin assured her of their authenticity and this seems to have carried some weight. The foreskin was removed by a German *lanzknecht* during the sack of Rome in 1527 and subsequently lost. The Lateran basilica contained by far the most celebrated relics of Christ's body venerated during the middle ages. But it had several rivals. At the very end of the eleventh century the monastry of Charroux in Poitou claimed to possess a foreskin, and based its claim on a legend which is clearly modelled on the Roman one. This relic enjoyed an uneven popularity for four centuries until the destruction of the church by the Huguenots in the 1560s, and there was even a brief attempt to revive the cult in the nineteenth century. Another foreskin was venerated in the Benedictine abbey of Coulombs: it was sent to England in 1421 in the baggage of Henry V's bride, Catherine of France, in the hope that it would bring good fortune on her marriage bed. Pope Martin V proclaimed an indulgence for a foreskin at Boulogne, while at Antwerp another had made its appearance by the beginning of the fifteenth century.

The blood of Christ was venerated in a growing number of churches after the eleventh century. A phial of Christ's blood was discovered in Mantua as early as 804, and created a profound sensation. Charlemagne asked the pope to investigate its authenticity but the outcome of this inquiry and the subsequent fate of the relic are not known. However, the memory of the event was revived when a second phial of blood was unearthed in the garden of the hospice of St. Andrew in Mantua in 1048. On this occasion, the cult took root, and Mantua became an important stage on the pilgrim's route to Rome. We do not know how the clergy of Mantua explained the existence of their relic or reconciled it with the doctrine of the resurrection. But when relics of the blood of Christ began to multiply in the thirteenth century, the commonest explanation given was that the blood had been miraculously exuded by a eucharistic host or an image of the Lord struck by heretics or Jews (see plate II b). This legend, which has an ancient lineage, served to account for the relics of the Divine Blood exhibited in many western churches in the late middle ages, especially in the Low Countries. A typical variation on the theme was given out by the clergy of Aasche in the fourteenth century. A woman had been inveigled by the Jews into stealing a consecrated host one Easter Sunday, but on the way home she took fright and hastily buried the incriminating host in a tree trunk at the side of the road. There it bled profusely until the inhabitants of the area alerted the local clergy, who took the bloodstained wood away and preserved it in the church at Aasche. Stories of this kind were already common-place in the time of Thomas Aquinas who declares them to be theologically sound, though he does not speak of them with any enthusiasm. A number of churches traced the origin of their phials of blood to the celebrated wooden statue of Christ at Beirut which had begun to bleed when pierced with nails by Jews. A small quantity of it kept by the Franciscans of La Rochelle aroused 'certain dissentions' in the diocese, which were referred in 1448 to the arbitration of the university of Paris. The faculty of theology declared that the veneration of the blood was in no way repugnant to the faith, and their opinion was confirmed by pope Nicholas V.

More controversial was the blood which was alleged to come from the very wounds of Christ. This Thomas Aquinas declared to be impossible. But several churches, notably the Norman abbey of the Trinity at Fécamp, claimed to possess it, and when a vase of blood was presented to Henry III of England by the military orders in 1247, Robert Grosseteste applied his considerable scholarship to its defence. Nothing was more probable, he argued than that when Christ was taken down from the cross, His blood had splashed over Nicodemus and Joseph of Arimathea. Grosseteste listed five occasions when His blood had been shed and suggested that the disciples would naturally have gathered it up and preserved it.

In the fourteenth and fifteenth centuries churches which displayed the divine blood found powerful defenders in the Franciscan order, which had espoused the cult of the Passion of Our Lord since its inception. In 1351 the Franciscan prior of Barcelona stated in a public sermon that the blood shed at the crucifixion thereupon lost its divinity and so remained on earth after the resurrection. He was immediately prosecuted by the Inquisitor of Aragon and obliged to make a humiliating retraction. But more than a century later another Franciscan, Giacomo della Marca, revived the forbidden doctrine in a sermon at Brescia and was accused by the Dominicans of heresy. In December 1463 a formal debate between representatives of the two orders was held in the presence of Pius V, at which the matter was argued with such vehemence that although it was December the protagonists were shortly bathed in sweat. As the Franciscans pointed out, the relics venerated at Rome, Mantua, Bruges, and countless lesser shrines depended on the outcome. Perhaps it was for this reason that the jury of cardinals adjourned the debate, and no decision was ever made public.

This softening of the official attitude was the result of continuous popular pressure. The great processions in honour of the Holy Blood at Bruges were spectacular displays of popular devotion, and the plebeian nature of such cults was increasingly recognized by the growing band of critics. John Hus observed that there were now 'innumerable places where the Devil has moved the people through the wickedness of greedy priests to worship the body and blood of the Lord as a relic'. It was in the fourteenth century that the practice began of displaying the host from the altar in a monstrance. Tabernacles made their appearance at the same time, where the Eucharist would be placed for the adoration of the faithful instead of being left in the sacristy between services.

The extensive devotional literature surrounding the pilgrimage to the Holy Blood at Fécamp demonstrates beyond doubt that belief in the bodily relics of Christ was a form of eucharistic piety. The blood of Fécamp was already venerated in 1120 when Baudri of Deuil visited the abbey of the Trinity and remarked on 'the blood of Christ, buried by Nicodemus, . . . and now solemnly revered by large crowds of pilgrims'. In a twelfth-century poem composed for the abbey, pilgrims are urged to come to win their redemption at Fécamp by beholding the precious blood of Christ 'not as you do in the sacrament but just as it flowed from the Saviour's side when he died for us':

> *Non pas comment u sacrement*
> *Mes en sa fourme proprement*
> *Vermel comment il le sengna*
> *Quant pour nous mort soufrir degna.*

The same passionate desire to translate the mysteries of the faith into realities is reflected in every aspect of the cult of relics. Ordinary men looked on the saints as individuals no less immediate, no less visible and tangible in death than they had been in life. It was essential to this view of things that a saint should be considered to inhabit the place where his relics were preserved, and in that place he should above all be venerated. Hence the fact, observed in the fifteenth century by Reynold Pecock, that many of those who went on pilgrimages to Mont-St.-Michel expected to find there the bones of the archangel. From this Pecock drew the perceptive conclusion that 'without rememorative signs of a thing, . . . the rememoration or remembrance of that thing . . . must needs be feebler, as experience sufficiently witnesseth. And therefore, since the body, or the bones, or other relics of any person is a full rememorative sign of the same person, it is full reasonable and full worthy that where the body or bones or any relic of a saint may be had, it be set up in a common place to which people may have their devout . . . access.'

The process by which the veneration of the saints became associated with particular places is especially striking in the case of the Virgin Mary. The earliest collections of miracles of the Virgin, which date from the early twelfth century, were not associated with any particular sanctuary. The stories are set as far apart as Germany and Spain, Pisa and Mont-St.-Michel, and in none of them is there any question of relics. Pilgrimages to shrines of the Virgin were common in the east, but there is no mention of them in the west until the tenth century, when a monk of Bobbio observed that the Blessed Virgin frequently worked miracles for the benefit of those who came to the abbey of St. Columban with their troubles. Bodily relics of the Virgin were almost unknown, and thus when Geoffrey de Montbray, bishop of Coutances (d. 1110), discovered some of her hair in his cathedral, accompanied by imposing certificates of authenticity, some of the canons objected on the ground that 'hitherto no relic of the Virgin was known to exist on earth.' The popularity of the cult of the Virgin spread rapidly in the twelfth century, and as it did so countless relics came into existence. Laon cathedral had a 'splendid little reliquary' containing some hair of the Virgin at the beginning of the twelfth century, when it was carried about England and northern France to raise money for the rebuilding of the cathedral. More hair existed at Astorga in northern Spain; this caused some astonishment to Ida, countess of Boulogne, who arranged for eleven of the hairs to be sent to Boulogne and subjected them to the ordeal of fire. Most early relics of the Virgin consisted of parts of her clothing. The most celebrated of these was undoubtedly the tunic preserved in Chartres cathedral, which had a mass following in northern France, and was believed to ease the pains of pregnancy. But others, sometimes older than that of Chartres, were claimed by churches in Germany and eastern France. The bishops of Verdun possessed a tunic, 'somewhat battered and torn', in the tenth century, while another is found at Munchsmunster in a list of relics

compiled in 1092. Other tunics were venerated at Regensberg and
Trier at the same time. The church of S. Maria Maggiore in Rome
was alleged to have a large number of relics of the Nativity, including the original crib, together with parts of the Virgin's hair,
milk, and clothing. Milk of the Virgin made its appearance in the
same period, though the days of its greatest popularity were yet to
come. The famous *arca santa* of Oviedo Cathedral was believed to
contain a phial of milk of the Virgin; it is one of the items listed on
the inscription which Alfonso VI caused to be engraved on the outside in 1075. The relic list of Munchsmunster includes 'milk of the
Virgin which flowed from her breast', presumably labelled thus in
order to distinguish it from 'miraculous' milk which was already
appearing at Chartres and elsewhere.

Thus the first result of the popularization of the cult of the Virgin
during the eleventh and twelfth centuries was that the cult became
'localized' in a number of relatively new shrines. Pilgrimages did
not, of course, supersede other forms of devotion to the Virgin, but
they were the principal means by which that devotion was expressed
by uneducated people. These people did not see the Virgin as the
ubiquitous power, uncramped by time or place, who was venerated
by St. Anselm or St. Bernard. To them she was Our Lady of Chartres or Our Lady of Soissons, and the distinction between them
loomed large in the eyes of contemporaries. The author of the
Miracles of Our Lady of Chartres tells of a lady of Audignecourt who
was cured of a skin disease by praying to the Virgin. As she was
about to set out for Notre-Dame de Soissons to give thanks, the
Virgin appeared to inform her that it was by Notre-Dame de
Chartres that she had been healed. The purpose of the miracle collection of Rocamadour was declared to be to demonstrate that 'the
Blessed Virgin Mary has chosen Rocamadour in Quercy above all
other churches'. The enemies of Coutances cathedral attempted to
dissuade a pilgrim from going there by asking her, 'why go to a
strange church to seek the help of the Blessed Virgin whose power
is universal and could just as easily cure you in your own home?'
But they were confounded when the woman returned, fully cured,
from Coutances. Indeed, the author of the Coutances miracle
collection devoted much of his work to refuting opinions of this
sort. He pointed, for example, to the fate of Vitalis, a Norman who
came to the 'insipid conclusion' that 'the Blessed Mary of Bayeux
and the Blessed Mary of Coutances were one and the same person,
that is, the mother of God; and that consequently the Virgin of
Coutances could not possibly be more merciful or more powerful
than the Virgin of Bayeux.' Vitalis accordingly refused to accompany his fellow villagers on a mass pilgrimage to Coutances, for

which the Virgin severely chastised him. Already pilgrims had accepted a plurality of Virgins inhabiting defined places, the view caricatured in the pleasant conversation once overheard by Sir Thomas More: ' " of all Our Ladies, I love best Our Lady of Walsingham"; "and I", saith the other, "Our Lady of Ipswich." '

The Image of the Saint

The saint was physically present in the altar of his church. When his relics moved, he moved with them. He was the protector of the sanctuary, and offerings were made to him personally. The saint was quite capable of defending his property from his shrine. Thus, when, shortly after 946, the monks of Fleury quarrelled with the bishop of Orléans over the possession of a vineyard, they came to harvest the grapes bringing with them the remains of St. Benedict, whereupon the soldiers posted there by the bishop made way and departed. The monks of Bobbio brought the body of St. Columban to the royal court of Pavia in order to complain about the invasion of their lands by powerful noblemen. The notion of the saint re-siding in his reliquary is literally portrayed in the stained glass of Canterbury cathedral, where St. Thomas is seen climbing out of his shrine in order to appear to a sleeping monk (see plate II a).

The very atmosphere of a pilgrimage church encouraged the im-pression of the saint's physical presence. From the eighth century onwards relics were placed on the altar in the east end of the church, or else in a crypt designed for that purpose. At Santiago, Conques, St. Sernin of Toulouse, and St. Martin of Tours there were vast double aisles through which, on feast days, superb processions made their way towards the gilded shrine. The sense of the saint's latent power was often fostered by the fact that his relics were contained in a statue. These statue-reliquaries originated in southern France in the tenth century. Stephen, bishop of Clermont ordered a statue of the Blessed Virgin in 946 to house some of her relics. Stephen was also the abbot of Conques in the Rouergue, whose monks had recently stolen the relics of St. Foy from Agen, and it seems likely that he commissioned the celebrated statue-reliquary which is still preserved there (see plate I). The Conques statue, which is of gold encrusted with precious stones, shows St. Foy seated on a throne stretching out hands which once held a model of the grid on which she had supposedly been martyred. It survives as a solitary reminder of the enormous number of such statues which were once venerated in southern France. At the synod of Rodez in 1013, Bernard of Angers, a stranger to the south, described how each church was represented by its clergy carrying the statue-reliquary of its patron saint beneath a splendid canopy: St. Armand of Rodez, St. Marius of Vabres, St. Sernin of Toulouse, a golden statue of the Virgin, and St. Foy herself were all carried processionally round the walls of the city before the opening of the council. 'Hitherto', Bernard wrote, 'I have always believed that the veneration of images and paintings of the saints was improper, and to raise statues to them would have struck me as absurd. But this is not the belief of the inhabitants of these parts, where every church contains a statue of its patron made of gold, silver, or base metal, depending on the wealth of the church. And inside it they place the head or some other important relic of the saint . . . Jupiter or Mars might well have been venerated like this.' The statue of St. Foy was a potent means of impressing the saint's presence not only on pilgrims but on the population of the remotest valleys of the Auvergne. Whenever the possessions of the abbey were threatened or an epidemic ravaged the area, the statue was drawn through the valleys mounted on a horse and surrounded by young monks clashing cymbals and blowing ivory horns. The inhabitants of the villages would gather at the side of the road on these occasions, and in an atmosphere of extreme religious excitement repeated cries would signal the occurrence of new miraculous cures.

These reliquaries, which so faithfully reflected the popular piety of the tenth and eleventh centuries, passed out of fashion in the twelfth. Few of them have survived. But at one time they were venerated not only in the Midi but throughout northern France and even in England. A gold statue-reliquary with one hand outstretched in blessing was made for the abbey of St. Martial of Limoges in 952. The famous black wooden statue of the Virgin at Chartres (the existing one is a copy of it) may have been modelled on that of Conques. A statue-reliquary was venerated at St. Bertin in the late eleventh century, and in England bishop Brithnod of Ely had four of them made for his cathedral out of gilded wood. Even after the pilgrimage churches had ceased to commission new statue-reliquaries, artistic representations of the saints continued to exercise a potent influence on the popular imagination. When Guibert of Nogent's mother dreamed of the Blessed Virgin she dreamed of the Virgin of Chartres cathedral. Witbert, the blind peasant whose sight was restored by St. Foy, had a vision of her corresponding exactly to the statue-reliquary which can be seen today at Conques. Similarly when a young monk of Monte Cassino saw St. Michael taking away the soul of a dead brother, he saw him 'exactly as he is usually depicted by painters'. Indeed, it seems possible that the special reputation which St. Foy acquired for healing the blind was due in part to the staring jewelled eyes of her statue at Conques.

*

The cult of relics brings into sharp relief the classic problem of the mediaeval Church. It has often been accused by enlightened historians of fostering popular superstition and resisting the intellectual development of the laity. Usually this has been attributed to the avarice of the clergy and indeed there are many mediaeval writers who could be found to support such a view. Nevertheless it overlooks the fact that the mediaeval Church not only did not but could not control and direct popular religion. In the broadest sense of the word, it did not have the educational resources to convey anything but the most elementary formulae to the people *en masse*. For the most part the parish clergy must be regarded as splinters from the same wood as their parishioners, sharing their misconceptions and their simplified view of life. In fact, in so far as one can trace the movement of ideas in the history of mediaeval piety it is often in the reverse direction. Popular religious practices continually influence the behaviour of the establishment. With a few eminent exceptions such as Guibert of Nogent, few churchmen were found who appreciated this fact, still less made a conscious effort to resist it. The following chapter will show how popular influences of the same sort determined the attitude of the Church to miracles.

CHAPTER IV

THE PURSUIT OF THE MIRACULOUS

Until relatively recent times the overwhelming majority of men have believed in modern miracles. Mediaeval men in particular had no doubt that miraculous events occurred not occasionally but with such continuous regularity as to be almost part of the natural operation of the universe. Some of them indeed, intelligent and experienced men, not only described miracles of which they had heard but claimed to have witnessed them with their own eyes. Moreover the belief in the miraculous, although predominantly a characteristic of the mediaeval Church, is found in the ancient world as it is in the modern. Few mediaeval saints had as many miracles attributed to them as the Quaker leader George Fox who died at the end of the seventeenth century, leaving behind him a *Book of Miracles* recounting more than a hundred and fifty marvellous feats for the edification of his followers.

The phenomenon poses serious evidential problems which have, on the whole, exercised the minds of philosophers more than historians. More than two centuries ago David Hume disturbed the fat slumbers of the eighteenth-century Church by declaring in his *Essay on Miracles*

> 'A miracle is a violation of the laws of nature; and as a firm and unalterable experience has established these laws, the proof against a miracle, from the very nature of the fact, is as entire as any argument from experience can possibly be imagined. . . . The plain consequence is . . . that no testimony is sufficient to establish a miracle unless the testimony be of such a kind that its falsehood would be more miraculous than the fact which it endeavours to establish.'

Hume's argument turned on his definition of a miracle as a 'violation of the law of nature', a question-begging phrase which is open to legitimate theological objections. But the historian, limited by the evidence at his disposal, can only work on the basis that miracles have never happened, though the descriptions of them which contemporaries have left may provide valuable evidence of the attitudes of those who wrote them.

Hume was inclined to believe that the evidence for miracles was fabricated, either for missionary purposes or else for reasons of self-interest and greed. Self-interest and greed were, indeed, the principal explanations offered by the Protestant tradition for the phenomenon of mediaeval miracles. The view propagated by the Reformers was that miracles were concocted by a conspiracy of clergymen in order to induce simple men, who knew no better, to part with their money. This was the opinion of Thomas Cromwell, whose injunctions to the English clergy in 1536 require them to desist from such activities in future.

On the eve of the Reformation there was considerable evidence to support such a view, and the Church's critics made full use of it. In his diatribe against the pilgrimage to Wilsnack, John Hus alleged that the clergy paid handsome sums to beggars to wander from town to town announcing that they had been cured or exorcized at Wilsnack. Hus had himself sat on a tribunal convened by the archbishop of Prague to examine those citizens of Prague who asserted that they had been cured there. These included a boy whose deformed foot was found to be worse than ever, and two women who were said to have recovered their sight 'but who, on clear investigation, were found never to have been blind.' One witness testified that after three days and nights of fruitless vigils at Wilsnack he was suddenly seized by a priest who cried out 'A miracle! A miracle! Come and see this citizen of Prague whose withered hand has been healed.' 'O priest, why do you lie thus', the man exclaimed with unusual presence of mind, 'see my hand is as withered as ever.' On the eve of the Reformation many orthodox Catholics were found who made similar allegations. Thomas More's imaginary heretic gave it as his opinion that all miracles were based on fraud, and More himself was constrained to admit that this was sometimes true:

'Some priest, to bring up a pilgrimage in his parish, may devise some false fellow feigning himself to come and seek a saint in his church and there suddenly say that he hath gotten his sight. Then ye shall have bells rung for a miracle, and the fond folk of the country soon made fools. Then women coming thither with their candles. And the parson buying of some lame beggars three or four pair of their old crutches, with twelve pence spent in men and women of wax thrust through divers places some with arrows and some with rusty knives, will make his offerings for one seven year worth twice his tithes.'

The commissioners for the dissolution of the English monasteries found some evidence that miracles were simulated by various histrionic contraptions. Such was the notorious rood of grace at Boxley, a life-size figure of Christ which rolled its eyes, shed tears, and foamed at the mouth and which was found to have 'certain engines and old wires with old rotten sticks in the back of the same'. John Hoker wrote to the Swiss reformer Bullinger exulting over the public destruction of a similar device from Kent which nodded its head, winked its eyes, and bowed at the waist to receive the prayers of pilgrims.

The rapid expansion of popular pilgrimages in the fifteenth century undoubtedly encouraged frauds, particularly in the smaller and less well-established shrines. The disappearance of all restraints on popular religious enthusiasm in the later middle ages deserves a chapter of its own. But to make an assessment of mediaeval religion solely on the basis of the last hundred and fifty years of its history is a seriously misleading procedure which, moreover, avoids the principal historical problem. For most of the period under consideration miracles were proclaimed without the assistance of elaborate mechanical devices and without obvious fraud. Moreover, the evidence for them was accepted by intelligent men who made some attempt to ascertain the truth. Evidently they were deluded, but the basis of their delusion is worth examining.

The Missionary Church

The missionaries who converted northern Europe were dealing with people whose religion was fundamentally pantheistic. To them it seemed that the entire natural world was inhabited and controlled by unseen powers; every tree had its own spirit, every pool its devil, every mountain its god. This being so, there was no distinction drawn between the laws of nature and those of God, and the suspension of the one by the other did not arise. In so far as pagans embraced Christianity they did so because they believed Christ to be a more powerful God than their own, and missionaries would endeavour to prove this, for example by felling the holy oak of Thor at Geismar and remaining unscathed. The converts expected the new God to intervene as often and as powerfully in nature as the old, and if He failed to do so they would frequently revert to their old beliefs. Thus, when plague attacked the region of Melrose in the time of St. Cuthbert the people 'forgot the sacrament of the Gospel which they had received and returned to the delusive cures of idolatry'. It was quite common for new converts to Christianity to continue to worship pagan gods, like Redwald king of the East

Saxons, who used the same temple to worship Christ and offer sacrifices to devils. Such people insisted on miracles, and the Church was not willing to endanger the success of the missions by denying them. Gregory the Great recommended to Augustine that the cult of the saints and martyrs be presented to the English as the equivalent of pagan pantheism, 'for one cannot efface everything at once from their obstinate hearts. He who would climb the highest peaks must ascend by steps and not by leaps.'

Thus the first thing that was required of missionaries was the performance of miracles, and we are told that Augustine proved the truth of Christianity to king Ethelbert of Kent by working miracles daily, on which pope Gregory congratulated him: 'Rejoice that the souls of the English are drawn by outward miracles to inward grace.' No less decisive was the role of miracles in the conversion of Gaul. The only resurrection from the dead performed by St. Martin in his lifetime had the effect of converting a large body of pagans, and even the posthumous miracles of St. Martin were believed to have convinced heretics as well as pagans of the truth of the Catholic religion. According to St. Nizier, Clovis was brought nearer to the faith by an early visit to St. Martin's basilica at Tours, and it was after seeing evidence of the miracles performed there that he promised to be baptized. In a letter of about 565, addressed to Clovis' granddaughter, St. Nizier observed that 'such miracles never occur in Asian churches thus proving that God and his saints do not reside in them.' In this context the numerous exorcizings of demons were particularly important for 'no demon can survive in the habitation of the saints whence it follows that God resides in places where demons are exorcized.'

It was broadly recognized that miracles were necessary to assist the propagation of the faith, and that when the faith was established they would cease. Consequently each new missionary enterprise, every threat to the orthodox faith, convinced the Church that the age of miracles was not yet past, a process which can be clearly seen, for example, in the mind of Augustine of Hippo. In his treatise *On the true faith* written in 390, Augustine asserted that the apostles had enjoyed power to work miracles in order to assist the foundation and expansion of the Church in the most vulnerable period of its history. 'But now that the Church is established across the whole world, miracles no longer occur.' However, in the face of powerful assaults on the orthodox creed by the Donatists and Pelagians, Augustine changed his mind, and in the last two decades of his life he made good use of the miracles of St. Stephen at Uzalis and Hippo, in support of Catholicism. Moreover, in describing these miracles Augustine was avowedly bidding for the support of precisely those popular elements in the Church which he had once despised. The problem of the cessation of miracles continued to perplex later generations. Gregory the Great compared miracles to the watering of plants. We water plants when we plant them but as soon as they have taken root we stop watering them. Similarly, now that Christianity has taken root in men's minds, we no longer have need of miracles. Yet Gregory's *Dialogues* are largely devoted to miracle stories, often of the most improbable kind. It is clear that in Gregory's mind there were two divergent tendencies, the theological (that there are no modern miracles) and the hagiographical (that for didactic purposes miracles continue). This dichotomy was very common amongst Gregory's contemporaries and while it survived no actual theory of miracles was possible.

In later generations the received view was that miracles would continue for as long as there were holy men alive. The age of miracles, thought Bede, had ended, but some men, by their extraordinary holiness had recovered the power of working miracles which others had lost. In an unspeakably wicked age miracles would cease altogether. Orderic Vitalis, writing in the twelfth century, took this proposition for granted. In his view his own age was one of unparalleled wickedness, and he asserted that miracles had indeed ceased.

The true explanation of the continuance of miracles is that the plant of Christianity never took root as firmly as Gregory had hoped. At a popular level pantheistic notions survived throughout the mediaeval period, and constant efforts utterly failed to eradicate them. It is perhaps true, in the broadest possible sense, to speak of the middle ages as an 'age of faith', but it was an age of extremely varied and heterodox faith, in which the missionary aspect of the Church's work was kept alive by ignorance and heresy. With it survived those missionary attitudes which are so characteristic of the Church's teaching on miracles. Gregory of Tours once described a dispute on some doctrinal issue between an Arian preacher and a Catholic priest. When all argument had failed the priest ordered a cauldron of boiling water to be brought forward and said: 'enough of these futile arguments. Let works speak louder than words. Let us heat up a cauldron of boiling water and throw this ring into it. Whoever first takes the ring out with his bare hands will be proved right.' A theological argument in these circumstances took on the character of a trial by ordeal, and orthodoxy is said to have triumphed in such ordeals not only against Arians but later against Albigensians, Hussites, Protestants and even Moslems. Conflicts between rival magicians are frequently recorded in connection with the Albigensian heresy at the end of the twelfth cen-

tury. Two heretics at Besançon, for example, attempted to impress
their doctrines on the inhabitants by walking on flour without
leaving footprints, jumping on burning coals, and standing on the
surface of water all of which, we are told, they achieved by means
of elaborate stunts. The officials of the bishop of Besançon were
obliged to work their own miracles in order to expose these frauds.
St. Dominic, in very similar circumstances, claimed to have demonstrated the truth of the orthodox doctrine by a process akin to the
testing of relics by fire. At a formal disputation, so he told the
historian Pierre des Vaux-de-Cernay, he had cast a written statement of his beliefs into the fire and watched it jump out uncon-
sumed. A hundred and fifty Albigensians are said to have been
converted on this occasion, and the memory of the miracle was
potent enough, two centuries later, to inspire a painting by Fra
Angelico.

The serious threat posed to the Church in the twelfth century
by heresy and by Islam undoubtedly contributed to striking expansion of the cult of the miraculous. The miracles of St. Thomas
Becket, for example, by frequently transmuting water into milk are
alleged to have confirmed in the minds of the onlookers the doctrine of the real presence. Frequent revivals of the dead provided
graphic confirmation of the doctrine of the resurrection amongst
the ignorant and faithless. The bishop of Evreux knew of a rich
Moslem merchant of Palermo who was converted to Christianity by
the stories of St. Thomas's miracles.

It was axiomatic that no heretic or unbeliever could perform a
miracle, and reports that any such had done so invariably provoked
the authorities to displays of indignation and alarm. In the case of
the Albigensians of Besançon the bishop had retorted that it was
'impossible that God should work miracles through men of impure
doctrine'. Nevertheless a community of heretics at Moncoul in
southern France claimed to have a miraculous statue of the Virgin,
and orthodox writers such as Lucas of Tuy were most anxious to
discredit it. In 1440, miracles were alleged to have occurred at the
grave of Richard Wyche, a Lollard executed in London some weeks
earlier; a royal writ complained that certain of the King's subjects
openly averred that Wyche had been a holy man and that miracles
had been performed by him which they had not. Such claims,
irritating enough when made by heretics, posed a serious intellectual
problem when uttered by Moslems. In the late middle ages scholars
became aware of the fact that the Koran attributes many miracles
to Mohammed, and that in parts of the Islamic world holy men still
claimed to have performed them. Ricoldo of Monte Croce, a
thirteenth-century Italian Dominican who lived for many years in

Baghdad studying Islamic religion, indignantly denied the Arab assertion that God worked miracles amongst them just as he did amongst Christians. Miracle-workers in Baghdad, 'sons of perdition every one of them', were constantly deceiving large audiences in this way. The occurrence of miracles in the Latin west remained, to Christian minds, a conclusive argument against Islamic theology. Thus in the fifteenth century Denis the Carthusian not only denied that Mohammed or his latter-day followers had worked miracles, but cited the miracles of Christian saints as proof of the Christian faith. In his imaginary dialogue with a Moslem he argued that 'no one who denies the divinity of Christ can work miracles.' Christians on the other hand have always worked miracles. The dead have been raised, the deaf, the dumb, the blind and the lame have been healed. No one who has read the miracles of St. Martin, St. Nicholas, St. Servatius, St. Germanus, St. Bernard, or St. Francis can possibly doubt the reality of the God they worshipped.

That the need for miracles was as strong on the eve of the Reformation as it had ever been, is clear from the career of John of Capistrano, vicar-general of the Observant Franciscans and a preacher of remarkable powers. During his mission to the Hussites (1452–6) he drew audiences which contemporaries reckoned at 120,000 and which, even allowing for exaggeration, must have been unusually large. In his sermons he would condemn heresy with fierce fanaticism and would perform astonishing miracles, all of which were immediately recorded at his direction, together with the names and depositions of witnesses. One of these stories is typical enough. At Breslau some Hussites advanced through a crowd during a sermon, bearing a coffin in which there was a Hussite feigning death. They demanded that John resuscitate him and he refused. Thereupon one of the heretics announced that he would bring him back to life, but there was no response, for the unfortunate youth was found to be really dead. A contemporary who followed John of Capistrano through central Europe recalled that he sometimes performed thirty miracles or more in the course of a sermon, most of them miraculous cures, and that these exhibitions were usually followed by large-scale conversions from among the audience.

The mediaeval Church never formally abandoned the notion that miracles were the milk-teeth of the Church, superfluous after the earliest years of its life. But during the bitter schisms of the fourth and fifth centuries miracles became bound up with the moral teaching of the Church, and thus the ambivalent attitudes of Augustine of Hippo and Gregory the Great survived as long as the belief in the supernatural itself. Not only were miracles presented to the faithful as evidence of the truth of the Church's teaching at times when that teaching was questioned, but they were constantly used as *exempla* or illustrations of the spiritual life. This is plainly true of preachers like Jacques de Vitry or teachers like Caesarius of Heisterbach, whose collections were avowedly made for this purpose. But it is no less true of historians such as Bede or Gregory of Tours, addressing a limited audience and not professing to preach a sermon. For they, like all mediaeval historians, wrote in accordance with the prevailing belief that history should be written for the edification of its readers by showing them the perpetual action of God in the physical world. Their purpose was not to inform posterity but to teach their contemporaries. It was essentially didactic, though that is not to say that they did not believe everything that they wrote to the letter. 'For all chroniclers', as a twelfth-century author thought, 'have a single purpose: to relate noteworthy matters so that the invisible power of God may clearly be seen in the march of events, and men may, by stories of reward and punishment, be made more zealous in the fear of God and the pursuit of justice.'

Miraculous Tales and their Audience

The authors of mediaeval miracle stories were not completely unconcerned with truth, nor were their readers invariably simpletons who believed all that they were told. It is clear from the terms in which some of the miracles were couched that there was a considerable body of opinion which looked on miracles with a jaundiced eye and which may even have rejected the possibility of modern miracles altogether. Gregory of Tours found it 'impossible to pass over in silence the tale of what happens to those heretics and unbelievers who doubt the miracles which God has wrought on earth to reinforce the faith of his people.' The author of *The Miracles of St. John of Beverley* knew that some men regarded his work as the delusion of a simple mind and so many old wives' tales, but he confidently anticipated that they would suffer the fate of all blasphemers. Nicholas of Clun laughed aloud when it was suggested that he should go and witness the miracles of St. Wulfstan at Worcester. At least one parish priest of Worcestershire did not believe in St. Wulfstan's miracles, and used to recommend herbs and blood-lettings when his parishioners were sick. The chronicler who described this aberration remarked that the man was 'of a frivolous turn of mind . . . and quite unlike other men', but in fact we have no evidence on which to decide what proportion of mediaeval men did not believe in modern miracles. Those who appear in the sources are almost invariably those who repented or suffered punishment for their scepticism, but there must have been many who did neither.

Exalted and educated persóns were probably more inclined to doubt marvellous stories than their inferiors. Robert II, count of Namur (d. 1031), protested against the miracles of St. Gengulph of Florennes on the grounds that that saint had been a pagan. The courtiers of William Rufus declined to believe that the body of St. Edmund had been found incorrupt by the monks of Bury in 1094. The revelation that St. Cuthbert had been found incorrupt at Durham at the beginning of the twelfth century provoked similar suspicions and amongst those who demanded to see the body were Ranulf Flambard, bishop of Durham, Ralph, abbot of Seez, and Alexander, brother of the king of Scotland. Two bishops (they are not named) refused to believe the miracles attributed to Ailred of Rievaulx in Walter Daniel's *Life*. Wise men would not believe in miracles until they had seen the evidence. When king William of Scotland heard that a knight had been miraculously saved from drowning in the Tweed, he sent the bishop and archdeacon of Glasgow to question the man. A ducal official in Périgord in the time of Henry II would never believe tales of miraculous cures until he had seen the sufferer with his own eyes.

At the opposite extreme a surfeit of miracles might be accepted at the expense of its significance. So many miracles were performed by St. Swithin of Winchester on the occasion of his translation at the end of the tenth century, that the monks began to find them wearisome. William of Canterbury complained that so many exaggerated stories were told in the twelfth century that interest in them was waning at the very time that he was composing his massive collection of the miracles of St. Thomas. 'It is well-known', Thomas of Monmouth declared, 'that the occasional reading of miracle stories is a valuable stimulus to devotion. But as each miracle follows the last and the astonishing is succeeded by the spectacular, I must take care to restrain my enthusiasm, or else the piety of my readers will be dampened by the tedium of reading so many marvels.'

The churches which suffered most from public scepticism were those which used their relics for the purposes of self-aggrandisement. Churches with the patronage of a great saint were always enriched by offerings, many of which consisted of land, and vigorous efforts were made by the monks to acquire intervening holdings which would consolidate their estates. The miracles of the saint and the acquisitions of his monastery were intimately connected. A lady of Brabant, for example, presented the title deeds of her estates at the altar of the abbey of Lierre near Malines, in gratitude for a miraculous cure. But the document adhered to her fingers for it was improperly made out; she had kept some of her possessions to herself. 'And St. Gummarus delivered her from her physical bonds once he had acquired full legal rights over her. As for her, she was reinforced in faith and her worldly goods multiplied exceedingly.' Many miracle collections, notably the *Miracles of St. Benedict*, are largely concerned with showing how the saint had miraculously intervened to defend the estates of his abbey. The acquisitiveness of houses such as St.-Denis or Fleury made them many local enemies, who regarded the miracle stories as so many fabrications designed to justify the encroachments of the abbey. Thus we learn that many ill-disposed persons doubted the miracles of St. Denis in the ninth century and the same complaint is made in the eleventh. Some of them went as far as to reject 'all such modern miracles'. The growing wealth of the abbey of Conques can be traced in the four books of the miracles of St. Foy. We have already seen how the statue-reliquary was carried through the valleys of the Auvergne when the abbey's lands were threatened. It is clear that the relics of St. Foy were the means by which the monastery acquired enormous landed wealth in the Rouergue as well as psychological control over the minds of the inhabitants. Consequently, as Bernard of Angers, the author of the miracle stories, admits, the saint had many detractors and it was a source of quiet satisfaction to the monks that many of them met untimely ends. A group of scholars from Angers once encountered a man of the Rouergue on the road to Le Puy. 'You must know that man Bernard who left Conques this year', he said; 'how many lies has he written about St. Foy this time? Does he expect me to believe all that nonsense about eyes gouged out and then restored, dead animals brought back to life, and other absurdities?' 'Truly', Bernard observes in relating these words, 'this man was a son of Satan, an enemy of truth, and a minister of Antichrist.'

When the consequences of a miracle were of more than local importance, the temptation to doubt it was correspondingly greater. The miracles of Thomas Becket, for example, were an important political phenomenon. Not only were they regarded as vindicating Becket's case against Henry II, but they were also believed to have justified the claims of Alexander III against the anti-pope. Many interested parties, including Richard de Lucy and Joscelyn, bishop of Salisbury, publicly proclaimed their disbelief, and some asserted that the monks had brought about the miracles by dabbling in the black arts with the assistance of the Devil.

Faced with an increasingly astute public, the clergy of the pilgrimage churches began to examine miracles more carefully before publicizing them. There is no doubt that the miracles reported in the eleventh and twelfth centuries are less fantastically improbable than those of earlier periods, while some writers show an interest in names, dates, places, and witnesses which is altogether absent in their predecessors. At the beginning of the eleventh century the monks of Fleury held an investigation before accepting that miracles had occurred in one of their Burgundian cells; two women who claimed to have been healed there were interrogated at length and the findings were given the greatest possible publicity. When miracles occurred at St. Frideswide's, Oxford, in the twelfth century, a formal enquiry was always held, followed by a solemn announcement of the details. Correspondents who wrote to the monks of Christ Church Canterbury, describing the more distant miracles of St. Thomas, were careful to enclose the depositions of witnesses and testimonials as to their good character. When pilgrims came to Canterbury and told of marvellous happenings in their home villages, the monks would normally write to the local bishop or civic authorities asking them to investigate it. How detailed these investigations were is not usually revealed, and no doubt some churches made more strenuous efforts than others to discover the truth. At Worcester in the thirteenth century witnesses seem to have been required before any miracle was inscribed in the record. When a boy of Droitwich was miraculously saved from drowning he was brought to Worcester by his mother, together with several local worthies who attested the absolute truth of his story. Another boy was shortly afterwards revived from the dead at Petton in Shropshire but the bishop refused to allow premature exhibitions of jubilation until the villagers had been summoned to give evidence in the cathedral and the boy's parents had solemnly sworn an affidavit on the tomb of St. Wulfstan.

In the course of time these enquiries became more thorough and a higher proportion of alleged miracles were rejected as spurious. This was chiefly due to the stricter rules imposed by Rome before permitting the canonization of a saint. After the twelfth century, miracles were usually collected with a view to canonization, and in many cases they were no longer recorded after the process of canonization had been brought to a successful conclusion. In the cases of Thomas Becket and Gilbert of Sempringham, whose miracles were recorded for some years after their canonizations, it is noticeable that those which occurred after canonization are much more fantastic than the earlier ones, and the intrusion of hearsay evidence becomes more common. The commissioners who investigated miracles during a process of canonization performed their work with rigour. The instructions issued to the commissioners in the process of Gilbert of Sempringham, who was canonized in

1202, required them to interrogate all those who claimed to have been miraculously healed. How long had they been ill? What was the nature of their illness? Had their cure been complete? Were there any trustworthy witnesses? In reputable pilgrimage churches the same questions were asked even when no process of canonization was pending. At Mont-St.-Michel, those who alleged that they had been healed by the Almighty were sometimes interrogated for three days. Humble people who indiscriminately boasted of the miracles from which they had benefited frequently found themselves facing an imposing judicial tribunal. Thus ten inquisitors with a staff of clerks and notaries were appointed to examine one Moriset de Ranton who asserted that St. Louis had healed his wounded leg.

The Evidence

If the majority of educated men of the twelfth and thirteenth centuries accepted the evidence for miracles, it was not because they were unduly credulous or irrational, still less because they cared nothing for the truth. It was rather because in assessing the evidence they applied criteria very different from those of David Hume. They may often have been misled by lying witnesses, but the fundamental cause of their error was that they considered a miracle to be a normal, though nonetheless remarkable, incident of life. It was the natural consequence of that combination of humanity and omnipotence which they ascribed to the saints. Thus they did not require the same high standard of proof as the eighteenth-century philosopher, and indeed they were inclined to attribute events to the intervention of the Almighty which could quite easily have been explained without. Men accepted the evidence for particular miracles because they passionately desired to believe in miracles in general. Their beliefs on this subject become intelligible when we consider them in relation to their other beliefs, as part of a system of thought which, although quite unlike our own, is nevertheless based on perfectly rational deductions from a number of faulty premises.

'We speak of a miracle', thought Caesarius of Heisterbach, 'whenever anything is done contrary to the normal course of nature, at which we marvel.' Few mediaeval men would have quarrelled with that definition, but their understanding of the 'normal course of nature' was limited. Their ignorance of the causes of the simplest natural processes evidently made them more inclined to proclaim a miracle. The doubts of intelligent men when considering the physical world were reflected in the sensitive mind of St. Augustine. Augustine was fascinated by the sight of the two halves of a centipede wriggling across a writing desk, and the behaviour of a magnet seemed to him to be little less than miraculous. In his attack on the 'rationalism' of Julian of Eclanum, he listed several observable natural phenomena, such as the grafting of olive branches, which appeared to have no natural explanation. Augustine was profoundly aware of the limits of human knowledge, and he argued that in the existing state of man's knowledge, rational criticism of the evidence for miracles was misguided. 'Where in all the variety of created things is there anything that is not wonderful, even if our familiarity with them has reduced our amazement. How many common things are trodden underfoot when, if we stopped to pick them up, we might be astonished. Take, for example, the seeds that grow into plants: does anyone really understand . . . the secret power which makes them evolve from such small beginnings into such great things?' Why then, he concludes, should we look for rational explanations of the resurrection or the miracles of the saints and martyrs?

Underlying Augustine's arguments was the belief in a 'higher law of nature' which was synonymous with God. 'God does nothing against nature. . . . When we say that he does so, we mean that he does something against nature as we know it. . . . But he no more acts against the highest laws of nature than he acts against himself.' Looked at in this way the 'laws of nature' became mere conventions of God. God controlled the entire natural world from moment to moment. Everything that happened was his doing, from the most sublime to the most insignificant. Although human beings might, in their ignorance, accustom themselves to the fact that God normally worked in a particular way, there was no reason why He should not behave quite differently if the circumstances of the moment seemed to call for it. Thus the true significance of a miracle was not its rarity but its usefulness as a means of discerning the will of God. 'These things are indeed marvellous', wrote abbot Samson after describing the miracles of St. Edmund, 'but only to those who consider the ordinary laws of matter instead of the nature of the Creator. For if He created the laws of matter in accordance with His whim, why should He not alter them whenever he chooses?'

This characteristically mediaeval view of causation suggests why it was that perfectly natural explanations of events were constantly discarded in favour of supernatural ones. Amongst the 'miracles' collected by Gregory of Tours are included the author's recovery from headaches, eyesores, pimples, and even indigestion; 'truly, I cannot count how often the miraculous power of God has healed my headaches, fevers, blocked ears, tiredness in the eyes and pains in my limbs', the bishop confessed. The monk of Fécamp did not hesitate to proclaim as a miracle the story of a child whose throat was blocked by a large piece of meat until he drank a glass of water in the abbey of Fécamp. William of Canterbury saw the hand of God in the tale of a knight who lost his horse while riding in the forest of Ponthieu. After invoking the aid of St. Thomas and walking through the forest for the rest of the day, he found his horse in a clearing and hurried away to announce the miracle to the local clergy. These events prompted in William some rare reflections on the problem of causation:

'Some would say that the finding of the horse was due to chance, that it had no cause at all. Others would argue that if it had a cause then that cause was directed towards some other end, and the recovery of the horse was merely an incidental consequence. There are others who would hold that it was a combination of causes. . . . But the truth is that not a leaf falls from a branch without cause, for to admit the power of chance in the physical world is to detract from the power of the Creator. The Creator has ordained the laws of matter such that nothing can happen in His creation save in accordance with His just ordinance whether good or bad. If we are to seek the cause of things, we must look for the original cause, which is not itself caused by something else. And the original cause (that is, God) is the true cause of the miracle I have just described.'

This argument is, of course, a licence to find miraculous explanations in everything that occurs, however trivial. It was readily accepted because it was more flattering for a man who had recovered his horse to believe that God had intervened on his behalf, than to admit that a chance encounter in a forest clearing had brought the beast back into his possession. Indeed a very high proportion of surviving miracle stories, especially after the eleventh century, can be explained without recourse to the supernatural. A particularly striking example is the story of the prisoner whose escape was assisted by a miracle. Such tales were legion, especially in the twelfth century, when most of the beneficiaries were crusaders in the hands of the infidel, either in Spain or in the Middle East. St. Foy seems to have been the first saint to specialize in the release of prisoners, and at the beginning of the eleventh century she was already 'famous above all others for releasing prisoners who invoke her, casting aside their chains and ordering them to hurry thankfully to Conques'. Crusaders were frequently released by St. Gilles, St. James, or St. Leonard. Similarly, during the Hundred Years War, St. Martial acquired a reputation for releasing prisoners of war on both sides. These miracles followed no discernible pattern, for although most of the captives were deserving prisoners of war, some were less deserving criminals, such as the various cattle thieves released by St. Gilles and the convicted murderer who owed his freedom to St. Mary Magdalene. In almost every case the escape was entirely due to the cleverness of the escaper or the carelessness of his jailors, but the escaper preferred to attribute it to the intervention of the Almighty. The release of Bohemond prince of Antioch from a Turkish prison in 1103 was universally attributed to St. Leonard, notwithstanding the fact that his friends had paid a ransom of 100,000 besants to the Danishmend emir. Bohemond himself certainly encouraged the legend, for he swore to make a pilgrimage to the shrine of St. Leonard and actually did so some years afterwards. There seems to have been a presumption, at any rate amongst the authors of miracle stories, that any release from captivity was miraculous. Hence the twelfth-century legend of Gregory bishop of Tarsus who, on being released from the custody of a middle eastern slave-owner, travelled to all the principal shrines of Europe in an attempt to discover which saint was responsible. Stories of this sort were still popular in the fifteenth century when John Hus acidly pointed out their illogicality:

'Peter Layman is a thief and a murderer, justly imprisoned for life. He vows to go to the Holy Blood of Wilsnack if he is freed. He breaks his chains and escapes by brute force, and everyone exclaims that the blood of Wilsnack has freed him. Henry, out of sinful pride, challenges Frederick to a duel and promises to go to Wilsnack if he wins. He slays Frederick in armed combat and then invites us to believe that this was the work of the Holy Blood of Christ.'

Yet the explanation was not, as Hus thought, the lies spread about by the clergy, but the desire of Peter Layman and Henry to be considered the beneficiaries of a miracle. As Guibert of Nogent judiciously observed, 'many miracles owe more to the vanity of men than to the power of the saints.' Those who visited distant shrines not only desired but expected that their prayers would be answered. When, for example, a Welsh girl failed to recover her sight at the shrine of St. Wulfstan, her mother went away vowing angrily that she would never pray to St. Wulfstan again, 'for such', commented the chronicler, 'is the nature of that simple-minded and bad-tempered race.' At Montserrat, the celebrated Marial shrine in Catalonia, pilgrims were exhorted 'not to lose their tempers if they failed to obtain a miraculous answer to their prayers . . . for God, from whom all benefits proceed, knows better than we do what is right and fitting for our souls.' Indeed some unsuccessful pilgrims became objects of derision at home, especially if they lived far from the shrine in places where the achievements of the saint had been exaggerated by much repeating. Two blind women returning from Canterbury were openly laughed at as they passed through the streets of Leicester. On the other hand those who returned with visible proof of a miraculous cure were treated as heroes and were flattered by the obvious implication that God had thought it worth intervening on their behalf. Pilgrims who believed that they had witnessed or experienced a miracle were usually most anxious that the fact should be recorded. The monks of Christ Church Canterbury received a constant stream of letters informing them of astonishing occurrences, not all of which were believed. When Samson of Bury was writing his book on the miracles of St. Edmund, he was visited by three Londoners who demanded to be mentioned in it on the ground that St. Edmund had once sent them a fair wind when sailing to St.-Gilles.

Evidently the wish was frequently father of the thought. The combination of a pilgrim who had convinced himself that he had experienced a miracle, and a public which was overwhelmingly anxious to believe him, was impossible for the clergy to resist, even if they wished to. Many miracles were proclaimed, without any supporting evidence, in circumstances which ruled out the possibility of a cool and judicious examination of the facts. Thus, a knight who had come to believe that St. Gilles had released him from the Moors, repaired to the saint's Provençal shrine and there 'before the altar of the saint, and in the presence of a great crowd of people, publicly recited the facts, praising God and St. Gilles.' Another knight died in battle and was raised from the dead by St. Mary Magdalene; a friend of his, who had witnessed the miracle, rushed to Vézelay where he announced it to a jubilant crowd of pilgrims. Every major shrine was perpetually besieged by a motley crowd of pilgrims, hawkers, musicians, beggars and idlers whose appetite for new wonders was insatiable. Amid the scenes of collective euphoria that followed each announcement, no churchman could publicly voice his doubts without doing serious damage to the prestige of his church. An increase in demand could, in this way, stimulate a corresponding increase in supply. A striking instance of this economic law at work occurred at Fleury in the late eleventh century. A mason working on the roof of the new basilica fell from the scaffolding and was gravely injured. The monks took him into the monastery and attended to him, praying fervently for his recovery because, they averred,

'we were afraid that if he died the whole building programme would be interrupted as a result of a sudden fall in contributions to the building fund. For the vulgar mob is very fickle and bends like a reed whatever way the wind blows it. If the mason had died they might have murmured that St. Benedict did not care about his own monastery or the troubles that befell it.'

It must be admitted that this is an unusually blatant example of the invention of miracles for self-interested purposes, but the same dilemma must have presented itself whenever the clergy at a shrine were informed of a miracle and asked to take note of it.

Their position was particularly delicate because the mediaeval notion of sanctity was inextricably linked with the performance of miracles, not only in the popular mind but also in canon law. In the bull of canonization of St. Cunegonde, Innocent III stated that 'merit without miracles and miracles without merit are both equally insufficient if a saint is to be venerated by the Church Militant.' But long before the Church had made them a prerequisite for canonization, the populace had shown that it would not venerate a saint who performed no miracles. Their attitude was grounded in the proposition that since God's will was expounded to men by means of miracles, the only certain proof that He had designated a particular saint for their veneration was the occurrence of miracles at his shrine. To deny these miracles was therefore tantamount to denying the sanctity of the person venerated. Similarly, if miracles were reliably attributed to a man after his death, then he was to be venerated, be his reputation in life never so black. Thomas Becket, for example, was a man who aroused bitter controversy both before and after his death. The parish priest of Nantes spoke for many of his contemporaries when he declared that Becket was a 'traitor against his lord the king, and the King of Kings will no more glorify him than he will that dog over there'. This situation was, however, transformed by the frequent miracles, skilfully publicized, which made the hysterical and somewhat unattractive archbishop into the 'holy blissful martyr' of later days. Joscelyn, bishop of Salisbury, Gilbert Foliot, and Richard de Lucy, all of them prominent opponents of Becket in his lifetime, all confessed themselves converted to his merits by the news of his miracles, though Richard tartly expressed his astonishment that a man who, as chancellor, had been so harsh on the Church, should become its foremost miracle-worker. Two obstinate canons of St. Frideswide's, Oxford, would not be convinced of Becket's sanctity till one of their colleagues was miraculously relieved of his constipation. 'I shall never believe that St. Thomas is a saint', declared the sacristan of St. Remy at Rheims, 'until he returns my lost service-book.' Indeed in a debate in the University of Paris the miracles were held to be conclusive evidence that his life was pleasing to God, notwithstanding all arguments to the contrary. Master Roger, we are told,

> 'swore that he had deserved to die (though not to die in such a manner), and judged the constancy of the blessed saint to be mere obstinacy. Master Peter on the other hand asserted that he was a worthy martyr of Christ, since he had died for the liberty of the Church. But the Saviour himself resolved their debate when he glorified him with many wonderful miracles.'

This definition of sanctity gave rise to the most perverse conclusions, on account of the popular tendency to proclaim miracles in unpredictable circumstances. Abbot Odo of Cluny protested against the universal prejudice of his contemporaries who, like doubting Thomas, refused to believe anything which they could not see with their own eyes. The cult of a saint ceased with his miracles. Guibert of Nogent argued that it encouraged the populace to proclaim bogus saints and firmly declared that God had been known to work miracles through evil men as well as good. Indeed Guibert had himself seen Louis VI, no saint he, touching for the king's evil. This feeling gained in force in the fourteenth and fifteenth centuries as the consequences of unrestrained popular enthusiasm manifested themselves. Wyclif's comments on miracles are substantially the same as Guibert's. Jean Gerson, chancellor of the University of Paris and an indefatigable critic of popular religion, pointed out that St. Jerome and Gregory the Great performed no miracles though no one had ventured to doubt their sanctity. But these were the parting shots of a brilliant, though ineffective, rearguard. The miracle remained the decisive test of sanctity as far as ordinary people were concerned, and no pilgrimages succeeded without them. As the Lollard William Thorpe complained, 'both men and women delight now more for to hear and know miracles than they do to know God's word.'

Every pilgrimage church faced, on a smaller scale, the same missionary problem as the Church as a whole. They could not convey their message, in this case the virtues of their patron saint, without adducing supernatural arguments. They took an indulgent view of the aberrations of the faithful, partly because they were powerless to do otherwise, and partly, no doubt, because they felt that even misdirected faith was better than no faith at all. As Chaucer's parson remarked of charm-healing, 'it may be peradventure that God suffereth it for (that) folk sholden geve the more faith and reverence to His name.'

The initiative for the proclamation of miracles almost invariably came from the laity, and those who fabricated the evidence for miracles were more often the pilgrims themselves than the clergy of the shrine. Every popular cult drew its share of charlatans. The growing reputation of St. Thomas of Canterbury attracted so many that the authors of his miracles had difficulty in distinguishing true miracles from false. Geoffrey Musard, a knight of Gloucestershire, pretended to be blind and asked for miracle-working water to be smeared over his eyelids. A woman of Lichfield asserted that her son had been crushed to death beneath a mill-stone and then revived by St. Thomas, but she was unable to find witnesses to corroborate her story. A noble lady who claimed to have been raised from the dead did indeed produce witnesses, but they were found to be 'mendacious sluts'. Many pilgrims were evasive and obstructive when questioned about the miraculous cures that they had experienced, and one of them, a pauper from Woodstock, lost her temper when Benedict refused to inscribe her name in the book of miracles. The miracles of St. Thomas were probably more closely scrutinized than any other miracles of the twelfth century. Even so the authors could do no more than eliminate the more obvious liars, while those who had convinced themselves that they were speaking the truth went undetected. At other, less scrupulous shrines, both classes were indiscriminately recorded and thus achieved a brief moment of celebrity before the crowd passed on to more recent wonders and consigned them once again to oblivion.

CHAPTER V

THE MEDICINE OF THE SICK

Mediaeval Afflictions and Their Treatment

Mediaeval men were pathetically vulnerable to the hazards which contemporary life held for their health. Their sense of impotence before the forces of nature was at no time stronger than during the great famines and epidemics of the middle ages. 'Neither by bleeding nor by clysters nor by any precautions could anyone who had once caught this plague escape it, except by death,' recorded a Parisian diarist during an epidemic in 1433. 'In Florence', Boccaccio wrote at the time of the Black Death, 'all human wisdom was unable to avert the onset of the terrible disease. The city had been cleansed and sick folk kept outside the walls. . . . But nonetheless, towards the beginning of spring, the first appalling symptoms of the plague began to appear. . . . Which plague set at naught the skill of the physicians and the virtues of their science.' The incidence of disease, unpredictable, irresistible, bred a kind of fatalism which inclined men to look to the supernatural for their only hope of relief.

Bread was the chief source of the B vitamins and almost the only source of carbohydrates. Its supply depended on an agricultural system whose productivity was low at the best of times. A yield of ten bushels an acre was considered exceptional, and in most regions a normal harvest did little more than feed the immediate locality. Grain was difficult to transport and expensive to store, with the result that a bad harvest might threaten a whole region with starvation. It was thus possible for a traveller to pass in the space of a single day from an area of plenty to one where fodder was unobtainable and men were dying of starvation at the side of the road; such was the experience of John, bishop of Norwich, when travelling through central France in 1176. After the end of the thirteenth century, certain climatic changes occurred in western Europe, and famines followed each other with increasing frequency, with the consequent weakening of men's resistance to petty illnesses and major epidemics alike.

Even in times of plenty, the diet of both rich and poor was far from healthy. A shortage of green vegetables and fresh fruit in winter was responsible for a serious deficiency of vitamin C which manifested itself in muscular pains and mild scurvy. Mediaeval men depended chiefly on milk, eggs, and fish for vitamin A. Fish was often scarce in inland areas, and in winter the low quality of the feed given to cows and hens must have caused a progressive fall in the intake of vitamin A by all classes. In the towns, where milk was almost impossible to keep, this problem presented itself throughout the year. Thus arose the most characteristic of mediaeval maladies. Stone in the bladder and urinary tract was probably due to a deficiency of vitamin A combined with a very high intake of calcium, while the same dietary deficiencies weakened resistance to infections and caused the appearance of skin lesions. The widespread complaints of sore eyes and fading sight (xeropthalmia) have the same ultimate origin.

The result was that men suffered from an interminable succession of minor afflictions as well as the occasional major one. Indeed a sense of complete physical well-being was probably extremely rare. Gregory of Tours tells us that he constantly suffered from headaches, inflammations of the ears and throat, sore eyes, and muscular pains. The letters of Peter the Venerable perpetually refer to his ill-health and physical discomfort; he was often constipated and afflicted throughout his life by what appears to have been a mild form of malaria. Digestive problems were common complaints. In 1171 Robert, count of Leicester, was reported to have suffered from chronic indigestion ever since a tour of duty in Ireland, while Geoffrey of Binbrooke, a pilgrim to Canterbury in the same year, had never recovered from the effects of eating unwashed fish. Benedict of Peterborough, who took some pride in his medical knowledge, warned against the evil effects of excessive eating and drinking, and reported that female pilgrims at St. Thomas's shrine were occasionally suffering from an incautious choice of diet during pregnancy or lactation.

It was in part because so many mediaeval ailments had dietary origins that contemporary medicine was unable to offer a cure or even a good diagnosis. It is true that special diets were prescribed for sick men. They were an essential adjunct to Hippocratic medicine. But their object was not to restore nutritional deficiencies; it was to correct supposed imbalances between the four 'humours' in the patient's body, and when this failed to cure the patient's afflictions, he tended to look elsewhere for relief. The malady often disappeared quite suddenly when the dietary deficiency had been made good, for example by a journey to another province or a change of season. In these circumstances it seemed plausible to attribute both the original affliction and its ultimate disappearance to divine intervention. The frequent outbreaks of ergotism in northern Europe afford a classic instance of this. Ergotism, which was known to contemporaries as '*Ignis Sacer*', or 'Holy Fire', was caused by eating rye infected by a specific kind of mould or fungus. Outbreaks of it commonly occurred after a wet summer. Large numbers of people were afflicted simultaneously by its alarming symptoms, severe gangrene accompanied by a sharp burning sensation in some cases, convulsions and nervous disorders in others. The most serious epidemics occurred in England and France in the first half of the twelfth century, and the result in almost every case was a mass pilgrimage to one or other of the sanctuaries of the Blessed Virgin.

'This horrible disease', wrote Hughes Farsit of the epidemic of 1128, 'spreads beneath the stretched blue skin, separating it from the bones and slowly consuming it. The pain and heat steadily increase until the victims long for death as their only hope of release. As the fever wastes the limbs, a raging fire burns the internal organs, yet it produces no heat and it never abates, however much the wretched victims pour cold liquids over themselves. . . . It was horrible to behold the sick and the recently cured, the sign of death still visible on their bodies and in their faces. Yet the mercy of God is even greater than the afflictions of men. When no human remedy could be found, . . . the sick, even as the fire ranged inside them, took refuge in the benevolence and healing power of the ever-virgin Mother of God, and she did not disappoint them in their hopes.'

Sufferers crowded into Coutances cathedral in the closing years of the eleventh century. In the autumn of 1128 they came from every part of northern France to the church of Notre-Dame at Soissons. In 1132, after another wet summer, several hundred citizens of Beauvais suffering from ergotism trekked in a body to Chartres. Notre-Dame in Paris was the object of a similar mass pilgrimage during the outbreak of 1206. In each case the disease passed away in the course of time and the Virgin acquired a growing reputation as a healer of the sick. 'She is the sovereign remedy for the sick', proclaimed the prior of Sauxillanges, 'for she can obtain from her son all that she desires. She is merciful on our sins and relieves us in all our troubles.'

There were physicians available throughout the middle ages, and in parts of Europe, such as southern France, they were organized in powerful corporations. But the medicine which they practised was of a somewhat rudimentary and unscientific nature. It was based on the distant influence of Arab science, and on the works of Hippocrates and Galen, manuscripts of which were conserved at Salerno and in many monasteries during the 'dark ages'. It consisted in examining the patient, particularly his urine, and in diagnosing an imbalance of the four humours, namely blood, phlegm, green bile and black bile. The imbalance could then be corrected by means of purges, blood-letting, special diets, and so forth. Peter the Venerable's doctor diagnosed in his patient an excess of phlegm, the qualities of which were cold and moist; he therefore prescribed myrrh which was hot and 'actively wet yet potentially dry'. Even formal medicine of this sort was usually available only to a small number of wealthy and important persons. The medical attention which these persons received was certainly no more effective than the folk medicine of the villages, and it may in some cases have been positively harmful. Peter the Venerable's health was not improved by the 'baths and stoves, fumigations and poultices, pills under the tongue, pills for catarrh, balsam potions, gargles and similar things' which were recommended to him. William, dean of Coutances, was brought to death's door by the potions which his doctor prescribed. One John Chadleton made a pilgrimage to St. Frideswide's, Oxford, in order to recover from the effects of a near-fatal blood-letting, while pilgrims at Rocamadour complained that the hot baths recommended by the celebrated physicians of Montpellier had done grave injury to their health.

Many of the pilgrims who were cured at the shrine of St. Thomas had already received the best attention that the medical profession could offer. The son of a knight of Surrey was taken to London to see the foremost consultants of the day, but they were unable to cure his liver disease. A 'copious supply' of surgeons laboured in vain to remove an arrow-head from Tancard de Carew's right eye. Robert of Bromton's physician inspected his urine with great diligence, diagnosed an imbalance of the humours, prescribed pills and potions and laxatives, and finally gave the case up as hopeless. William of Dene was close to death after unwisely entrusting his health to 'mere human physicians, with whom there is no hope of recovery'. Some doctors, indeed, are alleged to have admitted their shortcomings and advised their patients to go forthwith to Canterbury.

Consequently the practice of medicine was not held in high esteem, and writers from Sidonius Apollinaris onwards spent their harshest invectives on the ignorance and incompetence of the medical profession. One of them, a canon of St. Frideswide's, Oxford, stoutly declared that any surgeon who operated for the stone was guilty of murder. Ordinary people preferred to rely on herb doctors, charm-healers and 'wise women' of the locality. Although these were normally found in rural areas, their services were much in demand even in the towns. In Langland's day,

Londoners used to resort to witches at Southwark and Shoreditch. These unorthodox physicians probably did more for their clients than most doctors, and what we know of their methods suggests that they were sometimes soundly based on common sense and traditional herbal medicine. A twelfth-century witch at Palinges in the Loire valley used to prescribe 'herbs and potions, beet or the juice of local plants, or even the fat of various animals', a mixture which may well have been effective in restoring certain dietary deficiencies. But Raoul Tortaire, who tells us of this lady, had nothing but contempt for her remedies which, he averred, served only to raise false hopes in ignorant people.

Such sentiments were common enough among the clergy of pilgrimage churches who constantly upheld the invocation of the saints as the only sure remedy for sickness. 'Why waste your breath in calling for a mere human doctor', a Merovingian bishop asked a dying nobleman, 'when a celestial doctor is at hand, . . . the body of St. Andrew?' By the time of Gregory of Tours the denigration of 'human medicine' had become a commonplace of hagiography. 'Physicians', explained a twelfth-century churchman, 'are out to enrich themselves in any way they can; their promises are mere verbiage designed to augment your hope and their fees'; only by a pilgrimage to the shrine of St. Donatian could one be certain of good health. The *Liber Sancti Jacobi* echoes these feelings. It is better to study the divine medicine by which Christ brought salvation to men than the pseudo-medicine of Hippocrates, Dioscorides, and their ilk. Whether the medical profession resented the success of its celestial rivals is not recorded. The doctors of Montpellier apparently regarded a miraculous statue of the Virgin there with some envy. The physicians of the prior of Chaalis, according to Guillaume de St.-Pathus, were dismayed to learn that their patient had been cured by the miraculous intervention of St. Louis, 'for if this is indeed the case, we shall all be out of a job.' As for the patients, there must have been many like Raoul le Cavetier of Fourmont, who made three pilgrimages to Noyon and paid a fortune to his doctors before concluding that 'neither doctors nor pilgrimages were any use at all to his wounded leg.'

Medicine and Religion

In all the great miracle collections of the middle ages, miraculous cures account for an overwhelming majority of the stories, and it is clear that the desire to witness or experience a miracle was the principal motive for many pilgrimages. Pilgrims to St. Thomas were 'not merely attracted by the miracles but, as it were, compelled by them'.

The association of pilgrimage with the healing of the sick was so close that a youth of Warbleton is reported to have refused to go to Canterbury 'for I am neither dumb nor lame, and my health is perfectly sound.' 'I am in excellent health', protested another, 'what need have I of St. Thomas?' His father gave him a sound beating, but his was nevertheless the prevailing attitude among those unruly pilgrims who in Chaucer's day still trekked to Canterbury

> *The holy blisful martir for to seke*
> *That them hath holpen when that they were sick.*

This was not only a reflection of the inadequacy of medical science. At the root of it was a powerful conviction that physical diseases had spiritual causes. Illness was brought on by sin, from which it followed that penitence at the shrine of a saint effaced not only the sin but the illness as well. Frequently enough, the malady had been deliberately inflicted by the saint as a punishment for sacrilege or for some other offensive behaviour. In the Latin west, the healing function of the saints was originally regarded as the natural corollary of their spiritual function. As early as the sixth century, diseases are inflicted in punishment for sin, and no sooner is the sin absolved but the symptoms pass away. Thus the sixth-century biographer of St. Hilary of Poitiers informs us that a woman who worked on the Lord's Day received a withered hand which was healed at the moment of her absolution on the following Sunday. Similarly, a blind woman recovered her sight as soon as a bishop laid hands on her in blessing. King Clothaire, whose sins caused him great physical suffering, visited the tomb of St. Germain and applied the pallium of the saint to his bleeding wounds; as soon as he had confessed his sins aloud, the pain disappeared. This notion was already well-established when Gregory of Tours was writing at the end of the sixth century. In his works we discover that a man who violated the sanctuary of St. Julian's basilica at Brioude was struck blind until the moment of his confession. A woman who had baked bread on the Lord's Day went every month to beg forgiveness at the shrine of St. Martin, but her withered arm was not healed until after she had received absolution.

The basic form of these punitive miracles did not greatly change through the centuries. It did, however, become broader in scope with the growing conviction that not only 'punitive' sickness but all sickness was caused by sin. After the fall of man, it was said, original sin had given Satan power over the bodies of men as well as their souls. Baptism might afford some protection against sickness, but only by remaining in a state of grace could a man preserve his health; as soon as he sinned the Devil was able to reclaim his body.

'There is no doubt', John Chrysostom had thought, 'that sin is the first cause of bodily disease.' The author of that most popular of hagiographical collections, the *Golden Legend*, believed that illness in unbaptized infants was due to original sin, and that children generally recovered after baptism.

Gregory of Tours had spoken of illness as an '*incursio diaboli*', an invasion of the body by the Devil, and it is clear that many people entertained the most literal notions as to how this came about. Gregory himself had described how the Devil could be vomited up with one's bile. Peter the Deacon, the historian of the abbey of Monte Cassino, claimed to have seen a devil fleeing from the mouth of an epileptic recently cured by St. Benedict. When Guibert of Nogent's cousin was gravely ill, the arm of St. Arnoul was brought to his sick-bed, with results which Guibert described in the following terms:

'When the arm of the blessed martyr was laid upon him, the sickness shifted its ground and settled in another part of the body. Then the virulence was put to flight again and the holy arm pressed hard against it. The whole force of the disease ran up and down his face and limbs and finally flowed into the region of his throat and shoulders, the skin being a little raised like a mouse. Then gathering into a ball it vanished without pain.'

Similarly, infection could be explained as the physical transfer of a devil out of one body and into another.

The diabolic theory of sickness seemed particularly plausible to contemporaries in the case of mental illness. 'Possession by the Devil' was the usual synonym for any kind of delirium. The expression seemed natural to Bede, who tells us, for example, that at Bardney abbey in the late seventh century

'there came a guest who used very often to be troubled in the night without any warning by an unclean spirit. . . . When he lay down on his bed he was suddenly possessed by the Devil and began to gnash his teeth and foam at the mouth, while his limbs were twisted by convulsive writhings. . . . A great crowd tried vainly to hold the man down while the priest pronounced an exorcism and did all that he could to sooth the wretched creature. Then the abbess suddenly remembered the soil from the shrine of St. Cuthbert and ordered a servant to go and fetch the casket in which it was kept. No sooner was it brought . . . but the demoniac was suddenly silent and laid his head down as if in relaxed sleep, while his limbs became quiet and composed.'

The thirteenth-century *Miracles of St. Wulfstan* contains a remarkable account of the methods used to exorcize demons from delirious pilgrims at Worcester. From this it appears that a madwoman, dragged screaming to Worcester, was repeatedly struck blows, and a potter who suddenly lost his mind was bound to the altar and passers-by invited to scourge him with sticks. The basis of this treatment was that the patient's body became uncomfortable for the devil who was presumed to be inhabiting it. One boy who recovered his sanity at Worcester actually saw the devil departing, shaking his fist at the shrine as he did so. Other shrines are known to have been more gentle in their methods, but their attitude was broadly similar. An Italian madwoman at St.-Gilles was taken into the crypt, where passages were read from the Gospels and the names of Jesus, Mary, and St. Gilles solemnly invoked; no devil, it was alleged in defence of this procedure, could survive in the house of God or bear to hear such holy names pronounced.

The conviction that sin was the origin of sickness does much to account for the confidence with which some men relied on healing saints. It explains also the unconcealed hostility with which the Church at various times regarded the medical profession, which attempted to cure the bodily symptoms while ignoring the spiritual origins of the patient's complaint. For this reason the Lateran council of 1215 forbade physicians to visit a patient for the second time unless a priest had seen him beforehand. 'Since bodily ailments usually spring from sin', the fathers of the council added, 'we decree hereby, and strictly enjoin, that all doctors . . . shall warn their patients that they stand in need of a spiritual physician, not a physical one.' This injunction was frequently repeated by diocesan synods. Indeed, a synod meeting in Paris in 1429 went so far as to forbid physicians to give any treatment at all to patients who were in a state of mortal sin. Public preachers constantly returned to this theme. Jacques de Vitry urged his audiences that their only hope of good health was to look to the salvation of their souls, to which the instructions of doctors were positively deleterious. 'God says keep vigils; the doctors say go to sleep. God says fast; the doctors say eat. God says mortify your flesh; the doctors say be comfortable.' The fifteenth-century preacher Olivier Maillard could think of no words harsh enough to describe those physicians who would not call the priest until it was clear that the patient was dying: 'of what use is such treatment; take care in future that you recommend spiritual remedies to your patient before applying physical ones.' For the same reasons the Church made several attempts to prevent Jews from practising medicine for, the root cause of sickness being sin, the ministrations of a heathen could not possibly be effective. The council of Béziers (1246) excommunicated all Christians who allowed themselves to be treated by a Jew, and similar prohibitions were uttered wherever Jews practised medicine. In Spain, where the tradition of Jewish medicine was strong, decrees to this effect were issued at regular intervals, but equally regularly ignored.

Some afflictions were particularly liable to be regarded as divine punishments. Leprosy, for example, was often regarded as the punishment for fornication. Gonorrhoea was invariably diagnosed as 'leprosy', and the fact that it is usually acquired through sexual intercourse could only reinforce in contemporary minds the connection between sin and disease. Odo of Beaumont, whose symptoms are described in some detail in the *Miracles of St. Thomas*, had contracted gonorrhoea by frequenting brothels, as a result of which he was segregated as a leper. The same fate had befallen a debauched Norman knight whom abbot Samson once met at Bury St. Edmunds. In India, leprosy is still regarded as a divine chastisement, even though the distinction between leprosy and venereal disease is now well-known.

Female fertility was taken to be the gift of God, from which it followed that barrenness was a sign of God's displeasure. Particularly common were cases in which women who married within the prohibited degrees of affinity, or committed adultery, were unable to conceive. In 1063 we hear of a Norman couple who travelled to Rome 'on account of their sterility'. At the end of the eleventh century a landowner presented two estates to the abbey of Conques, in the hope of an heir. Thereafter, such donations became fairly common, and in some cases, the connection between sin and barrenness was heavily underlined. A Frenchman who visited Santiago in 1108 to pray for the birth of a son, 'as is customary', found his request refused on account of the gravity of his sins; not until he 'wept, cried out, and prayed with all his heart' did he have his way. No class was immune from the curse of barrenness and its occurrence, especially among princes, tended to provoke dramatic displays of penitence. When Wladislaw Hermann, king of Poland, was unable to beget an heir in 1085, he underwent a rigorous programme of fasts, vigils, and prayers, and lavishly distributed alms to the poor. Finally, on the advice of a French missionary bishop, he sent an embassy to the shrine of St. Gilles in Provence, bearing numerous gifts, including a small golden model of a baby boy. His son, the future Boleslaw III, was born shortly afterwards.

Miraculous Medicine

On the feast days of the saints the crowds of the sick and the dying filled the great basilicas. Around the shrine they lay in makeshift beds or wrapped themselves in blankets, surrounded by a host of relatives and well-wishers, the wealthier among them attended by their own physicians and servants. Many of them waited for weeks and even months as the clergy of the basilica fulfilled their daily rounds of offices and ceremonies. Some dramatically recovered and the miracle was proclaimed amid scenes of hysterical rejoicing; others died within sight of the shrine.

The rituals for the treatment of the sick differed from century to century and from church to church. Pilgrims were not normally permitted to touch the relics themselves. Public exhibitions of relics were rare and imposing ceremonies, while private views were enjoyed only by the great or the exceptionally persuasive. In 1088 a woman with withered hands asked to be allowed to touch the body of St. Gilles 'asserting that if this was done she would undoubtedly be cured, for so much had been revealed to her in a dream the night before'. Her request was granted, but in terms which show that this was an unusual favour, to be explained only by the possibility that her dream was of divine origin. Most pilgrims never saw the relics of the saint who had healed them.

Instead they applied to their bodies objects such as dust, stones, or scraps of paper which had been in contact with the saint or his shrine. Eating or drinking such substances was believed to be particularly effective, perhaps because it underlined the similarities between human and celestial medicine. In the time of Gregory of Tours sick men ate wax from the candles which burned before the shrine and some even ate the charred wicks. During an epidemic of dysentery in the Loire valley at the end of the sixth century, many of the sick drank water containing dust from the tomb of St. Martin, while others drank the water used to wash down the sarcophagus before Easter. Both methods, according to Gregory, were equally effective. Sick men drank water in which a splinter of the True Cross had been immersed or chewed the length of silk in which it had been wrapped. Gregory himself had been cured of an inflammation of the eyes by drinking wine poured into a footstep of St. Benigne preserved in the ground at Dijon.

The dipping of relics in water or wine remained the commonest method of healing practised in the pilgrimage churches of the eleventh and twelfth centuries. It was a convenient way of parcelling out the miraculous power of the relics among large numbers of people. At the end of the eleventh century a crowd estimated at several thousand gathered at Chateau-Gordon during an epidemic to receive jars of the wine that had been used to wash down the tomb of St. Benedict. 'Experience has repeatedly proved', explained

Raoul Tortaire, 'that whenever a sick person washes any part of the shrine with wine or water and then drinks it with faith, he will immediately recover.' At Norwich cathedral, pilgrims drank water mixed with scrapings of cement from the tomb of St. William. At Reading abbey the hand of St. James was dipped in water, phials of which were sent off to cure the sick in their own homes. After swallowing it, they would usually vomit violently, suffer a high fever for several hours, and then suddenly recover. Much the same effects are recorded at Canterbury, where 'water of St. Thomas' was one of the most celebrated medicines of the twelfth century. This consisted of the blood of St. Thomas, wiped up from the floor of Canterbury cathedral after his murder and diluted in a large cistern of water, thus ensuring, says Becket's biographer, both that there was plenty available and that it would not be too repulsive to drink. The water was continually diluted as demand for it rose, and one of the monks of Christ Church priory was charged with the task of preparing it and pouring it into little *ampullae* for the use of the sick. A London priest was cured by this concoction within a week of Becket's death. Not only was it drunk by the sick and smeared on the eyelids of the blind, but cases were reported in which it was used for the magical detection of thieves and even for extinguishing fires. A small *ampulla* worn around the neck became the badge of a Canterbury pilgrim. Parallels with eucharistic piety obviously suggest themselves and Benedict of Peterborough did not hesitate to draw them: 'just as St. Thomas in his lifetime sought to achieve the same perfection as the Son of Man, so, after his death, he was honoured in the same fashion, by the partaking of his blood.'

There are some indications that sensitive persons found this practice repellent. This was one reason why the blood of St. Thomas was so heavily diluted. A sick monk of Mont-St.-Michel refused a draught of the wine which had washed the skull of St. Aubert, 'preferring to die than drink wine swilled in the head of a corpse'. It may be that growing sensitivity on this point explains the fact that these macabre beverages passed out of fashion after the twelfth century.

Any genuine cures which occurred at the shrines of the saints evidently occurred in spite of such methods rather than because of them. In most cases the sick no doubt owed their recovery to the strength of their constitutions, and the symptoms disappeared in the natural way. Since they frequently remained at the shrine until they recovered or died, sometimes indeed for several months at a time, it would be surprising if there were not many 'cures' of this kind. Such factors as a change of diet or climate may well have assisted the natural recovery of these pertinacious pilgrims. Moreover, it must not be forgotten that the clergy, although relying principally on the celestial medicine of their patron saints, were not above practising terrestrial medicine as well. Many pilgrimage centres had excellent medical libraries which included parts of the Hippocratic corpus and the works of Galen. Canterbury cathedral priory had an enormous library of medical books, with which William, one of the authors of the *Miracles of St. Thomas*, seems to have been familiar. Bury St. Edmunds too had a substantial collection. Among the French abbeys where book-medicine thrived were Cluny and St. Martial of Limoges, both of them major pilgrimage churches. The practice of medicine by monks was quite common, though the Church made periodic attempts to discourage it. Thus, the celebrated Baldwin, physician to Edward the Confessor and William the Conqueror, was first a monk of St.-Denis and then abbot of Bury St. Edmunds. William of Malmesbury tells us that one of the monks of his abbey, a certain Gregory, was a very famous physician in his day, and would occasionally give consultations to pilgrims at the shrine of St. Aldhelm.

At these churches it seems likely that the cult of the saints was superimposed upon a pre-existing body of medical lore, some of which may conceivably have been sound. Some of the miraculous streams visited by the sick probably had a genuine therapeutic value. Pilgrims came from as far away as Burgundy and Aquitaine to the one which flowed past the Norman monastery of St. Evroul, thus causing great distress to local farmers whose crops were trampled down by the crowds. St. Thomas is said to have recommended a variety of homely medicines to his devotees. One woman was healed after he had instructed her in a vision to drink the juice of certain herbs in her garden and then to have a long sleep. A physician of Bergerac was told to cure his dropsy by making an incision in his stomach in accordance with contemporary surgical practice. The daughter of Ralph Raison, who for two years had suffered from boils on her feet, was recommended by a vision of St. Gilbert to go to his shrine at Sempringham and there apply a poultice to them. If the treatment was successful it was, of course, attributed to the saint on the ground that no medicine could be effective without God's merciful intervention. Baldwin of Bury himself hesitated before claiming the credit for healing a patient. When he successfully healed the bishop of Thetford's eye, the feat was acclaimed as a miracle of St. Edmund for, as the bishop's amanuensis pointed out to him, 'not even Hippocrates or Galen themselves could have cured you unless you had been found deserving of God's mercy.'

The less spectacular miracles can often be explained in psychological terms. In addition to the physical ailments suffered by pilgrims, a very high proportion of them suffered from mental illnesses signified by dumbness, delirium, epilepsy, and the like. This is particularly true of the Merovingian and Carolingian periods; approximately half the miraculous cures recorded by Gregory of Tours involved some form of insanity or mental abnormality. Moreover, contemporaries were only too ready to diagnose insanity in persons who were suffering from nothing more than temporary depression or nervous tension. The English peasantry, according to William of Canterbury, looked upon melancholy or broodiness as symptoms of insanity. Even purely physical afflictions may have been cured, at least temporarily, by psychosomatic means, for physical discomfort, even severe physical discomfort, can be induced by hypochondria, a fact which was not realized by orthodox medical practitioners until the nineteenth century. It almost certainly explains the supposedly miraculous cures achieved by some clergymen and Christian Scientists to this day.

The powerful belief that sin was the cause of sickness may itself have been responsible for a number of maladies of psychological origin. 'Punitive' miracles in particular are well attested in primitive societies today, where those who have broken a universally accepted taboo go into a state of excitement and panic which can have serious effects culminating often in paralysis, occasionally in death. The victim's expectation of death is a powerful factor in bringing on his illness. Recent research into Voodoo and battle shock has suggested that this can be explained by prolonged adrenal overexcitement and a sharp fall in blood pressure, leading to a state analogous to surgical shock. Such seems to have been the fate of Waldo, a youth of Matrignac at the close of the eleventh century, who had a spell laid on him by a witch whom he had slighted; as a result, he lost his memory and became dazed, aimless, and finally delirious. Similarly fourteen-year-old Luciana Torel of Austrey (Worcestershire) lost her speech and was partially paralysed when her father cursed her for sewing on St. Cecilia's day. The closeness of mediaeval society greatly intensified the feelings of guilt experienced by those who had flouted the more formidable moral canons. Helen of Luttershall arrived at St. Frideswide's, Oxford, in the 1180s suffering from chronic insomnia and nervous exhaustion, the result of having allowed herself to become the concubine of a priest for three months. After confessing her sin and praying at the shrine, her anguished feelings of guilt appear to have been relieved and she made a complete recovery. Such conditions as hysterical loss of appetite can almost invariably be traced to psychological causes and were consequently amenable to psychological treatment. In this category falls the case of Nicholas of Dover, who refused all food and drink for eighteen days and was saved from death only by being carried to the shrine of St. Thomas.

Sickness, even when it is not caused by stress, is easily aggravated by it. Illnesses tended to be long lasting for lack of the simplest curative measures, and in the absence of a comprehensive system of 'social security' they posed a serious threat to the economic survival of a family. They were therefore accompanied by very considerable emotional stress. William of Malmesbury gives us the case history of a woman of Malmesbury 'of moderate means' who was suddenly paralysed. For five years she was bedridden and paid out the bulk of her wealth in medical fees. Her family were gradually reduced to poverty until at length they were unable even to buy bread. The husband at this stage deserted her, leaving her dependent on charity. It is clear from the sequel that her paralysis was not permanent but had been prolonged by the distressing social consequences which it produced. The woman was ultimately cured at the shrine of St. Aldhelm in Malmesbury.

In circumstances such as these, 'miraculous' cures contained two essential ingredients which had the effect of relieving psychological stress. First came the diagnosis (i.e. sin) accompanied by the confident assurance of the possibility of a cure. Then followed the ceremonies at the shrine or the making of a vow, accomplished with formality and pomp, marking the moment of dramatic recovery. The patient, given his desire to be cured and his conviction that he would be, usually persuaded himself that he had recovered and may actually have done so. 'Hope invited her; faith instructed her,' Thomas of Monmouth percipiently remarked of a woman healed in Norwich cathedral. Persuasion was the most important element of miraculous healing in the middle ages. Modern research has suggested that persuasion, or 'faith-healing', can have marked physiological effects, which can be observed by injecting saline into a hypochondriac who believes it is morphine; the patient's symptoms are relieved by the strength of his own belief. Caesarius of Heisterbach admitted that a man might be cured by a false relic, provided that he believed that it was genuine. Benedict of Peterborough told an unusually candid story of a young man who lay on his death-bed and begged his friends to bring him some 'water of St. Thomas'.

'But unfortunately none of them had any, so one of the friends ran to a nearby fountain and filled a glass with fresh water. "Here", he said, "here is the saint's water for which you asked." The sick man believed it and drained the glass. Happily deceived, he immediately felt himself much improved; and thus, he who had lately been staring death in the face, got out of bed feeling nothing worse than a slight stiffness.'

If the sickness was a serious one, a psychosomatic cure would normally have been short-lived. But any relapse would have occurred after the pilgrim had left the shrine and returned to his former environment. The authors of the miracle stories either did not know of them, or chose to ignore them. The *Miracles of St. Thomas* are unique in that they not only describe the symptoms and case histories of each patient, but sometimes they record what became of him. From this it appears that relapses were remarkably common. A madwoman of Rouen recovered her sanity at Canterbury but lost it when she returned home. A monk of Poitiers found that his leprosy returned once he had left Canterbury. A Fleming called Gerard was only temporarily relieved of his ulcer. The authors found it hard to explain such occurrences. In one case the relapse is attributed to the patient's immediately engaging in hard agricultural labour. Very common are cases in which the patient relapsed because he omitted to express proper gratitude to the saint, or did not fulfil a vow of pilgrimage, or did fulfil it but failed to make a sufficiently generous offering. But there are others where the authors are frankly mystified and are driven to the conclusion that the patient had committed some obscure and horrible sin. Ralph of Langton was cured of leprosy in May and relapsed in December 'owing to some hidden judgement of God, . . . for the cause of this relapse only He can know.' Defective cures at one shrine were commonly recorded by the clergy of another, and from this it is plain that relapses were by no means confined to Canterbury pilgrims. Thus Ralph Attenborough, a mental defective, was cured as soon as he accepted from a priest the staff of a pilgrim of St. James; but his afflictions returned three months later, after he had come back from Santiago, and he was finally cured at Sempringham in September 1201. Hubald, archdeacon of Salisbury, was relieved of pains in his neck by touching the shrine of St. Aldhelm, but on his return home the pains began once more and continued until he made a second pilgrimage to Malmesbury.

Some of those who visited the great sanctuaries of the middle ages did undoubtedly enjoy a genuine recovery, for reasons which can quite easily be explained in the light of modern medical and anthropological knowledge. It is possible to accept most of the facts as contemporaries stated them while maintaining scepticism as to their miraculous causation. The British Medical Association has suggested six factors which account for most miraculous cures reported in modern times: 1. mistaken diagnosis; 2. mistaken prognosis; 3. apparent alleviation of symptoms; 4. periodic remission of the symptoms; 5. spontaneous cure; 6. simultaneous use of physical remedies. All these factors can be found in the exceptionally well-documented miracles of St. Thomas of Canterbury, and some of them are present in almost every miracle collection. Such considerations will not, of course, explain every miraculous cure. Many stories must be regarded as fabrications or pious legends. But it should be remembered that a very small number of genuine cures will suffice to excite general belief in a large number of fictitious ones. To cite a modern parallel, in the last century less than a hundred cures at Lourdes have been officially certified by the Roman Catholic Church as being of miraculous origin; but this tiny proportion has been enough to draw many millions to St. Bernadette's grotto in the Pyrenees. In an earlier age, ill-equipped to understand the mysteries of sickness and health, it would be surprising if men did not put their faith in unorthodox medicine and magic rituals.

CHAPTER VI

ORIGINS AND IDEALS

The Steps of the Master

It is a striking paradox that the most celebrated tomb visited by pilgrims in the middle ages was empty, the tomb, once prepared for Joseph of Arimathea, in which the dead Christ had lain for three days and then risen from the dead. The pilgrimage to Jerusalem had a longer history than any other, and it remained throughout in a class of its own. Time brought to the Holy Places most of the abuses which popular enthusiasm had already created in the west, but the Jerusalem pilgrimage was nonetheless consistently the most spiritual pilgrimage of the middle ages.

For the first three centuries after the death of Christ there was very little to see in Jerusalem. Most of the city which Christ had known was utterly destroyed by Titus in A.D. 70. Christian travellers were chiefly interested in its remarkable library which made it, by the end of the second century, a meeting place for the foremost scholars of the first age of Christian philosophy. Melito, bishop of Sardis (d. c. 190), visited Palestine in order to copy out extracts from the Old Testament. At the beginning of the third century, bishop Alexander greatly expanded the library, which was visited by Origen and Fermillian of Caesarea. It was in this library that Eusebius gathered the materials for his great *History*.

Few mediaeval pilgrims to the Holy Land were scholars, and yet they shared with these early travellers a desire to recreate in their imagination the scenes of Christ's ministry and passion. Origen declared that he had come to 'walk in the footsteps of the Master'. At the close of the fourth century Paulinus of Nola wrote:

'No other sentiment draws men to Jerusalem than the desire to see and touch the places where Christ was physically present, and to be able to say from our very own experience "we have gone into his tabernacle and adored in the very places where his feet have stood" (Ps. CXXXII. 7). . . . Theirs is a truly spiritual desire to see the places where Christ suffered, rose from the dead, and ascended into heaven. . . . The manger of His birth,

the river of His baptism, the garden of His betrayal, the palace
of His condemnation, the column of His scourging, the thorns
of His crowning, the wood of His crucifixion, the stone of His
burial: all these things recall God's former presence on earth and
demonstrate the ancient basis of our modern beliefs.'

The deeds of the Old Testament prophets and the events of Christ's
life, so remote from the minds of men, took on a thrilling immediacy
when they were recited on the very soil which they had trodden. It
was a common practice amongst the early pilgrims to read out aloud
passages from the Scriptures in the places to which they related.
'Etheria', the remarkable Spanish lady whose travels at the end of the
fourth century took her as far afield as Sinai and Edessa, had read
not only the Scriptures but the *Ecclesiastical History* of Eusebius and
the Acts of the more important Christian martyrs. Coming to the
cave of Moses in the side of Mount Sinai she and her party paused to
read out the passage of Exodus (33.22): '. . . and it shall come to
pass . . . that I will put thee in a cleft of the rock and cover thee with
my hand while I pass by.' With the Old Testament in her hand she
was able to follow, as she thought, the exact route of the Israelites
in their flight out of Egypt. At the shrine of St. Thecla near Seleucia
she had the *acta* of the saint read to her. It was a feeling for the Holy
Places compounded of imagination and romanticism, an attempt
not merely to read the Scriptures but to relive them in her own
actions.

The services held at Jerusalem during Holy Week were designed
to reinforce this feeling. On each day of the week the congregation
met at the site of the events which had occurred on that day in the
first Holy Week. Most of these sites were now covered by churches
and the crowds moved from one to the other while the relevant
passages of the Gospels were recited to them. Thus on the Wednesday they met in the Garden of Gethsemane, where a deacon read
from the Gospel of St. Matthew the account of the betrayal. On
Good Friday, the climax of the pilgrim's journey, the relics of the
Passion were displayed and the account of the crucifixion read to the
crowd, together with passages from the Old Testament foretelling
it. When Etheria was there in c. 382 'every one present was overwhelmed by emotion and the strongest men there could not contain their tears.'

St. Jerome, who lived at Bethlehem for the last thirty-five years
of his life, was the foremost exponent of this scholarly attitude to
the Holy Places. He could not conceal his contempt for those pilgrims who supposed that their souls would benefit by the mere
fact that their bodies were in Jerusalem. In a famous and often

quoted letter Jerome observed that a pilgrim should 'not merely live
in Jerusalem but live a holy life there'. It was at Bethlehem that
Jerome made his great translation of the Bible, and in pungent
letters to admirers in the west he asserted that only in Palestine was
a true understanding of the Scriptures to be had. To study the Bible
anywhere else was like learning Greek at Lilibaeum or Latin in
Sicily. 'One may only truly understand the Holy Scriptures after
looking upon Judaea with one's own eyes.' Jerome himself lyrically
described the emotions of his protégée Paula when she visited the
Holy Places for the first time:

'She threw herself down in adoration before the cross as if she
could see the Lord himself hanging from it. And when she
entered the tomb, she kissed the stone which the angel had
rolled away. . . . What tears she shed there, what sighs of grief,
all Jerusalem knows. . . . After this she came to Bethlehem and
entered the cave where the Saviour was born; and when she
looked upon the inn, the stall, and the crib . . . she cried out in
my hearing that with the eyes of her soul she could see the infant Christ wrapped in swaddling clothes and crying in the
manger.'

Paula's pilgrimage was a constant effort of imagination, a mystical
experience as intense in its own way as that of St. Francis at La
Verna. But before long this mystical adoration of the Holy Places
had crystallized into a naïve and literal view which attached the
greatest importance to the physical survival of relics of the Passion.
The practice of collecting soil from the Holy Land, already common
in the time of St. Augustine, was a popular echo of the words of
the psalmist, 'we have adored in the places where his feet have
stood.' Augustine's contemporary, Paulinus of Nola, commended
it on the ground that 'we must not ignore the simple and literal
sense of this passage, even though it may contain a deeper one as
well.' Indeed, Paulinus believed that the footprints of Christ were
physically preserved in the ground at the point whence He had
ascended into Heaven 'so that we may adore the imprint of the
divine feet in the very dust trodden by the Lord, and then we may
truly say that "we have adored in the place where his feet have
stood."' At the end of the seventh century the Gallic traveller
Arculf observed these footprints exactly as Paulinus had described
them, and reported that pilgrims took pinches of dust from them as
souvenirs of their visit.

The veneration of the Holy Places as a living and visible commentary on the Bible did not, of course, die with the generation of St.
Jerome, any more than did the tradition of meditation on the Passion

which these early pilgrims had inaugurated. Arculf, for example, was described by a contemporary as 'learned in scripture'. At Bethany he was able to follow in the synoptic Gospels the very path of Christ and the apostles. In later times, the mendicant orders, who ultimately acquired control of the Holy Places, encouraged meditation on the Scriptures, and on the Passion in particular. A Franciscan novice who visited the Holy Land in the middle of the thirteenth century remembered how, reading his Bible in the Holy Places, he had felt as if he was witnessing with his own eyes the tortures inflicted on Christ. At the end of the fifteenth century the Dominican Felix Faber remarked that experienced Biblical exegetes were regularly confounded by the arguments of those who had been to the Holy Land.

The growing emphasis on the humanity of Christ in the spiritual literature of the eleventh and twelfth centuries found its reflection in the behaviour of pilgrims in the Holy Land. The pilgrimage of Richard of St.-Vanne to the Holy Land in 1026–7 followed a prolonged period of meditation on the Passion and death of Christ. What the Holy Places meant to this man is indicated by his actions in Jerusalem in Holy Week:

'It is not for me', his biographer wrote, 'to describe the anguished tears which he shed when at last he reached those venerable places. When he saw the pillar of Pilate in the Praetorium he witnessed in his mind's eye the binding and scourging of the Saviour. He thought of the spitting, the smiting, the mocking, and the crown of thorns. Then, on the place of Calvary, he passed through his mind an image of the Saviour crucified, pierced with a lance, reviled and mocked by all around him, crying out with a loud voice, and yielding up his spirit. And meditating on these scenes, he could no longer hold back his tears, and surrendered to the agony which he felt.'

Richard's experience was not uncommon. St. Silvinus, according to his ninth-century biographer, stood on the mount of Calvary and 'although he could not see God with his bodily eyes he could nevertheless see Him with his spiritual eyes, standing in the very place where He had saved humanity from the power of Satan by the shedding of His precious blood.' The twelfth-century ascetic Rayner Pisani used to pray so fervently on Mount Tabor that he would actually see Christ with Moses and Elias, exactly as Peter, James and John had once seen Him.

These ascetics and visionaries saw themselves as reliving the life of Christ. They often referred to their pilgrimage as an *imitatio*

Christi. By re-enacting in their own lives the sufferings of Christ they felt that they were performing an act of personal redemption just as Christ, by His death, had made possible the salvation of all men. On Maundy Thursday 1027, Richard of St.-Vannes knelt down in the square in front of the Holy Sepulchre, and washed the feet of the poor. Rayner of Pisa fasted for forty days on Mount Tabor in remembrance of Christ's forty days in the desert. All pilgrims who could baptized themselves in the Jordan at the point where John the Baptist was believed to have baptized Christ. Some, like St. Bona of Pisa (d. 1207), spent several months following the exact path of Christ's ministry, beginning at the Jordan and ending at the place of Calvary. Others, like Fulk Nerra, count of Anjou, flagellated themselves before the basilica of the Holy Sepulchre, and in the latter half of the twelfth century it was common for pilgrims to have themselves flagellated at the very pillar preserved in the church of Mount Sion. One contemporary went so far as to describe Henry II's visit to Canterbury in July 1174 as an *imitatio Christi* for, like Christ, he allowed himself to be beaten with scourges; 'save that Christ did this for the remission of our sins whereas Henry did it for the remission of his own.'

At its highest level, the pilgrim's life in Jerusalem was conceived as a continuously repeated drama of the life of Christ. The rituals which he performed, more than a mere passion play, had something of the regenerative qualities of the celebration of the Eucharist. In this idea lies the distant origin of the modern liturgical practice of the Roman Catholic Church known as the 'stations of the Cross'. Already in 1231 the exact route which Christ was believed to have followed from Pilate's prison to Calvary was marked out in the streets of Jerusalem. Some seventy years later Ricoldo of Monte Croce 'followed the path which Christ ascended when he carried the Cross', which took him past the house of Pilate, the place where Simon of Cyrene was made to help him, and thence to the Golgotha chapel in the basilica of the Holy Sepulchre. The sire d'Anglure followed the same route in 1395 with a few stations added, 'a thing which every pilgrim who makes this journey can and ought to do.' The journey of the ideal pilgrim could be presented, as Franco Sacchetti presented it at the beginning of the fourteenth century, as an elaborate allegory of the life of Christ from the Nativity to the Resurrection. The pilgrim's entry into a roadside hospice was likened to the incarnation in the womb of the Blessed Virgin. The dangers of the route found their counterpart in the Passion of the Lord. The pilgrim may be betrayed and killed by his companions as Christ was betrayed by Judas and killed by the Jews. He may be betrayed and killed by his host, as Christ was welcomed into Jerusalem by those same Jews who later killed him. Robbers may waylay and despoil him just as the soldiers divided Christ's belongings amongst themselves. It is a naïve picture which must have been offered to countless groups of pilgrims departing to the Holy Land. Yet it conceals one of the profoundest sentiments of an age which reduced all spiritual ideas to images. At a popular level men sought to associate themselves with the life of the Saviour, to express literally their conviction that he had saved them by his death. They wished to tear down the barrier of remoteness that separated a man of the thirteenth century from the events of the first. At the highest levels of Christian mysticism they sought, like St. Francis, to 'enter into the mind and body of the crucified Christ and take on Christ's sufferings in their own persons'.

The Rejection of the World

Contempt for the society which they left behind was at least as important to the followers of St. Jerome as their longing for the promised land. His entourage at Bethlehem saw in their pilgrimage an act of self-denial, of voluntary exile whose object was to take them away from Rome and thus from the 'damnation to which the rest of the world is destined'. Equally negative were the motives of the younger Melania, who left Rome in 410 allowing the wind to take her ship where it would; it took her not to Palestine but to north Africa, where she passed seven years before setting eyes on the Holy Places. 'Depart from the midst of Babylon', Jerome urged a friend who had stayed behind in Rome, 'for it is the house of Satan, the stronghold of iniquity and sin.'

The desire to renounce civilization as contemporaries knew it was a powerful spiritual impulse of the late classical period. Born in the deserts of Egypt in the third century, it remained until the twelfth a strong element of Christian piety. Its inspiration in Jerome's day was the *Life of St. Anthony* by Athanasius. The decisive moment of Augustine's 'conversion' had come when he had heard of two ordinary soldiers who had abandoned the world to live as hermits after reading the *Life of St. Anthony*. Jerome's friend Marcella had had a similar experience in Rome. During his three years in Rome between 382 and 385 Jerome gathered round him a self-conscious group of ascetics, most of them women, who felt that the Christian society of the city had compromised with paganism, come to terms with the world and the flesh. They saw themselves as an elite corps, besieged on every side by flabby worldliness, forced by the ordinary necessities of life to descend to the level of those around them. The true spirit of Christianity they saw in the communities of hermits in the Egyptian desert, and it was these communities, as much as the Holy Places, that drew western pilgrims to the east. Paula, who visited Egypt in Jerome's company in 386, 'threw herself at the feet of these holy men and seemed to see the Lord himself in every one of them.' The elder Melania spent five years in Egypt in the 370s before proceeding to Jerusalem. Etheria would not return home until she had visited the Egyptian monasteries, and the younger Melania returned to Egypt after only a few weeks in the Holy Land 'in order to learn about the perfect life from her spiritual superiors, the desert hermits.'

Pilgrimage in the early Church was very often motivated by a purely negative rejection of urban values. Jerome spoke of himself as 'forsaking the bustling cities of Antioch and Constantinople so as to draw down upon myself the mercy of Christ in the solitude of the country.' It was a process of self-exile, of social and physical isolation. To Jerome, a pilgrim was not a vulgar tourist, an audience for the lying guides who plied their trade in the Holy City. He was a monk. His place of exile did not matter; how he lived was more important than where, and even the sites of the Crucifixion and Resurrection were of no intrinsic spiritual value unless the pilgrim was ready to carry the cross of the Lord and be resurrected with him. St. Anthony, whom Jerome intensely admired, had never seen Jerusalem.

Jerome was well aware that his austere views were visibly rejected by most pilgrims of his own day. But they are worth dwelling on, because Jerome bequeathed a tradition to mediaeval Christianity, and his works were on the book-lists of serious pilgrims for ten centuries after his death. The monastic ideal remained for many years inseparable from contemporary notions of pilgrimage, though Egypt lost its fascination for western pilgrims after the fifth century. During the monastic revival of the eighth century, pilgrims regarded Rome in much the same light as they had once seen Egypt and Palestine. Four Anglo-Saxon kings retired to die there in the space of fifty years. The Lombard king Ratchis walked to Rome with his wife and children in 749 and accepted the monastic habit at the pope's hands. Just as in the fifth century the empress Eudoxia, estranged wife of Theodosius II, had exiled herself to Jerusalem to escape her enemies, so in the eighth century Pippin's brother Karloman left the Frankish court and settled in a Roman monastery on Monte Soracte.

Jerome's attitude to pilgrimage as an escape from civilization was unconsciously revived by the Irish. Their distinctive contribution to the spiritual life of the 'dark ages' was the idea of the aimless wanderer whose renunciation of the world was the most complete of which man could conceive, far more austere than the principles of Benedictine monasticism. In the wandering Irish hermits of the sixth and seventh centuries, western Europe came as near as it would ever do to those 'athletes of Christ', the desert fathers of Egypt and Syria in late antiquity. By wandering freely without destination, the Irish hermit felt that he had cut himself off from every material accessory to life. In his eighth sermon St. Columban dwells on the transitory nature of life, and declares: 'I know that if this earthly tent of mine is taken down, I shall get a new home from God made by no human hands. It makes me sigh, this longing for the shelter of my heavenly habitation . . . for I know that while I am in my body I am travelling away from God.' The notion of a specific destination did not enter into Columban's thinking; his only destination was the heavenly Jerusalem. The spirit of Columban's teaching was precisely expressed by an Irish pilgrim of the twelfth century, who quoted with approval Jerome's strictures against 'Babylon' (i.e. Rome) and urged his hearers to 'be exiles for God's sake, and go not only to Jerusalem but everywhere, for God himself is everywhere.' The same conviction brought three Irishmen to the court of king Alfred in 891 'in a boat without any oars, because they wished for the love of God to be in foreign lands, they cared not where.' Only in the ninth century did some Irish begin to regard Rome as a place of special spiritual merit, and even then a marginal annotation in an Irish hymn-book informs us that 'going to Rome involves great effort and little reward, for the King whom you seek there you will not find unless you bring him with you.'

Bede has left us the spiritual portrait of an Englishman of his own day, the Northumbrian monk Egbert, who passed much of his early life in Ireland and became deeply imbued with Irish spiritual values. According to Bede's informant, Egbert had once suffered from a serious illness during which he became terrifyingly conscious of his own sinfulness. He persuaded himself that even the slender material ties which kept him in an Irish monastery were dragging him to perdition. He determined to become an aimless wanderer fulfilling in exile the daily rituals of the monastic life. 'He would live in exile and never return to his native Britain. In addition to the solemn psalmody of the canonical offices, he would recite the entire psalter in praise of God, unless prevented by illness. Every week he would fast for a day and a night.'

Religious wandering was recognized by contemporaries as a peculiarly Irish practice. 'Why is it', asked the hagiographer Heiric in a letter to Charles the Bald, 'that almost the entire population of Ireland, contemptuous of the perils of the sea, has migrated to our shores with a great crowd of teachers? The more learned they are the more distant their chosen place of exile.' 'Wandering is an ineradicable habit of the Irish race,' observed a ninth-century monk of St.-Gall. The popularity of aimless pilgrimage in the seventh and eighth centuries on the continent can usually be traced to Celtic influence. Irish missionaries spread their ideas amongst the Anglo-Saxons, many of whom exiled themselves to monasteries in Ireland. St. Colman built a monastery in Mayo in 667 exclusively for their use, and Englishmen were still living there more than a century later. St. Cyran (d. 697), founder of the abbey of Lonrey, was converted to the wandering life by an Irish hermit whom he encountered. When the Norman monk Wandrille was commanded in a vision to abandon his home and friends, he made straight for the Irish monastery at Bobbio in northern Italy. Some Irish wanderers, like St. Cadroe at the beginning of the eleventh century, were joined by ever-growing bands of disciples as they trod their erratic paths across western Europe.

Isolated examples of this eccentric behaviour can be found in Germany well into the twelfth century, but as a way of life it had died more than two hundred years earlier. As the missions conquered paganism in central and northern Europe, formal Churches were established with the hierarchical organization familiar to older Christian lands. The wandering of priests across diocesan boundaries and the departure of monks from their monasteries were discouraged by St. Boniface after the 740s, and strenuously condemned by his successors. The reorganization of the monastic life in the ninth century, which is associated with the name of Benedict of Aniane, reinforced the hostility of the authorities to wandering monks. A Frankish synod forbade them to go without permission to Rome 'or anywhere else' as early as 751. The same prohibition was embodied in the capitularies of Charlemagne, which rehearsed that these unauthorized wanderings were destructive of ecclesiastical discipline and instrumental in spreading 'unnecessary doubts' among the people. The spiritual ideals of the Irish thus found themselves in conflict with the tendency of the Carolingians to make use of Benedictine monasticism as a stabilizing force, a propagator of what one might call the 'cultural colonialism' of the ninth century. Henceforth renunciation of the world was to mean entering a monastery or a fixed hermitage. Itinerant clerics were to find themselves condemned even by such fierce ascetics as Peter Damian. When Everard de Breteuil, *vicomte* of Chartres, suddenly renounced the world in 1073, he became a hermit living a 'life of freedom', and earned his living by burning charcoal; he was persuaded, however, that the irregularity of his life was unpleasing to God, and so entered the monastery of Marmoutiers.

CHAPTER VII

THE PENITENTIAL
PILGRIMAGE

Penance and Pilgrimage

An age which loved definition and codified religious observances, also divided pilgrims into categories. The lawyers and theologians of the thirteenth century distinguished between voluntary pilgrimages undertaken as an act of personal piety, and compulsory ones imposed by confessors or courts of law. Yet the distinction was unreal, for the need to expiate their sins was common to both classes. In the first centuries of Christianity sinners occasionally exiled themselves voluntarily to Jerusalem as an act of penitence. One of Jerome's correspondents, a notorious adulterer called Sabinianus, retired to expiate his sins at Bethlehem, though he shortly returned to his old ways. In Constantinople, St. Marcian persuaded several ladies of loose morals to withdraw to the Holy Land at the end of the fifth century. The monasteries of Palestine, like those of Egypt and Syria, drew a large number of penitents.

Yet the early Church knew neither judicial nor penitential pilgrimage. Rituals and panaceas had little place in a penitential system as strict as that which was known to St. Augustine. The notorious sinner was excluded from the life of the Church, and the conditions on which he was readmitted amounted to a promise to live an almost monastic existence for the rest of his days. Public penance was a 'second baptism'. Like baptism it could be performed only once in a lifetime, and in practice it was nearly always postponed to the eve of death. Pilgrimages were not imposed on penitents until the sixth century, when the whole notion of penance was transformed by the Irish missionaries. The Irish confessor imposed penances, which varied with the gravity of the sin, in accordance with a penitential 'tariff', of which several were already in circulation by the end of the sixth century. Here were found comprehensive lists of sins together with the appropriate penances ranging from short fasts to perpetual exile. Pilgrimage was much favoured by the Irish as a spiritual exercise. As a penance for the more enormous transgressions it was thought especially appropriate. Pilgrimages of varying duration are specified for murder (particularly by clerics), incest, bestiality, and sacrilege. The sins of monks and those of the higher clergy were visited more often with penitential pilgrimages than those of any other class.

In the Irish penitentials we have the origin of the distinction between 'public' and 'private' penance, which was defined and elaborated by the thirteenth-century schoolmen. Public penance, which usually meant pilgrimage, was imposed for public sins with overtones of scandal, notably the sexual offences of the clergy. It was a useful penance, wrote the canonist Raymond of Peñaforte, for 'those scandalous and notorious sins which set the whole town talking'; when they were committed by laymen the penance was described as 'solemn', when by clergymen as 'public'. This idea was still very much alive at the end of the middle ages when Chaucer's parson explained the distinction to his fellow-travellers: 'commune penaunce', the *penitentia publica non sollemnis* of the schoolmen, was used 'when a man hath sinned openly, of which sin the fame is openly spoken in the country. . . . Common penance is that (which) priests enjoin men commonly in certain cases, as for to go, peradventure, naked in pilgrimages or barefoot.'

The scandalous overtones were obviously stronger in cases involving clerics or noblemen, and it was above all these classes who were wont to be sent on long pilgrimages. The emperor Otto III was advised by St. Romuald to walk barefoot to Monte Gargano after murdering a Roman senator in breach of his safe-conduct. Romuald's biographer Peter Damian imposed pilgrimages to Rome, Tours, and Santiago on the corrupt and rebellious clergy of Milan; a marquis called Renier he sent to Jerusalem 'on account of the grave sins which you have confessed to me.' A pilgrimage was thought the appropriate sentence for count Thierry who murdered the archbishop-elect of Trier in 1066, as it was, more than a century later, for Henry II after the murder of Becket, and for Raymond VI of Toulouse after the death of the papal legate on the steps of the abbey of St.-Gilles. These penances were in no sense voluntary. Even in the cases of kings the pressure of public opinion could be overpowering, and to ignore it would have been politically most unwise, as both Raymond of Toulouse and Henry II discovered to their cost.

For such notorious crimes the penitential pilgrimage remained in use throughout the later middle ages. During his regular visitations of the province of Rouen, archbishop Odo Rigaud constantly imposed pilgrimages on both clerics and laymen for their sexual indiscretions. Other offences which were punished thus included forgery, breaking sanctuary, and public irreverence towards the services of the Church. For seizing and imprisoning a cleric, Robert de Frechesne, *bailli* of Rouen, was sent to St. Michael's church in Rouen, there to recite fifty *Pater Nosters* and fifty *Ave Marias*, to fast for three days, and to distribute five shillings to the poor. In the province of Cologne a synod of 1279 recommended pilgrimages in cases involving self-indulgence of any sort. The publicity which long-distance pilgrims drew to themselves made it the obvious penalty for spectacular crimes. Roger da Bonito was sent to Rome, Santiago, and Jerusalem in 1319 for murdering the bishop of Fricento. For his attack on Boniface VIII at Anagni Guillaume de Nogaret, chancellor of the king of France, was ordered to visit Notre-Dame de Vauvert, Rocamadour, Boulogne, Chartres, St.-Gilles, Montmajour, and Santiago, and finally to exile himself to the Holy Land, though none of this did he actually do.

For those whose sins were venial or well-concealed, the penitential pilgrimage remained an act of personal piety, voluntarily undertaken. After the end of the tenth century growing numbers of the humble as well as the mighty performed distant pilgrimages to expiate crimes that weighed on their consciences. The reasons for this sudden upsurge are far from clear. Introspection and guilt were not inventions of the eleventh century, and the condition of western Europe at the millennium is not, on its own, enough to account for the phenomenon. There was, however, one aspect of contemporary religious life by which it could hardly fail to have been coloured. The period witnessed radical changes in the role of the sacrament of penance. Two centuries earlier the Carolingian reformers had taken exception to the penitential practices of the Irish which, to their thinking, failed to bring the penitent back to the straight and narrow path. Rabanus Maurus had insisted that penances should be performed under the direct supervision of the confessor who had imposed them, and that the penitent should not be absolved until it had been completed. This had always been the practice of the early Church. It gave a certain finality to the ritual of absolution which marked the sinner's readmission to the body of the Church. From the end of the tenth century, however, penitents were usually absolved and reconciled with the Church immediately after confession. Thus arose the distinction between sin and punishment: the former was expunged by confession; the latter remained to be suffered in Purgatory. The penitent was reconciled to the Church, but he still had to do satisfaction for his sins, and the view ultimately prevailed that by performing good works in this life he could reduce the punishment that awaited him in the next. Against this background the unprecedented number of monastic foundations and the extraordinary popularity of pilgrimages and the crusades which mark out the eleventh century, become intelligible.

This obsession with the remission of sins can be discerned in all the more notable pilgrimages of the period. Robert the Pious, king of France, did a tour of nine shrines including some as far away as Toulouse and St.-Gilles shortly before his death in 1031. His biographer tells us that he hoped in this way to 'evade the awful sentence of the day of judgement'. Robert, duke of Normandy, who was under strong suspicion of having murdered his brother, travelled barefoot to Jerusalem in 1035 'driven by the fear of God'. A contemporary who saw king Canute at St.-Omer on his way to Rome reported that he shed bitter tears and implored the pardon of the saints, beating his breast and heaving heavy sighs. The three (or perhaps four) pilgrimages of Fulk Nerra, count of Anjou, to Jerusalem were accompanied by exhibitions of repentance as spectacular as the crimes they were intended to efface. According to Radulph Glaber 'the fear of Gehenna' entered into him in the year 1000 on account of his slaughter of the Bretons at the battle of Conquereuil, and the murder of his wife can only have added to his feelings of guilt. His first journey to the Holy Land occurred about three years after this. On his last, which was accomplished at a great age in 1038–40, Fulk had himself dragged on his knees by a halter to the church of the Holy Sepulchre, while two servants followed behind flogging him with birches. 'Accept, O Lord, the wretched Fulk,' he cried from the steps of the basilica; 'I have perjured myself before thee and fled from thy presence. Receive, O Christ, this my unworthy soul.'

These pilgrims were as different as they could possibly have been from the Celtic wanderers of an earlier age. They had a particular destination in mind and, having spent a short time there, they returned home to resume their normal lives. Fulk Nerra and his contemporaries took it for granted that certain places were intrinsically holier than others and this, as we have seen, was very far from being the view of the Irish. The penitential pilgrim, according to an Anglo-Saxon writer of the tenth century, underwent 'the most profound of penances': 'he throws away his weapons and wanders far and wide across the land, barefoot and never staying more than a night in one place. . . . He fasts and wakes and prays by day and by night. He cares not for his body and lets his hair and nails grow freely.' A pilgrimage of this sort is in fact a development of the penalty of judicial exile which is so common in primitive legal systems. The offender became an outcast. In the words of the *Penitential of St. Columban* he was to be 'like Cain a wanderer and a fugitive on the face of the earth, never to return to his native land.'

The destination of this penitent was immaterial. Indeed it was often laid down that in the case of particularly heinous offences the pilgrimage was to be perpetual. In 585 the council of Mâcon decreed that a bishop guilty of murder should pass the rest of his life in pilgrimage. In the Irish penitentials perpetual exile is ordained for incest, bestiality, the murder of clerics or close relatives, and various kinds of sacrilege. As late as c. 1000 some Irish canons collected at Worcester require that the murderer of a bishop's servant be condemned to perpetual exile, while lesser offences are visited with pilgrimages of up to twenty years. Indeed it was still possible for a preacher in the middle of the twelfth century to speak of pilgrims at Santiago as being 'sent into exile by their parish priests'.

In no other period was it so much better to travel hopefully than to arrive. But these wanderings were not devoid of religious significance, and penitents were often reported to have been pardoned by the intercession of the saints. Gregory of Tours had observed in the sixth century that 'by praying to the saints sinners can often obtain the remission of their sins and thus be saved from the torments of Hell. . . . Those who have fallen into grave sin should therefore pay special reverence to God's saints.' In some miracle stories of the period the saint signified that the penitent was pardoned by causing his chains to break asunder in front of the shrine. Typical of such stories is the tale of the priest Willichar, whose enemies were unable to imprison him because the fetters fell from his feet every time he invoked the name of St. Martin. Two criminals are reported to have been released from their chains by St. Nizier in the sixth century, and at the church of St. Victor in Marseilles a traveller saw with his own eyes the rows of broken fetters hanging before the altar. But no one shrine was the special destination of these pilgrims, and when the chains broke the place was usually fortuitous. They wandered from shrine to shrine as aimlessly as any Irish exile. The wanderings of one such outcast are described in a Norman text of the ninth century. He was a nobleman called Frotmund who, in 850, had murdered his father, a chaplain of the emperor Lothair. Together with a large company of others in a similar predicament, he first made his way to Rome and then proceeded to Jerusalem, then to the shrine of St. Cyprian at Carthage, and back to Rome. Divine pardon was not forthcoming in Rome, so he returned to Jerusalem by way of Mount Sinai, then back to Rome and across northern Italy and France, until his fetters broke in the church of St. Marcellin at Rédon.

The notion that a pilgrim had only to go to a particular shrine to be pardoned is scarcely found before the ninth century and did not command universal acceptance until the eleventh. At the very beginning of the ninth century we are told that St. Mestrille went to Tours in order to be pardoned for his sins. In the same period we find pilgrims commanded in visions to go to particular shrines. A ninth-century editor included in the works of Gregory of Tours the story of a penitent who was directed by a vision of Christ to the shrine of Moutiers-St.-Jean near Lyon. Another story in the same vein told of St. Peter and St. Paul appearing to a criminal on the road to Rome and directing him to the shrine of St. Bavo at Ghent.

Bishops and confessors only now begin to impose specific pilgrimages on penitents. Rome was the usual destination. An Irish penitential written at the end of the ninth century suggests that parricides should be sent there to receive their penance from the pope in person. A certain Ratbert, who battered his mother to death in c. 870, was sent by the archbishop of Sens on two pilgrimages to Mont-St.-Michel and one to Rome. Such penances were still fairly uncommon a century later when the renowned confessor Abbo of Fleury sent Bernard, abbot of Beaulieu, to Jerusalem, and on learning that the roads east were blocked, to Rome and Monte Gargano instead. Bernard had confessed to having obtained his abbacy by simony, and Abbo's biographer believed that the penance was 'almost the first of its kind in France'.

Thus arose the characteristic mediaeval belief in the automatic remission of sins by formal visits to particular shrines. The story of the criminal whose fetters burst asunder was gradually replaced by still more dramatic indications of divine forgiveness. Charlemagne, for instance, was stated in a legend of the eleventh century to have written out his sins on a sheet of paper, which was then wiped clean by the miraculous power of St. Gilles. This story, with its simple, literal approach, plainly struck a sympathetic chord in contemporary minds, for other pilgrims are alleged to have had similar experiences. A woman who visited Vézelay in the early twelfth century laid on the altar a *scedula* of her sins, which were immediately erased. The same happened to an Italian, whose sins were so vile that his bishop refused to absolve him, and sent him instead to Santiago with a written list of his enormities. 'From this', writes the author of the *Miracles of St. James*, 'it is plain that whoever goes truly penitent to St. James and asks for his help with all his heart, will certainly have all his sins expunged.' Writing at the beginning of the twelfth century, Hughes de Sainte-Marie saw this as the principal function of the saints. The Merovingian saints had healed the sick and punished iniquity; those of the twelfth century did so too, but they were also pastors, concerned above all with the moral welfare and eventual salvation of their flock. 'Who can say how many souls have won God's mercy by the merits of St. Benedict; how many men have been reformed, turned away from the vain prattle of the world, and subjected to the light yoke of Christ. For in so doing, St. Benedict revives the dead and heals the open wounds of sin.'

Pilgrimages Imposed by the Law

The responsibility for introducing the judicial pilgrimage into the civil law of Europe probably belongs to the Inquisition. The systematic juridical persecution of heresy, which began in southern France in the early years of the thirteenth century, left its mark on several aspects of mediaeval law. An organized system of tribunals, possessed of established rules and procedures, the Inquisition was active at one time or another in every country of Europe except England. For those who confessed to minor offences against the faith, pilgrimages were amongst the commonest penances which it imposed.

The Inquisition of Languedoc classified pilgrimages as 'major', 'minor', or 'overseas' (i.e. to the Holy Land). The nineteen minor pilgrimages were all in France, while the four major ones were Canterbury, Santiago, Cologne, and Rome. Depending on the gravity of his offence, the penitent might be sent to any number of these shrines or even to all of them. It was nevertheless regarded as one of the lighter penances and was commonly used when large numbers of people were suspected of heresy without there being any definite evidence against any of them. When the inquisitors visited the small towns of Gourdon and Montcuq in 1241, most of those brought before them were sentenced to one major pilgrimage and a host of minor ones. Ninety-eight people were sent to Santiago via Le Puy and St.-Gilles; thirty-eight citizens of Gourdon were obliged to visit Canterbury by way of St.-Léonard de Noblat, St. Martial of Limoges, and St.-Denis. By comparison, Bernard Gui, inquisitor of Toulouse, who dealt with more serious cases and was in any case reckoned a hard judge, made much more severe use of pilgrimage as a penance. In his surviving book of sentences, which covers the years 1308–22, only sixteen out of 636 offences were considered so venal as to merit a mere pilgrimage. Even these sixteen had to undergo long journeys on foot. Three offenders who had unwittingly attended a Waldensian meeting in their childhood were directed to visit seventeen 'minor' sanctuaries as far apart as Vienne and Bordeaux.

Civil courts had occasionally ordered malefactors to make distant pilgrimages in the twelfth century. Not very often, however. It was not until the middle of the thirteenth century that they came into general use. Most early examples are found in the ecclesiastical

principalities of the Low Countries where, at first, they were reserved for offences against the Church. They were rapidly adopted
by criminal lawyers as a convenient, easily enforced penalty which
brought about the temporary disappearance of the offender without
the expense of imprisoning him. In Liège the *Paix aux Clercs*, a code
of ecclesiastical law issued in 1207, ordains that assaults inside
churches shall be punished with pilgrimages. Two months later, a
code of civil law was published which specified pilgrimage as the
penalty for all assaults resulting in mutilation. By 1328, when the
next major legal code of Liège appeared, pilgrimage had become an
all-purpose penalty for violent crimes. A similar process can be
traced in almost every city of the Low Countries, and by the fourteenth century it was firmly established in France and Italy as well.
Only in England did the secular courts ignore it.

Pilgrimages of this sort were little more than the traditional
penalty of banishment renamed. City-states have almost invariably
banished serious disturbers of the peace, and in Flanders, for example,
this tradition had an uninterrupted history going back well beyond
the eleventh century. Pilgrimage and banishment were almost in-
terchangeable terms. Hence the practice of the kings of France of
periodically commuting short banishments to even shorter pilgrimages; thus did Philip VI allow the town of Douai in 1346 to
commute all banishments of less than five years. The religious element in these journeys was usually small, a fact which became
apparent in the later middle ages when Arab hostility sometimes
made it impossible to visit Jerusalem. On settling his quarrel with
the count of Namur in 1402, Robert de Roux promised to go to the
Holy Land or, if that proved impossible, to Cyprus. Indeed it was
to Cyprus, a place of little spiritual importance, that the most
heinous offenders were sent. There they were required to stay for a
specified number of years. It was very rare for the judges to require
from the offender any display of religious enthusiasm. Perhaps it was
a reflection of the ecclesiastical character of the government of
Liège that criminals sent from thence to Rome were required to
mount the steps of the Lateran basilica on their knees and to remain
kneeling for the duration of five masses. Other cities did not think
it worth including such details in their statutes.

Pilgrimage, like banishment, was a particularly suitable punishment for those enormities which threatened the tight-knit urban
communities of the late middle ages. Thomas Aquinas regarded it as
the obvious penalty for a grave breach of public order. Murder and
wounding, riot and affray, conspiracies of various sorts all carried
the penalty of exile. At Liège in the fourteenth century any person
who committed an assault that caused bleeding but broke no bones,

who sheltered some one involved in a vendetta, or who obstructed the course of justice, was liable to be despatched to Rocamadour, a distance of some six hundred miles. Arson, the most terrifying crime that a mediaeval townsman could commit, was punished by a pilgrimage to Jerusalem or Santiago as early as 1186, when Frederick Barbarossa issued a constitution to this effect. Arson was punished at Namur in the late middle ages with a visit to Cyprus, and it is probable that the same practice prevailed in other cities of the Low Countries. Cyprus too was the destination of twenty-five citizens of Nieuport who had been amongst the crowd which in 1235 lynched the ambassadors of the neighbouring town of Furnes. In 1483 insulting a town councillor of Namur was added to the list of offences which were held to merit a pilgrimage to Rocamadour. Indeed by this time pilgrimage had become a convenient and flexible penalty for all those whose continued presence in a small community was felt to be a nuisance. Henri le Kien, a painter of Tournai who was sent to Rocamadour in 1428, was accused of no crime at all except that he 'made a habit of insulting and criticizing other people . . . and thus caused great dissensions and troubles'; it was resolved that the unfortunate artist was 'never to return to the city unless the citizens gather together in their guilds and districts to re-admit him.'

Mediaeval lawyers did not make the same rigid distinction between civil and criminal law as their modern counterparts. The victim of a violent crime, or the victim's heir, was held to be the prosecutor and the sentence inflicted on the malefactor was at least partly for the victim's satisfaction. The honour of the injured party was satisfied by the banishment of his assailant. This is an attitude as old as the penitential pilgrimage itself. One of the oldest Irish penitentials, the *Penitential of Finnian*, prescribes that a cleric found guilty of murder shall pass ten years in exile, after which 'he shall be received into his own country and make satisfaction to the friends of him whom he slew and compensate his father and mother, if they are still alive. . . . But if he does not fulfil this obligation he shall never be allowed back.' This outlook did not disappear, even in the more formal circumstances of thirteenth-century law. Thus in Frederick Barbarossa's constitutions of 1186, men banished for crimes of violence are not to return until they have compensated the victim or his family. Grave crimes might be settled by private agreement, the courts intervening only to ensure that the agreement was kept. In 1434, for instance, a certain Gerard de Rostimont of Namur was obliged to make peace with the relatives of a man whom he had killed in a brawl, the condition being that he should go immediately to Cyprus. A document of 1333 in the town archives of

St.-Omer records the return of a clerk called William Bondulf from a pilgrimage to St. Andrew's in Scotland. He showed his testimonials to the judge to prove that he had been, and paid twelve *livres* for the repose of his victim's soul. Then the victim's heir, who was present in court, publicly acquitted him of all further responsibility. Indeed at Liège the victim's claim was considered quite separately from that of the state, and in cases of assault in churches the evil-doer might be required to go twice to Santiago, once to the profit of the Church and once to that of the victim.

From the state's point of view these arrangements had the advantage of settling a potential vendetta. Indeed, most of the earliest judicial pilgrimages are the result of timely agreements designed to avoid family feuds. In 1264 the four murderers of Godfrey and Jaquemon de Clermont, two brothers of a wealthy Flemish family, agreed to depart to the Holy Land until the victims' relatives allowed them to return. Pilgrimages were often imposed by arbitrators in private quarrels. Beaumanoir records the case of a villager who killed another's horse under him, and repenting of his rashness, promised to submit his quarrel to the arbitration of three other villagers. These decided that he should go barefoot to Boulogne, Santiago, and St.-Gilles, before finally exiling himself to the Holy Land for three years. According to Beaumanoir the sentence was considered excessive and it was never executed. But when two families of Dieppe submitted a blood-feud to the archbishop of Rouen in 1264, he sent the head of one of them to St.-Gilles and Santiago, observing that in this way 'the honour and peace of mind of the aggrieved parties will be saved.'

The judicial pilgrimage was more fearsome in theory than it was in practice, for the sinner could usually be released from his penance by paying a fee to the state or damages to the injured party. The Inquisition scarcely ever allowed its victims to escape their penances in this way. According to the inquisitor Bernard Gui, only the old and the infirm were permitted to make a money payment in lieu of a pilgrimage, and even then the cost was high – fifty *livres* for the old, a hundred for the infirm. By contrast, the civil courts allowed criminals to buy their way out of the journey for quite small sums. Nothing more clearly illustrates the slender spiritual basis of these pilgrimages than the lists of tariffs in which the price of evading each pilgrimage was advertized. Here is one such list, which was in use at Oudenarde in the fourteenth century:

To Santiago	*livres* 12– 0–0
To Rome	*livres* 12– 0–0
To St. Julian of Brioude	*livres* 4– 0–0

To St. Simeon of Paris   *livres*   0–40–0
To St. Martin of Tours   *livres*   3–10–0
etc.

The sum required varied considerably from place to place. A pilgrimage to Rocamadour could be bought off for five *livres* at Alost, while at Ypres it cost seven; Oudenarde charged eight *livres* and Limburg ten gold florins. Occasionally a court would refuse to allow commutation at all in serious cases. At Maestricht, for instance, murderers were allowed to buy their way out of a pilgrimage if it was imposed to the profit of the victim's family, but if it was imposed on behalf of the town it had to be performed. In general it was assumed that the malefactor would pay if he could afford to. After the sentence had been announced there was usually a pause of several weeks during which he would try to raise the money from friends or moneylenders. If the money was not paid, the victim or his family would then apply for a court order enforcing the sentence. Many French towns enjoyed royal privileges which entitled citizens to buy off pilgrimages as of right. In confirming the privileges of Corvins and Epinoy in 1371, Charles V found it necessary to warn them that the pilgrimage must be enforced if the offender could or would not pay. Similar privileges were granted to Bergues, Furnes, and several other towns of Flanders, Artois, and Brabant.

Pilgrimages were imposed not only by law courts and arbitrators, but by any corporation which exercised a quasi-judicial authority over its members. Universities, guilds, and similar corporations were all entitled to send recalcitrant members to distant parts and often did so. For breaking a minor rule, the armourer's guild at Malines sent one of its members, barefoot, bareheaded, and fasting on bread and water to the shrine of Battel. The draper's guild at Malines had been known to send rebellious members as far as Rocamadour. Contemporaries appreciated the humiliation which was thus inflicted on the victim. For this reason pilgrimages were commonly inflicted on whole towns after an unsuccessful war or rebellion. At the treaty of Arques (1326), which marked the defeat of the Flemish towns in their revolt against Charles of France, Bruges and Courtrai were required to send a hundred prominent citizens to Santiago, a hundred to St.-Gilles, and a hundred to Rocamadour. On this occasion the offending towns commuted the penalty to a payment of 10,000 *livres*, but they were not always let off so lightly. Robert de Cassel paid for his part in the same rebellion by visiting Santiago, Rocamadour, Le Puy, and St.-Gilles, and bringing back testimonials to prove it. Sixty citizens of Bruges performed a civic pilgrimage to Avignon in 1309, and in 1393 dignitaries of the town were sent to Rome and Jerusalem after an unsuccessful quarrel with the Hanseatic League. In 1468 a hundred inhabitants of Haut-Pont presented themselves at Notre-Dame de Boulogne bearing wax candles weighing three pounds each in penance for their seditious designs against Charles the Bold, duke of Burgundy.

Enforcement

The solemn and exemplary character of a judicial pilgrimage was emphasized by the way in which it was performed. The practice of sending the convict on his way loaded with chains belongs to the Merovingian and Carolingian periods, but it did not altogether die out until the end of the twelfth century. Even in 1319 the murderer of the bishop of Fricento was despatched to Rome and Santiago with an iron collar round his neck. Fetters were attached to the convict's arms and sometimes to his legs, neck, and waist as well. In the case of murderers it was usual to hang the murder weapon from one of the fetters as a permanent advertisement of the crime. In the early mediaeval period these awful wanderers were a familiar sight in every part of Europe, but in the eleventh and twelfth centuries most of the victims came from southern France, Germany, or Scotland. When chained convicts are reported at English shrines they are almost invariably foreigners. A pilgrim who came to Norwich priory in the 1150s 'clothed in a coat of mail on his bare flesh, fettered with his own sword' was a nobleman of Lorraine. Scottish convicts were constantly arriving at the shrine of St. Cuthbert at Durham. In 1164, great interest was aroused by the appearance of a murderer wearing an iron girdle made of the sword with which he had killed his victim. Another Scotsman had been fettered by the arm, waist, and neck, and had already been to the Holy Land and St. Martial of Limoges before coming to Durham. At each place part of his load had broken away, 'and thus', explained Reginald of Durham, 'St. Cuthbert can free the body from its chains just as he frees the soul from the bonds of sin.'

It is difficult to know what to make of these stories of the spontaneous bursting of iron chains, especially when they are reported by those who claim to have been present. Thomas of Monmouth complained that some of his contemporaries were inclined to doubt them, ascribing them to fraud or rust, but Thomas asserted that he had watched with his own eyes as the fetters of Philip of Lorraine fell to the ground. A high proportion of these stories must have been pure fiction, Thomas's own tales among them. But many of the pilgrims who clanked their chains along the roads of Europe in the eleventh and twelfth centuries had probably put them on voluntarily and may have removed them themselves as soon as they felt that God had pardoned them. In such cases the 'miracle' consisted of the sudden relief of their feelings of guilt, a circumstance which it is rather easier to visualize. A penitent who arrived at Fleury at the end of the eleventh century is stated to have confessed his crimes out of fear of God's vengeance and then placed the fetters on his own arms 'in the firm conviction that as soon as God deigned to remit his sins the chains would fall away of their own accord.' A pilgrim released at the shrine of St. Egwin of Evesham had loaded himself with chains. So had a fratricide of Cologne who confessed his sin to the archbishop and then wandered for seven years from shrine to shrine. It was an extreme form of mortification of the flesh, following an ancient and still powerful tradition. A twelfth-century penitent called Bernard, who ended his days in the abbey of St. Bertin at St.-Omer, had committed the most trivial of crimes. His biographer does not reveal what it was, but observes that 'no one would think ill of him even if the stories were true. He had done nothing particularly vile or bestial, nothing we would consider sinful nowadays. But it is the mark of a saint to look upon everything worldly as loathsome.' Accordingly Bernard had condemned himself to wander for seven years with seven tight irons around his limbs and neck. It seems likely that by this time the majority of fettered pilgrims seen at the great shrines had chosen to add thus to the discomforts of their penance.

Those who had been sentenced by the Inquisition were not chained and fettered, but they were required to wear on their back and front two large crosses made of saffron-coloured cloth, and there were severe penalties for tearing them off. It is quite probable that these crosses subjected the wearer to scourging at each of the shrines he visited. Certainly the crosses were regarded as the most humiliating part of the penance. Those who wore them were ostracized by their fellow-travellers and excluded from inns and hospices, in spite of the orders of the inquisitors that they should be sheltered like any other pilgrim. Some complained that they found it hard to marry off their daughters, others that the stigma attached to wearing crosses lasted for many years after the pilgrimage had been completed. Even those convicted by civil courts found that the worst part of the sentence was the public humiliation which accompanied it. In the fifteenth century a rich man like Joos Pieterseune, who was ordered to Rocamadour for involuntary manslaughter, could do the journey in six months; but his conviction was quashed on appeal on the ground that judicial pilgrims were known as *amadours* and generally regarded as men of evil repute, a stigma which, it was felt, the unfortunate Pieterseune did not deserve.

The problems of enforcing compulsory pilgrimages were considerable. Successful evasions must have been frequent though it is, on the whole, the unsuccessful ones which are recorded. Convicts who pleaded illness were required to prove it. Bodechon de Bourges, who was convicted by the magistrates of Namur in 1413, produced a posse of witnesses to testify that he could scarcely lift himself from his bed. He was allowed to put off his departure for forty days, but six months later he was still in Namur trying to borrow the money to buy his release. Victims of the Inquisition were constantly being reminded of their unperformed pilgrimages, and in 1251 the inquisitors of Carcassonne issued a general warning of the awful consequences of leaving a pilgrimage unperformed. Corporations which punished their members by despatching them to distant shrines often had some difficulty in enforcing their sentences. Much of the *acta* of the university of Louvain for the year 1448 are taken up with the transgressions of one Jan Vogel van der Elst, a servant of the mayor of Louvain who had conceived a virulent hatred of the university, and had repeatedly assaulted its students and dignitaries. For this he was ordered by the rector of the university to go on a pilgrimage to Milan cathedral. Vogel's reaction was to insult the rector loudly, and declare that he would not go to Milan unless he was tied to a cart and driven there by force. He then stood outside the university hall as the officers of the university passed by, and shouted 'Where is the cart? Is it not ready yet?' Vogel was ultimately arrested for his contumacy and was only released on the understanding that future assaults on students would result in his execution or perpetual banishment. He did not, however, go to Milan.

Many offences for which pilgrimages were imposed were capital offences, and this brief period of exile was often a merciful alternative to execution. When Lambert de Soif was sent to Rome in May 1515 for seizing his cousin by the hair and threatening his wife with a razor, the sentence was described as a 'merciful one, preferable in the circumstances to the full rigour of the law'. If the malefactor failed to perform the pilgrimages the full rigour of the law might be enforced. Pierot the Porter, who left Namur for Santiago after murdering a lawyer in 1405, turned back a few miles outside the town and settled in a quiet suburb. When he was discovered there a few weeks afterwards, he was immediately beheaded. In France, many of the letters of pardon which the crown habitually granted to convicted felons were made conditional on the performance of a pilgrimage. In 1393, for example, two cut-throats of Azay le Brulay (Poitou) escaped death by carrying a candle to Le Puy and buying a hundred masses for the soul of their victim. In urban communities, where evading a sentence was easier to detect, the simplest method of enforcing it was to refuse to let the evil-doer return unless he could prove that he had performed his pilgrimage. At Liège, failure to perform the relatively mild pilgrimage to Walcourt meant banishment for a year; to Vendôme, for two years; to Rocamadour, for four, and to Santiago, for five. When he returned, the convict sent his certificates ahead of him and waited outside the boundaries of the city until the magistrates signified that they were content to readmit him.

These certificates or 'testimonials' were first devised by the Inquisitors of Languedoc, who required their penitents to collect signed documents from the clergy of the shrines they visited, proving that they had been there. Like other Inquisitorial practices, they were quickly adopted by secular judges. Those of Namur, for example, ordered criminals to bring back a certificate 'showing that they had visited the said places in person without any kind of dishonesty or deceit, and without evading any of the obligations traditionally fulfilled by pilgrims.' On his return, the penitent showed his testimonials in court, and collected a certificate of acquittal for which he might have to pay a small fee.

The judicial pilgrimage had always had its opponents. Even in the heyday of the chained pilgrim, there was a substantial body of opinion which doubted how effective it was in reforming the sinner. This view is rehearsed in a capitulary of Charlemagne in 789 and it became in the following century part of the orthodoxy of reforming churchmen such as Rabanus Maurus. Not only did compulsory pilgrimages endanger the salvation of the sinner, but they also set loose upon the roads large numbers of dangerous criminals who terrorized peaceful travellers. This was the reason for Charlemagne's complaint against them in 789, and it remained a serious problem in later periods. In the thirteenth century Jacques de Vitry had occasion to complain of the hordes of 'wicked, impious, sacrilegious, thieves, robbers, murderers, parricides, perjurers, adulterers, traitors, corsairs, pirates, whoremongers, drunkards, minstrels, jugglers, and actors', who were unleashed on the Holy Land by the courts of Europe. A growing appreciation of the force of these arguments is found in writers of the later middle ages. Thomas Aquinas reflected the views of most of his contemporaries when he protested against the imposition of pilgrimages on women or by ordinary parish priests. At the beginning of the fourteenth century Durand de Saint-Pourçain held that their moral effects were disastrous and that they were too often imposed by ignorant parish priests. He proposed to restrict the power of inflicting them to bishops and confessors appointed by them, but in practice pilgrimages were rarely imposed by any spiritual authority after the middle of the fourteenth century. After the gradual decay of the Inquisition of Languedoc the secular courts of northern Europe were the only tribunals which still had recourse to them. This they continued to do until some decades after the Reformation. It was a source of some surprise to count Mansfeld, Philip II's lieutenant in the Low Countries, to discover in 1592 that convicts were still being sent to Rocamadour and Santiago, in spite of the bitter civil war raging in France. But penances of this kind were not spiritual exercises. For most sinners of the later middle ages the decision as to whether to undertake a pilgrimage was one which the Church was content to leave to their own consciences.

CHAPTER VIII

THE GREAT AGE OF PILGRIMAGE

'Some three years after the year 1000', wrote the Burgundian chronicler Radulph Glaber, 'there was a sudden rush to rebuild churches all over the world, and above all in Italy and France. Although most of these churches were in perfectly sound condition, Christians everywhere vied with each other to improve them. It was as if the world itself had thrown aside its old rags and put on a shining white robe of churches.' In southern France, broad strips of Glaber's 'white robe' still stand as evidence of the extraordinary spiritual intensity of the eleventh century, of a mood which manifested itself in the climax of monastic history, in the crusades in Spain and the middle east, and in the transformation of Christianity by a world of emotion and sentiment. In an age of religious sensitivity, pilgrimage fulfilled a real spiritual need. By inflicting severe physical hardship on the pilgrim, it satisfied a desire for the remission of his sins and opened up to him the prospect of a 'second baptism'. By showing him the places associated with Christ and the saints, it gave him a more personal, more literal understanding of his faith.

Profound changes in the spiritual life of Europe coincided with political developments which made it possible, for the first time, for large numbers of people to travel long distances overland. The barbarian invasions of the ninth and tenth centuries had had a particularly destructive effect on the shrines of western Europe. These wealthy churches, protecting tombs of precious metal encrusted with jewels, proved an irresistible prey to raiding parties of Arabs, Vikings, and Magyars. Many of the more famous relics led a peripatetic existence as their owners carried them from church to church, fleeing before the invaders. When the Normans invaded the Loire valley in 853 the body of St. Martin was carried to Corm' ery and thence to Chablis, Orléans, and Auxerre. It was more than a hundred years before it returned to its home at Tours. After suffering a succession of Viking raids at the end of the ninth century, the monks of Lindisfarne took the body of St. Cuthbert and 'wandered across the whole of Northumbria, having no settled home, like sheep fleeing before wolves'. The body was venerated at Chester-le-Street for more than a century before the monks fled once again from the Vikings and found a permanent home at Durham. In such conditions regular pilgrimages were impossible. The exact location of the relics might be changed or it might be forgotten altogether. Libraries were dispersed or burned, collections of saints' lives lost. No one knew, in Orderic Vitalis's time, the exact location of the fifteen hermitages founded by St. Evroul. Recurrent raids, and the political disintegration which accompanied them, made it unsafe to travel long distances on the roads. The monk Bernard, returning from the Holy Land in the 860s, observed that it was safer for a Christian to travel in the dominions of the Caliph than on the high-ways of southern Italy. In the tenth century, Arab raids in the Alps made a pilgrimage to Rome an extremely hazardous undertaking. Even if the pilgrim escaped ambush and death, he was unlikely to find a monastery or hospice to receive him. Successive edicts emanating from the chancery of the Frankish Emperors failed to halt the decay of the Irish hospices, and a document of 841 shows that by then all the hostels maintained by the abbey of Monte Cassino were in ruins.

By mediaeval standards the period which followed the millen-nium was a peaceful one. All over Europe the barriers to travel were lifted. Most dramatic of all was the opening of the overland route to Jerusalem at the end of the tenth century. The victories of the Byzantine emperor Nicephorus Phocas placed Antioch once more in Christian hands and secured the route through Asia Minor. Basil II (976–1025) overthrew the Bulgarian empire and extended his dominions to the Danube. When duke Geysa of Hungary announced his conversion to Christianity in 985 the whole land route from western Europe to northern Syria was brought under nominal Christian rule. Geysa's son Stephen accommodated pilgrims at court and founded hospices for their use. The great monastery of Melk on the Danube was founded at this time by 'wealthy Christians from neighbouring provinces for the accommodation of pilgrims and the poor'. The overland route to Palestine was cheaper and safer than the sea voyage. The chance of a pilgrimage to the Holy Land was now embraced by an 'enormous multitude, both noble and common' whose grandfathers could never have afforded it.

At the opposite end of Europe developments of the same kind marked the rise of the great sanctuary of Santiago de Compostella. The decline of the Ummayad caliphate of Cordova left northern Spain in peace and freed the route from France to Santiago. The reign of Sancho the Great of Navarre (970–1035) marks an epoch as significant for the Spanish pilgrimage as the reign of Stephen of Hungary was for the Palestinian one. Hospices were constructed along the *camino de Santiago* by kings, bishops, and noblemen, and by a horde of immigrants from France. In the middle years of the century, Alfonso VI rebuilt every bridge between Logroño and Santiago. Diego Gelmirez, the great archbishop of Santiago, who completed the existing cathedral, made it his chief concern to keep open the 'Frenchmen's road'. To this end he rebuilt one ruinous town on the route, bought up another, and sprinkled northern Spain with churches and *mansiones* for the use of pilgrims. In his time the *camino* was probably the busiest trunk road in Christendom. When, in 1121, the ambassadors of the Almoravid Caliph of Cordova traversed the route on their way to León, they were taken aback by the crowds of travellers using it, and confessed that 'they had not thought so many people could be found in all Spain.'

Yet Santiago is scarcely heard of before the end of the ninth century, and no pilgrim is known by name until Gottschalk bishop of Le Puy visited it in 950. It was lifted to the front rank of mediaeval shrines by a combination of shrewd promotion and excellent communications. Other towns attempted, though less successfully, to do the same, and the eleventh century was probably the last in which totally specious 'discoveries' of relics could command universal acceptance. In France, England, and Italy, new shrines sprung up like mushrooms after rain, sometimes taking firm root, sometimes provoking a brief spurt of enthusiasm before falling back into oblivion. At Sens, archbishop Leoteric 'discovered' part of Moses' rod in the foundations of his cathedral, 'at the news of which the faithful converged on Sens not only from every province of France but even from Italy and overseas.' This, according to Radulph Glaber, was the first of an unprecedented spate of discoveries. In Italy the citizens of Salerno rediscovered their lost relics of St. Matthew the apostle in 1080, while the monks of Monte Cassino rediscovered in the rubble beneath their church the body of St. Benedict. Reading abbey was not founded until 1121, yet by the 1190s its list of relics contained 242 items, including twenty-nine relics of Our Lord, six of the Virgin, nineteen of the patriarchs and prophets, fourteen of apostles, seventy-three of martyrs, fifty-one of confessors, and forty-nine of virgins.

Several saints were more or less invented under the stimulus of the pilgrimage to Santiago. St. Leonard, who was venerated in a small town near Limoges on one of the busiest roads to Spain, was completely unknown to any writer before the eleventh century. He began to corruscate in miracles around 1017, and the first biography of the saint (a tissue of falsehoods) was written in about 1030.

Almost as fraudulent as the cult of St. Leonard were those of St. Eutrope at Saintes and St. Gilles near Arles, both of which owed their considerable prosperity to the fact that they lay on one or other of the roads to the great Galician sanctuary.

Lay Piety and the Monasteries

The strongly local character of eleventh-century piety is one of its most remarkable features. Glaber's boast that 'men of every nation' filled the roads to Jerusalem was the truth, but it was far from being the whole truth, for a very high proportion of them came from a few provinces of France and the Rhineland. Burgundy and Lorraine, Gascony, and above all Normandy and Aquitaine, were the homes of these long-distance pilgrims.

South-western France in particular was struck with great force by the spiritual movements of the eleventh century. The delicate civilization of Languedoc and Aquitaine thrived in an atmosphere of harsh religious extremes. In Limoges, Périgueux, and Angoulême, the proclamation of the millennium and the forcible baptism of the Jews were greeted with enthusiasm several decades before the same distressing symptoms appeared in the Rhineland. It was here that the movement for the moral reform of the Church took its most violent form. In 1031 the councils of Limoges and Bourges published canons of draconian severity against clerical immorality, pronouncing the bastards of priests to be slaves of the Church on whom no one could confer property and whom no judge could set at liberty.

Shortly after the millennium, Guy count of Limoges and his brother bishop Hilduin led a large party of pilgrims to the Holy Land ranging from the great seigneurs of his court to the most obscure citizens of Limoges. Another unwieldy band departed in 1010 under the leadership of the bishop of Périgueux and the count of Malemart. The army of pilgrims who accompanied William, count of Angoulême, to Jerusalem in 1026 was believed to be the largest mass pilgrimage which had left France since the opening of the overland route. Nor was it only to Jerusalem that these Aquitainian pilgrims went. Among local shrines, St.-Jean d'Angély, St. Eutrope at Saintes, and St.-Léonard de Noblat all leapt to prosperity in the wake of the pilgrimage to St. James. William V, duke of Aquitaine, apparently visited Santiago or Rome every year. Gerald of Corbie, founder and first abbot of La Sauve-Majeure had been to both Rome and Jerusalem in his time.

The Christian faith of the dukes of Normandy dated only from the middle of the tenth century, but few princes were more assiduous in sending alms to the Holy Places. Their subjects were notoriously the most energetic pilgrims of the eleventh century and became the leaders of the early crusades. The considerable cost of the pilgrimage of the abbot of St.-Vannes to Jerusalem was met by duke Richard, and the army of hangers-on who accompanied the abbot across central Europe included a substantial Norman contingent. Robert, duke of Normandy, went to Jerusalem in person in 1034. His grandson, Robert Curthose, was a prominent figure in the first crusade. In spiritual matters, as Orderic Vitalis remarked, the Normans tended to follow the example of their rulers. Normans were among the leaders of the Spanish crusades, and many of them visited Santiago. In Rome there were hostels which specialized in the business of accommodating them, and the horde of coins discovered beneath the walls of the basilica of St. Paul in 1843 includes a large number of eleventh-century coins minted in Rouen.

The aggressive habits of Norman travellers, pilgrims, and soldiers of fortune alike, earned them an unsavoury reputation which made it wise for them to make their pilgrimages in large, well-armed bands. In Italy, Norman pilgrims met with intense local hostility after a group of their compatriots, gathered at the shrine of Monte Gargano, had embarked with astonishing success on the conquest of Apulia. John, abbot of Fécamp, complained to pope Leo IX that Norman pilgrims were being robbed, imprisoned, or murdered 'every day' by enraged Italian peasants. The Norman conquest of southern Italy also earned them the undying hatred of the Greeks. For three years in the 1020s, every Norman who passed through Constantinople on his way to Jerusalem was cast into prison. Few Normans needed to travel far to find an enemy. Roger I de Tosny had made so many in his violent lifetime that he was afraid to make a pilgrimage to Conques lest he should meet one of them on the road. Instead he founded a church at Conches in Normandy and dedicated it to St. Foy.

In both Normandy and Aquitaine there were powerful movements of monastic revival. From the abbey of St. Martial at Limoges the influence of Cluny radiated through south-western France, while in the Bordelais a succession of monastic foundations enjoyed the patronage of the counts of Aquitaine. At La Sauve-Majeure Gerald of Corbie created a strange mixture of the monastic and eremitical lives which, by the time of his death in 1095, had been implanted in twenty priories throughout Gascony and Aquitaine. The same pattern can be discerned in Normandy, where the ancient foundations of Mont-St.-Michel and Jumièges combined with the new ones at Bec and Caen to produce a spiritual revival with a strong local character. The third area which sent pilgrims and crusaders in large numbers to Spain and Palestine was Burgundy, and here the influence of Cluny was overpowering. The Clunaic monk Radulph Glaber recorded a steady stream of departures for the Holy Land including several of those strange mass-pilgrimages which are so characteristic of the eleventh century. The enthusiasm for these distant shrines seems to have been strongest at Autun whence, in 1024–5, an immense leaderless mob of pilgrims left for the Holy Places. The news of their doings created a considerable stir in the surrounding provinces. Radulph Glaber's friends came to tell him in his priory at Bèze. Two years afterwards Richard of St.-Vannes confessed that their example had prompted him to make his own pilgrimage to the Holy Land. Aganon, bishop of Autun, visited the Holy Places at an advanced age in 1083, and lived to see the synod, held at Autun in 1094, which first proposed the launching of the crusade.

The enthusiasm which the fate of the Holy Places aroused in these three provinces of France had much to do with the monastic revival. The interest of the monks in the Holy Land was reflected in their libraries. The library of St. Martial at Limoges was a mine of topographical information on the Holy Land. It included a manuscript of the pilgrimage of Etheria which, had it survived, might have contained the part missing in our text. The library of Moissac contained several itineraries, including a manuscript of the fourth-century 'Bordeaux pilgrim' and another written in the vernacular ('*simplice sermona scripta*'). The books which they read, the hymns which they sang, the sculptures which they passed on their way through the cloister to the chapter house, all betray the same passionate interest in the Holy City. Several monasteries of southern France administered estates on behalf of the basilica of the Holy Sepulchre, which had by now acquired extensive endowments in the west.

The abbey of Cluny is often credited with having organized the pilgrimage to the Holy Land. Certainly the abbots looked on it with favour, and had done much to produce the spiritual environment which nurtured it. But of active direction there is no evidence at all. Much more significant is their role in promoting the pilgrimage to Santiago. The Spanish crusades were followed with great interest at Cluny, and the Burgundian knights who took part spent much of their spoil on the enrichment of the abbey. In the reign of Alfonso VI of Léon and Castile (1065–1109), Cluny obtained a firm grip on the Church in north-western Spain. In 1094 a Clunaic monk became bishop of Santiago. By the close of the eleventh century many of the shrines and monasteries on the pilgrims' roads to Santiago had become dependencies of Cluny, including Vézelay, St. Martial of Limoges, St.-Gilles, Moissac, and St. Eutrope at Saintes.

Particularly interesting is the hand of Cluny in composing the elaborate promotional literature put out by the church of Santiago. Most of it is contained in the *Liber Sancti Jacobi*, an exquisitely produced manuscript in the cathedral library. The *Liber* consists of five quite separate books bearing on the pilgrimage to St. James, proclaiming at the beginning and end that it was written for the benefit of the abbot of Cluny by pope Calixtus II. The attribution is fictitious, for there are parts which could not have been written by any Cluniac. But the second book, which consists of the *Miracles of St. James*, bears strongly the imprint of Cluny. Most of the miracles occurred to inhabitants of Burgundy, the Viennois, or the Lyonnais, and some happened within a few miles of the abbey. A few are attributed to a canon of Besançon, while another was related by an abbot of Vézelay. Three miraculous stories which St. Anselm told to abbot Hugh during a prolonged visit to Cluny in 1104 all appear with minor alterations in the *Miracles of St. James*. These miracles were Cluny's greatest contribution to the pilgrimage of St. James. They were plagiarized by every collector of marvellous stories, copied out in a great number of manuscripts from the twelfth century to the sixteenth, set forth in sculpture and stained glass throughout Europe. Arnaldo de Monte, a monk of Ripoll who saw the *Liber Sancti Jacobi* at Santiago in 1173, justly remarked that it was these miracles which had made the apostle 'shine forth as bright as the stars in every part of the world'.

Cluny's message faithfully reflected the spiritual values of the age. It insisted on the overriding importance of the remission of sins, and although men like St. Hugh had no doubt that the best possible chance of remission lay in taking the monastic habit, they appreciated the value of pilgrimage for those whose responsibilities prevented them from abandoning the worldly life. Abbot Mayeul, according to his twelfth-century biographer, 'knew that life itself was but a pilgrimage and that man lived as a fleeting guest upon the earth. He would often undertake the hardships of a pilgrim's life, expending all his bodily strength . . . on travelling across the Alps to Rome.' One of Mayeul's contemporaries, who knew him well, recorded that tears would come to his eyes as he approached the city 'for he knew that he would shortly behold the glorious apostles as if he were standing face to face with them.'

The message was addressed with special urgency to the nobility, whose social responsibilities forced on them a worldly existence and exposed them to the temptations of power. The abbots of Cluny, like so many reforming churchmen of their day, believed in knighthood as an order of the Church, upholding the values of the Church not only in war but also in peace. So, in his treatise *On the*

Christian Life, Bonizo of Sutri devoted a whole chapter to the duties of knights – the keeping of the peace, the protection of the poor, the defence of the Church, the persecution of heresy. The aristocratic poetry of the period shows that the nobility itself was acutely aware of its special spiritual needs. The *troubadour* William IX, duke of Aquitaine (d. 1127), sang of the dissipation of his youth and the imminence of death and judgement. A new age of religious sensitivity made William's contemporaries deeply uncomfortable about the inevitable sinfulness of their way of life. A century later the seigneur de Berzé was induced to join the fourth crusade by his overpowering feelings of guilt for the sins which his social status had forced on him:

> Li un de nous sont usurier
> Li autre larron et murdrier
> Li autre son plain de luxure
> E li autre de desmesure;
> Li autre sont plain d'envie
> E d'orgueill e de tricherie,
> E tantes manières pechommes
> Nous qui en ce vill siècle sommes
> Que molt grant merveille sera
> Se ja Diex de nul en ara
> Misericorde ne merci.

Some of us are usurers, others thieves and murderers. We sin by self-indulgence, by excess, pride, and deceit. We who live the worldly life are drawn so deeply into sin that it will be a miracle indeed if God has mercy on us.

But by almsgiving, pilgrimage, or taking the Cross, such men were offered an immediate opportunity of bringing that miracle about. 'Every day we see with our own eyes the death of men', wrote Roger count of Foix when presenting a church to Cluny; 'we know that we too must shortly die, and mindful of these things we have given much thought to the salvation of our souls and the remission of our most terrible sins.' It was a pity, as the seigneur de Berzé naïvely remarked, that one could not be warned of one's approaching death a year or two in advance, so as to prepare one's soul for the great tribunal 'where I shall have no essoins to delay the awful verdict.'

In the early tenth century, abbot Odo of Cluny presented to his contemporaries an idealized portrait of the model knight in his *Life of Gerald, count of Aurillac*. Gerald, who died in 909, is shown as a man who renounced the brutal and worldly side of knightly life, its hunting, revelry, and violence. He did not, like many aristocratic hermits, renounce his knightly status, but used it to keep the peace and protect his vassals and tenants. He remained in the world and yet above it, and he chose devotional exercises which were in keeping with his noble status. Pilgrimage was the foremost of these. Gerald first visited Rome in the 880s, accompanied by several knights of his household, and on his return he founded a monastery at Aurillac dedicated to St. Peter. Thereafter he went every other year to Rome, and in the intervening years visited other shrines, including those of St. Hilary at Poitiers, St. Martial at Limoges, and St. Martin at Tours. Odo believed that these pilgrimages were the outcome of his feelings of guilt, born of the conflict between his semi-monastic way of life and his knightly status.

'When he prayed to God from his innermost heart . . . he was afraid that God would not listen to him as long as evil thoughts remained in his mind. . . . For his sins, which might perhaps seem trivial to us, weighed heavily on his conscience and he was always thinking of ways to atone for them and secure the remission of them from a merciful God. And so God, in his mercy, showed him the way, that is, the way of prayer . . . and he developed the habit of going regularly to Rome.'

Idealized as it was, Odo's description did much to mould contemporary notions of lay piety. According to Adémar de Chabannes, William V, duke of Aquitaine, was 'amiable to all, of good counsel, generous with his wealth, a defender of the poor, the father of monks, and a builder and lover of churches, particularly the Church of Rome'. Like Gerald, he found pilgrimage a congenial method of expiating his sins, compatible with his almost royal status as the principal feudatory of the French Crown. From his earliest youth, 'he was accustomed to go every year to the tombs of the apostles in Rome, and if he could not get there, to St. James of Compostella. . . . Such was the splendour of his retinue and the nobility of his bearing on these occasions, that onlookers took him for a king rather than a duke.' The annual or biennial pilgrimage became a recognized mark of aristocratic piety. An Aquitainian knight whom St. Mary Magdalene raised from the dead in the mid-twelfth century used to go annually to Vézelay, as did Adalard, another knight who benefited from the Magdalene's miraculous powers.

No materials exist to make a statistical analysis of the clientele of a great mediaeval shrine, but the pilgrimage to Canterbury in the decade after Becket's death is probably typical of other major sanctuaries of the twelfth century. The two massive collections of miracles identify a total of 665 pilgrims who visited Canterbury between 1171 and 1177. The authors describe the social status of nearly two-thirds of these pilgrims, from which it appears that more than eight per cent of them were of the higher nobility (i.e. earls, great magnates, *potentes*, etc.), and no less than twenty-six per cent were knights. Some allowance should be made for the fact that the arrival of a nobleman was more likely to be recorded than that of a peasant, but these figures are out of all proportion to the numerical importance of the nobility in the population at large. Moreover the scraps of evidence which survive from continental shrines suggest that they are no means untypical. It was very different in the fourteenth century, when the Florentine diplomat Paolo Vergerio was told by his guide in Rome that bishops and princes had long abandoned the Lenten 'stations', which were now given over to the scum of the earth. Very different too from the situation in England on the eve of the Reformation, when the commissioners for the dissolution of the monasteries could dismiss the pilgrims they found at Bury St. Edmunds as poor fools and old women.

The Mortification of the Flesh

One of the less admirable characteristics of aristocratic pilgrimages was the comfortable, sometimes luxurious manner in which they were often performed. William V of Aquitaine was not the only nobleman whose manner of travelling led onlookers to believe that he was a king. The official historian of the dukes of Normandy recorded that such was the magnificence of duke Robert when passing through Constantinople in 1035, and such the largesse which he dispensed to the inhabitants, that they concluded that he was the king of France. Ealdred, bishop of Worcester, travelled through eastern Europe in 1059 'in such state as none had displayed before him'. Gunther, bishop of Bamberg, who led several thousand Germans on a mass pilgrimage to the Holy Land in 1064, informed the canons of his cathedral that the citizens of Constantinople, seeing his splendid array, had assumed him to be a king disguised as a bishop in order to avoid capture by the Arabs. Gunther had every reason to fear capture by the Arabs, for he and the other leaders of the host of pilgrims travelled in litters carried by liveried retainers; their tents were hung with silk and they ate splendid repasts nightly off gold and silver plate which was carried behind them on long trains of packhorses. As a result they found themselves attacked at every stage by the covetous inhabitants of eastern Europe and Palestine, losing much of their treasure and suffering heavy casualties. At least one contemporary, the annalist Lambert of Hersfeld, regarded this as a proper punishment for their sinful pride.

Others were inclined to agree with him, and for this reason there is a certain ambivalence amongst churchmen of the twelfth century towards the pilgrimage to the Holy Land. When a knight called Hugh Catula decided to go to Jerusalem instead of entering the monastery of Cluny, Peter the Venerable wrote to him protesting that although pilgrimage might be a valuable spiritual exercise if properly performed, it could not offer the same prospect of salvation as the monastic habit: 'it is better to serve God in humility and poverty for ever than to set out in grandeur and luxury for Jerusalem. Whence it follows that if it is good to visit the Holy Land and survey the places where Our Lord trod, then it is even better to enter Heaven where you will see Our Lord face to face.' Salvation, he remarked on another occasion, was 'achieved by holy lives, not holy places'. Yet Peter's attitude is not as straightforward as it appears. Writing to an abbot of his acquaintance, Peter commended his decision to go to Palestine, observing that a pilgrimage to the Holy Sepulchre over such a distance would be as pleasing to God as that first pilgrimage of the holy women to the tomb on Easter Sunday. In Peter's opinion, the ideal pilgrim was one whose pilgrimage was a monastic exercise as exacting as that which St. Jerome had required of his followers in the fourth century. Jerome's ideal was thus reasserted in all its rigour at a time when the coming of the penitential pilgrimage had made it very largely meaningless.

In the first book of the *Liber Sancti Jacobi* there is a remarkable sermon, known from its opening words as the sermon *Veneranda Dies*. It was attributed (wrongly) to pope Calixtus II, and intended to be read to pilgrims on the vigil of 30th December, one of the two feasts of St. James. 'The way of St. James', it begins, 'is fine but narrow, as narrow as the path of salvation itself. That path is the shunning of vice, the mortification of the flesh, and the increasing of virtue.' The preacher's purpose was to deny that pilgrims to St. James would automatically be saved as if the apostle had waved a magic wand over them, 'for a wand', he told them, 'is an external, material thing, whereas sin is an internal, spiritual evil.' Having thus dismissed the spiritual ideas of most of his audience, the preacher urged them to make their pilgrimage a monastic exercise of the most austere sort:

'The pilgrim may bring with him no money at all, except perhaps to distribute it to the poor on the road. Those who sell their property before leaving must give every penny of it to the poor, for if they spend it on their own journey they are departing from the path of the Lord. In times past the faithful had but one heart and one soul, and they held all property in common, owning nothing of their own; just so, the pilgrims of today must hold everything in common and travel together with one heart and one soul. To do otherwise would be disgraceful and outrageous. . . . Goods shared in common are worth much more than goods owned by individuals. Thus it is that the pilgrim who dies on the road with money in his pocket is permanently excluded from the kingdom of heaven. For what benefit can a man possibly derive from a pilgrimage undertaken in a spirit of sin?'

The preacher then turned his attention to those comfortable persons who ate and drank their way across the roads of Europe in the hope of salvation.

'Truly, these are not real pilgrims at all, but thieves and robbers who have abandoned the way of apostolic poverty and chosen instead the path of damnation. . . . If the Lord chose to enter Jerusalem on a mule rather than a horse, then what are we to think of those who parade up and down before us on horseback? . . . If St. Peter entered Rome with nothing but a crucifix, why do so many pilgrims come here with bulging purses and trunks of spare clothes, eating succulent food and drinking heady wine? . . . St. James was a wanderer without money or shoes and yet ascended to heaven as soon as he died; what, then, will happen to those who make opulent progresses to his shrine surrounded by all the evidence of their wealth?'

Turning from the general to the particular, the preacher directed his invective against those who entered Santiago fattened on the profits of usury, lying and swearing, joking, and singing bawdy, drunken songs. In fact, a pilgrimage was worthless unless it was accompanied by a total moral reformation in the pilgrim. Not only must he go to Santiago in the right spirit, but he must persevere in that spirit for the rest of his days. 'If he was previously a spoliator, he must become an almsgiver; if he was boastful he must be forever modest; if greedy, generous; if a fornicator or adulterer, chaste; if drunk, sober. That is to say that from every sin which he committed before his pilgrimage, he must afterwards abstain completely.'

These opinions were not simply mouthed in vain by a few idealistic churchmen. A small minority of pilgrims attempted to put them into practice, not, perhaps, on the roads to Santiago, but certainly in Palestine during the century of Christian rule. Some of them, like St. Godric, the hermit of Finchale who visited Jerusalem in the early twelfth century, tended the sick in the Hospital of St. John. Others chose the traditional eremetical life and retired to an isolated cabin in the desert wastes of Palestine. The Greek monk John Phocas, who visited the Holy Land in about 1175, met several of these lonely 'men of God'. In a hut by the Jordan, he encountered an aged Spaniard, 'a very pleasing and admirable person from whose conversation we derived great benefit.' Another hermit, this time an Italian from Calabria, was found with twelve brethren inhabiting a shed by the ruins of Mount Carmel. Even after the disaster which engulfed the Christian kingdom of Jerusalem in 1187, communities of Christian hermits survived in Syria, at the Quarantana, in the valley of the Jordan and the district of Galilee. Jacques de Vitry, writing in the 1220s, regarded the preservation of their way of life as a legitimate reason for launching another crusade. Those pilgrims who became hermits and recluses were drawn chiefly from the noble and well-to-do. Rayner Pisani, who suddenly went to live alone on Mount Tabor in the middle of the twelfth century, was a wealthy merchant of Pisa whose 'conversion' occurred when he listened to a sermon on the humanity of Christ, during a business visit to Tyre. 'Because the life of the world was onerous', wrote his biographer and disciple, 'he prayed to God day and night to help him put aside all his wealth, to put on the pilgrim's habit and be worthy of it.' Many of these hermits came from northern Italy, the birthplace of the eremitical movement of the eleventh and twelfth centuries. William of Mallavalle, who ended his days as a recluse in the wilderness north of Pisa, was a knight who had marked his 'conversion' to the spiritual life by 'throwing aside his breastplate' and making a pilgrimage to the Holy Places. Such figures were the spiritual heroes of the twelfth century, and their example was frequently highly infectious. In June 1200, when Berthold von Neuenburg sold all his belongings and retired to a hermitage in Palestine, he found many followers in the Breisgau region; 'a large number of noblemen, together with their wives and children, sold all their goods and vowed to become serfs of the Holy Sepulchre.' The ideal of renouncing the world was adopted by some crusaders. Jacques de Vitry knew a crusader who had his family brought before him as he left in order to make his departure the more bitter and meritorious. Indeed, the preacher complained that some crusaders were worthless as fighting men on account of the austerities which they inflicted on themselves. Nevertheless it was generally agreed that a crusading army was bound by spiritual conventions which would not have applied to any other army. Hence when Saladin offered to accommodate Hubert Walter at his expense in Jerusalem, the archbishop refused on the ground that 'we are pilgrims and can never accept such comforts.'

For pilgrims and crusaders alike the normal method of renouncing the world was to enter a monastery on their return. Peter the Venerable heartily approved of those knights whose pilgrimages were merely the prelude to taking the monastic habit. Cluny received many of them. Peter tells us of a knight who gave his horses, fine clothes, and money to Cluny and proceeded 'as a pauper' to Jerusalem before ending his days in the abbey. Another spent forty days in Rome and then took the habit at Cluny.

Even those who made no attempt to live up to this ideal, usually made some conventional gestures towards the mortification of the flesh. Pilgrimages on foot were very common, and among sincere penitents almost obligatory. A long tradition of the Church held that walking was the most virtuous method of travelling. According to Sulpicius Severus, St. Martin had expressed his contempt for priests who went mounted about their duties. St. Hilary of Arles (d. 449) is stated to have walked to Rome at the end of his life 'because he so much admired the ideal of poverty that he insisted on doing without horse or mule.' As so often happened, the hagiographic tradition of the early Church moulded the behaviour of later generations. Thus the idealized 'holy man' of the eleventh century, in this case St. Aibert, travelled on foot:

'Walking completely barefoot, clothed in a simple tunic, and with scarcely a penny on them, he and his companions set out for Rome rich in the abundance of their poverty. They rode on horseback rarely or never, and used their mule only to help weak and infirm pilgrims whom they met on the road.'

Matilda of Thornbury walked to Canterbury on her crutches at the end of the twelfth century, and even so august a pilgrim as the countess of Clare threw away her shoes as she began her pilgrimage. Barefoot pilgrims were particularly esteemed, and at Limoges in the fourteenth century there is even a reference to pilgrims arriving completely naked. The author of the *Life of St. Godric of Finchale* gloried in the austerities of the saint during his journeys to Jerusalem. Not only did he go barefoot till his feet were covered in hideous sores, but he ate nothing but dry barley bread; if only fresh bread could be obtained he would keep it in his bag until it was hard and almost unbreakable. Pilgrims rode on horseback at their peril, risking not only the imprecations of idealistic churchmen, but also the possibility of divine chastisement. A canon of Dol, riding to Chartres at the close of the eleventh century, began to feel ill as he approached Orléans, and so thought it prudent to do the rest of the journey on foot. John King found his horse unusually restless on the road to Canterbury and took it as a divine warning to dismount. A woman who suffered from deformed feet was obliged to go to Reading abbey in a carriage and pair, but she was healed during the journey, and thereupon dismounted and proceeded on foot. Thus, although the austere warnings of the Santiago preacher fell on deaf ears, a distant echo of his voice was sometimes heard on the pilgrimage roads.

Renewal and Death

One of the stories which Jacques de Vitry collected for use in his sermons told of two brothers, the one an assiduous visitor of shrines, the other not. When they died, the pilgrim was escorted to heaven by flights of angels, while the other made his way alone. At the tribunal of St. Peter both brothers were found wanting, but only the pilgrim was admitted: 'open to him', the Lord commanded, 'for he was a pilgrim.' The story, like so many of Jacques de Vitry's, expresses in the simplest pictorial fashion the aspirations of his audiences. The overwhelming majority of mediaeval pilgrims expected to have their sins expunged from their souls as if by a magic wand, and the austere warnings of the preacher of *Veneranda Dies* fell on deaf ears. The moral theology of the Church laid an overpowering emphasis on the sinfulness of men. The material world they lived in, everything they touched and saw, all that they enjoyed, drew them towards sin, and the few introspective writings which survive are all characterized by a morbid obsession with the accumulated burden of guilt. The penitential system of the eleventh and twelfth centuries offered only a partial solution, for by preserving an elaborate distinction between guilt and punishment, it left the sinner with most of his burden. The prospect of a second baptism, of starting his spiritual life anew, stood before him like a mirage, irresistibly attractive.

This was what the great shrines offered, with increasing openness, to the sinner. Baptismal imagery constantly recurs in the devotional literature which they put out. At the shrine of Thomas Becket criminals were reformed, sinners amended, debauchers returned to the path of holiness: 'the moment they approach the shrine . . . they promise to mend their ways as if rebaptized in the font of their own tears.' Sentiments of this sort became a commonplace of the later middle ages. Christ informed the Swedish mystic St. Bridget in a vision that she was cleansed of her sins at the moment of entering the basilica of the Holy Sepulchre 'as if she had just arisen from the baptismal font'. When a noble woman of Bologna entered the Franciscan church of the Portiuncula in 1336, a voice declared to her: 'just as you were freed of all sin in the baptismal font, so you are now, by the act of entering this church, relieved of the entire burden of your sins.'

One of the most popular legends of the middle ages was the story of St. Mary the Egyptian, a prostitute who was purified by a visit to the Holy Land. On the feast of the Invention of the Cross she attempted to enter the basilica of the Holy Sepulchre together with the crowds of other pilgrims, but a miraculous force prevented her from passing through the door. Then Mary realized that she alone was unworthy to enter that place. Guided by the Blessed Virgin she walked to the point in the Jordan where Christ had been baptized, and swam across, to live a hermit's life on the other side. In the eleventh and twelfth centuries the story enjoyed an undying popularity. Honorius of Autun preached on St. Mary the Egyptian, and Hildebert of Tours wrote her life in verse. Her story was sculpted on the capitals of the church of St. Etienne in Toulouse. Within a decade of the Christian conquest of Jerusalem, the door which she had been unable to enter and the place where she had immersed herself in the Jordan were marked out for the benefit of pilgrims.

St. Mary the Egyptian had purified herself by reliving the baptism of Christ. The sins of her past had been obliterated and her spiritual life begun afresh. It was this process of regeneration which mediaeval pilgrims to the Holy Land tried to repeat by bathing in huge numbers in the Jordan. The biographer of St. Silvin, writing at the beginning of the ninth century, recorded that the saint walked to the Jordan 'to the very place where Christ, the son of God, was baptized ... and immersed himself totally in the holy waters. Overcome with elation, he emerged from the river as if reborn, his spiritual ills cured, and his life's desire fulfilled.' This symbolic act eloquently explains what it was that brought pilgrims to the Holy Land in such numbers. It became, in the eleventh century, an almost obligatory part of any pilgrimage to Jerusalem to trek the twenty miles to the Jordan and baptize oneself in its waters. After the capture of Jerusalem by the crusaders a large detachment of the victorious army, led by Raymond of St. Gilles and the visionary Peter Bartholomew, marched to the Jordan and swam, fully clothed, across the river. On emerging from the water Raymond was presented by the hermit with a palm of Jericho and, having fulfilled thus the object of his pilgrimage, he began his homeward journey. The ritual was not peculiar to western Europeans. The Danish hero Thorstein Ricardson baptized himself in the Jordan in about 1025. The Russian princess Euphrosine, as she lay dying in Jerusalem, was unable to go to the Jordan, but one of her companions brought her some of the precious water in a bottle, 'which she received with joy and gratitude, drinking it and spreading it over her body to wash away the sins of the past'. When Dietrich of Wurzburg visited the Holy Land in c. 1172, he counted 60,000 pilgrims (an exaggeration, no doubt) standing with candles in their hands on the banks of the

Jordan. So popular had the ritual become that it was adopted at Santiago. Two miles before the city there was a stream where French pilgrims were in the habit of totally immersing themselves 'for love of the apostle'.

According to Jacques de Vitry there were three reasons for the pilgrim to immerse himself in the Jordan. First, the waters of the Jordan were a relic which Christ had sanctified by the touch of His flesh. Secondly, every pilgrim should seek to imitate, however inadequately, the perfection of Christ; by bathing in the Jordan, Christ had bestowed upon it regenerative powers through which the pilgrim could enjoy a second baptism. Finally, Naaman the Syrian had been cleansed of his leprosy in the Jordan 'which was the model of purification for future generations'.

The tendency of the later middle ages was to venerate the Jordan exclusively as a relic. In a guide-book written at the end of the thirteenth century, the three reasons given by Jacques de Vitry are reduced to one, namely that 'these are the very waters which came into contact with the body of Christ, our Redeemer.' In 1483 Felix Faber reported that several knights of his party dived into the Jordan fully clothed, in the belief that their clothes would become impenetrable to the weapons of their enemies. Others brought small bells with them which they dipped in the water in the hope that, if they were rung thereafter, no thunder or lightning would threaten any area within earshot. 'However whether these vulgar opinions are true or false', the Dominican discreetly added, 'I leave for the sensible reader to decide for himself.' Certainly it was by now common for pilgrims to bring bottles of Jordan water home with them, for in 1480, as a pilgrim ship lay becalmed in the bay of Jaffa, its passengers vigorously debated the question whether the boat was capable of movement so long as part of the Jordan remained on board. One of them stood on the rail and announced that he had himself seen a papal bull at St. Peter's in Rome excommunicating those who removed water from the Jordan. This statement was evidently found convincing, for most of the pilgrims hastily threw their phials of water overboard, and the wind rose immediately.

When princess Euphrosine came to Jerusalem in 1173, it was with the fixed intention of dying there. A desire to die in Jerusalem was in fact expressed by several of those pilgrims of the eleventh century who believed that the end of the world was imminent. It is closely allied with the notion that the Holy Places offered to the sinner the means of wiping clean the slate of his past sins. Pilgrims who felt that they had just experienced a process of spiritual renewal hoped to die while they were still in their perfect state. The notorious sinner Eskill Sveinsson prayed: 'I am afraid, O Lord, that when I return to my native country, I shall be seduced by Fortune and tempted into sin, and then I shall return to my old ways. I pray you therefore that for the good of my soul, you will deliver me now from the bonds of this earthly life and from the weight of my sins, and lead me to everlasting rest.' 'Lord Jesus Christ, who knowest all things', another begged, 'if I cannot purge myself of my former vices, then permit me not to return to my country but grant that I may die here . . . and be saved.' According to Caesarius of Heisterbach his prayer was answered, 'and thus, a few days later, he was united with the citizens of the heavenly Jerusalem.' The field of Aceldama, where pilgrims who died in Jerusalem were buried, bore eloquent witness to the vast number of pilgrims who died far from their homes, happy in the conviction that the stains of sin had been washed away.

The place of a man's burial was a matter of some importance to him, for the mediaeval Church firmly believed in the bodily resurrection of the dead. Those who were buried near the shrine of a great saint would rise in that very place on the Last Day, in the company of the saint. He would throw a mantle of protection over them at the tribunal of Christ, and they would ascend to Heaven in his wake. In Rogier van der Weyden's great altarpiece of the *Last Judgement*, in the hospital at Beaune, the blessed and the damned can be seen emerging from the ground and reaching out to grasp the robes of the saints above them. In the early Church this was a very powerful idea which shaped the attitudes of churchmen to the burial of the dead. Paulinus of Nola had his son buried near the martyrs' tombs at Alcala, in Spain, 'so that the proximity of their blood might purify his'. When the early Christian cemetery at Arles was excavated, it was found that all the sarcophagi were piled, one on top of the other, over the tomb of a local martyr. In the middle ages this notion was held with the same immovable conviction. When abbot Suger closed his biography of Louis VI with an account of the obsequies of the dead king at St.-Denis, he concluded with these words: 'in that place he awaits the resurrection of the dead at the last day. At St.-Denis he is closer in spirit to the army of the saints because his body is buried close to the holy martyrs Denis, Eleutheria, and Rusticus. And so at the Last Day he will benefit by their advocacy.'

At the Last Day Christ too would be found in the place where he had been buried, and would dispense judgement to men from his sepulchre. The author of a guide to the Holy Land, written at the beginning of the twelfth century, states as a fact that the Last Judgement would be held in the valley of Jehosaphet on the eastern side of Jerusalem, not far, in fact, from the pilgrims' cemetery of Aceldama. Some seventy years later a German pilgrim reported that the tribunal would be set up in a field in the valley of Ennon and that simple-minded pilgrims were in the habit of reserving stones for themselves to sit on and enjoy a good view. This belief still prevailed at the end of the fifteenth century, when several of Felix Faber's companions set about claiming seats not only for themselves but also for their friends at home. The pilgrim who was buried within yards of the site of the Last Judgement would be resurrected in the holiest place on the earth. Just as Louis VI would enjoy the patronage of St. Denis at the awful tribunal, so the pilgrim who died in Jerusalem would have the favour of the divine judge himself. This is what the Autun pilgrim Lethbald meant when, in 1025, he entered the basilica of the Anastasis in Jerusalem, and prayed to be allowed to die there, 'for I believe that thus . . . my soul shall follow in the track of yours and enter Paradise.'

In the eleventh century, millenarian fears, always a strong undercurrent of mediaeval thought, gave a peculiar urgency to the quest for the remission of sins. No period had such a strong belief in the imminence of divine judgement. To mediaeval men history was not an ever-continuing process. It had a formal, dramatic unity, for the events of which the chroniclers wrote were the direct consequences of the fall of Man and they led directly to the end of the world. The chronicle of Otto of Friesing, who died in 1158, begins at the Creation and ends with the Last Judgement. 'Manifest signs portend the destruction of the world, and ruin builds up around us', began a charter of the seventh century. These fears were strangely linked with political events, for chaos and disorder in the affairs of men were certain portents of the Last Day. In the middle of the tenth century the notion was embodied in a little book, the *Libellus de Antichristo* of Adso of Montiérender, which held the field amongst millenarian writings until it was replaced in the later middle ages by the even stranger works of Joachim of Fiore. Adso borrowed from the Book of Daniel the prophecy that there would be four empires in the history of the world, asserting that the fourth and last of these empires was the Roman empire. Like all his contemporaries, Adso recognized in the Christian German empire of his own day a continuation of the Roman empire, and it followed that when the Christian German empire ended, so too would the history of the world.

Adso himself had every confidence in the resilience of the empire. But he wrote at the end of a century of political chaos during which western Europe had been continuously raided and pillaged by Arabs, Norsemen, and Magyars, and its political fabric had come close to total dissolution. His contemporaries had no reason to be confident of the future, and the imminence of divine retribution was their constant preoccupation. They not only knew that the world was drawing near to its end, but they had clear ideas as to how and where the Last Judgement would occur, and what signs would precede it. There would be famine, earthquakes, and other natural disasters, followed by the dissolution of all political power, as the Apocalypse had foretold. Then Antichrist would be born in Babylon of the tribe of Dan and would rule the world until the descent of Christ and his saints. When the time came for the dissolution of all political power the emperor would march to Jerusalem and surrender the insignia of office in the church of the Holy Sepulchre. There he would witness with his own eyes the Last Judgement. The polemicist Benzo of Alba saw his contemporary, the emperor Henry IV, in this role. He would be the last emperor, and would lead his army to Jerusalem 'where he will visit the Holy Sepulchre and be crowned by He who lives for ever and ever, and whose tomb shall shine forth in glory.' At that moment the earthly and the celestial Jerusalem would be one.

In his youth, Abbo of Fleury had heard a popular preacher in Paris promise his audience that the world would end in the year 1000. A profound fear of imminent destruction undoubtedly existed in the tenth century, but the millennium itself was an uneventful year. It required some portentous event to liberate these suppressed feelings, and this event occurred in 1009 with the total destruction of the Holy Sepulchre in Jerusalem by caliph Hakim. The destruction, which was the result of a short-lived outburst of hysteria in an unbalanced caliph, had profound effects in the west. Suddenly it was clear that Hakim was the Antichrist of whom the Apocalypse had spoken. In parts of France the prevailing view was that Hakim's act had been suggested to him by the Jews of Orléans, and the mob reacted by invading the ghettos and murdering or forcibly baptizing the inhabitants. In some towns, particularly in Aquitaine, they were actively encouraged by the clergy. From western France, Normandy, and Burgundy departed the first of a series of mass pilgrimages to the Holy Land. The bulk of these pilgrims were obscure, frightened men, but amongst them were several distinguished churchmen and a few lay princes to testify to the striking homogeneity of eleventh-century piety. Gauzlin, abbot of Fleury and later archbishop of Bourges, a bishop of Périgord, Raymond count of the Rouergue, and Fulk Nerra were amongst the pilgrims of that year.

An even larger exodus followed the thousandth anniversary of the death of Christ in 1033. The year was ushered in by famine and torrential rainstorms, which lasted throughout the spring and flattened the crop in many parts of France. 'Men thought', wrote

Radulph Glaber, 'that the very laws of nature and the order of the seasons were reversed, that those rules which governed the world were replaced by chaos. They knew then that the end of the world had arrived.' Glaber was born in Burgundy and lived there all his life. His work gives us an insight into the religious imagination of the eleventh century, for he shared the moods and enthusiasms of those whom he described. A superstitious and emotional man, he was several times possessed by the devil and was plainly an embarrassment to his superiors, who moved him from one monastery to another at frequent intervals. In 1033 Glaber was living at Cluny, and from behind its sheltered walls observed the growing panic of his fellow-countrymen. Beginning in Aquitaine, the terror had reached Burgundy by summer. Large assemblies of men joined in public displays of repentance and swore to keep the 'peace of God'. 'The entire people, great and small, willingly attended, each one ready to obey the instructions of his pastor as if he had heard a voice from the sky speaking to all men on earth.' The wealthier pilgrims who returned from Jerusalem at that time, expressed their relief and gratitude for the survival of mankind by founding churches. 'I Hictor', wrote one of them, 'mindful of the compassionate kindness of God the supreme judge, do hereby found this church on the occasion of my return from Jerusalem. For I know that the fleeting life of the world is brittle and yet harsh; I know too how great is the reward of the virtuous, and how dreadful the torments of the damned.' Hervé, archdeacon of the church of Ste.-Croix d'Orléans had been convinced in 1033 of the approaching dissolution of the earth:

> 'The life of the world is uncertain and fragile. No one knows when his passage on earth will end, for does not the whole world rush rapidly to its destruction? . . . I pondered many nights on the frailty of life and so came to live in fear of sudden death. I went to Jerusalem to atone for my sins and to beg for mercy on my knees. . . . Now, God having permitted me to return safely, . . . I have endowed this church, . . . not only for the remission of my own most grievous sins but for the salvation of the souls of my family; for my parents Havranus and Adela and my brother Peter, all dead, as well as for the rest of my family who are still, thank God, alive.'

The mass pilgrimage of 1033, though probably the most dramatic, was not the last occasion on which eschatological fears were to send frightened hordes to the Holy Land. The turn of Germany came in 1064. The army of pilgrims which left Passau in that year seem to have been persuaded that the world would end when Easter Sunday fell on the 26th March, the date given in some mediaeval calendars for the original resurrection. This coincidence occurred in 1065 for the first time in seventy-three years. Again, on 15th July 1099, when the crusading army entered Jerusalem, some of them saw in their achievement the prelude to the end of the world, and the dazed remnants of the Provençal contingent waited, silent and inactive, for the descent of Christ and his saints.

Two images of God drew the attention of men to the Holy Places. The religion of the eleventh and twelfth centuries was characterized by a new devotion to the humanity of Christ, to his nativity and childhood as much as to his death and resurrection. The formal, stylized, infinitely distant, God of the Moissac tympanum gave way to the human God of Chartres cathedral, and thus to the suffering God of Cimabue and Giotto. But the same Christ who took on the weakness and vulnerability of manhood was also the terrible judge portrayed with frightening realism on the west fronts of Conques or Autun. Here indeed, carved in stone, was the *rex tremenda majestatis* whom the pilgrim sought to appease with his prayers. In contemporary eyes these two notions offered no contradiction: the one led on naturally to the other.

'Tell me then', wrote Peter Damian in his treatise on flagellation, 'you who proudly mock the Passion of Christ, you who disdain to be stripped and scourged with him, you who laugh at his nakedness and sufferings and dismiss them as the triflings of pious old fools, tell me what you will do when he who hung naked on the Cross appears in glorious majesty, surrounded by angels and the incomparable splendour of all creation. What will you do when he who took on the ignominy of humanity and death, comes to judge the living and the dead?'

Only by imitating Christ the man could one placate Christ the judge. In this way the romantic desire to relive in one's imagination the life of Christ, was combined with a very real fear of His anger, and a firm conviction that by renouncing one's ordinary life and following His footsteps in the Holy Land, the force of that anger could be deflected. Thus it was to a stern and vengeful God that the author of the *Dies Irae* addressed his impassioned plea for mercy:

> *Iuste iudex ultionis*
> *Donum fac remissionis*
> *Ante diem rationis.*

The minority of pilgrims who lived according to the precepts of the sermon *Veneranda Dies* felt that they had fully earned this mercy.

They had, at least temporarily, renounced the world and entered an order of the Church, an elite body whose chances of salvation were infinitely greater than those of the mass of humanity. This feeling of belonging to an initiated caste of holy men, as formal in its own way as the monastic order itself, the pilgrim expressed by wearing a distinctive 'uniform', and by receiving at his departure the blessing of the Church. The great monastic reformer William of Hirsau, who always had the 'mot juste' for everything, distinguished five orders of the Church in Germany, for each of which he had a separate spiritual message. To the order of bishops and priests, he would teach theology and ecclesiastical law; to the order of monks, humility and piety; to the order of laymen, faith and submission; to the order of virgins, chastity; and the order of pilgrims and hermits he would teach to be content with their lot 'for their faith has made them glorious in the sight of God and the world is at their feet'.

CHAPTER IX

THE LEGACY OF THE CRUSADES

The first crusade is the central event in the history of mediaeval Christianity. In proclaiming the holy war at the council of Clermont in 1095, Urban II promised salvation to a world obsessed with its own sinfulness. 'God has invented the crusade', Guibert reflected, 'as a new way for the knightly order and the vulgar masses to atone for their sins.' In the two centuries which followed, the crusade offered a route to salvation which eclipsed every other spiritual exercise. In the celebrated phrase of Gibbon, the pope had unwittingly 'touched upon a nerve of exquisite feeling'. Yet, although it was born in the mood of intense spiritual feeling which hung over the eleventh century, the crusading movement was ultimately to destroy the spiritual values of Christian Europe. Those who fought on the crusades or contributed to their cost, received a 'quantum of salvation' which was precisely defined and measured. In the course of time their rights and duties were embodied in the codes of canon and civil law. This uncompromising precision greatly simplified the moral values of Christendom, and it was without doubt the root cause of the astonishing success of crusading preachers from Peter the Hermit to Jacques de Vitry. The crusades brought a new formality to the notion of pilgrimage, a formality which radically altered its character. Thus the doctrine of indulgences, whose development was greatly assisted by the crusades, transformed the pilgrim's journey into a ritual, devoid of the intensely personal and spiritual quality of the pilgrimages of the eleventh century. The enforcement of the crusading vow became the principal method of recruiting crusaders, and in its wake came an apparatus of dispensations and financial commutations with far-reaching consequences for the spiritual life of the west.

These symptoms affected every aspect of spiritual life in varying degrees. Pilgrimages were, perhaps, affected more than any other because the crusaders regarded themselves as pilgrims, and in contemporary eyes, so they were. They shared the same hopes of spiritual rebirth, performed the same rites, enjoyed the same legal privileges and expected the same esteem from their fellow men. They were surprised and angry when the inhabitants of Asia Minor refused to sell them food 'taking us to be no pilgrims but mere bandits and plunderers'. Moreover, the early crusades were joined not only by 'armed pilgrims' of this sort but by crowds of unarmed hangers-on who travelled in the unshakeable conviction that God would reward their piety by delivering Jerusalem into their hands without a battle. The expeditions of 1096 and 1146 were both accompanied by a lunatic fringe which castigated in violent terms the bearing of any arms at all. This fifth column was brutally excluded from the later crusades, but their ideal of conquest by holiness alone lived on. Even the sober Jacques de Vitry believed that the crusaders had lost Jerusalem on account of their degenerate and sinful ways. The notion of the true crusader remained inseparable from that of the pilgrim.

The Pilgrim's Vow

'Is there anything that a man can do to atone for a vow unfulfilled?' asked Dante of Beatrice in Paradise; 'nothing', she replied, 'for when you consent, God consents, and nothing can stand in place of God's consent.'

Though the vow of pilgrimage was as old as pilgrimage itself, the age of its greatest impact began with Urban II's momentous pronouncement at Clermont. Towards the end of his speech, the pope required every crusader to swear a solemn oath to fulfill his pilgrimage and, when he had raised his hearers to a high pitch of emotion, the pope had crosses quickly distributed among the crowd 'for whoever accepted this sign . . . could never go back on his decision.' Fifty years later St. Bernard too had crosses sewn to the tunics of his audience when he was preaching the second crusade at Vézelay. In 'taking the cross' the pilgrim, often unwittingly, passed a point of no return. So much so that a thirteenth-century satirist warned his readers against attending revivalist meetings lest they should suddenly find themselves 'imprisoned by crosses'.

Canon law prescribed that no one could break a vow of pilgrimage and be saved. Whether the culprit was a peaceful pilgrim or an armed crusader was immaterial. The vow was enforced by excommunication and in parts of Europe failure to fulfil it was punished by both secular and ecclesiastical courts. Such sanctions were rarely necessary in the twelfth century, but as enthusiasm for the crusade began to wane, so the authorities became more vigorous in their attempts to enforce vows. The fourth crusade, which developed into a war against the Christian empire of Byzantium, was the first to encounter really serious recruiting problems. Innocent III sternly reminded the Hungarian king of his crusading vow. The doge of Venice was informed that his salvation should be regarded as unlikely 'if, ignoring the wrath of God, you fail to do as you are told.' The fifth crusade drew a similar series of testy letters from Honorius III. The tardiness of the emperor Frederick II in fulfilling his vow involved him in a prolonged dispute with the papacy which culminated in his excommunication.

In some circumstances a pilgrim might even be bound by the vow of another. In a letter to duke Andrew of Hungary, Innocent III declared in general terms that if a pilgrim died before fulfilling his vow, his heir might be made to do it for him. This ambitious idea cannot have been enforced in practice, but it had a certain moral authority even when the pilgrim was not a crusader. In the 1170s a parish priest in Lincolnshire was cured of a fatal illness after two women had vowed in his name to visit the shrine of St. Thomas of Canterbury. A vision of St. Thomas made it quite clear that he was bound by the vow: 'others promised for you; the fulfilment of their promise is your duty.'

Until the thirteenth century, these stern rules admitted few exceptions. It was agreed that vows made in childhood were not binding, and Alexander III formally declared this to be a principle of the canon law. Would-be crusaders who were prevented by illness or some other impediment had always been allowed to send a substitute, as Thierry, duke of Lorraine, did in 1096. Such dispensations were common enough in the twelfth century, and in 1200 Innocent III laid down a procedure for granting them. The procedure applied to crusaders and non-crusaders alike, but in the course of the thirteenth century a distinction was gradually recognized. The canonist Henry of Susa appreciated that there was a difference between 'pilgrims who fight and pilgrims who pray'. In practice an ordinary pilgrim obtained his dispensation without much difficulty.

As dispensations became increasingly common, the crusading vow imperceptibly ceased to be a spiritual act. The growing difficulty of recruiting volunteers made the thirteenth-century crusades dependent to some extent on expensive mercenaries. In 1240 Gregory IX made an important pronouncement to the effect that all crusading vows could be commuted for money whether or not the would-be crusader was capable of fighting in person. According to the jaundiced English chronicler Matthew Paris, large numbers of women, children, and old men took the cross in order that they could buy a dispensation and still gain the crusading indulgence. Thereafter, an excuse was sometimes required, sometimes not. The friars who preached the crusade in 1290 were empowered to commute vows for two hundred *livres* of Tours, and the same authority was given to them in 1308.

Until the end of the fourteenth century the Church did not concern itself much with vows of pilgrimage, other than those involving the Holy Land. Such vows were, however, enforced by strong spiritual pressures especially if they had been made in public. Countless popular stories related the fate of those foolhardy persons who broke a promise to the saint. One was struck blind, another afflicted with paralysis or leprosy. Infirmities cured by the saint returned if the patient failed to show his gratitude by praying at his shrine. An English knight whose broken arm was healed by St. James forgot to visit the hand of St. James at Reading, and the apostle therefore broke his other arm. 'And by this example', the author of the tale concluded, 'one may see how powerful is faith and how dreadful it is to break an oath.' By promising to visit a shrine, the pilgrim conceived that he was uniting himself to the saint by a bond of mutual self-interest: the saint wished to be venerated and desired offerings for his clergy; the pilgrim wanted to be protected against sin, disease, and natural disasters. Failure to fulfil a vow was both sinful and imprudent. This notion was implicit in the prayer of a Polish nobleman who visited St. Gilles-de-Provence towards the end of the eleventh century, after narrowly escaping death in a hunting accident: 'Holy St. Gilles, on condition that you offer me your good offices with the Lord and preserve me from human perils, I solemnly agree that I shall mend my ways and forthwith make a pilgrimage to your shrine.'

Bargains of this sort were particularly common in the fourteenth and fifteenth centuries, when fewer miracles were reported at the shrines themselves. In large miracle collections of this period, the great majority of stories tell of marvellous happenings near the pilgrim's own home. He has come to the shrine, not to beg for a miracle, but to give thanks for one which has already occurred. When, in 1388, St. Martial of Limoges suddenly began to corruscate in wonders, in almost every case the miracle occurred before the pilgrimage; the one was, in fact, conditional upon the other. A citizen of Limoges declared that 'if the ever-glorious St. Martial were to heal my sick son, I would offer a candle at his shrine'; the son recovered and the father presented his candle in the saint's basilica. A cowherd swore to visit St. Martial if he protected his cows from English bandits. Another would do so if ever he found his lost gold pennies. Thus the subtle idea that human troubles were caused by sin and removed by penitence slowly lost its force, and was replaced by the simpler notion of a contract, freely entered into, between the saint and his votary.

Indulgences

When a Christian confessed his sins and sought absolution, a penance was imposed on him. An indulgence was a formal act of the Church by which that penance was remitted. An indulgence did not pretend to release the sinner from his guilt (only confession and absolution could do that), but in the words of a thirteenth-century schoolman it 'excused him from suffering the temporal punishment due for his sins'.

The indulgence grew from modest beginnings. In the tenth century the Frankish Church allowed penitents to redeem their penances by payment if they were physically incapable of performing them, and remissions of this sort were pronounced to be legitimate by the council which met at Rheims in 923–4. Such indulgences were only granted if the circumstances of the individual case warranted it. The earliest general indulgences, offered to anyone who was prepared to fulfil the conditions, did not make their appearance until the eleventh century, when Christendom was becoming morbidly preoccupied with the problems of *remissio peccatorum*. The rapid development of indulgences, like that of the vow of pilgrimage, owed everything to the crusades. At the council of Clermont, Urban II declared in unequivocal terms that 'every man who sets out for Jerusalem with the army to liberate the Church of God shall have the entire penance for his sins remitted.' Urban was offering them a 'plenary' indulgence, that is, an indulgence which erased all the penance due for the sins of a lifetime. It was, in the words of the Lateran council of 1215, a guarantee of salvation.

The crusading indulgence was the first plenary indulgence, and for two centuries it remained the only one. But partial indulgences, which remitted a stated proportion of the sinner's outstanding penance, made their appearance at about the same time. The earliest papal indulgence which can be accepted as authentic dates from 1091, when Urban II promised that all who assisted the restoration and repair of the Norman monastery of St. Austreberthe at Pavilly would enjoy the remission of 'a fourth part of the penance enjoined by a bishop or priest'. During Urban's tour of France in 1095 several pilgrimages were favoured with indulgences of this kind. 'It is right to consent to pious requests', one of them begins, 'in order to help the sinner to achieve his salvation. . . . We recommend therefore that the church of St. Nicholas of Angers be honoured, protected, and visited by the faithful . . ., and we accordingly remit a seventh part of the penance imposed for any sins, for all those who visit the church in a devout frame of mind on the anniversary of its dedication.'

During the twelfth century the papacy granted indulgences sparingly, and made only modest claims for them. Others, however, were less restrained. The churches which received indulgences grossly exaggerated their efficacy, while those that did not, forged them. Moreover, bishops also claimed the right to issue indulgences and showed themselves much more generous to local shrines than the papacy. Their indulgences were far more numerous than those issued by the papacy, and their impact on contemporary religious life correspondingly greater. In 1215 the Lateran council addressed itself to the problem. Bishops were forbidden to issue indulgences of more than forty days for the feast of a patron saint or one year for the anniversary of a dedication. Within a few years, however, the excessive indulgences granted by some bishops to insignificant shrines had attracted the hostile attention of the university of Paris. The decree of 1215 was reissued with a frequency which suggests that it was widely ignored. In 1339 the council of Aquilea complained that bishops not only exceeded the limits laid down by the Lateran fathers, but even granted indulgences outside their own dioceses.

Towards the end of the thirteenth century the issue became less important as the papacy itself started to issue indulgences more generously. The charity of the popes began, naturally enough, at home. In the reign of Alexander III (d. 1181), the basilicas of the apostles already offered indulgences which were extremely large by the standards of other pilgrimage churches. A century later, at the death of Nicholas IV (1292), indulgences of astounding generosity were available in every church of Rome, and at every altar of the basilicas of the apostles. But no pilgrimage offered a plenary indulgence until 1294, when Celestine V 'opened the treasury of mercy confided to him by Christ and bestowed it upon those who were truly confessed and penitent.' In fact, he issued a plenary indulgence to the church of Collemaggio, near Aquila, for the feast of John the Baptist. After Celestine's abdication in the following year, this act was quashed by his robust successor Boniface VIII together with all his other indulgences issued 'in ignorance of the canon law and of all his pastoral responsibilities'. But only five years later Boniface issued a plenary indulgence of his own, to the basilicas of the apostles on the occasion of the first Roman Jubilee.

The indulgence which finally opened the floodgates was the indulgence of the Portiuncula. St. Mary of the Portiuncula was the small chapel near Assisi which had been made over to the use of St. Francis and his earliest followers. It was here, in 1226, that Francis had died. By the middle years of the thirteenth century the Franciscans were claiming that the founder had secretly obtained from Honorius III a plenary indulgence for the chapel which would, if genuine, have been the only plenary indulgence in existence other than the crusading indulgence. Its authenticity was disputed from the outset on several grounds. It was said to be prejudicial to the reconquest of the Holy Land. The Portiuncula chapel was said to be too obscure to enjoy an indulgence which was denied to the greatest churches of Rome. It was an incitement to sin, others alleged; it brought other indulgences into contempt. These arguments, which could never have been advanced a hundred years later, are alone sufficient to show how novel and unfamiliar the idea of a plenary indulgence for pilgrims was in the thirteenth century. A commission of enquiry met in 1277 to examine the authenticity of the indulgence, and much scholarly ink has been spilt over the matter ever since. It is, on the whole, unlikely to be genuine, and even if Honorius III did grant an indulgence to the Portiuncula, it was certainly not a plenary one. None of these considerations, however, weighed very heavily with contemporaries. By 1295 the number of pilgrims was already greater than the friars serving the chapel could deal with, and in the early years of the fourteenth century the brothers were stated to be dealing daily with cardinals, archbishops, bishops, abbots, priors, kings, dukes, counts, and barons. However dubious its origins, the pilgrimage of the Portiuncula was among the most prosperous in Europe. It was the first pilgrimage which owed its success entirely to the skilful advertisement of an indulgence. Other shrines were quick to learn the lesson of the Portiuncula, and Celestine V undoubtedly had the Franciscan indulgence in mind when he declared a plenary remission of sins for pilgrims to Collemaggio.

No indulgence ever purported to release pilgrims from guilt as well as penance. Confession was therefore an essential preliminary to every pilgrimage. The preacher of the sermon *Veneranda Dies* inveighed fiercely against those who imagined that a pilgrimage to Santiago would erase their sins without it. However, there is no doubt that many, perhaps most, pilgrims did not appreciate this point. Many of those who flocked to Assisi to claim the Portiuncula indulgence, or to Rome to claim the Jubilee indulgence of 1300, had dispensed with the formality of confession, and in strict canon law their journey was wasted. Their error is scarcely surprising in view of the extravagant claims made for some indulgences by preachers and writers of miracle stories. In the fourteenth and fifteenth centuries these claims were regularly made notwithstanding repeated declarations that priests responsible for them were automatically excommunicate. In unlettered minds the confusion was exacerbated by the use of the misleading term '*a pena et culpa*' ('free from guilt and penance') to describe plenary indulgences. This phrase did not in fact mean what it said. Almost every papal document which used it, even the notorious Jubilee indulgence of 1510, insisted in the next breath that those claiming it must be 'truly confessed and penitent'. But few pilgrims would have seen these documents and fewer still would have read the learned commentaries of the canon lawyers. Their mistake would be discovered, if at all, only when they reached the shrine. By then it was often too late, for until the fourteenth century the Church insisted that confession be made to one's own parish priest before departing and, outside Rome, very few pilgrimage churches enjoyed the privilege of confessing visitors on the spot. At Rocamadour in the twelfth century, pilgrims were asked whether they had confessed and were sent home if they had not. A favourite anecdote of mediaeval preachers told how unconfessed pilgrims had suffered every kind of disaster, or how a mysterious force had physically prevented them from entering the church. A Burgundian pilgrim was physically unable to climb the steps of Mont-St.-Michel until she had confessed her sins. Ten strong men were unable to push a French nobleman through the entrance to the church of Our Lady at Villalcazar de Sirga on the road to Santiago, for his mortal sins had not yet been absolved. 'And the moral of this is that no man may enter the church of God who has not first confessed his mortal sins.' These considerations applied just as strongly in the later middle ages, when the doctrine of indulgences had provided a measuring-stick with which to assess the merit of a pilgrimage. The fourteenth-century *Miracles of St. Martial* tell of a pilgrim who was struck to the ground when he tried to kiss the sarcophagus of the saint, and this, says the author, was because he tried to claim an indulgence recently granted by pope Gregory XI without first going to confession.

The canonists and theologians of the later middle ages fought hard against the more extreme versions of the doctrine of indulgences. But even if the orthodox view had been universally understood, which it was not, the widespread use of indulgences would still have had the inevitable consequence of transforming the spiritual life of many laymen into a sequence of elaborate rituals. The indulgences of the twelfth and thirteenth centuries almost certainly did make pilgrimages more popular. On the other hand, they invited the pilgrim to measure the worth of his pilgrimage by standards which were mathematical, not spiritual. At the end of the twelfth century we find Gerald of Wales in Rome attending 395 masses in the shortest possible time, in order to obtain a total of ninety-two years of indulgences; finding that he was only eight years short of a century, he enrolled himself in the confraternity of the Holy Spirit which offered an indulgence of one-seventh of the penance due for his sins. Yet Gerald of Wales was an intelligent man, though not perhaps a very spiritual one. How many simpler souls must have raced from church to church, guide-book in hand, in the hope of collecting even more than a century of remission.

CHAPTER X

THE GROWTH OF A CULT

Canonization

The first stage in the rise of a great pilgrimage was the recognition of a saint. In the modern Roman Catholic Church this is a formal process, conducted with deliberation and ceremony. But it was not always so. In the earliest years of the cult of the saints, during the persecutions of the later Roman empire, veneration was accorded only to martyrs. The fact of their martyrdom being fairly easily ascertainable, no formal process of 'canonization' was necessary. It was only in the course of the fourth century, after the last of the great persecutions, that the veneration began to extend to 'confessors', i.e. those who had witnessed the true faith in their lives but not in their deaths. The *Life of St. Anthony* by Athanasius was a landmark in this respect, for it showed how a holy man might achieve sanctity by the spiritual quality of his life. In time, however, the broader definition of sanctity created problems of its own, notably the problem of deciding whether the sanctity of the holy man was such as to warrant his public veneration by believers. What was needed was some kind of official procedure by which sanctity could be recognized.

No such procedure existed until the eleventh century, and even after that it was imperfectly respected. In its place, saints were usually recognized by spontaneous popular acclaim, assisted by the enthusiasm of the local clergy. It was an unreliable method at the best of times. Guibert of Nogent tells us at the beginning of the twelfth century that he had known many bogus popular 'canonizations' in his time, and mentions a striking example which had occurred in a small village near Beauvais in recent memory.

'A young man of low birth, the squire of some knight I believe, died on Good Friday and was spontaneously venerated as a saint, simply because of the holy day on which he died. The peasants, looking for something novel, brought offerings and candles to his grave from the entire surrounding area. Then a tomb was erected on the site, and after that a chapel, while troops of pilgrims, all of them peasants with not a nobleman among them, arrived from the furthest confines of Brittany. The learned abbot and his holy monks observed all this and, won over by the gratifying flow of offerings, allowed themselves to be convinced by all manner of spurious miracles.'

Guibert is at pains to point out the popular character of this pilgrimage. The dead squire was of low birth and so were those who came to venerate him; men of good birth were conspicuously absent. The resistance of the monks was weakened by greed, and the reserves of the authorities swept away by popular enthusiasm.

When the Normans conquered England they encountered spiritual traditions very different from their own, and they viewed with considerable suspicion some of the most popular saints of the Anglo-Saxon Church. Lanfranc was astonished and displeased to learn, on becoming archbishop of Canterbury, that Elphege, one of his predecessors, who had been killed by the Danes in 1012, had been solemnly translated to the cathedral and was revered there as a martyr. 'These English amongst whom we live', he complained to the abbot of Bec, 'have set up certain persons whom they revere as saints. At times, when I reflect upon the lives of these persons, . . . I entertain serious doubts as to their sanctity.' Abbot Paul of St. Albans, who also found his predecessors venerated as saints, dismissed them as 'boors and half-wits', thus giving deep offence to his monks. When Warin, the second Norman abbot of Malmesbury, arrived at the abbey, his first act was to throw out the remains of St. Meindulf and other saints of doubtful worth.

Nominally, the power of authorizing a cult rested with the bishop. Laymen and local clergymen had been forbidden since the fifth century to set up shrines without his approval, but in the west it was several centuries before the bishops achieved even a limited measure of control. Before the eleventh century, the normal method of inaugurating the cult of a saint was by 'elevation', which involved disinterring his relics and placing them on an altar. In 688, eleven years after the death of St. Cuthbert, the monks of Lindisfarne opened his tomb and, finding the body uncorrupt, they resolved to 'replace them in a new coffin in the same place but above the floor, where they could be more worthily venerated.' Before doing this they consulted their bishop, and this seems to have been the usual practice. In the Frankish territories the bishop's consent was made mandatory by the ecclesiastical legislators of the Carolingian period. How much care the bishop took to investigate the candidate's claims to sanctity varied from place to place. When the bishop of

Cambrai authorized the 'elevation' of St. Hadulph at Arras in the ninth century, he was satisfied with an assurance from the sacristan that miracles had occurred. Salomon bishop of Constance, on the other hand, asked for a copy of the life of St. Otmar before proceeding to his 'elevation' and, having duly found the life edifying, he summoned a synod to consider the matter.

When vested interests were involved, obtaining approval for a new cult might be a prolonged and complex business. In 918 St. Gerard founded the monastery of Brogne near Liège, and translated to it the relics of an obscure Spanish saint called Eugenius, which he had been given by the abbey of St.-Denis. On his way back to Brogne with the relics he stopped to ask the bishop of Liège for permission to perform a translation. This was readily granted. But when the relics were enshrined at Brogne the popularity of the new cult spread so rapidly that other churches of the locality became jealous. A number of priests complained to the bishop that it was wrong for an unknown saint to be venerated in this way. The bishop decided to intervene. At this point, the contemporary historian of Brogne alleges, the Lord struck him down with a fatal disease. The bishop, who had correctly divined the cause of his illness, summoned a diocesan synod at which a life of the saint was read and the cult approved.

Papal consent was rarely sought before the tenth century and was not considered to be essential until the end of the eleventh. The first papal canonization known to history was that of St. Udalric of Augsburg, whose cult was officially approved by John XV in 993 at an imposing ceremony in the Lateran palace. Even so, John's consent was more or less a formality, no attempt being made to investigate the saint's life in any detail. Popes and synods were usually satisfied with the *acta* of the saint, hastily compiled by the local bishop. The first sign of any significant papal enquiry is found in 1099 when Urban II was invited by the clergy of southern Italy to authorize the cult of St. Nicholas of Trani. Urban commissioned the archbishop of Trani to investigate the case and, after hearing the *acta* and miracles of St. Nicholas recited in council, the pope duly performed the canonization. When, shortly afterwards the abbot of Quimperlé asked Urban to canonize his predecessor as abbot, the pope replied that this would not be possible 'unless witnesses can be found who will attest that they have seen his miracles with their own eyes.' We should probably regard Urban II as the father of the modern process of canonization.

One consequence of the new state of affairs was that canonizations no longer occurred on the spur of the moment. The canonization of Thomas Becket within three years of his death was regarded by some observers as excessively hasty, and so indeed it was by comparison with other processes of canonization. Lengthy judicial formalities were already the rule at the end of the twelfth century. The cardinals appointed to examine the miracles of St. Edmund of Abingdon in 1247 pointedly remarked that few of the fathers of the Church would have been canonized if this procedure had always been applied. Indeed, after about 1300 relatively few canonizations were performed although the flow of applications to Rome continued unabated. The canonization of St. Louis of Toulouse (d. 1297) was applied for in 1300 by his father, Charles of Anjou. Seven years elapsed before the investigation even began, and the business then proceeded slowly with five proctors, twenty witnesses, and a crowd of clerks, notaries, and dignitaries. A favourable verdict was announced in May 1313, but the canonization did not finally occur until April 1317. No wonder that it was necessary for John XXII to explain patiently to the earl of Lancaster that the canonization of archbishop Winchelsea was not as simple a matter as he imagined. It had to be 'debated in consistory by experienced persons from amongst the prelates, clergy, and people of England, attesting the archbishop's saintly life and miracles'. Winchelsea was never canonized.

For all the care with which the popes considered canonizations it is unlikely that their deliberations were of great interest to ordinary pilgrims. Except, perhaps, in so far as canonizations and translations were the occasion for splendid ceremonies at the shrine. Becket and Louis IX, for example, were both canonized by the populace long before their veneration was officially authorized by the Church. Louis IX, indeed, was almost venerated in his lifetime. One of the pilgrims who visited the tomb at St.-Denis shortly after the king's death, had this to say to the commissioners investigating his miracles: 'It is my belief that Louis is a saint because of all the miracles that I have heard about and because of his worthy life. But most of all I believe it because everybody round here says that he is a saint and calls him St. Louis.'

Publicity

What considerations dictated a pilgrim's choice of shrine is as much a mystery to us as it must have been to contemporaries. Sometimes the choice was determined by such factors as the pilgrim's name or trade. Sometimes it was determined by lot. Reginald of Durham knew of several pilgrims who had decided on a visit to the shrine of St. Cuthbert after drawing lots between the various alternatives. One had named three candles after different saints and decided on the shrine whose candle burned out first; another had drawn twigs. According to William of Canterbury, this was a common practice in Wales and the west of England.

·The ebb and flow of fashion was undoubtedly the most important factor. Notable events such as inventions of relics, canonizations, or translations served to draw attention in dramatic fashion to the existence of a saint and to provoke an outburst of popular enthusiasm which rarely lasted more than half a century. A minor cult might be forgotten within a few weeks. The tendency of the laity was always to visit the saint whose cult was the most recently established. St. Wulfstan of Worcester, who was canonized in 1203, is referred to shortly afterwards as 'the new saint'. St. Thomas of Canterbury was the 'new saint' *par excellence* of the late twelfth century. His cult was established within a fortnight of his death and was propagated with exceptional skill by the monks of Christ Church, Canterbury. William of Canterbury, who was the author of a great deal of this propaganda, reflects that all saints have their period of miracle-working then they command the veneration of Christians; then they withdraw gracefully and leave miracle-working to saints of more recent creation, such as St. Thomas. The French pilgrim Hugh Brustins, who had been possessed by the devil, visited St.-Denis only to discover that that saint had 'left to his colleague St. Thomas the business of curing the sick . . . in order that a new and relatively unknown martyr might make his name.' It is often forgotten how sporadic was the cult even of a great saint like St. Thomas. Canterbury was a shrine of European importance, probably the most prosperous in Christendom, for about ten years after Becket's brutal death. But only a few years later a canon of St. Frideswide's is found expressing the opinion that Canterbury is now old hat, and Caesarius of Heisterbach felt that St. Thomas was not as potent as most older martyrs. In the early thirteenth century pilgrims who used to go regularly to Canterbury are reported to be abandoning it in favour of the holy rood recently acquired by Bromholm priory. A renewed outburst of popular devotion to St. Thomas marked the translation of the relics to the choir of the new cathedral in 1220, but by the middle of the thirteenth century the great days of the pilgrimage were past. In the fourteenth century a miracle at the shrine was so unusual as to be the subject of a special letter of congratulation from the king. A Jubilee indulgence of 1370 served to bring large crowds to Canterbury, including the poet Chaucer, and other Jubilees were held in 1420 and 1470. But except on these famous occasions the cult of St. Thomas scarcely deserved the hostile attention which it received from the sixteenth-century reformers. The history of the Canterbury pilgrimage was in this respect very typical. Amongst its rivals only Rome, Jerusalem, and Santiago were able to attract pilgrims throughout the mediaeval period.

By far the most effective advertisements for a saint were his miracles. Contemporaries followed the posthumous doings of the saints with extreme interest and the news of miraculous happenings could be relied upon to spread without any active assistance from the clergy of the sanctuary. When, for example, a blind man was healed by St. Eutrope as he sat by the side of the road outside Saintes, 'a deafening clamour arose and all the nearby villages resounded with the news. People rushed to the spot and young men clapped their hands in delight. The whole city of Saintes throbbed with excitement and everyone was increased in love of Christ and of his holy saint, Eutrope.' On another occasion a pilgrim who had visited the shrine of St. Eutrope is described as going back home and inviting in all his neighbours to persuade them to go too. How far the news carried by word of mouth depended on the importance of the saint and the quality of the miracle. The canons of Laon who toured England in 1113 in search of funds for the rebuilding of their cathedral, returned with stories of the miracles of St. Swithin at Winchester and St. Edmund at Bury. News of the miracles at St.-Gilles-de-Provence is known to have penetrated as far as Denmark, and Poland.

Although the most spectacular miracles needed no advertisement, the clergy of the greater sanctuaries did go to considerable lengths to publicize them by compiling collections of miracle stories known as *libelli miraculorum*. The habit of recording every marvellous event as it occurred dates back at least to the time of St. Augustine, who collected depositions from the pilgrims healed by St. Stephen at Hippo. These accounts were then included in Augustine's sermons and circulated in neighbouring dioceses. In the west the classic miracle collection of the early middle ages was the celebrated account of the miracles of St. Martin by Sulpicius Severus, which was written at the beginning of the fifth century. The extraordinary repetitiveness and lack of originality which characterize almost every mediaeval miracle collection, is in a large measure due to the fact that their authors were modelling themselves on Sulpicius Severus. The clergy of every major shrine conceived that they owed a duty to their patron saint to increase his glory by writing down his miracles. Geoffrey, prior of Canterbury, believed that God had brought misfortunes upon his head to punish him for his failure to record a miracle he had witnessed. The monk who wrote up the miracles of St. James at Reading pointed out that the servant who increased his talents found more favour with God than the one who buried them in the ground; 'and in just the same way, we who by God's gracious favour have seen the miracles worked by St. James . . . have a solemn duty to pass the knowledge of them on to posterity, that their faith may be strengthened and that God may be glorified.'

Most collections of miracles were pure propaganda and few of them had the slightest literary merit. The rivalry between competing shrines found expression in aggressive assertions that this or that saint was more consistently effective than any other. The authors never fail to point out how many other celebrated shrines a pilgrim has visited in vain before he is restored to health at the shrine of St. Benedict, St. Foy, or St. Thomas as the case may be. 'Why are you wasting your time here?' a mysterious voice is alleged to have declared to a sick Englishman in St. Peter's at Rome; 'go back home to England and make your offering at the monastery of St. Egwin at Evesham, for there alone will you be healed.' A lady of Luton apparently went blind after visiting St.-Gilles-de-Provence when she ought to have gone to St. Thomas of Canterbury. But it was above all the rivals of St. Thomas who excelled at this kind of competitive propaganda. The sudden rise of Canterbury as a major shrine eclipsed every other English pilgrimage. The literature put out by the older English shrines in the late twelfth century is therefore full of slighting references to the inability of St. Thomas to cure a pilgrim who later found his health at Durham, Bury St. Edmund's, St. Frideswide's, or Reading. The Reading author, who was much the most aggressive of this group, reports the following conversion between an apparition of St. James and a pilgrim in the choir of Canterbury cathedral:

'What are you doing hanging about here?'
'I am waiting to be healed by the merits of the blessed apostle Thomas.'
'You will wait in vain. What you ought to do is go back to my abbey at Reading. There, and there alone, will you be healed.'
'I know nothing of Reading and I have never heard of your abbey. How do you think I can get there in my state of health?'

This pilgrim was punished for her contumely but she was ultimately cured by the hand of St. James at Reading.

The twelfth century saw the first attempts to influence the decisions of pilgrims by advertizing techniques which strike a surprisingly familiar note in modern ears. Much of the fame of Canterbury in the 1170s was due to skilful promotion by its monks, who sent abstracts of St. Thomas's miracles to numerous prelates and religious houses in England and France. Other churches proclaimed the benefits of their pilgrimage in pamphlets, rhymes and jingles.

The monks of the abbey of the Trinity at Fécamp composed a poem in French entitled 'Why everyone ought to love and visit the holy church of Fécamp and hear the story of the Precious Blood.' Jerusalem, it pointed out, was far away, 'so remember that you are never far from Fécamp where the Lord has sent his Precious Blood for your benefit'. In the early years of the twelfth century when both St. Adalbert's abbey in Rome and the church of Benevento claimed to possess the body of St. Bartholomew, the pamphlets issued by St. Adalbert's abbey sang this untranslatable jingle:

> Roma tenet corpus, tu famam, tu modo tumbam;
> Roma tenet corpus, tu non nisi corporis umbram . . .
> Fraus male subvenit Benevento non benevenit,
> Ob detrimentum Benevento fit maleventum.'

With the growing popularity of public preaching in the later middle ages, the advertisement of pilgrimages became an elaborate and expensive business. Both mendicant orders offered their services as preachers of indulgences, and individual preachers enjoyed European reputations for their persuasiveness. When the church of St. Lambert at Liège received an indulgence from Eugenius IV in 1443, they employed two Franciscans to preach it in the town, and two Dominicans to compose pamphlets for distribution further afield. The accounts of Lyon cathedral in the early sixteenth century show that the canons paid ten *sous* to the Augustinian who preached their indulgence, five *sous* to the town crier who advertized his sermons, and twenty *sous* to the sacristan for the cost of his dinners.

Attractive packaging was an essential element in the saint's appeal. Pilgrims expected to be received by a magnificent and costly reliquary, and those who were not sometimes put their disgust on record. Shortly after the translation of some new relics to the German monastery of Prüm in the mid-ninth century,

'a certain woman arrived with a wagon full of food and drink and precious things which she proposed to offer to God and to the holy martyrs. But, seeing that the saint's tomb did not glitter with gold and silver, she uttered a contemptuous guffaw, as is the wont of foolish and irreligious minds. Then, rushing back home, she bade her friends retrace their steps saying "you won't find anything holy in that place." '

This lady's attitude was as familiar to the twelfth century as it was to the ninth. Superb reliquaries and sumptuously decorated sanctuaries were not only subtle indications of the power of the saint but they testified to the devotion and the generosity of past pilgrims and invited offerings from present ones. Preachers of the later mediaeval period pointed out this lesson most explicitly. 'Look at all these gold and silver reliquaries, these chalices and jewels, rich tapestries and vestments', intoned the fourteenth-century preacher at the shrine of Our Lady of Montserrat; 'all these costly and holy things were presented by pious persons.' A grey friar of Canterbury preaching at Herne in 1535 declared that he knew of people who had travelled two hundred miles to see the shrine of St. Thomas 'and when they . . . see the goodly jewels that be there, how they think in their hearts "I would to God and that good saint that I were able to offer such a gift." '

From the fourth century onwards a dazzling display of wealth was to be found in every pilgrimage church of any importance. In the lifetime of the emperor Constantine the Holy Sepulchre was adorned with 'gifts of indescribable beauty including gold, silver, and precious stones'; a traveller of the sixth century found the Sepulchre completely invisible beneath a carpet of jewellery. Golden ornaments and silk wall-hangings decorated the relatively minor shrine of St. Felix of Nola in the fourth century. 'Truly', observed John Chrysostom, 'the sanctuaries of the saints are more lavishly decorated than the palaces of kings.' After the eighth century the western Church allowed reliquaries to be put on permanent display on the altar, instead of being 'elevated' only on special feast days. From this moment onwards, sanctuaries became ever more ornate and expensive. When Suger became abbot of St.-Denis in 1122 his first act was to order new reliquaries for his church. In his time St.-Denis employed an *atélier* of goldsmiths and jewellers which made the abbey for a brief while the artistic centre of Europe. The arm of St. James was enclosed in a reliquary of crystal mounted in gold. The panels of the sarcophagus of St. Denis himself contained forty-two marks of gold studded with diamonds, rubies, sapphires, emeralds, topazes, and pearls. Suger bought the entire stock of every jeweller he encountered and even removed the rings from his fingers to add to the magnificence of his patron's shrine. Suger was justly proud of this splendid array. He was surprised and offended when pope Paschal II, visiting St.-Denis in May 1107, showed no interest in it, but humbly prostrated himself before the relics themselves. In Suger's mind a superb reliquary was a material symbol of the spiritual grandeur of the saint whose relics it contained. In devoting a substantial proportion of his revenues to the decoration of the sanctuary, Suger was in no way untypical of the wealthy churchmen of his day. The tomb of St. Thomas of Canterbury, completed at enormous expense in c. 1220, astonished even seasoned travellers. A Venetian diplomat who saw it at the beginning of the sixteenth century reported that is 'surpassed all belief':

'Notwithstanding its great size it is entirely covered with plates of pure gold. But the gold is scarcely visible beneath a profusion of gems, including sapphires, diamonds, rubies and emeralds. Everywhere that the eye turns something even more beautiful appears. The beauty of the materials is enhanced by the astonishing skill of human hands. Exquisite designs have been carved all over it and immense gems worked delicately into the patterns. Finest of all is a ruby, no larger than a man's thumbnail, which is set into the altar at the right hand side, and which . . . I believe, was the gift of the King (Louis VII) of France.'

When Henry VIII dissolved the cathedral priory, the jewels and precious metals from this tomb filled twenty-six carts. In England, none of these fine works of mediaeval jewellery survived the Reformation. In France almost all were destroyed in the revolution. Today we must go to Germany or Spain, to Cologne, Marburg, Oviedo, or León, to receive even a faint impression of the treasures which confronted a pilgrim at St.-Denis in the time of Suger.

Contemporaries differed as to the morality of spending such large sums on the decoration of churches. Guibert of Nogent correctly divined that magnificent tombs were an appeal to popular piety at the expense of more genuine spiritual feelings, and the reaction of Paschal II on being shown the sanctuary of St.-Denis tends to bear this out. St. Bernard stated the classic case against them when he delivered his celebrated invective against the excessive splendour of the Benedictine churches.

'Look at their churches, glistening with gold while the poor are starving and naked outside. . . . Their object is to excite the devotion of the vulgar masses who are incapable of truly spiritual feelings. . . . But what kind of devotion do they produce? They do not bring men to prayer but tempt them into making offerings. Thus is wealth squandered on creating more wealth and money spent on attracting more money. . . . Here the saints are displayed for veneration enclosed in the exquisite workmanship of teams of goldsmiths. Ordinary people think them that much more holy if they are plastered with precious stones; they crowd forward to kiss them and make offerings to them. But what are they really venerating? Not the spiritual beauty of God's saints but the mundane prettiness of their shrines.'

St. Bernard's strictures were a little unjust. It should be remembered that every rich church had to keep a reserve of liquid wealth in case of a sudden disaster, and in a non-money economy this could only be done by hoarding precious stones and metals. Hence the fact that many a fine example of the goldsmith's art was melted down within a few years of being made; this was part of its purpose. When abbot Mayeul of Cluny was captured by the Arabs in 972, his monks paid a ransom of a thousand pounds of silver by melting down ornaments from the church. The abbey of Malmesbury, when asked to pay tribute at short notice to William Rufus, stripped the silver and gold from twelve Gospels, eight crucifixes, and eight reliquaries. Reading abbey settled its accounts with Richard I by removing the gold leaf from its most famous relic, the hand of St. James. All these raids on the reserves would have been made good out of surplus income when the opportunity arose.

But the insatiable appetite of wealthy churches for precious reliquaries was more than just a prudent financial precaution. It arose out of a deeply engrained habit of mind which found it hard to imagine spiritual grandeur without material wealth. Because the saints were poor in their lifetimes, argued Theofrid, abbot of Epternach (d. 1110), they are entitled to untold riches when they are in Paradise; with untold riches, therefore, they should be honoured on earth. Splendid apparel and costly jewellery were part of the popular image of the saints triumphant. St. Cuthbert, for example, appeared to a youth of Coupland dressed in full pontificals shining with gold and glistening with precious stones. Indeed, contemporaries imagined Christ himself in this way, until in the thirteenth century Franciscan preachers impressed upon their hearers the image of a God who was at the same time poor and human. The English anchorite Christina of Markyate, who died in about 1160, dreamed of Christ as 'a man of indescribable beauty wearing a golden crown thickly encrusted with precious stones which seemed beyond the skill of any human craftsman. Hanging over his face, one on either side, were two bands delicate and shining, and on top of the gems small pearls could be seen shining like drops of dew.' The material glory which clothed the risen Christ was reflected by his saints. In this respect abbot Suger and the monks of Cluny were closer to the mainstream of Christian sentiment than St. Bernard.

The saint's sanctuary served above all as a reminder of the miracles attributed to him. Written accounts of these miracles were always available on request. A Burgundian nobleman at Mont-St.-Michel is found asking for a list of St. Michael's miracles, 'and on reading the account which was shown to him he conceived a high opinion of the holiness of the place.' In 1319, when the monks of Canterbury were actively pressing for the canonization of Robert Winchelsea, a description of his miracles was hung in front of the tomb. In many sanctuaries murals, sculptures, and tapestries illustrated the life and miracles of the saint. At St.-Benoit-sur-Loire, for example, the miracles of St. Benedict, drawn from the *Dialogues* of pope Gregory, are sculpted on the capitals of the church. At Canterbury, those of St. Thomas can be seen in the stained glass windows of the Trinity Chapel, exactly as they are described by Benedict of Peterborough and William of Canterbury. How many long-faded murals must once have decorated the great sanctuaries of England and France, offering to the sick and infirm the distant hope of a miraculous end to their sufferings.

Perhaps the most curious reminders of past miracles were the *ex-voto* offerings which are still a characteristic feature of modern pilgrimages in Italy and France. These were offered by pilgrims to commemorate a miraculous cure, and were usually wax models of whatever part of the body had been healed. *Ex-voto* offerings were also made by those who had not been cured but hoped to be. As early as the fifth century, visitors to eastern shrines left 'pictures of their eyes or models of their feet or hands. Some are made of wood, others of gold. The Lord accepts them all, great or small. . . . These objects are kept as evidence of countless miraculous cures, mementoes offered by people who have recovered their health.' Models of part of the human body were much the most common *ex-voto* offerings. A pilgrim cured of a continuous head-ache by St. Martial left a wax model of his head. Another, with an abscess on her nose, presented a silver nose to the church of Notre-Dame de Rocamadour. Occasionally, sick men sent full-size models of themselves to a local shrine in the hope of hastening their recovery. One Adam of Yarmouth sent a wax model as tall and broad as himself to Norwich cathedral in the late twelfth century, but extravagant gestures like this remained uncommon until the close of the middle ages. John Paston was one of the many well-to-do persons who sent wax models to Our Lady of Walsingham in the fifteenth century. Between 1535 and 1538 the commissioners for the dissolution of the monasteries constantly refer to the accumulation of such models in English sanctuaries. At Canterbury, gruesome relics of afflictions cured were to be found in the piles of *ex-voto* offerings. Henry of Maldon's tapeworm was hung up in the cathedral as an *ex-voto*. Iselda of Longueville, in gratitude for the recovery of her hearing, made an offering of part of her hair. A shepherd from Durham left his withered finger on the altar in the hope that another would grow in its place. So many wax models hung in the church of Rocamadour that at least one pilgrim accused the monks of making them themselves. In general, however, such offerings were a useful advertisement for the healing powers of the church's relics, and the clergy of the shrine were assiduous in collecting a memento of every cure. The guardian of St. Thomas's shrine was dismayed when an archdeacon was relieved of a cherry-stone stuck in his nostril, but insisted on taking it home with him.

Although the sick were responsible for the great majority of *ex-voto* offerings, in principle any pilgrim could make one. The crew of a Dunwich fishing boat which had been saved from a storm by St. Edmund hung up a wax anchor in his basilica. A knight who had lost his hawk took a wax hawk to the church of Our Lady at Villalcazar de Sirga. Guillaume Bataille, whose house had been preserved from a fire by the Virgin, brought a wax house to Rocamadour. The chains of prisoners liberated by the saint would normally be hung up in his basilica, and at sanctuaries where the saint specialized in this kind of miracle, almost all the *ex-voto* offerings on display were ruptured chains. This was so as early as the sixth century. A deacon of Tours returning from a visit to Rome in 590 was astonished by the number of chains hanging in the basilica of St. Victor at Marseilles. Later generations ceased to be amazed as knights delivered from the infidel and criminals released from prison became familiar sights on the roads of Europe. The author of the *Guide for Pilgrims to Santiago* counted several thousand iron chains in the church of St.-Léonard de Noblat, together with various contraptions in which prisoners had been trapped, injured, or tortured. The church of St. Foy at Conques was full of the chains of Spanish crusaders delivered from the Moors; indeed, in the extreme left-hand corner of the celebrated sculpted tympanum, an iron fetter can be seen hanging from a beam behind the figure of St. Foy. In a few sanctuaries the mounting pile of *ex-voto* offerings posed serious problems. Abbot Geoffrey of Vézelay (d. 1052) had a new set of altar rails made from the chains left behind by pilgrims. Other churches were more ruthless. At Santiago the guardians of the shrine had strict instructions not to accept any incense, bread, staves, crucifixes or 'models made out of lead or wax'.

Offerings

Offerings were an essential ingredient in the rise of a great shrine because they paid for the imposing church which housed it. A pilgrim was expected to be as generous as his means would allow, and there were some who asserted that without an offering a pilgrimage was of no value. The authors of the miracle stories were foremost in putting forward this proposition. 'Come to my shrine at Conques and give me all your gold bracelets', St. Foy is said to have told the wife of Guillaume Taillefer, count of Toulouse. A woman who bought a valuable ring at Conques and failed to give it to St. Foy was cursed with fevers and nightmares. Another, who emerged from the basilica of Conques with her ring still on her finger, fell ill in a nearby hospice, and did not recover until the ring was removed by one of the guardians of the shrine and placed in the abbey treasury. Perhaps the most striking story in this vein was the tale of Sir Jordan Fitz-Eisulf, a knight of Pontefract who had known Thomas Becket in his lifetime. Some time after Becket's death Fitz-Eizulf and his family were saved from the ravages of the plague by drinking 'water of St. Thomas'. Fitz-Eisulf put aside four silver pieces to offer at St. Thomas's shrine, but the pilgrimage was constantly postponed until St. Thomas reminded the knight of his obligations by allowing the plague to return and strike down his eldest son. In the stained glass of the Trinity Chapel at Canterbury Fitz-Eisulf can be seen recovering his health by pouring a great sackful of money onto the shrine. The notion of the offering as an essential part of the pilgrimage received the sanction of the canon law when the popes began to issue occasional indulgences conditional on an appropriate donation being made. An indulgence of 1147 offered remission of seven days to those who visited the chapel of St. Denis at Montmartre 'and who bestow their alms upon the nuns according to the resources which God has given them.'

Offerings were frequently described as 'tribute money', akin to the services which a vassal owed to his feudal lord. This interesting notion makes its appearance in the tenth century. In his life of St. Gerald of Aurillac, Odo of Cluny remarks that the holy man used to travel to Rome wearing ten silver shillings round his neck as a sign of his vassalage to St. Peter. A charter of 1090 describes an offering made by a pilgrim at the church of St. Vincent of Le Mans as a *censum donum*, i.e. feudal tribute. In the twelfth century it became a common practice to vow oneself a 'perpetual serf' of the Holy Sepulchre in Jerusalem. Rudolf count of Pfullendorf did this in 1180 at the abbey of St.-Gall, before departing for the Holy Land. In June 1200 a large group of noblemen of the Breisgau renounced their property and proclaimed themselves 'vassals of the Holy Sepulchre' before they in turn left for Jerusalem. Several monarchs of the period, in declaring themselves vassals of God, offered tribute money to one of his saints. Thus the kings of Aragon described their annual gifts to the shrine of Santiago as the 'tribute which is owed to God and the holy apostle James'. It is this sentiment which explains the iconography of the shrine of the three Magi at Cologne (plate IV. 6). This magnificent gold and jewelled shrine was the gift of the emperor Otto IV, and on the side of it Otto can be seen behind the figures of the three Magi, presenting his offering to Christ. It was characteristic of an age in which feudal imagery constantly intruded into the realm of spiritual practice. By making themselves the 'serfs' or 'vassals' of a saint, men supposed that they were placing themselves under the saint's protection. 'Know then that I am a serf of St. Gilles', Raymond Feraldo told those who had captured him in the course of a local vendetta; 'and therefore you have no power to do me ill except in so far as he shall permit.'

The statutes of Santiago cathedral, dating from the end of the thirteenth century, contain an elaborate ritual for the presentation of offerings, and it is probable that similar formalities were observed at other churches. After the morning mass the sacristan and another priest stood behind the shrine with rods in their hands and with these they would tap each pilgrim on the back or on the arms or legs. A third priest, wearing a surplice, invited them to make an offering, addressing each pilgrim in his own language. Pilgrims were then asked whether their offering was for St. James, i.e. for alms and general purposes, in which case it was placed on the altar; or whether it was for the building fund, when it was placed on a side-table. This ceremony marked the moment at which the pilgrim 'received' his indulgence. Only cash or jewellery was accepted.

The more important sanctuaries undoubtedly received very large sums in offerings. The exact amount varied from one year to the next and from sanctuary to sanctuary. Canterbury cathedral, for example, received an average of £426 a year in offerings between 1198 and 1213, although these were troubled years in the history of the monastery. In 1220, the year of the translation of St. Thomas to the choir, the receipts amounted to £1,142, nearly two-thirds of the total income of the monastery. Yet three centuries later, in 1535, offerings accounted for a mere £36. Our Lady of Walsingham, on the other hand, was still getting £260 a year from pilgrims in 1535. Even if one takes the twelfth and thirteenth centuries as the heyday of pilgrimages, it is clear that no English shrine could match the prosperity of Canterbury at the height of its fame. St. Edmund's abbey, for example, received £142 a year from pilgrims at the end of the thirteenth century and was well satisfied with it.

The best evidence of the wealth which even a short-lived pil-grimage could bring to a church, is to be found in the ambitious enterprises which were financed out of offerings. Under the rule of abbot Gontran (1034–55) miracles began to occur in the monastery of St.-Trond, near Liège. Gontran was a modest man, and he kept the details to himself, but his successor, Adelard, had influential connections and high ambitions for his abbey. He spread the news of the miracles abroad and skilfully promoted a pilgrimage. In time, so many pilgrims arrived at St.-Trond that the small village at the gates of the abbey was unable to contain them. 'Almost every day', wrote the chronicler of the abbey, '. . . they filled the roads for half a mile around. Across the fields and meadows came such a crowd of pilgrims, being nobles, freemen, and peasants of both sexes, that they had to be put up in tents, which made them look like a besieging army. . . . And offerings beyond belief piled on up the altar. Herds of animals were offered every day, palfreys, cows and bulls, pigs, lambs, and sheep. Linen, wax, bread, and cheese arrived, and above all purses full of money.' So much money was given that in the evening several men were needed to collect it up and put it in a safe place, and a number of monks worked full-time as guardians of the shrine. Indeed, says the chronicler, the offerings exceeded all the other revenues of the abbey combined and continued to do so throughout abbot Adelard's lifetime. The abbey was able to build itself powerful walls and retain a large body of knights and servants. It bought the seigneurial rights over most of the neighbouring towns and villages and acquired estates as far away as Laon. The monastery was completely rebuilt, and henceforth its servants and officials were treated with respect and fear wherever they went.

The story of St.-Trond was repeated in countless churches and abbeys across the face of Europe. Many French churches made their fortunes in the religious revival of the eleventh century. The flood of relics which reached the Latin west after the fall of Constantinople in 1204 drew immense sums of money from pilgrims. The cathedrals of Amiens and Troyes were among the great churches built on their offerings. The bishop of Châlons-sur-Marne, who had acquired the elbow of St. Stephen in Constantinople, felt confident enough to pawn all his future revenues to pay for the completion of his cathedral 'in view of the great numbers of people who will certainly come to venerate such a relic.' The astonishing growth of devotion to the Virgin in the fifteenth century produced a very similar result. Shrines of the Virgin in isolated places like Avioth and Notre-Dame de l'Epine were suddenly covered by great flamboyant Gothic churches. 'Do you see this spacious and beautiful church, perfect in its elegance and style (except for the tower which is being restored)?' asked the parish priest of Bollezeel in Flanders of a pilgrim who visited it in 1483; 'all this was paid for out of the offerings of pilgrims who appeared in droves, receiving consolation from our Blessed Lady and buying badges at the door.'

But while offerings could bring unheard-of wealth to minor sanctuaries in the space of a few weeks, churches which depended too heavily on the generosity of pilgrims might see their revenues

dry up as suddenly as they had first appeared. The most distinguished sanctuary to suffer this fate was the abbey of St.-Gilles in
Provence. The abbey had seen its greatest days between about 1050
and 1250, when its position on one of the most frequented routes to
Santiago had brought it very considerable wealth. Much of this
wealth had been invested in magnificent buildings. But at the opening of the fifteenth century the roof had partly collapsed, the bell-
tower was only half-completed, and the fabric of the church was in
a dangerous state of disrepair. The rival armies of the Hundred Years
War, the undisciplined bands of *routiers*, and a succession of savage
epidemics, had combined to drive pilgrims onto roads passing well
north of St.-Gilles. In 1417 the monks addressed a petition for help
to the emperor Sigismund. In it they lamented that 'the devotion of
Christians to St.-Gilles has altogether ceased and the faithful no
longer come to visit his tomb. In former times the great affluence
of pilgrims was a wonderful boon to the abbey and town of St.-
Gilles, but now the place is deserted and impoverished.' The population of the town had fallen to eighteen taxable families and the
number of monks to twenty-six. The abbey's income, which had
once stood at four thousand gold francs a year, was now so small
that the monks could not afford food or winter clothing. The story
of St.-Gilles exactly balances that of St.-Trond. Today the church is
partially ruined, but the noble crypt and fine sculpted façade survive
as monuments of its departed greatness.

The clergy of a sanctuary were usually entitled to a share of the
offerings, and this was a fertile source of disputes throughout the
mediaeval period. Some churches were governed by statutes which
laid down with admirable clarity exactly what should be done with
the money. The basilica of St. Martin at Tours had an arrangement
dating back to 832 whereby one-third of the offerings went to the
canons, except for precious fabrics and jewellery, which were used
to decorate the church. At the Sainte-Chapelle the proportions destined for the canons and those set aside for administrative expenses
were meticulously laid down in the statutes of 1303. At many other
churches, however, ill-defined rules based on obscure traditions and
notions of fairness were a recurrent source of undignified squabbles.
The Vatican basilica in particular was governed by rules of extreme
complexity as a result of which the pope, the canons, and the
chantors were regularly locked in combat. During the Jubilee of
1350, when exceptionally large sums were being received at the
altars, the canons forced the door of the treasury and helped themselves to what they considered to be their due. The offerings at the
Vatican were of special importance because of the large sums
involved; in 1285-6, during the least prosperous period in the history

of the Roman pilgrimage, a total of 1,097 *livres* was received in the basilica. But even where lesser sums were at stake the fate of the offerings was constantly left to be decided by argument and litigation.

In principle the papacy was not entitled to any share of the receipts of churches outside Rome itself. Bulls of indulgence, like all bulls, were taxed when they left the papal chancery in accordance with a fixed scale of fees. But the sum raised was negligible and most of it went to the chancery officials. In the fourteenth and fifteenth centuries, however, most sanctuaries came to depend heavily on papal indulgences and the papacy began to exploit them as a source of revenue. By the end of the fifteenth century the cost of a plenary indulgence of a year's duration was an initial payment of four or five hundred gold florins and a proportion of the proceeds. This proportion was usually a third. The duties of Richard Wily, who became papal receiver in England in 1463, included the collection of one third of the proceeds of papal indulgences. Sometimes the papal share was a high as three-quarters. In May 1442 Eugenius IV granted an indulgence to Eton College which specified that a quarter of the offerings were to go to the fabric fund and three-quarters to the papacy, nominally for the needs of the Holy Land. To ensure that the pope got his share, the bull provided that all the oblations were to be kept in a chest with two locks, the provost to have one key and the papal collector the other. The exact share claimed by Rome was always a matter to be negotiated between the pope and the church concerned. In the opening years of the sixteenth century, however, the papacy was beginning to price itself out of the market. The monks of Canterbury were unable to get a Jubilee indulgence in 1520 as they had done every fifty years since 1320, because they could no longer afford the cost. Their agent in Rome, Dr. Grig, was informed by cardinal Campeggio that 'it is not possible that the pope will grant you this for no money or favour.'

The clergy of the great sanctuaries were accused by their contemporaries as well as by later historians of exploiting pilgrims for their own avaricious purposes. There is some justice in this charge, but it has been considerably over-stated. A clear distinction should be drawn, first of all between the periods before and after the papal schism of the fourteenth century, and secondly between sanctuaries that were served by monks and those that were not. The papal schism, and in particular the pontificate of Boniface IX, marks the beginning of a century and a half of ruthless commercialization which radically altered the character of some of the more popular spiritual exercises of the late middle ages. The fifteenth century also saw a large increase in the number of new sanctuaries, almost all of which were served by the secular clergy, while some of the older monastic sanctuaries began to fall into 'decay. Some monastic sanctuaries, like Walsingham, were actually refounded as colleges of canons. Monks were not personally entitled to a share of the offerings, whereas secular canons almost invariably were. Monks, moreover, had extremely expensive obligations of hospitality which were, on the whole, respected throughout the mediaeval period. The receipts of a monastic sanctuary might therefore be enormous while the profits remained very modest; when the surplus had been swallowed up by the fabric fund, it was difficult to argue that the monks had made gross gains at the pilgrims' expense.

Some early indulgences expressly require the pilgrimage church to offer hospitality to visitors. The indulgence which Urban II conceded to St. Nicholas of Angers in 1096 included a condition that on the day of the indulgence the monks were to feed a hundred poor people. Most monasteries, even when their duties were not explicitly laid down in this fashion, offered food and shelter as the Benedictine rule required. This might impose a serious strain on the abbey's finances, as it did at the mountainous Catalonian shrine of Montserrat in the fourteenth century. There, the preacher would remind pilgrims of the difficulty and expense of carting provisions up the steep mountain tracks to the church, and ask them to bring their own food unless they were poor or disabled. Another mountain shrine, Notre-Dame de Rocamadour, was driven deeply into debt by the number of pilgrims; in 1181, when the church was at the pinnacle of its fame, the monks were obliged to pawn the tapestries and curtains to moneylenders of the town. An inquest into the revenues of the abbey of Mont-St.-Michel in 1338 established that the monks received 1,100 *livres* a year in offerings, about one-sixth of their total income. But far from bringing joy to the abbot, the mass of pilgrims was a source of deep anxiety 'for the abbey is situated on the borders of Normandy, Brittany, Anjou and Maine, wherefore it receives enormous numbers of pilgrims passing to and fro. Many of them have to be accommodated in the monastery and this costs the monastery so much that other equally important charges on our revenues have to be neglected.'

The nearest approach to a balance sheet comes from Canterbury, where a number of account books survive. These show that the allowance made to the cellarer, who was the official responsible for entertaining pilgrims, rose and fell in tune with the income from offerings. In 1220, the year of the translation of St. Thomas to the choir, the offerings received rose from £227 to £1,142, while the expenses of the cellarer rose from £422 to £1,155. Pilgrims, of course, did not account for all the cellarer's expenses, and if testamentary bequests made by pilgrims are taken into account, there was probably a small surplus in both years. But as popular interest in St. Thomas declined, the surplus became a deficit. The four Canterbury Jubilees of the late middle ages drew large crowds of pilgrims but the great and wealthy stayed away. The declining social status of pilgrims was a general phenomenon of the four-teenth and fifteenth centuries, and its immediate effect was to reduce the income from offerings while increasing the number of visitors who needed free food and board. The first Jubilee, in 1320, brought in offerings of £671, but left the monastery with an overall deficit of £83. Thereafter the years in which offerings were highest were usually years of deficit.

Even the Vatican basilica, without doubt the most visited church in Europe over the whole mediaeval period, was sometimes in deficit. At the end of the twelfth century the pope received three-quarters of the offerings made at the high altar and the *confessio* of St. Peter. Out of this came the cost of several thousand candles burned every day in the basilica, of repairs to the fabric, and of the stipends of non-canonical priests. Innocent III, according to his biographer, devoted all that was left to alms for the poor and hospitality for pilgrims. Alexander IV, half a century later, devoted a quarter of his share of the offerings to alms. Innocent was indeed extremely sensitive to accusations of profiteering. In 1212 he an-nounced to pilgrims gathered in Rome that all the offerings received at St. Peter's were devoted to the maintenance of the basilica and the entertainment of its visitors and he asked them to publicize the fact in their own countries. It seems unlikely that pilgrims to St. Peter's were a significant source of revenue before the age of the great Jubilee indulgences.

The clergy of the sanctuaries were undoubtedly ambitious. How-ever, what they wanted was status rather than money. Status for themselves, and above all for their patron saint. This was more than mere vainglory, for a great deal of ecclesiastical power ulti-mately rested on status. The possession of St. Peter's body was cited as the basis of Rome's spiritual authority from Leo I in the fifth century to Innocent IV in the thirteenth. Jerusalem itself had achieved metropolitan status in the fifth century owing largely to its importance as a pilgrimage centre. In 969 Benevento was erected into an archbishopric with twelve diocesan bishops 'because it is a holy place where St. Bartholomew lies and is therefore entitled to much greater respect than it has hitherto received.' Salerno became the seat of an archbishop after acquiring the remains of St. Matthew.

The church of Santiago was perhaps more successful than any

other in making use of its pilgrimage as a means of ecclesiastical aggrandisement. In the tenth century its bishops were already employing the title 'bishops of the apostolic see' and signing themselves '*servus servorum domini*' after the fashion of the popes. These pretensions were encouraged by the kings of León, who were claiming the imperial dignity for themselves and may have hoped that Santiago would become to them what Rome was to the German emperors. As the fame of St. James expanded, so did the ambitions of his bishops. The episcopal official who greeted the papal legate at Santiago in c. 1065 had been instructed to give him no greater honour than he received in return. The incident is said to have inspired in pope Alexander II the fear that Santiago 'would shortly assume a dignity appropriate to its possession of the body of an apostle; that is, that it would dominate the churches of the Spanish kingdoms by virtue of St. James, just as Rome dominates other kingdoms by virtue of St. Peter.' Whether Alexander or his successors ever entertained any such fear is open to doubt, but these words precisely describe the ambitions of the formidable Diego Gelmirez. Gelmirez, who was consecrated as bishop in 1101 and completed the existing cathedral, went as far along this path as he dared. He called his canons cardinals, gave them mitres, and enforced surplices, copes, and shaving on them (formerly they had entered the church booted and spurred and with three days' growth of beard). Finally, in 1120, he persuaded an unwilling pope to erect Santiago into a metropolitan see. Three centuries before, Santiago had not even been the seat of a bishop.

The offerings at Santiago must have been considerable, but the active promotion of the pilgrimage by successive bishops and archbishops cannot be explained by offerings alone. Ecclesiastical status was their constant obsession, and they spent their offerings on a visible symbol of their status, the superb cathedral of St. James. In doing this they exemplified the ambitions of almost every sanctuary in Europe. In financial terms those who profited most from the pilgrimage to St. James were not the clergy but the citizens of Santiago. Their city, which had scarcely existed in the ninth century, was one of the major entrepôts of Spain in the twelfth. The *camino de Santiago* became a thriving commercial highway. In 1130 a merchant train carrying silver worth 22,000 marks was attacked by robbers at Padrón. Carrión de los Condes is now a wretched little town, dusty and decayed, but eight hundred years ago it was a station on the road to Santiago, described in the *Guide for Pilgrims* as 'industrious and prosperous, rich in bread and wine and every kind of meat'. This was the true revolution worked by the rise of a great sanctuary, and many travellers must have agreed with the German mathematician Hieronymus Munzer, who left Santiago in 1494 with the reflection that its citizens were 'fat as pigs and slothful at that, for they have no need to cultivate the soil when they can live off the pilgrims instead.'

CHAPTER XI

THE JOURNEY

Preparations

'He that be a pilgrim', declared the London preacher Richard Alkerton in 1406, 'oweth first to pay his debts, afterwards to set his house in governance, and afterwards to array himself and take leave of his neighbours, and so go forth.'

His first act, if he was a man of substance, was to make his will. Pilgrims enjoyed the special privilege of disposing of their property by will, a privilege which, until the late middle ages, was accorded to very few. As well as naming his heirs, the will would deal with such matters as the administration of his property in his absence and the length of time which was to elapse before he should be presumed dead. In Normandy local custom required every landowner to make a will which would automatically be executed if he did not announce his return within a year and a day. Some pilgrims also made private agreements with their wives as to how long they should leave before remarrying. The Church did what it could to ensure that the terms of a pilgrim's will were respected. In Spain, for instance, it made his companions responsible for looking after his personal effects. Failing companions, the local clergy were expected to keep them for a year and a day and, if they remained unclaimed, to sell them and apply the money to endowing masses for the repose of the dead pilgrim's soul.

In his absence, a pilgrim's property was immune from all civil claims in a court of law. The service which he owed to his feudal lord was usually suspended during the pilgrimage, and in northern France, according to Beaumanoir, pilgrims were exempt from the obligation to take part in family vendettas. In effect, there was no legal remedy to be had against a bona fide pilgrim, so long as he returned home to face his adversaries within a reasonable time. Illegal remedies were *a fortiori* forbidden, and those who had recourse to them faced both civil and ecclesiastical sanctions. In the bull *Quantum Praedecessores* of December 1145, Eugenius III proclaimed that the wife and children, goods and chattels of every

pilgrim or crusader were 'placed under the protection of the Holy
See and of all the prelates of the Church of God. By our apostolic
authority we absolutely forbid anyone to disturb them until their
return or death.' Before the first crusade this principle had probably
been honoured chiefly in the breach. But effective protection was
essential if crusaders were to be recruited for the defence of the Holy
Land, and by the end of the twelfth century, flagrant violations of a
pilgrim's rights never failed to arouse indignant protest. The invasion of Normandy by Philip Augustus of France while Richard
Coeur-de-Lion was in the Holy Land was bitterly criticized, and
some of Philip's own vassals refused to follow him. When, at the
beginning of the thirteenth century, it seemed that the entire
Angevin empire in France must shortly fall into the hands of the
French king, loyal vassals of John were afraid that Philip would
seize their lands. Some of them regarded a pilgrim's privileges as
the best guarantee of the rights of their heirs. This, at any rate, was
the reason given by Archambert de Monluc when he joined the
fourth crusade, appointing as trustees of his property a formidable
list of ecclesiastical personages.

Although few pilgrims went to the extremes recommended by
the preacher of the sermon *Veneranda Dies*, most of them made
some concession to the principle that a pilgrimage should be accomplished in poverty. Rich pilgrims often made generous donations to
the poor before leaving. The cartularies of monasteries, from the
eleventh century onwards, are full of deeds recording the gifts made
by departing pilgrims and crusaders. A donor could have the best of
both worlds by making his gift conditional on his not returning
alive. Then, when he returned home, he could demand the usufruct
of his property for the rest of his life, after which it would become
the unencumbered possession of the Church. When Aimeric II,
count of Fézensac, gave some windmills to the canons of Auch in
1088 as he was about to leave for the Holy Land, he insisted that 'if
I come back alive from Jerusalem, I can have them back until my
death.' If the knight never returned, the monks were often required
to give a pension to his widow and sometimes even to his children.
In fact, even if no such conditions were explicitly mentioned, they
were almost certainly implied by both parties. When Leteric de
Chatillon died in Palestine in 1100, the monks of La Charité allowed
his widow half the revenues of his estates, although no such arrangement is found in the deed whereby Leteric had made the monks his
heirs. Hughes de Lurcy, on returning from the Holy Land in the
1080s, claimed back his lands from the monks, promising to leave it
to them on his death. Pilgrims probably adopted this roundabout
procedure in order to ensure that their lands were safe in their

absence. Some of them may also have borrowed the cost of the journey from the monks and left the lands with them as a pledge.

The true pilgrim, urged the preacher of the sermon *Venerenda Dies*, ought before his departure to make amends to all those whom he has offended, and to ask the permission of his wife, his parish priest, and anyone else to whom he owed obligations. The most important of these, for a layman, was his feudal lord, whose consent would be necessary if the pilgrim wished to nominate his heir or safeguard the position of his wife. Even the kings of France, Louis VII in 1146 and Philip Augustus in 1190, sought formal permission to leave with the crusade from St. Denis, whose vassals they recognized themselves to be. A cleric was required to ask the permission of his superior before making a pilgrimage, and until the fourteenth century this obligation was enforced with vigour. The German annalist Lambert of Hersfeld recalled how he had set out for Jerusalem in 1058, immediately after his ordination, without asking his abbot:

'I was afraid that since I had set out without his blessing, I might have given him offence. If he had died in my absence I would have remained forever unreconciled to him and would thus have committed a terrible sin in the eyes of God. But God's favour was with me, . . . for I returned in safety, confessed my sin, and was received with kindness. I felt as if I had just escaped alive from the fires of Hell.'

He was, in fact, only just in time, for the abbot became feverish that very evening and died a week later.

A pilgrim who left without making amends to those he had wronged could not possibly make a sincere confession, and without a sincere confession, it was generally agreed that his pilgrimage would be worthless. 'In order that my devotion may be the more acceptable to God', reflected Odo, duke of Burgundy, before joining the crusade in 1101, 'I have decided that I should set out at peace with everybody.' Accordingly he wished to make amends for the damage he had done, in a lifetime of violence, to the abbey of St.-Bénigne de Dijon. He begged forgiveness in the nave of their church for the trespasses he had committed against their lands and the insults he had heaped upon their heads. 'And my promises of amendment and offers of compensation have been accepted by the monks of St.-Bénigne; they have pardoned and absolved me and have agreed to pray for me, that I may keep my promises and enjoy a safe journey to the Holy Land.' Bertrand de Moncontour, who had seized some land belonging to the abbey of the Trinity of Vendôme, wished to go to the Holy Land in 1098 but 'realized that the path of God would be closed to me while such a crime remained on my conscience.' Aggrieved monks were not the only beneficiaries of these acts of last-minute repentance, though they were the main ones. The Santiago preacher had reminded his audience that they must make their peace with neighbours and friends, great or humble. The most spectacular exercise in this direction was the *enquête* launched by St. Louis in January 1247 before his departure with the crusade. Commissioners, most of them drawn from the mendicant orders, toured the provinces of Louis's kingdom enquiring into wrongs alleged to have been done in his name. That this process of conscience-clearing was not confined to the king is shown by the behaviour of Louis' biographer Joinville, who summoned his vassals and family before joining the expedition and told them 'if I have wronged any of you, I shall now make amends to you one by one, as I have always done.'

When his enemies had been placated and his creditors satisfied, the pilgrim sought out his parish priest or, occasionally, his bishop, and received a formal blessing. Texts of these blessings for travellers survive from the early eighth century, though they did not pass into general use until the eleventh. Blessing ceremonies reflected the growing feeling among pilgrims that they belonged to an 'order' of the Church, distinguished from other men by a uniform and by a solemn ritual of initiation. Mass departures to the Holy Land or Santiago were marked by public ceremonies in the cathedrals. But most pilgrims received their blessing privately from their parish priest, or else from a monk whose sanctity they respected. The hermit St. Godric of Finchale was said to have performed the ceremony regularly. Joinville, in 1248, sought out the Cistercian abbot of Cheminon on account of his saintly reputation, and then, after receiving his blessing, made his way on foot without shoes or coat to the embarkation point of the crusade at Marseilles.

Pilgrims' Dress

Once initiated into the 'order' of pilgrims, he signified his attachment to a new way of life by wearing a uniform, as distinctive in its own way as the tonsure of a priest. 'When the debts be thus paid and the meine is thus set in governance', continued Richard Alkerton in 1406, 'the pilgrim shall array himself. And then he oweth first to make himself be marked with a cross, as men be wont to do that shall pass to the Holy Land. . . . Afterwards the pilgrim shall have a staff, a sclavein, and a scrip.' The staff, a tough wooden stick with a metal toe, was the most distinctive as well as the most useful part of the pilgrim's attire. The 'sclavein' was a long, coarse tunic. The scrip was a soft pouch, usually made of leather, strapped to the pilgrim's waist; in it he kept his food, mess-cans, and money. Such was the attire of every serious pilgrim after the end of the eleventh century. Much later, probably in the middle of the thirteenth century, pilgrims began to wear a great broad-brimmed hat, turned up at the front, and attached at the back to a long scarf which was wound round the body as far as the waist.

The origin of this curious garb is not at all clear. The staff and pouch were used by the migrant monks of Egypt in the fourth century, but they were obvious and sensible accessories for any traveller on foot, not only for pilgrims and not only in the middle ages. The tunic, on the other hand, whose practical usefulness is not as readily apparent, seems to make its first appearance at the beginning of the twelfth century. Canute, setting out for Rome in 1027, 'took up his scrip and staff as did all his companions', but there is no mention of the tunic. St. Anselm, in 1097, 'took his scrip and staff like a pilgrim', but again, no tunic. Orderic Vitalis, writing in about 1135, said that he could remember a time when pilgrims were indistinguishable from other travellers, except by their unshaven faces. Indeed it is probably about this time that the normal clothing of the traveller took on a sudden rigidity and became peculiarly the garb of the spiritual traveller.

This was almost certainly due to the fact that at the end of the eleventh century the Church began to bless the pilgrim's clothes and sanctify them as the uniform of his order. A special order of ceremony for pilgrims, as opposed to ordinary travellers, was now coming into existence. This usually took the form of blessing the pilgrim's pouch and mantle and presenting him with his staff from the altar. The ceremony has its origin in the blessing conferred on knights departing with the first crusade, and it is referred to in 1099 as a 'novel rite'. Behind the 'novel rite' is the pronounced tendency of the Church in the eleventh and twelfth centuries to stimulate lay piety by assigning to laymen certain defined spiritual functions. Those who fulfilled these functions were clothed with a special, almost ecclesiastical, status; they enjoyed spiritual privileges and ultimately secular ones as well. Hence the religious ceremony which now almost invariably accompanied the dubbing of a knight. Indeed, the ritual presentation of the pilgrim's staff bears a striking resemblance both to the dubbing of a knight and to the ordination of a priest. To the more austere pilgrim, the act of putting on his travelling clothes might have the same significance as taking the monastic habit. One such pilgrim was Rayner Pisani, an Italian merchant who experienced a sudden conversion during a business visit to Tyre in about 1140. Rayner took his pilgrim's tunic under his arm to the Golgotha chapel in Jerusalem and, in full view of an astonished crowd, removed all his old clothes and gave them to beggars. He then placed his tunic on the altar and asked the priest serving the chapel to invest him with it. This the priest did, and Rayner passed the remaining twenty years of his life as a hermit in Palestine.

In the course of time the Church invested the pilgrim's uniform with a rich and elaborate symbolism. Already in c. 1125 the author of the sermon *Veneranda Dies* is found explaining that the pilgrim's pouch is the symbol of almsgiving, because it is too small to hold much money and the pilgrim who wears it must therefore depend on charity. The pilgrim's staff is used for driving off wolves and dogs, who symbolize the snares of the Devil; the staff is the pilgrim's third leg, and three is the number of the Trinity; the staff therefore stands for the conflict of the Holy Trinity with the forces of evil, etc. This kind of imagery became very popular in the fourteenth and fifteenth centuries and it provided the theme for most of the sermons delivered to congregations of pilgrims before their departure. To Franco Sacchetti, the pilgrim's tunic stood for the humanity of Christ. The staff recalled the wood of the Cross in which lay the pilgrim's hope of salvation. Perhaps the most involved as well as the most popular of these allegories was the work of Thomas of London, a Dominican who taught in France and who wrote, in c. 1430, an *Instructorium Peregrinorum*. Here the staff, pouch, and tunic stand for faith, hope and charity, respectively, for reasons which are pursued as far as scholastic subtlety will permit. These arid academic exercises make dull reading today, but at the close of the middle ages they were much enjoyed.

On his way home, the pilgrim usually wore a badge or token showing where he had been. The best known and probably the earliest of these souvenirs was the palm of Jericho which pilgrims customarily brought back from Jerusalem. It is the origin of the English word 'palmer'. Like so many of the rituals associated with the pilgrimage to the Holy Land, this seems to have had its origin in the eleventh century. The palms, which were collected in the plain between Jericho and the Jordan, were regarded as a symbol of regeneration, of the victory of faith over sin. Peter Damian refers to the picking of palm leaves as 'customary' in c. 1050, and the soldiers of the first crusade all travelled *en masse* to the Jordan in July 1099 to baptize themselves in the river and collect their palms. William of Tyre, writing in c. 1180, remarks that the palm of Jericho was 'the formal sign that the pilgrim's vow has been fulfilled'. And so it remained throughout the middle ages, though later generations did not have to travel as far as the Jordan for their palms. After the twelfth century palm-vendors carried on a thriving trade in the market of the 'Rue des Herbes' in Jerusalem and stalls piled high with palms could be seen beneath the walls of the Tower of David.

Equally famous were the cockle shells worn by pilgrims returning from Santiago. The preacher of the sermon *Veneranda Dies* ascribed to them much the same symbolic significance as the palm of Jericho. 'In the sea near Santiago there are certain fish with two shells, one on either side of their body. . . . These shells the pilgrims of St. James gather up and sew onto their caps, carrying them home in triumph to their own people.' In Santiago, as in Jerusalem, enterprising tradesmen soon began to collect the shells themselves and by c. 1120, pilgrims had already given up the long trek to the sea and begun to buy their shells in the animated market which was held every day outside the north door of the cathedral.

Before the end of the twelfth century real cockle shells had been replaced by small lead badges in the shape of a shell, whose sale was strictly regulated by the archbishop of Santiago. Lead badges had by now been adopted by almost every major sanctuary. Most of them consisted of a simple disc with a roughly moulded representation of the patron saint of the sanctuary. Canterbury, for example, had a badge showing the mitred head of St. Thomas between two erect swords. The badge of Mont-St.-Michel showed St. Michael with his standard and shield weighing souls at the last judgement. The Virgin, as protectress of all pilgrims, appears on many badges, for instance the emblem of a minor sanctuary of St. Catherine in Lorraine, which shows two pilgrims with staffs, protected by the mantle of the Virgin. Others depicted well-known miracles of the saint. St. Leonard, protector of prisoners, is shown on his badge listening to the prayer of a chained captive. The miraculous survival of a man wrongly condemned to be hanged is commemorated in the emblem of St. Eutrope of Saintes. The horse miraculously shod by St. Eloy was depicted on the badges sold to pilgrims at Noyon in the thirteenth century. Much-travelled pilgrims would cover the brims of their hats with badges until their heads were bowed beneath the weight of lead. Langland's pilgrim had

> An hundreth of ampulles on his hatt seten,
> Signes of Synay and shelles of Galice
> And many a cruche on his cloke and keyes of Rome
> And the vernicle bifore; for men shulde knowe
> And se bi his signes whom he soughte had.

Louis XI of France, who was well-known for his simple but intense piety, assiduously visited almost every notable French shrine of his day. His hat, according to one of his enemies, was 'brim-full of images, mostly of lead and pewter, which he kissed whenever good or bad news arrived or whenever the fancy took him.'

Pilgrims' badges were much prized, not only as souvenirs, but as magic charms. A badge of Rocamadour was said to have cured a pilgrim's ailing son. Miraculous powers were often attributed to *coquilles-Saint-Jacques*, one of which was alleged in c. 1120 to have healed an Apulian knight suffering from diphtheria. Badges were also used to prove that the wearer was entitled, as a pilgrim, to exemption from tolls and taxes. Some courts of law accepted them as evidence that the wearer's property was immune from distraint for debt. The wearing of a cross was certainly *prima facie* evidence that the wearer was entitled to a crusader's privileges. All these factors ensured that the demand for badges far outstripped the supply, and the sale of emblems to pilgrims was an extremely profitable business. The Valon family made their fortune in the fourteenth century by buying the monopoly of the sale and manufacture of badges at Rocamadour. They were obliged to give a large slice of their profits to the bishop of Tulle, and this appears to have been the usual arrangement. The archbishop of Santiago took a percentage from licensed badge-sellers after 1200 and it was for many years a major source of revenue. Unlicensed sellers, however, sold at least as many badges as licensed ones, and not only to genuine pilgrims. The archbishops of Santiago often complained that copies of their badges were being sold throughout France and northern Spain. Indeed, in 1228 this nefarious trade was being carried on by no less a man than the neighbouring bishop of Lugo.

Travel Overland

A long journey in the middle ages was not a thing to be lightly undertaken. The great sanctuaries were separated by hundreds of miles of unmade, ill-marked roads, many of them running through unpopulated tracts of Europe infested with bandits. 'O Lord, heavenly father', ran a blessing commonly conferred on pilgrims in the twelfth century, 'let the angels watch over thy servants N.N. that they may reach their destination in safety, . . . that no enemy may attack them on the road, nor evil overcome them. Protect them from the perils of fast rivers, thieves, or wild beasts.' The outbreak of a war could interrupt the flow of pilgrims to an important sanctuary or even choke it altogether. Thus the disordered state of central Italy brought about the serious decline of the Roman pilgrimage in the tenth century and again in the thirteenth. The Hundred Years War ruined the abbey of St.-Gilles and many other shrines of

southern France, and significantly affected the prosperity of Santiago itself. In the fifteenth century a sudden Arab or Turkish descent
on Rhodes might prevent all travel to the Holy Land for a year.

The condition of the roads was the first obstacle. Europe relied,
throughout the middle ages, on the network of roads bequeathed to
it by the Roman empire. This network was far from comprehensive,
but new roads did appear from time to time in response to changing
needs. Thus the Roman road from Lyon to the south-west was
diverted in the eleventh century through the hard granite mountains
of the Ségalas to take it past the abbey of Conques; when the pilgrimage to Conques was forgotten, in the fourteenth century
travellers returned to the old road. In France, the roads were never
allowed to fall into complete disrepair, as they were in parts of
England. Nevertheless travel was not easy and even an experienced
rider could not expect to cover more than thirty miles in a day. The
seigneur de Caumont, who rode from Caumont to Santiago in
1418, was reduced to six miles a day in the Pyrenees and the Asturias,
but he was capable of doing twenty-seven miles when the terrain
was good.

The manor was responsible for the upkeep of the roads, but too
often it had few resources and little enthusiasm for the work. Important roads, particularly if they were used by pilgrims, were
frequently maintained by volunteers. For the maintenance of roads
was regarded as a work of charity equivalent, for example, to almsgiving. Bridge-building was particularly meritorious, 'a service to
posterity and therefore pleasing to God', declares a charter of 1031
concerning the construction of a bridge over the Loire at Tours.
French hermits in northern Spain were active road-builders at the
time when the great road to Santiago was being rebuilt by the
Castilian kings. Their names are preserved in the *Guide for Pilgrims
to Santiago*, 'and may their souls and those of their companions rest
in everlasting peace.' The bridge over the river Miño at Puerto
Marin was rebuilt after a civil war by Peter the Pilgrim. St. Domingo
'de la Calzada', another French immigrant, founded a celebrated
hospice on the site of his hut by the river Oja, and spanned the
stream with a wooden bridge; he built the first cobbled road across
the marshy expanse between Nájera and Redecilla. Several mediaeval roads and bridges still survive in Spain and southern France,
built under the impulsion of the pilgrimage to Santiago. At St.-
Chély d'Aubrac and St.-Michel Pied-de-Port the old track, its
stones worn or displaced, can still be followed for a few hundred
yards. The fine stone bridges which span the river at Orthez and
Oloron in Gascony date from the fourteenth century and replaced
older, wooden ones. At Puente la Reina one can still see the great

five-arched bridge where the two roads from southern France to Santiago came together.

The *Guide for Pilgrims to Santiago* catalogues the full range of catastrophes which could overcome the traveller on the roads in the twelfth century. It is both a historical guide and a route-book, offering its readers information about towns and hospices, a few useful words of the Basque language, an architectural description of Santiago cathedral, and precise directions on how to get there. The pilgrim is warned that the eight-mile ascent of the Port de Cize, the principal pass over the Pyrenees, is a steep climb; that in Galicia there are thick forests and few towns; that mosquitoes infest the marshy plain south of Bordeaux where the traveller who strays from the road can sink up to his knees in mud. Some of the rivers are impassable. Several pilgrims had been drowned at Sorde, where travellers and their horses were ferried across the river on hollowed-out tree trunks. Other rivers were undrinkable, like the salt stream at Lorca, where the author of the *Guide* found two Basques earning their living by skinning the horses who had died after drinking from it. Pilgrims were in theory exempt from the payment of tolls, but nevertheless the *Guide* reports that the local lords exacted payment from every traveller in the Béarn. At the foot of the Port de Cize, pilgrims were searched and beaten with sticks if they could not pay the toll. The author demanded immediate action by the bishop and the king of Aragon, but it was more than half a century before the extortionists suffered retribution at the hands of Richard Coeur-de-Lion.

The supply of food and fodder is a constantly recurring theme in the *Guide*, and an important one at a time when it dictated the beginning and end of the travelling season much more effectively than the weather. There was no fodder to be had in the Landes south of Bordeaux, and the horseman was well-advised to bring three days' supply with him. There were parts of the route where the pilgrim would find it hard to buy a good meal for himself, even in summer. The food and wine were excellent in Gascony but dreadful in the Basque country. Fish caught in the river Ebro were disgusting, even poisonous. In general, concludes the *Guide*, Spanish meat should be avoided by those who are unused to it, 'and if any one can eat their fish without feeling sick, then he must have a stronger constitution than most of us.'

Against wild animals, bad roads, and natural catastrophes, the traveller had no protection. But, in theory, he enjoyed a measure of protection against man-made hazards. Every criminal code imposed special penalties on those who molested travellers, and synods of bishops regularly threatened them with the severest ecclesiastical

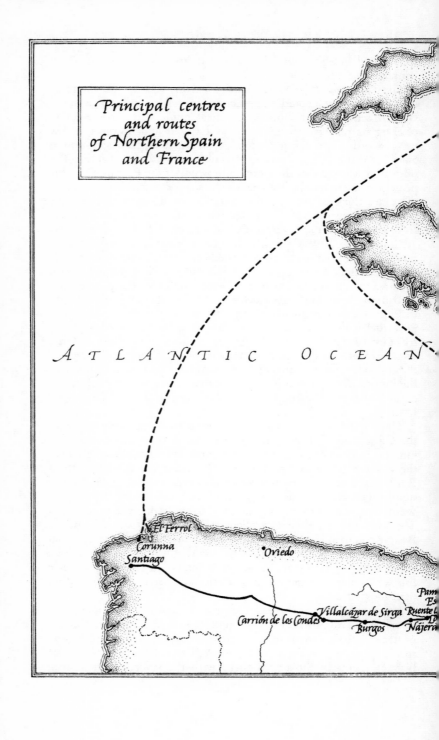

Principal centres
and routes
of Northern Spain
and France

ATLANTIC OCEAN

El Ferrol
Corunna
Santiago
Oviedo
Pam
Es
Villalcázar de Sirga Puente L
Carrión de los Condes
Burgos
Nájera

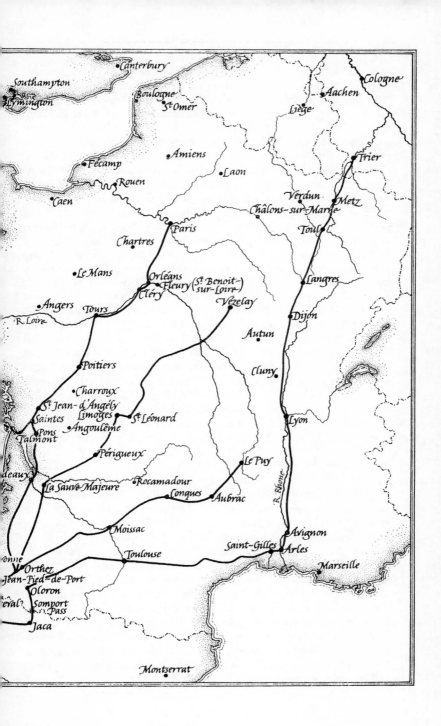

censures. In 1096 a steward of the king of France was excommunicated for seizing a vassal of his on the road to Vézelay during Lent.
'But you should know', the archbishop of Lyon pointed out, 'that
all those who travel to the shrines of the saints are protected against
attack at all times, and not only in Lent. Those who disturb their
journey will suffer the harshest penalties of the Church, so that the
fear of God may remain for ever in their eyes.' From 1303 onwards,
molesters of pilgrims were included in the annual bull *In Coena
Domini*, in which the pope solemnly anathematized an ever-length-
ening list of obnoxious persons. But although it is true that pilgrims
were marginally safer from attack than other travellers, they can
never have felt secure. In the eleventh century the Tuscan nobleman
Gerard of Galeria supported himself in part by attacking rich
pilgrims on the roads north of Rome. King Harold's brother Tostig
was one of his victims. The French robber-baron Thomas de Marle
owed much of his notoriety to his practice of holding pilgrims to
ransom and mutilating them if the ransom was not paid. He terrorized the roads of northern France for many years before Louis VI
mounted a military expedition against him in 1128. From the constant complaints of the ecclesiastical authorities, it is clear that
Thomas had many imitators. We are better informed, however, of
the bandits of the fourteenth and fifteenth centuries, most of whom
were never brought to justice. The Roman Jubilee of 1350 brought
considerable prosperity to one Berthold von Eberstein, who descended daily on the long processions of pilgrims winding through
the Rhine valley. The German *routier* Werner von Urslinger was
another bandit who enriched himself in 1350. His hunting-ground
was Tuscany, where several of the main routes to Rome met.
Jacopo Gabrielli, the papal rector of the Patrimony, was allowed
14,000 florins to raise mercenaries against him, the cost to be de-
frayed from the offerings at the Roman basilicas. The banditry of the
later middle ages is remarkable for its international quality. The
roads of northern Italy were infested with German robbers. On the
roads which crossed northern Spain to Santiago, many of the
bandits seem to have been Englishmen. In 1318 the provost of
Estella spent several weeks in pursuit of one John of London, who
had robbed pilgrims as they slept in a local hospice. In the following
year a number of English bandits were captured at Pamplona. It was
the same in the middle east. After the disappearance, in 1187, of the
crusading kingdom of Jerusalem, the hills of Palestine were terrorized by brigands from every western nation, Englishmen, Frenchmen, and Germans, common criminals and former knights Templar,
living side by side with Arabs for whom brigandage had been a way
of life for centuries.

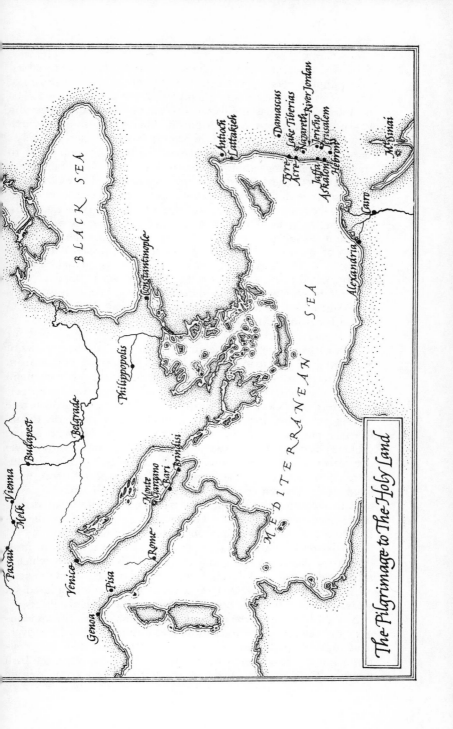

The Pilgrimage to The Holy Land

To the depredations of professional robber bands were added those of innkeepers and villagers, who found the constant stream of pilgrims passing their doors a temptation too great to resist. The inhabitants of the coastal villages of southern Normandy repeatedly waylaid pilgrims bound for Mont-St.-Michel. Those of northern Italy were said, in 1049, to be murdering Norman pilgrims 'daily'. Rather later, the villages of Navarre and the Basque country took to preying on pilgrims passing on the roads to Santiago; at the border towns of Sorde and Lespéron this was even described as 'customary'. Lawlessness on this scale was a familiar problem whenever the rise of a great sanctuary drew its seasonal flux of pilgrims onto the roads. The anarchic state of Italy in 1350 encouraged whole villages to seize and despoil pilgrims travelling to the Roman Jubilee. Peter, bishop of Rodez, and his companion were ambushed outside the village of Sant' Adriano in Sabina and were saved only by the timely arrival of Napoleone Orsini. The Romans themselves were reported to be mounting expeditions to rob pilgrims on the roads north of the city. One observer believed that half the pilgrims who set out for Rome in 1350 were robbed or killed on the way.

Innkeepers, never the most popular of men, were blamed for many thefts and murders. The most celebrated of all the miracles of St. James told of a man wrongly hanged for stealing money from the pockets of some wealthy German pilgrims as they slept in an inn at Toulouse. The true culprit, it transpired, was the innkeeper, 'wherefore it is clear that pilgrims should take great care before staying at an inn lest a similar fraud be perpetrated on them.' German pilgrims were notoriously the victims of these frauds, probably because they travelled in a somewhat more showy style than others. Tales of gruesome murders of pilgrims in lonely inns were commonplace. In the forest of Châtenay, near Mâcon, there lived, at the beginning of the eleventh century, an innkeeper who used to accommodate travellers at night and murder them as they slept. According to Radulph Glaber, an investigation by the authorities revealed eighty-eight bodies hidden in his hut.

No one doubted that the journey to Jerusalem was by far the most dangerous that a pilgrim could undertake. Every hazard which a mediaeval traveller could encounter is exemplified in the experiences of those who walked three thousand miles or endured six weeks in a tiny, unstable boat, in order to visit the Holy Places.

At the beginning of the eleventh century the conversion of Hungary and the revival of Byzantium had brought most of the overland route to Jerusalem under nominal Christian rule. Latin pilgrims learned how nominal that rule was in 1053, when the Irish pilgrim, Colman, was battered to death at Stockerau outside

Vienna, after an angry mob had taken him for a government spy. Although travellers now passed the frontier of the Byzantine empire at Belgrade, behind that frontier lay tracts of untamed territory which never recognized Byzantine rule. Lietbert, bishop of Cambrai, found Christian slaves being sold here in the summer of 1054. The valley of the Danube was so insecure in 1053 that travellers were being turned back by border guards at Belgrade. Pilgrims passed the southern extremity of the Byzantine empire at the coastal town of Lattakieh in northern Syria. Here again, they encountered a deeply hostile and suspicious population. Gerald of Saumur was battered to death by Syrian peasants in 1021, while others, like Anselm of Ardres, fell into the hands of Moslem fanatics and were lucky to escape by renouncing their faith.

Conditions were probably at their worst in 1064–5, when seven thousand unarmed German pilgrims made their way overland to Jerusalem under the leadership of Gunther, bishop of Bamberg. 'Truly we have been through fire and water', Gunther wrote to the canons of his cathedral from Lattakieh; '. . . we have been harassed by the Hungarians, attacked by the Bulgars, and driven to flight by the Turks, we have endured the insults of the arrogant Greeks of Constantinople and the rabid fury of the Cilicians. But we are afraid that even worse disasters lie ahead of us.' And so it was. On Good Friday 1065, as the long column of pilgrims was passing through an abandoned village near Caesarea, a terrifying scream of triumph was heard as hordes of mounted Arabs descended on them 'as famished wolves leap upon their prey'. The pilgrims in the front of the procession were cut down in hundreds and their leader, the bishop of Utrecht, left half dead in the sand. Those at the rear fled to a nearby farmhouse where they held out for three days until the arrival of the Arab governor of Ramleh.

The Arab authorities in Palestine were weak rather than malevolent, and they were well aware of the economic benefits which Christian pilgrimages brought to them. The only point of conflict was at the gates of Jerusalem, where pilgrims were required to pay a toll of one gold piece each. This was a large sum of money, which many pilgrims did not have by the time they reached Jerusalem. When Robert, duke of Normandy, arrived there in 1036 he found several hundred pilgrims lying starving beneath the walls, begging for alms with which to pay the keepers of the toll-gate. The Greeks also levied tolls on pilgrims. Basil II demanded payment from all western travellers arriving in Constantinople by sea, and his successors set up toll-gates at two points on the overland route. Pilgrims were charged half a gold piece each, three gold pieces if they were mounted. These exactions were the source of some bitterness in the west. In 1056 pope Victor I addressed a long complaint to the empress Theodora, pointing out that her officials were taking advantage of the neutrality of the Arabs to levy taxes within the precinct of the Holy Sepulchre itself.

The conquest of parts of Palestine and Syria by the crusaders served to increase the number of pilgrimages to the Holy Land without making their journey any safer. Guerrilla raids constantly cut the roads leading to Jerusalem. In 1172 a traveller reported that churches lying within a mile of the city were fortified against the infidel. Ascalon, which remained in Arab hands until 1153, was the base from which raids were launched against the roads west to Joppa and south to Hebron. The Joppa road was the lifeline between Jerusalem and the sea, along which travelled almost every pilgrim who visited the Holy Land in the twelfth century. An English pilgrim who followed the road in October 1102 described how the Arabs 'lay hidden in caves and crevices, waiting day and night for people travelling in small parties or straggling behind their groups. At one moment they are everywhere, the next they are gone. Their presence is felt by every one who passes on that fatal road.' The road to Jericho and the Jordan, where most pilgrims went to baptize themselves and collect their palms, was no safer than it had been in the time of the good Samaritan, although the Templars regularly patrolled it. At Easter 1120, thirty pilgrims were killed and sixty captured out of a party of some seven hundred. As for the road north to Nazareth and Acre, it was scarcely attempted except during the periodic wars between the kings of Jerusalem and the emirs of Damascus, when enterprising pilgrims would attach themselves to the Frankish army. In 1106, the Russian pilgrim abbot Daniel managed to penetrate as far north as Lake Tiberias in the entourage of king Baldwin. But travelling with the army was not as safe as it appeared, for many pilgrims are reported to have died on this particular expedition.

The eleventh century had been the heyday of the overland route to the Holy Land, but the growing instability of eastern Europe sharply reduced its popularity in the twelfth. Wealthy pilgrims with large escorts might fight their way through the Balkans as Henry the Lion, duke of Saxony, did *cum magna gloria* in 1172. But for most men, a pilgrimage to the Holy Land involved a long and expensive journey by sea. After the final disappearance of the crusading states at the end of the thirteenth century, there is scarcely a single case on record of an overland pilgrimage to Jerusalem.

Travel by Sea

A voyage by sea in the middle ages was an uncomfortable experience. Pilgrims were crowded like grains of corn into small, unstable boats where, for six weeks or more, they endured stale food and water, boredom, disease, and intense discomfort.

> Men may leve alle games
> That saylen to seynt James,

sang an Englishman of the fifteenth century with bitter memories of a voyage to Santiago. The seamen shouted at him and rushed to and fro, continually ordering him out of their way. The bark swayed and tossed so violently that he did not feel like eating and could not hold a tankard to his lips. The poorest pilgrims, stowed in the most uncomfortable part of the ship, slept next to the bilge-pump, and had to make do with bread and salt and water.

The well-to-do pilgrim could mitigate the discomfort of the journey by paying a little more for his passage. Two types of ship were available at Venice. There were large, oared galleys which were safe, comfortable, and expensive; and small ships for the use of the poor, which were crammed to overflowing. Sebald Rieter, the opulent merchant of Nurnberg, paid sixty-seven ducats for his fare to the Holy Land in 1479 and shared the ship with only sixty-three other passengers. On the other hand an anonymous German pilgrim who travelled in the cheap ship paid only thirty ducats. The Florentine, Lionardo Frescobaldi, took the expensive ship to Alexandria in 1384 and watched the cheap one foundering in the first storm with two hundred pilgrims on board. When the demand for places fell, both rich and poor would share the same ship but occupied different parts of it. 'Chose yow a place in the sayd gallery in the overest stage', advised William Wey, 'for in the lowst under hyt is ryght smoulderyng hote and stynkyng.' When Hans von Mergenthal sailed to the Holy Places in 1476, the place allotted to poor pilgrims was so narrow that it was impossible to turn over in one's sleep. Sleepers were bitten by insects and trampled over by large rats. The animals penned up on the deck to be slaughtered for food broke out from time to time and trod on the sleeping bodies. When the sea was rough, passengers could not stand upright for fear of being struck by swinging booms and ropes.

Pilgrims were advised to bring mattresses and warm clothes with them. Frescobaldi, Gucci, and Sigoli, the three Italians who travelled together in 1384, brought several mattresses, a large number of shirts, a barrel of Malmsey wine, a Bible in several volumes, a copy of the *Moralia* of St. Gregory, a silver cup, 'and other delicate things'.

Santo Brasca, who did the journey in 1480, recommended a long thick coat, and also suggested some provisions which every pilgrim would need to supplement the ship's meagre diet: a good supply of Lombard cheese, sausages, salted meat, white biscuits, sugar loaves, and sweetmeats. He should also bring some strong spices for curing indigestion and sea-sickness, 'and above all a great quantity of fruit syrup, for this is what keeps a man alive in hot climates.' William Wey agreed that the prudent pilgrim should arm himself with laxatives, restoratives, ginger, flour, figs, pepper, saffron, cloves, and other 'confections and comfortaciouns'; it was essential to have half a dozen chickens in a cage 'for ye schal have need of them many tymes.' All travellers were agreed on the appalling quality of ship's food. 'Sum tymes', declared William Wey, 'ye schal have swych feble bred, wyne, and stynkyng water, that ye schal be ful fayne to eate of yowre owne.'

The manner in which the food was served was not calculated to stimulate the appetite. At the sound of a trumpet the passengers separated into two groups, those whose fare included food, and those who were seeing to their own wants. Members of the first group then scrambled for a place at one of three small tables in the poop. After dinner another trumpet signalled for the diners to retire, while their place was taken by the ship's officers and crew. Their food was even more frugal than that of the pilgrims, but it was served with great pomp on silver dishes, and their wine was tasted before it was offered to them. The galley was a scene of unending chaos. 'Three or four hot-tempered cooks struggle with the food in a narrow passage lined with pots and pans and provisions, while a fire crackles away in the middle. Sounds of angry shouting issue forth from the room while, outside, crowds of passengers shout each other down in the effort to order special meals from the cooks.'

After hunger and sleeplessness, boredom was the principal problem of the passengers. 'Unless a man knows how to occupy himself, he will find the hours very long and tedious', Felix Faber observed. Saxons and Flemings, 'and other men of low class', usually passed the days drinking. Others played dice or cards. Chess was very common. Communal singing went on in the background all the time. A small group of contemplative pilgrims gathered in a corner to read or pray. Others slept day and night. Many wrote travel diaries. A number of pilgrims, Faber remarked with contempt, amused themselves by running up and down the rigging, jumping up and down on the spot, or weight-lifting. 'But most people simply sit about looking on blankly, passing their eyes from one group to another, and thence to the open sea.' During Faber's first pilgrimage, in 1480, the news of Turkish naval activity in the eastern

Mediterranean caused the passengers to agree on measures of moral reform which would preserve them from capture. All games were forbidden, together with quarrels, oaths, and blasphemies. Disputes between the French and the Germans were to cease, and the bishop of Orléans promised to give up gambling. Extra litanies were added to the daily service.

Sermons were the only organized recreation. The company who travelled with canon Casola in 1494 were fortunate enough to have amongst them one Francesco Tivulzio, 'a holy friar with a wonderful library in his head'. Whenever the ship was becalmed, he would rise and deliver an elaborate and learned sermon, many hours in length. On the eve of the feast of St. John, he delivered a sermon on the merits of that saint in nine parts which lasted from 5 p.m. to sunset, and promised to deliver the rest of it on the following day. While waiting for permission to disembark at Joppa, the pilgrims listened to another sermon from friar Tivulzio on the allegorical significance of sailing ships, followed, a few hours later, by 'a beautiful sermon on trade'. Such discourses, however, were not always received in rapturous silence. On Faber's first pilgrimage his preaching was repeatedly interrupted by inane laughter, after which he refused to utter again. On his second pilgrimage the company was more polite, and he favoured them with regular sermons. Even so, a number of noblemen disliked his preaching, which Faber attributed to the fact that they practised the vices that he castigated, 'and truth ever begets hatred.'

The tedious serenity of a long sea voyage was occasionally disturbed by the appearance of pirates. The law of the sea required all passengers to assist in defending the ship, and although pilgrims were exempt from this obligation on account of their religious calling, they usually fought as hard as any. In 1408, a Venetian galley returning from the Holy Land was attacked by a Turkish pirate in the gulf of Satalia. The captain was found to have no cross-bows on board, and it was only after the pilgrims had beaten off their assailants in fierce hand-to-hand fighting that the ship escaped capture. In consequence, the Venetian senate enacted that a proper supply of bows, arrows, and lances was to be carried on every pilgrim-ship.

The pilgrim's troubles did not end with his arrival at Joppa. After the fall of Acre to the Arabs (1291), Joppa was the point at which almost all pilgrims disembarked, and it was here that they first encountered Arab officialdom. An English pilgrim who was there in 1345 described them as a group of 'revolting and corpulent men with long beards', mounted on tall horses on the foreshore. The master of the ship gave them a list of the pilgrims' names and paid a toll of six Venetian *gros* a head. The column was then escorted by two Arab guides to Jerusalem. This pilgrim was fortunate to find the officials waiting for him. Usually it was necessary to send word to the Arab governor of Jerusalem, and until the arrival of his minions the travellers were incarcerated in three large underground cellars in the ruins of the town. Fifteenth-century pilgrims made a virtue of this necessity by attaching an indulgence of seven years to these comfortless cellars. The Franciscans of Jerusalem, who enjoyed considerable influence with the caliphate, did all they could to ease the pilgrim's lot. At the beginning of the fifteenth century they even succeeded in taking over the administration of the tolls and the issue of visas. The prior of the Franciscans met the pilgrim-ship at Joppa, clutching a wadge of visas which he had obtained from the governor in advance. He collected the names of the pilgrims and took their money on the governor's behalf before escorting them inland.

In addition to the heavy toll which had to be paid before leaving Joppa, the pilgrim was required to pay the poll-tax which Islamic law imposed upon non-Moslems. This was exacted in Jerusalem, usually under the eyes of the governor himself. The English pilgrim of 1345 found the governor at the end of a large hall. In front of him scribes were seated on the floor recording the proceedings with huge quills. At that time the poll-tax stood at four gold florins, but a large sum from the party as a whole was accepted instead, for some of them had come without any money at all. However, the attitude of the Arab authorities was constantly changing. Only a year later, the governor threatened a penniless Franciscan pilgrim with flogging and imprisonment unless he could find someone to pay his poll-tax for him. As relations between Islam and the west deteriorated, the tolls and taxes demanded of pilgrims sharply increased. In 1440, a German pilgrim was asked for one *gros* from Joppa to Ramleh, one *gros* from Ramleh to Lydda, two *gros* at Emmaeus, and five at the gates of Jerusalem. Mariano da Sienna paid thirteen ducats to be exempted from all tolls, though even this did not spare him the payment of the poll-tax. The Dominican writer Guillaume Adam, an early advocate of economic warfare, calculated in 1317 that the sultan received thirty-five *gros tournois* every time a pilgrim visited the Holy Land, and he suggested to John XXII that this was a good reason for forbidding pilgrimages to the Holy Land altogether. 'Pilgrims are the only people who freely assist the Saracens without having to fear excommunication.'

The fact that pilgrims continued to visit the Holy Land in large numbers, in spite of the obstacles in their way, was largely due to the enterprise of the Venetians. The ship-owners of Venice provided the earliest all-inclusive package tours. Galleys licensed by the republic left for Joppa every year as soon as possible after Ascension

Day and returned in the autumn. When the demand for passages was high, two fleets sailed from Venice, one in March and one in September. The fare included food and board throughout the journey as well as in the Holy Land itself; the ship-owner, who was generally the master as well, paid all tolls and taxes, and met the cost of donkeys and pack-horses, guided tours of Jerusalem, and special expeditions to the Jordan. The popularity of these tours was entirely due to the high reputation of Venetian ship-owners. The stiff regulations of the serene republic enforced on them standards of safety and commercial morality which were uncommon in other ports. The anonymous English pilgrim of 1345 was advised by the inhabitants of Brindisi that it was unsafe to travel in any ship but a Venetian one. If he entrusted his life to a Sicilian or a Catalan master 'he would undoubtedly enjoy eternal rest at the bottom of the sea.' The ship-owners of Genoa and Pisa were suspected of selling their passengers into slavery at Arab ports. Francesco da Suriano gave four reasons for sailing from Venice in the latter half of the fifteenth century. It was so busy that a traveller never had to wait more than a few days before a ship sailed for his destination; the port was safe from pirates; the Venetian navy patrolled much of the route; and Venetian sailors were 'the finest travelling companions in Christendom'. He might have added that the Venetian currency was among the most stable in the west, and it was the only one which passed for legal tender in Arab territories. 'And so', counselled Santo Brasca, 'travel via Venice, for it is the most convenient embarkation point in the world.'

The Venetian republic began to license and regulate the traffic of pilgrims at the beginning of the thirteenth century. The maritime statutes of 1229 laid down the maximum number of pilgrims which one ship could carry and the date of sailing. At that time there were two fleets per year. The first, which reached the Holy Land in time for Easter, was to return not later than 8th May, while the second was to leave Joppa before 8th November. Further regulations, in 1255, enjoined officers of the republic throughout the eastern Mediterranean to inspect every pilgrim ship calling at their ports and to impose heavy fines if they were overloaded. Mariners were required to swear an oath not to steal more than five shillings from the passengers. The rights and duties of the pilgrim were set out in a lengthy contract, which was signed by both parties. Some of these contracts have survived. The contract between Jan Aerts and the shipowner Agostino Contarini, signed in April 1484, is in every way typical. It permits the pilgrim to go ashore whenever the ship is in port, and to visit Mount Sinai instead of returning with the ship, in which case Contarini will refund ten ducats of his fare. Contarini undertakes not to take on too many passengers or too few crewmen and not to appropriate the pilgrim's chattels if he dies during the journey; he promises to supply enough arms for twenty-five men in case of attack, and to accompany his passengers wherever they go in Jerusalem. The passengers may elect two of their number to oversee him. But there were no standard forms of contract, and pilgrims occasionally insisted on a special term. A contract dating from 1440 provides for a four-day stop at Nicosia, in Cyprus. William Wey advised English pilgrims to insist on a clause forbidding the owner to call at Famagusta on account of its unhealthy air. Once signed, the contract was lodged with a magistrate in Venice who would hear any disputes that arose. In 1497, for example, pilgrims protested that the space allotted to them was too small; port officials boarded the ship and resolved that each passenger should have one and a half feet of deck on which to sleep. On another occasion, pilgrims complained on their return to Venice that they had been manhandled and ill-fed and that their sleeping-quarters had been filled with cargo. Some of them had refused to return with the ship and had instead taken a passage from Beyrut in a Genoese vessel. The rest returned to Venice in an exceedingly hostile mood and, as they included a number of 'great lords', the Senate hastily sequestered the vessel and ordered the owners to refund the fares.

Disputes had become so common by the early fifteenth century that in 1437 the republic took the extreme step of suspending the annual pilgrim fleets. When they were restored, in 1440, it was on a somewhat different footing. The republic decided to encourage the process by which the pilgrim trade was monopolized by a small group of reputable shipowners. The smaller shipowners were excluded by a new maritime statute forbidding the masters of pilgrim-ships to carry any cargo at all. The number of annual licences issued by the republic was severely restricted, and those were sold for huge sums by public auction. Should any particularly distinguished pilgrims request a passage to the Holy Land, the republic reserved the right to make an extra charge. Thus in 1446, when a number of noblemen arrived with letters of commendation from the duke of Burgundy, the licensees of the year were charged an extra six hundred ducats for the exclusive privilege of fleecing these august personages. For some years after 1440, the traffic was monopolized by the Loredano family. But within ten years they were facing powerful competition from a syndicate headed by the brothers Contarini. The Contarini conducted their business with a degree of professionalism hitherto unheard-of, employing commission agents as far away as the Netherlands. In the last three decades of the fifteenth century, Agostino Contarini enjoyed an unofficial monopoly of the pilgrim traffic which did not end until he was forced to retire in 1497 after frequent complaints of misconduct.

But it was not misconduct which brought Agostino Contarini's career to an end, so much as the disturbed state of the eastern Mediterranean and the increasingly hostile attitude of the Arab authorities in Jerusalem. The Turks attacked Rhodes four times in the 1440s doing considerable damage to the port. William Wey, returning from his first visit to the Holy Land in 1459, saw the ruin left after a recent Turkish descent, and heard stories of fearful atrocities. In 1480 another Turkish attack on Rhodes seriously disrupted the shipping routes. Although Venice had signed a treaty with the Porte only the year before, the pilgrim's galley of that year had to take refuge for a week in Corfù. Twenty of the pilgrims decided to return to Venice in another ship, and Agostino Contarini had to refund ten ducats to each of them.

In Palestine, toll-gates multiplied unceasingly and the Arab governor made unpredictable demands on the shipowners which they were unable, by the terms of the contract, to recover from the passengers. In 1479 Agostino Contarini had to pay peace money to Arab officials because another Venetian shipowner had given offence to them in the previous year. The anarchic state of Palestine made it impossible to bathe in the Jordan that year, and the passengers complained bitterly. In 1480 Contarini's troubles began anew when the pilgrims of his galley demanded that he hire an armed escort to accompany them to the Jordan. They pointed out that a trip to the Jordan was included in the contract. Contarini replied that nothing in the contract obliged him to spend so much extra money and that if he hired an escort it would be at their own expense. The pilgrims finally left in high dudgeon, without an escort. A further dispute broke out when the Arabs forced Contarini to pay more than the customary fee for the hire of donkeys and pack-horses. Contarini refused to allow the pilgrims to re-embark for Venice until they had paid him a further ducat and a half to cover this unforeseen expense. Needless to say, he made large losses in both years.

It was shortly after these disasters that the Venetian package tour was abandoned and the pilgrimage to the Holy Land suffered a prolonged decline. Pietro Casola learned from the Franciscans of Jerusalem in 1494 that no pilgrims had visited the city for several years. The fleet of 1499 had to be cancelled when war broke out between Venice and the Porte, and the licensee had to refund all the fares which he had received. The news of these events deterred the pilgrims from Italy and northern Europe who had once gathered in

crowds for the Ascension Day sailing. In the early years of the sixteenth century the fleet, when it sailed at all, consisted of a single
ship. In 1533 the French pilgrim Gréffin Affagart arrived in Venice
to find that it had not sailed for many years. Interest in the Holy
Land had declined, and it was no longer possible for enterprising
shipowners to offer cheap passages by filling their decks with human
cargo.

Strange Customs and Foreign Languages

It would be pleasant to learn that pilgrims returned from their
travels with minds broadened by the experience of strange people
and unfamiliar customs. But it would be the reverse of the truth.
Such exchange of ideas as had occurred in the 'dark ages' of the west
did not survive the onset of an age of mass-pilgrimage. All too often,
those who lived on the pilgrimage roads regarded pilgrims as fair
game to be plundered at will. The pilgrims in turn had little in-
centive to understand their hosts, and viewed them with that un-
comprehending contempt which uneducated people commonly
accord to foreigners. The impressions of French pilgrims in Spain
are a case in point. So loathsome a race as the Basques, thought the
author of the *Guide for Pilgrims to Santiago*, could only have originated in Scotland. After describing their national dress, he goes on
to comment on their food and language in the following terms:

'Not only are they badly dressed, but they eat and drink in the
most disgusting way. The entire household, including servants,
eat out of the same pot and drink from the same cup. Far from
using spoons, they eat with their hands, slobbering over the
food like any dog or pig. To hear them speaking, you would
think they were a pack of hounds barking, for their language is
absolutely barbarous. They call God *Urcia*; bread is *orgui* and
wine *ardum*, while meat is referred to as *aragui* and fish *araign*.
. . . They are in fact a most uncouth race whose customs are
quite different from those of any other people. They have dark,
evil, ugly faces. They are debauched, perverse, treacherous and
disloyal, corrupt and sensual drunkards. They are like fierce
savages, dishonest and untrustworthy, impious, common,
cruel and quarrelsome people, brought up in vice and iniquity,
totally devoid of human feeling. . . . They will kill you for a
penny. Men and women alike warm themselves by the fire,
revealing those parts which are better hidden. They fornicate
unceasingly, and not only with humans. . . . That is why they
are held in contempt by all decent folk.'

PLATE I: STATUE-RELIQUARY OF ST. FOY AT CONQUES (AVEYRON).
The statue dates from the mid-tenth century, and its outstretched
arms once held a model of the iron bed on which she was supposed to
have been martyred. It was carried with clashing cymbals through the
valleys of the Rouergue whenever the abbey's lands were threatened.

PLATE II: A. ST. THOMAS APPEARS TO A SLEEPING MONK. Like all saints, he was thought to be a conscious being who physically inhabited his shrine. From a stained glass window of Canterbury cathedral (13th. century).

B. A BLEEDING IMAGE OF CHRIST. From a manuscript of Marco Polo's travels (14th. century). In the fourteenth and fifteenth centuries, the blood of Christ was venerated in this form in many churches of the Low Countries.

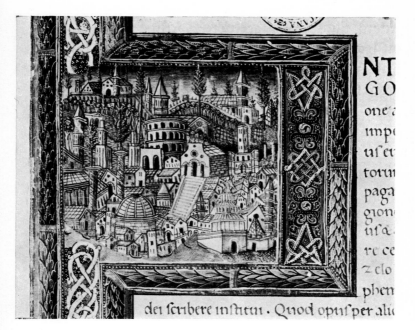

PLATE III: A. A VIEW OF ROME IN 1456. From a manuscript of St. Augustine illuminated by Giacomo Fabriano for a Roman monastery.

B. PILGRIMS PAYING TOLL AT THE GATES OF TYRE (15th. century).

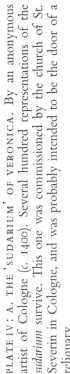

PLATE IV: A. THE 'SUDARIUM' OF VERONICA. By an anonymous artist of Cologne (c. 1400). Several hundred representations of the *sudarium* survive. This one was commissioned by the church of St. Severin in Cologne, and was probably intended to be the door of a reliquary.

B. SHRINE OF THE THREE KINGS IN COLOGNE CATHEDRAL (early 13th. century). The artist, Nicholas of Verdun, was probably trained at St.-Denis in the time of abbot Suger. The shrine was presented by the emperor Otto IV, who is depicted on the side, paying homage to the Virgin and Child.

In the *Chanson de Roland* the Basques appear in an extremely sinister light, and the influence of this celebrated poem may well be responsible for the contempt which many pilgrims expressed for them. But this alone will not explain the venom of the *Guide*, which entertains a remarkably similar opinion of the Gascons, characterizing their way of life as impious, immoral, and 'in every way detestable'.

If a Poitevin could write thus of the Gascons, he was unlikely to feel closer in spirit to the Greeks and oriental Christians, let alone to the Arabs. Throughout this period, relations with the Greeks were marked by a bitterness which can only be understood in the light of the tortuous relations of Byzantium with the crusaders. Most Latin Christians despised the Greeks as effeminate schismatics and believed with immovable conviction that they had betrayed the twelfth-century crusades. A guide-book written at the end of the century refers to them characteristically as 'cunning men who do not bear arms and who err from the true faith. . . . They also use leaven bread in the Eucharist and do other strange things. They even have an alphabet of their own.' This mood of suspicion was aggravated by the widespread belief that the Byzantine authorities deliberately obstructed pilgrims passing through Constantinople. The emperor Alexius Comnenus was once described by an eminently sane Latin writer as 'that great oppressor of pilgrims to Jerusalem who hinders their progress by guile or by force.' Indeed, it never struck western pilgrims that their habit of helping themselves to whatever they required, and of insulting and attacking local people, might arouse justifiable resentment on the part of their hosts. The importance which Greeks attached to their own traditions was regarded by some Latin pilgrims as nothing less than a calculated insult. Jacques de Vitry denounced them as 'foul schismatics moved by sinful pride', and then went on to consider the Jacobite and Armenian Christians, 'barbarous nations who differ from both Greeks and Latins . . . and use a peculiar language understood only by the learned.'

Language was indeed the principal barrier. Few mediaeval men, however cultivated they were, understood more than a few words of any language but their own or Latin. Travelling through regions such as eastern Europe or Egypt, where pilgrims were rare and Latin unknown, was a difficult and dangerous undertaking. Lietbert, bishop of Cambrai, who passed through the Danube valley on the way to Jerusalem in 1054, listed 'the strange and foreign language of the Huns' amongst the perils which he had encountered, together with mountains, swamps, and impenetrable forests. During the twelfth century, French was the language of Jerusalem, and this is said to have made difficulties for the Germans. At any rate, one of

the reasons given for the foundation of the German hospice in
Jerusalem was that 'in such a place Germans might talk in a language
they can understand.' In Venice the authorities were constantly
embarrassed by the activities of sharp traders or shipowners who
took advantage of foreigners bound for the Holy Land. 'It is well-
known that many scandalous mistakes have been made of late, on
account of the great number of pilgrims boarding ships at Venice',
the senate noted in 1398; 'for the said pilgrims are of divers tongues
. . . and unless a remedy is found, still greater scandals will
follow.'

It is worth following the Burgundian pilgrim Bertrandon de la
Brocquière in his efforts to learn a few words of Turkish. Bertrandon visited the Holy Land in 1432–3, but he avoided the Venetian
package tour because he wished to spy out the land at leisure, with
a view to planning a crusade. In Damascus he made the acquaintance
of a Turk who spoke Arabic, Hebrew, Turkish, and Greek. Bertrandon spoke none of these languages, but he had a working
knowledge of Italian, and the Turk found a Jew who knew a little
Italian and some Turkish. The Jew compiled a list of everything that
Bertrandon would require on his journey, in parallel columns of
Turkish and Italian. On the first day after leaving Damascus,
Bertrandon had occasion to ask a group of peasants for some fodder
for his horse. He consulted his piece of paper and made his request,
but there was no reaction. He showed the paper to the leading
peasant, who began to roar with laughter. The group then gave him
an impromptu lesson in Turkish, picking up various articles and
pronouncing their names very carefully several times. 'And when I
left them I knew how to ask in Turkish for almost everything I
wanted.'

Italian was the only European language known to a significant
number of Arabs. Pilgrims who visited Mount Sinai via Egypt
could usually find an Italian-speaking interpreter at Alexandria or
Cairo, but this was an expensive luxury of which few travellers
availed themselves. In 1384 Lionardo Frescobaldi's party spent more
than forty-nine ducats on interpreters between Alexandria and
Damascus. In addition, one of their interpreters stole eight ducats
from them, and another was in league with a group of Bedouin
bandits. More than a hundred ducats was spent on bribing the personal interpreters of various Arab officials to present their requests
for safe-conducts in a favourable way.

Phrase-books, then as now, were the simplest way to overcome
the language difficulty. As early as the ninth century, we find a
phrase-book entitled *Old High-German Conversations* (*Altdeutsche
Gespräche*) being used by Franks travelling in Germany. It consists

of orders to servants, requests for information, and demands for hospitality such as 'I want a drink':

'Erro, e guille trenchen; id est, ego volo bibere.'

A number of early phrase books of Greek and Hebrew survive, most of which were clearly intended for the use of pilgrims to the Holy Land. The abbey of Mont-St.-Michel had, in the eleventh century, a Greek phrase-book containing useful demands like

'Da mihi panem: DOS ME PSOMI.'

An interesting manual for crusaders, dating from the twelfth century, includes such tactful requests as 'What is the news about the Greek emperor? What is he doing? He is being kind to the Franks. What good things does he give them? Much money and weapons.' During the period of mass-pilgrimages in the late middle ages, an immense number of phrase-books was available, some of them very comprehensive. The library of Charles V of France contained a manual for pilgrims entitled *How to ask in Arabic for the necessities of life*. Another French-Arabic phrase-book, preserved in the Swiss abbey of St.-Gall, has a long section on how to ask one's way in a strange town.

Some pilgrims found oriental alphabets a source of limitless fascination. *Mandeville's Travels*, that strange mixture of fact and fantasy, sets out the Greek, Hebrew, Arabic, and Persian alphabets, though they contain many mistakes and the Hebrew one is incomprehensible. Johann Schiltberger appended to the account of his travels the *Pater Noster* in Armenian and Turkish. But the most proficient linguist amongst the pilgrims of the fifteenth century was certainly Arnold von Harff, a wealthy young nobleman of Cologne who, between 1496 and 1499, travelled through Italy, Syria, Egypt, Arabia, Ethiopia, Nubia, Palestine, Turkey, and Spain. He was a worldly pilgrim of the type mocked in the *Canterbury Tales* and the *Quinze Joies de Mariage*, but he took a genuine interest in the people of each country and particularly in their languages. Von Harff collected alphabets. His memoirs contain many oriental alphabets (some of them are undecipherable), as well as useful phrases in nine different languages, Croatian, Albanian, Greek, Arabic, Hebrew, Turkish, Hungarian, Basque, and Breton. He was a cultivated man, a gallant knight and an aristocrat whose range of phrases was broader than that of most conventional pilgrims. Thus, 'Wash my shirt for me – I do not understand – Will you sell me that? – How much is this? – Madam shall I marry you? – Madam shall I sleep with you? – Good woman, I am already in your bed.'

But Arnold von Harff was scarcely typical even of his own worldly age. He was an acute observer who was interested in such diverse matters as wild animals in the Nile valley, and the Mamluk system of government. He doubted the authenticity of the body of St. James at Santiago, and openly disputed the claims of several Roman relics. He considered the Turks closer to the spirit of Christianity than the Spanish. A more faithful reflection of the mentality of pilgrims is found in the account of the Arab way of life in the travel diary of one of Frescobaldi's companions, which begins, 'now let me tell you of their bestial habits.'

Companions

The criticism directed at pilgrims at the close of the middle ages owed much of its vehemence to the fact that they generally travelled in large and raucous bands. The carnival atmosphere in which Chaucer's thirty pilgrims left Southwark, piped out of town by the miller, ill-accorded with the spiritual sentiments which they professed. But then, as the host of the Tabard Inn reflected, 'trewely confort ne mirthe is noon, to ryde by the weye doumb as a stoon'; in fact he 'ne saugh this yeer so mery a companye.' William Thorpe, an itinerant Lollard preacher who was examined for heresy in 1407, had this to say about such vulgar gatherings:

> 'I know well that when divers men and women will go thus after their own wills, and finding out one pilgrimage they will ordain beforehand to have with them both men and women that can well sing wanton songs. And some other pilgrims will have them bagpipes so that every town that they come through shall know of their coming, what with the noise of their singing and the sound of their piping, what with the jangling of their Canterbury bells, and the barking out of dogs after them. They make more noise than if the King came thereaway with all his clarions and many other minstrels.'

The first pilgrims to travel in bands did so for reasons of self-defence, not amusement. Before the eleventh century, pilgrims generally had two or three companions with them at the most. Indeed, it was thought to be specially virtuous to travel alone. The dangerous state of the roads to Jerusalem forced pilgrims to abandon this prejudice, and by the middle years of the eleventh century the departure of an abbot or a great nobleman was the signal for pilgrims from all the surrounding provinces to gather together and follow in his suite. Richard, abbot of St.-Vannes, who set out from Verdun in 1026, found himself the leader of several hundred

Normans and Aquitainians. Each group had picked up hangers-on
on their way to Verdun, and as the whole unwieldy column proceeded up the Rhine valley they were constantly joined by new
recruits. By the time they left the frontiers of Germany behind
them, they were more than seven hundred strong. Robert, duke of
Normandy, was followed to Jerusalem in 1035 by an imposing
retinue of bishops, abbots, and noblemen, whose expenses he had
promised to pay. The ill-fated expedition of Gunther, bishop of
Bamberg, was estimated at seven thousand.

Few pilgrims travelled alone after the eleventh century, whatever
their destination. The growing popularity of pilgrimages made it
easy to find companions. Indeed, on the busy roads to Rome and
Santiago it was impossible to avoid them. Pilgrims were exhorted
to choose their friends with care, for there were regular reports of
travellers killed or robbed by their companions. Particularly notorious was the stretch of the road to Santiago which ran from
Saintes to the Pyrenees. Here, theft was a well-organized industry.
In one incident a blind man was robbed by his companions of his
money, his horse, and all his luggage, and left without a guide at the
side of the road. The 'companions' were of course professional
thieves of the sort described in the *Liber Sancti Jacobi*, who dressed as
pilgrims or priests in order to gain the confidence of their victims.
'Take care, then, not to join up with bad companions', warned the
French jurist Beaumanoir, after telling of a pilgrim who was hanged
as a felon on being found in the company of thieves; 'for however pleasant they appear, you never know what evil will befall
you.'

Even if he was honest a companion might well be quarrelsome or
a bore. He might walk too fast, as Margery Kempe's companion
did on the road to Wilsnack. He might talk too much, as Margery
herself was inclined to do. Her visit to the Holy Land in 1413 is a
classic illustration of the difficulty of living up to high spiritual ideals
in the company of a happy band of Chaucerian pilgrims. As a
woman, she could not travel alone, and so she fell in with a group of
English pilgrims of somewhat conventional piety. These were embarrassed by her constant fasting, weeping, and lamentation, and
her long sessions in prayer. They left Constance without her, but
she caught them up again at Bologna, where an agreement was made
in an effort to restore harmony. 'Ye shall not speak of the Gospel
when we come,' they warned her, 'but ye shall sit still and make
merry as we do.' At Venice, her habit of quoting passages from the
Bible brought about another rupture. In Jerusalem her trances and
visions caused them intense discomfort. 'Some shunned her; some
wished she had been left in the haven; some would she had been at

sea in a bottomless boat; and so each man as him thought.' The Franciscans of Jerusalem, however, were impressed by her piety. So, strange to say, were the Arabs, who provided her with an escort about the Holy Places.

Hospitality

A pilgrim, according to an eighth-century text, was entitled to a roof over his head, a fire, wholesome water, and fresh bread. The principle of free hospitality, though often honoured in the breach, remained throughout the mediaeval period a corner-stone of Christian charity. The *Guide for Pilgrims to Santiago* ends with a collection of stories illustrating the unwisdom of refusing hospitality to a pilgrim of St. James. 'For all pilgrims, rich or poor, who go to St. James ought to be received with charity by all. Whoever receives them receives St. James and God himself.'

The early Church placed this obligation squarely on the shoulders of the bishops. But although some bishops, such as John Chrysostom and Augustine of Hippo, took their duties seriously, it was from the very first the monasteries who bore most of the burden. In the earliest monastic rules of the eastern Church, monks are required to receive pilgrims, and in the western Church this tradition was incorporated into the Benedictine rule. In this form, it survived for as long as the monasteries themselves. In the great restatement of the Benedictine rule at the beginning of the ninth century the importance of hospitality was, if anything, increased, and monasteries were expected to put aside a fixed proportion of their revenues to it. Naturally, in the succeeding centuries this rule was unevenly observed, but there were some monasteries justly famous for their hospitality. The chronicler of Evesham abbey remarks that abbot Agelwy was known as far afield as Ireland and Aquitaine for his habit of washing the feet of pilgrims in person, a practice which was required by the rule but had been abandoned in some houses. The hospitality dispensed at Maria Laach outside Bonn was described in c. 1225 as 'unequalled'.

On busy roads it proved impossible to accommodate the droves of pilgrims in the monastery itself, and instead large guest halls were built for the purpose. Abbot Otmar built one at St.-Gall as early as the eighth century. Another, dating from the thirteenth, can be seen today at Battle abbey. The logical extension of this policy was the foundation of independent hospices away from the monasteries, governed by small autonomous communities of monks or canons. This was first practised on a large scale in the eighth century by Irish monks on the continent. Major Irish hospices sprang up at

Péronne, Honau, and elsewhere; others at St. Omer and St.-Gall ultimately became great monastic houses. So important were the Irish houses that their disappearance during the ninth and tenth centuries was a source of genuine concern to successive emperors. The council of Meaux in 845 attributed it to the disordered state of the Frankish dominions, and asked Charles the Bald to do something about it. Charles promised to take measures to halt the decline. What these measures were is not at all clear, but there is no doubt that they were unsuccessful, for a century later most of the hospices of western Europe had entirely disappeared. When, in the eleventh century, pilgrims began to reappear in thousands on the roads of Europe, the task of building hospices to receive them had to be begun anew.

In the *Guide for Pilgrims to Santiago*, three hospices are singled out as 'columns built by God for the support of his poor people'. They were the hospices of Jerusalem, the Great St. Bernard Pass, and St. Christine in the Pyrenees. 'These hospices have been sited in the places where they are most needed. They are holy places, houses of God himself, ordained for the comfort of pilgrims, the restitution of the needy, the consolation of the sick, the assistance of the living, and the salvation of the dead.'

There had been a Latin hospice in Jerusalem since the beginning of the ninth century. Its foundation was traditionally, and probably rightly, ascribed to Charlemagne. The Frankish monk Bernard found much to approve of when he stayed there in 870, at which time it had a chapel, a library, and a vineyard. The tenth century, however, was a troubled period in the history of Jerusalem and the hospice probably ceased to exist shortly after Bernard's departure. The great hospice referred to by the *Guide* was the Hospital of St. John, which owed its foundation to the community of merchants of Amalfi, and maintained a precarious existence from about 1060. After the capture of Jerusalem by the first crusade it became the headquarters of a crusading order, but it remained above all a pilgrims' hospice. The Hospital made a strong impression on visitors if only by its sheer size. One of them, who saw it in about 1165, counted two thousand beds, many of then occupied by the sick. About fifty patients a day died in the Hospital, he casually observed. Their beds were immediately filled by others, and a crowd of pilgrims was perpetually milling about outside the doors waiting for the daily distribution of alms. After the disappearance of the crusading states, the Hospital became a Moslem establishment, but Christian pilgrims were still admitted to it on payment of two Venetian pennies, a courtesy which, in its Christian days, had never been extended to Moslems.

The Great St. Bernard hospice, which stood on the highest and bleakest pass of the Alps, received almost every English or French pilgrim bound for Rome. It was a younger institution than the Hospital of Jerusalem, but its origins are still far from clear. It owed its foundation to St. Bernard of Aosta, who flourished at a somewhat uncertain date, and who gave his name to both the hospice and the pass. It was certainly in existence by 1081, and within a century its buildings were already bursting out from its narrow site, crushed between two steep walls of rock.

Still more obscure are the origins of the hospice of St. Christine, on the Somport pass over the Pyrenees. It opened its doors, according to a popular song, 'not only to catholics, but to pagans, Jews and heretics, to the idle and the vain alike'. But its real importance was that it formed part of a remarkable chain of hospices which had sprung up in the space of a few decades along the roads to Santiago, both in Spain and in France. By the middle of the twelfth century there was scarcely a hospice on these roads which was not within a day's journey of the next. Several of them, like the hospice of St. Christine and its great rival at Ronceval, founded by the bishop of Pamplona in 1132, were in the hands of Augustinian canons. Others were attached to Cluniac priories, like Leyre, Nájera, or Carrión de los Condes. A number of religious orders devoted themselves entirely to running hospices, the confraternity of Santo Spirito, for example, a twelfth-century foundation which had establishments at Montpellier and Rome. The Spanish military orders, like their opposite numbers in the middle east, devoted a great deal of their immense wealth to building hospices and repairing roads. Most active of all were the orders of Santo Sepolcro and Santiago, one of whose functions was declared to be 'to offer shelter and food to travellers and poor people'. These hospices were not commercial enterprises, but that did not prevent them from indulging in an intense and often bitter rivalry. The hospices of Ronceval and St. Christine stood on the two principal passes over the Pyrenees, and each stridently proclaimed its own special advantages over the other. The prior of Villafranca complained to the abbot of Cluny in 1088 that a rival establishment had 'usurped his rights over pilgrims'. In 1122 the monastery of Oboña in the Asturias secured a privilege forbidding anyone to 'divert its pilgrims elsewhere', though how effective this document was is not revealed.

The variety of functions which hospices fulfilled is reflected in the thirteenth-century statutes of Aubrac in the Rouergue. Its principal purpose was declared to be the assistance of 'all pilgrims passing this way towards Notre-Dame de Rocamadour, Santiago, Oviedo, St. Dominic of Estremadura, or any other sanctuaries, not least the sepulchre of Our Saviour at Jerusalem'. But it was also enjoined to 'receive, welcome, and comfort the sick, the blind, the weak, the lame, the deaf, the dumb, and the starving'. The foundation of Aubrac in about 1100 was an act of thanksgiving. Its founder and first 'commander' was a Flemish nobleman who had narrowly escaped death in a snowstorm on his return from Santiago. The community lived under the Augustinian rule but its organization was peculiar to itself. There was a small body of priests, who sung the daily office and administered the sacraments. A force of monk-knights, not unlike the Templars, patrolled the roads of the Rouergue and protected pilgrims against bandits. Side by side with them lived brothers and nuns (described as 'ladies of good birth') who administered the hospice and its charitable activities. Finally, there were lay brothers, who worked in the fields and granges of the church. In the thirteenth century it acquired considerable wealth and extensive buildings though, like most churches of southern France, it fell upon hard times during the Hundred Years War. The Romanesque church, surrounded by the remnants of its buildings, can still be seen on the high windswept plain beside the Roman road from Lyon to Rodez.

When the hospice of Aubrac was full, the statutes provided that alms were to be distributed at the gate. In 1523 it was reported that between 1,200 and 1,500 poor gathered every day to receive their pittance. This kind of outdoor relief was commonly practised by wealthy hospices. When the roads were crowded and every bed full, it might be as much as the pilgrim could get. At St.-Léonard de Noblat and at St.-Jean d'Angély, every pilgrim received his pittance at the church door, and at Santiago itself all offerings received at the high altar before terce each Sunday were given to lepers in the city.

Life in a pilgrims' hospice was monotonous and comfortless, though most pilgrims were thankful to be there at all. Renart, in the popular twelfth-century fable, received eggs, cheese, bread and salted meat at a pilgrims' hospice. This must have been one of the wealthier establishments, for in many hospices no food was served at all, and pilgrims were expected to see to their own wants. At Villamartín, a hospice maintained by the order of Santiago, pilgrims received two loaves of bread every day; only the poorest travellers were given a little wine and meat on three days a week. A more varied diet was to be had at the hospice of Pamplona cathedral, where pilgrims ate bread and a salad, with meat or vegetables according to the season. Beds, like food, were only provided in well-endowed establishments. Elsewhere, the inmates slept on straw-covered floors:

Bedding ther is nothing faire,
Many pilgrimez it doth apaire:
Tabelez use thei non of to ete,
But on the bare flore thei make ther sete.

So sang an anonymous English pilgrim of the fourteenth century. Testators often left bedding to hospices where they had once passed a sleepless night; one of them, who died in 1297, left money to buy 'one bed, equipped with a good bolster, one cushion, and one pillow, with two good linen sheets, and a blanket'. Where there were beds, they were usually dirty, and fleas were a common incident of life in a hospice or cheap inn. A curious French phrase-book, composed for English travellers at the end of the fourteenth century, deals with this subject in some detail. The wise traveller is recommended to send his servant ahead to enquire whether there 'be no fleas, nor bugs, nor other vermin'; 'no sir', was the reply, 'for please God you will be well and comfortably lodged here – except that we suffer much from rats and mice.' There is a full section on how to converse with another traveller with whom you have just shared a bug-ridden bed: 'William, undress and wash your legs and then dry them with a towel and rub them well on account of the fleas, that they may not leap on your legs. For there is a mass of them about in the dust under the rushes. . . . Ow, the fleas bite me so and do me great harm, for I have scratched my shoulders till the blood flows.'

'Taverns', remarked one pilgrim, 'are for the rich, and for lovers of good wine.' Life was certainly more comfortable in the inns and taverns, but it was far from luxurious, and well below the standard which even a modestly rich man of the late middle ages could expect in his own home. They were more likely to contain beds, but no one had a bed to himself. A room would contain several beds, each shared by two, three, or even four travellers. During the Roman Jubilee of 1350, pilgrims were paying thirteen pennies to share a bed with three other people. In England, observed the poet and diplomat Eustache Deschamps, 'no one sleeps alone but two or three to a bed in a darkened room'; the fleas were bigger in an English tavern than in the habit of a monk of Cîteaux. Deschamps preferred the more refined manners of his own country, but the inns were scarcely better on the pilgrimage roads of France. They generally served better food than the hospices, but even this could not be relied upon. A Flemish draper who visited the Holy Land in 1518 took a poor view of the food and wine served in most of the inns of south-eastern France. At Montmélian 'we were promised good wine but it was undrinkable and cost eight *gros*'; at St.-

Michel de Maurienne 'we were swindled at the dinner table'; 'appalling fare' was served at Lanslebourg; it was a relief to find a good meal at last at Novalese.

On busy roads every house became an inn and rival hoteliers were ruthless in canvassing for customers. The innkeepers on the road to Santiago sent their boys out to the gates of the towns with instructions to kiss and embrace pilgrims as if they were long-lost friends, and then lead them to the inn. Those of Santiago itself sent their servants with placards as far outside the city as Barbadella or Triacastellos. In 1205 the municipality of Toulouse had occasion to reprove those hoteliers who forced pilgrims to employ their services by taking the reins out of their hands or dragging them in by the lapels.

Bitter disputes arose out of the attempt by innkeepers to claim the chattels of pilgrims who died in their houses. By custom they were certainly entitled to a share of the chattels, but what that share was was nowhere defined. One innkeeper confiscated a dead pilgrim's money and the donkey on which his children were riding; St. James caused him to break his neck in a fall, and threatened to visit the same fate on all other 'wicked innkeepers plying their trade on my road'.

Mediaeval innkeepers were not much loved. The author of the sermon *Veneranda Dies* could scarcely find words to describe them. There was no crime that they did not commit. They displayed fine wines and served cheap ones. Their fish was bad and their meat putrid. Their candles did not burn. Their beds were filthy. They gave change in bad coin. Their inns were often brothels and always dens of drunkenness. The preacher believed that they were responsible for the exaggerated and theologically unsound miracle stories which circulated amongst pilgrims. 'Truly, Judas lives in every one of them.' What was more, these vices were found not only amongst the innkeepers of Santiago but at Rome, St.-Léonard de Noblat, Le Puy, Vézelay, Tours, St.-Jean d'Angély, Mont-St.-Michel, Benevento, and Bari. Everywhere, in fact, that a few pence could be made out of gullible pilgrims. When the judgement day arrived, the saints concerned would come forward and say 'these, O Lord, are the ones who defrauded our pilgrims and practised on them all manner of iniquitous crimes.'

Cost

Inns, at least, were relatively cheap. A bed in fourteenth-century England generally cost a penny a head, which was less than the price of a simple dinner. Although guests complained frequently of extortionate rates, their protests were more often directed at the cost of meals and the pilferings of servants. Chaucer's parson, in reproving those who encouraged the misdeeds of their subordinates did not forget 'thilke that holden hostelries', who 'sustenen the theft of their hostilers'. The hire of a horse, to name but one expense, cost more than bed and board combined: twenty-four pence to ride from Southwark to Canterbury in Chaucer's time. Many pilgrims recorded their expenses on the route, sometimes in great detail. But it is almost impossible to draw general conclusions from their experiences. Prices varied from year to year, and some pilgrims travelled in greater comfort than others. In France, where there were a large number of free hospices, travel was cheaper than it was in Germany. Rome was not accounted an expensive place, but during a Jubilee the price of a bed more than doubled and bread sold for a penny an ounce.

The pilgrimage to Jerusalem was notoriously the most expensive of all. 'Good intentions, stout heart, ready tongue, and fat purse' were needed, according to Gréffin Affagart, who knew from experience. He reckoned the cost at two hundred ducats. Santo Brasca agreed; every pilgrim 'should carry two purses, one right full of patience, and the other containing two hundred Venetian ducats', one hundred and fifty for normal expenses and fifty for emergencies. 'And for this reason', advised Affagart, 'I would recommend every pilgrim to choose his destination according to his pocket.' The most revealing statement of accounts which survives is that of Giorgio Gucci, one of the companions of Frescobaldi in 1384. Theirs was a relatively expensive expedition, consisting of six pilgrims with six servants. They travelled by ship to Alexandria and thence overland to Mount Sinai, Jerusalem and Damascus. They finally took ship at Beirut and arrived in Venice ten months after their departure. All this came to an average of one hundred and fifty gold ducats a head, or three hundred gold ducats for each man and his servant. It was made up as follows:

Fares from Venice to Alexandria and from Beirut to Venice	96 ducats each
Fees to officials, guides, and interpreters; authorized tolls on roads and in churches	25 ducats each
Illicit tolls and bribes to powerful officials to prevent them from confiscating baggage or interrupting their progress with red tape, 'which expenses the populace over there call "mangerie", that is, robbery'	$4\frac{1}{2}$ ducats each
Hire of asses, mules and camels, and of boats on the Nile between Alexandria and Cairo	10 ducats each

Food and supplies, wine, travelling clothes,
  and tent   10 ducats each
Utensils, saddlery, weapons, cutlery, candles
  and torches, inns and miscellaneous ex-
  penses   4½ ducats each

The large sums expended on fees, bribes, and tolls are recorded in
every travel diary of the period unless the traveller took the Venetian package tour, in which case the burden fell on the unfortunate
shipowner. Thomas Swynburne, the English castellan of Guines,
who followed exactly the same route as Frescobaldi eight years
later, spent even more on bribes, including a gratuity of three ducats
to the chief cameleer 'that he might behave himself', and three
ducats to the customs official who overlooked his barrel of wine.

Venetian shipowners generally charged half fares to the poor, but
even this amounted to thirty ducats, a sum which was well beyond
the means of most 'poor pilgrims'. One problem was that the pilgrim had to carry the entire cost of the journey with him in cash.
Thus a pilgrim who lodged at the monastery of St. Etienne de Caen
in the late eleventh century was found to have on him the enormous
sum of thirty-three *livres*, which made him a tempting prey for
bandits and pick-pockets. Frescobaldi arrived in Alexandria in 1384
with six hundred gold ducats, a truly prodigious sum, which he had
hidden in the false bottom of his trunk for fear that the Arabs might
confiscate it. At this primitive stage in the history of international
banking, even a well-to-do pilgrim might run out of money or lose
his purse to a thief, and find himself utterly dependent on the charity
of others. Caesarius of Heisterbach tells the story of a young girl
whose father took her to Jerusalem at the end of the twelfth century.
The father died at Tyre, and his manservant absconded with all
his money, leaving the girl to subsist by beggary until at length a
wealthy German pilgrim was persuaded to pay for her passage
home.

Gerald of Wales ran out of money in Rome in 1203, leaving all
his bills unpaid. He attempted to flee, but his creditors pursued him
to Bologna, where they demanded payment. No one in Bologna
would lend him money unless he could find a local inhabitant to
guarantee that he would repay the lender's agent in England. But
guarantors were reluctant to step forward. Only a few weeks earlier
a number of Spanish students and priests in Bologna had been imprisoned after they had kindly offered security for a compatriot, who
had then defaulted. Still followed by his creditors, Gerald continued
north until they were finally induced to accept a promissory note
drawn on merchants at the Troyes fair. The following year, when

Gerald returned to Rome, he called at Troyes and bought bills of exchange worth twenty gold marks of Modena from merchants of Bologna. Even then, he had difficulty in changing them at Faenza. With the development of a more sophisticated banking system in the fourteenth and fifteenth centuries, the life of the wealthier traveller became easier. Hoteliers often acted as bankers. Those of Toulouse, for example, would lend money, transfer it to the traveller's next stopping place, guarantee debts, or accept bills of exchange. Italian pilgrims used bills of exchange even on quite short journeys. A group of Milanese in Rome for the Jubilee of 1390 had brought with them bills of exchange for five hundred florins.

The variety of currencies and rates of exchange was another pitfall for the unwary. Hoteliers would change coin willingly, but it was well known that they gave an unfavourable rate. In 1350 the innkeepers of Rome were offering only forty shillings for a gold florin. When Denis Possot tried to change four hundred French *écus* in a hostelry in Venice, he was furious to receive only 350 gold ducats and forty marks for them. William Wey noted in 1458 that 'at Sienna a bolyner of Rome ys worth but fyve katerynes and an halfe, and the same bolynar ys worth at Rome, six katerynes.' The account of his pilgrimage to Jerusalem begins with a lengthy list of exchange rates, but it was wisest, Wey thought, to bring with one a supply of coins of Tours, Candi, and Modena, as well as the ubiquitous Venetian coins which came nearest to being the international currency of the Mediterranean.

A pilgrim who intended to visit Jerusalem in the style that befitted his station, might expect to pay at least a year's income. How did he raise this money? If he was a landowner, he might sell his land to a monastery, as the soldiers of the first crusade, according to Guibert of Nogent, sold their fields, vineyards and chattels to buy armour and horses. If the land was worth more than the cost of the journey, he might give it to a monastery in return for alms to meet his expenses; in this way William Arnold parted with extensive lands to the abbey of Conques in the late eleventh century, and received a contribution of one hundred shillings towards the expenses of a pilgrimage to the Holy Land. Many 'sales' of this sort were in fact mere assignments of land as security for a loan. Monasteries readily lent money to crusaders and often to ordinary pilgrims as well. Guy I, count of Limoges, paid for his expensive pilgrimage to the Holy Land in c. 1000, by borrowing 15,000 shillings from the abbey of St. Martial. The canons of Auch cathedral paid for the pilgrimage of Raymond Aimeric II de Montesquieu in 1180. Monasteries, of course, were not the only source of loans. Thibault de Marly borrowed 140 *livres* from his lord before setting out for the Holy Land in 1173. A document of 1172 records that Josbert de Précigny, a Christian usurer of Tours, lent thirty *livres* to a pilgrim to go to the Holy Land; but Josbert died before the loan was repaid, and his heirs remitted the debt on condition that the pilgrim paid twelve pennies a year for the repose of his soul. Before his departure on the crusade with Louis IX, Joinville mortgaged his property to the moneylenders of Metz, leaving himself with only a thousand *livres* of unencumbered income, scarcely enough for the maintenance of his widowed mother. 'I was reluctant', he explained, 'to pay my way by pillage.'

If he could, a pilgrim would find a wealthy patron to participate in the benefits of his pilgrimage by contributing to the cost. This practice, an early form of vicarious pilgrimage, was regarded as extremely meritorious. 'Many rich men who never leave their own homes . . . are well rewarded by God for their charity to the poor', St. Bernard observed; 'whereas those who go in person to Jerusalem may come away without any reward if they have not performed some work of charity.' The expenses of Richard of St.-Vannes and all his seven hundred followers in 1026 were met by Richard II, duke of Normandy. Guy, count of Limoges, needed a huge loan from the abbey of St. Martial because he was paying the expenses of his companions, some of whom witnessed the document in which he acknowledged the loan. Similarly Henry the Lion, duke of Saxony, paid for the large company of vassals, *ministeriales*, and campfollowers whom, according to his biographer, he 'induced' to accompany him to the Holy Land in 1172. But in 1172, the large mass-pilgrimages which had been such a boon to the poorer pilgrims, were already a thing of the past.

In parts of France a lord was entitled to a feudal aid from his vassals on the occasion of his departure on pilgrimage. This was the case in Brittany, where it was stated to be immaterial whether it was a devotional pilgrimage or a crusade. The abbey of the Trinity at Vendôme was customarily expected to contribute three thousand shillings if the count of Vendôme decided to visit the Holy Land. These customary rights, where they existed, aroused considerable protest as they were often exacted ultimately from those who could least afford to pay. The second council of Chalons complained, as early as 813, that pilgrimages had become occasions for levying crushing taxation on tenants. The twelfth-century theologian, Honorius of Autun, who was profoundly suspicious of pilgrimages, gave it as his opinion that they were entirely valueless if the cost was extracted by force from unwilling vassals.

The poorer pilgrims lived roughly and hoped for alms and free hospitality. Fortunately for them, the virtue of charity was a constantly recurring theme in sermons and devotional literature. 'Pilgrims and poor men of God' were generally singled out as the most deserving categories, and pilgrims at least were exempted from the ordinances against begging passed in many towns of the Low Countries at the end of the middle ages. Alms flowed into their hands from a variety of sources. A tradesman, for instance, could normally expect a contribution from the members of his guild, and occasionally this was a right enshrined in the guild's statutes. If any member of the fullers' guild of Lincoln went on a pilgrimage to Rome, the Holy Land, or Santiago, his fellow members were required to accompany him out of the city gate as far as Queen's Cross and to give him at least a halfpenny each. The Dominican Felix Faber received a grant from his order. Municipalities could often be induced to help out a penniless pilgrim if only, as the town clerk of Damme put it, 'that he might not stay with us longer.' However, it is likely that most alms were given by other pilgrims. The author of the sermon *Veneranda Dies*, who had harsh words to say of pilgrims who carried money on them, made an exception in favour of those who did so only to distribute it in alms. This may seem a somewhat pointless exercise, but we hear of one Heimrad, a priest of Hesse at the end of the tenth century, who, as soon as he received alms gave them to another pilgrim more needy than himself. Gerald of Aurillac was famous for the largesse which he displayed on his biennial pilgrimages to Rome, and his biographer naïvely remarks that other pilgrims assembled at the side of the road when they had been warned of his coming. Certainly, the generosity of some pilgrims to others was an open invitation to fraud. On the roads to Santiago, professional beggars painted blood on their arms, and simulated lameness or leprosy, waving palms of Jericho in the air to arouse the sympathy of passing travellers.

According to his ninth-century biographer, the wanderer and hermit St. Cyran refused to support himself by begging on his way to Rome. Instead he worked in the vineyards on the route, carrying the grapes to the wine-presses. Not many pilgrims worked their way to the sanctuaries, because it took so long to reach one's destination. Brother Giles, the first Franciscan friar to visit the Holy Land, took pride in the fact that he would 'never eat the bread of idleness'. He fetched water from the wells and sold it in the streets of Ancona, and he carried bodies to the cemeteries at Acre. 'He was not ashamed to humble himself, and stoop to any menial and honest work that he could get.' Felix Faber first visited the Holy Land as tutor and companion to the son of a Bavarian nobleman. Three years later he returned as chaplain to John Truchsess von Waldburg, whom he had encountered at Ulm before his departure.

Less respectable but very much more lucrative was the practice of engaging in commerce on the route. This was viewed with disfavour by the Church because it derogated from the spiritual quality of the pilgrimage, and also by the state, for many of these amateur merchants claimed a pilgrim's exemption from tolls. The English, Charlemagne complained to Offa king of Mercia, were the principal offenders. 'True pilgrims travelling to Rome for the love of God and the salvation of their souls may pass in peace. But if there are any amongst them who serve Mammon and not God, then they must pay the ordinary tolls.' The *Siete Partidas* of Alfonso IX repeated this injunction in the thirteenth century. Penitential pilgrims were strictly forbidden to turn their punishment into a profitable venture by selling their wares on the road. The strong implication was that trade was intrinsically base and for this reason alone incompatible with pilgrimage. Hence the request of Philip the Fair to the pope that ships carrying troops to the projected crusade should be forbidden to carry merchandise as well, lest God's disfavour be brought down upon the expedition. Nevertheless pilgrims of otherwise impeccable motives surrendered to the temptation. When St. Willibald left England in the summer of 721 he brought with him a boat-load of goods to sell in Rouen, and paid for his journey to Rome out of the proceeds. On his way back from Jerusalem, Willibald smuggled some balsam past the Arab customs officials at Tyre in a jar with a false bottom, remarking to his companion that had he been discovered he would have 'suffered there and then a martyr's death'. Plainly, Willibald saw nothing wrong in his behaviour. Neither did St. Godric, the half-legendary hermit of Finchale, whose biographer calls him *mercator simul et peregrinus*, merchant and pilgrim combined. Many pilgrims found it impossible to resist the temptation to buy spices and precious cloth in Jerusalem and sell them for much more at home. The Arab traders of Palestine 'never sleep when the pilgrims are in Jerusalem', a fifteenth-century writer noted with disgust. Even in the church of the Holy Sepulchre itself they set up their stalls and haggled with pilgrims over beads, jewels and silk cloth.

The shrewdest pilgrim, however, could not have hoped to recover more than a part of the two hundred ducats which his journey had cost him. Against the undeniable excitement of discovering an alien world, he had to set not only the cost, but the difficulties which followed a year's absence from home, the hardships of a long journey, and the possibility that he might never return. Few men would have disagreed with that experienced pilgrim Eberhard of Wurtemburg, whom Felix Faber consulted before setting out on his first pilgrimage.

'There are three acts in a man's life which no one should advise him either to do or not to do. The first is to contract matrimony the second is to go to the wars, and the third is to visit the Holy Sepulchre. These things are all good in themselves, but they may turn out ill, in which case he who gave the advice will be blamed as if he were the cause of it.'

CHAPTER XII

THE SANCTUARY

The pilgrim was greeted at his destination by a scene of raucous tumult. On the feast day of the patron saint a noisy crowd gathered in front of the church. Pilgrims mingled with jugglers and conjurers, souvenir sellers and pickpockets. Hawkers shouted their wares and rickety food stalls were surrounded by mobs of hungry travellers. Pilgrims hobbling on crutches or carried on stretchers tried to force their way through the crush at the steps of the church. Cries of panic were drowned by bursts of hysterical laughter from nearby taverns, while beggars played on horns, zithers, and tambourines. The noise and vulgarity which accompanied a major pilgrimage changed little from the fourth century, when Augustine of Hippo spoke of 'licentious revels', to the fifteenth, when the French preacher Olivier Maillard demanded an end to these sinful carnivals.

The practice of holding fairs outside churches on the feast days of the saints was too deeply engrained to be eradicated by a handful of moral reformers. Any annual gathering of large crowds was certain to attract merchants and itinerant salesmen. Many of them were selling guide-books, lead badges, or candles. In the eleventh century one merchant expected to make his fortune by selling wax for *ex-voto* offerings outside the abbey of Conques, and many of those who bought official monopolies of the sale of candles or badges did make fortunes. Every kind of wares was sold outside church doors. Deorman, a rich London merchant of the late twelfth century, used to bring his entire stock of silks and spices to Bury on the feast of St. Edmund. Some visitors came solely on account of the fair, like the servant-boy mentioned by Reginald of Durham, who attended the celebrations of St. Cuthbert's day in order to find a good price for his horn. Others had both purposes in mind, and thus, remarks Reginald, they were able to atone for a day of usurious commerce simply by crossing to the other side of the cathedral square. The fairs, and their attendant jollifications, were viewed by the clergy with mixed feelings. Augustine had uncompromisingly condemned them, but his contemporary and friend, Paulinus of Nola, permitted them with reluctance on the ground that misguided piety was better than no piety at all. On the whole it was the latter view which prevailed. Indeed the fairs were often held with the permission of the clergy on land belonging to the church. The monks of St.-Denis drew considerable revenues from the Lendit fairs, which were timed to coincide with displays of the abbey's relics. So long as this remained a typical arrangement there was little point in the constant complaints of ecclesiastical synods against the pollution of churchyards on feast-days by 'games and competitions, rowdy singing, loose women, and lewd songs'.

The inside of the church was almost as noisy as the outside. Here the scenes of mass enthusiasm were reserved for the vigils of the saints, when pilgrims passed the entire night in the nave or by the shrine. The sick were carried in on litters or stretchers, and it was during vigils that most miraculous cures occurred. Vigils were always held on the eve of the saint's feast-day, but in some churches they occurred more often. At the shrine of St. Wulfran in the Norman abbey of Fontenelle, there seems to have been a vigil every Saturday night. Evesham too had vigils on Saturdays 'and scarcely a Saturday passed when some unfortunate was not freed from the bonds of sickness.' Except on official 'vigil-days', no one was permitted to watch by the shrine at night. At Mont-St.-Michel not even the night watchman was allowed into the basilica before the morning bell had rung, and at Santiago the doors were locked at sunset. When Pontius de St.-Gilles and his companions arrived in Santiago at night, only a miracle enabled them to enter the cathedral.

The atmosphere which enveloped the shrine of a saint was at its most intense during the vigil of his feast-day. 'Let us prostrate our bodies before their relics,' urged the Canterbury monk Eadmer; 'let us bend our knees to the ground and throw ourselves before them in supplication. What saint in God's court could fail to be moved by such devotion?' At the end of the eleventh century a rich man whose son lay dying came to light a candle at the altar of St. Egwin at Evesham.

> 'Humbly inclining his head to the ground, he made his offering, adored his God, and prayed with great intensity to St. Edwin for his son's recovery. With tears in his eyes he passed the whole day and the following night in vigil and prayer. Candle in hand, he knelt on the ground, beating his breast until morning came. Then he returned to see his son.'

At Rocamadour the sound of lamentations drowned the words of the Mass. At Canterbury, tears of sorrow and moans of gratitude mingled with the howls and the shrieks of the sick and the newly healed. Crowds pushed forward to investigate as each new miracle was announced, and the clergy had to force their way through to examine the patient for themselves. At the back of the church the less devout pilgrims gathered in their national groups trying to sleep in spite of the noise and the close heat from thousands of candles. Some of them had brought bottles of wine with them, and as they became more inebriated they began to shout abuse at each other or broke into community singing. At Santiago on the eve of St. James's day 'all sorts of noises and languages can be heard together, discordant shouts, barbarous singing in German, English, Greek, and every other language under the sun.' The 'worldly songs' which so infuriated the clergy of Santiago were a familiar sound wherever pilgrims gathered in large numbers. At Conques the litany was drowned by 'rustic sing-songs', and a special chapter was summoned at the end of the tenth century to consider this 'absurd and detestable practice'. It concluded, very typically, that pilgrims should be allowed to express their devotion in the only way known to them, even though this might strike cultivated persons as 'inappropriate and rude'. Some sanctuaries, like Durham cathedral, employed muscular stewards to keep order. Others, especially towards the end of the middle ages, tried to suppress vigils altogether, or else strove manfully to impose some order on them. But the attempt was a failure, and disorderly vigils remained an inseparable part of the cult of the saints.

At dawn on the feast-day itself, the congregation was turned out of the church, and the pilgrims returned to their lodgings. Auxiliaries cleaned up the mess and prepared for the services of the day. At these services the crowds were larger still, for the pilgrims of the night before were joined by most of the local inhabitants. The simplest techniques of crowd control seem to have been beyond the clergy of the sanctuaries, and accidents were frequent. This was the reason given by abbot Suger for rebuilding the abbey church of St.-Denis in the 1130s.

'As the numbers of the faithful increased', Suger wrote, 'the crowds at St.-Denis grew larger and larger until the old church began to burst at the seams. On feast-days it was always full to overflowing, and the mass of struggling pilgrims spilt out of every door. Not only were some pilgrims unable to get in, but many of those who were already inside were forced out by those in front of them. As they fought their way towards the holy relics to kiss and worship them, they were so densely packed that none of them could so much as stir a foot. A man could only stand like a marble statue, paralysed, and free only to cry out aloud. Meanwhile the women in the crowd were in such intolerable pain, crushed between strong men as if in a wine-press, that death seemed to dance before their eyes. The blood was drained from their faces and they screamed as if they were in the throes of childbirth. Some of them were trodden underfoot and had to be lifted above the heads of the crowd by kindly men, and passed to the back of the church and thence to the fresh air. In the cloister outside, wounded pilgrims lay gasping their last breath. As for the monks who were in charge of the reliquaries, they were often obliged to escape with the relics through the windows. When first, as a schoolboy, I heard of these things from my monastic teachers, I was saddened and conceived an earnest desire to improve matters.'

It was the same in Jerusalem, where hundreds fainted in the airless crush outside the basilica of the Holy Sepulchre on Easter Friday. The author of the *Liber Sancti Jacobi* was present one day at St.-Gilles when the crush developed into a riot between French and Gascon pilgrims resulting in at least one death. There were eighteen deaths when the head of St. Martial was displayed in the presence of the Black Prince in 1364. Such incidents were so common that the clergy of St.-Gilles and Santiago received special permission to re-consecrate their church immediately with holy water, instead of following the usual elaborate ceremony.

Nor were these the only perils which threatened pilgrims as they stood squashed together before the shrine. There were few exits and fire precautions were non-existent. Thus, when fire broke out in the abbey of Vézelay during the vigil of the feast of St. Mary Magdalene, 1,127 pilgrims were burned to death. Pickpockets throve. In a typical day at Worcester, one pilgrim lost sixteen shillings to pickpockets, another lost forty. At Fécamp a pilgrim standing on a box to police the crowd had his pocket picked as he did so. Large crowds were not only uncomfortable and liable to be robbed, but usually unable to see or hear what was going on. During the Canterbury Jubilee of 1420, the preacher had to repeat his sermon in four different places so that every pilgrim could hear it.

Public exhibitions of relics were rarer than vigils and, perhaps for that reason, provoked the most spectacular of all outbursts of mass piety. They generally marked moments of national or local crisis. Thus, when Philip Augustus departed on crusade in 1191, the royal abbey of St.-Denis exposed its relics on the high altar, where they were inspected by the queen mother, the archbishop of Rheims, and a cortège of dignitaries. Every serious epidemic occasioned a display of relics. When plague was decimating the population of Rouen in

1053, the body of St. Wulfran was carried to the city from Fontenelle. The head of St. Martial was publicly exhibited in 1388, the reasons given being that Christendom was divided by the papal schism, that the harvest had failed, and that Limoges had just endured a close siege. The diary of a Parisian citizen in the first half of the fifteenth century reveals that relics were brought out of the churches almost every time that reverses on the battle-fields of northern France threatened the city's precarious food supply. In 1423, for example, the war was going badly and famine threatened. The bishop of Paris 'had processions made for forty consecutive days, praying that God might, by His grace, bring peace to Christendom and calm the weather which had prevented the sowing of the crops for four months past.' In the summer of 1427, when the Seine broke its banks, some five or six hundred people from the suburban villages wound processionally through the streets of the city, barefooted, singing hymns, carrying banners of the saints, and calling on God to have mercy on their vineyards. Lesser catastrophes were marked in much the same way. The monks of Durham used their relics to prevent fires in the town from spreading to the cathedral. Those of St.-Gilles hoped to restore their depleted finances by displaying their relics, and proposed to commission an unusually costly reliquary for the purpose. Their hopes were disappointed in the event but they were by no means absurd, for exhibitions of relics could be relied upon to provoke enthusiasm degenerating at times into violence. The crowd which gathered at Bury one Whitsun was so impressed by the relics of St. Edmund that it forced the preacher to show them again. The preacher took this in good part, unlike the monks of Conques who refused to display the relics of St. Foy except at fixed intervals, thus causing riots outside their church. Urban II was asked to forbid the populace to display the relics of Conques without the consent of their owners.

In normal times, displays were rare. The head of St. Martial was displayed only once in seven years, as was the celebrated foreskin of Christ at Charroux. Other churches never displayed their relics. This surprising reticence dates from the beginning of the thirteenth century and was largely due to one of the pronouncements of the Lateran council of 1215. Faced with a number of impostors who claimed to have stolen relics while they were on public display, this council and its successors forbade the exhibition of relics except on feast-days, and then only in a reliquary. Amongst other things, this required a new kind of reliquary, like the one used at Limoges in 1388 with little doors in the side which opened to reveal the head of St. Martial. The legislation of the thirteenth century had been intended to prevent thefts, real or imagined. Its actual result was to diminish the visual element of the cult of relics, and to invite doubts as to the authenticity or even the existence of some relics. An inquiry into the affairs of the abbey of Vézelay in the 1260s concluded that its revenues had declined owing to the failure of the monks to exhibit the relics of St. Mary Magdalene, thus reinforcing 'certain hesitations and scruples as to the authenticity of the said relics'. Arnold von Harff's doubts about the body of St. James were confirmed when the clergy of Santiago refused to lift the lid of the sarcophagus. 'Any one who does not believe that the body of St. James lies under that altar', they told him, 'will certainly go as mad as a dog.' By this time, however, most churches had abandoned their objections to regular exhibitions of relics. In 1424 Martin V permitted churches to show their relics to the faithful whenever they wished, subject to the characteristic proviso that they were not to do it merely to satisfy the idle curiosity of pilgrims. This was followed by a succession of well-attended public exhibitions, notably in Germany. The visual element was once more respectable.

CHAPTER XIII

ROME

When the emperor Aurelian rebuilt the walls of Rome in the year 271 he defined the outer limits of the city for sixteen centuries. The old walls, traditionally attributed to Servius Tullius, had long outlived their usefulness. From every gate of the city thin ribbons of houses, the slums of the poor and the residences of the nobility, had extended into the suburbs, defenceless against attack from outside. Now they were contained by walls eleven miles in length, which remained the principal defence of the city throughout the middle ages. Rome, like many mediaeval cities, occupied but a fraction of the space enclosed by its ancient walls. But although they no longer marked the true limits of the city, Aurelian's walls determined its spiritual geography. Roman law forbade the burial of the dead within the city. Because they believed in the resurrection of the dead, Christians found the practice of cremation repugnant, and they buried their martyrs in deep graves along the roads which led out of the city.

The tradition of the Roman Church held that St. Paul had been buried on the Via Ostia, and St. Peter in the pagan necropolis on the Vatican Hill, north-west of the city. In the reign of Constantine their obscure graves were covered by great basilicas. On the Vatican Hill a cruciform church arose with great speed, arranged (at the expense of all architectural convenience) on an east-west axis, such that the high altar stood directly above the remains of the apostle. It symbolized the triumph over paganism by obliterating part of the circus of Caligula, where many of the early martyrdoms had occurred. St. Paul's was built at a more leisurely pace, and was said to have been even finer. Both of them had broad naves with double aisles on either side. Despite the continual process of repair and reconstruction, they preserved this form throughout the middle ages. At the southern extremity of the city, Constantine donated to the Church a tract of land within the walls, which had once belonged to the Laterani family and was now part of the estate of his wife. It contained a decayed palace which was now reconstructed as the papal residence, and a cavalry school which was transformed into

the Lateran basilica. Such were the three great sanctuaries of mediaeval Rome.

They were far from being the only sanctuaries. The persecutions
of the third century had left Rome richer in martyrs than any other
city. The *Depositio Martyrum*, compiled in 354, lists thirty-two
martyrs whose anniversaries were remembered by the Christian
community. A revised list, drawn up at the beginning of the fifth
century, added some seventy more. Most of them were buried in
extensive underground cemeteries outside the walls, such as the
celebrated Calixtine cemetery and the cemetery '*ad catacumbas*' on
the Appian Way, which subsequently gave its name to all the others.
Before the peace of the Church, the catacombs were used on the
feast-days of the martyrs, when services were held by their tombs.
It is unlikely that they were ever used as refuges during the persecutions, for the Roman authorities were well aware of their existence,
and kept them under constant surveillance. When the emperor
Valerian issued his decree against the Christians in 258, the catacombs were among the first places to be searched and pope Sixtus
II, who was found worshipping in the Calixtine cemetery, was beheaded with six of his deacons. After the conversion of Constantine,
the catacombs began to fall into decay. Now that Christians could
worship openly, they built imposing churches within the city, where
the ordinary services of the church were held. In the course of the
fourth century, a number of underground galleries collapsed, thus
making some parts completely inaccessible.

Only the interest of pilgrims saved the catacombs from oblivion.
Graffiti on the walls record the visits of pilgrims from Greece and
north Africa, Spain and southern France. 'Holy Souls, pray for a
safe crossing for us . . .', 'grant us a safe journey over the sea.' It
became fashionable to be buried there, and Romans used to amuse
themselves on holidays by groping their way along the dark passages. When St. Jerome was in Rome as a young man, he used to go
with other students on Sundays to explore them.

> 'We used to go down into the catacombs buried deep in the
> ground. Inside, all was silence and graves were everywhere
> around us. It was so dark that at times I had the impression of
> descending bodily into Hell. . . . Only the occasional faltering
> light broke the horrid darkness as we stumbled onward with
> faltering steps, immersing ourselves in the black night. I re-
> called the line of Virgil, which goes "Horror ubique animos,
> simul ipsa silentia terrent." '

The preservation of the catacombs was largely the work of Damasus,
who ascended the papal throne in 366. Damasus was not himself a

Roman, but a Spaniard who had come to Rome during the reign of his predecessor. He is famous as the founder of the papal archives, as the patron of St. Jerome, and above all as the restorer of the catacombs. The crumbling galleries were rebuilt, and new staircases installed. Fallen masonry was removed, and forgotten galleries reopened. Skylights were made in the ceilings, to reduce the oppressive darkness of which Jerome had complained. Damasus's greatest work was to begin the long process by which the graves of the martyrs were identified and marked with inscriptions, instead of being known only from unreliable local traditions. Frescoes were restored and chapels were built where services could be held on feast days. New burials, which required extensive works and did irreparable damage, were now strongly discouraged. When Prudentius visited the catacombs a few years afterwards, he found them greatly improved since Jerome's youth.

'A sloping path led into the ground, doubling back on itself again and again, reaching deep unlit chambers. The daylight scarcely lit up the outer porch of the first chamber. As we penetrated further, the darkness intensified, but now and again it was broken by a simple ray of light from a skylight pierced in the ceiling. In the middle of the dark maze formed by poky chambers and narrow galleries, a little daylight was thus brought into the bowels of the earth. Even in the deepest chambers, it was possible to follow the strained glow of the absent sun.'

The churches within the city had to wait three centuries before acquiring the remains of the saints to which they were dedicated. The Roman Church had originally held the graves of the dead to be inviolate. But a succession of destructive sieges, from the Gothic siege of 410 to the Lombard one of 756, forced the popes to reconsider the matter. In 537–8 many of the most important cemeteries were pillaged by the Arian Goths. In the catacombs of the two Via Salaria, where the Gothic army had been encamped, the tale of destruction was told in the inscriptions left by those who came to repair them afterwards. 'Here the fury of the enemy violated the sanctuary of the saints.' 'Here the blind rage of the invader violated the church and carried off its treasure.' Now that the liturgical cult of the saints was concentrated in the great urban basilicas, it was natural that the Romans should wish to translate their relics from the catacombs to more formal and imposing sanctuaries within the city. The martyrs Primus and Felicianus were removed from their graves on the Via Nomentana as early as the 460s, and reburied in the church of S. Stefano Rotondo. Leo II (682–3) built a new basilica in Rome and translated to it three martyrs from the catacomb on the Porto road. The process was greatly accelerated after the Lombard siege of 756, when the major cemeteries suffered appalling devastations. Some of the bodies, including that of St. Cecilia, were carried off to Pavia. Others were destroyed. At the accession of Paul I in 757, the catacombs had 'fallen into ruin as a result of neglect and cupidity. The bodies had been desecrated or stolen, the surrounding area utterly desolated.' It was Paul who began the long business of distributing the relics among the titular churches and monasteries of the city, an operation which continued until well into the ninth century.

Such relics as remained in the catacombs were translated, stolen or simply forgotten. At least one of the deacons who had charge of them carried on a vigorous trade in the relics of the lesser-known martyrs. The powerful ecclesiastical lords of northern Europe, no longer content to have mere *brandea* beneath their altars, attempted by fair means or foul to acquire some of the surplus relics of Rome. Some of them arrived with letters from the emperor, and were able to obtain important relics by applying political pressure to an enfeebled papacy. The export of bodies to the north had reached such alarming proportions by the middle of the ninth century that the populace, which regarded these saints as its protectors, began to object. The abbot of St. Médard of Soissons had some difficulty in escaping with the body of St. Sebastian in 826, even though the pope had been prevailed upon to part with it. Eight years later the rumour that St. Alexander was to be carried off to Friesing was enough to provoke serious riots.

By this time scarcely any of the more significant saints were still buried in the catacombs. Only the apostles were left in their original graves. But after a particularly disastrous Arab raid in 846, Leo IV extended the walls of Rome across the Tiber to swallow up the Vatican Hill. Some thirty years later, St. Paul's was in turn surrounded by its own walls. In the space of a century, the spiritual geography of the city had been transformed. No longer the centre of a network of cemeteries and graveyards, Rome had become a museum of relics, second only to Constantinople. After the sack of Constantinople by the fourth crusade, Rome stood unrivalled.

Impressions of Rome, 1100–1250

But Rome was more than a museum. Few pilgrims, even in the obdurately anti-classical mood of the 'dark ages' could look on the city of the apostles and blind themselves to the capital of a lost civilization. In the eleventh and twelfth centuries it still inspired a romantic fascination which would have marked it out as a resort of travellers even if St. Peter and St. Paul had never been there and the popes had never established it as the headquarters of a religious bureaucracy. One pilgrim recalled his first sight of the city 'from a far off hill beyond which lay those innumerable palaces bristling with a cornfield of towers; I was overwhelmed, and imagined how Caesar would have seen it from that spot.' Countless other pilgrims following the northern road and reaching the summit of Monte Mario must have experienced the same feelings and sung the words of the famous hymn which began:

> O Roma nobilis, orbis et domina,
> Cunctarum urbium excellentissima.

But the grandeur of distance disappeared as the pilgrims approached the city, and many of them may well have been dismayed by the closer sight of the shrunken mediaeval Rome in the centre of the vast open space enclosed by its ancient walls. When Master Gregory, who had been so exhilarated by the distant view of the cornfield of towers, reached the centre of the city he saw in it a certain sign that the world itself was drawing to an end. No one was indifferent to Rome. Many hated it. Few were as uncritically enthusiastic about it as the author of O Roma Nobilis. Rome, proclaimed William of Malmesbury, 'once mistress of the earth seems slight nowadays in comparison with its glorious past. And the Romans, whose ancestors wore the toga and ruled the earth, are now a miserable lazy race who live by selling justice for gold and putting price tags on every canon of the law of the Church.' The English satirist Walter Map knew it only as the seat of the papal curia, whose name stood for 'Radix Omnium Malorum Avaritia' – greed is the root of all evil.

The admiration of mediaeval poets was tempered by their admission that the beauty of Rome was the beauty of the past, the pathetic contrast between her noble classical ruins and her modern degeneracy. This feeling was voiced by Hildebert archbishop of Tours in a famous poem, in which he reflected that 'not even the decay of years, nor fire nor sword have eclipsed the splendour of her ascendance':

> Par tibi Roma nihil, cum sis prope tota ruina
> Quam magna fueris integra fracta doces.

Nothing can equal Rome, even Rome in ruins.
Your ruins themselves speak louder than your former greatness.

Hildebert had first seen Rome as the Norman leader Robert Guiscard left it in 1084. In the course of the fighting and the three days of plundering that followed, the quarters around the Colosseum

and the Lateran, the districts of St. Silvester and St. Lawrence in
Lucina were razed to the ground. Rome bore the marks of its
violent history until the fifteenth century, and for many years
writers describing it quoted Hildebert's words with approval.

The architectural revolution which transformed the face of
northern Europe and of the great cities of northern Italy left Rome
virtually untouched. The popes of the twelfth and thirteenth centuries were great restorers and decorators of existing buildings. The
churches of S. Maria in Cosmedin and S. Maria in Tastevere were
sumptuously redecorated in this period, the church of St. Lawrence
Without the Walls greatly enlarged. But the only entirely new
building of any importance erected before the fifteenth century was
the Gothic church of S. Maria sopre Minerva, begun under Nicholas
III in 1280.

St. Peter's was the principal attraction. Although damaged in each
successive riot and siege it was on each occasion tolerably restored.
Until the beginning of the thirteenth century it was still possible to
enter the *confessio* or shrine of St. Peter beneath the high altar, and
thirteen lamps burned perpetually before it. But towards the end of
the twelfth century a new relic began to rival the body of the apostle.
This was the *sudarium* of Veronica, believed to be the napkin on
which Christ had wiped his face on the road to Calvary, leaving the
impression of his features. How St. Peter's came to possess this relic
is not at all clear, but it had certainly been there since the eighth
century, when it was one of the subsidiary relics kept in the *confessio*.
In 1208 Innocent III instituted a liturgical station at the hospital of
S. Spirito on the first Sunday after the Epiphany, and ordered that
the *sudarium* should be taken from St. Peter's on that day and displayed in a special reliquary 'of gold and silver and precious stones,
so constructed that it might be carried solemnly in processions'. In
response to the clamorous demand of pilgrims the relic was displayed at regular intervals, and in 1289 the pope conferred a generous
indulgence on the 'precious image that the faithful call the Veronica'.

It was only in the eleventh century that the Lateran palace and
basilica began to command as much attention as St. Peter's. The
'*Sancta Sanctorum*', which was the private chapel of the popes, was
the scene of some of the most solemn services of the Roman calendar, particularly those which occurred around Easter. It contained a
formidable collection of relics, notably the heads of both apostles
preserved in splendid reliquaries on the main altar. The ark of the
covenant was there (it attracted a certain amount of cynical comment), as were the tablets of Moses, the rod of Aaron, a golden urn
of manna, the tunic of the Virgin, various pieces of clothing worn
by John the Baptist including his hair shirt, the five loaves and two

fishes which fed the five thousand, and the table used at the Last Supper. The chapel of St. Lawrence in the papal palace contained other spectacular relics, including the foreskin and umbilical cord of Christ preserved in a gold and jewelled crucifix filled with oil; and a piece of the true cross enclosed in a small reliquary of gold and silver with engraved panels.

The superb processions held at Easter impressed upon more than one onlooker the contrast between the mediaeval papacy and its classical setting. After the service in S. Maria Maggiore, the pope passed in procession to St. Peter's and thence back to the Lateran palace by a route which took it past some of the city's classical finest monuments. A contemporary described the papal train passing 'beneath the triumphal arches of Theodosius, Valentinain, and Gratian, past the Capitol and the Mamertine prison, . . . under the triumphal arch [of Severus], between the arch of Janus and the Temple of Concord. Then they walk between the forum of Trajan [i.e. Nerva] and the forum of Caesar . . . crossing the very spot where Simon Magus fell near the Temple of Romulus. . . . Finally they reach the arch of Titus and Vespasian which is called the seven-branched candlestick . . . and so past the Colosseum to the Lateran.' Many of these monuments were in an advanced state of decay. In particular most of them were disfigured by being converted into fortresses. Master Gregory's abiding impression of Rome was that of a 'cornfield of towers' for it was the practice of the noble families of Rome to build towers on top of the classical monuments from which to assail their enemies in times of civil war. The arch of Titus was called the 'seven-branched candlestick' because it formed part of the fortress of the Frangipani family who had covered it with fortifications. The enemies of Gregory VII accused him of carrying out this practice to excess, adding battlements to every bridge, tower, or triumphal arch in the city. Even churches were not exempt, for St. Peter's was fortified by the mob in 1145. The lamentable condition of the arch of Severus is revealed by the judgement of Innocent III in a lawsuit between its two owners. Half of it had been converted into the church of St. Sergius and St. Bacchus while the other half was the property of a certain Ciminus who had built on it a small embattled tower with an observation platform. In times of peace many proprietors found a commercial use for their towers by charging pilgrims for the right to climb up and enjoy a panoramic view of Rome. The monastery of S. Silvestro in Capite owned the column of Marcus Aurelius, which was leased out for this purpose and provided them with a lucrative source of revenue.

Some attempt, it is true, was made to preserve the monuments. The senate, which restored itself during the republican revolution of

1143, threatened with death all persons who defaced or damaged the column of Trajan, 'so that it should remain as it stands to honour the Roman people as long as the world endures.' But the task was made impossible by the looting of builders. To the depradations of the builders were added those of prelates and even pilgrims,·who met their need for marble by removing it from the classical monuments. The churches of Hildesheim were adorned with marble from Rome, looted by bishop Bernard. Desiderius abbot of Monte Cassino did the same when he was rebuilding his abbey church. Even the canons of Durham cathedral knew that marble was easily to be had in Rome and asked a pilgrim to obtain enough to cover the floor of their church. Many pilgrims who came to Rome for reasons of piety or ecclesiastical business found their interest unexpectedly aroused by the visible testimony of its classical past. The wealthier amongst them took to collecting antiquities. Abbot Suger of St.-Denis confessed that he would gladly have removed the columns from the baths of Diocletian and shipped them to France for the adornment of his abbey. Henry of Blois, bishop of Winchester and brother of king Stephen, obtained the pope's permission to buy up old statues and take them back to England. John of Salisbury, who was in Rome at the time, recorded the astonishment of the papal courtiers at the sight of the bishop 'conspicuous by his long beard and philosophical solemnity, engaged in buying up idols carved by pagan hands'.

The most celebrated classical monument in Rome was the equestrian statue of Marcus Aurelius, which in the middle ages was generally believed to represent the emperor Constantine. The statue emerges from obscurity in 962, when a rebellious official is recorded to have been hanged by the hair from it. At that time it stood in front of the Lateran palace. Although scholarly opinion held that the horseman was Constantine, unlearned pilgrims, encouraged by their guide-books, permitted themselves unlimited speculation as to his identity. The most popular guide-book gave it as its opinion that the statue commemorated a great hero who had saved the city from its enemies in the days of the republic. This hero had ridden bareback into the besieging army and kidnapped the enemy king, 'which is why we see today a statue of a man without a saddle, his right hand stretched out as it was when he seized the king.' The English visitor, Master Gregory, was perplexed by the variety of opinions. The cardinals called it Marcus or Quirinus, the Romans called it Constantine, and the pilgrims Theoderic. Each of them justified his opinion by reciting some popular story from Roman history. All, however, were agreed that it was a 'memorable work, executed with remarkable skill'. They paid it the compliment of copying it when they returned home. In western France equestrian statues of Constantine can still be seen on the west fronts of churches of Chateauneuf, Melle, Civray, Parthenay-le-Vieux, and elsewhere.

In his attempt to identify all the churches and classical ruins the pilgrim was assisted by guide-books which told him in a reasonably digestible form everything he needed to know. The book which held the field from the twelfth century to the fourteenth was the *Mirabilia Urbis Romae*, the 'Wonders of Rome'. It is a remarkable work, which testifies both to the passionate interest of the Romans in their past, and to their profound ignorance of it. Nevertheless, few guide-books have ever enjoyed a greater reputation. It appeared in innumerable Latin editions, and was translated and versified in every language. Each century brought it up to date, and amended it in accordance with current tastes. The *Mirabilia* is a mine of extraordinary information. 'The walls of Rome', it begins, 'have 361 towers, 49 bastions, and 12 gates. They are 22 miles in circumference.' Continuing the statistical survey of the city in a tone reminiscent of tour guides in French public monuments, it lists the 12 gates, the 12 triumphal arches, the 7 hills, and the 10 baths. It gives the names of the palaces, theatres, churches, bridges, and cemeteries. Then the tone changes. The author discusses the legend of the statue of Constantine and tells his readers a few anecdotes about the principal buildings of Rome. At the church of S. Maria in Ara Coeli he recounts how the emperor Octavian had a vision there of the Virgin and child and resolved that he would refuse to be deified by the senate. As pilgrims wandered through the city they were given garbled versions of the persecution of Decius, the story of Anthony and Cleopatra, and other well-known incidents from classical history. Sometimes the author takes liberties with his classical myths. In one version Rome is founded not by Romulus and Remus but by Noah, who landed there after the flood and left behind his son Janus, from whom all Roman emperors were descended. The pages are filled with a nostalgic feeling for the Roman past, scattered with a few summary aesthetic judgements on its monuments. 'The Capitol was once the capital of the world; there the consuls and senators governed the whole earth.' 'The circus of Priscus Tarquinius is very fine; the seats are stepped in such a way that no Roman's head obstructed the view of the person behind him.' But it is not the learned nostalgia of a Gibbon that pervades the *Mirabilia*. It is something more earnest and more naïve, a desire for knowledge without the means of gratifying it. 'All these temples and palaces', the guide concludes, '. . . we have described as we have read of them in old chronicles, heard of them from tradition, and seen them with our own eyes.'

One of the more sophisticated travellers who read the *Mirabilia* was Master Gregory, an Englishman who visited Rome at the beginning of the thirteenth century. Gregory, perhaps wisely, did not allow the *Mirabilia* to colour his judgement, and spoke with contempt of the unlettered pilgrims who believed all that they were told. Instead, he relied on the opinions of the 'cardinals and clergy of Rome' and on a small tract on 'The Seven Wonders of the World', *De Septem Miraculis Mundi*, which was generally, though wrongly, attributed to Bede. Standing on the Capitoline Hill, Gregory was struck by the sight of a nude statue of Venus in Pavian marble, a thing quite outside his experience, which prompted him to quote a few lines from Ovid's *Ara Amandi*. 'This inexplicably perfect work of craftsmanship', he wrote, 'looks more like a living figure than a statue. The face is a deep purple colour as if it were blushing at its own nudity, or as if a trickle of blood were flowing through its snow-white mouth.' Gregory found the sight of this statue so compelling that he visited it three times, even though his hospice was more than two miles away. Continuing with his tour, he visited the baths of Diocletian, which had so impressed abbot Suger, and agreed that they were the finest classical buildings in the city. 'I cannot do justice in writing to their ample dimensions and superb proportions. They are so large that one cannot take them in in one view. The columns that crown them are so tall that their summits were beyond a pebble's throw.' Gregory was informed by the cardinals that it would have taken a hundred men an entire year to build them. 'But I shall say no more for if I were to tell you the truth, you would not believe me.' The waterworks of Rome, although but a shadow of what they had once been, were still imposing enough to an Englishman. Gregory examined the Claudian aqueduct and observed that 'the river Tiber, though all right for horses, is no good for men and indeed positively poisonous. Wherefore in four parts of the city, ancient artificial aqueducts bring fresh water in.' He visited the sulphur baths near the aqueduct, paid the set charge to the attendant, and tested the water with his fingers; but the disgusting smell of the sulphur was too much for him and he left without bathing. Decay is a recurring theme in Gregory's work and provoked some bitter reflections. He was disgusted by the pillaging of marble from the Domus Augustana on the Palatine Hill. The neglect or mutilation of statues in the forum of Nerva shocked him. The gold which once covered the roof of the Pantheon had all disappeared owing to the 'boundless cupidity of the Romans, for whom no crime is too awful.'

Gregory's description of Rome is the last account which survives until we come to the age of the great Jubilee indulgences. There is, indeed, some evidence that the Roman pilgrimage underwent a serious decline in the thirteenth century. The reputation of the city as a spiritual centre continued to diminish, and the almost continual warfare which afflicted Italy and Rome itself seem finally to have choked the flow of pilgrims. During his quarrel with Becket, Henry II of England is reported to have prevented his subjects from embarking for Rome. The emperor Frederick II discouraged his subjects from undertaking pilgrimages to Rome, thus earning him a stiff rebuke from Innocent IV who accused him of putting the salvation of his subjects in jeopardy. The few national pilgrims' hospices which survived began to disappear at the end of the twelfth century. The Irish hospice of the Holy Trinity ceased to exist at about this time. The deacon responsible for the English national hospice complained that its income from offerings was declining and that hardly any clergy or laymen could be found to serve in it; in 1203 it was finally dissolved and the buildings transformed into the hospital of S. Spirito. Doubtless simple men came to Rome as they had always done. But they came quietly, undramatically, and the sources are silent about them. The great and powerful recognized in Rome an important political capital, and they visited it because they had to. But they no longer came in the spirit of Canute, or even of Gerald of Wales. Richard I passed within a few miles of the city on his way to the crusade in 1190 but refused an invitation to visit it. On his way back from the east in 1273 Edward I passed through Rome and turned aside to discuss political affairs with the pope at Orvieto. But he did not trouble to visit the Roman shrines.

The Fount of Forgiveness

Gregory the Great used to tell how St. Peter once appeared to the empress Galla Placidia on her deathbed and told her that all her sins were forgiven; the same miracle, he remarked, was performed every day in the Vatican basilica. Even in the dark years of the Arab invasions of the tenth century, the city of the apostles meant to one writer the mental and spiritual salvation of countless pilgrims from all over the Christian world. The theme appealed to an English king of the eleventh century, just as it had done to his predecessors in the eighth. 'God has granted me', Canute wrote in 1027, 'the privilege of praying at the shrines of the blessed Peter and Paul and in every sanctuary within the city of Rome. And this privilege I have sought because wise men have told me that the apostle Peter has received from God the power of binding and loosing, and carries the keys of Paradise.'

Above all other places, Rome was the destination of those '*nudi*

homines cum ferro' who plagued the roads in the time of Charlemagne, the convicted criminals who had been exiled by their communities and sent to wander across the face of the earth. Rival
sanctuaries recognized this when they advertized their saints as
having the same powers as St. Peter. One of them described how a
convict lost one of his fetters in the Vatican basilica and the other at
the shrine of St. Austremoine in Auvergne; 'which proves', the
author reflected, 'since one fetter was removed by St. Peter and the
other by St. Austremoine at the instigation of St. Peter, that St.
Austremoine partakes of the merit of the great apostle and that their
power is equal.' So important had Rome become as an object of
penitential pilgrimage, that a writer of the ninth century surprised
no one by asserting that 'penance is synonymous with going to
Rome.'

Rome owed its unique prestige to a variety of factors. Its role as
the converter of northern Europe was certainly one of them.
Another was the gradual process by which the absolution of grave
offences, originally the prerogative of the bishops, passed into the
hands of the papacy. This important change had its roots in the
eighth century, when bishops began to consult the popes in particularly difficult cases. St. Boniface asked the advice of Gregory III on
parricides and of Zacharias on fornication and clerical murderers.
Nicholas I was consulted by the archbishop of Rheims on the case of
a man who had killed his three sons, and again about a monk who
had killed his brother. In the ninth century, bishops began to send
the malefactor to Rome together with the letter asking for advice.
The pope would then prescribe the penance directly. Several penitential manuals of the period recommend this procedure, and
Nicholas I began to insist that some crimes, such as incest, must be
referred to him in this way. In theory the bishop retained control
over the case. The pope did not actually absolve the sinner, but
merely prescribed the penance and returned him for absolution to
the bishop. The bishops did what they could to impress this narrow
distinction on sinners, fearing that criminals would come to the
conclusion that they could by-pass the bishop's jurisdiction by a
simple pilgrimage to Rome. This, indeed, was precisely what
happened. Haito, bishop of Basle, warned his diocesans in vain that
the power of absolution was his alone. The council of Seligenstadt
(1022–3) tried to forbid all pilgrimages to Rome without the written
permission of the bishop, and breaches of this principle sometimes
created sore conflicts. In the 1020s Pontius, count of Auvergne,
received absolution from the pope without the knowledge or consent of the bishop of Le Puy, as a result of which the council of
Limoges ordered him to do another pilgrimage to Rome, this time

in proper form with a letter from the bishop. The bishops struggled hard to preserve their authority and prevent the Roman pilgrimage from becoming a general fountain of forgiveness. They failed, however, and by the end of the twelfth century the canonists had set the seal on their failure by the principle of 'reserved cases' which could be absolved by the pope alone. Sacrilege, murder of priests or monks, robbery of churches, and a continually increasing number of lesser crimes, were all 'reserved cases'. The pope delegated the business of absolving sinners in reserved cases to the officers of the papal penitentiary. The penitentiars could absolve in person or by brief, though in many cases the penitent came to Rome to receive his penance. For the remainder of the middle ages the prospect of confessing to an anonymous penitentiar and of being absolved from even the most enormous transgressions added considerably to the spiritual attractions of Rome.

In the newly converted countries of Scandinavia the papacy made ample use of these powers. When Alexander III was informed that incest was particularly common in Sweden he instructed the bishop of Upsala to send offenders to Rome 'to visit the Holy See and the blessed apostles Peter and Paul so that by the sweat of their brow and the hardships of the journey they may soften the anger of the supreme judge and be found worthy of His mercy.' Behaviour which had been normal in the pagan society of the north suddenly became sinful, and a pilgrimage to Rome enabled converts to relieve themselves of their guilt. Two pilgrims mentioned in the *Grettis Saga* reflected that 'to another King we have much more to pay, . . . for we have lived according to our own worldly desires instead of following the teachings of Christ, . . . and now we are growing old. Then they journeyed to Rome, and when they appeared before the penitentiar they told him everything truthfully, just as it had happened, and with what pagan hocus pocus they had been married. They humbly submitted to such penance as he deigned to impose on them and promised to amend their ways.' These pilgrims had asked no one's consent before approaching the penitentiar, and had avoided all the normal preliminaries to absolution. This appears to have been regarded at Rome as a point in their favour, 'since they had voluntarily turned their minds to atonement without being prompted or instructed by the Church.' Unusual cases were commonly submitted to the pope in person. When Gunnhildr, the mother of a Norwegian king, confessed to the penitentiar that her son had been born in adultery, the diplomatic importance of the case was held to call for the personal attention of the pope, Alexander III. Alexander may have been untypical in the interest which he took in the penitential function of the papacy, but he was certainly not the only pope who heard confessions himself. It was said of Adrian IV, the only English pope, that no business was so urgent as to prevent him from talking with northmen who wanted to see him.

The advantages which the Roman churches enjoyed over other sanctuaries were greatly increased by the development of the doctrine of indulgences. Already in the latter half of the twelfth century a pilgrim could get more remission by attending the Lenten stations than he could find in any sanctuary outside Rome. The stations were the churches in which the Pope said Mass on certain appointed days, especially in Lent. It was Gregory the Great who was traditionally supposed to have assigned to each station its special church. Pilgrims were expected to attend each of the forty stations in turn, and from the middle of the twelfth century indulgences were believed to be attached to them. Gerald of Wales gained all the stational indulgences during his visit to Rome in 1195, though there was some doubt as to how generous they were. Gerald thought that they amounted to ninety-two years. His contemporary, the Parisian theologian William of Auxerre, computed them at fifty years. It was not until 1297 that Boniface VIII settled the matter by laying down that pilgrims would get one year and forty days at each station in addition to any indulgences that might be attached to the stational churches in their own right.

The stational indulgences came into existence more or less spontaneously, but individual churches generally received their indulgences by formal grant. At the end of the twelfth century, visitors to St. Peter's on Maundy Thursday won an indulgence of two years if they were Italians, three if they came from further afield. Peter Mallius dated this concession from the foundation of the basilica by Constantine, though in fact it had almost certainly originated in his own lifetime. Alexander III (d. 1181) used to tell Swedish pilgrims that all those who made a good confession to the papal penitentiars before the shrine of the apostle would receive an indulgence of one, two, or three years, depending on the distance they had travelled; Scandinavians could certainly count on winning three years. In Alexander's reign only the basilicas of the apostles could offer indulgences in their own right, but within twenty years of his death pilgrims could gain the same indulgences at many of the shrines of the martyrs on their feast days. The result was an inflation of indulgences in which those of the greater basilicas were constantly increased in order to preserve their superiority. In 1240 the pope declared an indulgence of three years and three quarantines for those who visited the basilicas of the apostles between Pentecost and the octave of the feast of the apostles. In the time of Gregory X (1272–6) the indulgence offered at the Lateran on Maundy Thursday had risen to four years and four quarantines, and Thomas Aquinas reported that pilgrims from overseas could sometimes win five years or more. By the end of the thirteenth century indulgences were being attached to individual altars in St. Peter's.

Although the process was a continuing one, no pope was so prodigious a dispenser of indulgences as Nicholas IV (1288–92). He increased the largest indulgences obtainable at St. Peter's to seven years and seven quarantines and shortly afterwards awarded the same privilege to the Lateran basilica. St. Paul's received indulgences for every day of Lent, every Sunday of the year, and the octave of the feast of the apostles in addition. S. Maria Maggiore was raised to the status of the basilicas of the apostles; it received a similar indulgence for every day of Lent and every Saturday of the year, the Epiphany, the anniversary of its foundation, and a number of other feasts. In the year of Nicholas's death a pilgrim who passed Lent in Rome could be sure of getting at least ten times the remission earned by Gerald of Wales a century before. The stage was set for the Jubilee indulgence of Boniface VIII.

1300: The Year of Jubilee

The Jubilee was originally a Jewish concept. It was an amnesty proclaimed every fifty years, when prisoners were released, ill-gotten gains restored, and penance performed for past transgressions. In the language of mediaeval preachers it came to mean any year in which men were offered an unusual chance to earn their salvation. The word was often applied to the indulgences given to crusaders. St. Bernard proclaimed that the year 1146 was 'a year of remission, a veritable year of Jubilee' in which men could be saved by going to the aid of the faltering Frankish kingdoms of the middle east. Those who fought on the Albigensian crusade also won a 'Jubilee' indulgence. 'See, this is our year of Jubilee', cried Humbert of Romans when urging young men to go and defend Acre against the infidel; 'not the Jewish one but a Christian Jubilee which will be far greater.'

In the autumn of 1299 a notion spontaneously arose that the year 1300 would be a year of Jubilee in which pilgrims to St. Peter's would win huge remission. The rumour spread through northern Italy that visitors to Rome would gain a plenary indulgence on the first day of January and at least a hundred days of remission on every other day of the year. On New Year's eve a great crowd gathered in St. Peter's between vespers and midnight, pressing round the high altar, pushing and trampling on each other to get a glimpse of it. It was assumed that the special remission would begin at midnight and most of them proposed to spend the whole of the following day in the basilica. In the tightly-packed mass, rumours circulated rapidly. Some said that God had proclaimed a Jubilee in a tract handed down from the sky; others that every centennial year was a year of Jubilee. On New Year's day itself the news of these happenings passed like wildfire through the city and surrounding countryside, and the crowds in the Leonine city became uncontrollably large. 'Give us your blessing before we die', they cried, 'for we have heard that whoever visits the bodies of St. Peter and St. Paul in a centennial year shall be freed from both sin and guilt.'

That this seminal event should have occurred unprompted and unplanned was altogether characteristic of the religion of the late middle ages. Far from provoking this display of enthusiasm, the pope, Boniface VIII, was taken aback by it. After hasty consultations, the cardinals were sent to look up the canons and peruse various old books to see whether the popular rumour had any basis. The matter was very obscure. Nothing could be found in the writings of the fathers about Jubilees, and various opinions were canvassed. While these enquiries were proceeding, a few temporary measures were taken. The treasures of St. Peter's were displayed, and in the middle of January the *sudarium* of Veronica was exposed in the basilica. Boniface received some of the pilgrims in person. He was particularly impressed by an old man of 107 years who told him that he remembered his father describing a visit to Rome in 1200 and assured him that there had been a Jubilee in that year. This intelligence was confirmed by several other centenarians, most of them Italians, but including one Frenchman from Beauvais; the belief, declared this last, was widespread in France. The cardinals were unable to discover any authoritative basis for this nonsense. They concluded, however, that a tradition so general ought to be respected. The time was ripe to spread the fame of St. Peter, and to encourage the faithful to pay tribute to the prince of the apostles in his own basilica. It was decided that the aspirations of the crowd should be given authoritative support. On 22nd February, 1300 Boniface issued the bull *Antiquorum Relatio*. 'The tradition of our ancestors', it began, 'affirms that great indulgences for our sins are granted to those who visit the venerable basilica of the apostles in Rome. We who, in accordance with the dignity of our office, must strive to secure the salvation of every man, do hereby hold all these indulgences to be authentic. We confirm them and approve them and do now grant them afresh.' All those who visited the basilicas of the apostles during the centenary year and made a truly penitent confession would receive a plenary indulgence. They must visit each basilica on fifteen separate days (thirty for Italians); nevertheless, the bull vaguely adds, the more frequently they visited the basilicas the more efficacious would be their indulgence. The bull was accompanied by a brief excluding from its benefits all excommunicates and rebels against the Church, merchants who traded with the infidel, the pope's enemies in Aragon and Sicily, and the Colonna family.

It was clear from the terms of the bull that the Jubilee indulgence did not pretend to release sinners from guilt as well as penance. John the Monk, one of the cardinals whom Boniface had consulted, insisted that 'this indulgence remits penance after the sinner has been absolved of his guilt by a true and contrite confession; the guilt is remitted by God in the sacrament of penance.' Theological subtleties of this sort were, however, wasted on most of those who came to Rome. Probably very few of them had confessed their sins and they thought that they were gaining an indulgence which dispensed them from such formalities. The chroniclers William Ventura and Giovanni Villani, both of whom claimed the indulgence, were under this impression. At Tournai a large band of pilgrims assembled for the journey to Rome in the belief that the indulgence released them from the need to confess. Various friars were trying to persuade them of their error 'and for this reason everyone was perplexed by doubt and confusion.' The abbot of St. Martin, who was in the crowd, asked a papal penitentiar in Rome to settle the question. The penitentiar, who was a doctor of theology, replied that so many pilgrims had asked this question that the papal confessors had gone in a body to Anagni to seek an authoritive ruling from the pope. Boniface had then 'formally declared that a full remission would be granted to all who made a true and contrite confession as the canons and decretals require.'

Copies of the bull *Antiquorum* were despatched to every part of Europe accompanied by a slight commentary explaining the circumstances and pointing to various Biblical precedents. 'Wherefore', it continued, 'you who are called, drive away your cares and preoccupations. Come and pray and atone for your sins without delay. For now is the time, and this is the very day of salvation. . . . Think how near is the means of your salvation, . . . of washing away the stains of sin from your souls, of exchanging the wretchedness of your earthly lives for everlasting glory.' The missive concluded with the following jingle which the Siennese inscribed on the walls of their cathedral:

> *Annus centenus Romae semper est jubilaeus.*
> *Crimina laxantur, cui paenitet ista donatur*
> *Hoc declaravit Bonifatius et roboravit.*

Every hundredth year is held the Roman Jubilee.
To he who is penitent all crimes are forgiven.
Thus says Boniface.

In Rome, pilgrims were handed copies of the bull on the steps of St.
Peter's, and invited to preserve them as a reminder that the next
Jubilee would occur in 1400.

The response was overwhelming. Italy was unusually peaceful in
1300 and the pope had overcome his enemies within the city. The
summer was fine and the harvest excellent. 'Innumerable Christians
of both sexes, young and old, Italians and foreigners, came to Rome.
They came on horseback, on other animals, even on foot. Amongst
them one could see many young people, full of hope and without a
penny, carrying their parents on their shoulders.' The Roman populace were the first to claim the indulgence. Flying in the face of
tradition, fathers allowed their unmarried daughters to leave the
house by night accompanied by reliable chaperons, to perform their
thirty visits. Stephaneschi lyrically describes the crowd of paupers in
rags entering the city side by side with proud noblemen. Almost
every Italian bishop claimed the indulgence, and some French ones.
The English, he thought, preferred to come later in the year, when
Rome offered the same dank climate as their own country. No
kings attended, but Philip of France was represented by his Italian
agent Musciatto Francesi and Edward I by one of the Cerchi of
Florence.

The influx of pilgrims imposed a considerable strain on the resources of the city. From the summit of the gate-towers they looked
like a swarm of ants or an invading army, and there was scarcely
enough room in the city to contain them. After three months there
was a serious prospect of famine which was only averted by an
abundant harvest. 'The land smiled on us and the earth gave forth
fruit. It was a miracle no less impressive than the feeding of the five
thousand with five loaves and two fishes.' But the miracle was
accomplished, for when William Ventura came to claim the indulgence he found an 'abundance of flesh, fish and oats'. Villani too had
no difficulty in feeding himself and his horse. It was, however,
accomplished at a price. The cost of food rose steeply and the
Romans made enormous profits out of the Jubilee. Ventura had to
pay a *gros tournois* per day for a bed for himself and a stable for his
horse; even this did not include fodder which was extremely dear.
A number of pilgrims accompanied their devotions with austerities,
fasts, vigils, and even flagellation 'to prepare themselves for the vast
influx of the Holy Spirit'. The great amorphous mass of men taxed
the papal police to the limit of their endurance. On the bridge below

the Castel St. Angelo pilgrims were made to keep to one side when entering the Leonine city and the other when leaving it. On the city side of the bridge a new street had to be opened in the walls to allow easier access.

Boniface was often asked by pilgrims to reduce the number of days that they had to spend in the city but he usually refused. According to Stephaneschi he made only three exceptions. On Maundy Thursday he appeared in front of the Lateran basilica and announced that all those in the crowd might claim the indulgence after only one visit to each of the basilicas of the apostles. This concession was repeated on 18th November, the anniversary of the consecration of the basilicas. Finally, as the end of the Jubilee year approached, he agreed that foreign pilgrims who had already begun the journey or the fifteen visits might complete them after the end of the year.

Many pilgrims who attended the Jubilee later had occasion to remember it as a formative episode in their lives. Giovanni Villani, the Florentine merchant and historian, 'wandered amongst the great monuments of the city and read the histories and chronicles of ancient Rome by Sallust, Lucan, Livy, Valerius, Paulus Orosius, and other masters of the historical art; I resolved then to copy their style and form.' It was here that he formed the design of his great history of Florence, daughter of Rome and destined for equal greatness. 'And so with the help of God's grace I turned back from Rome in the year 1300 and began to write this book.' Dante was almost certainly in Rome in the Jubilee year and set the *Divine Comedy* at Easter 1300. William Ventura, the chronicler of Asti, spent fifteen days there, departing on Christmas Eve, the last day of the Jubilee. 'As I rode away from Rome I saw the roads encumbered with a countless multitude of pilgrims. . . . Again and again I saw men and women trodden underfoot in the press and I myself was often hard put to it to escape the same fate. It would be a fine thing and agreeable to every true Christian to repeat the festival every centennial year.'

There were widely varying estimates of the number of pilgrims who visited Rome in 1300. Villani's figure of 200,000 is almost certainly too low, while William Ventura's claim of two million is plainly excessive. Every one agreed, however, that the pope and the Romans had made large profits. 'From the offerings of the pilgrims', one remarked, 'the Church gained great treasures and all the Romans were much enriched.' In the basilica of St. Peter, Ventura saw two priests standing day and night at the high altar drawing in the money with rakes. The rumour in Tuscany was that the offerings had amounted to a thousand *livres* of Perugia every day. But the truth was less spectacular. According to Stepheneschi the offerings in a normal year amounted to 30,405 florins whereas in this year there were rather more than 50,000. Most offerings were in small coin and many pilgrims were too poor to give anything at all. The nobility were particularly mean and kings absented themselves altogether. All of this, he adds, was swallowed up by the very heavy expenses of the Jubilee; 'money piously given was piously spent', on the accommodation of pilgrims and the upkeep of the two basilicas.

The Jubilee of 1300 was in a sense the swan-song of the mediaeval papacy. No pope had exercised the substance of power like Innocent IV and none was to display the shadow of power more splendidly than Boniface VIII. After the terrible fall of Boniface in 1303 many were inclined to attribute the Jubilee to his ambition and vainglory. In the posthumous 'trial' of Boniface, the bull *Antiquorum* was cited as evidence of heresy and he was even accused of murdering pilgrims in Rome. A French pamphleteer depicted the Jubilee as a commercial enterprise designed to impoverish pilgrims for the pope's benefit:

> *Tel y ala en belle guise*
> *Qui s'en revint en sa chemise . . .*
> *Lors alèrent plusieurs à Rome*
> *Qui retournèrent mains preudhommes.*

> Many went there richly dressed
> Who later came back in their shirt-sleeves . .
> Many went to Rome
> And came back wiser men.

But this was the verdict of his enemies after his fall. Those who attended the Jubilee felt that they had achieved something, that a similar opportunity would not arise again in their lifetime. Stephaneschi emphasized that it offered a unique opportunity to restore the soul to its state as after baptism and, like baptism, it could not be repeated. How many vile crimes had until then lain hidden in the deepest recesses of men's consciences? 'Who can say how many grievous wounds were laid bare to the healing hand of the confessor?' Dante was no friend of Boniface VIII but when he entered Purgatory at Easter 1300 he was told by the shade of his friend Casella that for three months not one sinner had been refused admittance to the cleansing of Purgatory; 'for three months he has taken in peace all who would embark.'

The Avignon Papacy and the Jubilee of 1350

The years which followed the Jubilee were amongst the most dismal in Roman history. In 1305 Bertrand de Got, archbishop of Bordeaux, was elected pope and, fleeing the turbulent politics of Rome, established the papacy in France. On 6th May, 1308 the Lateran basilica was almost entirely destroyed by fire. In the absence of the popes the social and economic life of Rome stagnated while successive papal legates waged incessant warfare against the rebellious magnates of central Italy. Those Romans who remembered the Jubilee of 1300 saw the only hope of reviving their fortunes in the staging of another Jubilee as soon as possible.

In the autumn of 1342 a delegation of thirteen citizens drawn from various classes of the population made its way to Avignon and petitioned that the Jubilee be brought forward to 1350 and held every fifty years thereafter. The Jewish Jubilee, they pointed out, had been held every fifty years and, besides, such was the frailty of human life that many people born after 1300 would not live to see the year 1400. The pope, Clement VI, approved their request. He embodied his consent in the bull *Unigenitus*, one of the most celebrated pronouncements of the mediaeval Church. Borrowing a concept of the thirteenth-century schoolmen, Clement declared that Christ, the Blessed Virgin, and the saints and martyrs, had accumulated in their lifetimes more merit than they needed for their personal salvation. The excess was collected in a 'treasury of merit' controlled by the Church. The pope, who held the keys of St. Peter, could alone unlock this treasury and use it to release men from their sins by remitting the punishment (not the guilt) due to those who had made a true and contrite confession. Turning to the case in point Clement referred to 'the clamour of our own people of Rome who have humbly beseeched us on behalf of all peoples of the world' to release some of the merit of Christ and the saints for the salvation of mankind. The Jubilee would be held in 1350. The arrangements would be the same as those of 1300 except that the Lateran basilica was added to the list of churches to be visited.

The condition of Italy had changed for the worse in the past fifty years. No time could be less auspicious, as Petrarch remarked, than one in which 'all France, the Low Countries, and Britain, are engulfed in war; Germany and Italy are crippled by civil strife, their cities reduced to ashes; the Spanish kings turn on each other in armed combat, and throughout Europe Christ is unseen and unknown.' As the news of bitter fighting in northern Italy reached Avignon, Clement VI sank into a state of depressed lethargy, punctuated by the regular issue of bulls reproving Christendom for its violent ways and lamenting that 'if our reports are correct many pilgrims flocking to gain our indulgence will be seriously impeded.' Clement's efforts to secure a brief truce in the war between England

and France ended in failure. Both countries forbade their citizens to attend the Jubilee on the ground that the drainage of currency and manpower would do irreparable damage to the war effort. Nevertheless the prohibition was widely ignored in France, and in England a large number of individuals obtained licences to visit Rome. English pilgrims travelling through France had to chose their route with care. Several were arrested as subjects of Edward III, and some French pilgrims who innocently travelled with parties of Englishmen found their property sequestered by royal officers when they returned.

Three months before it was due to begin, the Jubilee suffered another blow in the form of a violent earthquake. Much of the population was reduced to living in tents, and a number of monuments were entirely destroyed. The campanile and loggia of St. Paul's collapsed and the roof of S. Maria Maggiore fell in. The Lateran basilica, which had only recently been rebuilt after the fire of 1308, was partially ruined. 'In the two thousand years since the foundation of the city', Petrarch wrote, 'no worse disaster had befallen it. Its grandiose monuments, stunning to the foreign traveller, ignored by the Romans, have fallen to the ground. . . . An icy pall of gloom is cast over the Jubilee year.'

In spite of the difficulties, and somewhat to the surprise of contemporaries, the roads were shortly filled with crowds of pilgrims reminiscent of those of 1300. Matteo Villani observed them passing through Florence 'enduring the hardships of the time, the unbelievable cold, the ice, the snow, and the floods'. By day the roads were crowded out, by night the inns. The Germans and Hungarians travelled in enormous bands and spent the nights in the open air huddled round large bonfires. The innkeepers sold all the food, wine, and fodder that they could find and, as usual, were accused of making excessive profits. So were butchers and grocers. 'But there was no disorderliness or grumbling; everything was born patiently without fuss.' Inside Rome the citizens were invited to lay in ample stocks of food 'so that no pilgrim will suffer penury or starvation, but will be restored and satisfied not only spiritually but bodily as well.' Aniballe de Ceccano, the papal legate, was instructed to provide for pilgrims, needs at his own expense if necessary.

Counting the pilgrims was a matter of guesswork. Matteo Villani calculated that the peak was reached at Easter when there were rather more than a million pilgrims in Rome; even at Ascension and Pentecost there were 800,000 and the number never at any point fell below 200,000. Peter of Herenthals was probably closer to the truth when he estimated that about 5,000 pilgrims entered the city every day, which would mean that no more than 50,000 were there at any one time. On the last day of the Jubilee, Rome was still full of pilgrims completing their visits to the three basilicas. 'Every Roman became an innkeeper and filled his house with pilgrims and horses.' As a result of the earthquake, accommodation was harder to find than it had been in 1300. A pilgrim could expect to pay one and a half or two *gros tournois* per day for himself and his horse, falling perhaps to one *gros* in a slack period. The demand for wine and meat outstripped the supply throughout the year, allowing enterprising merchants to make large sums by importing food from northern Italy. Bread cost a penny an ounce; a bottle of wine three, four, or even five shillings; a sack of fodder fetched five *lire*. Every kind of meat was unbelievably expensive and some of it was of very poor quality.

Visiting the three basilicas involved a walk of eleven miles which was accomplished in some discomfort. 'The streets were so crowded that every one, whether they were riding or walking, had to reconcile themselves to moving extremely slowly.' Similar inconveniences attended the public exhibitions of the Veronica, which were held every Sunday afternoon at St. Peter's. Three or four pilgrims were suffocated or trampled underfoot on each of these occasions, and on some days the number rose to six or even twelve. On Easter Sunday Heinrich von Rebdorff saw several pilgrims crushed to death in the crowd. The more distinguished pilgrims took the precaution of applying in advance for a private view. It is clear that the *sudarium* of Veronica had by now supplanted the body of St. Peter as the principal relic of Rome. For Petrarch, Rome was no longer the city of the apostles but the city of Christ, whose relics eclipsed every other exhibit. Although Petrarch paid a cursory visit to the Calixtine cemetery and the site of Peter's crucifixion, his overpowering desire was to see 'the features of the Saviour wherever he might find them, on the napkin of Veronica or on the walls of S. Maria Maggiore'. He would 'gaze on the place where Christ appeared to St. Peter and would worship his footsteps on the hard ground. Then he would enter the *sancta sanctorum* of the Lateran . . . and see the relics of the birth and circumcision of his Lord, and the flask of the Virgin's milk by which so many had been restored to health.'

There was another side to Rome in 1350 which stood in pathetic contrast to the celebration of the Jubilee. St. Bridget of Sweden found the sight of the city in the aftermath of the earthquake profoundly depressing, and the absence of the papacy in France pained her. In the churches 'cracks and rifts had appeared in the arches so that bricks and pieces of masonry fell down on the heads of praying pilgrims. The pillars were buckling and the roofs on the verge of collapse. Mosaic floors, once fresh and beautiful, were now broken in pieces and the faithful stumbled into holes in the floor, doing themselves great injury.' Beneath the physical ruin, the Swedish visionary detected the signs of a deeper, spiritual decay. Bridget added her voice to the chorus of her contemporaries who pointed to the Avignon papacy as a symptom of religious decline and, although it is hard for a historian to share this view, the sorry condition of Rome must have done much to confirm it in the eyes of the pilgrims. 'In times past it was a city in which dwelt warriors of Christ, its streets strewn as if with gold and silver. Now all its precious sapphires are lying in the mire and few of its inhabitants live the Christian life.'

As in 1300, there were 'many altercations' about the meaning of the indulgence. The confusion was increased by the fact that alongside the official bull *Unigenitus* there circulated a number of unofficial bulls which were almost certainly forged by the Romans in order to attract more pilgrims to the city and keep them there longer. In these pseudo-bulls the pope was supposed to have urged priests and monks to visit Rome with or without the permission of their superiors. Italians were 'required' to remain in the city for at least a month and extra churches were added to those that were to be visited. In one version pilgrims were required to visit seven churches on at least fifteen occasions before they could claim the indulgence. The pope, it added, 'would order the angels to admit straight to heaven all pilgrims who die on the route having made a good confession'. These bulls were widely distributed. The canon lawyer Alberic of Rosate, who claimed the indulgence together with his wife and children, knew nothing of *Unigenitus* and reproduced two of the forged bulls in his handbook of canon law. Peter of Herenthals, the abbot of Floresse near Namur, reproduced them in his biography of Clement VI, and the jaundiced English chronicler Thomas Burton cited them as proof of Clement's wickedness. John Wyclif denounced them as blasphemy. It may seem unfair to condemn Clement for a bull which he had never issued, but although he had not in fact invited clerics to visit Rome without permission he certainly behaved as if he had done. Many monks did go to Rome without permission; others conjured up ecclesiastical business taking them to Avignon and then made off to claim the Jubilee indulgence in Rome. Most of these illicit pilgrims were able to obtain letters from the pope forbidding their superiors to punish them. Nor was Clement as firm as Boniface VIII in refusing the pressing demands of pilgrims for a reduction in the number of visits required. The papal legate Guy of Boulogne was empowered to reduce the number of days if the crowds in Rome became unmanageable. Alberic of Rosate, who inspected the bull conferring this power, was allowed to leave after six days with the full indulgence. After Easter the shortage of food became acute and Guy reduced the number of visits from fifteen to eight. This had its effect. The crowds diminished, 'at which the Romans were exceedingly vexed.'

Louis of Hungary was the only king who came to claim the Jubilee indulgence in person. The others asked to be granted it without having to make the irksome journey to Rome. Philip VI of France protested that he was too old and infirm to go to Rome, Hugh of Cyprus that he lived too far away. Edward III of England sent the celebrated preacher Richard Fitzralph, archbishop of Armagh, to plead on his behalf. Fitzralph pointed out that travelling to sanctuaries had no place in the Jewish Jubilee which Clement professed to be reviving. Jews were simply commanded to behave exceptionally well towards their neighbours in Jubilee years. Could not the English do the same and gain the indulgence by, say, bestowing alms on hospices and schools? This interesting argument carried no weight. The pope affirmed in reply that 'no one of any status or condition whatever may gain the indulgence without visiting the basilicas in person.' Clement's attitude softened, however, when the Jubilee had ended. In May 1351 Edward III, the queen, the prince of Wales, and the earl of Lancaster were all formally 'granted' the Jubilee indulgence. Many of Edward's subjects were accorded the same privilege in return for a sum equal to the cost of a journey to Rome, the money to go to the needs of the Holy Land. Queen Elizabeth of Hungary was permitted to appoint a confessor and receive 'the same indulgence as those who visited the basilicas of St. Peter and St. Paul and St. John of the Lateran in the year 1350'. More spectacular was the concession of an indulgence *ad instar Jubilaei* to the entire population of Mallorca in June 1352, perhaps as a reward for their resistance to the pope's great adversary, Peter IV of Aragon. Any Mallorcan could claim the indulgence if he paid eight visits to Mallorca cathedral and to every parish church of the city; he was also to contribute to the endowment of new churches a sum equal to the cost 'in conscience assessed' of travelling to Rome and staying there for fifteen days. This was not enough for the Mallorcans, who complained that 'it was hard to reckon what the cost of going to Rome would be, and the gross errors that would occur might lose some people the benefits of the indulgence. Moreover there are many sons of families, servants, retainers, and paupers who could never afford to go to Rome, and if it were only the rich who could win salvation it would be a grave scandal which would endanger the souls of the entire population of the kingdom.' It was therefore agreed that the Mallorcans would be granted the indulgence in return for a single official payment of 30,000 gold florins to the papal treasury. This curious transaction established a precedent of which Boniface IX would make full use when the time came to celebrate the next Jubilee.

The Papal Schism

In non-Jubilee years the Roman churches depended on the modest indulgences awarded to them by the popes of the thirteenth century. At the death of Nicholas IV, in 1292, no single church in Rome offered an indulgence of more than seven years and seven quarantines, and it required an unusually energetic pilgrim to collect as much as a thousand years of remission in one visit to the city. This proved to be insufficient to draw the pilgrims of the fourteenth century, bored by Rome and enticed by the excitement of the Holy Land. After the Jubilee of 1350, the churches of Rome attempted to revive their fortunes by claiming enormous indulgences, indulgences so large that it is difficult to understand why their authenticity was not challenged before the sixteenth century. 'Suffice it to say', wrote the papal secretary of state Signorili, 'that they exceed in indulgences all other churches in the world combined. Which is why every year an unending throng of pilgrims from every corner of the earth comes to the city of the apostles to pray, to gain the indulgences, and to venerate the holy relics of its churches.' The first that is heard of these indulgences is the report of Leopold, prior of the Augustinian house in Vienna, who toured the churches of Rome in 1377. Leopold bought a *Liber Indulgentiarum*, or book of indulgences, from which he learned that seven years of remission were gained when he ascended each of the twenty-nine steps in front of St. Peter's. Each of the eighty altars in St. Peter's offered twenty-eight years and five of them were worth thirty-two. At the altar of the *sudarium* of Veronica 'I, Leopold, unworthy sinner that I am, spent three sessions of twenty-seven hours in prayer. For you must know that for every hour that a Roman looks on this image of the Lord he gains an indulgence of three thousand years; the Italian gets nine thousand years, and the foreigner twelve thousand years.' Each visit to the basilica carried twenty-eight years or a third of all one's sins, whichever was the greater. The high altar apparently offered a plenary indulgence, which was as much as could be obtained by spending fifteen days in Rome in a Jubilee year. The basilica of St. Paul now carried forty-eight years and forty-eight quarantines every day; extra indulgences of a thousand years were available there on the feast of the apostles, and of seven thousand years on the anniversary of the dedication of the basilica. Leopold's booklet informed him that pope Silvester (d. 335) had declared most of these indulgences, and that they were particularly effective in effacing the sin of anger against one's parents, so long as one had not actually struck them.

The *Mirabilia* no longer satisfied the demands of pilgrims. One of them, who was in Rome in 1344, complained that it was impossible to buy a reliable guide to the churches and monuments. Books of indulgences like Leopold's began to fill this vacuum towards the end of the fourteenth century. They reproduced some of the more interesting stories from the *Mirabilia* and added a mass of information about the indulgences of the city's churches, together with specious accounts of their origins. Forged papal bulls were quoted at length. William Brewyn, the author of an English book of indulgences, proved to his own satisfaction that the indulgences at the altar of the Veronica originated in a bull of Gregory XI. John Capgrave in 1450 read an 'old legend' to the effect that the indulgences at the church of St. Lawrence had been personally declared by the saint himself. From the end of the fourteenth century new editions of these works appeared in verse and prose in every major language. An English edition, written in about 1400, begins

> *Whoso wol his soule leche*
> *Listen to me; I wol him teche*
> *Pardoun. Is the soule bote*
> *At grete Rome, there is the roote.*
> *Pardoun a word in Frensch it is*
> *Forgiveness of thy synnes i-wis.*

Translations often contained slight alterations to suit national tastes. The church of S. Maria Maggiore claimed to possess some relics of the apostle Thomas, but in English versions the relics become those of Thomas Becket. An English pilgrim in Rome in 1344 was shown a picture of the Virgin which Becket, who had never been to Rome, was supposed to have held in special reverence. English guide-books asserted that Becket had been to school in Rome, and the clergy of S. Maria Maggiore displayed his right arm 'and a parte of his brayne'. John Capgrave believed these fables in 1450 and wrote them down, but on his return home he thought better of it and erased them from his manuscript.

Those who did not buy hand-books were left in no doubt that plentiful indulgences were to be had. At most churches notices or inscriptions proclaimed what spiritual benefits were available inside. A bill-board outside the church of St. Lawrence promised daily indulgences of seven thousand years and seven thousand quarantines. At the spot where Christ had once appeared to St.

Peter an inscription announced remission of two thousand years. In the church of S. Maria Maggiore a list of indulgences was posted at the east end of the church:

> And written it is all there
> On a table at high altere,
> Pardoun there is that men may see
> Graunted of popes that there han be.

The obvious purpose of these frauds was to re-establish the Roman pilgrimage in rivalry with that of Jerusalem, which was now at the summit of its popularity. The theme which runs through all the Roman hand-books of the period is that greater benefits can be obtained with less trouble at Rome. If men only knew about the indulgences available at Rome, wrote the author of the *Stacions of Rome*, they would never bother to visit the Holy Land.

> Pope Bonifas telleth this tale
> If men wuste grete and smale
> The pardoun that is at grete Rome
> They wolde tellen in heore home
> It were no need to man in Christiante
> To passe into the Holy Lond over the see
> To Jerusalem ne to St. Katheryne,
> To bring man's soule out of pyne
> For pardoun ther is without ende.

One pilgrim remarked that the road from the Lateran to St. Peter's was called the Via Sacra 'because from one end to the other there are as many indulgences to be had as can be won by a voyage to Jerusalem.'

The attitude of the papacy to these claims was somewhat equivocal. An official memorandum of 1382 is remarkably reticent, contenting itself in most cases with the observation that the remission to be had was 'very great'. Some of the books of indulgences gave the impression the popes had acquiesced in the claims of the Roman churches. The *Stacions of Rome* says as much of Boniface IX, who was almost certainly alive when it was written. After the beginning of the great schism, in 1378, the Roman popes would have found it hard to protest even had they wished to. They were too heavily dependent on the prestige of Rome to indulge in damaging quarrels with its clergy on a matter which so closely touched that prestige.

The Avignon anti-popes were acutely conscious that their rivals enjoyed a considerable advantage in the actual possession of Rome. Pilgrimages to Rome reinforced the prestige of the Roman pope, and in countries loyal to Avignon sporadic attempts were made to suppress them. In 1382 the Avignon pope, Clement VII, took the extraordinary step of transferring the indulgences of the major basilicas of Rome to the churches of Marseilles. The indulgences of St. Peter's on the feast of the apostles were transferred to Marseilles cathedral, while those of S. Maria Maggiore were awarded to the abbey church of St. Victor. The Franciscan church of Marseilles received the indulgences of the Lateran on the grounds that all Italy was in the hands of 'that pestiferous and tyrannical schismatic', Urban VI. The Roman pope, for his part, made the maximum use of his possession of the city by bringing forward the Jubilee of 1400. One of the last acts of Urban VI before his death was to declare that Jubilees would henceforth be held at intervals of thirty-three years, in honour of the thirty-three years of Christ's life on earth. A fourth church, the basilica of S. Maria Maggiore, was added to those that must be visited. The bull was issued in April 1389 and the next Jubilee was announced for 1390. The anti-pope immediately denounced the Jubilee as having no validity and forbade all the faithful within his obedience (it consisted of little more than France and Spain) to attend it. In this strident document, Clement castigated the Roman pope as a pseudoprophet and a serpent, his Jubilee as 'a fraud, concocted under the false colours of piety and clemency in the hope of enticing the faithful into his detestable obedience, . . . and thus into the jaws of Hell.' The contest which followed gravely damaged the prestige of the Roman Jubilee. As in 1350, requests were made for the benefit of the indulgence without the burden of going to Rome and Boniface IX, who was elected pope in Rome in November 1389, was in no position to resist them. He could not afford to offend princes like the duke of Bavaria, who was awarded the indulgence, together with his wife and family, before the Jubilee had even begun. But Boniface's generosity was by no means confined to princes. Some bishops were empowered to grant the indulgence to any of their diocesans whom they chose. Countless unimportant individuals like the mayor of Berwick-on-Tweed applied for the indulgence and got it. Boniface undoubtedly hoped to placate his friends and win over his enemies, and in this policy he enjoyed a measure of success. The municipal authorities of Cologne appear to have been won over to his cause by the promise of a Jubilee indulgence. In Spain, Boniface's agents were instructed to offer the indulgence to all who would convert to his obedience.

Boniface IX was not only diplomatically weak but chronically short of money, and it was he who first transformed the Jubilee into an instrument of financial policy. He appropriated half the offerings made at all the Roman basilicas including St. Paul's and S. Maria

Maggiore which he did not directly control. Special representatives were installed at these churches, to ensure that he got his share, and the management of the Jubilee receipts was placed in the hands of the banking firm of Michael de Guinigi. As soon as the Roman Jubilee was over, Boniface sold the indulgence to those who had been unable to attend. This had been done in a small way by Clement VI in 1350, but Clement had not attempted to market the indulgence far and wide. Boniface on the other hand set up an elaborate organization to sell the Jubilee indulgence north of the Alps. One of his bitterest critics described his agents as extracting large sums from the rich and simple-minded. One province alone was said to have yielded 100,000 florins. 'And so these agents with painted faces and fat bloated stomachs made their way to Rome with their trains of servants and fine horses . . . and poured their spoils into Boniface's coffers.' In most parts of Europe pilgrims were permitted to gain the Jubilee indulgence by making fifteen visits to a local church and paying whatever sum they would have expended on a journey to Rome. At Milan six thousand florins were raised, part of which went to the cathedral building fund. Other local Jubilees were declared in Germany at Munich, Prague, Meissen, Magdeburg, and Constance.

The Avignon pope watched the affair in idle frustration. Some members of his own obedience had visited Rome in 1390, but most of them accepted that the next valid Jubilee would be held in accordance with the bull *Unigenitus* in 1400. Many Frenchmen appeared in Rome in that year and they were joined by members of the Roman obedience who looked forward to the prospect of any Jubilee, even an unofficial one. Indeed, the unofficial Jubilee of 1400 appears to have been more popular than the official one of 1390, and one monk of St. Paul's asserted that it was the most crowded Jubilee in his experience; the offerings at St. Paul's, said he, came to 60,000 ducats 'partly because there were more people and partly because they were more generous'. A more reliable source than the reminiscences of an aging tourist guide suggests that the offerings in the four Jubilee churches combined had reached 16,000 florins by June and may have amounted to about half as much again in the whole year.

All this presented Boniface IX with a delicate problem. He could not recognize the Jubilee of 1400 without casting doubt on that of 1390. But plainly he could but ignore it, and early in the year he took steps to claim his share of the offerings. In March he announced in somewhat opaque language that all the indulgences of his predecessors for the fiftieth and hundredth years were confirmed. In July, without actually declaring a Jubilee, he conceded a Jubilee indulgence to all who contributed to the rebuilding of the ruinous

basilica of St. Paul. His embarrassment was complete when princes
whom he could ill-afford to displease wrote to ask for the Jubilee
indulgence. The queen of Denmark, who had claimed the indulgence of 1390 now wrote in for that of 1400. Boniface replied
cagily to such requests. Without mentioning the Jubilee he offered
them 'the same indulgence and remission as those who visit the
basilicas of St. Peter, St. Paul, St. John Lateran, and S. Maria
Maggiore in this present year'. The news of these happenings caused
dismay in the Avignon obedience. The Carthusians loyal to Avignon
heard as early as 1399 that Frenchmen were planning to attend the
Jubilee and forbade their members to join them. The French
government, which was the principal supporter of Avignon, forbade all pilgrimages to Rome and instructed its officers to prevent
them by force if necessary. This was easier said than done. Early in
the year reports indicated that the roads were daily covered with
nobles, clergy, bourgeois, and peasants on their way to Rome, and
royal officials were constantly exhorted to greater diligence. The
bailli of Mâcon was threatened with dire penalties. The *bailli* of Sens
was told that droves of pilgrims were passing freely through his
jurisdiction, 'from which it appears that you have ignored our instructions.' The hospice of St. Didier at Nevers was filled to capacity
with pilgrims, and the master had to appeal to the town for a
special subsidy.

The problem of the Avignon obedience was posed in a particularly acute form in Spain. Although the Spanish kingdoms had
consistently supported Avignon, their subjects had never altogether
accepted this policy, and pilgrimages to Rome had continued
throughout the schism. Indeed, a hospice for Catalans in Rome was
partially financed by the king of Aragon. But the prospect of a mass
pilgrimage to Rome in 1400 stirred the Aragonese government to
action. An embassy was sent to Paris, which expressed the opinion
that all those who went to Rome were excommunicates, schismatics, and destined for everlasting damnation. The problem of
applying these sentiments in practice was underlined by the case of
the Cistercian abbey of Poblet in southern Catalonia, where a
number of monks had formed the intention of claiming the Jubilee
indulgence at Rome. Poblet was a royal monastery. Pedro IV of
Aragon was buried there, and Martin I was even then in the process
of building a palace in the monastery. The king indicated his displeasure and embarrassment; he was astonished that they were
prepared to suffer excommunication at the hands of the true (i.e.
Avignon) pope, 'especially as our lord the pope has proclaimed that
monks remaining in their monasteries shall have the same indulgences as those who go to Rome in person, in view of the present

situation of the Church.' Accordingly the abbot was to forbid such pilgrimages and to punish monks who disobeyed. The monks appear to have taken no notice of this letter for, some weeks later, a second letter gave expression to the king's anger that certain monks had persisted in their intention of going to Rome 'into the territory of that detestable intruder and to the great detriment of our holy mother the Church'. If the rest of them would promise not to go, he would ask the Avignon pope to nominate some convenient Spanish sanctuary where pilgrims could claim the Jubilee indulgence or else, perhaps, to permit the voyage to Rome. The affair throws an interesting light on the resilience of the Roman pilgrimage in the least creditable period of its history.

The Return of the Popes

'Pity Rome', a papal official cried at the beginning of the fifteenth century, 'once thronged with princes and crowded with palaces, now it is a place of hovels, thieves, wolves, and worms.' In later life, Adam of Usk's memories of Rome were of wolves howling at night outside his house and fallen buildings blocking the narrow streets. The campanile of St. Peter's had been struck by lightning in 1352 and the rubble remained for many years strewn across the Vatican Hill. The triumphal arch of Arcadius fell down in the time of Urban V. The last years of the papal schism brought Rome to the nadir of its fortunes. In the absence of the popes the splendid ceremonies were curtailed and finally abandoned. The Neapolitan troops who entered Rome in 1408 found St. Peter's abandoned by the canons, and not even on the feast of the apostles could any one be found to celebrate Mass. One of the canons recorded in his diary that there was not enough money to light the candles in the basilica on the feast of the apostles in 1414. 'At Corpus Christi we celebrated Mass in great poverty on account of the war and the tribulations of St. Peter's. We carried the Eucharist on foot in a small crystal tabernacle, . . . lighting our way with six torches . . . for the canons could not afford any oil.'

The Jubilee of 1423 was a miserable affair. It occurred automatically thirty-three years after that of 1390, but no one troubled to proclaim it, and it was so little publicized that some historians have doubted whether it ever took place. The pope, Martin V, made no special arrangements. This may have been because he was reluctant to revive the controversies which had accompanied the Jubilees of the schism, or perhaps because he was anxious not to set up an indulgence in rivalry with the Hussite crusade. Nevertheless Poggio Bracciolini, then in the service of the papacy, complained that he was 'oppressed by a monstrous mob of barbarians' (i.e. non-Italians) who brought with them their dirt and uncouth manners. Perhaps more pilgrims would have attended but for the war which had engulfed northern Italy. John, abbot of St. Albans, waited for several weeks at Siena for a safe-conduct from Filippo-Maria Visconti, duke of Milan, and when at last it was forthcoming he was horrified by the desolation he found north of Rome.

Martin V entered Rome for the first time in his reign in September 1420. With the exception of nine years in the reign of Eugenius IV, the popes resided in Rome for the rest of the fifteenth century. The artistic patronage of the papacy returned to the city for the first time in a century and a half, and with it came some of the vigorous religious life of an earlier age. The arrival of new relics in Rome contributed to the atmosphere of revival. Martin V presided in person over the translation of St. Monica from Ostia. A few relics of Constantinople found their way to Rome after the fall of the city to the Turks in 1453. Thomas Paleologus, despot of the Morea, fled to Italy in 1460 bringing with him the head of St. Andrew and the right arm of St. John. The translation of the first of these relics to St. Peter's in April 1462 was marked by a formal oration from Pius II and a special plenary indulgence. The Sienese ambassador had not seen so many pilgrims in Rome since the Jubilee of 1450. Thus the last notable item from the greatest collection of relics that the mediaeval world had known, painfully assembled over seven centuries by successive Byzantine emperors, found its place in a Latin church.

The imposing ceremonies which visitors to Rome had missed in the fourteenth century now reappeared. Martin V ordered a new golden tiara from Lorenzo Ghiberti, together with embroidered vestments, banners, and ceremonial swords. Ever-increasing splendour attended the publication of the annual bull *In Coena Domini* in which the pope solemnly excommunicated the enemies of the Church, followed by cries of 'so be it, so be it' from the assembled cardinals. When Arnold von Harff witnessed it in 1497 it took a full hour to read and the watching crowd filled the entire Leonine city. The Easter celebrations of 1437 prompted in one pilgrim the reflection that 'Rome, which used to be the highest among nations and is now the lowest, yet retains these superb ceremonies from the days when they signified her mastery over all men.'

The *sudarium* of Veronica reached the zenith of its fame in the fifteenth century. Popular belief attributed miracles to it, and the indulgences attached to it were the largest in Rome, seven thousand years for Romans, ten thousand for Italians, fourteen thousand for foreigners. The 'vernicle', which had by now replaced the horse of Constantine as the emblem of Rome, was worn by every returning pilgrim. Langland's palmer pinned it to his hat, as did Chaucer's pardoner. Public displays of the Veronica were occasions for mass exhibitions of fierce repentance which astonished more than one visitor to Rome. Francesco Ariosto, a lawyer in the service of the duke of Modena, witnessed one of these ceremonies when he was in Rome on official business in 1471. A thin, fragile, almost transparent veil of silk was brought forward bearing the features of a bearded man. The entire crowd was silent and fell to its knees.

'It would be well beyond my powers to describe the feelings of devotion and piety which overcame the crowd then, or to tell you what public displays of repentance and humility were to be seen; what beating of breasts, what mental anguish in so many faces; what weeping, crying, and howling broke the silence of the square as sinners humbly begged for pardon; with what anguish they raised their hands to Heaven imploring mercy. They beat themselves repeatedly, causing themselves great pain, for they felt that by their sins, they had inflicted on Christ those wounds whose marks they saw before them; and now they hoped to wash away their guilt with tears, to purge the stains of sin with groans of pain. And from so much weeping and anguish, such general lamentation, there emerged consolation, rejoicing, happiness, and even jubilation at having experienced a spiritual renewal. A sudden change of mood from sorrow to joy overcame the crowd.'

The catacombs experienced a revival in the fifteenth century. They had never been entirely forgotten, but in the absence of the popes, the continual work of repair had been neglected. Several of the galleries had fallen in and some of the altars had been looted. A commission was appointed in 1424 to survey them. Repairs were undertaken, and pilgrims were once again reminded of these curious survivals from the earliest age of the Christian Church. The most famous were those on the Appian Way, which were entered from the church of St. Sebastian. The Florentine Giovanni Rucellai explored them in 1450 and reported that the bodies of St. Fabian and St. Sebastian carried a plenary indulgence. John Capgrave's first impression was of a 'grete pitte, for we go down thereto on 28 steps'. When his eyes had become accustomed to the gloom, he found himself in 'a cave or ellis a myre under the ground. . . . The cymytery is thus long that if a man tary not in the chapeles but go rit forth he schal walk it by the time that he hath said four times the *miserere mei Deus*. In this place were buried 46 popes and eche of them gave grete indulgence to the same place. . . . The comoun opinion is there of this place that who so evyr out of synne visit it . . . clene shreve and contrite, he is assoiled as clene as a man may be by the power of the Church.' As for the other catacombs, they were now 'desolate for horrible darknesse and disuse of peple', and few pilgrims visited them.

When they were not visiting the churches pilgrims amused themselves in various ways. Arnold von Harff saw a passion play performed at the Colosseum in which 'everything was acted by living people, even the scourging, the crucifixion, and the death of Judas.' The actors were all children of the well-to-do 'and therefore it was fittingly and richly performed.' Some of the more discerning pilgrims visited the Vatican library, recently refounded by Nicholas V and Sixtus IV largely on the proceeds of the Jubilee of 1450. The Burgundian pilgrim Georges Lengherand explored it in 1485, and found five large rooms full of books, of which one was available for private study, the rest reserved for curial officials.

The pilgrims brought prosperity to Rome, and to no one more than to its innkeepers. *Alberghi* multiplied prodigiously in the fifteenth century, and according to one pilgrim there were 1,022 of them functioning in 1450. Some of them achieved international repute, like the Albergo della Luna, where Francesco da Carrara stayed during the imperial coronation of 1355. Most of them were too expensive for the ordinary pilgrim. When the retinue of Borso d'Este were accommodated in Rome at the pope's expense in 1471, the bill came to seven thousand gold florins. Those who had to pay their own bills preferred to hire a room in a private house or else to bring an introduction to some compatriot living in Rome. Arnold von Harff was accommodated by one Johann Payll, a German doctor who kept a small guest-house for German pilgrims and offered his services as a guide. Large parties were well advised to arrange their accommodation in advance, especially at Easter and the feast of the apostles. There was no room for Otto, duke of Bavaria, when he arrived unexpectedly in the city in 1489, and he was obliged to withdraw to the villages of the Campagna. On the whole the hoteliers of Rome were an unpopular group of men. Erasmus thought their chances of salvation limited. Villon's friend Guillaume Bouchet derived the word 'host' from the Latin 'hostes' for they were all enemies to him.

Towards the end of the middle ages the resources of private enterprise were supplemented by national hostels. National hostels had existed before, but none had survived the decline of the Roman sanctuaries in the thirteenth century. The English house, which had been the last to disappear was the first to be revived. Opposite the church of St. Thomas on the Via Monserrato, now the site of the Venerable English College, stood a small house belonging to one

John Shepherd, an English rosary-seller living in Rome. He sold it in 1362 to the 'community and society of the English in the city, . . . for the benefit of the poor, infirm, needy, and wretched people coming from England to the city, and for their convenience and utility.' Shepherd and his wife Alice stayed on to run the hospice at a wage, and thus was born the English hospital of the Holy Trinity and St. Thomas. In the course of three decades it expanded into neighbouring houses, and by the end of the sixteenth century it could accommodate sixty pilgrims. A second English hospice was founded in 1396 by a wealthy London merchant, and became the hospital of the Holy Trinity and St. Edmund, king and martyr.

Other national hospices sprung up in much the same fashion, originating in the generosity of a few rich men and expanding haphazardly into neighbouring houses. In 1389 Dietrich of Niem, a curial official from Westphalia, joined with a merchant of Dortrecht to found the German college of S. Maria dell' Anima. It consisted originally of three adjoining houses, of which the central one was a chapel and the other two for the accommodation of male and female pilgrims. The college became by far the wealthiest and most celebrated national hospice in Rome. It was continually enriched by bequests from German pilgrims and residents. Successive popes conferred indulgences on its benefactors, and Eugenius IV gave its chaplains the valuable privileges of administering the Eucharist and hearing confessions, privileges normally reserved for parish churches. The Anima rapidly acquired all the surrounding houses and within a few years the three original houses were all used as the chapel, the middle one being the nave and the outer two the aisles. Few Germans of note passed through Rome without visiting it and inscribing their names in the book of benefactors. Among other national groups which could boast their own hospices were the Italians, Portuguese, Swedes, Irish, Castilians, Aragonese, Sicilians, Flemings, Bretons and Hungarians. Not all were organized in the same way and some were richer than others. Some, such as the Portuguese hospice of St. Anthony, were little more than a chapel where the Portuguese of the city worshipped. The German hospice was packed out every night while the Irish one was so little used that it was shortly turned into a seminary for Irish priests. The services they offered to pilgrims depended largely on the extent of their endowment. The Swedish hospital of St. Bridget occupied the palace in which the saint had lived out her last years, and it was operated by the rich Bridgetine order. Pilgrims were allowed to stay there for as long as they liked and were given free bread and wine for the first three days; only the more opulent pilgrims were asked for payment. The impoverished Flemish hospital of St.

Julian was more stringent, pilgrims being obliged to leave after three nights. No food was served at all. Vagabonds, soldiers of fortune, and the rich, were altogether excluded. One exception only was made for poor priests who might stay for eight days so long as they promised to say at least two masses in the chapel.

In January 1449 the crisis of the papacy had passed and Nicholas V considered the moment appropriate for the proclamation of the fifth Roman Jubilee, to be held from Christmas 1449 to Christmas 1450. It is probable that more pilgrims attended this Jubilee than any previous one, and the chroniclers competed with one another in devising suitable hyperboles to describe the throngs of travellers. The Sienese diplomat Agostino Dati watched Frenchmen, Germans, Spaniards, Portuguese, Greeks, Armenians, Dalmatians and Italians on the roads to Rome singing hymns in every language. The crowd of Burgundians who joined them was '*noble et sainte chose et devote a veoir*'. The first rush of pilgrims ended in February. 'The crowds diminished so rapidly that the innkeepers became discontented and every one began to think that it was all over. Then, in the middle of Lent, so many pilgrims appeared that there was no room for them in the inns and many had to sleep out in the vineyards . . . or beneath the porticoes of the basilicas.' Pilgrims begged for the love of God to be allowed in for the night at any price. Such was the shortage of food and beds that Nicholas several times reduced the number of days which pilgrims were required to spend in Rome. In the autumn he reduced them to one, on account of the threat of famine, but even so, on Saturdays and Sundays, when relics were displayed at St. Peter's and the pope gave his benediction, the crowd filled the entire Leonine city and the vineyards and cemeteries beyond. Most of them could see nothing at all. In mid-summer a serious epidemic thinned out the crowds arriving in Rome. Mortality in the city itself was high, and pilgrims fleeing from the crowded streets spread the plague along the roads leading north. Panic gripped the papal court, which made hurried arrangements to depart for Fabriano. The ambassador of the Teutonic Order had it on good authority that Nicholas had forbidden infected persons to come within seven miles of him on pain of excommunication. Nevertheless it was officially estimated that for most of the year 40,000 pilgrims were entering Rome every day, and Giovanni Ricci reckoned that a million were there at Easter.

The Florentine merchant Giovanni Rucellai had fled his native city to escape the plague and, finding himself in Perugia, he reflected that 'confession may liberate me from the fires of Hell but only a plenary indulgence can free me from Purgatory as well.' He departed for Rome with his family and three friends in February. Rucellai was

one of the first pilgrims to record his impressions of some of the
modern works of art in the city; Giotto's frescoes in the chapter-
house of St. Paul's, the gold reliquaries of S. Maria Maggiore, the
bronze tomb of Martin V in the Lateran, all of which struck this
Florentine as 'extremely fine'. He prayed at all the altars in St.
Peter's, diligently examined the relics proffered for his veneration,
and returned satisfied to Perugia less than a month after his departure.

John Capgrave, the Augustinian prior of King's Lynn, experienced like many others the frustration of having no reliable guide to
the city. The Colosseum he pronounced to be 'a marvellous place
whech was made round of schap and grete arches', but he could find
no book to tell him what its function had been. Capgrave wrote his
own guide, a scholarly work for its time, in the hope that it would be
found 'ful solacious' to his countrymen who had never been to
Rome. For their benefit he described the relics of each church in
extreme anatomical detail. His interest was stirred by a 'pees of the
flesch of seynt Laurens and coals joyned therto rit as thei fried in
his passioun'. In Holy Week he inspected the heads of St. Peter and
St. Paul in the Lateran. St. Peter, he reported, was 'brood . . . with
much hair on his berd and that is of grey colour betwixt whit and
blak. The hed of Paule is a long face, balled with red hair both berd
and hed.' In the church of St. George the head of the saint was kept
in a tabernacle with a removable lid to enable pilgrims to kiss it.
Capgrave took part in the many processions of Easter week and
stated that they were originally ordained by Christ, the reason given
for this opinion being that 'saynt Austin gevyth us swech a rule in
his boke *De Moribus Ecclesiae* . . . that when we cannot see hem
grounded in scripture we schul suppose that Christ taut hem.'

Towards the end of the Jubilee year the pope's satisfaction was
marred by a serious incident. The Ponte Molle in front of the Castel
St. Angelo had caused anxiety to the papal police ever since the first
Jubilee of 1300. The narrow bridge was the only means of access
from the city to the Vatican. The shops which had once lined both
sides were destroyed in the fighting of 1405, thus greatly reducing
the crush in Jubilee years. Even so, the crowds of 1450 were too
large for it. At Easter, soldiers from the Castel St. Angelo, together
with some youthful volunteers, had to drive back the pilgrims with
sticks in order to avert a serious accident. Families and friends lost
each other in the mêlée and 'it was pitiful to see pilgrims wandering
aimlessly about in search of missing fathers, sons, or companions.'
On another occasion, when the crowds in front of St. Peter's were
so tightly packed that none could move, a messenger on horseback
tried to get through the crowd. The horse panicked and reared,

killing several pilgrims with his hooves and throwing the rider to his death.

On Saturday 19th December, a week before the end of the Jubilee, the crowds had gathered to attend the weekly display of the Veronica and receive the pope's blessing. For some reason there was an untoward delay and at four o'clock it was announced that owing to the lateness of the hour the benediction would not take place that day. The unwieldy crowd of pilgrims turned back in disappointment and swarmed across the Ponte Molle into the city. In the middle of the bridge a mule, bearing Pietro Barbi, cardinal of St. Mark, was trying to move in the opposite direction. The narrow bridge was blocked for a few seconds but those behind did not notice and pushed forward, trampling some underfoot and forcing others over the side into the river. With some presence of mind the castellan of St. Angelo recruited some citizens on the spot, closed the bridge, and dispersed some pilgrims on the northern side of it. It took a further hour to clear the mob on the bridge itself and the crushed bodies of 178 pilgrims were recovered. A further seventeen bodies were pulled out of the river at Ostia, some still clutching each others' clothes for safety. All were taken to the nearby church of St. Celsus for identification. As evening closed appalling scenes were witnessed there as 'fathers, sons, and brothers wandered among the bodies as if in Hell itself, . . . pathetically holding candles in their hands and looking through rows of corpses, then collapsing with grief as they recognized those for whom they were looking.' The Medici agent in Rome was told of the disaster by a servant who had not seen such carnage since his service in the Turkish war. No one was more horrified than Nicholas V who tried to avert a similar disaster in future by clearing some of the buildings at either end of the bridge. Two small chapels were erected near the scene to commemorate the dead and warn those who crossed in future.

As usual the Jubilee indulgence was enjoyed by many who did not go to Rome. At Salzburg in February 1451 Nicholas of Cusa, papal legate in Germany, proclaimed that all those who made a good confession and visited local churches on fifteen separate days would earn the indulgence; they were also to fast for seven Fridays, abstain from meat on seven Wednesdays, and give half the cost of a journey to Rome to the bishop. At the special request of Nicholas V this offer was not available to simonists, adulterers, and notorious sinners, who would obtain only a partial remission of their sins. Those who had actually been to Rome in 1450 were invited to claim a second Jubilee indulgence and in their case no payment was required. The proceeds were to go to pious uses appointed by the pope. These concessions, which originally applied only to the province of Salzburg, were repeated throughout western Europe. Henry VI of England no doubt expressed the prevailing view when he declared that 'the whole population will rejoice to see the light for the remission of their sins.'

As a result of the Jubilee very great sums of money came into the papal coffers, 'an almost infinite quantity of gold and silver', says the pope's biographer. Most of it was spent on the Jubilee itself, particularly on buying in large stocks of grain. What was left went partly to the upkeep of the basilicas and partly to the purchase of the priceless collection of Greek and Latin manuscripts which is still one of the finest possessions of the papacy. But the most important results were intangible. The Jubilee marked the revival of the prestige of the papacy after a century of conciliar conflict. The last anti-pope had abdicated only a few months before the beginning of the Jubilee. Nicholas's biographer assures us that his design in proclaiming the Jubilee was to 'increase the dignity of the Holy See', and that many pilgrims came not only to claim the indulgence but to behold the person of Nicholas V, now universally recognized as pope. No doubt this is the exaggeration born of enthusiasm. But the Sienese diplomat Agostino Dati later had occasion to record that 'the memory of those days is a warm one for me, for they made manifest the triumph and glory of the Christian religion. From the most distant parts of the world, all these pilgrims travelled to Rome to visit the head of the universal church and the tomb of the prince of the apostles. Truly this was a year worthy to be remembered throughout all ages.'

CHAPTER XIV

THE LATER MIDDLE AGES I

'Light-Minded and Inquisitive Persons'

Tourists

Rome was the principal tourist resort of the middle ages, but it was far from being the only one. 'Some light-minded and inquisitive persons', Jacques de Vitry remarked, 'go on pilgrimages not out of devotion, but out of mere curiosity and love of novelty. All they want to do is travel through unknown lands to investigate the absurd, exaggerated stories they have heard about the east.' As travelling became easier and cheaper, tourism, lightly disguised as pilgrimage, became extremely popular. It would be a gross exaggeration to suggest that simple curiosity had displaced the intensely spiritual feelings of an earlier age, but in the fifteen century, it was certainly the predominant motive of many pilgrims.

This new interest is reflected in their guide-books. The guide-books of twelfth-century pilgrims in the Holy Land were condensed, factual and turgid; most of their topographical information was still derived from the seventh-century writings of Bede and Adamnan. A few pilgrims supplemented these arid tomes by writing travel diaries. Soon after the first crusade an Englishman called Saewulf wrote a long personal account of his experiences in the Holy Land. Four years later the Russian abbot Daniel composed another, having found it impossible to buy a good guide-book in Jerusalem. Pilgrims were still complaining about the inadequacy of guide-books in the 1160s, when John of Wurzburg observed that the city had been largely rebuilt since the beginning of the eleventh century, and Bede was no longer a useful companion. 'For this reason', he thought, 'my own detailed description will not be found superfluous.' Even more interesting are the accounts of thirteenth-century travellers, some of whom penetrated to Damascus or Baghdad and recorded their impressions of Islamic society. Exactly what audience they had in mind when writing these lengthy 'itineraries' is not at all clear. Dietrich, bishop of Wurzburg, declared that his itinerary, written in c. 1172, was intended to 'satisfy the desires of those who cannot go there themselves'. But in this it was plainly unsuccessful for, like almost every other account of this period, it was read by a few friends of the author, and then allowed to gather dust in a monastic library. The only itinerary which was much read at the time was the *Jerusalem History* of Jacques de Vitry, a book more interesting for its pungently expressed prejudices than for its information.

All this changed in the fourteenth century. If one event deserves to be singled out as a landmark in this change it was the appearance, shortly after 1357, of *Mandeville's Travels*. This purported to be an account of the travels of Sir John Mandeville to Palestine, Turkey, Persia, India, and Egypt, but it was in fact a compilation of stories drawn from various itineraries of the previous century with a few colourful fictions added. The author of this audacious literary forgery is still unknown, though the evidence points to Jean d'Outremeuse, a prolific collector of legends, who lived in Liège. Despite his improbable details, the fraudulent 'Mandeville' was treated with a respect that was denied to the truthful Marco Polo, whose work was dubbed *Il Milione* for its supposed exaggerations. *Mandeville's Travels* immediately became one of the most popular books of the age. Well over three hundred manuscripts survive. Within half a century it had been translated from the original French into Latin, English, high and low German, Danish, Czech, Italian, Spanish, and Irish. With the advent of printing it appeared in countless editions, and in England alone Wynkyn de Worde printed four different versions before the death of Henry VII. It was the first really popular book to portray travel as an adventure and a romance. For a hundred and fifty years after its appearance the public devoured each new travel book as it was written. 'Mandeville' was plagiarized and abridged by lesser writers, while a glut of reminiscences came from the pen of every Holy Land pilgrim with pretensions to literacy. The English Augustinian John Capgrave was inspired to write his account of Rome by reading Marco Polo and 'Mandeville'. When Felix Faber returned from his round trip to the Holy Land, crowds gathered to listen to his experiences. Most of the annual pilgrim-fleets which sailed from Venice in the fifteenth century carried at least one diarist; there were four on the fleet of 1479 and five on that of 1483. By this time, too, pilgrims' diaries were issuing in thousands from the printing presses.

Travel-books both reflect and create interest in the places that they describe. 'Mandeville' and his imitators stand at the beginning of the first chapter in the history of mass-travel, and the *Travels* reflect the growing romanticism and enthusiasm with which men were beginning to look on distant lands. Many pilgrims returned from their travels as little Mandevilles and, as the Lollard William Thorpe observed, 'if they be a month out in their pilgrimage, many of them shall be an half year after great janglers, tale-tellers, and liars.' This is the world of Chaucer's knight, who had 'ridden no man further, as well in Christendom as hethenesse'. So it was of the Wife of Bath:

> And thryse had she been at Ierusalem.
> She hadde passed many a straunge streem.
> At Rome she hadde been and at Boloigne,
> In Galice at seint Iame and at Coloigne.
> She coude much of wandring by the weye.
> Gat tothed was she, soothly for to seye.

Official arrangements are now made for tourists for the first time. Information offices appear at Rome and consulates in Egypt and Palestine. The Venetian package tour is at the height of its popularity. Governments begin to encourage tourism. Thus a safe-conduct issued by the Aragonese chancery in 1387 to a band of German travellers and their wives describes their purpose as being 'to fulfil their pilgrimage and observe the Spanish way of life'. The commercial treaty made between England and France in 1471 envisaged the possibility that English gentlemen might wish to cross the Channel 'to see and observe the country *pour leur plaisance*'. The invitation was probably taken up, for John Wyclif believed that the English were especially addicted to pilgrimages on account of their restless curiosity. Gréffin Affagart, on the other hand, thought it a peculiarly German vice. But both were agreed that it was deplorable. 'Let no man go to the Holy Land just to see the world', wrote the impeccably orthodox Santo Brasca, 'or simply to be able to boast "I have been there" and "I have seen that", and so win the admiration of his friends.'

In several respects these early tourists behaved exactly like their modern counterparts. They carved graffiti on walls, for example. Noblemen were in the habit of inscribing their coats of arms inside the Holy Sepulchre itself while pretending to be praying, and some of Felix Faber's companions had brought chisels and mallets with them for the purpose. Ghillebert de Lannoy's graffiti, carved in the refectory at Mount Sinai, can still be seen. They also bought gaudy souvenirs, like the coral paternosters and shaped semi-precious stones which were on sale outside the sanctuaries of Le Puy. The nagging wife in the *Quinze Joies de Mariage* bullied her husband into buying some of these. Nompar de Caumont bought several pieces of fine coloured silk at Jerusalem, together with four pieces of rope the length of the Holy Sepulchre, three silk purses, thirty-three silver rings and twelve silver crucifixes which had touched the Holy

Sepulchre, a number of relics of doubtful worth, a bag of Jerusalem soil, a black embroidered purse, two pairs of golden spurs, four roses and a phial of Jordan water. These he distributed amongst his relatives and tenants when he returned.

Primitive postcards were sold at the more popular sanctuaries. In Rome pictures of the *sudarium* of Veronica, painted on pieces of stiffened paper torn out of old books, were mass-produced and sold to pilgrims in the streets. Bernard van Breidenbach, dean of Mainz cathedral, brought a professional painter with him to Jerusalem in 1483 'to record all the principal cities from Venice onwards, which he did in a masterly and accurate fashion.' These drawings were reproduced in the earliest edition of Breidenbach's account of his journey, a beautiful octavo volume printed in Mainz in 1486. They include 'pull-out' drawings of Venice and Rhodes, the west front of the basilica of the Holy Sepulchre, and several animals which the artist claimed to have seen in Palestine, amongst them a unicorn and a strange hairy-looking man with a frog-like face. The French edition, printed in Lyon in 1489, is the earliest known example of copper-plate printing in France.

Books like Breidenbach's were probably read at leisure at home, not carried about on long journeys. Felix Faber, it is true, took a small library with him to the Holy Land, but he was an unusually thorough tourist. Most of the books carried by pilgrims in their hip-bags would have been route-books, like the *Guide for Pilgrims to Santiago* or the curious Anglo-Saxon guide to the sanctuaries of England, which dates from the eleventh century. Route-books did not vary much through the years, but as the routes became better-organized after the thirteenth century they passed out of fashion and were replaced by books of indulgences. The *Pilgrimages and Pardons of Acre*, written in French in about 1280, is an early example, altogether typical of its species. The *Mirabilia Urbis Romae* comes nearest, perhaps, to our own concept of a guide-book. In the Holy Land there were eight anonymous 'descriptions', all but one dating from the twelfth century, but they were cursory and inaccurate and, although much used, they were found wanting even by the uncritical pilgrims of the twelfth century.

Pilgrims who were not satisfied with these sketchy hand-books were obliged to hire a local guide. Professional guides had been found in Jerusalem as early as the fourth century, when their inaccuracies and exaggerations had earned them the implacable hostility of St. Jerome. The Russian abbot Daniel, in 1106, was lucky enough to find an 'old man, extremely learned' who spoke Greek and accompanied him on expeditions to all the outlying parts of Palestine. John of Wurzburg was guided round the Jacobite convent of St. Mary Magdalene by a monk who proclaimed the scriptural associations of the place with dramatic emphasis and many flamboyant gestures. In some cities, guides were licensed and organized. Venice, with its bureaucratic tradition, was naturally one of these. The republic provided guides whose duties included showing visitors the sights, finding them lodgings, helping them with their shopping, and introducing them to shipowners.

It is a measure of the greater sophistication of late mediaeval pilgrims, more critical and better-read than their predecessors, that they listened with suspicion to the untruths peddled by guides. Felix Faber was a devout man, but not a naïve one. He prepared for his second pilgrimage to the Holy Land by reading every pilgrim's account he could lay hands on, numerous histories of the crusades, and the writings of St. Jerome. He doubted whether the Lord's Sepulchre was 'really his own, or another, built afterwards'. He did not believe the Arab guides who told him that the bodies of the Holy Innocents were preserved at Bethlehem. Arnold von Harff, who was neither naïve nor particularly devout, was caustic in his remarks on the 'confusions' of the clergy on the subject of relics. He 'did not know' whether the tablets at S. Spirito in Rome were those which Moses received on Mount Horeb. Although von Harff did not question the value of relics as such, he had seen arms of St. Thomas at Rhodes, Rome, and Maestrich, as well as in India; heads of St. James the Less had been shown to him at Santiago and Venice. On being told that St. Matthew the apostle was buried in Rome he recalled that he had seen shrines of St. Matthew in Padua and in Lombardy 'and they tell me that his head is at Trier in Germany, so I will leave it to God to resolve the confusions of these priests.' 'On the right hand side of the altar I was told that there lies St. Jerome, but was he not buried in Bethlehem and subsequently carried off to Constantinople? How he came to be in Rome as well, I shall leave to the learned to decide.' It was no more than Guibert de Nogent had said four centuries before, but the growing popularity of travel was bringing these disconcerting truths to a wider audience.

Women

The circle of Latin pilgrims which grew up around St. Jerome at the close of the fourth century was dominated by women. The most celebrated pilgrims of the late classical period, Paula, Etheria, Melania, were all women. Even in the 'dark ages' of the west, female pilgrims were a familiar sight on the roads. Their sins and their illnesses are recorded by Gregory of Tours, their restless addiction to travel unequivocally condemned by St. Boniface. For most of the middle ages, however, women were not particularly noted as pilgrims. So much so that the sudden reappearance of large numbers of female pilgrims in the fourteenth and fifteenth centuries called for comment, usually hostile comment. Chaucer's wife of Bath became the epitome of the worldly, pleasure-seeking pilgrim. In the *Quinze Joies de Mariage*, it is the nagging wife, not her husband, who decides on a pilgrimage to Le Puy, where all rich and fashionable ladies go. Berthold of Regensburg and Giordano da Rivalta both devoted whole sermons to the virulent condemnation of female pilgrims. It is possible that at the close of the middle ages women formed the majority of visitors at many shrines. This was certainly true of several sanctuaries visited by Henry VIII's monastic commissioners in the course of their travels, notably of Bury St. Edmund's, where they reported that 'there was such frequence of women coming and resorting to this monastery as to no place more.'

The fickle tastes of women seem to have been partly responsible for the abrupt rise of obscure shrines which is such a marked characteristic of the cult of the saints in the late middle ages. At the end of the fourteenth century, the Cistercian abbey of Meaux in Yorkshire commissioned a sculptor to carve a large wooden crucifix for the church. Miracles were reported as soon as the crucifix was completed and local people began to make pilgrimages to it. 'It was thought', wrote abbot Thomas Burton, 'that if women were admitted to the abbey church the general atmosphere of devotion would be greatly increased, which would be most advantageous to our monastery. We therefore requested the abbot of Cîteaux for permission to admit honest men and women to the crucifix, which was granted on condition that the women did not enter the conventual buildings.' This was, in fact, a common problem at monastic sanctuaries. The monks of St.-Benoît-sur-Loire had solved it by erecting a marquee at the back of their church where much venerated relics could be seen by both sexes on Saturdays. Some important sanctuaries, however, adhered to the letter of the Benedictine rule and excluded female pilgrims altogether. In the first half of the twelfth century, Symeon of Durham boasted that no woman had ever been admitted to the sanctuary of St. Cuthbert and that when Judith, wife of earl Tostig, had tried to enter, she had been paralysed at the door. The same fate befell a chambermaid who tried to enter the sanctuary in the following of king David of Scotland, dressed as a monk.

A more practical objection to the presence of women was that it was usually members of the weaker sex who were trampled underfoot in the rush to venerate the relics of the church. Most of the casualties at St.-Denis in Suger's time were women, as they were at other public exhibitions of relics. A pregnant woman was crushed to death in the crowd that gathered to see the head of St. Martial in 1388. In many Roman churches the authorities excluded women for this very reason. This rule originated in the fourteenth century when women first appeared in Rome in large numbers. An anonymous Englishman who visited Rome in 1344 remarked that the women gathered round the shrines were the most devout he had ever seen. Nevertheless, they were not allowed to set foot in the chapel of St. John the Baptist in the Lateran basilica but were directed to gain the indulgence by touching the outside of the door. No women were allowed in the chapel of the Saviour, or even in the *Sancta Sanctorum*, where the most important relics were housed. Various explanations were advanced. Women, it was alleged, were inclined to vanity, hysteria, or vice. In one of the forbidden chapels of St. Peter's a rich lady was said to have demanded that a crucifix be washed after a poor woman had kissed it. According to another school of thought, a woman had 'once uttered such things that she burst asunder'. John Capgrave sagely remarked that the exclusion of women was attributed to 'many lewd causes to which I wil give no credens'. His own theory probably represents the truth of the matter. 'All those whech have be at Rome knowe wel that the women there be passing desirous to goo on pilgrimage and to touch and kiss every holy relik. Now in very soothfastness these places which are forbode to them are rit smale. . . . And uphap some woman in the press, eithir for sikness or with child, be in grete perel there, and for this cause they were forbode the entre of these houses as I suppose.'

Noblemen

The Roman Jubilee of 1450 was remarkable not only for the numbers who attended but for their high social standing. They included the archbishop of Mainz with a suite of 140 knights, as well as the duke of Austria, the margravine of Baden, and the landgrave of Hesse. John, duke of Cleves, was seen passing on foot from church to church. Jacques de Lalaing led a large party of Burgundian noblemen to Rome, celebrating his departure from Châlons with a 'joyeux et plaisant banquet'. The same phenomenon was observed in 1475, when the Mantuan ambassador informed his master of the arrival of thousands of courtiers from every western kingdom, come to atone for their notoriously scandalous lives. Two periods stand out as being pre-eminently those of the noble pilgrim. The first came to an end at the close of the twelfth century, when the established shrines of Europe began to lose their hold on educated minds. Apathy and war combined to destroy shrines like Vézelay and St.-Gilles, while others, like Canterbury and Conques, were abandoned by their more distinguished clientèle. The great spiritual revival which marked the hundred and fifty years before the Reformation brought new life to a few of these ancient sanctuaries and threw up a large number of obscure new pilgrimages. The greater shrines, like Le Puy, became fashionable resorts; otherwise the intensely fashion-conscious wife satirized in the *Quinze Joies de Mariage* would never have wanted to go there. At Le Puy then, and at other major sanctuaries, the nobility were once more to be found in large numbers. Although the cult of the Virgin was primarily a popular one, the kings of England were assiduous pilgrims at Walsingham, just as those of Aragon and Castile were at Montserrat. Philip the Good, duke of Burgundy, visited Notre-Dame de Boulogne on at least a dozen occasions. Louis XI of France, who was well-known for his intense, rather simple-minded piety, made pilgrimages to Mont-St.-Michel, Notre-Dame de Cléry, Puy Notre-Dame in Anjou, and Le Puy, amongst other sanctuaries. He was constantly attributing to the intervention of the Virgin his salvation from every kind of mishap, and at his death in 1483 he was buried beside the shrine of Notre-Dame de Cléry, to whom he had so often attributed his victories in battle.

The motives of noble pilgrims of the fifteenth century were less straightforward than those of the twelfth. Worldly motives were certainly prominent and some pilgrimages were accomplished with a degree of ostentation which would have surprised churchmen of an earlier age. Nevertheless, they paid lip-service to traditional ideals, and often more than lip-service. Nompar de Caumont, who departed for the Holy Land in 1418 with several servants and equerries, shared the obsession of his more spiritual contemporaries with death and remission. 'Know then that death has no mercy on kings, princes, or lords, but takes them all with equal abandon', he wrote, in a passage that might have been a commentary on the *danses macabres* that now decorated the walls of so many churches and cemeteries; 'every man must know that the world is but a temporary habitation, and that death, harsh and unpitying, is imminent.' Some noble pilgrims cast off their status and travelled without attendants or fine clothes. Hence the curious complaint of the Venetian senate in 1437 that noblemen were bringing the pilgrim fleets into disrepute by travelling dressed as commoners and complaining when they were treated as such. 'Everyone knows', they declared, 'about the abominable way in which princes, counts, and foreign noblemen travel to the Holy Sepulchre disguised as common pilgrims.' There may have been more in this 'abominable' practice than Christian humility. When Gréffin Affagart advised his readers to dress as poor hermits on their travels, he added that this would save them from being preyed upon by shipowners, robbers, pirates, and Turks. Indeed, the stately fashion in which most noble pilgrims travelled is often revealed to history by their complaints that they had been robbed of their treasures. Earl Rivers, brother-in-law of Edward IV, complained to the pope in 1475 that he had been ambushed outside Bracciano on his way to attend the Roman Jubilee, and robbed of a large quantity of precious gems, gold trinkets, silver goblets, cash, 'and other things of very great value'.

The Venetian republic occasionally arranged luxurious passages to the Holy Land, either in return for money or else, as in the case of the earl of Derby in 1392, in return for 'the favours which might be granted to Venetian merchants trading or resident in England'. The earl's accounts of the expenses of his voyage include the hire of a warehouse in Venice to store supplies. His agents, accompanied by interpreters, visited fairs in nearby towns, and bought several whole oxen, 2,250 eggs, 2,000 dates, 1,000 pounds of almonds, several dozen butts of sweet wine, and large quantities of mattress stuffing, live hens, water, cheese, oil, fish, vegetables and spices. The total sum thus expended was 2,379 ducats, or nearly forty times the all-inclusive fare usually demanded by shipowners. In addition, the earl and his company enjoyed the bounty of the Serenissima, which instructed its agents not to disclose the cost to the earl himself, but to hint at it delicately in the presence of the English ambassador. The earl's needs were not untypical. Indeed they were modest by comparison with those of some aristocratic pilgrims. The ship which carried Pietro Casola to the Holy Land in 1494 was joined at Corfù by a nephew of Ferdinand of Aragon, a young clergyman destined for a rich benefice who was going, by way of preparation, to take the Franciscan habit on Mount Sion. His baggage, which included several horses and falcons, was carried in a separate cargo boat sailing alongside the ship.

In the last years of the fifteenth century German and Italian princes were renowned for the unmatched ostentation which surrounded their pilgrimages. Ernest, duke of Saxony, arrived in Rome in 1480 to fulfil a vow of pilgrimage with a suite of two hundred mounted retainers dressed in black livery, their horses in jewelled halters. The papal camera recorded the expenditure of a hundred gold florins on entertaining him. Otto, duke of Brunswick, was accompanied to Rome in 1489 by physicians, apothecaries, courtiers, and twenty-seven personal servants. Perhaps such splendid expeditions should not be regarded as pilgrimages at all, though those who participated in them vigorously asserted that they were. Ernest of Saxony's pilgrimage may have been prompted by the

desire to extend his political influence in Germany by securing the
election of his relatives to important bishoprics, an object in which
he succeeded handsomely. But no such considerations will explain
the magnificent progress of Niccolo d'Este to the Holy Land in
1413. Apart from an official historiographer, his suite included
several dozen orderlies, four chamberlains, a chef, a sub-chef, a
tailor, a barber, a page, a chaplain, and two trumpeters.

The interest of the nobility in the Holy Land was in a large
measure due to the practice of dubbing knights in the Holy
Sepulchre. This was a survival of the ideology of the crusades after
the shattering disaster which had overcome the last crusading
expedition at Nicopolis in 1396. The dubbings were originally conducted under the auspices of the Order of St. John of the Hospital,
which now had its headquarters at Rhodes. Nompar de Caumont
stopped at Rhodes on his way to the Holy Land and persuaded a
Navarrese knight of the order to accompany him to Jerusalem, and
to dub him a knight of St. John in the Holy Sepulchre itself. This is
the first trace of a practice which was to enjoy a considerable popularity in the fifteenth century. By 1480, newly dubbed knights are
found calling at Rhodes on their way back from the Holy Land,
enrolling their names in a book kept by the king of Cyprus, and
receiving a certificate in return. It was only by degrees that the
practice of dubbing knights in the Holy Sepulchre acquired a status
quite independent of the Order of St. John. Thus dubbings were not
only performed by Hospitallers. Niccolo d'Este knighted several of
his courtiers on his expensive expedition of 1413. Guillaume de
Chalons was knighted by one of his companions in 1451. Alterna-
tively, the senior pilgrim present might be asked to perform the
ceremony. The reason for its popularity lies in the prevailing view
that the institution of knighthood had been devalued in an age when
Louis XI, for example, could permit rich bourgeois to buy knight-
hoods, and indeed compel them to do so. Some hint of this was given
by Guillaume de Chalons when he remarked to his companion that
he was proposing to be knighted in the Holy Sepulchre because he
'did not wish to be a cardboard knight, but a true knight'. Much the
same sentiments were expressed by the father of George van Ehingen, who sent him to the Holy Land because it was 'not his wish that
I should pass my time in unwarlike idleness at some princely court
. . . or else in taverns'. Indeed, as Felix Faber remarked in his lengthy
panegyric of the 'order of the Holy Sepulchre', it was the only order
of knighthood universally recognized in an age when bogus orders
sprang up in every province. But it seems that the order was
already passing the way of its predecessors, for Faber hints that
'nowadays base-born men are occasionally admitted.'

CHAPTER XV

THE LATER MIDDLE AGES 2

'Base-born Men'

The Climate of Opinion

The mobs who converged on Limoges in 1388 to witness the display of St. Martial's relics were not alone in regarding the papal schism as God's punishment on human wickedness. Contemporary opinion, reflected in the impassioned protests of St. Catherine of Siena, saw in it the culmination of an era of appalling spiritual decay. Some reaction to the sterility of the fourteenth century was perhaps to be expected in the fifteenth, and the flagellant processions of 1399 were early symptoms of it. In the same year St. Vincent Ferrer left Avignon to begin a preaching-tour of southern France, the first of a spectacular series of nomadic missions conducted by the two mendicant orders. What Vincent Ferrer did for France, Manfred of Vercelli and Bernardino of Siena did for Italy, their pupils for Germany and Spain. The immediate effects were certainly impressive. In Rome, which, more than any other city, had felt the impact of the schism, the arrival of Bernardino in June 1424 was marked by a great bonfire of playing-cards, lottery tickets, musical instruments, wigs, 'and such-like effeminate vanities'. In March 1411 the magistrates of Orihuela in Murcia reported to the bishop the moral transformation of their town:

> 'All those who are heard blaspheming are visited with swift punishment. The gambling hall has been closed down. Conspiracies and secret societies have been abandoned, and diviners and sorcerers have gone out of business. We have never seen so many people going to confession, and churches which used to be too large are now too small. The citizens, overcome by a common feeling of goodwill and a strong love of God, have forgiven each other their trespasses.'

No generation should be judged by its moments of enthusiasm, the contemporaries of St. Bernardino least of all. Christianity remained in their eyes a ritual framework of life, rather than a body of coherent beliefs and commanding ideals. Like the great merchant of Prato, Francesco Datini, they recited prayers at fixed hours, uttered pious formulae when they were appropriate, gave alms when it was expected of them, and marked the passing stages of their lives by receiving the sacraments of the Church. But the over-powering conventionality of religious life was punctuated by brief outbursts of hysteria which, although by no means new, were highly characteristic of the century which preceded the Reformation. Even the sober Datini, who spoke of the Roman Jubilee only as a source of profit, joined the flagellant processions of 1399. It was typical both of the man and his age that he should have given as his reason the fact that 'all men, or at least the greater number of Christians, were moved to go on pilgrimage in that year.'

By halting, irresolute steps, Christendom entered upon a period of spiritual revival. The revival accentuated some of the traditional characteristics of lay piety, and created new ones of its own. The literal, pictorial interpretation of dogma is taken to new extremes; this is above all others the century of religious drama and eucharistic miracles. The strong desire of laymen to feel that they were part of an 'order' charged with special spiritual functions, finds expression in their enthusiasm for confraternities, lay brotherhoods whose activities ranged from running hospitals to flagellation. The con-fraternities are also the symptom of something new: the special importance attached to the performance of spiritual exercises *en masse*. The public procession is the typical spiritual observance of the late middle ages. Flagellant processions first appear in Perugia in 1260 and their most hysterical pitch is reached in the towns of northern Italy and the Low Countries at the end of the fourteenth century. Mass-pilgrimages are made to hitherto obscure shrines. The religion of the laity was above all a religion of external observances, marked by a strong element of ritual. Men joined confraternities because in doing so they automatically acquired a measure of merit which brought them closer to salvation; their own, personal spiritual needs had very little to do with it. It was an attitude which bred extreme conformity and a somewhat unhealthy view that the clothes make the man. Wearing a pilgrim's badge or the emblem of a confraternity became pious works in themselves. Hence the curious remark of Christine de Pisan that priests could not possibly be possessed by devils because they knew the formulae which chased them away. An earlier age would have felt that possession by devils had more to do with the spiritual condition of the victim.

Amongst external observances, pilgrimage remained by far the most important, but the shrines which pilgrims visited changed. Some of the traditional saints, St. Thomas of Canterbury for example, still drew crowds on their feast day or in Jubilee years, but there was no continuous cult as there had been in the twelfth century. The loyalty of the masses was transferred to an enormous number of minor shrines which commanded attention for a few weeks before relapsing into obscurity and being replaced by others. Fifteenth-century pilgrims were creatures of passing fads; they rarely needed to travel far to their destinations. 'You tell me that your new saints have displaced the old ones', Sacchetti had once protested; 'what business have you to enshrine their relics and light candles in their honour, when images of the Blessed Virgin and Christ himself lie forgotten in darkened corners?'

The 'new saints' of the late middle ages were often humble men who were acclaimed as saints by local people. Their cult was rarely recognized by the Church and did not generally extend beyond the immediate locality. Many of them were working class, like the multitude of peasant-saints venerated in parts of France. St. Zita of Lucca was one of the more celebrated examples. She was a serving maid who died in 1272 and became the object of a cult which continued for several centuries. Despite the popular origins of the cult, cardinals, archbishops, and secular magnates are known to have visited her tomb, and chapels were dedicated to her in many parts of Europe. But she was not canonized until 1696. The death of Henry of Bolzano, a labourer of Treviso, in 1315 was followed by a prolonged outburst of popular enthusiasm. Three notaries were appointed to record the miracles which occurred at his tomb in Treviso cathedral, and in 1381 his relics were even displayed in public on his feast day. He was never canonized.

Parish priests of great saintliness were frequently the objects of these spontaneous and unauthorized cults. Margery Kempe used to weep at the grave of the vicar of St. Stephen's, Norwich, 'the good vicar, for whom God showed high mercy to his people'. In 1361 John de Grandison, bishop of Exeter heard ('not without amazement and irritation, I assure you'), that Richard Boyle, parish priest of Whitestone, who had recently committed suicide, was being revered as a saint by his parishioners. Ordinary folk from the area were making pilgrimages to his tomb, and twelve miraculous cures had been reported. The veneration of parish priests was not always opposed by the authorities. In 1260 the bishop of Coutances built a magnificent chapel over the grave of Thomas Hélye, parish priest of Biville, who had died three years earlier. Although Hélye was never canonized, the shrine was visited by pilgrims until the nineteenth century. A similar fate befell John Schorne, parish priest of North Marston in Buckinghamshire, who died in 1314. His shrine, and a well which he had blessed, were visited throughout the fourteenth and fifteenth centuries, and were believed to cure ague. His cult, like that of Thomas Hélye, was never authorized by the Church, but it was so well established in 1478 that his remains were translated to the Lincoln chapel in St. George's, Windsor.

More common still was the veneration of miraculous statues. Most were statues of the Virgin, of the sort whose origins were pungently described by the Lollard author of the *Lanterne of Light*.

'The painter maketh a live image forged with divers colours, till it seem in fools' eyes as a lively creature. This is set in the church in a solemn place, fast bounden with bonds for it should not fall. Priests of the temple beguile the people with the foul sin of Balaam in their open preaching. They say that God's power in working of his miracles loweth down in one image more than in another and therefore come and offer to this, for here is showed much virtue.'

It was just such a statue which had drawn troops of women to the abbey of Meaux in the early fourteenth century, thus causing so much trouble to the monks. The artist, we are told, spent several months carving it and used a nude model. The spoils of the dissolution of the English monasteries included several much-venerated statues like the rood of Boxley which rolled its eyes, shed tears, and foamed at the mouth, and the Kent statue burned at Smithfield in 1538 which bowed to receive the prayers of pilgrims. The attitude of the authorities was highly equivocal. The abbot of Meaux was delighted by the arrival of pilgrims until he found that they were more trouble than they were worth. Bishops generally turned a blind eye to unauthorized images, and earnestly defended them against Lollards. Archbishop Warham assured Wolsey that Boxley was 'so holy a place where so many miracles are showed'. The inaction of the bishops was really a reflection of their impotence, for a popular cult could survive any number of anathemas. In 1386 bishop John Buckingham of Lincoln ordered an enquiry into rumours he had heard of certain doings in Rippingdale. 'Many of our subjects have made for themselves a certain pretended statue, vulgarly known as Jordan Cros, in the fields of Rippingdale. They have begun to adore it, and allege that miracles are occurring there. They preach, ring bells, and hold processions for the deception of the people and for their own gain. Indeed, laymen are said to be embezzling the offerings for their own use.' But the bishop's letter was not the end of the matter for, in 1392, the parishioners succeeded in getting the pope's permission to build a chapel over the statue and to worship there with or without the bishop's consent. The reason given was 'the great number of miracles wrought there, and the multitudes who arrive with offerings from all over England.'

The discomfort of the Church in the face of unauthorized popular shrines was the symptom of a deeper malaise. Ever since the thirteenth century there had been a tendency on the part of many educated churchmen to withdraw from the more popular forms of piety. The outspoken views of non-conformists like St. Bernard gradually became the orthodoxy of a generation of scholastics and canon lawyers which had little else in common with the great abbot of Clairvaux. The change of heart coincided with the climax of that long process of spiritual centralization which had begun with the papacy's claim to a monopoly in the canonization of saints. A substantial and influential body of churchmen began to look with profound suspicion on extreme symptoms of popular devotion. This they did partly because they felt, as Guibert of Nogent had done, that popular religion was vitiated by superstition and ignorance; and partly because they disliked spiritual exercises which by-passed the sacramental function of the Church and offended its claims to spiritual authority. Their attitude was crystallized in the prolonged crisis in the Franciscan order in the thirteenth and fourteenth centuries. The tendencies within the order to depart from the spirit of St. Francis' *Testament*, with its strict prohibition of the possession of property, were officially encouraged. The minority of Franciscans who wished to abide by it were deliberately prevented from doing so, while the *fraticelli* who asserted the doctrine that Christ had lived in absolute poverty and that the order should do likewise, were persecuted as heretics. In so far as the late mediaeval Church had a 'policy' towards popular religion, it was summed up in a marked distaste for 'enthusiasm' when it occurred outside the framework of ecclesiastical institutions. The origin of this 'policy' should perhaps be sought in the bull *Quo Elongati* of 1230, in which Gregory IX declared the *Testament* of St. Francis to be invalid.

The 'policy' was, of course, neither formally proclaimed nor consistently followed. The encyclopaedic works of Jean Gerson, chancellor of the University of Paris (d. 1429), are full of contradictions and conflicts between the thinker who felt that popular superstitions were theologically unsound, and the indulgent pastor who took the traditional line that they were better than nothing. Gerson was completely opposed to the practice of mass-flagellation, and the Church's opinions on this subject are a microcosm of its attitude to popular religion in general. Flagellation became a common spiritual practice in the western Church in the tenth and eleventh centuries. Peter Damian gave it an elaborate theological justification, arguing that it was the supreme manifestation of humility and love of God, a perfect imitation of the sufferings of Christ himself. Flagellation was still practised in private in the late middle ages, particularly by the Carthusians. In the thirteenth century, however, the Church was first confronted with flagellation practised, not privately by individual ascetics, but by thousands of laymen in the main squares of Italian cities. That which had been acceptable as an act of personal piety, was condemned when it became an expression of hysterical enthusiasm. The change of heart is epitomized in the behaviour of Clement VI, who himself instituted flagellant processions in Avignon in 1349, in the hope of warding off the Black Death. But the arrival of an unofficial band of wandering flagellants in the city began to sow doubts in his mind, doubts which were reinforced by the arguments of a deputation of masters of the University of Paris. The deputation dwelt on the popular nature of the flagellant movement. Not only were the flagellants uneducated laymen, *indocti, ignari, rudes*, but they were a sect, purporting to offer an independent route to salvation, flouting the spiritual authority of the Church. In October 1349 Clement declared the flagellants to be heretics, and ordered the suppression of their processions throughout Europe.

The mood of critical suspicion was not confined to mass movements. Visions and revelations, which had played so important a part in the spiritual life of an earlier age, were now subjected to increasingly hostile scrutiny. Those of St. Bridget of Sweden were critically examined for heretical leanings by a commission of the council of Constance. In England, the visions of Margery Kempe brought upon her accusations of Lollardy. She was three times arrested after experiencing trances in public, and although her beliefs were found to be orthodox, the distaste of the clergy for her particular brand of enthusiasm was not one whit abated. 'We know well that she knows the articles of the faith', the canons of York minster stated, 'but we will not suffer her to dwell amongst us, for the people hath great faith in her dalliance, and peradventure she might pervert some of them.'

The harshest strictures were reserved for the cult of the saints, and the miracles associated with them. As well as inveighing against clerical avarice in terms not unlike those used by St. Bernard, John Wyclif condemned the cult of saints as such. He denied that miracles were the proof of holiness, or that canonizations were a good guide to sanctity. He abhorred the multitude of festivals. 'Some men trowen truly that all such saints profit not men unless they make them love Christ. So if men would better love Christ without such feasts, it were better for them to do without such saints.' Wyclif's Lollard admirers were almost unanimous in their objections to pilgrimage. The cult of St. Thomas of Canterbury was the object of particularly venomous criticism. Several Lollards had occasion at their trials to inveigh against Becket himself, and one of them told the bishop of Norwich that the martyr was a false traitor and a cowardly knave who had been killed at the cathedral door while attempting to flee, and was even then suffering in Hell. Pamphlets against the cult of St. Thomas were still being written in the sixteenth century, when the pilgrimage to Canterbury was ridiculously unimportant.

Wyclif's views, important as they are as a foretaste of things to come, are less interesting than the opinions of churchmen who accepted the structure of the late mediaeval Church. The council of Constance unequivocally condemned the opinion of John Wyclif, but many of the most prominent reformers at Constance themselves believed that the cult of the saints ought to be restricted. The canonization of St. Bridget in 1391 provoked some sharp criticism, not only because her revelations were suspect, but because it was felt that there were too many saints and that their veneration occupied too important a place in the religious life of the age. Henry of Langenstein asked 'whether it were right to canonize her, given the great multitude of saints already venerated. Is it seemly to proclaim new saints to be celebrated with greater solemnity than the apostles themselves?' Nor was Henry's an isolated voice. Jean Gerson repeated his words with approval. Pierre d'Ailly laid before the council a programme of reforms which included the demands 'that images and pictures in churches be not permitted to multiply so, that new shrines be forbidden, and that so many new saints be not canonized.' In the sermons of Nicholas of Clamanges, these sentiments became part of a general assault on all external observances. 'It is vain to preach to the outer man', he urged, 'if Christ does not resound within him.'

On miracles, the views of the heretical Wyclif can scarcely be distinguished from those of the orthodox Gerson. The Carthusians, Gerson pointed out, were renowned for their sanctity but they performed no miracles. Indeed, miracles were generally reported only at shrines where the sanctity of the person venerated was in doubt. No one doubted the sanctity of St. Jerome or Gregory the Great, and no miracles were attributed to them. However, none of these sentiments had the slightest effect on popular practice. Both before and after the council of Constance, conscientious prelates laboured in vain to prevent ordinary people from proclaiming miracles. The problems of Oliver Sutton, bishop of Lincoln (1280–99), are altogether typical of those of a late mediaeval bishop of a large diocese. In April 1296 he closed down the private chapel of Edmund, earl of Cornwall, at Hambledon. It had only recently been constructed, it was not officially consecrated, and now it was the scene of 'various superstitious practices and vain inventions, . . . rash assertions of miracles not authorized by the Church'. Two years later bishop Sutton had to deal with more unproven miracles and an eager throng of pilgrims at Great Crawley. Problems constantly arose in connection with holy trees, magic wells, and the like. The bishop has heard that the vicar of Linslade is encouraging the cult of a well in his parish by spreading stories of miraculous cures; the usual prohibitions follow. Bishop Grandison of Exeter, another reforming prelate, did not mince his words on such occasions. 'I find these miracles hard to believe and impossible to prove', he wrote in 1340; 'I fear that the people have given themselves over to idolatry and strayed from the path of the true catholic faith, . . . deluded by insane and untrue visions, inspired by the Devil and his agents, and deceived by false superstitions. It is our experience that they are frequently led on by cupidity as well.' His commissory was to visit the offending villages and stamp out the cults, if need be with excommunication and anathema.

Nicholas of Clamanges was satisfied that no age had witnessed so few miracles as his own, and that saints, like Peter and Paul, who used to corruscate in wonders, no longer did so. But he was speaking of 'genuine' miracles, i.e. those recognized by the Church. They had indeed dwindled almost to nothing, but the unrecognized sort were probably commoner in the fifteenth century than ever before. The attempt to reform popular religion was a failure. Its true effect, as John of Trittenheim pointed out in 1513, was merely to widen the gulf between the minority of highly educated clergy and most ordinary Christians. John himself believed strongly in miracles, and held that more men had been saved by reading about them than by listening to a thousand philosophical discourses. He hated the learned of his own day for separating themselves from the people, and accused them of turning instead to mysticism, writing poetry, and sexual indulgence. Only the simple and the poor still believed in miracles, and practised the traditional religion of the Church.

It was an exaggeration, as the author's own career amply demonstrated. But fundamentally John of Trittenheim's diagnosis was correct. The Church in the fifteenth century was a very much more rigid institution than it had been in the twelfth. It was no longer capable of absorbing overpowering spiritual movements, and those movements therefore occurred outside the framework of the Church. As a cause of the Reformation, this was a fact of greater importance than the abuses which are often supposed to have discredited the late mediaeval Church.

The Cult of the Virgin

The story of Theophilus is amongst the most attractive and expressive mediaeval legends. Theophilus was the steward of a bishop in Cilicia, and he was anxious to succeed his master on the episcopal throne. With the assistance of a Jewish sorcerer, he arranged to sell his soul to the Devil. The contract was drawn up and signed by both parties in the presence of witnesses, and from that moment Theophilus succeeded in all that he attempted. But his enjoyment was marred by pangs of remorse, and he began to think of ways in which he could rescind the contract. After he had passed several nights in prayer, the Blessed Virgin dramatically intervened, wresting the parchment from the hands of Satan and restoring it to Theophilus. It is, of course, the ancestor of the Faust legend. Like many legends of the Virgin, the origins of this story are Greek and it does not appear in the Latin Church until the ninth century. Nevertheless, if the number of editions, translations, and surviving manuscripts is any guide it was by far the most popular legend of the Virgin known to the middle ages. The reason for its extraordinary appeal is not far to seek. The story of Theophilus's compact with the Devil accorded exactly with current notions about the personality and power of evil. At the same time it offered, in the veneration of the Virgin, a guarantee of protection from evil. This was the function of the Virgin in the religious literature of the middle ages. She intervened to save those whom justice, human or divine, had condemned. She offered an escape from the rigorous teaching of the Church on the subject of damnation and punishment. Thus it was that already in the late eleventh century, the office of the Virgin sung in churches hailed her as the 'mother of mercy, who took pity on Theophilus and saved him from the trough of sin and misery':

> Tu mater es misericordiae
> De lacu faecis et miseriae
> Theophilum reformans gratiae.

The early collections of miracles of the Virgin, dating from the twelfth century, are so many variations on the same theme. A knight of ill-repute was saved on account of his devotion to the Virgin. A monk who used to slip out of his monastery at night was saved because he never passed an altar of the Virgin without saying 'Ave Maria'. A loose-living nun found that her pregnancy was miraculously concealed from her superiors. Another nun, who died unconfessed, was saved because of her daily invocations of the Virgin. A monk learned in his sleep that he was already inscribed in the book of the elect because of the care with which he had painted the

Virgin's name in an illuminated manuscript. 'By her intercession', Caesarius of Heisterbach told his novice, 'sinners are enlightened, the despairing are brought to confession, the apostate is reconciled, and the righteous comforted with revelations.' The salvation of those who deserved to be damned is the theme of all Caesarius's stories. 'Wonderful indeed is the compassion of Our Lady', says the novice after hearing of the salvation of an unworthy priest, rightly deprived of his benefice; 'for thus she defends a feeble-minded priest who ought to have been deprived, and by her intervention he was able to keep his benefice.'

The theme was capable of being simplified to the point of distorting the moral precepts of the Church. Jacques de Vitry illustrated his sermons on the power of the Virgin with the story of a gambler who was enabled to amass Croesian riches by regularly invoking her name. All pilgrimages appealed to a universal desire to wash away sin by a simple, ritual act, but none more so than pilgrimages to the Virgin. The popular view was reflected in the dying words of John, abbot of Belleville, to his attendants: 'Only one thing do you need to know from me; he who would be saved need only honour the Virgin.' This simple idea is very far from the profoundly spiritual concept of the Virgin's role entertained by St. Bernard. Its appeal was to a more popular audience. The early Marial shrines were almost exclusively patronized by ordinary people and, although they were joined in the late middle ages by more august pilgrims, the shrines never lost their popular character.

Outside the village of Essones, near Corbeil, there stood a ruined chapel dedicated to the Virgin. In the 1120s the villagers believed that they had seen mysterious candles burning there on Saturday nights. Subsequently, several peasants were miraculously cured of various ailments, and the fame of the miracles began to draw pilgrims from further afield. The abbey of St.-Denis, which owned the chapel, learned of these happenings and sent a group of monks to serve there. The incident, which is related by abbot Suger, is typical of the popular, and more or less spontaneous, origins of many Marial pilgrimages. Indeed the earliest of the hysterical mass-pilgrimages which are so characteristic of the fifteenth century occurred in connection with Marial sanctuaries of the twelfth. Chartres, Soissons, Beauvais, and Paris all received processions of peasants afflicted with ergotism during the severe epidemics of the early twelfth century. More remarkable still were the 'building crusades' which began in 1145, when thousands of Norman pilgrims arrived at the shrine of Notre-Dame de Chartres, intending to assist in the building of the western towers of the cathedral. For some months men and women volunteered to haul heavy wagons of

stone up the steep slope on which Chartres is built, flagellating themselves as they did so, and singing hymns in honour of the Virgin.
The crowds who pulled carts of building materials to the abbey of
St.-Pierre-sur-Dives regarded it as a form of homage to the Virgin.
As the building continued, services in her honour were continually
held in the abbey, while in the yards outside the volunteers held
services of their own, modelled on those in use at Chartres. As at
Chartres, flagellation was an important part of the ritual. The
phenomenon was repeated when Chartres cathedral was rebuilt
after the disastrous fire of 1194. The 'entire population' of Pithiviers,
in the Loire valley, made a collective pilgrimage to Chartres,
dragging a wagon of corn as an offering. More corn came from the
villages of Batilly, Chateau-Landon, and Bonneval. Some Breton
villages dragged building stone over rough roads for two hundred
miles to assist the rebuilding of the Virgin's cathedral.

'Building crusades' reflected the view that pilgrimages performed
en masse were more meritorious than those performed alone. We
find the pilgrim-builders forming themselves into sects, or 'brotherhoods', performing their penitential rituals in common, and solemnly expelling those members who showed signs of returning to their
old ways. The same thought lies behind the processional pilgrimages
of whole villages to a Marial shrine. The parish priest of Issigny, in
the Bessin, was so impressed by the processions in honour of the
Virgin at Bayeux that he organized a collective pilgrimage to
Coutances from his own parish, in which the entire population,
with one exception, took part. Coutances, he explained to his congregation, was 'the dwelling of the Holy Ghost and the scene of
many miracles. Their pilgrimage would therefore be the more
acceptable to the Blessed Virgin if they accomplished it together, by
a common vow.' The one parishioner who refused to go was struck
down for his presumption.

After the end of the eleventh century, some Marial sanctuaries
had relics of the Virgin. But the cult of the Virgin remained relatively independent of relics. They were certainly not considered
essential, as they would have been in any other cult. Their place
was taken by statues which eventually received the same veneration
as relics, and worked miracles. Coutances cathedral had a miracle-
working statue of the Virgin in wood, in addition to its relics of the
Virgin's body. Chartres cathedral possessed the tunic of the Virgin,
but it also had a celebrated statue in the crypt which, by the beginning of the fifteenth century, entirely monopolized the attention of
pilgrims. These statues were always painted, sometimes in bright
colours, like the four figures of the Virgin in the extraordinary
vision of the monk of Eynsham, recorded in 1196. But the most

famous of all, including the one at Chartres, were painted black. The black Virgin of Rocamadour is first mentioned in 1235, when it was trodden underfoot by an armed band of the abbey's enemies. The black Virgin of Le Puy was brought back from Palestine in 1254 by Louis IX and immediately made the fortune of the city. Special indulgences were offered on the first feast-day, in May 1255, and several hundred were killed in the crush under the very eyes of the king. In the fourteenth century the floodgates were opened, and miraculous statues appeared in thousands of obscure churches. England and the Low Countries were particularly affected. Some achieved more than local fame, and in 1356, archbishop Fitzralph pointed out in a sermon 'a certain danger from the veneration of images, which some frequently and wrongfully call by the name of those they are intended to represent, such as St. Mary of Lincoln, St. Mary of Walsingham, St. Mary of Leicester, and so forth.' Particularly reprehensible were 'the oblations which are offered to such images on account of the false and fabricated miracles wrought by their intercession.'

Any event which abruptly drew attention to a statue might be the beginning of a cult. In the Flemish village of Beveren the parish priest had only to build a small oratory in 1330, and to light a lamp in front of a statue of the Virgin, and pilgrims began to arrive immediately. Miracles were recorded within weeks and episcopal indulgences followed. An old and faded statue at Antwerp was venerated as soon as it was repaired, repainted in bright colours, and removed to Brussels. Sometimes, as at Beveren, the parish priest deliberately provoked the cult; sometimes he was taken aback by the sudden rush of pilgrims to venerate a new statue. The vicar of Kernetby reported to his superiors in 1310 that 'there have suddenly and unexpectedly arisen new offerings in the said church, in honour of God and the most glorious Virgin Mary, at a certain *new* image of the said Virgin there.' Three years later, it was eclipsed by another miraculous statue in nearby Foston. There archbishop Greenfield had to put an end to the 'great concourse of simple people who come to visit a certain image of the holy Virgin, *newly placed* in the church.' The mere appearance of a roadside statue was often enough to draw pilgrims. In an alcove in the wall of the Franciscan convent at Trier, there was a small statue of the Virgin which was alleged to have wept tears. For four months the street was impassable for the crowds, until the enthusiasm died away. A street statue in Heilbronn, which was believed to have spoken, had a longer life. The pilgrimage began in 1442 and was still prosperous sixty years later.

All these obscure cults had in common the suddenness of their origins. Elaborate justificatory legends were composed afterwards to clothe them with a spurious antiquity. The great pilgrimage to Notre-Dame de Boulogne began abruptly in 1211, but the absurd legend placing its origins in the seventh century only became current about two hundred years later. Similarly the legend of the Virgin's miraculous intervention at the battle of Rozebeke (1382) grew up many years after the first pilgrims had visited the oratory on the site. The legend and miracles of Notre-Dame de l'Epine in Champagne, date from the seventeenth century.

Aachen, Walsingham, and Boulogne long retained their place among the great sanctuaries of Europe, but most Marial pilgrimages were short-lived. They sprang up without warning, burned bright for a while, and then quite suddenly ended. Many of them left no literary or architectural monument to their existence. At the beginning of the sixteenth century John of Trittenheim recorded a few that had sprung up in the previous century in the diocese of Wurzburg, none of which would be known but for his strange rambling works. In the wine-growing town of Deitelbach a man was injured in a brawl and healed by a statue of the Virgin in the parish church. There had been many such miracles in the diocese in recent years and the authorities were hostile. The pilgrimage quickly ended. The parish church of Tynbach was the object of a great Marial pilgrimage for a few brief weeks. No one wrote down the miracles and now they were forgotten 'but the church, which was built from the offerings of the faithful, remains as a testimony to what happened there.' There had been great Marial pilgrimages in Wurzburg itself at one time, but now both miracles and pilgrims had ceased.

The crowds who crammed into these small oratories and parish churches contained no noblemen, no bishops or deacons. They consisted entirely, as John of Trittenheim admitted, of the 'simple people of Christ'. He attributed this, as we have seen, to the arrogance of the learned and the simple devotion of the poor. But his other explanation is probably closer to the truth. Peasants and artisans could not afford to go on distant pilgrimages and they were ashamed to beg, so they honoured the only saint whose shrine was always nearby. Thus it was that the *populus simplex et rusticanus* was devoted to the Virgin above all saints. In England, where educated opinion of the early sixteenth century turned sharply against pilgrimages, the sanctuaries of the Virgin were the only ones which did not share in the general decline. Our Lady of Walsingham, with £260 *per annum* on the eve of the dissolution, was the only church which still drew a substantial income from offerings. In the two days that the dissolution commissioners passed in the priory, nearly seven pounds was offered. St. Anne's Well at Buxton, the commissioners reported, was as much visited as ever on account of the 'fond trust that the people did put in these images'. As for the image of Our Lady of Cardigan, it was 'used for a great pilgrimage to this present day'.

Political Saints

Nowhere was the tendency of the populace towards the spontaneous veneration of heroes more pronounced than in the case of political saints. In an age which attached incalculable importance to miracles as an indication of God's will, it was perhaps to be expected that miracle-working would be harnessed to political causes. Writing to the bishop of Metz in March 1081, Gregory VII pointed to the miracles of the saints as an argument for the superiority of the spiritual over the temporal power. 'Where among all the emperors and kings can a man be found to compare with St. Martin, St. Anthony, or St. Benedict, not to speak of the apostles and martyrs? What emperor or king has raised the dead, cured the leprous, or opened the eyes of the blind?' Eighty-four years later, on Christmas Day 1165, the emperor Frederick Barbarossa answered Gregory's question by having Charlemagne 'canonized' at Aachen in the presence of the anti-pope Paschal III, thus giving formal recognition to a popular cult of long standing.

Political saints were found in every country, though more, perhaps, in England than anywhere else. There they included Edmund king and martyr, Elphege archbishop of Canterbury, Edward the Confessor, Thomas Becket, Simon de Montfort, Thomas of Lancaster, Edward III, Richard Scrope archbishop of York, and Henry VI. Some of these men lived lives of exceptional piety by the standards of their day. But with the exception of Edward the Confessor, they all died by violence, and it was almost certainly the circumstances of their deaths rather than the manner of their lives that earned them the veneration of the faithful. For the equation of violent death with martyrdom and sanctity there were many continental parallels. Canute II king of Denmark was murdered in 1086 and buried where he lay. His death was followed by several years of famine and epidemic, during which the dead king was frequently reported to have worked miracles and appeared in visions. In about 1100 the legates of king Eric persuaded the pope to declare him a saint.

After Becket, none of the English political saints was canonized, nor was their cult in any way sanctioned by the Church. Indeed in some cases, the cult is only known from the vigorous denunciations and prohibitions of the authorities. Whereas popular devotion sufficed to make a saint in the ninth century, or even in the twelfth, it was clearly inadequate by the fourteenth. In the cases of Thomas of Lancaster and Edward II the pope repeatedly refused even to appoint a commission of inquiry, although pressed to do so by powerful interests. The extent of the change can be measured by comparing two political saints separated by a gulf of seven centuries. St. Leger, bishop of Autun, was blinded and beheaded by his opponents in 679 after becoming involved in a civil war between two rival claimants to the throne. Yet this most political of saints was the object of a liturgical cult of continuing importance throughout the middle ages. In Guibert of Nogent's time he was renowned for curing fevers. The canonization of Becket in 1173 suggests that it was still possible for equally unattractive persons to achieve sanctity by a refined version of this process in the twelfth century. The story of Thomas of Lancaster shows that it was no longer possible in the fourteenth, even with the energetic support of the king.

In the civil wars of Edward II's reign, both sides were inclined to venerate their dead leaders as saints. Thomas, earl of Lancaster, was accounted a saint after his execution in March 1322. Pilgrims visited his tomb at Pontefract daily until the king's envoys, sent to investigate, placed an armed guard on it. Early in the following year, two of the guards were killed by a mob of politically motivated pilgrims from Kent, and in June, reports reached the king's ears that images of the earl were being venerated at St. Paul's in London. In 1327 the political situation changed. Most of Thomas's enemies met violent ends. In parliament the earl's cause triumphed, and the commons pressed for his canonization. Nothing came of it, but the popular cult continued unabated. In the fifteenth century a hagiographical life appeared. His hat and belt, preserved at Pontefract, cured minor ailments until the Reformation. Thomas's antagonist, Edward II, enjoyed a similar apotheosis after his defeat and murder. His body was carried to Gloucester abbey and enclosed in a superb alabaster tomb. The cult received official encouragement in the reign of Richard II, who was often threatened with the fate of his great grandfather and may have hoped to silence such threats by procuring Edward's canonization. Urban VI and Boniface IX were plied with bribes, and a list of Edward's miracles was despatched to Rome for their perusal. But no decision had been made by 1399, when Richard's own deposition and murder made the whole affair an irrelevance.

These pilgrimages, although political, were in no sense official. They arose spontaneously and largely amongst the common people. After the death of Simon de Montfort on the battlefield of Evesham, miracles were quick to manifest themselves and the pilgrims they drew were mostly poor men from areas such as London, which had supported de Montfort in his lifetime. Within a year of his death the Dictum of Kenilworth forbade anyone to venerate him as a saint or give any credence to 'these vain and fatuous miracles attributed to him by certain persons'. As for the cult of Edward II, the streets of Gloucester could scarcely contain the 'enormous concourse of plebs' come to see his shrine. Within six years the offerings had yielded enough to pay for the rebuilding of a transept of the abbey church. It is tempting to see in this a religious manifestation of those early murmurings of social discontent which made themselves heard in the late middle ages, but the evidence does not permit it. What it does reflect is the tendency of ignorant people to look for a golden age in the past, and a hero in any prominent figure who met a sudden and violent end.

Mass-Pilgrimages

The first pitched battle between the ecclesiastical authorities and a major, but unauthorized, popular pilgrimage ended in a complete defeat for the authorities. It occurred at Wilsnack, a small town near Wittenberg in Saxony. In August 1383 the parish church was burned to the ground. In the rubble, the parish priest alleged, three consecrated hosts had been found, unharmed, but marked with drops of blood. The news spread, and the ruins of the church became a great pilgrimage centre almost immediately. Within two years, a fine new oratory stood on the spot, and by the early years of the fifteenth century it was a sanctuary of international repute. Margery Kempe, who walked there in 1433, knew it as a place of 'great worship and reverence, and sought from many a country'.

At first, the authorities looked benevolently on the new pilgrimage. Urban VI granted it an indulgence in March 1384, and in the same month the archbishop of Magdeburg joined with his suffragans in commending it to the faithful on account of the 'manifest miracles already famous in every part of Germany, which Our Lord Jesus Christ has worked through the real presence of his body in the holy sacrament.' But in 1387 they were disturbed by the reports that large mobs of the poor, many of them hysterical, were gathering at Wilsnack, and within twenty years of the shrine's abrupt beginnings, the Church was withdrawing its favour. The first to act was the archbishop of Prague, who had received reports of fraudulent miracles from pilgrims of his diocese. In 1405 he appointed a commission to consider the matter. Its members included John Hus, who had not yet fallen foul of the Church in Prague. On the basis of their report, a synod meeting in Prague in June 1405 condemned the

pilgrimage and instructed the clergy of the diocese to preach against
it at least once a month. This was followed, a year later, by a vehement pamphlet *On the Blood of Christ*, the work of Hus himself. In
1412, the archbishop of Magdeburg in turn ordered an investigation,
from which he learned that the pilgrims were almost all 'plebeian
persons who cannot be trusted'; a hysterical atmosphere pervaded
the place, with pilgrims crying 'help my Holy Blood', and 'free me
Blood of Christ'; in so far as these pilgrims were venerating the
drops of blood as well as the host, the commissioners reported, they
were being led into heresy. These disturbing facts were presented to
a synod in the summer of that year, and the pilgrimage was sharply
condemned as the product of overripe imaginations and clerical
avarice. There matters rested for forty years. No active steps were
taken to suppress it, and in 1446 the local clergy successfully applied
for a papal indulgence. It was unwise of them thus to reopen old
wounds, for the then archbishop appointed another commission of
enquiry which reported in much the same terms as their predecessors of 1412. By the skilful handling of crowds, fraudulent miracles
were passing for real ones every day. An atmosphere of extreme
religious excitement was engendered by forceful preaching and by
lighting an enormous number of candles in the church. Several false
indulgences were on display in the church, and pilgrims were shown
a shelf-ful of fat volumes in which the miracles of the Holy Blood
were said to be recorded. The whole affair, concluded the commissioners, was an open invitation to heretics to deny the real presence
altogether. Support for these views came from a surprising quarter.
Several citizens of Wilsnack complained that the general suspension
of excommunications at pilgrimage centres had made the town a
haven of bandits and usurers. This weighty dossier was submitted to
a provincial synod which met in 1451 under the presidency of the
papal legate Nicholas of Cusa. In June the legate issued a new bull,
forbidding the display of blood-stained hosts and ordering the
sanctuary at Wilsnack to be closed.

How long the church of Wilsnack remained closed is not clear.
Probably the pilgrimage never altogether ceased, though it undoubtedly suffered a decline. But in 1475 the archbishop of Magdeburg was abruptly reminded of its existence by another mass-
pilgrimage, this time involving several thousand children aged
between eight and twenty. The children came from the regions of
Franconia, Meissen, and Hesse. They left without informing their
parents, and without money. The town of Erfurt alone lost 324
children as well as several dozen from each of the suburban villages.
Hettstadt lost 300, Eisleben 1,100. Another mass-pilgrimage of
children occurred in 1487, when 'an enormous concourse of boys,

girls, and household servants of both sexes, all of them peasants and people of lowest class, flocked to the blood of Wilsnack inspired, it is believed, by a sort of giddy feeling (*spiritu vertiginis*)'. Rumour estimated their number at about 10,000, though there were probably much fewer than that. Thereafter, children's pilgrimages occurred at regular intervals, despite vigorous attempts to frustrate them.

'And men knew not the meaning of such a prodigy', the Erfurt chronicler wrote. The children's pilgrimages provoked controversy in all the towns they passed through. 'Some said it was the Devil's work, others that it was a wonderful miracle and praised God for it.' The chronicler himself thought it resulted from an imbalance of the humours in their bodies, a view which many shared, including the author of a searing tract *On the Pilgrimage of Foolish People to the Holy Blood in the Year 1475*. 'There are many who cannot in their natures stay quiet', this writer explained; 'this is due to a defect in their humours and the influence of the stars, or else perhaps to some work of the Devil.' Noting that almost all the child-pilgrims were from poor homes, the writer suggested that the bad harvest of the previous year might have had something to do with it:

'for the days are very long and empty of things to do and many are driven to pilgrimage for lack of bread to eat. . . . Having no bread, and being too poor to stay with friends or neighbours, they were ashamed to go begging near their own homes. And so they decided to go on this pilgrimage and beg in each town on the route, reckoning that it was better to beg in a strange district than from people they knew. And that is why there were so many young boys among them. . . . When curious onlookers asked them why they did it, they sought to explain themselves by saying that they were driven by an irresistible impulse.'

Other voices were added to the chorus of disapproval. An Augustinian of Erfurt pointed out the theological unsoundness of the pilgrimage, and somewhat futilely reminded the pilgrims that the journey would avail them nothing if they had not made a true confession and obtained the permission of their bishop. In July 1479, Marcus Spickendorff, *ratmeister* of Halle, recorded in his diary that he had heard an edifying sermon on the wickedness of going to Wilsnack. But no amount of thundering from pulpits succeeded in reducing the popularity of the pilgrimage until the village became Protestant in 1552. In that year the miraculous hosts were publicly consigned to the flames by the formidable evangelical preacher Joachim Ellefeld.

In fact, pilgrimages of children were by no means as uncommon as the preachers and pamphleteers suggested. The pilgrims who volunteered to build the church of St.-Pierre-sur-Dives in 1145 included a large number of children. The children's crusade of 1212 was a still more extraordinary outburst of this kind. A child called Stephen from the village of Cloies, near Vendôme, collected an army of children from central and northern France and announced his intention of marching to recapture the Holy Land. They embarked at Marseilles in several large ships. Two ship-loads were drowned in a storm off Sardinia, and the masters of the five remaining ships sold their passengers into slavery in north Africa. Another army of children was assembled simultaneously in Germany by a child called Nicholas. They penetrated as far as Genoa but failed to persuade the Genoese to transport them to the Holy Land, whereupon the 'army' broke up in disorder. Many of the children died of starvation on the roads of northern Italy while trying to return to their homes. Almost as interesting as the phenomenon itself was the reaction of contemporaries, who were far from unanimous in condemning it.

'Many people', one wrote, 'believed that the children should be taken seriously, and not laughed at. They believed that it was the work of God and a sign of pure devotion. They gave them food and money and everything they needed. But there were others, including most of the clergy, whose view was saner. They thought the enterprise useless and doomed to failure, and they denounced it. The populace, however, ignored them and shouted them down, saying that it was only their avarice which had turned them against the holy expedition, and not their sense of justice or love of truth.'

Only when the 'crusade' had ended in disaster did they come to agree with the clergy. An angry mob demanded the arrest of Nicholas's father, who had apparently encouraged the boy out of vainglory. He was seized and hanged.

The same violent disagreements surrounded children's pilgrimages whenever they occurred. The abbey of Mont-St.-Michel attracted the largest and most dramatic mass-pilgrimages of children. At Pentecost in 1333 'St. Elmo's Fire' was seen on the top of the spire of the abbey church. Large bands of children began to arrive almost immediately, and the continuous procession did not end until the first week in July. All were from poor, peasant families. They called themselves *pastoureaux*, a significant name, recalling the strange agrarian revolt of 1320, which had announced itself as having been called into existence by the Virgin to exterminate the Jews and deliver the Holy Land from the infidel. The children of

1333 had come from north-western France, most of them from Normandy and Brittany, but thereafter they came from further afield. In 1393 several hundred children aged between eleven and fifteen gathered at Montpellier, intending to march to Mont-St.-Michel. Another crowd of children left Millau in the summer of 1441 carrying a banner of St. Michael before them. The pilgrimage of children to Mont-St.-Michel was now common enough in southern France to merit a diatribe from the bishop of St. Papoul. In April 1442 he alleged that they were motivated by restlessness, impatience of hard labour, and a reprehensible desire to escape from the poverty of their homes; in future such journeys were to be forbidden on pain of excommunication.

The disease spread to Germany and the Low Countries in 1457. The circumstances were identical, except that the children came from the towns, and not from the depressed countryside. Several thousand of them, in groups up to eight hundred strong, began to arrive at Mont-St.-Michel after Pentecost, singing hymns in honour of the archangel. More than a thousand were counted passing through Wissemburg alone in the week after Christmas. Some were only nine years old. Again they were enthusiastically applauded by ordinary people and fed and lodged in the towns on the route. Again the clergy and the civil authorities tried in vain to prevent them. Denis the Carthusian wrote an angry pamphlet (now lost) *On the Processions of Young Boys to Mont-St.-Michel*. The town council of Regensburg tried to send them before the ecclesiastical courts and treated them to a sermon showing that the Christian faith 'in no way required of its devotees a pilgrimage to Mont-St.-Michel'. But their protests fell on deaf ears. In the following year more armies of children gathered in northern Germany and the Rhineland announcing that they had received 'certain revelations', instructing them to venerate the shrine of St. Michael, this time at Monte Gargano.

Why the cult of St. Michael should have appealed so strongly to children is far from clear, but it does seem that social factors were more important than spiritual ones. So much was apparent to contemporaries, who are all agreed that the children came from the poorest classes. 'They were but the children of poor folk', a citizen of Wissemburg reported, 'though there were a small number of noble ones among them.'

The disturbing possibilities of the situation became fully apparent in the summer of 1476, when the small village of Nicklashausen in the territory of Wurzburg became the scene of a popular Marial pilgrimage with overtones of social revolution. In the church of Nicklashausen there was a statue of the Virgin which was credited with miraculous powers. It had attracted a thin trickle of pilgrims for more than a century. Here, in the middle of Lent 1476, a young shepherd called Hans Böhm began to preach with astonishing eloquence before ever-growing audiences. His theme, a familiar one, was repentance. He called on all his hearers to go in their multitudes to venerate the statue, in order to appease the wrath of God on the sins of mankind. The Virgin had promised him that those who obeyed his call would have a plenary indulgence and those who died there would immediately ascend to heaven.

It was exactly a year after the great mass-pilgrimage to Wilsnack. In south Germany the harvests had been poor, and in the territory of the prince-bishops of Wurzburg, crushing taxation added to the burdens of the poor and provoked considerable social unrest. An atmosphere of intense religious excitement was heightened by the preaching of the Roman Jubilee indulgence, which had begun a few weeks earlier. The response to Böhm's call was unexpectedly dramatic. From the towns of the Rhineland and Thuringia, which had supplied most of the pilgrims to Mont-St.-Michel in 1457, from Saxony, whence pilgrims had rushed to Wilsnack the year before, there came many thousands of repentant poor. Others arrived from Bavaria and Swabia, then facing the threat of severe famine. It was estimated, no doubt with much exaggeration, that 40,000, or even 70,000 people could be seen encamped in the fields outside Nicklashausen every morning. The offerings of gold and silver coins, clothing, and wax, were prodigious. Böhm's preaching began conventionally enough. He called on his audience to abandon their effeminate clothing and to renounce swearing and gaming, much as Barnardino of Siena had urged half a century before. But Böhm did not leave matters there. He went on to preach against the loose-living and avarice of the clergy, a topical subject in the prince-bishopric of Wurzburg. From this he proceeded to a full-blooded egalitarianism. 'Bishops, princes, counts and knights should be allowed to possess as much as ordinary folk and no more. There will come a time when even they will have to work for their living.' Böhm finally urged his followers to withhold all payments of taxes, tithes, and rents, and summoned them to meet at Nicklashausen on an appointed day to overthrow the civil and religious authorities. 'Truly', John of Trittenheim remarked, 'the common people are always chasing after novelties, and trying to shake off the yoke of their masters.'

The pilgrimage, which had begun in March, came to an abrupt end in July. On the eve of the day appointed for the great meeting, Böhm was seized by a party of horsemen in the service of the bishop, and was later burned for heresy. His followers were dispersed with cannon. Further pilgrimages were forbidden by the secular authorities throughout Germany, and an interdict was laid on the village of Nicklashausen. Early in 1477, the church was razed to the ground on the orders of the archbishop of Mainz. The political consequences of Böhm's pilgrimage were obvious enough. The religious consequence was to intensify still further the profound suspicion of spontaneous popular movements in the minds of the educated establishment. Even John of Trittenheim, who was no friend of that establishment, was constrained to admit that 'simple unlettered folk are very easily taken in, and are inclined to believe in false miracles without proof. We know this from our experience of the pilgrimages of recent times. . . . It was the cause of the events at Nicklashausen.'

CHAPTER XVI

MEDIAEVAL CHRISTIANITY

Religion to Ritual

The progression from private austerity to popular enthusiasm and thence to abstract ritual, is a recurring theme in the religious life of the middle ages. The Catholic moralists of the fifteenth century and the Protestant reformers of the sixteenth had in common a strong dislike of the overpowering element of ritual in the religion of the late middle ages. Commenting on the popularity of the blood of Christ at Hailes, the English reformer Hugh Latimer complained that 'the sight of it with their bodily eye doth certify them, and putteth them out of doubt that they be in clean life and in state of salvation without spot of sin.' The roots of this situation penetrated very deep into the soil of mediaeval religion. The reduction of dogma to literal images, the localization of God's power in a few sanctuaries, the hope of automatic salvation, these were not novel 'superstitions' in 1533 when Latimer was writing. It might have surprised him to know that the second council of Chalons in 813 had protested, in terms very similar to his, against the 'simple-minded notion that sinners need only catch sight of the shrines of the saints and their sins will be absolved.'

Pilgrimage, like almsgiving, had begun as an accessory to the moral teaching of the Church, and ended as an alternative. In extreme cases it could be regarded as a licence to sin. The pilgrims in William Langland's dream 'had leave to lie all their life after'. 'He who goes to St. James and then kills his father commits no mortal sin,' asserted a Poitevin contemporary of Langland's. It was this attitude, and less extreme variants of it, which disturbed moral reformers of the late middle ages. Berthold of Regensberg once took the occasion of a sermon against the pious excesses of women to launch into a diatribe against pilgrims who pursued the illusion of the ritual purgation of sin. Another German Franciscan of the thirteenth century conjured up before his audience an image of the pilgrims standing at the brink of Hell and calling out to those below, 'did any of you try going to Rome when you were alive?' and the thousands replied, 'yes, we all went to Rome, but much good did it do us. . . . You who are still living, put not your trust in almsgiving, pilgrimages, or chantries, for they are all vain without true contrition. At the seat of judgement it will avail you nothing that you have been to the tombs of the apostles.' 'All these journeys', echoed the Italian friar Giordano da Rivalta, 'I hold for nothing worth.'

This plea for a more spiritual religion found its most eloquent supporter in William Langland, the obscure Englishman of the late fourteenth century who wrote *The Vision of Piers Plowman*. *Piers Plowman* is much the most powerful of those allegorical dreams of the late middle ages, of which the *Roman de la Rose* is the best-known example. Langland objected to pilgrimage because it was a ritual which eased the conscience of the sinner without improving the moral quality of his life:

> *And ye that seek St. James and saints of Rome,*
> *Seeketh St. Truth, for he may save you all.*

In their great quest for truth, Christians have been diverted by smooth promises and bright illusions. Hope seizes a horn and blows it. A thousand men throng together hoping to find truth but no one knows where to look, and the blind mass 'blundered forth as beasts over banks and hills till late was and long'. At last, they meet a pilgrim, wearing his pouch and scarf and carrying badges from all the great sanctuaries. 'Knowest thou a saint named truth?' 'Where dwells he?', they ask. To which the pilgrim replies, 'nay, so me God help. I saw never a palmer with pike ne with scrip asking after him till now in this place.' Piers Plowman then appears and tells them the road to truth. They must go through Meekness till they come to Conscience; next cross the brook called Be-buxom-of-speech by the ford called Honour-your-fathers. Pass by Swear-not-in-vain and Covet-not, by Steal-not and Slay-not, over the bridge of Pray-well where Grace is the gate-keeper and Amend-you his assistant, and thence through the narrow gate to Paradise.

The Devaluation of Indulgences

Indulgences were sometimes identified as the sole cause of the preoccupation with external observances at the end of the middle ages. This was an over-simplified view, but an important one, for it came not only from root-and-branch enemies of the ecclesiastical order, but from a vocal element in the council of Constance and from many Catholic reformers. The modern sinner, wrote the outspoken Thomas Gascoigne, says to himself 'I do not care how many sins I commit for I can easily and speedily have a plenary remission of guilt and punishment, by acquiring a papal indulgence.' Indulgences, once a valuable stimulus to pilgrimage, had become an alternative. Collecting them was an object in itself, and by the close of the middle ages, few pilgrimages could prosper without them. The almost complete dependence of the cult of the saints on papal indulgences can be seen in the volumes of petitions addressed to successive popes of the fourteenth and fifteenth centuries by decayed sanctuaries which saw their only hope of revival in the grant of a generous indulgence. Thousands came from French churches ruined in the most destructive phase of the Hundred Years War. St.-Gilles was one of the abbeys which hoped to restore its depleted income with the help of an indulgence. Canterbury was unable to hold its fifth Jubilee pilgrimage in 1520 for lack of money to buy the indulgence from Leo X.

The sale of indulgences replaced the hardship of the actual journey by a simple payment equal to the cost of making it. It had begun in a very small way in the twelfth century. Crusaders were early allowed to send substitutes to fight in their place and still gain the plenary indulgence. The synod of Santiago (1125) permitted all Spanish crusaders to do this if they were 'truly confessed and penitent'. A simple money payment, the cost of a mercenary, was almost as good as a substitute. In 1147 Eugenius III offered half a crusading indulgence to those who contributed a tenth of their income and moveables to the cost of the second crusade. A firm stride forward was taken in the thirteenth century when crusaders were allowed to commute their vows for a money payment, and it was not long before commutation was extended to all pilgrimages. The Roman Jubilee of 1350 was the turning point. In 1352 Clement VI allowed the population of Mallorca to claim the Jubilee indulgence without actually going to Rome, in return for a money payment equal to the cost of the journey. The precedent thus established was ruthlessly exploited forty years later by Boniface IX, who stood in dire need of both the money and the popularity which the sale of indulgences brought.

As bishops of Rome, the popes could plausibly claim the right to sell Jubilee indulgences to all comers. Very soon after the Jubilee of 1350, they began to sell dispensations from vows to perform other pilgrimages. Minor churches could obtain not only an indulgence for themselves, but the right to commute vows of pilgrimage to major sanctuaries, thus in effect upstaging churches vastly more important than themselves. The Gilbertine church of Mattersley in Yorkshire was allowed to commute vows of pilgrimage to anywhere except Rome or Santiago. The same concession, with the same exceptions, was given to Canterbury cathedral on the occasion

of the fourth Jubilee, in 1470. By 1470, however, it was common to
offer dispensations even from pilgrim's vows of Rome and Santiago.
Thomas Walsingham recorded with indignation that the cardinal
who came to England in 1381 to negotiate the marriage of Richard
II and Anne of Bohemia was openly selling dispensations from pilgrimages to Rome, Santiago, and Jerusalem. Ten years later, papal
legates were offering the same concessions in Germany and Castile.
The price of these dispensations had only the vaguest connection
with the cost of the journey. Thus in April 1330, Arnaud Rocelli, of
the diocese of Saintes, paid four shillings and twopence to be spared
the journey to Rome; but a year later it cost Agnes de Rocquefort
133 gold lambs and five shillings to evade a pilgrimage to Santiago.
The difference in price reflected the difference in their social status.
At the end of the fifteenth century the papal Datary was using a
tariff which was weighted according to the wealth of the applicant and the comfort in which he was thought likely to travel.
Even this degree of flexibility was abandoned in the instructions
given to the sellers of the Jubilee indulgence of 1500 in England.
Here the price was related strictly to the applicant's income, ranging
from one shilling and fourpence for those earning twenty pounds a
year or less, to three pounds six shillings and eightpence for those
with incomes above two thousand pounds.

Less direct but equally damaging was the practice of offering indulgences *ad instar*, that is, of offering the indulgences of major
shrines to minor ones. This again began in the fourteenth century
with the marketing of the Roman Jubilee indulgence. Most Christians were able to win the Jubilee indulgence of 1390 at churches
within a few miles of their homes. The commonest indulgence *ad
instar* was the indulgence of the Portiuncula which, like the Roman
Jubilee indulgence, was reputed to be plenary. Boniface IX began
to grant it to other churches in 1392. Franciscan churches, appropri-
ately enough, were the first to benefit, beginning with the church of
La Verna where St. Francis had received the stigmata. Subsequently,
ninety-five other churches received the indulgence of the Portiuncula. In England some forty churches gained a plenary indulgence
by this indirect route, including sanctuaries as obscure as the Gilbertine priory of St. Saviour at Hitchen and the Augustinian priory
of Langlete. Indulgences of other churches, notably of St. Mark's in
Venice, were also common. As well as devaluing indulgences as
such, Boniface's policies gave deep offence to important vested
interests. In December 1402 he was forced to yield to mounting
protests, and issued a bull formally 'revoking and annulling every
indulgence of the Jubilee, of the Holy Sepulchre, of Monte Gargano,
of Santiago, St. Mark's Venice, the Portiuncula, Collemaggio, or

any indulgences whatsoever *ad instar indulgentiarum* of any other church.' The retraction was impressive, and no doubt humiliating. Although the popes continued to distribute Jubilee indulgences with the same undiscriminating generosity, the indulgences of other great sanctuaries remained inviolate for more than a century. There were no doubt many churches like St. Nicholas of Calais which still advertized their Portiuncula indulgences as if Boniface had never spoken. But the popes themselves scrupulously avoided a return to this questionable experiment.

Their exact effect in discouraging long journeys to the major shrines thus abused is impossible to measure, but it must have been considerable. Indulgences *ad instar* could never displace pilgrimage altogether, for there was always the pleasure of travel and the strength of tradition to draw pilgrims to the major sanctuaries. But the fact remained, as a Parisian diarist pointed out, that if Notre-Dame de Pontoise had the indulgences of Rome then it was 'as good as going to Rome but less time-consuming'. This man cannot have been the only one to draw the obvious conclusion. Sixtus IV recognized as much when he declared in August 1473, that all indulgences *ad instar Jubilaei* were to be suspended during the actual Roman Jubilee of 1475. The reason given was that so many Jubilee indulgences had been granted to other churches 'that the rush of pilgrims to Rome may be discouraged and the celebrations of the Jubilee year diminished or even curtailed altogether, to the great detriment of the salvation of souls.'

The responsibility for this unedifying state of affairs rested largely with the papacy, but not entirely. The sanctuaries themselves were unscrupulous in extracting indulgences from the enfeebled popes of the schismatic period. Many otherwise reputable churches had no compunction in forging those which they could not obtain legitimately, and in magnifying those which they could. The Franciscans were believed to be the greatest offenders, but in fact the major secular cathedrals were just as aggressive. Cologne cathedral obtained a plenary indulgence *ad instar Jubilaei* in 1394 by playing one pope off against another. Others simply conferred plenary indulgences upon themselves, as Le Puy did in 1407. In 1420 the monks of Canterbury, after failing to obtain a Jubilee indulgence from Martin V, declared one of their own. The prior summoned four doctors of theology who pronounced this action to be legitimate, and the Jubilee was duly held, notwithstanding the fulminations of the pope.

The activities of the 'pardoners', or itinerant salesmen of indulgences, are well-known from the portraits of Langland and Chaucer. They were the butt of satirists and reformers not only in England but wherever there was an appetite for indulgences. The problem was extremely serious in fifteenth-century Spain, where a prodigious number of indulgences was available as a result of the close alliance between the dynasty and the papacy. Everywhere the pardoners owed their success to the fact that they were always slightly in advance of official thinking on the subject of indulgences. They offered their clients on paper more than could be had at the great sanctuaries. As a result, people expected the same benefits from their pilgrimages and, after a decent interval, they usually got them. In 1312 the council of Vienne sternly condemned pardoners for pretending that their indulgences could release souls from purgatory; but within twenty years such indulgences were being offered at the Portiuncula chapel, and by the middle of the fifteenth century they were being granted by the popes. This argues a high degree of gullibility among uneducated people and a good many educated ones as well. Most of Europe accepted a forged version of the bull proclaiming the Roman Jubilee of 1350; learned canonists were deceived in spite of the extravagantly improbable terms in which it was couched. Nor is this surprising, in view of the faith placed in impressive-looking documents, and the inadequate grasp of diplomatic even amongst the highly literate. When Langland's pardoner wished to convince an audience that a forged indulgence was genuine, he had only to produce 'a bull with bishops seals'. When a group of Slav pilgrims arrived at the Franciscan church of Ancona on their way to the Portiuncula chapel, the friars tried to persuade them that there was as much indulgence to be had at Ancona as at Assisi. 'Look at our letters of grant,' they declared. The pilgrims saw and believed.

The ready acceptance of indulgences *totiens quoties* is a case in point. These were indulgences which could be claimed as often as the penitent could perform the conditions, by entering the sanctuary once a day for example. The popes did not grant such indulgences, even under Boniface IX, but some fourteenth-century theologians favoured them. Nicholas of Lyra was one. Churches were not slow in offering them. In the middle of the fifteenth century the seven major altars of St. Peter's in Rome boasted an indulgence *totiens quoties*. Judas's thirty pieces of silver, preserved immediately inside the door of the basilica, was stated to be worth 1,400 years of remission as often as the pilgrim set eyes on them.

In January 1418 the council of Constance decreed severe restrictions on the issue of indulgences, expressing the fear that 'by their great numbers, they may be brought into discredit.' But the damage had already been done. The chronicler of Paderborn, Gobelinus Persona, accused Boniface IX of bringing all indulgences into disrepute by granting them not only to great and ancient walled cities, but to small villages and monasteries of no importance. Gobelinus was deeply hostile to Boniface, but his words were echoed by others who looked on his cause with favour. The chronicler of Neuss, on the whole a supporter of Boniface, complained that plenary indulgences had been conceded to 'towns that were not even walled, to monasteries and country churches. . . . Some people suspected that he was moved more by greed than by religious zeal.' Yet it is clear that Boniface's liberality was very popular with ordinary people, and the attempts of the council of Constance to repair the breach, merely served to widen still further the gulf between educated piety and popular enthusiasm. The failure of the reform movement inaugurated at Constance has often been put down to the indifference and obstructiveness of successive popes. This explanation may have been good enough for the council of Basle but it is not good enough for history. The truth is that the ritual purgation of sin was exactly what most uneducated people wanted. There is a hint of this in the reasons given by the monks of Canterbury for requesting a Jubilee indulgence in 1470. Many Englishmen, they told the pope, were too old or infirm to go to Rome or Santiago. Others could not afford the cost. Traditionally the Church had allowed them to gain a Jubilee indulgence at Canterbury, and it would be imprudent to end the tradition now. 'Of all nations', the monks alleged, 'the English are the most attached to old habits and traditional devotions, and they will not easily be deprived of them without great uproar.'

Pilgrimage without Travel

During a tour of Ulster in the late 1260s, two Franciscan preachers were followed about from town to town by a mass of people 'both for their sermons and for the indulgences which they dispensed'. One of them, on his way home, stayed with a householder and offered to sell him all the indulgences he had acquired for the amount he had spent in getting them and a pot of beer in addition. In this case both parties were simple peasants, but it was not always so. An Italian knight known to Bartolus of Assisi offered to buy the Portiuncula indulgence from a servant of his who had recently been there. 'If you give the indulgence you gained at Assisi to my deceased brother, then I, as witness all these people here, will return to you the money you spent on the journey.' If indulgences taught men to regard merit as a commodity, then it was, perhaps, natural for them to think of it as transferable.

The belief that indulgences could release the dead from Purgatory was a corner-stone of late mediaeval piety, but its origins lay firmly

in the past. For centuries, penitents who confessed on their death-
beds and who died without performing the penance, had been
allowed to have it performed for them. This was usually done by
distributing alms from their estate. The idea is found in the penitential literature of the ninth century and in the canon law collections of the eleventh. A synod meeting at Arras in 1025 expressed
the opinion that penance was 'just as efficacious for the dead as it was
for the living'. The final development of the theory was, however,
the work of the thirteenth century. It was actively canvassed in the
early years of the century by the preachers of the crusade who
taught, according to a jaundiced contemporary, that by virtue of a
crusading indulgence, 'evil men who died without confession or
penance would be received into the Church.' The schoolmen did
not go so far, but Albert the Great and St. Bonaventure were agreed
that penance could be remitted after death if the penitent had made
a true confession. As Thomas Aquinas argued, a man could gain an
indulgence in two ways, by fulfilling the conditions himself or, if
this was impossible, by fulfilling them vicariously. The dead can
only fulfil them vicariously.

The concept of indulgences for the dead remained a somewhat
academic one. It was left to the Franciscans of the Portiuncula to
make practical use of it. Bartolus, the friar of Assisi who wrote up
the miracles of the Portiuncula in about 1335, told a number of
stories whose object was to impress the lesson on his readers. A
Venetian priest was stricken with a fatal illness just as he was about
to begin a pilgrimage to the Portiuncula. Summoning his closest
friend to his bedside he gave him the money which he had saved for
the journey and begged him to make the pilgrimage on his behalf.
After the priest had died, the friend put off his departure for month
after month until the priest appeared to him in a dream chiding him
for his delays. The friend left immediately for Assisi and on his
return the priest appeared again and revealed that 'at the very hour
that you entered the chapel I was liberated from the penance of
Purgatory.' It is an altogether typical story. Bartolus is at pains to
point out that it was at the Portiuncula and nowhere else that the
dead could be released from Purgatory. A Sicilian woman who was
preparing to leave for Santiago had a startling vision of her dead
son, who addressed her in the following terms: 'Dear mother, the
pilgrimage which you are about to make is a fine and worthy act,
but it will not do much for me. If you wish to liberate me from my
sins you must go not only to Santiago but also to the church of S.
Maria de Angelis at the Portiuncula. Only then shall I be released
from Purgatory.'

The pilgrimage of the Portiuncula did not for long enjoy the monopoly which Bartolus claimed for it. In the church of the Holy Sepulchre in Jerusalem St. Bridget of Sweden received a revelation informing her that her devotions had released many souls from Purgatory. Five years later, in 1377, a German pilgrim in Rome found a plaque in the church of St. Lawrence promising the release of a soul from Purgatory for every year of Wednesdays that a visitor passed in the church. By the middle of the fifteenth century nearly every church in Rome offered an indulgence for the souls in Purgatory.

The confidence which laymen reposed in indulgences for the dead is reflected in their wills. Already in 1269, William de Beauchamp died leaving two hundred marks to his younger son Walter to make a pilgrimage to the Holy Sepulchre on his behalf. An examination of the enormous number of surviving mediaeval wills proved in London suggests, however, that wills like this one did not become common until the middle of the fourteenth century. Some testators were highly specific in their instructions to pilgrims, who were expected to perform the pilgrimage in a manner befitting the status of the testator. In his will, drawn up in 1415, Thomas, earl of Arundel, left a substantial sum for the expenses of his pilgrim and instructed him to travel 'in the same way as I would have travelled, had I done the pilgrimage myself.' Thomas Poulton, who died in 1433, left the sum of £20 'for a clergyman of good repute, chosen by my executors, to travel in my name to Rome and there to remain for two years continuously doing the stations regularly, visiting all the holy shrines and relics, and celebrating masses in those places on my behalf. And before his departure, my executors shall exact an oath from him that during those two years he shall pursue no other occupation.' In an age in which testamentary conditions were imperfectly enforced, there was no guarantee that the pilgrimage would actually be performed. The testator could only rely on the conscience of his heirs. One George Fryng, citizen of London, instructed his widow to go to Santiago on his behalf, but her second husband refused to let her go, and she was obliged to seek a dispensation from the pope. Many obligations must have remained unfulfilled for years, some for ever. A Lincolnshire knight who died in 1389 left money to 'Roger my grandson to make a voyage against the Infidel to which I am bound in the sum of two hundred marks by the will of my grandfather.' These examples have been drawn exclusively from England because of the extraordinary wealth of surviving English wills, but there is no reason to suppose that they are untypical. Where continental wills survive, they follow a very similar pattern. The wills of wealthy Parisian lawyers enrolled in the parlement of Paris frequently contain directions to pilgrims. In the

Testamentarbuch of the imperial free city of Pressburg (1427–1529), almost every will has a provision for sending a pilgrim to Rome.

The laity accepted the efficacy of indulgences for the dead for many years before the popes granted them in formal terms. No genuine letter of indulgence promised the release of souls from Purgatory until the middle of the fifteenth century. The earliest known example dates only from 1457, when Calixtus III offered the release of a soul to every one who contributed two hundred *maravedis* to the crusade against the Moors. Shortly afterwards, the same pope issued indulgences for the dead to the cathedral of Tarragona and the Franciscan order. In 1476 Sixtus IV granted an important indulgence to Saintes cathedral, which recited that:

'It is our desire to use the Church's treasury of merit to assist those souls in Purgatory who would have gained this indulgence had they been alive. We therefore concede that parents, friends, or any others may secure the release of souls from the fires of Purgatory by donating a sum, to be assessed by the canons, for the repair of Saintes cathedral.'

Thus the authorities accorded formal recognition to a belief which had been universal among the laity for more than a century.

As soon as it was agreed that the dead could perform pilgrimages by proxy, it was a short step to holding that the living could do so too. Vicarious pilgrimages were not unknown in the twelfth century if the would-be pilgrim was prevented from going himself. Ralph the clerk was too ill to go to Canterbury; he sent his candle by messenger, and recovered as soon as it was lit in the cathedral. The wife of a Norwich baker was unable to walk for the swellings on her feet; her husband visited the shrine of St. William on her behalf. A cloistered nun who could not leave her nunnery sent her son to Canterbury to give thanks for a miraculous cure. Pure vicarious pilgrimages, by those who could have gone themselves but preferred not to, had to wait for a later, less demanding age. In the fifteenth century the idea seems to have been accepted without protest. This was due partly to the fact that crusaders had been sending substitutes to fulfil their vows for two hundred years; and partly, no doubt, to the influence of the judicial pilgrimage, which by now was almost invariably commuted to a fine. Vicarious pilgrimages were never entirely respectable. Soon after their marriage, William Cressewyc of London and his wife Alice vowed to go to Rome, but they deferred the performance of the vow until old age, and then sent a man to do it for them. Nevertheless they still felt uneasy about this vicarious road to salvation, for in 1391 they applied to a papal nuncio for absolution. No such reservations ever troubled

Isabel of Bavaria, queen of France (d. 1435). She sent a pilgrim with a fifteen-pound candle to Notre-Dame du Blanc-Mesnil, instructing him to pray there for fifteen days, burning a pound of wax per day. The queen, who was disgustingly obese, was forever worried about her health. She was particularly devoted to St. Eutrope, the healer of dropsy, and to the celebrated medical saints like St. Lazarus, and Cosmas and Damian. One of her chaplains was sent to Larchamp, another to Moutiers-au-Perche, a third to Avallon. Her accounts are full of entries recording payments made to professional pilgrims or members of her household despatched to shrines throughout France.

In spite of the demand, the institution of the professional pilgrim was slow to make its appearance. Several English testators of the fourteenth century envisaged the possibility that no pilgrim would be available, and made alternative dispositions of their wealth. This was probably because most vicarious pilgrims thought it necessary that the proxy should be of the same rank as themselves. Many wills require the pilgrim to be 'of honest condition', i.e. well-born. When John, duke of Brittany, was prevented by the diplomatic crisis of 1420 from fulfilling a vow of pilgrimage, he sent a man to the Holy Land on his behalf, stipulating that he was to be '*homme notable et suffisant*'; a hundred gold *écus* were allowed for his expenses, and a hundred gold florins for his offering. In Scandinavia, it is true, professional pilgrims were quite common, and many contracts for their services survive. At the Baltic port of Lübeck there was always a crowd of professionals willing to go to the Holy Land for sums ranging from twenty to a hundred marks. Further south, however, so many bona fide pilgrims passed regularly to and from the great sanctuaries that it was easy enough to find a man who was minded to go anyway. Most vicarious pilgrimages were informal arrangements like that of the bishop of Lincoln, who gave Margery Kempe twenty-six shillings and eightpence as she was leaving for Palestine, 'to buy her clothes with and to pray for him'.

Such indifference to the element of personal hardship inevitably devalued the very idea of pilgrimage, and invited the appearance of alternatives which were emotionally more rewarding. Mass-flagellation, for example, was not simply another pious exercise, but specifically an alternative to pilgrimage. Flagellant preachers of 1349 contrasted the 'natural' penance of the flagellants with the 'artificial' Roman Jubilee declared for 1350. In a sermon preached before the pope at Avignon, the sternly orthodox Jean du Fayt made the same point. The flagellants, he argued, imagined that they would gain the same indulgence from their processions as those who attended the Jubilee. This was no doubt one of the arguments which led Clement

VI to condemn them as heretics. There was a great deal of truth in the bitter observation of John of Trittenheim that educated men had abandoned the cult of the saints for abstruse mystical devotions. There was a vogue for mystical alternatives to pilgrimage, inspired by allegorical writings which likened the whole of human life to a pilgrimage. One of the earliest and most influential of these is a lengthy treatise in French, written in 1330–1, called the *Pèlerinage de la Vie Humaine*. The title gives ample indication of the contents. Its author was Guillaume de Deguileville, a Cistercian of the abbey of Chaalis. The *Pèlerinage* is the record of a dream in which the author undertakes a pilgrimage to the celestial Jerusalem. Dame Grace blesses him and offers him the scarf of faith and the stave of hope. On the road he is attacked by the deadly sins in the shape of wild beasts. Heresy, voluptuousness, and idleness lie in wait to attack and rob him. He is shipwrecked in the sea of worldliness and is near to drowning when he succeeds in saving himself by climbing onto the raft of the Cistercian order.

The imagery is old and the moral conventional. But the idea of performing a pilgrimage in the daily passage of life was capable of being used as a powerful argument against all external observances. 'We ben pilgrims when that we ben born . . .', a Lollard pamphlet, the *Lanterne of Light*, proclaimed; 'every citizen of the heavenly country is a pilgrim of this world for all time of this present life, and when we travailen sore to keep God's feasts, then we do our pilgrimage.' 'I call them true pilgrims', agreed William Thorpe at his interrogation, 'which travel towards the bliss of heaven . . . hating and fleeing all the seven deadly sins.' The *Lanterne of Light* was once described by a mayor of London as 'the worst and most perverse thing that ever I did read or see'; no less than fifteen heretical propositions were extracted from it by archbishop Chichele. But there is nothing intrinsically heretical about the ideas expressed here, all of which were openly expounded at the council of Constance. They are strongly represented in the poetry of Jean Gerson, whose *Meditations* on the true pilgrim were read with pleasure by Charles of Orléans and recommended to Charles VII of France by his confessor.

These allegorical sermons, though intended as a summons to a more spiritual life, in fact replaced one ritual by another. A new kind of devotional handbook became popular in the fifteenth century, which explained to the reader how to follow each stage of an imaginary pilgrimage in his own home, and gain the same benefits. A Franciscan manuscript from St.-Trond (it is the earliest example known) begins by pointing out that one can win all the indulgences of the Holy Land without leaving one's house, if one is prepared to follow in spirit every stage of Christ's passion, reciting thirty-three *Pater Nosters* for each halt on the road to Calvary. It is in fact a sort of mental 'stations of the cross'. An even more original product of its kind was written, probably at Oxford, for the benefit of those who could not or would not attend the Roman Jubilee of 1423. Here the frustrated pilgrim is invited to say the *Pater Noster* ten times daily to represent the ten leagues which he could expect to cover each day of his journey to Rome. When he had notionally arrived in the city, let him visit a local church once a day and distribute alms equal to the offerings which he would have made in Rome. 'And it is my belief that by doing all this he will gain as much or more than he would have done by going physically to Rome.' Many hundreds of such works, some of them of extreme naïvety, circulated in northern Europe in the fifteenth century.

The theme was enthusiastically taken up by popular preachers, who openly recommended it as a less irksome alternative to pilgrimage. Preaching in Strasbourg cathedral during the Roman Jubilee of 1500, Johann Geiler addressed himself to the question whether a prisoner, locked up in a dungeon and unable to go to Rome, was thereby excluded from the benefits of the Jubilee indulgence. Calculating that it would take twenty-one days to reach Rome, another seven to visit the churches, and twenty-one to return, Geiler suggested that the prisoner could walk round his cell for forty-two days and devote himself to prayer for seven. Erasmus had this kind of exercise in mind when he poked fun at contemporaries who liked to acquire the indulgences of the Roman 'stations' without actually going to Rome.

> 'I walk about my house. I go to my study. I check on my daughter's chastity. Then I go to my shop and see what my servants are doing. Then into the kitchen to make sure that nothing is amiss there. And so from one place to another to see that my wife and children are all right and every one is at his business. These are my Roman stations.'

Even when the taunts of satirists and the impact of the Reformation had sharply reduced the popularity of real pilgrimages, imaginary ones showed no signs of dying the same death. The most elaborate of them all, the work of Jan van Paesschen (d. 1532), outlined a course of prayer extending over 365 days of the year and corresponding to every stage of a journey to the Holy Land. This manual was published posthumously at Louvain in 1563 and immediately went into several editions. A French translation appeared three years later, and in c. 1605 there was even an anonymously printed version in English.

The continuing popularity of these works testifies to the extra-ordinary resilience of late mediaeval piety. Erasmus believed that few offerings were made at the sanctuaries in his day, and that the pilgrimage to Santiago was nearly forgotten 'on account of the new opinion that has been spread throughout the world'. That conserva-tive Frenchman Gréffin Affagart agreed in blaming the decline of the great sanctuaries on the Reformation and particularly on 'that evil knave Luther and his band of accomplices like Erasmus, with his *Colloquies* and *Enchiridion*'.

But cultural change is seldom as straightforward as this. Progress is ragged. Successive periods overlap. A major intellectual transfor-mation may alter the climate of opinion but old ideas have a habit of persisting. 'Superstitions' were condemned with such vehemence by the Protestant reformers, that it is easy to forget how, even in Protestant societies, pilgrimages and shrines, relics and miracles, survived the Reformation by more than a century. Writing in the 1520s, Erasmus looked forward to the rapid demise of the pilgrim-age to Santiago. Yet the great Galician sanctuary was probably more prosperous in the seventeenth century than it had ever been in the middle ages. The offerings of the eleventh century had built the great Romanesque façade of St. James's cathedral; the offerings of the eighteenth century tore it down and replaced it with the Baroque extravagances of Casas y Nóvoa. In Catholic Europe of the eight-eenth century, obscure shrines rose to fame with the same facility as their fifteenth-century ancestors. Vierzehnheiligen was to Baroque Christianity what Notre-Dame de l'Epine had been to Gothic.

Pilgrimage did not mean the same thing to every generation. But it was practised in one form or another from late antiquity to the Reformation, and has maintained a fitful existence ever since. It affords a unique reflection of mediaeval religion at every stage of its complicated development. Almsgiving has a longer history, but its practice was confined to the relatively rich. It was, moreover, a spiritual duty to give alms, and although some religions (notably Islam) insist on pilgrimages, Christianity is not amongst them. If Christians have at times travelled long distances to venerate the remains of spiritual heroes, then it was because in doing so they satisfied an emotional need.

ABBREVIATIONS

Aa. Ss.	*Acta sanctorum Bollandiana*, ed. J. Bollandus *et al.*, 61 vols., Antwerp, Brussels, etc., 1643– (in progress).
Aa. Ss. OSB.	*Acta sanctorum ordinis S. Benedicti*, ed. L. d'Achéry and J. Mabillon, 9 vols., Paris, 1668–1701.
An. Boll.	*Analecta Bollandiana.*
AOL.	*Archives de l'orient latin*, 2 vols., Geneva, 1881–4.
Arch. Nat.	Archives Nationales de France, Paris.
Arch. Vat.	Archivio Vaticano, Rome.
ASRSP.	*Archivio della Società Romana di Storia Patria.*
BBB.	G. Golubovich, *Biblioteca bio-bibliografica della Terra Santa e dell' oriente Francescano*, 5 vols., Florence, 1906– (in progress).
BEC.	*Bibliothèque de l'École des Chartes.*
BEFAR.	*Bibliothèque des Écoles Francaises d'Athènes et de Rome.*
BEHE.	*Bibliothèque de l'École des Hautes Études.*
BHP.	*Bulletin historique et philologique du Comité des Travaux Historiques et Scientifiques.*
Bibl.	Bibliothèque de la ville de . . .
Bibl. Nat.	Bibliothèque Nationale, Paris.
BLVS.	*Bibliothek des literarischen Vereins in Stuttgart.*
Brit. Mus.	British Museum, London.
CCH (Bruxelles).	*Corpus codicum hagiographicorum Bibliothecae Regiae Bruxellensis, Pars i: Codices latini membranei*, 2 vols., Brussels, 1886–9.
CCH (Paris).	*Catalogus codicum hagiographicorum latinorum in Bibliotheca Nationali Parisiensi*, 3 vols., Brussels, 1889–93.
CJC.	*Corpus juris canonici*, ed. A. L. Richter and A. Friedberg, 2 vols., Leipzig, 1879–81.
CPR. Letters.	*Calendar of entries in the papal registers relating to Great Britain and Ireland. Papal letters*, ed. W. H. Bliss *et al.*, 13 vols., London, 1893– (in progress).
CRH.	*Comptes rendus des séances de la Commission Royale d' Histoire.*
CSEL.	*Corpus scriptorum ecclesiasticorum latinorum.*
DACL.	*Dictionnaire d'archéologie Chrétienne et de liturgie*, ed. F. Cabrol, H. Leclercq, *et al.*, 15 vols., Paris, 1907–53.
DDC.	*Dictionnaire de droit canonique*, ed. R. Naz, 7 vols., Paris, 1935–65.

DHGE.	*Dictionnaire d'histoire et de géographie ecclesiastiques*, ed. A. Baudrillart *et al.*, 17 vols., Paris, 1912– (in progress).
DTC.	*Dictionnaire de théologie catholique*, ed. A. Vacant, *et al.*, 15 vols., Paris, 1903–67.
EETS.	Early English Text Society.
EHR.	*English historical review.*
ES.	*España sagrada*, ed. H. Florez *et al.*, 51 vols., Madrid, 1754–1879.
Fonti.	*Fonti per la storia d'Italia.*
GC.	*Gallia Christiana*, 16 vols., Paris, 1715–1865.
G. Itin.	P. Geyer, *Itinera Hierosolymitana saeculi iv–viii, CSEL.*, xxxix, Vienna, 1898.
IS (1).	*Italia sacra*, ed. F. Ughelli, 1st. ed., 9 vols., Rome, 1644–62.
IS (2).	*Italia sacra*, 2nd. ed., 10 vols., Venice, 1717–21.
L. Peregr.	J. C. M. Laurent, *Peregrinatores medii aevi quattuor*, Leipzig, 1864.
MAH.	*Mélanges d'archéologie et d'histoire de l'École Francaise de Rome.*
MC.	*Sacrorum conciliorum nova et amplissima collectio*, ed. J. D. Mansi *et al.*, 55 vols., Florence and elsewhere, 1759–1962.
MD. Thes.	E. Martène and U. Durant, *Thesaurus novus anecdotorum*, 5 vols., Paris, 1717.
MD. Vet. Script.	E. Martène and U. Durant, *Veterum scriptorum et monumentorum amplissima collectio*, 6 vols., Paris, 1724–9.
MGH. Auct. Antiq.	*Monumenta Germaniae historica. Auctores antiquissimi.*
MGH. Constit.	— *Constitutiones imperatorum et regum.*
MGH. Epp.	— *Epistolae.*
MGH. Epp. Sel.	— *Epistolae selectae in usum scholarum.*
MGH. Leges.	— *Leges.*
MGH. Libelli.	— *Libelli de lite imperatorum et pontificum, saeculis xi et xii conscripta.*
MGH. Merov.	— *Scriptores rerum merovingicarum.*
MGH. Poet.	— *Poetae latinae medii aevi.*
MGH. Rer. Germ.	— *Scriptores rerum Germanicarum in usum scholarum.*
MGH. SS.	— *Scriptores.*
MR. Itin.	H. Michelant and G. Raynaud, *Itinéraires à Jérusalem et descriptions de la Terre Sainte redigés en francais aux xie, xiie, et xiiie siècles, SOL.*, iii, Geneva, 1882.
PG.	J-P. Migne, *Patrologia graeca*, 161 vols., Paris, 1857–66.
PL.	J-P. Migne, *Patrologia latina*, 221 vols., Paris, 1844–64.
PPTS.	Palestine Pilgrims Text Society.
RHC. Arm.	*Recueil des historiens des croisades. Documents Arméniens*, 2 vols., Paris, 1869–1906.
RHC. Occ.	— *Historiens occidentaux*, 5 vols., Paris, 1845–95.
RHF.	*Recueil des historiens des Gaules et de la France*, ed. M. Bouquet, *et al.*, 24 vols., Paris, 1738–1904.
RISS (1).	*Rerum Italicarum scriptores*, ed. L. A. Muratori, 25 vols., Milan, 1723–51.

RISS (2).	*Rerum Italicarum scriptores*, nuova edizione, Citta di Castello, Bologna, etc., 1900– (in progress).
RM. Pilg.	R. Röhricht and H. Meisner, *Deutsche Pilgerreisen nach dem heiligen Lände*, Berlin, 1880.
ROL.	*Revue de l'orient latin*, 12 vols., Paris, 1893–1911.
RS.	*Rolls series. Chronicles and memorials of Great Britain and Ireland during the middle ages, published under the direction of the Master of the Rolls.*
SATF.	Société des Anciens Textes Francais.
SHF.	Société de l'histoire de France.
SOL.	*Société de l'orient latin. Série géographique*, 5 vols., Geneva, 1879–89.
TM. Itin.	T. Tobler and A. Molinier, *Itinera Hierosolymitana et descriptiones Terrae Sanctae bellis sacris anteriora*, SOL., i–ii, Geneva, 1879–85.
VZ.	R. Valentini and G. Zucchetti, *Codice topografico della citta di Roma, Fonti*, 4 vols., Rome, 1940–53.

NOTES

Original sources listed in the bibliography are cited by author and/or shortened title. Secondary works listed in the bibliography are cited by author alone. In cases of doubt, the initials OS or SW are used. Works not listed in the bibliography are cited in full.

I. INTRODUCTION

11 English villages and towns: Stubbs, *Charters*, pp. 464–6.
Henry of Susa: Quoted in G. Le Bras, *Institutions ecclésiastiques de la Chretienté médiévale*, vol. i, Paris, 1964–5, p. 204.
No strangers in church: O. Dobiache-Rojdestvensky, *La vie paroissale en France d'après les actes épiscopaux*, Paris, 1911, pp. 87–8.

12 Confession once a year: Conc. Lateran (1215), canon XXI, *MC*. xxii. 1007–10. On its enforcement in France, Conc. Saintes (1280), *MC*. xxiv. 379–80; and in England, Conc. Exeter (1287), Powicke and Cheney, *Councils*, vol. ii, p. 992.
Held in public: *MC*. xxiv. 527. Cf. Powicke and Cheney, *Councils*, vol. ii, p. 144; for fifteenth century, Gerson, *De Officio Pastoris*, ed. Glorieux, vol. v, p. 141.
Confessional hand-books: e.g. Powicke and Cheney, *Councils*, vol. ii, pp. 220–6. W. A. Pantin, *The English Church in the fourteenth century*, Cambridge, 1955, pp. 270–6.
Prostitute repents: *Mirac. S. Mariae Carnotensis* XVII, pp. 533–4.
Busybodies: 'Visitation returns of the diocese of Hereford in 1397', ed. A. T. Bannister, *EHR*. xliv (1929), pp. 279–89, 444–53, xlv (1930), pp. 92–101, 444–63. Guérin and Célier (ed.), *Documents concernant le Poitou*, vol. xxiv, pp. 134–6, 287–9 (nos. 780–1, 836); late fourteenth century. John Myrc, *Instructions for parish priests*, ed. E. Peacock, *EETS.*, vol. xxxi, London, 1868, p. 23.

13 London lady dying: Benedict, *Mirac. S. Thomae*, II. 42, p. 90.
'Curiosity to see . . .': Wattenbach (ed.), 'Beitrage', p. 605.
Guilt overcome by travel: Orderic Vitalis, *Hist. Eccl.*, ed. Chibnall, vol. ii, pp. 44–6. Adam of Eynsham, *Vita S. Hugonis*, IV. 2, vol. ii, pp. 7–10. Paul Walther, *Itin.*, pp. 7–8.

14 'Signs' inspire terror: Gregory of Tours, *De Virtut. S. Martini*, III. 54, p. 645 (darkness). *Vita S. Genovefae*, V. 19, ed. C. Kohler, *BEHE*, vol. xlviii, Paris, 1881, p. 24; *Vita S. Aridii*, in Mabillon (ed.), *Vet. Anal.*, p. 204 (thunder). Eligius (attrib.), *Homilia*, IX, *PL*. lxxxvii. 628 (eclipse of moon). Gregory of Tours, *Hist. Francorum*, VI. 14, IV. 31, 51, pp. 284, 164–5, 187 (red sky, eclipse of sun).
Survival of these fears: Burchardt, *Decr.*, XIX. 5, *PL*. cxl. 971. Guibert, *De Vita Sua*, I. 15, p. 56. *Mirac. S. Benedicti*, VI. 11, pp. 233–6 (death of

Robert the Pious). Langland, *Piers Plowman*, B.V. 13–5, pp. 57–8.
Roman de la Rose, 11. 18,257–18,468, vol. iii, pp. 48–55.

15 Evil in the wind: Gregory of Tours, *De Virtutibus S. Martini*, III. 16, p. 636. Toussaert, p. 365 (Dunkirk abbey). Delaruelle *et al.*, pp. 831–2 (German Dominicans). Bruno, *Expositio in Ep. ad Ephesianos*, II, *PL.* cliii. 325. Yvo, *Panormia*, VIII. 68, *PL.* clxi. 1322.
Devil in wild animals: Sulpicius Severus, *Vita S. Martini*, XXI, pp. 130–1. Peter the Venerable, *De Mirac.*, I. 14, 18, cols. 877–8, 883–4, etc. Thomas of Monmouth, *Mirac. S. Willelmi*, III. 12, pp. 137–8 (pig at Norwich). Reginald of Durham, *De B. Cuthberti Virtut.*, XVII, pp. 32–3. Guibert, *De Vita Sua*, I. 21, pp. 81–2.

16 Devil as deformed man: Athanasius, *Vita S. Antonii*, V, VI, XXI, XL, XLII, LIII, *PG.* xxvi. 845–9, 876, 901, 904–5, 920. Cf. Peter the Venerable, *De Mirac*, I. 8, col. 869 ('parvi et nigerrimi Aethiopis specie assumpta'); Orderic, *Hist.*, *Eccl.*, VIII. 17, ed. Chibnall, vol. iv, pp. 242–4 ('agmen Aethiopum . . . nigerrimi cornipedis').
Dreams: William, *Mirac. S. Thomae*, III. 5, V. 8, pp. 262–4, 381. Benedict, *Mirac. S. Thomae*, I. 13, pp. 44–5. Rackham, p. 85.

17 'One night as he lay . . .': Orderic, *Hist. Eccl.*, III, ed. Chibnall, vol. ii, pp. 42–4.
'Luxuria' in sculpture: Mâle, pp. 373–6. G. Zarnecki, *Gislebertus, Sculptor of Autun*, N.Y., 1961, pp. 64–5 and pl. iv.

18 'The cause that oghte . . .': *Canterbury Tales*, p. 575.
'Conversion' by preachers: Jacques de Vitry, *Exempla*, CXCIX, p. 83. Etienne de Bourbon, *Anecdotes*, I. 21, p. 29 (Bologna student); cf. Owst, p. 413 and n[3]. Caesarius, *Dial. Mirac.*, I. 6, 16, 18, 21, 25, 29–30, 5, vol. i, pp. 12–15, 22–3, 25, 28, 30–1, 35, 11.
Augustine's 'conversion': P. Brown, *Augustine of Hippo*, London, 1967, pp. 106–7.
'Conversion' in hagiography: Bede, *Hist. Eccl.*, IV. 5, p. 350; Du Cange, vol. ii, p. 547. See, in general, D. Baker, 'Vir Dei: secular sanctity in the early tenth century', in Cuming and Baker, pp. 40–1.
Majority damned: Bernard, *Sermo in Vigilia Nativitatis Domini*, III. 3, *PL.* clxxxiii. 96. Berthold, *Predigten*, XXIV, vol. i, p. 382. Herolt, quoted in Coulton, vol. i, p. 447. See references in A. Michel, 'Elus (Nombre des)', *DTC.*, iv. 2364–6.

19 Priest's vision: Orderic, *Hist. Eccl.*, VIII. 17, ed. Chibnall, vol. iv, pp. 236–50.
How far this view accepted: Coulton, vol. i, p. 71 (prior of Holy Trinity). Vincent of Beauvais, *Speculum Morale*, Douai, 1624, col. 840. Berthold, *Predigten*, XXIV, vol. i, p. 386. C. Douais (ed.), *Documents pour servir a l'histoire de l'inquisition dans le Languedoc*, vol. ii, Paris, 1900, p. 100. *Book of Margery Kempe*, I. 59, pp. 144–6.

20 Descriptions of Hell: Owst, pp. 522, 524 (sermons). Bede, *Hist. Eccl.*, V. 12, pp. 490–4. Felix, *Life of St. Guthlac*, ed. B. Colgrave, Cambridge, 1956, p. 105. Guibert, *De Vita Sua*, I. 18, p. 70. Caesarius, *Dial. Mirac.* I. 34, vol. i, pp. 39–43 (Landgrave Ludwig). *Visio Monachi de Eynsham*.

21 Salvation a miracle: Berthold, *Predigten*, XXIV, vol. i, p. 382. Theofrid of Epternach, *Flores Epitaphiorum Sanctorum*, I. 3, col. 384.

II. THE CULT OF RELICS

22 Victricius on saints: *De Laude Sancrotum*, XII, *PL.* xx. 454–5.
Early evidence of cult of relics: Eusebius, *Hist. Eccl.*, IV. 15, pp. 350–2 (Polycarp). Prudentius, *Peristephanon*, V. 41–5, p. 346 (St. Vincent). *Monumenta Ecclesia Liturgica*, ed. F. Cabrol, vol. i (2), Paris, 1900, p. 192 (nos. 4399–4401).
Jerome and Vigilantius: Jerome, *Contra Vigilantium*, cols. 346–8; *Ep.* CIX. 1, vol. ii, pp. 351–3. Cf. Augustine, *De Civitate Dei*, XXII. 9–10, vol. ii, pp. 613–15.

23 Cult of relics defended: Augustine, *op. cit.*, I. 13, VIII. 17, 27, vol. i, pp. 25–6, 382–3, 405; *Contra Faustum*, XXI. 21, *PL.* xlii. 384. Followed by Isidore of Seville, *De Ecclesiasticis Officiis*, I. xxxv. 1–6, *PL.* lxxxiii. 770.
Popular view: Cyprian, *Epp.* XIII. 5, LXXVI. 2, ed. W. von Hartel, *CSEL.* iii, Vienna, 1868–71, vol. i, pp. 507, 829. Cyril of Jerusalem, *Catachesis*, XVIII. 16, XIX. 7, *PG.* xxxiii. 1071. See Delehaye (4), p. 116.
Aquinas on relics: *Summa Theologica*, III, q. xxv, a. 6, vol. xi, p. 284.

24 *Brandea*: Cyril of Jerusalem, *loc. cit.* Gregory I, *Reg.* V. 57, vol. i, p. 364; *Dialogues*, II. 38, *PL.* lxvi. 204.
'He who wishes to pray': Gregory of Tours, *In Gloria Martyrum*, XXVII, pp. 503–4.

25 Gregory of Tours at Brioude: *De Virtut. S. Juliani*, XXXIV–XXXV, pp. 578–9.
Dust from Holy Land: Frolow, pp. 158–9 (funerary table). Augustine, *De Civitate Dei*, XXII. 8, vol. ii, pp. 602–3. Gregory of Nyssa, *De S. Theodoro*, *PG.* xlvi. 740.
Hung round neck: Gregory I, *Reg.* III. 33, vol. i, p. 192. Jerome, *Comm. in Evang. S. Matthaei*, IV, *PL.* xxvi. 168. Conc. III Bracarense, canon V, in *PL.* lxxxiv. 589–90. Aquinas, *Summa Theologica*, II, ii, q. xcvi, a. 4, vol. ix, pp. 334–5. Adam, *Vita S. Hugonis*, vol. ii, pp. 167–8.
Later use of *brandea*: Guibert, *De Vita Sua*, III. 18, p. 219. *Mirac. S. Michaelis*, pp. 880, 883. Faber, *Evagatorium*, vol. i, p. 94. Ghistele, *Voyage*, vol. xxxvii, p. 742.

26 Fourth-century 'inventions': Delehaye (4), pp. 75–8, 80–1 (Gervaise and Proteus, Stephen). Paulinus, *Vita S. Ambrosii*, XXXIX, *PL.* xiv. 37 (Vitalis and Agricola). Marcellinus, *Chron.*, *PL.* li. 928 (John the Baptist); on the date of this, see *Aa. Ss.* June, vol. iv, p. 713.
Augustine on dreams: see P. Courcelle, *Les Confessions de Saint Augustin dans la tradition littéraire*, Paris, 1963, pp. 127–33. F. van der Meer, *Augustine the bishop*, London, 1961, pp. 531–9.

27 Relics authenticated by dreams: Glaber, *Hist.*, IV. 3, pp. 96–8 (Moses' rod). Raymond of Aguilers, *Hist. Francorum*, X–XI, pp. 253–7 (Holy Lance).
Sinful to ignore dreams: e.g. *Acta S. Fulconis*, II–V, *Aa. Ss.* May, vol. v, p. 193.
Jean de Meung on dreams: *Roman de la Rose*, ll. 18257–64, vol. iii, p. 48.

Heads of the Baptist: Delehaye (4), pp. 82–3. *Aa. Ss.* June, vol. iv, pp. 722–46, 751–66.

Dreams criticized: Conc. Carthage, canon XIV, in *MC.* iii. 971. Augustine, *De Cura pro Mortuis Gerenda,* X, pp. 639–41. Guibert, *De Pignoribus,* I. 3, col. 624; elsewhere, he suggests that both were false, *Gesta Dei per Francos,* I. 5, p. 132.

Guibert on translations: *Gesta Dei, loc. cit.*

28 Translations in Greek Church: *Codex Theodosianus,* IX. 17, ed. T. Mommsen and P. Meyer, Berlin, 1905, p. 463. Delehaye (4), pp. 54–7.

Popes refuse to translate relics: Hormisdas, *Ep.* LXXVII, in Thiel (ed.), *Epp. Pontificum,* pp. 874–5. Gregory I, *Reg.,* IV. 30, vol. i, p. 264.

Dismemberment: Theodoret, *Graecarum Affectionum Curatio,* VIII, col. 1012. Victricius, *De Laude Sanctorum,* XI, col. 453. Gregory of Tours, *Hist. Francorum,* VII. 31, pp. 311–12. Baudonivius, *Vita Radegundis,* II. 15, *PL.* lxxii. 672.

Austerities before removing relic: Gregory of Tours, *In Gloria Martyrum,* XIII, pp. 497–8. Cosmas of Prague, *Chron. Boemorum,* II. 3–4, ed. D. Bretholz, *MGH. Rer. Germ.,* N. S. ii, Berlin, 1923, pp. 84–90. Jocelyn of Brakelond, *Chron. de Rebus Gestis Samsonis,* ed. H. E. Butler, London, 1949, pp. 112–14.

29 Relics needed to consecrate churches: Ambrose, *Ep.* XXI, *PL.* xvi. 1019. Bede, *Hist. Eccl.,* I. 29, p. 104 ('all things needed . . .'). Conc. Nicaea, session VII, canon VII, in *MC.* xiii. 427; cf. Hefele, vol. iii, pp. 781–2.

Relics acquired in Rome: Llewellyn, pp. 183–90.

Byzantine collection: William of Tyre, *Hist.,* XX. 23, p. 985 (Amaury). In general, see Ebersolt. On its dispersal in 1204, Riant (1).

30 Other collections: Bethel, p. 69 (Reading); Morand, pp. 9, 23, and preuves, pp. 7–9 (Ste. Chapelle). In general, Fichtenau.

Objects of national pride: S. Runciman, *The Emperor Romanus Lecapenus and his reign,* Cambridge, 1929, pp. 145, 229–30. William of Malmesbury, *Gesta Pontificum,* V. 268, p. 425. French monk quoted in Fichtenau, p. 72. Matthew Paris, *Chron. Majora,* vol. iv, p. 642 (Suffield).

31 Ferdinand of Carrion: *Vita B. Zoyli,* IV, *ES.* x. 495.

Early relic merchants: Delehaye (8), p. 200. Gregory of Tours, *Hist. Francorum,* VII. 31. pp. 311–12.

Deusdona: Einhard, *Translatio Marcellini et Petri,* I. 3, p. 241; Rudolph, *Mirac. Sanctorum in Fuldenses Eccl. Translatorum,* II, p. 330.

Emma: Eadmer, *Hist. Novorum,* ed. M. Rule, *RS.,* London, 1884, p. 108; William of Malmesbury, *Gesta Pontificum,* V. 263, p. 419.

Effect of sack of Constantinople: Conc. Lateran, canon LXII, in *MC.* xxii. 1050–1. Riant (1), p. 8 (d'Alluye). Rohault de Fleury, pp. 110, 396 (Baldwin).

32 Einhard: see his *Translatio Marcellini et Petri,* I. 2–5, pp. 240–2.

Relics stolen in teeth: Etheria, *Peregr.,* XXXVII. 2, p. 88 (in 385). *Gesta Consulum Andegavorum,* p. 91. *Mirac. S. Eadmundi* (Bod. 240), vol. i, pp. 373–4.

No property of a relic: see example quoted in Baynes, p. 170.

Theft of St. Benedict: Adrevald, *Hist. Translationis S. Benedicti,* in

Mirac. S. Benedicti, pp. 1–14. Oldest account (late seventh century?) in Mabillon (ed.), *Vet. Anal.*, pp. 211–12.

33 Theft of St. Nicholas: Nicephorus, *Translatio S. Nicolai in Barum*, IV–XL, pp. 170–89, esp. pp. 175, 178–9.

34 Saint has mind of his own: *Mirac. S. Benedicti*, I. 15–17, pp. 37–42. *Translatio Reliquiarum B. Emiliani*, VIII, ES. 1. 368–9. *Guide*, VIII, p. 46.

35 St. Hugh at Fécamp: Adam, *Vita S. Hugonis*, vol. ii, pp. 169–70.
Precautions against theft: Conc. Lateran, canon LXII, *MC*. xxii. 1049; Conc. Bordeaux, canon IX, *MC*. xxiv. 283. *Capitula de Mirac. S. Cuthberti*, VII. 11, pp. 258–9 (Durham). *Cartulaire de N-D de Chartres*, ed. E. de Lepinois and L. Merlet, vol. i, Chartres, 1862, p. 61. Pero Tafur, *Andancas*, p. 29.
Henry III and blood of Christ: Matthew Paris, *Chron. Maj.*, vol. iv, p. 643, vol. vi, pp. 138–44.

36 Guibert on false relics: *De Pignoribus*, I. 2, II. 4, cols. 621, 628–9. Cf. Caesarius, *Dial. Mirac.*, VIII. 69–70, vol. ii, p. 140.
Odo of Bayeux: Guibert, *op. cit.*, I. 3, col. 625.
Fulbert of Cambrai: *Vita Autberti Ep. Cameracensis*, IV. 30–2, ed. J. Ghesquierus, *Acta Sanctorum Belgii*, vol. iii, Bruxelles, 1785, pp. 562–3.
Dispute over St. Benedict: Peter the Deacon, *Historica Relatio*, I. 1, p. 288; Chamard, pp. 6–12. Cf. *Mirac. S. Benedicti*, VII. 15, pp. 272–4.
Dispute over St. Nicholas: Orderic, *Hist. Eccl.*, VII. 13, ed. Chibnall, pp. 70–2 (Venosa, Noron). F. Chamard, *Les vies des saints personnages de l'Anjou*, vol. i, Paris, 1863, pp. 411–16; cf. *GC*. xiv. 473 (Angers). *Hist. de Translatione S. Nicolai*, X–XXIX, *RHC. Occ*. v. 260–70 (Venice).

37 Indignation of the *Guide*: *Guide*, VIII, pp. 46, 52.
Mary Magdalene: Saxer, pp. 65–73, 185–7, 230–42.

38 Relics displayed when authenticity doubted: *Detectio Corporis S. Dionysii*, II–IX, pp. 166–9 (in *c.* 1050). Robert de Torigny, *Chron.*, vol. ii, p. 136; Rigord, *Gesta Philippi*, LXXX, vol. i, pp. 114–15 (in 1186). Secretly inspected first: Suger, *De Admin. Sua*, XXXIII, p. 203.

39 Inspection of St. Genevieve: *Vita S. Willelmi Roschildensis*, II. 22–4, *Aa. Ss.* April, vol. i, p. 629; *GC*. viii. 1450–5.
Trial by miracle; *MGH. Epp*. v. 338 (St. Felix). Eadmer, *De Sanctorum Veneratione*, V, pp. 362–3 (St. Ouen).

40 Trial by fire: *De S. Adalberto Diacono*, XXV, *Aa. Ss. OSB*. iii. 635–6 (St. Celsus). *Chron. Mon. Casinensis*, II. 33, p. 649. *Vita Meinwerki*, CCIX, ed. F. Tenckhoff, *MGH. Rer. Germ.*, Hannover, 1921, p. 122. Guibert, *De Vita Sua*, III. 20, pp. 230–1 (St. Arnoul). Conc. II Sarragossa (An. 592), *MC*. x. 471 (Arian relics). William of Malmesbury, *Gesta Pontificum*, V. 267, pp. 424–5; *Capitula de Mirac. S. Cuthberti*, VII. 7–11, pp. 254–9 (Anglo-Saxon relics). Mabillon (ed.), *Vet. Anal.*, p. 569 (Anna Gonzaga).

III. THE SAINTS AND THEIR RELICS

41 Saints punish mockers: Gerald, *Itin. Cambriae*, I. 2, vol. vi, p. 27. William of Malmesbury, *Gesta Pontificum*, V. 275, pp. 438–9. Orderic,

Hist. Eccl., VI. 10, ed. Chibnall, vol. iii, p. 318 (St. Evroul). *Mirac. S. Emmerammi*, II. 20, *Aa. Ss.* Sept., vol. vi, p. 500. Loomis, pp. 98–100 (woman displays posterior, and other examples).

42 Iconoclasm in the west: Claudius of Turin, *Adv. Theulmirum Abbatem*, *PL.* cv. 462; *Ep.* XII, in *MGH. Epp.* iv. 611; Hefele, vol. iv, pp. 43–9. See Séjourné, cols. 2353, 2355.

Eastern heretics in Spain: *ES.* x. 525–32, xv. 12–15. Cf. Conc. Seville (An. 619), canon XII, in *MC.* x. 556.

Guibert: See Lefranc, p. 298, for comparison with Calvin etc. But there are more sensible assessments in J. Chaurand, 'La conception de l' histoire de Guibert de Nogent', *Cahiers de Civilisation Medievale*, viii (1965), pp. 381–95; and in Morris.

43 His pamphlet: *De Pignoribus*, esp. I. 3, II. 1–6, III. 3, 5, cols. 624–5, 629–50, 659–60, 662–3. On the relics of Nogent, *De Vita Sua*, II. 1, p. 105. On the Holy Lance, *Gesta Dei der Francos*, VII. 34, p. 252. Accepts cult of genuine relics, *De Pignoribus*, I. 3, col. 625; but demands higher standard of proof, *ibid.*, I. 3–4, cols. 623–4, 627–8.

44 Guibert and the inner life: see his *Liber quo ordine sermo fieri debeat*, *PL.* clvi. 27; *De Pignoribus*, I.2, IV. 8, cols. 619, 678–9. In general, Morris, pp. 59–60.

'Crystallized into images': Huizinga, p. 136. But the tendency was not, of course, peculiar to the later middle ages.

Eucharistic images: Early examples in *Vita S. Basilii*, VII, *PL.* lxxiii. 301–2; and *Vitae Patrum*, V. 18, *PL.* lxxiii. 979. *Vita S. Gregorii*, IV. 19, *Aa. Ss.* March, vol. ii, p. 134: the passage is a late interpolation, see H. Grisar, 'Die Gregorbiographie des Paulus Diakonus in ihrer ursprung-lichen Gestalt', *Zeitschrift für katholische Theologie*, xi (1887), p. 160. Later examples: Guibert, *De Pignoribus*, I. 2, cols. 616–17; Peter the Venerable, *De Mirac.*, I. 1, col. 852; Jacques de Vitry, *Exempla*, CCLXX, p. 113. Coulton, vol. i, pp. 109–10 (priests' manuals). On late mediae-val Netherlands, see J. Wils, *Het Sakrament van Mirakel berustende in Sint Jakobs te Leuwen*, Louvain, 1905. 'Extracts from Lincoln episcopal visitations', ed. E. Peacock, *Archaeologia*, xlviii (1885), pp. 252–3 (George Carter).

45 Immaculate conception and Trinity literally portrayed: Inventory of 1420 in L. E. de Laborde, *Les Ducs de Bourgogne*, vol. ii, Paris, 1851, p. 264. Gerson, *Sermon: Puer Natus*, ed. Glorieux, vol. vii, p. 963. J. Sarrète, 'Vierges ouvertes, Vierges ouvrantes, et la Vierge ouvrante de Palau del Vidre', *Ruscino, Revue d'Histoire et d'Archéologie du Roussillon*, ii (1912), pp. 5–59, 449–57.

Theological scruples on relics of Christ: Aquinas, *Summa Theologica*, III, q. liv, a. 2, vol. xi, pp. 509–10. Innocent III, *De Sacro Altaris Mys-terio*, IV. 30, *PL.* ccxvii. 876–7.

Relics of Christ at Rome: John the Deacon, *Descriptio*, XIII, pp. 356–7; Innocent III, *loc. cit.* Bridget, *Rev.*, VI. 112, p. 525. *Aa. Ss.* Jan., vol. i, pp. 4–6.

46 Foreskin at Charroux: Montsabert (ed.), *Chartes*; see also Vigneras. At a diocesan synod in 1862, Mgr. Pie asserted that there could be 'no legitimate doubt about the authenticity of this quite unique relic', see

P. Saintyves, *Les réliques et les images légendaires*, Paris, 1912, pp. 181–4. Other foreskins: *GC*. viii (Instr.), p. 389 (Coulombs). Denifle, vol. i, p. 167n. (Boulogne). *Aa. Ss.* Jan., vol. i, pp. 6–8 (Antwerp).

Blood of Christ at Mantua: *Annales Regni Francorum*, p. 119. Herman of Reichenau, *Chron.*, *MGH. SS.* v. 127.

47 Bleeding images in Netherlands: L-J. Rogier, *Geschiedenis van het Katholicisme in Noord-Nederland*, vol. i, Amsterdam, 1945, p. 82; cf. Moreau, vol. iv, pp. 368–71.

Other bleeding images: Aquinas, *Summa Theologica*, III, q. liv, a. 2, vol. xi, pp. 509–10. *Chartularium Universitatis Parisiensis*, ed. H. Denifle and A. Chatellain, vol. iv, Paris, 1897, pp. 682–3 (no. 2634), on blood at La Rochelle. On bleeding images reported in Naples in 1972, see *The Times*, 22 August, 1972, p. 5.

Blood defended by Grosseteste: Matthew Paris, *Chron. Maj.*, vol. vi, pp. 138–44.

and by Franciscans: Wadding, An. 1351 (nos. 16, 18, 21), An. 1462 (nos. 1–18), An. 1463 (nos. 1–4), An. 1464 (nos. 1–6), vol. viii, pp. 59–62, vol. xiii, pp. 206–16, 264–6, 340–3. N. Glassberger, *Chron.*, *Analecta Franciscana*, ii (1887), pp. 393–5.

48 Bruges processions: Toussaert, pp. 259–66.

Hus on blood of Christ: *De Sanguini Christi*, XI. 38, pp. 28–9.

Monstrances and tabernacles: M. Andrieu, 'Réliquaires et monstrances eucharistiques', *An. Boll.* lxviii (1950), p. 398. Delaruelle *et al.*, pp. 749–52.

Fécamp: Baudri de Deuil in *Neustria Pia*, ed. A. du Monstier, Rouen, 1663, p. 232. *Poème sur le Précieux Sang*, 11. 12–15, in Kajava (ed.), *Etudes*, p. 95.

49 Pecock on relics: *Repressor*, II. 4, 8, pp. 155, 182.

Miracles at Bobbio: *Mirac. S. Columbani Bobbiensis*, I, p. 998.

Hair of B. V. M. at Coutances: John of Coutances, *Mirac. Eccl. Constantiensis*, XXII, p. 378. Some *brandea*, usually of eastern origin, are found earlier, see Beissel (2), pp. 296–7.

Other hair of B. V. M.: Herman, *Mirac. S. Mariae Laudunensis*, II. 1, col. 973 (Laon). On the hair at Astorga and Boulogne, Mabillon (ed.), *Vet. Anal.*, p. 433; Lambert of Ardres, *Chron. Comitum Ghisnensium*, *MGH. SS.* xxiv. 577; Gaiffier (2), p. 79. On hair in Germany, Beissel (2), p. 293n.[2].

Tunics of B.V.M.: *Mirac. S. Mariae Carnotensis*, I, p. 509. *Gesta Episcoporum Virdunensium*, XVIII, *MGH. SS.* iv. 44. Others are known from dedication records, *MGH. SS.* XV. 1073, 1095, 1097, 1098, 1270.

Relics of S. Maria Maggiore: John the Deacon, *Descriptio*, XIV, p. 359. Milk of B.V.M.: M. Gomez-Moreno, 'El Arca Santa de Oviedo documentada', *Archivio Espanol de Arte*, xviii (1945), p. 129. *Notae Sweigo-Monasterienses*, *MGH. SS.* xv. 1073. William of Malmesbury, *Gesta Regum*, III. 285, p. 341 (Chartres).

50 B.V.M. 'localized': *Mirac. S. Mariae Carnotensis*, XVIII, pp. 537–8. *Miracles de Rocamadour*, praefat., p. 63. John of Coutances, *Mirac. Eccl. Constantiensis*, VI, pp. 370–2. More, *Dyalogue*, fol. 22. For similar attitudes in modern Italy, see E. C. Banfield, *The moral basis of a backward society*, Glencoe, Illinois, 1958, pp. 130–1n.

51 Saint present in his shrine: *Mirac. S. Benedicti*, II. 19, pp. 123–5. *Mirac. S. Columbani*, XXII, p. 1008. On the Canterbury glass, Rackham, p. 91 and colour pl. XII.

Relics on altar: E. Bishop, *Liturgica Historica*, Oxford, 1918, pp. 25–6. Statue-reliquaries: *Mirac. S. Fidis*, I. 13, 28, 30, II. 4, pp. 46–7, 71–3, 75–6, 100–1. P. Deschamps, 'Etude sur la Renaissance de la sculpture en France à l'époque romane', *Bulletin Monumentale*, lxxxiv (1925), pp. 33–5. Mâle, p. 203.

52 Artistic representations of saints influence popular imagination: Guibert, *De Vita Sua*, I. 16, p. 61. *Mirac. S. Fidis*, I. 1, pp. 9–10. *Chron. Mon. Casinensis*, II. 34, p. 650 ('illa nimirum specie qua depingi a pictoribus consuevit'). On St. Foy and the blind, *Mirac. S. Fidis*, I. 1–2, 29, II. 1, 3, III. 6, 9, 11–12, 14, IV. 15, pp. 6–21, 73, 90–3, 98–9, 137–8, 144–5, 147–50, 152–3, 200–1.

53 Influence of popular piety: it will be seen that I differ on this point from G. Duby, 'The diffusion of cultural patterns in feudal society', *Past and Present*, no. 39 (1968), pp. 3–5.

IV. THE PURSUIT OF THE MIRACULOUS

54 Hume: *An Essay on Miracles*, in *An Enquiry concerning human understanding*, ed. L. A. Selby-Bigge, Oxford, 1894, pp. 114, 115–16.

55 Injunctions of 1536: in *Letters of Thomas Cromwell*, ed. R. B. Merriman, vol. ii, Oxford, 1902, p. 28.

Fraud alleged: Hus, *De Sanguine Christi*, XIV. 45–6, pp. 32–3. More, *Dyalogue*, I. 14, fols. 18–18vo.

56 Histrionic contraptions: H. Ellis (ed.), *Original letters illustrative of English history*, 3rd. series, vol. iii, London, 1846, p. 168. *Letters and Papers*, vol. xiii (1), p. 120 (no. 348).

Plague at Melrose: *Vita S. Cuthberti*, IX, p. 184.

57 Augustine of Canterbury and miracles: Bede, *Hist. Eccl.*, I. 26, 30, II. see pp. 76, 108, 190. Gregory I, *Reg.*, XI. 36, vol. ii, pp. 305–8. On this, 15, Colgrave.

St. Martin: Sulpicius Severus, *Dialogi*, II. 4, pp. 184–5. *MGH. Epp.* iii. 119–22 (Nizier).

Augustine on miracles: *De vera religione*, XXV. 47, *PL.* xxxiv. 142; *Sermo* CCCLVI. 7, *PL.* xxxix. 1577. See D. P. de Vooght, 'Les Miracles dans la vie de Saint Augustin', *Recherches de Théologie Ancienne et Mediévale*, xi (1939), pp. 5–16; P. Brown, *Augustine of Hippo*, London, 1967, pp. 384–6.

58 Gregory on miracles: *Homilia in Evang.*, XXIX, *PL.* lxxvi. 1215.

Bede on miracles: *Vita S. Cuthberti*, XXI, p. 224.

Orderic on miracles: *Hist. Eccl.*, V. 4, VI. 1, ed. Chibnall, vol. iii, pp. 8, 214.

Survival of missionary attitude to miracles: Gregory of Tours, *In Gloria Martyrum*, LXXX, pp. 542–3; cf. *In Gloria Confessorum*, XIV, p. 756. Caesarius, *Dial. Mirac.*, V. 18, vol. i, pp. 296–7 (Besançon heretics). Pierre des Vaux-de-Cernay, *Hystoria Albigensis*, II. 54, ed. P. Guébin and E. Lyon, *SHF*, vol. i, Paris, 1926, pp. 47–9; cf. Guillaume de

Puylaurens, *Chronicon*, IX, ed. Beissier, *Bibliothèque de la Faculté des Lettres de Paris*, XVIII, Paris, 1904, p. 128; the painting is in the Louvre.

59 Lessons of the miracles of St. Thomas: William, *Mirac. S. Thomae*, IV. 45, 49, VI. 159, pp. 355–6, 360–1, 534.

Heretics cannot perform miracles: Lucas of Tuy, *De Altera Vita*, II. 9, in *Magna Bibliotheca Veterum Patrum*, vol. iii, Cologne, 1618, pp. 259–61; cf. III. 9, 18, pp. 280–1, 282–3. *Calendar of Close Rolls, Henry VI*, vol. iii (1435–41), London, 1937, pp. 385–6 (Wyche).

Moslem miracles: Ricoldo, *Liber Peregrinationis*, XXXVI, p. 141. Denis, *Contra perfidiam Mahometi*, II. 3, 4, 9, *Dialogus disputationis inter Christianum et Sarracenum*, III, in *Opera Omnia*, vol. xxxvi, Tournai, 1908, pp. 275, 278, 287, 454–5. In 1121, the ambassadors of the Almoravid emir of Cordova, Ali ben Yúsuf, encountered crowds of pilgrims on the road to Santiago, and were impressed by accounts of the miracles of St. James, *Hist. Compostellana*, II. 50, p. 350.

60 John of Capistrano: Wadding, *Annales Minorum*, An. 1452 (no. 25), vol. xii, p. 142. Nicholas of Fara, *Vita S. Johannis de Capistrano*, VII. 81–4, *Aa. Ss.* Oct., vol. x, pp. 465–6. See J. Hofer, *Johannes von Capestrano. Ein Leben in Kampf um die Reform der Kirche*, Innsbruck, 1936, pp. 313–560.

61 'For all chroniclers . . .': John of Salisbury, *Hist. Pontificalis*, prologue, p. 2.

Sceptics punished: Gregory of Tours, *In Gloria Martyrum*, XXIV, p. 502. *Mirac. S. Joannis Beverlacensis*, proem. 1. *Aa. Ss.* May, vol. ii, p. 172 (saec. xii–xiii). *Mirac. S. Wulfstani*, II. 5, I. 18, pp. 151–2, 125 (saec. xiii).

62 Educated men more sceptical: *Mirac. S. Gengulphi*, XV, *MGH. SS.* xv. 793. Herman, *De Mirac. S. Eadmundi*, XLIV, p. 86. *Capitula de Mirac. S. Cuthberti*, VII. 7–11, pp. 254–9. Walter Daniel, *Ep. ad Mauricium*, ed. F. M. Powicke, *Walter Daniel's Life of Ailred of Rievaulx*, London, 1950, p. 67. William, *Mirac. S. Thomae*, III. 41, 4, pp. 298, 262.

Surfeit of miracles wearisome: William of Malmesbury, *Gesta Pontificum*, II. 75, p. 168 (St. Swithin). William, *Mirac. S. Thomae*, IV. 45, p. 355. Thomas of Monmouth, *Mirac. S. Willelmi*, V. 12, pp. 202–3.

Miracles as means of monastic self-aggrandisement: Theobald, *Vita S. Gummari*, XXII, *Aa. Ss.* Oct., vol. v, pp. 687–8 (saec. xii). *Mirac. S. Dionysii*, III. 4, *Aa. Ss. OSB.*, vol. iv, p. 364; *Detectio Corporis S. Dionysii*, XI, p. 170. *Mirac. S. Fidis*, I. 13, 7, pp. 46, 31. The use of relics as a means of psychological influence is found in other churches; compare, for example, a miracle of St. James at Reading (MS. Gloucester cathedral 1, fol. 173) with the Reading cartulary (Brit. Mus., MS. Cotton Vespasian E.V, fols. 24–31, 58–60ᵛᵒ, 75ᵛᵒ, 77). The effect of monastic acquisitiveness on lay society in the Mâconnais has been studied by Duby, pp. 61–2, 68–73.

63 Miracles of St. Thomas as political phenomenon: William, *Mirac. S. Thomae*, III. 41, 4, pp. 298, 262.

64 Miracles investigated: *Mirac. S. Benedicti*, III. 15, 17–18, pp. 161–2, 164–6. Philip, *Mirac. S. Frideswidae*, LXXIII, p. 582. Benedict, *Mirac. S. Thomae*, III. 51, IV. 2, 6, 65, pp. 153–5, 181, 183–5, 236–7; William, *op.*

cit., VI. 3–5, pp. 410–13. *Mirac. S. Wulfstani*, II. 12, 15, pp. 161, 167; cf. II. 21, p. 179.

Spurious ones rejected: Foréville (ed.) *Livre de S. Gilbert*, p. 10. On Mont.-St.-Michel, Huynes, vol. i, pp. 109, 126–7. Guillaume de Saint-Pathus, *Miracles de S. Louis*, XIV, p. 49.

65 Caesarius's definition: *Dial. Mirac.*, X. 1, vol. ii, p. 217.

Augustine on the physical world: *De Quantitate animae*, XXXI. 62–3, *PL.* xxxii. 1069–70; *De Civitate Dei*, XXI. 4, vol. ii, p. 519; *De nuptiis et concupiscentia*, I. 19. *PL.* xliv. 426; *Ep.* CXXXVII. 10–11, vol. ii, pp. 109–11; *Contra Faustum*, XXVI. 3, ed. J. Zycha, *CSEL.* xxv, Vienna, 1891, pp. 730–1.

66 'These things are indeed . . .': Samson, *De Mirac. S. Eadmundi*, I. 12, p. 143.

Natural explanations discarded for supernatural: Gregory of Tours, *De Virtut. S. Martini*, III. praefat., p. 632; cf. II. 60, IV. 1, pp. 629–30, 649–50. *Hist. Versifié de Fécamp*, 11. 3645–70, pp. 186–7. William, *Mirac. S. Thomae*, III. 24, pp. 282–3.

67 Miraculous escapes from captivity: *Mirac. S. Fidis*, I. 31, p. 76. *Mirac. B. Egidii*, II, VI, X–XII, XV, *MGH. SS.* xii. 317, 319, 320–2, *An. Boll.* ix (1890), pp. 394–6, 399–404. *Liber S. Jacobi*, II. 1, 22, pp. 261–2, 286–7. *Guide*, VIII, p. 54 (St. Leonard). *Mirac. S. Martialis*, passim. Salimbene, *Chron.*, *MGH. SS.* xxxii. 522 (Mary Magdalene).

68 Bohemond: *Mirac. S. Leonardi*, II. 2, *Aa. Ss.* Nov., vol. iii, pp. 160–8. Albert of Aix, *Hist. Hierosolymitana*, IX. 33–6, pp. 610–12. Orderic, *Hist. Eccl.*, X. 23, XI. 12, ed. Prévost, vol. iv, pp. 156, 210–11.

Gregory of Tarsus: Benedict (interpolated), *Mirac. S. Thomae*, VI. 6, pp. 273–9.

Hus on escape miracles: *De Sanguine Christi*, X. 35, pp. 26–7. Yet such a conclusion, though morally repulsive, would not be logically absurd; see the sensible observations of E. E. Evans-Pritchard, *Theories of primitive religion*, Oxford, 1965, pp. 89–91.

Vain pilgrims hope for miracle: Guibert, *De Pignoribus*, III. 5, col. 663. Baraut (ed.), *Llibre Vermell*, p. 35 (Montserrat, saec. xiv). Benedict, *Mirac. S. Thomae*, IV. 33, p. 206. Samson, *De Mirac. S. Eadmundi*, II. 7, p. 178.

69 Miracles proclaimed to crowd: *Mirac. S. Egidii*, IV, *MGH. SS.* xii. 318–19. *Mirac. S. Mariae Magdalenae*, *Viziliaci Facta*, ed. alt., I, *CCH.* (Paris), vol. ii, pp. 292–3 (no. 2).

Mason injured at Fleury: *Mirac. S. Benedicti*, VIII. 30, p. 328.

70 Miracles proof of sanctity: Fontanini (ed.), *Codex*, pp. 37–8 (St. Cunegonde).

Case of Becket: William, *Mirac. S. Thomae*, I. 12, II. 91, pp. 152, 251–2. Benedict, *Mirac. S. Thomae*, II. 50, III. 64, IV. 75, pp. 91, 162–3, 245. Letter of Peter of La Celle in *Becket Materials*, vol. vii, p. 566 (lost service-book). Caesarius, *Dial. Mirac.*, VIII. 54, vol. ii, pp. 127–8 (Paris debate).

71 This view criticized: Odo, *Sermo de S. Benedicto*, *Collationes*, I. 23–4, III. 39, *De combustione Basilicae S. Martini*, in *Bibliotheca Cluniacensis*, cols. 139, 175, 240, 147. Guibert, *De Pignoribus*, I. 1, III. 5, cols. 615–16,

662–3. Wyclif, *De Ecclesia*, II, XIX, pp. 45, 465; *Sermones*, II. 22, vol. ii, p. 164. Gerson, *Contra Impugnantes Ordinis Carthusiensium*, ed. Du Pin, vol. ii, cols. 711–14. *Examination of William Thorpe*, p. 137. 'It may be peradventure . . .': *Canterbury Tales*, p. 607. The same argument is found in Pecock's *Repressor*, II. 4, pp. 155–6, in defence of the veneration of images.

72 False miracles of St. Thomas: Benedict, *Mirac. S. Thomae*, IV. 32, III. 31, pp. 305, 140. William, *Mirac. S. Thomae*, IV. 34, VI. 139, pp. 346–7, 524.

V. THE MEDICINE OF THE SICK

73 Fatalism: *Journal d'un Bourgeois*, p. 295. Boccaccio, *Il Decamerone*, introd.

Ten bushels an acre: *Walter of Henley's Husbandry*, ed. D. Oschinsky, Oxford, 1971, p. 325.

John of Norwich: Ralph of Diceto, *Ymagines Historiarum*, in *Opera Historica*, ed. W. Stubbs, vol. i, *RS*, London, 1876, p. 416.

Famines: See F. Curschmann, *Hungersnöte im Mittelalter*, Leipzig, 1900; M. J. Larénaudie, 'Les famines en Languedoc aux xive et xve siècles', *Annales du Midi*, lxiv (1952), pp. 27–39. On the transport of food, see J. Glénisson, 'Une administration médiévale au prise de la disette', *Moyen Age*, lvii (1951), pp. 303–26.

74 Diet: for England, J. C. Drummond and A. Wilbraham, *The Englishman's Food*, 2nd. ed., London, 1957, pp. 40–1, 54–5, 75–86; Bonser, pp. 351–6. The conditions described in L. Stouff, *Ravitaillement et alimentation en Provence aux xive et xve siècles*, Paris, 1970, probably obtained in most of southern Europe. On central and eastern Europe, M. Dembinska, *Konsumpcja zywnosciowa w Polsce sredniowiecznej*, Warsaw, 1963 (with English summary).

Constant discomfort: Gregory of Tours, *De Virtut. S. Martini*, II. 60, III. praefat., 1, IV. 1, pp. 629–30, 632, 649–50. Peter the Venerable, *Letters*, vol. ii, pp. 247–51.

Digestive complaints: *Miracles de Rocamadour*, I. 45, p. 148 (Robert of Leicester). William, *Mirac. S. Thomae*, IV. 40, pp. 350–1 (Geoffrey of Binbrooke). Benedict, *Mirac. S. Thomae*, II. 45, pp. 92–3.

75 Ergotism: John of Coutances, *Mirac. Eccl. Constantiensis*, XVI, XXVII, pp. 376, 381. Farsit, *Mirac. S. Mariae in Urbe Suessionensis*, I, VII, cols. 1777–9, 1781–2. *Translatio S. Geremari*, V–VI, *Aa. Ss.* Sept., vol. vii. p. 705 (Chartres, 1132). L. Bourgin, *La chaire Francaise au xiie siècle d'après les manuscrits*, Paris, 1879, pp. 365–8 (Paris, 1206). The disease was not yet associated with the Virgin in the 1040s, when a grave outbreak occurred in the Limousin, see *Mirac. S. Benedicti*, IV. 1, pp. 174–7. Prior of Sauxillanges: *Miracles de Rocamadour*, II. 21, pp. 215–16.

76 Peter the Venerable's doctor: Peter, *Letters*, no. 158b, vol. i, p. 383.

Doctors harm patient: Philip, *Mirac. S. Frideswidae*, XL, p. 577. *Miracles de Rocamadour*, II. 32, p. 238.

Pilgrimage after doctors fail: Benedict, *Mirac. S. Thomae*, I. 15, II. 23, VI. 7, pp. 47, 73, 280. William, *Mirac. S. Thomae*, II. 20, 32, pp. 176, 187.

Surgeon guilty of murder: Philip, *Mirac. S. Frideswidae*, CX, p. 589. Cf. Owst, pp. 349–51.

77 Witches: Langland, *Piers Plowman*, B. xiii. 335–42, p. 228. *Mirac. S. Benedicti*, VIII. 47, p. 354 (Tortaire). On Merovingian charm-healers, Marignan, pp. 186–93.

Physicians denigrated: Gregory of Tours, *In Gloria Martyrum*, XXX, pp. 506–7 ('Why waste your breath . . .'). *Mirac. S. Donatiani, MGH. SS.* xiv 180. *Liber S. Jacobi*, I. 6, p. 50.

Saints rivals of physicians: Caesarius, *Dial. Mirac.*, VII. 24, vol. ii, p. 34 (Montpellier). Guillaume de St.-Pathus, *Miracles de S. Louis*, XII, p. 40. On Raoul le Cavetier, *ibid.*, XX, pp. 68–9.

St. Thomas as healing saint: Benedict, *Mirac. S. Thomae*, IV. 15, 51, pp. 195, 219. William, *Mirac. S. Thomae*, II. 37, p. 196. *Canterbury Tales*, 11. 17–18, p. 1.

78 Punitive illnesses: *Vita S. Hilarii*, III. 17, *Aa. Ss.* May, vol. ii, p. 30. *Vita S. Germani*, XXIII, *MGH. Auct. Antiq.* iv (2). 16. Gregory, *De Virtut. S. Juliani*, X, p. 569; *De Virtut. S. Martini*, III. 56, pp. 645–6.

79 All sickness caused by sin: John Chrysostom quoted in Delaunay, p. 10. Jacob of Voragine, *Legenda Aurea*, CXC, p. 877.

'Incursio diaboli': Gregory of Tours, *De Virtut. S. Martini*, II. 20, III. 14, pp. 616, 635. Peter the Deacon, *Historica Relatio*, I. 1, p. 288. Guibert, *De Vita Sua*, III. 20, pp. 229–30.

Infection explained: Foréville (ed.), *Livre de S. Gilbert*, p. 49.

'Possession by the Devil': Bede, *Hist. Eccl.*, III. 11, p. 248. *Mirac. S. Wulfstani*, I. 13, 15, II. 19, pp. 122–3, 123–4, 177. *Mirac. S. Egidii*, XXX, *An. Boll.*, ix (1880), pp. 421–2.

80 Church opposes medicine: Conc. Lateran, canon XXII, in *MC.* xxii. 1010–1. Conc. Paris (1429), canon XXIX, in *MC.* xxviii. 1110. Jacques de Vitry quoted in Lecoy de la Marche, p. 486. Maillard quoted in Samouillan, pp. 278–9. On opposition to Jewish physicians, Conc. Béziers, canon XLIII, in *MC.* xxiii. 702; Delaunay, pp. 11–12. These attitudes were still common among English Protestants of the seventeenth century, see Thomas, pp. 85–9.

81 Gonorrhoea: William, *Mirac. S. Thomae*, IV. 25, p. 340; cf. VI. 19, pp. 431–2. Samson, *Mirac. S. Eadmundi*, II, 20, pp. 204–5.

Sterility: *Cartulaire de l'abbaye de la Sainte Trinite du Mont de Rouen*, no. 108, ed. A. Deville, Paris, 1841, p. 452 (Normans in 1063). *Cartulaire de Conques*, no. 373, pp. 281–2. *Liber S. Jacobi*, II. 3, p. 263. *Gesta Principum Polonorum*, I. 30–1, *MGH. SS.* ix. 442–3 (Wladislaw Hermann). See also *Mirac. S. Fidis*, III. 9, pp. 144–5; William, *op. cit.*, III. 6, pp. 264–5; *Miracles de Rocamadour*, I. 23, p. 112.

82 Woman at St.-Gilles: *Mirac. S. Egidii* (interpolated), *MGH. SS.* xii. 317. *Brandea* eaten: Gregory of Tours, *In Gloria Confessorum*, X, p. 754; *De Virtut. S. Martini*, III. 50, II. 51, pp. 644, 626; *In Gloria Martyrum*, VI, L, pp. 491–2, 523.

Relics dipped in liquid: *Mirac. S. Benedicti*, VIII. 21, 25, pp. 308–9, 318–19. Thomas of Monmouth, *Mirac. S. Willelmi*, III. 22, p. 162 (Norwich). MS. Gloucester cathedral, 1, fols. 171vo, 172, 174vo (Reading).

83 'Water of St. Thomas': William FitzStephen, *Vita S. Thomae*, in *Becket Materials*, vol. iii, pp. 148, 150. Benedict, *Mirac. S. Thomae*, I. 12, II. 4, 50, III. 19, 21–2, IV. 6, pp. 42–3, 59–60, 96, 131, 133–5, 186–7. Found repulsive: *Mirac. S. Michaeli*, pp. 886–7.

84 Medical libraries: M. R. James, *The ancient libraries of Canterbury and Dover*, Cambridge, 1903, pp. 55–62; William of Canterbury quotes Galen in *Mirac. S. Thomae*, IV. 20, pp. 332–4. M. R. James, *On the abbey of St. Edmund at Bury. I. The Library; II. The Church*, Cambridge Archaeological Soc., xxviii, Cambridge, 1895, pp. 14, 66, 67–8. L. Delisle, *Inventaire des manuscrits de la Bibliothèque Nationale. Fonds de Cluny*, Paris, 1884, pp. 166–75. Catalogue of medical books at St. Martial, including many translations from the Arabic, in *Bulletin de la Soc. Archéologique du Limousin*, xxv (1870), pp. 397–400.
Monastic physicians: Herman, *De Mirac. S. Eadmundi*, XXII, p. 56 (Baldwyn). William of Malmesbury, *Gesta Pontificum*, V. 274, pp. 437–8.
Stream at St. Evroul: Orderic Vitalis, *Hist. Eccl.*, VI. 9, ed. Chibnall, vol. iii, p. 276.
Medical instructions in visions: William, *Mirac. S. Thomae*, II. 4, III. 4, pp. 160, 261–2. *Mirac. S. Gilberti*, II. 19, pp. 68–9.
Bishop of Thetford's eye: Herman, *De Mirac. S. Eadmundi*, XXVI, pp. 62–4.

85 Broodiness taken for insanity: William, *Mirac. S. Thomae*, II. 43, p. 204. Psychologically induced illness: on hypochondria, see examples given in *Divine Healing* (SW), pp. 33–45 (nos. 7–10, 12–17, 20, 26); and the comments of R. A. Hunter and I. Macalpine, 'Valentine Greatraks', *St. Bartholomew's Hospital Journal*, lx (1956), pp. 361–8. On the physiological effects of shock see the important article by W. B. Cannon, 'Voodoo death', *American Anthropologist*, N. S. xliv (1942), pp. 169–81; H. Webster, *Taboo: a sociological study*, Stanford, 1942; C. Levi-Strauss, *Anthropologie Structurale*, Paris, 1958, pp. 183–204. The examples in the text are from *Mirac. S. Benedicti*, VIII. 37, pp. 339–40 (Waldo); Benedict, *Mirac. S. Thomae*, III. 63, pp. 167–8 (Luciana Torel); Philip, *Mirac. S. Frideswidae*, XCVII, p. 586. William, *op. cit.*, IV. 4, pp. 315–16 (Nicholas of Dover).

86 Sickness aggravated by stress: William of Malmesbury, *Gesta Pontificum*, V. 272, pp. 434–5. Cf. similar case in *Miracles de Rocamadour*, II. 18, p. 210. On sickness and stress, J. D. Frank, *Persuasion and healing. A comparative study of psychotherapy*, London, 1961, pp. 38–9.
'Hope invited . . .': Thomas of Monmouth, *Mirac. S. Willelmi*, VI. 16, p. 254.
'Faith-healing': in general, Frank, *op. cit.*, pp. 45–53, 64–74; J. Gillin, 'Magical fright', *Psychiatry*, ii (1948), pp. 389–94. On its role in modern clinical medicine, L. Lasagna *et al.*, 'A study of the placebo response', *American Journal of Medicine*, xvi (1954), pp. 770–9.
Placebos (false relics): Caesarius, *Dial. Mirac.*, VIII. 70, vol. ii, p. 140. Benedict, *Mirac. S. Thomae*, IV. 47, p. 217; but such deceptions did not always work, see William, *Mirac. S. Thomae*, V. 14, pp. 384–5.

87 Relapses: Benedict, *op. cit.*, II. 49, IV. 3, 21, pp. 95, 183, 199–200.

William, *op. cit.*, II. 56, VI. 72, pp. 219, 471. *Mirac. S. Gilberti*, II. 15, p. 66 (Sempringham). William of Malmesbury, *Gesta Pontificum*, V. 270, pp. 429–31.

Six factors: *Divine healing* (SW), pp. 10–13. See the valuable discussions of seventeenth-century miracles in Thomas, pp. 204–11, and M. Bloch, *Les Rois thaumaturges*, Paris, 1924, pp. 420–9.

VI. ORIGINS AND IDEALS

89 Scholars at Jerusalem: Eusebius, *Hist. Eccl.*, IV. xxvi. 13–14, VI. xx. 1, xxvii, pp. 386–8, 566, 580. Jerome, *De Viris Illustribus*, LIV, LXII, *PL.* xxiii. 664–8, 673.
'Footsteps of the Master': Origen, *In Joannem*, VI. 24, *PG.* xiv. 269.
'No other sentiment . . .': Paulinus, *Ep.* XLIV. 14, pp. 402–3.
90 Etheria: see her *Peregr.*, III. 5–6, X. 7, XXIII. 5, pp. 40, 52, 70.
Holy Week services: *Ibid.*, XXIV–XLIX, pp. 71–101.
Jerome and Paula: Jerome, *In Lib. Paralipomenon*, praefat., *PL.* xxix. 401; *Epp.* XLVI. 9, LVII. 2, CVIII. 9–10, vol. i, pp. 339, 529, vol. ii, pp. 314–18.
91 Footprints preserved: Paulinus, *Epp.* XLIX. 14, XXXI. 4, pp. 402–3, 271–2. Adamnan, *De Locis Sanctis*, I. xxiii. 3–5, p. 247.
92 Following Gospels in Holy Land: Bede, *Hist. Eccl.*, V. 15, p. 506; Adamnan, *op. cit.*, I. xxv. 1–8, pp. 251–3 (Arculf). *BBB.*, i. 151 (thirteenth-century Franciscan). Faber, *Evagatorium*, vol. i, pp. 25–6.
Meditation on humanity of Christ: *Vita Richardi Abbatis*, XVIII, pp. 288–9; cf. Hugh of Flavigny, *Chron.*, XVIII, p. 393. Antenoris, *Vita S. Silvini*, I. 6–9, p. 30 (not historically reliable). Benincasa, *Vita S. Rayneri*, IV. 48, p. 436.
93 '*Imitatio Christi*': Hugh of Flavigny, *Chron.*, XXI, pp. 395–6 (Richard of St.-Vannes). Benincasa, *op. cit.*, IV. 47, p. 436. On baptism in the Jordan, see *infra*. *Vita S. Bonae*, I. 13, *Aa. Ss.* May, vol. vii, p. 149. William of Malmesbury, *Gesta Regum*, III. 235, pp. 292–3 (Fulk Nerra). Theoderic of Wurzburg, *De Locis Sanctis*, XXV, p. 63 (flagellation on Mt. Sion). Robert of Torigny, *Chron.*, vol. ii, p. 51 (Henry II).
Stations of the Cross: Ernoul, *Chron.*, XVII, p. 206 (1231). Ricoldo, *Liber Peregrinationis*, VI, p. 112. Ogier d'Anglure, *Saint Voyage*, pp. 13–14.
Sacchetti's allegory: in *Sermoni*, LXVIII, pp. 165–6.
94 'enter into the mind . . .': Thomas of Celano, *De Mirac. B. Francisci*, II. 2, *Analecta Franciscana*, vol. x, Quaracchi, 1926–41, p. 273.
Pilgrimage as escape from civilization: Jerome, *Contra Joannem*, XLI, *PL.* xxiii. 393. *Vie de S. Mélanie*, II. 19, p. 168. Jerome, *Ep.* XLVI. 12, vol. i, pp. 342–3.
Impact of *Life of St. Anthony*: Augustine, *Confessions*, VIII. vi. 14–15, ed. P. Knoll, *CSEL.* xxxiii, Vienna, 1896, pp. 181–3.
Jerome's circle and the desert hermits: Jerome, *Epp.* CXXVII. 5, CVIII. 14, vol. iii, pp. 149–50, vol. ii, pp. 324–5 (Paula). Palladius, *Hist. Lausiaca*, XLVI, vol. ii, pp. 134–5 (elder Melania). Etheria, *Peregr.*, XVII. 2, p. 60. *Vie de S. Mélanie*, II. 39, p. 200.

95 Pilgrimage as self-exile: Jerome, *Contra Joannem*, XLI, *PL*. xxiii. 393; *Ep*. LVIII. 2–4, vol. i, pp. 529–33.
Four Anglo-Saxon kings: Caedwalla of Wessex (Bede, *Hist. Eccl.*, V. 7, pp. 470–2). Ceanred of Mercia and Offa of Wessex (*ibid.*, V. 19, p. 516). Ine of Wessex (*Anglo-Saxon Chron.*, p. 27).
Ratchis: *Lib. Pont.*, vol. i, pp. 433–4.
Karloman: *Annales Regni Francorum*, pp. 6–7. On Eudoxia, see J. B. Bury, *History of the later Roman Empire*, London, 1923, vol. i, pp. 226–31.

96 Irish concept of self-exile: Columban, *Sermo* VIII, *Opera*, ed. G. S. M. Walker, Dublin, 1957, pp. 94–6. Dermatius, *Exhortatoria*, *MD*. *Thes*. i. 341–2 ('be exiles . . .'). *Anglo-Saxon Chron.*, p. 53 (three pilgrims of 891).
'Going to Rome involves . . .': Gougaud, pp. 158–9.
Egbert: Bede, *Hist. Eccl.*, III. 27, pp. 312–14.
Wandering peculiarly Irish: Heiric's letter in *RHF*. vii. 563. Gozbert, *Mirac. S. Galli*, II. 47, *MGH. SS*. ii. 30.

97 Anglo-Saxons in Ireland: Bede, *Hist. Eccl.*, III. 27, IV. 4, pp. 313, 346–8. Alcuin, *Ep*. CCLXXXVII, ed. E. Duemmler, *MGH. Epp*. iv. 445–6.
Celtic influence: *Vita S. Sigiranni*, VIII, p. 386 (saec. ix). *Vita S. Wandregisili*, II. 9, *Aa. Ss.* July, vol. v, p. 274. *Vita S. Cadroae*, XX, *Aa. Ss. OSB.*, vol. vii, p. 494.
Wandering forbidden: *Capitularia Regum Francorum*, vol. i, pp. 35, 102, 133, vol. ii, p. 122.
Everard de Breteuil: Guibert, *De Vita Sua*, I. 9, pp. 25–6. Damian's views are contained in *De Contemptu Saeculi* (*Opusc. XII*), IX–XIV, *PL*. clxv. 260–7. For later criticism of monk-pilgrims, see St. Bernard, *Epp*. LVI, CCCIC, cols. 162–3, 612–13. Cf. miracle stories with the same moral, e.g. *Chron. Mon. Casinensis*, II. 11, p. 636; M. Valla, 'Les Lyonnais à Compostelle', *BHP*. (1964), pp. 240–1n.

VII. THE PENITENTIAL PILGRIMAGE

98 Legal distinctions: Peter of Joncels quoted in Du Cange, *Glossarium* (OS), vol. vi, p. 269. Cf. Alfonso X, *Siete Partidas*, I. xxiv. 1, vol. i (1), fol. 151vo.
Early penitential exiles: Jerome, *Ep*. CXLVII, vol. iii, pp. 312–29. Symeon Metaphrastes, *Vita S. Marciani*, XIX, *PG*. cxiv. 452–3 (late). Cf. Kötting (3), p. 330.
Irish penitentials: G. Le Bras, 'Pénitenciels', *DTC*. xii. 1162–5. Vogel (2), pp. 44–8, 53–6.

99 Public and private penance: Raymond of Peñaforte, *Summa*, III. xxxiv. 6, Avignon, 1715, pp. 642–3; cf. Aquinas, *Summa Theologica*, III (suppl.), q. xxviii, a. 3, vol. xii, p. 53. *Canterbury Tales*, p. 572.
Especially used for clerics or noblemen: Peter Damian, *Vita S. Romualdi*, VII. 37–8, *Aa. Ss.* Feb., vol. ii, p. 112; on Damian's own sentences, Lib. VII, *Ep*. XVII, *PL*. cxliv. 455; *Opusc*. V, *PL*. cxlv. 98. Bernold, *Chron.*, *MGH. SS*. v. 428, 429–30 (Thierry).

100 and for scandalous crimes: Rigaud, *Reg. Visitationum*, pp. 164, 325–6, 344, 425–6, 477, 579, 665. On Cologne synod of 1279, Hefele, vol. vi, p. 262. Raynald, *Annales*, An. 1319 (no. 27), vol. v, p. 123 (Roger da Bonito). Clement V, *Reg.* 7503, Rome, 1884–92, vol. vi, pp. 420–1 (Nogaret).
Eleventh-century penitential practice: C. Vogel, 'Les rites de la pénitence publique aux xe et xie siècles', *Mélanges offerts a Réné Crozet*, ed. P. Gallais and Y. J. Riou, Poitiers, 1966, vol. i, pp. 137–44. H. E. J. Cowdrey, *The Cluniacs and the Gregorian Reform*, Oxford, 1970, pp. 122–8, points out the importance of this for the expansion of monasticism. Cf. H. E. Mayer, *Geschichte der Kreuzzüge*, Stuttgart, 1965, pp. 31–4.

101 Penitential pilgrims of eleventh century: Helgaud, *Vita Roberti Regis*, XXX, *RHF.* x. 114–15. Orderic Vitalis, *Hist. Eccl.*, III, ed. Chibnall, vol. ii, p. 10 (Robert of Normandy). *Encomium Emmae*, II. 40, ed. A. Campbell, Camden Soc., 3rd. series, vol. lxxii, London, 1949, p. 36 (Canute). Fulk Nerra: Glaber, *Hist.*, II. 4, p. 32. William of Malmesbury, *Gesta Regum*, III. 235, pp. 292–3. On the complex chronology of his pilgrimages, see K. Norgate, *England under the Angevin kings*, London, 1887, vol. i, pp. 192–6.
Penitential pilgrimage as judicial exile: *Canones sub Edgaro Rege*, X, in *MC.* xviii. 514 (attribution incorrect). *Poenit. S. Columbani*, B. 1, in Bieler (ed.), *Irish penitentials*, p. 98. Conc. Mâcon quoted in Gratian, *CJC.*, vol. ii, p. 195, but this canon is not in *MC.* M. Bateson (ed.), 'A Worcester cathedral book of ecclesiastical collections made *c.* 1000 A.D.', *EHR.*, x (1895), p. 722; cf. Ivo of Chartres, *Decr.*, XV. 187, col. 897. Twelfth-century preacher: *Liber S. Jacobi*, I. 17, p. 154 ('in peregrinatione propter transgressiones suas a sacerdote suo quasi in exilio mittitur').

102 'By praying to the saints . . .': *De Virtut. S. Martini*, IV. praefat., p. 649; cf. I. 40, p. 606.
Chains break: *Ibid.*, I. 23, p. 600 (Willichar). *Vita S. Nicetii*, XIII–XIV, *MGH. Merov.*, iii. 523–4 (St. Nizier). Gregory of Tours, *Vitae Patrum*, VIII. 6, p. 697 (Agilulf). *Gesta Sanctorum Rotonensium*, III. 8, *Aa. Ss. OSB.*, vol. vi, pp. 219–21 (A.D. 868–875).

103 Salvation found at particular shrines: *Vita S. Austregisili*, IX, *MGH. Merov.* iv. 205 (Mestrille). Gregory of Tours, *In Gloria Confessorum*, p. 803n. (interpolated) on penitent directed to Moutiers-St.-Jean; the story is based on Jonas of Bobbio, *Vita Joannis Reomanensis*, XX, *MGH. Merov.* iii. 517 (saec. ix). *Mirac. S. Bavonis*, III. 4, *Aa. Ss. OSB.*, vol. ii, p. 414. Other ninth-century examples: Alcuin, *Vita Willibrordi*, XVII, *MGH. Merov.* vii. 136; *Mirac. S. Floriani*, VIII, *MGH. Merov.* iii. 70; Wilfrid Strabo (attrib.), *Mirac. S. Galli*, XXXIV, *Aa. Ss. OSB.*, vol. ii, pp. 264–5; *Vita S. Godegrandi*, II. 19, *Aa. Ss.* Sept., vol. i, p. 771. Confessors impose specific pilgrimages: *Poenit. Ps.-Egberti*, IV. 6, in Wasserschleben (ed.), *Bussordnungen*, p. 333. *Vita et Mirac. S. Frodoberti*, XXXI–XXXII, *PL.* cxxxvii. 616–17 (Ratbert). Aimoin, *Vita S. Abbonis*, X, cols. 398–9 ('poenitentiae voto, ante omnes fere in hoc tempore Galliae habitatores coeptum').

Sins erased: *Vita S. Egidii*, XXXV–XXXVI, *An. Boll.*, viii (1889), pp. 117–18 (attrib. to Fulbert of Chartres). *Mirac. S. Mariae Magdalenae Viziliaci Facta* (ed. alt.), III, *CCH*. (Paris), vol. ii, p. 292 (no. 1). *Liber S. Jacobi*, II. 2, pp. 262–3. *Mirac. S. Benedicti*, IX. praefat., pp. 357–8 (Hughes de Ste. Marie).

104 Pilgrimages imposed by Inquisition: Gui, *Practica*, II. 3, p. 39. Dossat, pp. 210–11 (Gourdon and Montcuq). On Gui's sentences, Molinier, pp. 400–1. In general, Lea (2), vol. i, pp. 466, 494–5.

105 Liège legal codes: Cauwenbergh, pp. 23–4.
Tradition of judicial exile in Flanders: R. C. van Caenegem, *Geschiedenis van het Strafrecht in Vlanderen, Verhandelingen van de koninklijke Vlaamse Akademie*, xix, Brussel, 1954, pp. 147–56.
Douai commutations: Le Grand, p. 385n[1].
Robert de Roux: *Chartes de Namur*, no. 1303, p. 385.
Devotions required at Liège: Cauwenberghe, p. 164.
Breaches of public order: Aquinas, *Summa Theologica*, III (suppl.), q. xxviii, a. 3, vol. xii, p. 53. *Coutumes de Liège*, vol. i, p. 494.

106 Arson: decree of 1186 in *MGH. Constit.* i. 450 (no. 318, cap. 8). *Chartes de Namur*, nos. 1000, 1026, pp. 298–9, 306.
Nieuport lynchings: Cauwenberghe, p. 10.
Affray and abusing councillor: *Coutumes de Namur*, Rep. 1440 (no. 77), Rep. 1483 (no. 118), vol. ii, pp. 91, 225–6.
Henri le Kien: Rupin, p. 215.
Pilgrimage for victim's satisfaction: *Poenit. Vinniani*, XXIII, in Bieler (ed.), *Irish penitentials*, pp. 80–2. *MGH. Constit.* i. 450 (no. 318). *Coutumes de Namur*, Rep. 1483 (no. 87), vol. ii, p. 194 (Gerard de Rostimont). Pagart d'Hermansart (ed.), 'Certificat d'accomplissement de pèlerinage pour homicide en 1333', *BHP*, (1891), pp. 372–3 (Bondulf). *Coutumes de Liège*, vol. ii, p. 145.

107 Pilgrimage imposed by arbitrators: On murderers of 1264, *CRH.*, 1e serie, ix (1847), p. 49. Beaumanoir, *Coutumes*, nos. 1296–7, pp. 168–70. Rigaud, *Reg. Visitationum*, pp. 507–8. See also *Cartulaire de la Commune de Fosses*, no. 10, ed. J. Borgnet, Namur, 1867, pp. 32–3. In 1307 the count of Namur would only submit his quarrel with Charles de Valois to the arbitration of Philip IV of France on condition that no pilgrimage was imposed on the loser, *Chartes de Namur*, no. 334, p. 96.
No commutation for Inquisition: Gui, *Practica*, II. 23, p. 55.
Tariffs: Cauwenberghe, pp. 222–3 (Oudenarde), and other lists, pp. 223–36. Van den Bussche (ed.), 'Rocamadour', pp. 50–2.

108 No commutation at Maestricht: Cauwenberghe, p. 148.
Enforced if not commuted: *Coutumes de Namur*, Rep. 1440 (no. 18), vol. ii, p. 30. *Ordonnances*, vol. v, p. 460, vol. ix, pp. 586–7, 589.
Pilgrimages imposed by corporations: Cauwenberghe, pp. 42–3, 161n.
And by treaty: *Archives de Bruges*, vol. i, pp. 292–5, 357–8, 405, vol. ii, pp. 254–7 (Arques, 1326). On Bruges pilgrimages of 1309 and 1393, Van den Bussche (ed.), 'Rocamadour', pp. 38–40. *Cartulaire de N-D de Boulogne*, no. 156, pp. 239–40.

109 Fettered pilgrims: Raynald, *Annales*, An. 1319 (no. 27), vol. v, p. 123 (murderer of bishop of Fricento). Thomas of Monmouth, *Mirac. S.*

Willelmi, VI. 9–10, 11, pp. 231–41, 256–8 (Norwich). Reginald of Durham, *De B. Cuthberti Virtut.*, LXXXIV, LXXIX, pp. 177–8, 164–5; cf. XCIII–XCV, pp. 205–12.

Thomas of Monmouth on broken fetters: *Op. cit.*, VI. 9, p. 235.

110 Fetters worn voluntarily: *Mirac. S. Benedicti*, VIII. 19, pp. 303–4 (Fleury). *Chron. Evesham*, II, p. 34. William of Malmesbury, *Gesta Pontificum*, V. 268, pp. 425–6 (Cologne penitent). John of S. Bertin, *Vita B. Bernardi*, I. 5, *Aa. Ss.* April, vol. ii, p. 676.

Crosses worn: Gui, *Practica*, II. 19, 34, pp. 53, 60. Lea (2), vol. i, pp. 466, 468–9.

Pieterseune: Van den Bussche (ed.), 'Rocamadour', pp. 48–9.

111 Pleas of sickness: *Coutumes de Namur*, Rep. 1440 (no. 80), Rep. 1483 (no. 58), vol. ii, pp. 95–6, 175; cf. Rep. 1483 (nos. 52, 254), vol. ii, pp. 169–70, 325.

Inquisitors' warning (1251): Molinier, p. 404.

Jan Vogel: *Actes et procès-verbaux des séances de l'université de Louvain*, ed. E. Reusens and A. van Hove, vol. ii, Brussels, 1919, pp. 126, 129–30, 143–9, 183–4, 201.

Pilgrimage alternative to death: On Lambert de Soif, *CRH.*, 2e serie, vii (1855), pp. 78–9. *Coutumes de Namur*, Rep. 1483 (no. 131), vol. ii, pp. 228–31 (Pierot the Porter). Guérin and Célier (eds.), *Documents concernant le Poitou*, vol. xxi, pp. 329–31 (no. 720) (cut-throats of 1393); cf. vol. xxiv, pp. 129–32, 284–7.

112 Alternative to banishment: *Coutumes de Liège*, vol. i, pp. 496–7.

Testimonials: Gui, *Practica*, II. 3, 10, III. 13, pp. 38, 47, 95; Van den Bussche (ed.), 'Rocamadour', p. 47. *Coutumes de Namur*, Rep. 1483 (no. 118). The fee required by the authorities at Bordeaux in 1495 was seven francs, six liards, see Reg. Fabrique de S. Michel, Archives Departmentales (Gironde), G. 2252.

Judicial pilgrimage opposed: *Capitularia Regum Francorum*, vol. i, pp. 60–1 (Charlemagne). Rabanus Maurus, *Poenit.*, VII, *PL.* cx. 473–4; cf. Conc. Mainz (847), in *MC.* xiv. 908–9; Conc. Seligenstadt (1022), *PL.* cxl. 1062. Jacques de Vitry, *Hist. Hierosolymitana*, LXXXII, pp. 1096–7. Aquinas, *Summa Theologica*, III (suppl.), q. xxviii, a. 3, vol. xii, p. 53. Durand de S. Pourçain, *In Sententias*, IV. xv. 4, Lyon, 1595, p. 745.

113 Mansfeld's surprise: Van den Bussche (ed.), 'Rocamadour', pp. 22–3, 26.

VIII. THE GREAT AGE OF PILGRIMAGE

114 'Some three years . . .': Glaber, *Hist.*, III. 4, pp. 61–2. Cf. Anselm, *Hist. Dedicationis S. Remigii*, *PL.* cxlii. 1417–18.

Disruptions of barbarians: E. Mabille, *Les invasions Normandes dans la Loire et les péregrinations du corps de S. Martin*, Paris, 1869; also, Gasnault, pp. 55–61. On St. Cuthbert, Symeon of Durham, *Hist. Dunelmensis Eccl.*, II. 6–III. 1, vol. i, pp. 54–80 (with many apocryphal details). On St. Evroul, Orderic, *Hist. Eccl.*, VI. 9–10, ed. Chibnall, vol. iii, pp. 276, 282–4, 302–4. Bernard, *Itin.*, XXIV, p. 320.

115 Hospices decayed: *Capitularia Regum Francorum*, vol. ii, pp. 408, 434–5

(Irish hospices). *Bullarium Casinense*, const. XXX, vol. ii, Rome, 1670, p. 25.

Route to Jerusalem: Glaber, *Hist.*, IV. 6, pp. 106–7.

Hospices in Hungary: on Melk, Orderic Vitalis, *Hist. Eccl.*, III, ed. Chibnall, vol. ii, p. 68. Richard of St.-Vanne was entertained at the Hungarian court in 1027, see G. Morin, 'Un théologien ignoré du xie siècle: l'évêque-martyr Gérard de Czanad', *Revue Bénédictine*, xxvii (1910), pp. 518–19; as also was Lietbert of Cambrai in 1054, *Vita Lietberti*, XXXII, p. 703. On the royal hospice at Vashegy (Pécvarad), see A. Palla, 'Hospital in Hungary in the XIth century', *Atti del primo congresso Europeo di storia ospitaliera*, Reggio Emilia, 1962, pp. 278–85.

Route to Santiago: Defourneaux, pp. 67–8. Pelayo, *Chron.*, *ES*. xiv. 473–4. *Hist. Compostellana*, I. 30, 31, III. 9, pp. 69, 71, 489; on ambassadors' impressions, *ibid.*, II. 50, p. 350.

116 Gottschalk: Vazquez de Parga, *et al.*, vol. i, p. 42 (the fundamental work). New relics: Glaber, *Hist.*, III. 6, pp. 68–9 (Sens). Gregory VII, *Reg.*, VIII. 8, pp. 526–7 (Salerno). Peter the Deacon, *Historica Relatio*, I. 1, p. 288 (Monte Cassino). Bethell, pp. 61, 65 (Reading).

St. Leonard: Adémar de Chabannes, *Chron.*, III. 56, p. 181. *Aa. Ss.* Nov., vol. iii, pp. 139, 148–9. On the saints of the route to Santiago, *Guide*, VIII, pp. 35–83.

117 South-western France: on the councils of 1031, *MC*. xix. 502–6. Pilgrimages: Adémar, *Chron.*, III. 40–1, 48, 65–6, 68, pp. 162–3, 171, 189–90, 192–3, 194; *Vita S. Geraldi*, VII–IX, XVII, *Aa. Ss. OSB.*, vol. ix, pp. 880–2, 884–5, cf. pp. 869–71.

118 Norman pilgrimages: Hugh of Flavigny, *Chron.*, XIX, pp. 393–4 (Richard of St.-Vannes). William of Jumièges, *Gesta Normannorum Ducum*, VI. 11, pp. 111–13 (Robert). Orderic, *Hist. Eccl.*, III, ed. Chibnall, vol. ii, p. 10.

Norman hospices in Rome: *Mirac. S. Wulfranni*, II. 12, *Aa. Ss.* March, vol. iii, p. 154.

Rouen coins: J. Lafaurie, 'Le trésor monétaire du Puy', *Revue Numismatique*, 5e serie, xv (1952), no. 26, pp. 117–18.

Normans impeded: Letter of John of Fécamp in *PL*. cxliii. 797. On Normans imprisoned at Constantinople, Adémar, *Chron.*, III. 55, p. 178. *Mirac. S. Fidis*, III. 1, pp. 128–30 (Roger de Tosny).

119 Mass-pilgrimage of 1024–5: Glaber, *Hist.*, IV. 6, p. 106. Hugh of Flavigny, *Chron.*, XVIII, p. 393.

Aganon: *GC*. iv. 381–4.

Synod of 1094: *Chron. S. Benigni Divionensis*, MGH. SS. v. 43 ('ubi primo iurata via Hierosolymitana'); cf. *MC*. xx. 799. Pilgrims from the neighbouring provinces of Lorraine and the Rhineland included Poppo abbot of Stavelot in 990 (Everhelm, *Vita Popponis*, III, MGH. SS. xi. 295–6); at least one count and one bishop of Verdun (*Gesta Episcoporum Virdunensium*, IX–X, MGH. SS. iv. 49); Adalbert, count of Metz (*Notitiae Fundationis Mon. Bosonis Villae*, I, MGH. SS. xv. 977–8); from Trier went Hierocon, abbot of S. Maximin (Mabillon (SW), vol. iv, p. 291), an abbot of St. Martin in 1026 (Eberwin, *Vita S. Symeonis*, X, *Aa. Ss. OSB.*, vol. viii, pp. 375–6), and an archbishop in

1025 (*Gesta Treverorum*, contin., III, V, *PL.* cliv. 1182, 1186); and Richard of St.-Vannes, whose monastery lay just outside Verdun.

Monastic libraries: thirteenth-century catalogue of books at St. Martial in Duplès-Agier (ed.), *Chroniques*, pp. 326, 329, 333, 336, 343. Eighteenth-century catalogue of Moissac in Archives Communales (Moissac), JJ. 1; the Moissac MS of the Bordeaux pilgrim is now Bibl. Nat. MS. Lat. 4808.

Western possessions of the Holy Sepulchre: many of these are listed in a confirmatory papal bull of Sept. 1128 in *Cartulaire du Saint-Sepulchre*, XVI, ed. E. de Rozière, Paris, 1849, pp. 18–22. Among the monastic houses which administered them in the eleventh century were S. Michel de Cuxa (Riant (2)); Moissac (Bibl. Nat. Coll. Doat, CXXVIII, fols. 91–2, 216vo–217vo, CXXIX, fols. 58vo–60); and Conques (*Cartulaire de Conques*, nos. 329, 392, pp. 257, 290).

Spanish spoil enriches Cluny: Glaber, *Hist.*, IV. 7, pp. 109–10. On the interest of the abbots in the pilgrimage to Santiago, see *Vita B. Morandi*, in *Bibliotheca Cluniacensis*, cols. 501–3.

120 Miracles of St. James and Cluny: the stories in *Liber S. Jacobi*, II. 16–18, pp. 276–83, are taken from Alexander, *Dicta Anselmi*, XXI–XXIII, ed. R. W. Southern and F. S. Schmitt, *Memorials of St. Anselm*, London, 1969, pp. 196–209, cf. pp. 31–2. Arnaldo's letter, ed. J. Vielliard in *Guide*, p. 126. On the dissemination of the miracles, see Vazquez de Parga *et al.*, vol. i, pp. 176–7; David, vol. i, pp. 30–9; J. Lafond, *Les Vitraux de l'eglise de S. Ouen de Rouen*, *Corpus Vitrearum Medii Aevi*, France, IV (2), Paris, 1970, p. 94.

Mayeul's pilgrimages: Nalgod, *Vita S. Majoli*, II. 18, *Aa. Ss.* May, vol. ii, p. 662. Syrus, *Vita S. Majoli*, II. 15, 17, *Aa. Ss. OSB.*, vol. vii, pp. 797–8.

121 Bonizo on duties of knights: *De Vita Christiana*, VII. 28, ed. E. Perels, *Texte zur Geschichte des römisches und kanonisches rechts im Mittelalter*, I, Berlin, 1930, pp. 248–9.

Aristocratic guilt: William IX, *Chanson* XI, ed. A. Jeanroy, 2nd. ed., Paris, 1926, p. 28. *La 'Bible' au seigneur de Berzé*, ll. 777–87, ed. F. Lecoy, Paris, 1938, p. 49; cf. ll. 188–205, 809–22, 825–6, 843–6, pp. 30, 32–3, 50, 51. On Roger of Foix, *Chartes de Cluny*, no. 2991, vol. iv, pp. 189–90.

Gerald of Aurillac: Odo, *Vita S. Geraldi*, I. 8–11, II. 16–17, 22, III. 3, cols. 646–50, 679–80, 682–3, 691. On the authenticity of this version, Poncelet.

122 Annual pilgrimages: Adémar, *Chron.*, III. 41, p. 163. *Mirac. S. Mariae Magdalenae Viziliaci facta* (ed. alt.), I, VI, *CCH* (Paris), vol. ii, pp. 292–3 (no. 2), *An. Boll.*, xvii (1898), pp. 178–9.

Canterbury statistics: Benedict and William, *Mirac. S. Thomae*, passim. Allowance is made for pilgrims mentioned in both collections. Women are classified as their husbands or fathers, children as their parents.

123 Declining social standing of pilgrims: Vergerio, *Ep.* LXXXVI, p. 212. Wright (ed.), *Letters*, p. 85 (Bury).

Luxurious pilgrimages: William of Jumièges, *Gesta Normannorum Ducum*, VI. 11, pp. 112–13. *Anglo-Saxon Chronicle*, p. 134 (Ealdred).

German pilgrimage of 1064: *Annales Altahenses Maiores*, p. 67. Marianus Scottus, *Chron.*, *MGH. SS.* v. 559. Lambert of Hersfeld, *Annales*, pp. 93–4.

124 Peter the Venerable on pilgrimages: *Epp.* LI, LXXX, CXLIV, vol. i, pp. 151–2, 216, 358–9.
Sermon *Veneranda Dies: Liber S. Jacobi*, I. 17, pp. 141–76, esp. pp. 144–5, 152, 154, 156–7.

125 Palestine hermits: Reginald, *Vita S. Godrici*, XV. 43, pp. 57–8. Phocas, *De Locis Sanctis*, XXIII, XXXI, cols. 952–3, 961. Jacques de Vitry, *Hist. Hierosolymitana*, LII–LIII, pp. 1074–5. Benincasa, *Vita S. Rayneri*, II. 22, 26, pp. 430, 431. Theobald, *Vita S. Guilelmi*, V. 22, *Aa. Ss.* Feb., vol. ii, p. 457.

126 Berthold of Neuenburg: *Annales Marbacenses*, p. 75.
Crusaders' austerities: Jacques de Vitry, *Exempla*, LXXV, CXXIV, pp. 38–9, 57. Ambroise, *L'Estoire de la Guerre Sainte*, ed. G. Paris, Paris, 1879, col. 325.
Pilgrims become monks: Peter the Venerable, *De Mirac.*, I. 11, 18, cols. 874–5, 883.

127 Walking: Sulpicius Severus, *Dialogi*, I. 21, p. 173. Honoratus, *Vita S. Hilarii*, III. 22, *Aa. Ss.* May, vol. ii, p. 31 (not historically reliable). *Vita S. Ayberti*, I. 5, *Aa. Ss.* April, vol. i, p. 674. Benedict, *Mirac. S. Thomae*, III. 48, IV. 94, pp. 152, 257 (Matilda of Thornbury; countess of Clare). *Mirac. S. Martialis*, XXXIII, p. 427 ('totus nudus'). *Vita S. Godrici*, XIV. 39–40, pp. 53–5. Labande (2), pp. 104–5n[13] (canon of Dol). William, *Mirac. S. Thomae*, VI. 18, p. 430 (John King). MS. Gloucester cathedral 1, fol. 175 (Reading pilgrim).

128 'Open to him . . .': Jacques de Vitry, *Exempla*, CXXXIII, pp. 59–60.
Baptismal imagery: Benedict, *Mirac. S. Thomae*, III. 11, p. 126. Bridget, *Rev.*, VII. 14, p. 550. Bartolus, *Tractatus*, XXVIII, p. 56 (Portiuncula).

129 Mary the Egyptian: earliest version (saec. vii) in Sophronius, *Vita S. Mariae Aegyptiaca*, PL. lxxiii. 673–90. Other versions: Hildebert, *Vita B. Mariae Aegyptiaca*, PL. clxxi. 1321–40; Honorius, *Speculum Ecclesiae*, PL. clxxii. 906. P. Mesplé, *Toulouse: Musée des Augustins. Les sculptures romanes*, *Inventaires des collections publiques françaises*, vol. v, Paris, 1961, no. 33. Sites marked: Daniel, *Pèlerinage*, pp. 19, 28.
Bathing in Jordan: Antenoris, *Vita S. Silvini*, I. 9, p. 30. Raymond of Aguilers, *Hist. Francorum*, XX, pp. 301–2 (Raymond of St. Gilles). *Saga Olafs Konungshins Helga*, *Fornmanna Sogur*, V, Copenhagen, 1830, p. 314 (Thornstein). *Pèlerinage d'Euphrosine*, p. 34. Theoderic, *De Locis Sanctis*, XXX, p. 73.

130 Copied at Santiago: *Guide*, VI, p. 16.
Jacques de Vitry on Jordan: *Hist. Hierosolymitana*, LIII, pp. 1075–6.
Jordan water as relic: Philip, *Descriptio* (c. 1285–91), VIII, pp. 64–5. Faber, *Evagatorium*, vol. ii, pp. 36–7. *Voyage de la Saincte Cyté* (1480), pp. 101–2.
Desire for death: *Pèlerinage d'Euphrosine*, p. 33. Eskill's prayer quoted in Labande (3), p. 346. Caesarius, *Dial. Mirac.*, XI. 24, vol. ii, p. 291. Theoderic, *De Locis Sanctis*, IV, pp. 9–10 (Aceldama).

131 Importance of burial-place: Paulinus, *Carmina*, XXXI. 605–10, pp. 328–9. E. Le Blant, *Etude sur les sarcophages Chrétiens de la ville d'Arles*, Paris, 1878, p. xxxvi. Suger, *Vita Lodovici VI*, XXXIV, p. 286.

Site of last judgement: Innominatus I, *Descriptio*, p. 99. Theoderic, *De Locis Sanctis*, XXXII, p. 77. Faber, *Evagatorium*, vol. i, pp. 392–3.

132 Lethbald: Glaber, *Hist.*, IV. 6, pp. 106–7.
Millenarianism: Otto of Friesing, *De Duabus Civitatibus*. Marculf, *Formulae*, II. 3, *PL.* lxxxvii. 729 ('manifest signs . . .'). Adso, *Libellus de Antichristo*, *PL.* ci. 1291–8.

133 Last day described: Benzo of Alba, *Ad Heinricum IV Imperatorem*, I. 14–15, V. 6, *MGH. SS.* xi. 605, 653; cf. Ekkehard of Aura, *Hierosolymitana*, XXXIV, XXXV, *RHC. Occ.* v. 38–9. See Erdmann.
Paris preacher: Haimo, *Vita S. Abbonis*, IX, col. 397; cf. Abbo, *Ep.* X, *PL.* cxxxix. 471. On the year 1000, see Plaine.
Panic of 1009–10: Glaber, *Hist.*, III. 7, pp. 71–2. Adémar, *Chron.*, III. 48, 68, pp. 171, 194. *Vita Gauzlini*, III, ed. P. Ewald, *Neues Archiv der Gesellschaft für ältere deutsche Geschichtskunde*, iii (1887–8), p. 353. On Raymond's pilgrimage, M-A-F. de Gaujal, *Etudes historiques sur le Rouergue*, vol. ii, Paris, 1858, p. 38.

134 Panic of 1033: Glaber, *Hist.*, III. 3, IV. praefat., 5, pp. 62, 90, 103–6. On Glaber's own feelings, see Petit. *GC.* ii. 105 (instr. XXXIX), 24 Oct. 1036 (Hictor). J. Doinel (ed.), 'Un pèlerinage á Jérusalem dans la première moitié du xie siècle', *BEC.* li (1890), pp. 204–6 (Hervé). Cf. *Cartulaire de Conques*, nos. 419, 453, pp. 308–9, 328–9.
Panic of 1064–5: *Vita Altmanni Ep. Pataviensis*, III, *MGH. SS.* xii. 230; *Annales Altahenses Maiores*, p. 66; and see Eicken, p. 317. Millenarian formulae suddenly appear in Limousin charters of this year, e.g. *Chartes, chroniques, et mémoriaux pour servir á l'histoire de la Marche et du Limousin*, ed. A. Leroux and A. Bosvieux, Tulle, 1886, p. 13 (no. 9).

135 Provençals in 1099: Raymond of Aguilers, *Hist. Francorum*, XX, p. 296. 'Tell me then . . .': Peter Damian, *De Laude Flagellorum* (*Opusc. XLIII*), IV, *PL.* cxlv. 682–3.

136 William of Hirsau: Haimo, *Vita Willelmi Hirsaugiensis*, XXI, *MGH. SS.* xii. 218.

IX. THE LEGACY OF THE CRUSADE

137 'God has invented . . .': Guibert, *Gesta Dei per Francos*, I. 1, p. 124.

138 'Taking us to be no pilgrims . . .': *Gesta Francorum*, I. 4, p. 8.
Unarmed hangers-on: Raymond of Aguilers, *Hist. Francorum*, XVII, pp. 279–80 (first crusade). *Annales Herbipolenses*, *MGH. SS.* xvi. 3 (second crusade).
Jerusalem lost by sin: Jacques de Vitry, *Hist. Hierosolymitana*, LXXII, p. 1088.
'Is there nothing . . .': Dante, *Paradiso*, IV. 133–8, V. 16–84; cf. Aquinas, *Summa Theologica*, II, q. lxxxviii, a. 1–2, vol. ix, pp. 234–5, 238–9.
Crosses: Robert the Monk, *Hist. Hierosolymitana*, I. 2, II. 3, *RHC. Occ*, iii. 729, 741; Guibert, *Gesta Dei per Francos*, II. 5, p. 140 (in 1096). Odo of Deuil, *De Profectione Lodovici VII*, I, p. 22 (in 1146). H. Pflaum (ed.), 'A strange crusaders' song', *Speculum*, x (1935), pp. 337–9. In general, Villey, pp. 119–21.
Vows enforced: *CJC., Coll. Greg. IX*, III. xxxiv. 7, vol. ii, cols. 591–3;

Tardif (ed.), *Coutumiers*, vol. ii, pp. 64–6, 214–15. Innocent III, *Reg.* V, 103, XVI. 35, *PL.* ccxiv. 1100, ccxvi. 830. On Frederic II's vow. Hefele, vol. v, pp. 1411–27.

139 Bound by vow of another: *CJC., Coll. Greg. IX*, III. xxxiv. 6, vol. ii. cols. 590–1; see Villey, p. 126. William, *Mirac. S. Thomae*, II. 13, pp, 169–70.

Dispensations: *CJC., Coll. Greg. IX*, III. xxxiv. 2, 8, vol. ii, cols. 589, 593–4. On Thierry, J. Calmet, *Histoire de Lorraine*, vol. ii, Nancy, 1748, p. 240. Paulus (2), vol. i, pp. 209–11; Villey, p. 251.

Commutation for money: Matthew Paris, *Chron. Maj.*, vol. iv, pp. 6–7, 9, 133–4. Paulus (2), vol. ii, pp. 35–9. A. Gottlob, *Kreuzablass und Almosenablass*, Stuttgart, 1906, p. 308. On preachers of 1290 and 1308, *The Register of John de Halton, bishop of Carlisle*, ed. T. F. Tout, vol. i, London, 1906, p. 317.

140 Punishment for broken vows: MS. Gloucester cathedral 1, fols. 174vo–175 (St. James).

'On condition that . . .': *Mirac. B. Egidii*, IX, *MGH. SS.* xii. 321.

Bargain with saint: *Mirac. S. Martialis*, VII, XXV, XLIV, pp. 417–18, 424, 431.

141 'Excused him from suffering . . .': Henry of Ghent, *Quodlibeta*, XV. 14. Paris, 1518, p. 589.

Council at Rheims: in *MC.* xviii. 345–6. See Paulus (2), vol. i, pp. 99–119.

Crusading indulgence: Conc. Clermont in *MC.* xx. 816; Conc. Lateran in *MC.* xxii. 1067. H. Hagenmeyer (ed.), *Die Kreuzzugsbriefe aus dem Jahren 1088–1100*, Innsbruck, 1900, pp. 396–7.

Early papal indulgences for pilgrims: Paulus (2), vol. i, p. 153 (Pavilly); Urban II, *Reg.* CLXXV, col. 447–9 (Angers).

142 Episcopal indulgences: Delehaye (2), vol. xliv, pp. 351–79. *CJC., Coll. Greg. IX*, V. xxxviii. 14, vol. ii, cols. 888–9 (Lateran council). *DTC.*, vol. vii, cols. 1609–10 (Univ. Paris). Conc. Aquilea in *MC.* xxiii. 1119–20.

Collemaggio: *Vita S. Petri Coelestini*, XXX, *An. Boll.*, xvi (1897), pp. 418–19; text of indulgence in Bartolus, *Tractatus*, p. clxxxii. Boniface VIII, *Reg.* 770, 815, 850, vol. i, pp. 257–61, 274–5, 286–7.

Portiuncula: general discussions in Sabatier's introduction to Bartolus, *op. cit.*, pp. xvii–xcvi; Van Ortroy; Paulus (2), vol. ii, pp. 1–4, 319–20: Catholic historians have, on the whole, condemned the indulgence while the Calvinist Sabatier defended it. Arguments of thirteenth-century opponents cited by Peter John Olivi in his defence of the indulgence, written c. 1279, see Bartolus, *op. cit.*, pp. lvii–lix. On the popularity of the pilgrimage, Wadding, An. 1295 (no. 12), vol. v, p. 337; Bartolus, *op. cit.*, XLIV, p. 93.

143 Confession essential: *Liber S. Jacobi*, I. 17, pp. 144–5.

Extravagant claims for indulgences criticized: Simon of Cremona, *De Indulgentiis*, p. 86; cf. *CJC., Coll. Clem. VI*, V. vii. 1, vol. ii, cols. 1186–7. See Remy, pp. 9–10; Paulus (2), vol. ii, pp. 330–4, 340–2, 348–9.

144 Unconfessed pilgrims excluded: *Miracles de Rocamadour*, I. 5, pp. 79–82.

Mirac. S. Michaelis, pp. 880–2. Alfonso X, *Cantigas*, CCXVII, vol. ii, pp. 303–4 (Villalcazar). *Mirac. S. Martialis*, VIII, p. 418.
Gerald of Wales: see his *De Invectionibus*, V. 12, vol. i, pp. 137–8.

X. THE GROWTH OF A CULT

146 'A young man of low . . .': Guibert, *De Pignoribus*, I. 2, col. 621.
147 Normans in England: Eadmer, *Vita Anselmi*, I. 30, p. 51 (Lanfranc).
Gesta Abbatum S. Albani, ed. H. T. Riley, *RS.*, London, 1876–9, vol. i, p. 62. William of Malmesbury, *Gesta Pontificum*, V. 265, pp. 421–2.
Elevation: Bede, *Eccl. Hist.*, IV. 30, pp. 442–4 (Cuthbert). Delehaye (8), pp. 184–5. Kemp, pp. 37–40.
148 Relics of Brogne: *De Virtut. S. Eugenii Bronii Ostensis*, I–VI, *MGH. SS.* xv. 647–9. On the date, G. Morin, 'De translatione S. Eugenii', *An. Boll.*, v (1886), p. 386.
Udalric: *Aa. Ss.* May, vol. i, p. 283. Fontanini (ed.), *Codex*, vol. i, pp. 2–3. Delehaye (8), pp. 185–9.
Urban's canonizations: *Aa. Ss.* June, vol. i, p. 249; Fontanini (ed.), *Codex*, vol. v, p. 9. On abbot of Quimperlé, *Aa. Ss. OSB.*, vol. ix, p. 109.
149 Long delays: Kemp, pp. 86–9 (Becket). *MD. Thes.*, vol. iii, col. 1851 (Edmund). Toynbee, pp. 149–205 (Louis). *Lit. Cant.*, vol. iii, pp. 400–1 (Winchelsea).
'It is my belief . . .': H-F. Delaborde (ed.), 'Fragments de l'enquête faite à St.-Denis en vue de la canonisation de S. Louis', *Mems. de la Soc. de l'Histoire de Paris*, xxiii (1896), p. 62.
Lots drawn: Reginald, *De B. Cuthberti Virtut.*, XIX, CXV, pp. 38–9, 260. William, *Mirac. S. Thomae*, II. 82, p. 244.
150 Wulfstan 'the new saint': *Mirac. S. Wulfstani*, I. 37, p. 137.
Cult of St. Thomas sporadic: William of Canterbury, *Mirac. S. Thomae*, III. 33, 48, pp. 290, 304. Philip, *Mirac. S. Frideswidae*, LXXVI, p. 583 (c. 1190). Caesarius, *Dial. Mirac.*, VIII. 69, vol. ii, p. 139 (c. 1223). Ralph of Coggeshall, *Chron. Anglicanum*, ed. J. Stephenson, *RS.*, London, 1875, pp. 202–3 (Bromholm). *Lit. Cant.*, vol. iii, pp. 26–8 (fourteenth-century miracle). On Canterbury Jubilees, Foréville, pp. 41, 47–81.
151 Fame of miracles: *Mirac. S. Eutropii*, IV. 29–30, III. 19, pp. 742–3, 740. Guibert, *De Vita Sua*, III. 20, pp. 228–30 (canons of Laon). *Mirac. S. Egidii*, VIII–IX, *MGH. SS.* xii. 320–1.
Libelli miraculorum: Delehaye (6). Sulpicius's influence can be seen in Benedict, *Mirac. S. Thomae*, II. 1, IV. 58, pp. 119–20, 224–5; and in *Mirac. S. Fidis*, I. 34, pp. 84–5.
Duty to record miracles: Benedict, *op. cit.*, VI. 4, pp. 269–70. MS. Gloucester cathedral 1, fols. 171–171vo (Reading monk).
152 Efficacy of saints compared: *Chron. Evesham*, p. 47. William of Canterbury, II. 75, pp. 238–9.
Rivals of Canterbury: Reginald, *De B. Cuthberti Virtut.*, CXII, CXIV–CXVI, CXXVI, pp. 251–2, 256, 260–1, 271. Philip, *Mirac. S. Frideswidae*, XII, LXXVI, pp. 570, 583. MS. Gloucester cathedral 1, fols. 174–174vo, cf. fol. 173 (Reading).

Advertisement: *Becket Materials*, vol. ii, p. 49, vol. vii, pp. 564–6. Kajava (ed.), *Etudes*, p. 98 (Fécamp). *Carmen de translatione S. Bartholomaei*, p. 574: loosely translated, 'everyone knows that Rome alone has the tomb, Rome alone has the body; deceit will not benefit Benevento; a curse on Benevento'. Rémy, p. 122 (Liège). Sachet, vol. i, pp. 519–23 (Lyon).

153 Packaging: *Translatio SS. Chrysanti et Dariae*, IX, *Aa. Ss. OSB.*, vol. v, p. 613 (Prüm). Baraut (ed.), *Llibre Vermell*, pp. 28–9 (Montserrat). Elton, p. 16 (Canterbury. A hostile report).

154 Decoration of sanctuaries: John Chrysostom, *In Ep. II ad Corinthios*, XXVI, *PG.* lxi. 582; E. Bishop, *Liturgica Historica*, Oxford, 1918, pp. 25–6. On the Holy Sepulchre, Eusebius, *Vita Constantini*, III. 40, ed. I. A. Heikel, *Eusebius Werke*, vol. i, Leipzig, 1902, pp. 94–5; Antoninus, *Itin.*, XVIII, p. 171. On Nola, Paulinus of Nola, *Carmina*, XIV. 98–103, p. 49. On St.-Denis, Suger, *De Admin. Sua*, pp. 192–3, 200–1; *Vita Lodovici VI*, X, p. 54. On Canterbury, *An Italian relation of England about the year 1500*, ed. C. A. Sneyd, Camden Soc., vol. xxxvii, London, 1847, pp. 30–1; *Letters and papers*, vol. xiii (2), p. 49 (no. 133), cf. vol. xiii (2), p. 155 (nos. 401–2).

155 Expensive shrines criticized: Guibert, *De Pignoribus*, I. 4, IV. 1, cols. 626, 666. Bernard, *Apologia ad Guillelmum*, XII. 28, in *Opera*, ed. J. Leclercq and H. M. Rochais, vol. iii, Rome, 1963, pp. 104–6.

156 Reliquaries as cash reserves: Glaber, *Hist.*, I. 4, p. 11 (Cluny). William of Malmesbury, *Gesta Pontificum*, V. 271, p. 432. Dugdale (ed.), *Monasticon*, vol. iv, p. 44 (Reading). See Duby, p. 52.

Saints thought of as rich: Theofrid, *Flores Epitaphiorum*, II. 6, cols. 356–7. Reginald, *De B. Cuthberti Virtut.*, LXVIII, p. 140. *The Life of Christina of Markyate*, ed. C. H. Talbot, Oxford, 1959, p. 186.

Accounts of miracles available at shrines: *Mirac. S. Michaelis*, p. 880 (saec. xi). *Lit. Cant.*, vol. iii, p. 398.

157 'Pictures of their eyes . . .': Theodoret of Cyrus, *Graecarum Affectionum Curatio*, VIII, col. 1032.

Ex-votos: Examples can be found in almost every miracle collection. Those quoted are from: *Mirac. S. Martialis*, LI, pp. 433–4; *Miracles de Rocamadour*, I. 25, III. 11, pp. 116, 288–9; Thomas of Monmouth, *Mirac. Willelmi Norwicensis*, V. 19, pp. 210–11; Wright (ed.), *Letters*, pp. 143, 221, 224 (monastic commissioners). William, *Mirac. S. Thomae*, VI. 12, p. 424; Benedict, *Mirac. S. Thomae*, II. 60, 64, III. 36, pp. 105, 109, 143.

158 Unusual *ex-votos*: *Mirac. S. Eadmundi* (*MS. Bodley* 240), I, p. 367. Alfonso X, *Cantigas*, CCXXXII, vol. ii, pp. 321–2 (Villalcazar). *Miracles de Rocamadour*, III. 16, p. 297.

Ruptured chains: Gregory of Tours, *Vitae Patrum*, VIII. 6, p. 697. *Guide*, VIII, p. 54.

Problem of disposal: *Mirac. S. Mariae Magdalenae Magdalenae Viziliaci Facta*, IX, in Faillon (ed.), *Monuments inédits*, vol. ii, p. 739. Instructions of Santiago guardians in Lopez-Ferreiro, vol. iv, p. 67 (appendix XXV). Offering obligatory: *Mirac. S. Fidis*, I. 18–20, pp. 54–8. On Fitz-Eisulf, Benedict, *Mirac. S. Thomae*, IV. 64, pp. 229–34; William, *Mirac. S.*

Thomae, II. 5, pp. 160–2; Rackham, pp. 99–100. On St. Denis of Montmartre, Eugenius III, *Reg.* CXCIV, *PL.* clxxx. 1242, as corrected by Paulus (2), vol. i, p. 163.

159 Offering as tribute money: Odo, *Vita S. Geraldi*, II. 17, col. 680 ('decem solidos ad proprium collum dependentes, tamquam supplex servus domino suo quasi censum deferret'). *Cartulaire de S. Vincent du Mans*, no. 342, ed. R. Charles and M. d'Elbenne, Le Mans, 1913, cols. 204–205; see Du Cange, *Glossarium*, vol. ii, p. 257. *Notae Sangallenses*, *MGH. SS.* i. 71 ('se perpetualiter S. Sepulchri servitio dicavit'). On the Breisgau pilgrims, *Annales Marbacenses*, p. 75 ('perpetuo servicio sancti Sepulchri devoverunt'). Aragonese gifts to St. James: Celestine III, *Reg.*, CLXXXI, *PL.* ccvi. 1067 ('quasi tributa quae Deo et beato Jacobo apostolo in Hispania . . . exsolvenda'). On the Cologne reliquary, P. E. Schramm, *Denkmale der deutsche Könige und Kaiser*, Munchen, 1962, pp. 187–8, and pl. 192. *Mirac. S. Egidii*, XIII, *An. Boll.*, ix (1880), p. 396 (Raymond Ferraldo).

160 Santiago offerings ritual: in Lopez Ferreiro, vol. v, pp. 64–7 (appendix XXV).
Canterbury accounts: Woodruff, pp. 16–18. Savine, p. 103.
Bury St. Edmunds receipts: *Chron. Buriensis*, in Arnold (ed.), *Memorials*, vol. iii, p. 32.
St.-Trond: *Gesta Abbatum S. Trudonensium*, I. 9–12, vol. i, pp. 15–22.

161 St. Stephen's arm at Châlons: *GC.* x. 129–30.
Bollezeel: *Mirac. B. V. M. in Bollezeel*, in *Anecdota Gielemans*, III. 20, pp. 395–6.

162 St.-Gilles: text of petition in Bondurand (OS), pp. 441–4.
Partition of offerings: *RHF.* vi. 582 (Tours). Morand, pp. 220–2 (Ste.-Chapelle).
Disputes at Rome: in general, Fabre. On the incident of 1350, Rodo-canachi, p. 163. For disputes in other churches see, e.g., *Hist. Compostellana*, III. 9, p. 489; *Chartulary of Bridlington*, pp. 448–9; Sachet, vol. i, pp. 305–7, 502–3.

163 Papal share: Wily's instructions in *CPR. Letters*, vol. xi, p. 685. On Eton indulgence, *The Official correspondance of Thomas Bekynton*, ed. G. Williams, *RS.*, vol. ii, London, 1872, pp. 299–303. *Lit. Cant.*, vol. iii, pp. 340, 344–5 (Canterbury negotiations). See W. E. Lunt, *Papal revenues in the middle ages*, vol. i, N.Y., 1934, pp. 112–13, 125–8; L. Celier, *Les dataires du xve siècle et les origines de la daterie apostolique*, *BEFAR.*, vol. ciii, Paris, 1910, pp. 154–60.

164 Walsingham refounded: Dickinson, pp. 10–11.
Expenses against offerings: Urban II, *Reg.* CLXXV, col. 448. Baraut (ed.), *Llibre Vermell*, pp. 34–5 (Montserrat). Robert of Torigny, *Chron.*, vol. ii, pp. 99–100 (Rocamadour). Delisle (ed.), 'Enquête', pp. 367–8, 372 (Mont-St.-Michel). Cf. the pilgrims at Meaux in Yorkshire, who 'gave little and cost much', Burton, *Chron. Mon. Melsa*, vol. iii, pp. 35–6.
Canterbury balance-sheet: *Royal Commission on Historical Manuscripts*, 9th. Report, London, 1883, p. 124. Woodruff, pp. 17–24, 26.

165 Expenses at Vatican: *Bull. Vat.*, vol. i, pp. 96–7, 130, 134–5, 139–41,

156–7. *Gesta Innocentii III Papae*, CXLIII, *PL*. ccxiv, introd., p. cxcix. Pilgrims bring status: *MC*. xix. 19 (Benevento). *IS(2)*., vii. 363 (Salerno).

166 Pretensions of Santiago: *Hist. Compostellana*, I. 44–5, II. 3, 18, pp. 93–4, 255–8, 296. On the attitude of the kings of León, H. J. Hüffer, *La idea imperial Española*, Madrid, 1933, p. 20. Until 1095 the bishop's seat was technically at Iria.

Wealth of Santiago citizens: on silver-train of 1130, *Hist. Compostellana*, I. 18, p. 505. *Guide*, III, p. 7. *Itinerarium Hieronymi Monetarii*, ed. L. Pfandl, *Revue Hispanique*, xlviii (1920), p. 94.

XI. THE JOURNEY

168 Alkerton: Owst, p. 104.

Wills: Tardif (ed.), *Coutumiers*, vol. ii, p. 240. On agreement with wife, see, e.g., Caesarius, *Dial. Mirac.*, VIII. 59, vol. ii, p. 132. On enforcement, Vazquez de Parga *et. al*, vol. iii, pp. 110–12.

Judicial immunity: *Ancient laws of Ireland*, vol. i, ed. W. N. Hancock, Dublin, 1865, p. 266; vol. v, ed. R. Atkinson, Dublin, 1890, pp. 234, 296. Glanvill, *De Legibus et consuetudinibus Angliae*, I. 29, ed. G. D. H. Hall, London, 1965, pp. 16–17. Beaumanoir, *Coutumes*, nos. 265, 1689, vol. i, p. 135, vol. ii, pp. 364–5. Tardif (ed.), *Coutumiers*, vol. ii, p. 215. Property protected: bull of 1145 in Otto of Friesing, *Gesta Friderici*, I. 36, ed. B. de Simson, *MGH. Rer. Germ.*, Hannover, 1912, p. 57; cf. Alfonso IX, *Siete Partidas*, I. xxiv. 3, vol. i (1), fol. 151vo. Will of Archambert de Monluc in Arch. Nat. J. 1138/6.

169 Donations: *Cartulaire d'Auch, Cartulaire Noir*, XLVI, pp. 44–5; cf. *Chartes de Cluny*, no. 3712, vol. v, p. 59, and many others.

Pensions demanded: *Cartulaire de La Charité*, L, pp. 126–7.

Implied terms in case of return: *Ibid.*, XXXIV, XXXVIII, pp. 96–7, 104–5.

170 Make amends to all: *Liber S. Jacobi*, I. 17, p. 157.

French kings and St. Denis: Odo of Deuil. *De Profectione Lodovici VII*, I, p. 25 ('licentiam petiit'). Rigord, *Gesta Philippi*, LXIX, pp. 98–9 ('licentiam accipiendi'). On the vassalage of the kings to St. Denis, see R. Barroux, 'L'abbé Suger et la vassalité du Vexin en 1124', *Moyen Age*, lxiv (1958), pp. 1–26.

Lambert: *Annales*, p. 75.

Reparations to injured monks: E. Pérard (ed.), *Recueil de plusieurs pièces curieuses servant à l'histoire de Bourgogne*, Paris, 1664, pp. 202–3 (Odo). *Cartulaire de la Trinite de Vendôme*, CCCLXI, vol. ii, pp. 106–7 (Bertrand).

171 Louis' *enquête: RHF*. xxiv. 4*–5*.

Joinville: *Hist. de S. Louis*, XXV. 111, p. 64. Cf. *Book of Margery Kempe*, I. 26, p. 60.

'When the debts . . .': Owst, p. 104.

172 Origin of garb: John Cassian, *Collationes*, XI. 3, ed. M. Petschenig, *CSEL*. xiii, Vienna, 1886, p. 315 (fourth century monks). On Canute, *Fagrskinna*, quoted in Larsen, pp. 225–6. Eadmer, *Vita Anselmi*, II. 21, p. 97. Orderic, *Hist. Eccl.*, VIII. 10, ed. Chibnall, vol. iv, p. 188.

Blessings: in general, Franz (1), vol. ii, pp. 273–7, and Brundage, pp. 292, 297. 'Novel rite': Eckhard, *Chron. Universale*, *MGH. SS.* vi. 214. Cf. Eadmer, *loc. cit.*, 'peregrinantium more coram altari suscepit'.

Rayner: Benincasa, *Vita S. Rayneri*, II. 28, p. 431.

173 Symbolism: *Liber S. Jacobi*, I. 17, pp. 152–3. Sacchetti, *Sermone*, XLVIII, p. 165. Thomas of London, *Instructorium Peregrinorum*, Bibl. Nat. MS. Lat. 2049, fols. 229–30.

Palms: Du Cange, p. 536. Raymond of Aguilers, *Hist. Francorum*, XX, p. 295 (first crusade). William of Tyre, *Hist.*, XXI. 17, p. 1033. On palm-vendors, Ernoul, *Chron.*, XVII, p. 193; *Manuscrit de Rothelin*, III, p. 493.

174 Shells: *Liber S. Jacobi*, I. 17, IV. 9, pp. 153, 379–80.

Lead badges: Lopez Ferreiro, vol. v, pp. 38–9, 125–6, and appendices V, XXVII, pp. 15–17, 53–5 (Santiago). *Archaeological Journal*, xiii (1856), p. 105 (Canterbury). Maxe-Werly (Mont-St.-Michel; St. Catherine). Forgeais, *Plombs historiés*, vol. ii, pp. 154, 175, 184 (St.-Léonard; Saintes; Noyon). See also Guernes de Pont-St.-Maxence, *Vie de S. Thomas Becket*, ll. 5895–5900, ed. E. Walberg, Paris, 1936, pp. 181–2.

Badge-collectors: Langland, *Piers Plowman*, B. 527–31, pp. 86–7. Claude de Seyssel, *Les louanges du Roy Louis xii*ᵉ, Paris, 1508, sig. iii (Louis XI).

175 Badges as charms: *Miracles de Rocamadour*, I. 37, pp. 135–6. *Liber S. Jacobi*, II. 12, pp. 273–4.

As legal proof of status: Rupin, pp. 233–4. On crusaders, Benedict, *Mirac. S. Thomae*, IV. 12, p. 175.

Trade in badges: Rupin, pp. 235–7 (Rocamadour). J. Saenz de Aguirre (ed.), *Collectio Maxima Conciliorum*, vol. v, Rome, 1755, p. 140; Lopez Ferreiro, vol. v, p. 33 (app. XXXIII) (Santiago).

'O Lord, heavenly . . .': quoted in Franz (1), vol. ii, pp. 263–4.

176 Road to Conques: M. Bloch, 'Régions naturelles et groupes sociaux', *Annales d'Histoire Economique et Sociale*, iv (1932), p. 494.

Seigneur de Caumont: see text appended to *Guide*, pp. 133–40.

Road-building: Oursel, p. 56 (bridge at Tours). On *camino de Santiago*, *Guide*, V, VIII, pp. 12, 80; Defourneaux, pp. 67–8. On surviving roads and bridges, Oursel, pp. 51–5, 57–60.

177 *Guide*: see caps. VI–VII, pp. 12–32.

Richard punishes toll-keepers: 'Benedict' (i.e. Roger of Howden), *Gesta Henrici*, vol. i, p. 132.

Criminal penalties: *Capitularia Regum Francorum*, vol. i, 37, 191, often reiterated. In eleventh-century Normandy murderers of pilgrims were reserved to the duke's justice, see *Consuetudines et Justitiae*, XII, ed. C. H. Haskins, *EHR.*, xxiii (1908), p. 508.

180 Ecclesiastical censures: Conc. Rome (1059), in *MC.* xix. 873; Conc. Lateran (1123), in *MC.* xxi. 285. Conc. Rouen (1096), in Orderic Vitalis, *Hist. Eccl.*, IX. 3, ed. Prévost, vol. iii, p. 471; *RHF.* xv. 178–9. 'But you should know . . .': Hugh of Lyons, Ep. XVII, *PL.* clvii. 520. Cf. Yvo of Chartres, *Decr.*, IV. 60, col. 276.

Bull *In Coena*: bull of 1303 in Boniface VIII, *Reg.* 5345, vol. iii, p. 846.

Bandits: On Gerard of Galeria, William of Malmesbury, *Vita Wulf-stani*, X, ed. R. R. Darlington, Camden Soc., 3rd. series, vol. xl, London, 1928, pp. 16–17; Peter Damian, *Disceptatio Synodalis*, in *MGH. Libelli*, i. 91. On Thomas de Marle, Guibert, *De Vita Sua*, III. 11, 14, pp. 177–9, 198–202; Suger, *Vita Lodovici VI*, VII, XXIV, XXXI, pp. 30, 174–8, 254. On Berthold of Eberstein, see Matthias von Neuenburg, *Chron.*, contin. CXXXVII, ed. A. Hofmeister, *MGH. Rer. Germ.*, N. S. iv, Berlin, 1924–37, p. 446. Werner von Urslinger's activities are traced in Clement VI, *Reg. (Autres Pays)*, 2181, 2183, 2185–6, 2276, pp. 302–3, 317. On English bandits in Spain, Vazquez de Parga *et al.*, vol. i, pp. 269–70. On banditry in Palestine, Gregory IX, *Reg.* 4148, 4156, 4523, vol. ii, pp. 916, 919–20, 1131–2; Burchard of Mt. Sion, *Descriptio*, XIII, pp. 88–9; Jacques de Vitry, *Hist. Hierosolymitana*, LXXXII, pp. 1096–7.

182 Depredations of locals: Lanfranc, *Ep.* IX, *PL.* cl. 517–18 (Mont-St.-Michel). *PL.* cxliii. 797 (Italian peasants). 'Benedict' (i.e. Roger of Howden), *Gesta Henrici*, vol. i, p. 132 (Sorde and Lespéron). On Jubilee pilgrims of 1350, Clement VI, *Reg. (France)*, 4512, vol. iii, p. 84; *Reg. (Autres Pays)*, 2149, p. 298; *Vita Prima Clementis VI*, in Baluze (ed.), *Vitae Paparum*, vol. i, pp. 253–4; M. Villani, *Istorie*, I. 56, col. 56. Innkeepers: *Liber S. Jacobi*, II. 5, pp. 267–8; cf. *Mirac. B. Egidii*, II, *MGH. SS.* xii. 317–18. On German pilgrims robbed, see case of Gil Buhon in Wohlhaupter (2), pp. 227–8. Glaber, *Hist.*, IV. 4, p. 101. Hostile populations on route to Jerusalem: *Vita Lietberti*, XXIV, pp. 705–6. *Passio S. Cholomanni*, II–III, *MGH. SS.* iv. 675. *Vita Theoderici Andaginensis*, XV, *MGH. SS.* xii. 44 (travellers turned back in 1053). *Hist. S. Florentii Samurensis*, in Marchegay and Mabille (ed.), *Eglises d'Anjou*, pp. 265, 268 (Gerald). Lambert of Ardres. *Hist. Comitum Ghismensium*, CXIII, *MGH. SS.* xxiv. 615 (Anselm of Ardres). On the German expedition of 1064–5, *Annales Altahenses Maiores*, pp. 66–70; Lambert of Hersfeld, *Annales*, pp. 92–100.

183 Tolls levied by Arabs: Guibert, *Gesta Dei per Francos*, II. 4, p. 140. Wace, *Roman de Rou*, ll. 3159–3194, vol. i, pp. 278–80 (duke Robert). And by Greeks: Glaber, *Hist.*, III. 1, p. 52. Victor's complaint in *PL.* cxlix. 961–2, where it is wrongly ascribed to Victor III, see Riant (4), pp. 50–3.

184 Fortifications outside Jerusalem: Theoderic of Wurzburg, *De Locis Sanctis*, XXIII, p. 59.
Roads from Jerusalem: On raiders from Ascalon, Daniel, *Pèlerinage*, VII, LI, pp. 10–11, 42; Saewulf, *Relatio*, pp. 36–7. On incident of 1120, Albert of Aix, *Hist.*, XII. 33, pp. 712–13. On Baldwin's expedition of 1106, Daniel, *op. cit.*, LXXI–LXXVIII, pp. 56–61; Albert of Aix, *op. cit.* X. 9, p. 635.
Henry the Lion: Arnold of Lubeck, *Chron.*, I. 1–3, pp. 11–18.

185 'Men may leve . . .': *The pilgrim's sea-voyage and sea-sickness*, ed. F. J. Furnivall, *EETS.*, O. S., vol. xxv, London, 1867, pp. 37–40.
Comfort on ship: *Reisebuch Rieter*, pp. 37–8. Conrady (ed.), *Rheinische Pilgerschriften*, pp. 90–1 (anonymous German). Frescobaldi, *Viaggio*, p. 36. Wey, *Itineraries*, p. 4. Newett, pp. 91–2 (Hans von Mergenthal).

What to bring: Frescobaldi, *Viaggio*, pp. 32, 35. Brasca, *Viaggio*, pp. 128–9. Wey, *op. cit.*, pp. 5–6. Cf. the *Regimen in principium peregrinationis*, in Conrady (ed.). *Rheinische Pilgerschriften*, pp. 297–301.

186 How food served: Faber, *Evagatorium*, vol. i, p. 137.

Boredom: *Ibid.*, vol. i, pp. 37–8, 135–6.

187 Sermons: Casola, *Pilgrimage*, p. 231. Faber, *op. cit.*, vol. i, pp. 132–133.

Passengers obliged to defend ship: *Consolat de la mar*, in *Black Book*, vol. iii, p. 184; *Statut de Marseille de 1253 à 1255*, in Pardessus (ed.), *Lois Maritimes*, vol. iv, p. 271. On incident of 1408, Riant (ed.), 'Passage à Venise', pp. 246–7.

Reception at Joppa: *Itin. Cuiusdam Anglici*, VI, p. 449. On the cellars, Ghillebert de Lannoy, *Voyages*, pp. 139–40; Capodilista, *Itin.*, p. 181; on the indulgenges, Faber, *Evagatorium*, vol. i, p. 195. On Franciscan administration of landing formalities, Nompar de Caumont, *Voyaige*, p. 46; Pero Tafur, *Andancas*, p. 51.

188 Poll-tax collected by governor: *Itin. Cuiusdam Anglici*, VI, p. 451. Niccolo da Poggibonsi, *Libro d'Oltramare*, X, vol. i, pp. 32–6.

Tolls and taxes increase: Girnand von Schwalbach, *Pilgerschrift*, p. 98 (German of 1440). Mariano da Sienna, *Viaggio*, p. 118.

Sultan enriched: G. Adam, *De Modo Sarracenos Extirpandi*, II, *RHC. Arm.* ii. 528.

189 Advantages of Venetian ships: *Itin Cuiusdam Anglici*, IV, p. 443. Suriano, *Trattato*, I. 8, pp. 14–15. Brasca, *Viaggio*, p. 128.

Passengers sold as slaves: Gregory IX, *Reg.* 4150, vol. ii, p. 917. Innocent IV, *Reg.* 2122, vol. i, p. 316.

Venetian currency: *Itin. Cuiusdam Anglici*, I, p. 436. Frescobaldi, *Viaggio*, p. 47.

Statutes of 1229 and 1255: Newett, pp. 25–6.

Contracts: Neefs, pp. 322–3 (Jan Aerts). Hans Rot, *Pilgerreisen*, pp. 382–5 (1440). Wey, *Itineraries*, pp. 4, 90.

190 Disputes and reorganization after 1440: Newett, pp. 101–2, 56–7, 65–72, 74–5, 101. Claes van Dusen appears to have been Contarini's agent in the Netherlands, see his *Beschrijvinge*, in Conrady (ed.), *Rheinische Pilgerschriften*, p. 193.

191 Turks damage Rhodes: Wey, *Itineraries*, p. 78.

Disturbances in 1480: *Voyage de la Saincte Cyté*, pp. iv–viii, 42–3.

Contarini's troubles in 1479–80: *Ibid.*, pp. 24, 99–101.

Decline of Venetian package-tour: Newett, pp. 107–8, 283. Affagart, *Relation*, pp. 20–1.

192 Habits of the Basques: *Guide*, VII, pp. 26–30; cf. the author's views on the Gascons, pp. 18–20. The fifteen words given in the *Guide* are the oldest monument of the Basque language. By contrast with the author of the *Guide*, the highly educated, and usually aristocratic, pilgrims of the 'dark ages' had often transmitted cultural influences, see, e.g. W. Levison, *England and the continent in the eighth century*, Oxford, 1946, pp. 36–44, 52–3, 134, 170–2.

193 Contempt for Greeks: *Innominatus V*, III, p. 259 ('cunning men'). Fulcher of Chartres, *Hist. Hierosolymitana*, II. 38, ed. H. Hagenmeyer,

Heidelberg, 1913, p. 521 ('that great oppressor'). Jacques de Vitry, *Hist. Hierosolymitana*, LXXIV–LXXX, pp. 1089-95.

Language difficulties: *Vita Lietberti*, XXXI, pp. 702-3. Jacques de Vitry, *op. cit.*, LVI, p. 1077 (Germans in Jerusalem). Riant (ed.), 'Passage à Venise', p. 240.

194 Bertrandon: *Voyage d'Outremer*, pp. 59, 63-4.
Interpreters: Frescobaldi, *Viaggio*, pp. 65-6. Gucci, *Viaggio*, pp. 150-1.
Phrase-books: Bischoff, pp. 217-19, a fine essay.

195 Alphabets: *Mandeville's Travels*, vol. ii, pp. 288, 308-9, 314-15, 412-13 (Paris text). J. Schiltberger, *Bondage and Travels*, tr. J. B. Telfer, Hakluyt Soc., O. S., vol. lviii, London, 1879, pp. 102-3. Harff, *Pilgerfahrt*, pp. 64-5, 75-6, 112-14, 130-1, 139, 152, 187-9, 201-2, 209-10, 212-14, 227, 240-1.

196 'Now let me tell you . . .': Sigoli, *Viaggio*, p. 163.
Raucous bands: *Canterbury Tales*, ll. 565-6, 764, 773-4, pp. 17, 23. *Examination of William Thorpe*, pp. 140-1.
Expedition of Richard of St.-Vanne: Hugh of Flavigny, *Chron.*, XIX, pp. 393-4. Adémar, *Chron.*, III. 65, pp. 189-90. Eberwin, *Vita S. Symeonis*, X, *Aa. Ss. OSB.*, vol. viii, pp. 375-6.

197 Expedition of Robert of Normandy: Wace, *Roman de Rou*, Lib. III, ll. 2927-36, 2959-64, vol. i, pp. 270, 271. On the authority of Wace, see C. H. Haskins, *Norman Institutions*, Harvard, 1918, pp. 268-72.
7,000 followers of Gunther of Bamberg: Sigebert of Gembloux gives this figure, the lowest contemporary estimate, *Chron.*, *MGH. SS.* vi. 361.
Treacherous companions: *Mirac. S. Eutropii*, IV. 29-30, pp. 742-3 (blind man); cf. *Mirac. S. Walbergis*, II. 9-12, *Aa. Ss.* Feb., vol. iii, pp. 531-2 (saec. ix). *Liber S. Jacobi*, I. 2, 17, pp. 32, 164. Beaumanoir, *Coutumes*, vol. ii, pp. 490-1.
Margery Kempe: *Book of Margery Kempe*, I. 27-30, II. 4, pp. 63-75, 233-4.

198 Right to hospitality: *Capitularia Regum Francorum*, vol. i, p. 32. *DDC.*, vol. vi, col. 1314. *Guide*, XI, pp. 122-4.
Hospitality in early Church: Gorce, pp. 137-89.
Monastic obligations: *Regula S. Benedicti*, LIII, ed. R. Hanslik, *CSEL.* lxxv, Vienna, 1960, pp. 123-6. *Capitularia Regum Francorum*, vol. i, p. 347.
Famous monasteries: *Chron. Evesham*, III, pp. 91-2. Caesarius, *Dial. Mirac.*, IV. 71, vol. i, pp. 238-9 (Maria Laach).
St.-Gall guest-hall: *Vita S. Otmari*, II–III, *MGH. SS.* ii, 42-3.
Irish hospices: Gougaud, pp. 166-74.

199 'Columns built by God': *Guide*, IV, p. 10.
Charlemagne's hospice in Jerusalem: Bernard, *Itin.*, X, p. 314.
Hospital of St. John: on its origins, J. Riley-Smith, *The knights of St. John in Jerusalem and Cyprus, c. 1050-1310*, London, 1967, pp. 34-7. Described in c. 1165 by John of Wurzburg, *Descriptio*, XV, pp. 158-9. On its history as a Moslem hospice, Vincent and Abel (2), vol. II, pp. 648, 692. Christians admitted: Ludolph of Suchem, *Itin.*, XXXVIII, pp. 81-2 (c. 1340).

200 St. Bernard hospice: Donnet, pp. 109–10, 119–20.
Hospices on roads to Santiago: Vazquez de Parga *et al.*, vol. ii, *passim*.
'Not only to catholics': *ibid.*, vol. iii, pp. 111–12. On military orders, *ibid.*, vol. i, pp. 307–8.
Confraternity of S. Spirito: *Bull. Dipl.*, vol. iii, p. 191.
Rivalry: *Chartes de Cluny*, 4326, vol. v, p. 680 (Villafranca). Vazquez de Parga *et al.*, vol. i, p. 495 (Oboña).
Aubrac: *DHGE.*, vol. v, cols. 256–8. Statutes quoted in Rupin, p. 225n.

201 Outdoor relief: *Guide*, X, pp. 120–2 (St.-Léonard). Denifle, vol. i, pp. 179–80 (St.-Jean d'Angély). Also at Canterbury, see William, *Mirac. S. Thomae*, III, 54, p. 308.
Food: *Roman de Rénart*, br. IX, ll. 9092–3, ed. M. Roques, vol. iii, Paris, 1955, p. 109. Vazquez de Parga *et al.*, vol. iii, pp. 70–1.

202 Bedding: *Purchas his Pilgrimes*, VIII. 5, vol. vii, Glasgow, 1905, p. 529 ('bedding ther is . . .'). On bequests, Vazquez de Parga *et al.*, vol. i, pp. 324–5.
Fleas: *La Manière de langage*, III, XIII, ed. P. Meyer, *Revue Critique d' Histoire et de Littérature* (1870), pp. 388–9, 403.
'Taverns for the rich': Denis Possot quoted in Oursel, p. 56.
Beds shared: for Rome in 1350, see Buccio di Ranallo, *Cron. Aquilana*, p. 194. On England, Deschamps quoted in Jusserand, p. 61.
Flemish draper: Le Saige, *Voyage*, pp. 9–10.

203 Canvassing for customers: *Liber S. Jacobi*, I. 17, pp. 146, 160, 162.
Hotel regulations of Toulouse in R. Limousin-Lamothe (ed.), *La Commune de Toulouse et les sources de son histoire*, Toulouse, 1932, p. 358.
Claim to chattels: *Liber S. Jacobi*, II. 6, pp. 268–9. See Vazquez de Parga *et al.*, vol. i, p. 274.
Innkeepers denounced: *Liber S. Jacobi*, I. 17, pp. 160–71.
Price of inns: Jusserand, pp. 61–2.

204 Hire of horses: see regulations for hackney men in P. Q. Karkeek, 'Chaucer's Schipman and his barge *The Maudelayne*', *Chaucer Society Essays*, ser. II, no. 19, London, 1884, pp. 499–500.
Prices in Rome: see lists given for 1350 by Matteo Villani, *Istorie*, I. 56, col. 57; and Buccio di Ranallo, *Cron. Aquilana*, p. 192.
Cost of Jerusalem pilgrimage: Affagart, *Relation*, pp. 22, 24–6. Brasca, *Viaggio*, p. 128. Gucci, *Viaggio*, pp. 149–56. Brygg, *Itin. Thomae de Swynburne*, pp. 387–8. Cf. accounts of Claude de Mirabel in 1452, in Saint-Génois, pp. 35–6.

205 Half fares to poor: Suriano, *Trattato*, I. 9, p. 16. Brasca, *Viaggio*, p. 129.
Money carried by pilgrims: Musset, pp. 149–50. Frescobaldi, *Viaggio*, p. 38.
Girl stranded at Tyre: Caesarius, *Dial. Mirac.*, I. 40, vol. i, pp. 47–8.
Gerald's troubles: see his *De Jure et Statu Menevensis Eccl.*, IV, V, vol. iii, pp. 240–1, 289–90.

206 Hoteliers as bankers: P. Wolff, 'Notes sur les hôtelleries Toulousaines au moyen age', *BHP.* (1960), pp. 202–3.
Milanese bills of exchange: *Annali della fabrica del duomo di Milano*, vol. i, Milan, 1877, pp. 35–6.

Rates of exchange: Matteo Villani, *Istorie*, I, 56, col. 57 (Rome in 1350). Possot, *Voyage*, p. 87. Wey, *Itineraries*, pp. 1–3, 6.

Sale of land: Guibert, *Gesta Dei per Francos*, II. 6, pp. 140–1. *Cartulaire de Conques*, no. 514, p. 368.

Loans from monasteries: Bibl. Carpentras, MS. 1823, fols. 55–6 (Guy of Limoges). *Cartulaire d'Auch*, *Cart. Noir*, CXIII, pp. 128–32.

Other lenders: on Thibault de Marly's loan, Arch. Nat. K. 25, no. 5/13. *Catalogue analytique des diplomes, chartes, et actes rélatifs a l'histoire de Touraine*, ed. E. Mabille, *Soc. Archéologique de Touraine*, xiv, Tours, 1863, no. 1187, pp. 192–3 (Josbert de Précigny). Joinville, *Hist. de S. Louis*, XXV. 112, p. 64.

207 Expenses paid by patron: Bernard, *Ep.* CCCIC, col. 612. *Roman de Rou*, I. ll. 3047–9, ed. H. Andresen, vol. i, Heilbronn, 1877, p. 149 (Richard of St.-Vanne). Arnold, *Chron.*, I. 1, pp. 11, 12 (Henry the Lion).

Feudal aid for pilgrimage: Bertrand d'Argentré, *Consuetudines antiquissimi ducatus Britanniae*, LXXXVII. 3, Paris, 1608, cols. 381–2. Customs of Vendôme as confirmed in 1185, *Cartulaire de la Trinité de Vendôme*, no. 578, vol. ii, pp. 445–6. On protests, Conc. II Chalons, canon XIV, in *MC*. xiv. 96; Honorius Augustodunensis, *Elucidarium*, II. 23, *PL*. clxxii. 1152.

208 Alms: on exemption of pilgrims from begging laws, see *Inventaire des chartes et documents de la ville d'Ypres*, ed. I. L. A. Diegerick, vol. vii, Bruges, 1868, pp. 157–8. J. Toulmin Smith, *English Gilds*, London, 1870, p. 180. Faber, *Evagatorium*, vol. i, p. 28. On municipal charity to pilgrims, *Archives de Bruges*, vol. v, p. 491 and n. On begging from other pilgrims, *Liber S. Jacobi*, I. 17, pp. 156–7; Egbert, *Vita S. Heimeradi*, I. 6, *Aa. Ss.* June, vol. v, p. 388; Odo, *Vita S. Geraldi*, II. 17, col. 680.

Professional beggars: *Liber S. Jacobi*, I. 17, p. 165.

Working one's way: *Vita S. Sigiranni*, VIII–X, pp. 386–7. *Vita B. Egidii*, V, ed. R. B. Brooke, *Scripta Leonis, Rufini, et Angeli*, Oxford, 1970, p. 324; cf. *BBB*. vol. i, p. 105. Faber, *Evagatorium*, vol. i, pp. 28, 63–4.

209 Commerce: *MGH. Epp.* iv. 144–6 (Charlemagne). Forbidden to penitential pilgrims: Alfonso IX, *Siete Partidas*, I. xxiv. 2, vol. i (1), fol. 151vo; Van den Bussche (ed.), 'Rocamadour', p. 47. Request of Philip the Fair in Baluze (ed.), *Vitae Paparum*, vol. iii, p. 146. *Hodoeporicon S. Willibaldi*, VIII, XXVIII, pp. 252, 271. Reginald, *Vita S. Godrici*, V. 17, p. 31.

Traders 'never sleep': Faber, *Evagatorium*, vol. ii, pp. 92–3.

210 Eberhard of Wurtemburg: *Ibid.*, vol. i, pp. 26–7.

XII. THE SANCTUARY

211 Scene outside church: see, e.g. the descriptions by Augustine, *Ep.* XXII. 3–6, vol. i, pp. 56–9; *Enarr. in Psalmum*, XXXII. 5, ed. E. Dekkers and J. Fraipont, *Corpus Christianorum*, xxxviii, Tournai, 1956, pp. 250–1. And by Olivier Maillard, quoted in Samouillan, pp. 282–3, 301–2. On musical beggars, *Mirac. S. Eutropii*, III, 25, p. 741.

Merchants at churches: *Mirac. S. Fidis*, I. 24, p. 63. Samson, *Mirac. S. Eadmundi*, II. 11, pp. 183–4. Reginald, *De B. Cuthberti Virtut.*, XXIV, XLVIII, pp. 53–4, 98.

Church's attitude: Augustine, *Ep.* XXII. 3–6, vol. i, pp. 56–9; cf. in the eighth century, Boniface, *Ep.* L, pp. 84—5. Paulinus, *Carmen* XXVII. 552–67, pp. 286–7.

212 Lendit fairs: Bédier, vol. iv, pp. 154–6.

'Games and competitions . . .': Powicke and Cheney, *Councils*, vol. ii, p. 353, cf. p. 174.

Weekly vigils: *Invent. et Mirac. S. Wulfranni*, L, LV, pp. 65, 68. *Chron. Evesham*, II, p. 50.

Sanctuaries closed at night: *Mirac. S. Michaelis*, pp. 875–7. *Liber S. Jacobi*, II. 18, pp. 282–3. Cf. on Canterbury, Benedict, *Mirac. S. Thomae*, I. 12, p. 42; William, *Mirac. S. Thomae*, V. 2, p. 373.

'Let us prostrate . . .': Eadmer, *De Sanctorum Veneratione*, I. 2, p. 190.

'Humbly inclining . . .': *Chron. Evesham*, II, p. 57.

213 Noise at vigils: *Miracles de Rocamadour*, II. 36, pp. 245–6. Benedict, *Mirac. S. Thomae*, II. 1, 25, 28, 33–4, pp. 57, 77, 80, 85. *Liber S. Jacobi*, I. 2, 17, pp. 15–16, 19–20, 149. *Mirac. S. Fidis*, II, 12, pp. 120–2.

Stewards: Reginald, *De B. Cuthberti Virtut.*, CIV, p. 232.

Attempted suppression: Nantes statutes (saec. xiv), cap. VIII, in *MD. Thes.* iv. 963. Chartres statutes of 1368, cap. XXXVII, in *MD. Ampl. Coll.* vii. 1361. Cf. stories of saints forbidding pilgrimages to their shrines, Coulton, vol. iii, pp. 98–9.

Pilgrims crushed: Suger, *De Consecratione S. Dionysii*, II, pp. 216–17.

214 Daniel, *Pèlerinage*, XCVII, p. 77 (Jerusalem). *Liber S. Jacobi*, I. 17, p. 158 (St.-Gilles). Duplès-Agier (ed.), *Chroniques de S. Martial*, p. 200.

Rapid reconsecration permitted: Innocent IV, *Reg.* 1781, vol. i, p. 266 (St.-Gilles). Innocent III, *Reg.* X. 75, *PL.* ccxv. 1175 (Santiago).

Fire at Vézelay (in 1120): *Chron. S. Maxentii*, *RHF.* xii. 407. Robert of Auxerre, *Chron.*, *MGH. SS.* xxvi. 231.

Pickpockets: *Mirac. S. Wulfstanni*, I. 19, II. 22, pp. 126, 179 (Worcester). Kajava (ed.), *Etudes*, p. 66 (Fécamp). Both saec. xiii.

Sermon repeated: *Traité sur le cinquième jubilée de S. Thomas*, III. 4–5, p. 142.

Relics displayed in crises: Rigord, *Gesta Philippi*, LXXX, vol. i, pp. 113–14 (St.-Denis in 1191). *Invent. et Mirac. S. Wulfranni*, XXXVIII–LI, pp. 56–66 (Rouen in 1053). *Mirac. S. Martialis*, praefat., pp. 412–15 (Limoges in 1388). *Journal d'un Bourgeois*, pp. 191, 216, cf. pp. 20, 21, 22, 102, 144, 208, 372, 374, 376–8, 391–2. Reginald, *De B. Cuthberti Virtut.*, XXXIX, pp. 82–3 (fires at Durham). Bondurand (ed.), 'Détresse de St.-Gilles', p. 444.

215 Forced displays: Samson, *Mirac. S. Eadmundi*, II. 6, pp. 173–4. *Cartulaire de Conques*, no. 570, p. 399.

Displays once in seven years: *Mirac. S. Martialis*, praefat., p. 412. Montsabert (ed.), *Chartes de Charroux*, CCXXXII, pp. 364–7.

Displays restricted: Conc. Lateran (1215), canon LXII, in *MC.* xxii. 1049. Conc. Budapest (1279), canon XXVII, in *MC.* xxiv. 283. Conc.

Exeter (1287), canon XLVIII, in Powicke and Cheney, *Councils*, vol. ii, p. 1044. Conc. Bayeux (1300), canon XXXV, in *MC*. xxv. 67.
New reliquaries: *Mirac. S. Martialis*, X, p. 419. In the late middle ages the heads of St. Peter and St. Paul were displayed in such reliquaries, Capgrave, *Solace*, II. 4, p. 73. Cf. relics of church of St. George in Rome, *ibid*. II. 9, pp. 87–8; and head of St. Thomas at Canterbury, Erasmus, *Peregrinatio Religionis*, col. 783.

216 Infrequent displays raise doubts: Faillon (ed.), *Monuments inédits*, vol. ii, pp. 753–4 (Vézelay). Harff, *Pilgerfahrt*, p. 233.
Bull of 1424 and its effects: A. L. Mayer, 'Die heilbringende Schau in Sitte und Kult', in *Heilige Ueberlieferung (Festschrift I. Herwegen)*, Munster, 1938, pp. 245–9.

XIII. ROME

217 Three principal sanctuaries: R. Vielliard, pp. 55–9. *DACL.*, vol. xv, cols. 3296–8. Gregorovius, vol. i, pp. 90–1, 102–4.

218 Roman martyrs: Delehaye (4), pp. 260–3, 269–99.
Death of Sixtus II: *Lib. Pont.*, vol. i, p. 155.
Catacombs: *DACL.*, vol. xiv, col. 42 (graffiti). Jerome, *Comm. in Ezechielem*, XII. 5, *PL*. xxv. 375. On Damasus's restorations, *Lib. Pont.*, vol. i, p. 212; *DACL.*, vol. xiii, col. 2434; De Rossi (ed.), *Inscriptiones*, vol. ii (Rome, 1888), pp. 30, 66, 90, 102, 105. Prudentius, *Peristephanon*, XI. 155–68, pp. 417–18.

219 Damage of 537–7: De Rossi, *op. cit.*, vol. ii, pp. 83, 84, 100.
Translations to city: *Lib. Pont.*, vol. i, pp. 332, 360, 441–3, 444–5, 445–6, 451–2, 464, 520, vol. ii, pp. 52, 54, 56, 74, 93, 115.

220 Relics taken north: Llewellyn, pp. 183–90.
Basilicas walled: *Lib. Pont.*, vol. ii, p. 123 (St. Peter's). Gregorovius, vol. iii, pp. 186–7 (St. Paul's).

221 'From a far off hill . . .': Gregory, *De Mirabilibus Romae*, I, p. 543.
'O Roma Nobilis': full text in F. J. E. Raby, *Christian Latin Poetry*, 2nd. ed., Oxford, 1953, pp. 233–4.
Romans despised: William of Malmesbury, *Gesta Regum*, IV. 351, p. 402. Walter Map, *De Nugis Curialum*, II. 17, ed. M. R. James, Oxford, 1914, p. 82.
Hildebert's poem: in B. Hauréau, 'Notice sur les mélanges poétiques d'Hildebert de Lavardin', *Notices et extraits des manuscrits de la Bibliothèque Nationale*, xxxviii (2) (1888), pp. 334–5. It is quoted by, e.g., William of Malmesbury, *Gesta Regum*, IV. 351, pp. 402–3; Gregory, *De Mirabilibus Romae*, I. p. 543.

222 Restorations and new churches: Gregorovius, vol. iv, pp. 694–6, vol. v, p. 637.
St. Peter's: On the *confessio*, Mallius, *Descriptio*, XLII–XLIII, p. 425. On the *sudarium*, *Bull. Vat.*, vol. i, pp. 9, 89–90; Nicholas IV, *Reg.* 653, p. 131.
Lateran: John the Deacon, *Descriptio*, IV–V, XIII, pp. 337–42, 356–7. Gerald of Wales, *Speculum Ecclesiae*, IV. 3–4, vol. iv, pp. 272–6. *Graphia Aureae Urbis*, XX, pp. 83–4.

223 Processions: Benedict, *Liber Politicus*, XLV-LI, pp. 152-4.
Condition of monuments: Gregorovius, vol. iv, p. 691 (arch of Titus).
Accusations against Gregory VII in 1080 in *MGH. Leges*, iv (1), p. 119
Otto of Friesing, *De Duabus Civitatibus*, VII. 31, p. 360 (St. Peter's
fortified). Innocent III, *Reg.*, II. 102, *PL.* ccxiv. 651-3. *Regesto di S.
Silvestro di Capite*, IV, ed. V. Federici, *ASRSP.*, xxii (1889), p. 269.

224 Attempt to preserve them a failure: A. de Bouard, 'Gli antichi marmi di
Roma nel medio evo', *ASRSP.*, xxxiv (1911), pp. 239-45. Reginald of
Durham, *De B. Cuthberti Virtut.*, LXXV, pp. 155-6.
Collectors: Suger, *De Consecratione*, II, p. 219. John of Salisbury, *Hist.
Pontificalis*, XL, p. 79.
Horse of Constantine: *Lib. Pont.*, vol. ii, p. 252 (official hanged). *Mira-
bilia Urbis Romae*, XV, pp. 32-3 (guide-book). Gregory, *De Mirabilibus
Romae*, IV-V, pp. 544-6. On equestrian statues in France, see R.
Crozet, 'Nouvelles remarques sur les cavaliers sculptées ou peints dans
les églises romanes', *Cahiers de Civilisation Médiévale*, i (1958), p. 27;
perhaps also at Autun, D. Grivot and G. Zarnecki, *Gislebertus, sculptor
of Autun*, N.Y., 1961, p. 65 and pl. VI. Many others once existed, see
Mâle, pp. 247-9.

225 *Mirabilia*: see caps. I-XI, XXIII, XXVI, XXXII, pp. 17-29, 51-3, 58,
65; *Graphia Aureae Urbis*, XII, p. 79. On editions, A. Graf, *Roma nella
memoria e nelle imaginazione del medio evo*, vol. i, Turin, 1882, pp. 65-72.
The author was probably Benedict, canon of St. Peter's, see L. Duchesne in *Liber Censuum*, introd., pp. 102-4.

226 Gregory: *De Mirabilibus Romae*, IV, X, XII, XV-XVIII, XXI, pp.
544-5, 547-50. On him, see introduction to Rushforth's edition in
Journal of Roman Studies, ix (1919), pp. 17-18, 30-1. Text of pseudo-
Bede ed. H. Omont, *BEC.*, liii (1882), pp. 40-59.

227 Pilgrims obstructed: *Becket Materials*, vol. v, p. 357. Innocent IV, *Reg.*
1896, vol. i, p. 281.
Hospices disappear: on Irish hospice, A. M. Tommasini, *I Santi Irlandesi in Italia*, Milan, 1932, p. 74. On English hospice, *Becket Materials*,
vol. v, pp. 64-5; *Bull. Dipl.*, vol. i, p. 355, vol. iii, p. 191.
Gregory the Great: *Dialogi*, IV. 13, III. 25, *PL.* lxxvii. 340, 280. Cf., in
tenth century, Liutprand of Cremona, *Hist. Ottonis*, IV, ed. J. Bekker,
MGH. Rer. Germ., Hanover, 1915, pp. 161-2.
Canute: Florence of Worcester, *Chron.*, ed. B. Thorpe, vol. i, London,
1848, p. 186.

228 Rivals of St. Peter: *Vita S. Austremonii*, III. 17, *Aa. Ss.* Nov., vol. i, pp.
53-4 (saec. vii-viii).
'Penance is synonymous . . .': Jonas of Orleans, *De Cultu Imaginum*, III,
PL. cvi. 369.
Popes consulted: Yvo of Chartres, *Decr.*, X. 35, 179, cols. 701, 743; cf.
X. 20, 24, 29, 180, 185, cols. 697-700, 743-5. Nicholas I, *Epp.* CXXIX,
CXXXIII, CXXXVIII, *MGH. Epp.* vi, 650, 654, 658. Wasserschleben
(ed.), *Bussordnungen*, p. 333. I cannot accept, with Hausmann, pp. 28-33,
that the practice dates back to Gregory I.
Bishops by-passed: *Capitula Ecclesiastica*, XVIII, in *Capitularia Regum
Francorum*, vol. i, p. 365 (Haito). Conc. Seligenstadt, canon XVI, in

MC. xix. 398. Conc. Limoges, in *MC.* xix. 546. On reserved cases, Göller, vol. i (1), pp. 80–1.

229 Scandinavian penitents: Alexander III, *Ep*, 975, cols. 850–2. *Grettis Saga Asmundarson*, ed. R. C. Boer, *Altnordische Saga-Bibliothek*, viii, Halle, 1900, pp. 311–14. *Sverris Saga*, ed. G. Indrebo, Kristiana, 1920, pp. 3–4 (Gunnhildr). *Inga Konungs Saga*, quoted in Springer, p. 94n[24]. (Adrian IV).

230 Stational indulgences: John the Deacon, *Vita S. Gregorii*, II. 18, *PL*. lxxv. 94 (late). Gerald of Wales, *De Invectionibus*, V. 12, vol. i, pp. 137–8. William of Auxerre, Summa Aurea, quoted in Paulus (2), vol. ii, p. 295n[4]. Decision of Boniface VIII in *Bull. Vat.*, vol. iii (app.), p. 6. Indulgences of churches: in twelfth century, Peter Mallius, *Descriptio*, III, p. 385; Alexander III, *Ep.* 1520, cols. 1315–16; Petrus Cantor, *Summa de Sacramentis*, quoted in Paulus (2), vol. ii, p. 295n[2]. In thirteenth century, Gregory IX, *Reg.* 5228, vol. iii, p. 270, extended by Urban IV in 1263, *Bull. Vat.*, vol. i, p. 143 (basilicas of apostles); *Ceremoniale Romanum* XXII, in J. Mabillon, *Museum Italicum*, vol. ii, Paris, 1869, p. 238 (Lateran); Aquinas, *In Sentent.*, quoted in Paulus (2), vol. ii, p. 296; Nicholas III, *Reg.* 1042, p. 414 (individual altar in St. Peter's).

231 Nicholas IV: *Reg.* 425, 631, 633–4, 650–1, 653, 1432, 2030, pp. 78, 127–8, 130–1, 285, 361.

Idea of Jubilee: Bernard, *Ep.* 458, *PL*. clxxxii. 652–3. Albert of Trois-Fontaines, *Chron.*, *MGH. SS.* xxiii. 889; cf. G. M. Drèves (ed.), *Analecta Hymnica*, XXI, Leipzig, 1895, p. 166 (Albigensian crusade). Humbert of Romans, quoted in Paulus (2), vol. i, p. 101.

Jubilee: this account is based on G. Villani, *Hist. Fiorentine*, VIII. 36, cols. 367–8. W. Ventura, *Chron. Astense*, XXVI, cols. 191–2. Cardinal J. Stefaneschi, *De Centesimo*, I–IX, pp. 299–307.

232 Bull *Antiquorum*: text in Boniface VIII, *Reg.* 3875, vol. ii, pp. 922–3; accompanying brief in Stefaneschi, *op. cit.*, pp. 315–16. Commentary by Silvester Scriptor, ed. R. Scholz, 'Zur Beurteilung Bonifaz VIII und seines sittlich-religiösen Charakters', *Historisches Vierteljahreschrift*, ix (1906), pp. 513–15; cf. *Gesta Boemundi Archiep. Treverensis*, XXXIV, *MGH. SS.* xxiv. 487–8, and Sienese inscription in *IS* (1)., iii. 561. For doubts as to its meaning, John the Monk in *Extravagantes Communes* Lyon, 1506, fol. 36; Giles li Muisis, *Chron.*, pp. 188–9 (Tournai incident).

234 'Innumerable Christians . . .': *Annales Mutinensium*, *RISS (1)*, xi. 75. Kings represented: Thurston, p. 24.

235 Crowds on bridge: Dante, *Inferno*, XVIII. 28–33.

Offerings: for rumour in Tuscany, Ptolemy of Lucca, *Annales*, ed. B. Schmeidler, *MGH. Rer. Germ.*, N. S., viii, Berlin, 1930, p. 236.

236 Boniface posthumously accused: Article LXIX of charges, in P. Dupuy, *Histoire du différend d'entre le pape Boniface VIII et Phelippes le Bel, Roy de France*, Paris, 1655, preuves, pp. 358–9. *Chronique Rimée*, ll. 41–2, 55–6, *RHF*. xxii. 89.

Dante on the Jubilee: *Purgatorio*, II. 98–105.

237 Lateran burned: Ptolemy of Lucca, *Hist. Eccl.*, *RISS* (1)., xi. 1230.

Bull *Unigenitus*: *Vita III Clementis VI*, in Baluze (ed.), *Vitae Paparum*, vol. i, pp. 278–9, vol. ii, pp. 370–1. Text in *CJC., Extrav. Comm.*, V. ix. 2, vol. ii, cols. 1304–6. On 'treasury of merit', see Albertus Magnus, *In Sentent.*, IV. xx. 16, in *Opera Omnia*, ed. A. Borgnet, vol. xxix, Paris, 1894, pp. 847–9.

Wars damage Jubilee: Petrarch, *Lettere Familiari*, XV. 15, vol. iii, pp. 150–1. Clement VI, *Reg. (France)*, 4290, 4307, vol. iii, pp. 34, 37; *Reg. (Autres Pays)*, 2181, 2183, pp. 302–3, 317. On prohibition of pilgrimages, Rymer, *Foedera*, vol. v, p. 668 (England); Giles li Muisis, *Chron.*, pp. 385, 395–6 (France). For licences to English pilgrims, Rymer, *Foedera*, vol. v, pp. 677, 681–3. On troubles of pilgrims in France, Clement VI, *Reg. (France)*, 4717, 4724,° vol. iii, pp. 128–9.

238 Earthquake: Petrarch, *op. cit.*, XI. 7, vol. ii, p. 338.

Jubilee pilgrims: this account is based on M. Villani, *Istorie*, I. 56, cols. 56–7; Peter of Herenthals, *Vita Clementis VI*, in Baluze (ed.), *Vitae Paparum*, vol. i, pp. 302–3; Heinrich von Rebdorff, *Annales Imperatorum et Paparum*, ed. J. F. Boehmer, *Fontes Rer. Germ.*, iv, Stuttgart, 1868, p. 562; Buccio di Ranallo, *Cronaca Aquilana*, pp. 192, 194; Bridget, *Rev.*, III. 27, IV. 5, 78, VI. 112, pp. 189, 209–10, 293, 525; Petrarch, *Rime*, XVI, and *Lettere Familiari*, IX. 13, XI. 1, vol. ii, pp. 254–5, 322–3. On private views of the Veronica, Clement VI, *Reg. (France)*, 4734, 4746, 4750–1, 4778, 4785, 4790, 4792, 4795, 4816, 4835. vol. iii, pp. 131, 132–3, 139–43, 148, 151; *Reg. (Autres Pays)*, 2353, p, 329.

240 'Many altercations': *Breve Chron.*, ed. J. J. de Smet, *Corpus Chronicorum Flandriae*, vol. iii, Bruxelles, 1856, p. 14. Text of two forged bulls in Alberic of Rosate, *Dictionarium*, fols. 163–4; another in Peter of Herenthals, *Vita Clementis VI*, in Baluze (ed.), *Vitae Paparum*, vol. i, p. 299, cf. vol. ii, pp. 432–3. Burton, *Chron. Mon. Melsa*, vol. iii, pp. 88–9. Wyclif, *Trialogus*, ed. G. Lechler, Oxford, 1869, p. 357.

Clerical pilgrims pardoned: *CPR. Letters*, vol. iii, pp. 382–6, 388, 395–7, 429.

Visits reduced: Alberic of Rosate, *Dictionarium*, fol. 164, and accounts cited above.

241 Louis of Hungary: Rodocanachi, p. 162.

Indulgences without journey: for requests, see Clement VI, *Reg. (France)*, 4426, vol. iii, pp. 64–5 (Philip VI); Raynald, *Ann. Eccl.*, An. 1350 (no. 2), vol. vii, p. 502 (Hugh); Oxford, MS. Bodley 144, fols. 246vo–251vo (Fitzralph's sermon). Granted: *CPR. Letters*, vol. iii, pp. 49, 383; A. Theiner (ed.), *Vetera Monumenta Historica Hungariam Sacram Illustrantia*, vol. i, Rome, 1859, p. 791; on Mallorca, Vincke (4).

242 Large indulgences: Philip, *Liber de Terra Sancta (1377)*, pp. 519–20.

243 Guide-books unobtainable: *Itin. Cuiusdam Anglici*, III, p. 441.

Books of indulgences: Brewyn, *A fifteenth century guide-book*, pp. 22–3, 41. Capgrave, *Solace*, II. 6, p. 83. *Stacions of Rome*, ll. 1–6, p. 1. In general, Hulbert.

Translations altered: *Itin. Cuiusdam Anglici, loc. cit. Stacions*, ll. 497–9, 718–19, pp. 16, 23. Oxford, MS. Bodley 423, fol. 384 (Capgrave).

Notices: *Stacions*, ll. 215–16, 515–18, pp. 8, 17; cf. Philip, *Liber de Terra Sancta (1377)*, p. 522.

244 Rivalry with Jerusalem: *Stacions*, ll. 285–91, p. 10. Muffels, *Beschreibung*, p. 17.
Attitude of papacy: *Memoriale de Mirabilibus et Indulgentiis*, in *VZ.*, vol. iv, pp. 75–88.

245 Indulgences transferred to Marseilles: J. B. Guesnay, *Provinciae Massiliensis Annales*, Lyon, 1657, p. 435. *Bullarium Franciscanum*, ed. C. Eubel, vol. vii, Rome, 1904, pp. 237–8 (no. 645).
Jubilee of 1390: Urban's bull in Amort, *De Origine Indulgentiarum*, vol. i, pp. 84–6; Clement's denunciation in Vincke (1), pp. 68–9. Granted without journey: *Regesta Boicarum*, ed. C. H. Lang, vol. x, Munich, 1843, p. 255 (Stephen of Bavaria); Arch. Vat. Reg. Vat., 312, fols. 148vo–149vo (bishop of Camerino); *CPR. Letters*, vol. iv, pp. 323–6, 379–80 (mayor of Berwick etc.); Jansen, pp. 152–4 (Cologne); Vincke (1), pp. 69–71 (Spain).
Papal share of offerings: Arch. Vat. Diversa Cameralia 1, fols. 129vo–130 (St. Paul's); Arch. Vat. Reg. Vat. 347, fols. 78vo–79vo (S. Maria Maggiore). Commission to Guinigi, Arch. Vat. Reg. Vat. 312, fols. 148vo–149vo.

246 Indulgence marketed north of Alps: Arch. Vat. Reg. Vat. 313, fols. 187–187vo, 196 (instructions to legates in Poland). Dietrich of Niem, *De Scismate*, I. 68, pp. 119–20. On Milan, *Annali della fabrica del duomo di Milano*, vol. i, Milan, 1877, pp. 33–4, 41–3; Arch. Vat. Reg. Vat. 313, fol. 241. On German Jubilees, Jansen, pp. 145–62.
Jubilee of 1400: Dietrich of Niem, *op. cit.*, II. 28, p. 170; Laslowski, pp. 128, 148; monk of St. Paul's quoted by Rucellai in 1450, *Giubileo*, p. 579. Offerings calculated on the basis that the pope's share (8,000 florins) was half the total, Arch. Vat. Reg. Vat. 317, fols. 30–30vo.
Boniface's embarrassment: Arch. Vat. Reg. Vat. 316, fols. 342vo, 349–50; 317, fol. 8vo (offerings claimed). Boniface's pronouncements on indulgence in Arch. Vat. Reg. Vat. 316, fols. 341vo–342; 317, fols. 47–47vo. Granted to princes etc.: *Diplomatarium Norvegicum*, vol. v, Kristiana, 1860, pp. 251–2, vol. xvii, Kristiana, 1902, p. 201; Arch. Vat. Reg. Lateran 79, fol. 85vo; 87, fol. 231vo; Arch. Vat. Reg. Vat. 317, fols. 41–2.

247 Attempt to stop French pilgrims: N. Valois, *La France et le Grand Schisme d'Occident*, vol. iii, Paris, 1901, pp. 321–2.
Spain: on royal support for Catalan hospice, J. Vielliard (1), pp. 188–9. *Instructiones pro ambaxiadoribus in Franciam*, ed. F. Ehrle, 'Neue Materialen zur Geschichte Peters von Luna (Benedicts XIII)', *Archiv. für Literatur- und Kirchengeschichte des Mittelalters*, vii (1893), pp. 116, 118. On Poblet, J. Vielliard (2), pp. 287, 271.

248 'Pity Rome . . .': Adam of Usk, *Chron.*, pp. 91, 93.
State of monuments: Petrarch, *Lettere Familiari*, XV. 9, vol. iii, p. 162 (campanile). *De Rebus antiquis et situ urbis Romae*, in *VZ.*, vol. iv, p. 117 (arch of Arcadius).
Services abandoned: Antonio Petri, *Diarium Romanum*, *RISS* (1). xxiv. 1043, 1050.
Jubilee of 1423: Poggio, Lib. II, *Ep.* II, ed. T. de Tonellis, vol. i, Florence, 1832, p. 86. John Amundesham, *Annales Mon. S. Albani*, ed. H. T. Riley, *RS*, vol. i, London, 1870, pp. 131–2, 134–5, 143, 147.

249 New relics: Pastor, vol. i, pp. 231, 258–61.
Ceremonies: on new ceremonial trappings, E. Muntz, *Les arts à la cour des papes pendant le xve et xvie siècle*, Paris, 1878–82, vol. i, pp. 20–3, 36, 53, vol. ii, pp. 309–12. On the bull *In Coena*, Adam of Usk, *Chron.*, p. 97; Harff, *Pilgerfahrt*, pp. 31–2. Tafur, *Andancas*, pp. 34–5 (celebrations of 1437).
Sudarium: Muffels, *Beschreibung*, p. 10 (indulgences). On the 'vernicle', *Canterbury Tales*, I. 685, p. 20; Langland, *Piers Plowman*, B.V. 530, p. 86. F. Ariosto, *Dicta de la entrata in Roma de lo illustrissimo duca Borso*, ed. E. Celani, *ASRSP.*, xiii (1890), pp. 434–5.

250 Catacombs: Raynald, *An. Eccl.*, An. 1424 (no. 13), vol. ix, p. 10 (commission of 1424). Rucellai, *Giubileo*, p. 463. Capgrave, *Solace*, II. 3, I. 7, pp. 69, 20.

251 Other amusements: Harff, *Pilgerfahrt*, p. 31. Lengherand, *Voyage*, p. 72.
1022 inns: Number given by Rucellai, *Giubileo*, p. 453. On albergo della Luna, Galeazzo Gataro, *Istoria Padovano*, *RISS* (*1*). xvii. 45. Pastor, vol. iv, p. 185n. (Borso d'Este). Harff, *Pilgerfahrt*, p. 14. Burchard, *Liber Notarum*, ed. E. Celani, *RISS* (*2*), xxxii, vol. i, pp. 266–7 (Otto of Bavaria). On their unpopularity, see Romani, p. 79.
English hospices: Croke, pp. 568–72. Re, pp. 85–92. F. A. Gasquet, *A History of the Venerable English College, Rome*, London, 1920, pp. 30–5.

252 The Anima: Nagl (OS), pp. 58–63, 65–6. Shmidlin. Also, *Liber Confrat. B. M. de Anima*.
Other national hospices: many references in Delaruelle *et al.*, pp. 1150–1; and Pastor, vol. i, pp. 253–6. On Irish hospice, Pastor, vol. i, p. 254. F. Pascarelli, 'Origine e vicende dell' ospedale di S. Brigida di Svezia in Roma', *Atti del primo Congresso Europeo di Storia Ospitaliera (1960)*, Reggio Emilia, 1962, p. 1004. On Flemish hospice, Vaes (2), p. 91.

253 Jubilee of 1450: what follows is based on Paolo dello Mastro, *Memoriale*, LIV, pp. 95–7; Manetti, *Vita Nicolai V*, II, *RISS* (*1*). iii (2). 924–5. Olivier de la Marche, *Mémoires*, ed. H. Beaune and J. d'Arbaumont, *SHF*, vol. ii, Paris, 1884, p. 162; Pastor, vol. ii, pp. 74–137, 500–2.
Jubilee bull: partial text in Raynald, *Ann. Eccl.*, An. 1449 (no. 15), vol. ix, p. 543.
Rucellai: *Giubileo*, pp. 564–79.

254 Capgrave: *Solace*, preface, I. 14, II. 4, 9, 47, pp. 1, 33, 73, 87–8, 146–7.
Shops on bridge destroyed: Dietrich of Niem, *De Scismate*, II. 37, p. 192.

255 Indulgence without journey: C. Gärtner, *Salzburgische gelehrte Unterhaltungen*, vol. i, Salzburg, 1812, p. 114. Fredericq (ed.), *Codex*, pp. 80–2, 119–21, 132–6. Paulus (2), vol. ii, pp. 47, 188. C. Witz (ed.), 'Bullen und Breven aus italienischen Archiven', *Quellen zur Schweitzer Geschichte*, xxi, Basel, 1902, p. 517. *CPR. Letters*, vol. x, pp. 169–70. Amort, *De Origine Indulgentiarum*, vol. i, pp. 87–9. *Bull. Vat.*, vol. ii, p. 137. Henry VI's comment in Rymer, *Foedera*, vol. x, pp. 263–6, vol. xi, pp. 252–4.

256 Results of the Jubilee: Manetti, *Vita Nicolai V*, II, *RISS* (*1*). iii (2). 924–5. Dati, *Opera*, Venice, 1516, fol. 177.

XIV. THE LATER MIDDLE AGES: (1)
'LIGHT-MINDED AND INQUISITIVE PERSONS'

257 'Some light-minded . . .': Jacques de Vitry, *Hist. Hierosolymitana*, LXXXII, p. 1097.

Itineraries: bibliography in Rohricht (1), supplemented, for the years after 1290, by Atiya, pp. 490–509. Quotations are from John of Wurzburg, *Descriptio*, praefat., pp. 109–10; Theoderic of Wurzburg, *De Locis Sanctis*, praefat., pp. 1–2.

258 Jacques de Vitry: See list of MSS in Rohricht (1), pp. 48–50. He was used, e.g., by Burchardt of Mt. Sion, *Descriptio*, VI, pp. 45–6.

Mandeville: on editions and MSS, Rohricht (1), pp. 79–85. Valuable introductions to the editions by M. C. Seymour, Oxford, 1967, and G. F. Warner, Roxburghe Club, London, 1889. On his sources, see A. Bovenschen, 'Untersuchungen über Johann von Mandeville und die Quelle seiner Reiserbeschreibung', *Zeitschrift der Gesellschaft für Erdkunde zu Berlin*, xxiii (1888), pt. iv, pp. 177–306.

Capgrave's models: *Solace*, p. 1.

Interest in Faber's account: *Evagatorium*, vol. iii, p. 467.

259 'Little Mandevilles': *Examination of William Thorpe*, p. 141. *Canterbury Tales*, ll. 48–9, 463–8, pp. 2, 14.

Official arrangements for tourists: Heyd (consulates). Vincke (2), p. 263 (safe conduct of 1387: 'et ut patriae mores videant'). Rymer, *Foedera*, vol. xi, p. 686 (treaty of 1471).

Tourism criticized: *Fasciculi Zizaniorum*, ed. W. W. Shirley, *RS.*, London, 1858, p. 270 (Wyclif). Affagart, *Rélation*, pp. 22–3. Brasca, *Viaggio*, p. 128.

Graffiti: Faber, *Evagatorium*, vol. i, p. 213, vol. ii, pp. 94–6. On Lannoy's graffiti, Van de Walle, pp. 123–5.

Souvenirs: *Quinze Joies*, VIII, pp. 69–70. Nompar de Caumont, *Voyaige*, pp. 136–9.

260 Postcards: Vergerio, *Ep.* LXXXVI, p. 216 (Rome). Faber, *Evagatorium*, vol. i, p. 329 (Breidenbach); there is a fine copy of the 1486 edition in the Bodleian Library, Oxford (Douce 223), with good early colouring; cf. Davies, where all the drawings are reproduced.

Faber's books: *Ibid.*, vol. i, pp. 62, 327–8.

Route-books: On Anglo-Saxon one of eleventh century, F. Liebermann, *Die Heiligen Englands*, Hannover, 1889, pp. 9–19. Also, Adam of Bremen, *Gesta Pontificum Hammaburgensium*, V. 1, ed. B. Schmeidler, *MGH. Rer. Germ.*, Leipzig, 1926, pp. 228–9; *Annales Stadenses*, *MGH. SS.* xvi. 340–4; *Pèlerinages por aler en Iherusalem*, A route to Rome is given by Matthew Paris, accompanied in some MSS by a map, see Brit. Mus. MS. Royal 14 C. vii, fols. 2–5, reproduced in E-F. Jomard, *Les Monuments de la Géographie*, Paris, 1862, plates 39–41.

Indulgence-books: *Pèlerinages et Pardouns d'Acre*. On Roman indulgence-books, Hulbert.

Anonymous 'descriptions': Röhricht (1), pp. 28–9, 33, 35, 39–42, 45, 55, 665. John of Wurzburg, e.g., used *Innominatus VI*, see his *Descriptio*, III, pp. 117–19, and compare *Innominatus VI*, pp. 433–15.

Local guides: at Jerusalem, see Abel; Daniel, *Pèlerinage*, I, p. 5; John of Wurzburg, *op. cit.*, VI, pp. 132–4. In Venice: Newett, pp. 40–1. On disbelief of guides' stories, Faber, *Evagatorium*, vol. i, pp. 330–7; Harff, *Pilgerfahrt*, pp. 16–17, 30.

262 Female pilgrims criticized: Boniface, *Ep.* XLVIII, p. 169. *Quinze joies*, VIII, pp. 69–70. Berthold, *Predigten*, XXVIII, vol. i, pp. 458–60; Giordano da Rivalto, *Prediche recitate in Firenze dal MCCCIII al MCCCVI* vol. i, Florence, 1831, pp. 252–3; cf. Owst, pp. 388–9.

Women at Bury: Wright (ed.), *Letters*, p. 85.

Women in monastic sanctuaries: Burton, *Chron. Mon. Melsa*, vol. iii, pp. 35–6. *Mirac. S. Benedicti*, I. 28, pp. 64–5. On Durham, Symeon, *Hist. Dunelmensis Eccl.*, III. 11, vol. i, p. 95; Reginald, *De B. Cuthberti Virtut.*, LXXIV, pp. 141–4. Cf. Loomis, p. 97.

263 Pregnant woman crushed: *Mirac. S. Martialis*, XXXIX, p. 429.

Women in Rome: on their devoutness, *Itin. cuiusdam Anglici*, III, pp. 440–1. Excluded from sanctuaries, see Capgrave, *Solace*, II. 4, 5, pp. 71, 77; Harff, *Pilgerfahrt*, pp. 16, 23; Wey, *Itineraries*, p. 143. Muffels, *Beschreibung*, p. 24; Tafur, *Andancas*, pp. 29–30.

Nobles at 1450 Jubilee: Pastor, vol. ii, pp. 91–3. Chastellain, *Le livre des faits de Jacques de Lalaing*, LXV–LXVI, in *Oeuvres*, ed. Kervyn de Lettenhove, vol. viii, Bruxelles, 1866, pp. 245–7.

And in 1475: Pastor, vol. iv, pp. 280–2.

264 Royal pilgrimages to Virgin: Dickinson, pp. 33–45 (Walsingham). Carreras y Candi, pp. 341–56 (Montserrat). On Boulogne, Benoit.

Louis XI: See A. Gandilhon, 'Contribution à l'histoire de la vie privée de Louis XI', *Mémoires de la Soc. Historique, Littéraire, et Scientifique du Cher*, xx (1905), pp. 356, 362–3. P. Champion, *Louis XI*, vol. ii, Paris, 1927, pp. 204, 209–12.

Traditional ideals: Nompar de Caumont, *Voyaige*, pp. 18, 20.

Noble pilgrims disguised: Newett, pp. 65–6 (Venetian complaint). Affagart, *Rélation*, p. 4.

265 Earl Rivers robbed: *CPR. Letters*, vol. xiii, pp. 221–2.

Henry of Derby: Riant (ed.), 'Passage à Venise', pp. 238–40. Toulmin Smith (ed.), *Accounts*, pp. 204–24.

Ferdinand of Aragon's nephew: Casola, *Pilgrimage*, p. 188.

Ernest of Saxony: Jacopo Gherardi da Volterra, *Diario Romano*, ed. E. Carusi, *RISS* (2), xxiii (3), pp. 13–14. On his motives, see R. Koetzchke and H. Kretzschmar, *Sachsiche Geschichte*, vol. i, Dresden, 1935, p. 164.

Otto of Brunswick: see names of his attendants enrolled in *Liber Confraternitatis de Anima*, p. 39.

266 Niccolo d'Este: Luchino del Campo, *Viaggio di Niccolo da Este*, p. 105.

Dubbing of knights of St. John: Nompar de Caumont, *Voyaige*, pp. 45, 49–51. On enrolment on return, Faber, *Evagatorium*, vol. i, p. 42; see certificate granted to Peter Rindfleisch of Breslau in 1496, in his *Wallfahrt*, pp. 317–18.

Dubbing by non-hospitallers: Luchino, *Viaggio di Niccolo da Este*, p. 125.

Guillaume de Châlons: E. Clerc, *Essai sur l'histoire de la Franche Comté* vol. ii, Besancon, 1846, pp. 490–3.

Georg von Ehingen: see his *Reisen*, p. 11.
Faber's panegyric: *Evagatorium*, vol. ii, pp. 2-13.

XV. THE LATER MIDDLE AGES: (2)
'BASE-BORN MEN'

267 Nomadic missions: Delaruelle *et al.*, pp. 636-56. On Bernardino in Rome, Infessura, *Diario della citta di Roma*, ed. O. Tommasini, *Fonti*, Rome, 1890, p. 25. On Orihuela, M-M. Gorce, *Saint Vincent Ferrier 1350-1419*, Paris, 1924, pp. 174-6.

268 Datini: I. Origo, *The merchant of Prato*, London, 1957, pp. 306-7, 311-19.

Spiritual revival: in general, Delaruelle *et al.*, pp. 605-7, 688-90, 828-9, 872-4, 878. On mass observances, P. de Félice, *Foules en délire, extases collectives. Essai sur quelques formes inférieures de la mystique*, Paris, 1947. On flagellants, see *Disciplinati* (MW).

Priests never possessed: quoted in Delaruelle *et al.*, p. 872.

269 Sacchetti: *Ibid.*, p. 789.

Working-class saints: on peasant saints, G-A. Prevost, *L'Église et les campagnes au moyen age*, Paris, 1892, pp. 272-80 (an idealized picture). On St. Zita, *Aa. Ss.* April, vol. iii, pp. 497-8, 508; Dante, *Inferno*, XXI. 38. On Henry of Bolzano, *Aa. Ss.* June, vol. ii, pp. 375, 391.

Parish priests venerated: *Book of Margery Kempe*, I. 60, p. 147, Grandison, *Reg.*, pp. 1232-4. *Aa. Ss.* Oct., vol. viii, pp. 596-606 (Hélye). *Victoria history of the county of Buckingham*, vol. i, London, 1905, pp. 288-9 (Schorne).

270 Statues: *Lanterne of Light*, XII, p. 84. Burton, *Chron. Mon. Melsa*, vol. iii, pp. 35-6. On Boxley, *Letters and papers*, vol. iii (1), p. 284 (no. 754); G. Baskerville, *English monks and the suppression of the monasteries*, London, 1937, p. 22. On statue burned in 1538, *Letters and papers*, vol. xiii (1), p. 120 (no. 348). On the Rippingdale statue, Owen, p. 141.

271 Franciscans: on this complicated subject, see D. L. Douie, *The nature and effect of the heresy of the fraticelli*, Manchester, 1932.

Gerson: See Delaruelle *et al.*, pp. 855-7.

Flagellation: on early flagellation, J. Leclercq, 'La flagellazione volontaria nella tradizione spirituale dell' occidente', in *Disciplinati*, pp. 73-83. On Avignon incident of 1349, Cohn, pp. 140-1; Delaruelle (1), pp. 122-5; argument of Jean du Fayt, leader of the Parisian deputation, in A. Coville's notice in *Histoire littéraire de la France*, vol. xxxvii, Paris, 1938, pp. 403-4.

272 Revelations: Gerson's views in *De distinctione verarum revelationum ac falsis*, ed. Glorieux, vol. iii, pp. 36-56. On Bridget's revelations, Hefele, vol. vii, pp. 184-5. *Book of Margery Kempe*, I. 46-55, pp. 111-37, esp. I. 52, p. 125.

'Some men trowen . . .': *Select English works of John Wyclif*, ed. T. Arnold, vol. i, Oxford, 1869, pp. 329-30 (attributed). For Wyclif's views on pilgrimages, see *Sermones*, III. 1, 22, vol. ii, pp. 1, 164-5; *De Potestate papae*, XII, ed. J. Loserth, London, 1907, p. 329; *De Ecclesia*, II, XIX, pp. 44-5, 465.

273 Lollards: J. A. F. Thomson, *The later Lollards, 1414–1520*, pp. 28, 33, 34, 41, 44, 47, 56, 62, 69, 70, 78, 81, 104, 113, 126, 160, 184. For sixteenth-century pamphlets against St. Thomas, see list of proscribed books (1531) in F. J. Furnivall, *Political, religious, and love poems*, EETS., O. S., xv, London, 1866, p. 62; Wright (ed.), *Letters*, p. 6. On the official campaign against Becket's reputation in the 1530s, Elton, pp. 197, 257n[1].

Cult of saints attacked at Constance: Henry of Langenstein, *Consilium pacis de unione Ecclesiae*, in H. von der Hardt, *Consilium Constantiense Oecumenicum*, vol. ii, Frankfurt, 1697, col. 56; cf. vol. iii (1698), cols. 30, 33, 35–6. Pierre d'Ailly, *De reformatione Ecclesiae in concilio Constantiensi*, III, in Gerson, *Opera*, ed. du Pin, vol. ii, col. 911. Nicholas of Clamanges, *De novis celebritatibus non instituendis*, p. 153.

Gerson on miracles: *Contra impugnantes ordinis Carthusiensium*, ed. du Pin, vol. ii, cols. 711–14.

Attempt to suppress unproven miracles: *The rolls and register of bishop Oliver Sutton*, ed. R. M. T. Hill, vol. v (Lincoln Record Soc., lx), Hereford, 1965, pp. 143–4; vol. vi (*ibid.*, lxiv), Hereford, 1969, pp. 103–4, 186–7. Grandison, *Reg.*, pp. 941–2.

274 Nicholas of Clamanges on miracles: *Ep.* LXI, p. 175.

John of Trittenheim on miracles: *De Mirac. B.V.M. Helbrunnensis*, I. 3, II. 1, pp. 1136–9, 1158.

275 Legend of Theophilus: principal text in C. Neuhaus, *Adgars Marien-legenden*, Heilbronn, 1886, pp. 79–115. On its dissemination, H. Lundgren, *Studier över Theophiluslegendens romanska varianter*, Uppsala, 1913; Beissel (2), pp. 97–9; introduction to Ruteboeuf, *Le miracle de Théophile*, ed. G. Frank, Paris, 1969, pp. xii–xiv; E. Mâle, *Religious art in France of the thirteenth century*, tr. D. Nussey, London, 1913, pp. 260–1.

'*Tu mater es . . .*': U. Chevalier, *Poésies liturgiques traditionelle de l' Eglise catholique en occident*, Tournai, 1893, p. 134.

'Mother of mercy' in early miracle stories: Kjellman (ed.), *Miracles de la Vierge*, VIII, XI, XIII, LI, pp. 27–30, 44–5, 60–1, 219–20. Monk inscribed among elect: Étienne de Bourbon, *Anecdotes*, II. 139, pp. 119–20. On dates and origins, Southern.

276 Gambler enriched: Jacques de Vitry, *Exempla*, CCXCVI, pp. 124–5.

'Only one thing . . .': Etienne de Bourbon, *Anecdotes*, II. 117, p. 101.

Essones: Suger, *De Administratione sua*, XX, pp. 177–82.

Ergotism: see above, p. 75.

'Building crusades': on Chartres (1145), see Robert of Torigny, *Chron.*, vol. i, pp. 238–9; letter of Hugh, archbishop of Rouen, in *RHF.* xiv. 319. On S. Pierre-sur-Dive, Haimoin, *Lettre*, esp. I–IV, pp 121–5. On Chartres (post 1194), *Mirac. S. Mariae Carnotensis*, III–V, IX–X, pp. 514–17, 521–2.

277 Procession at Issigny: *Mirac. Eccl. Constantiensis*, VI, pp. 370–2.

Statues of Virgin: *Ibid.*, praefat., XIV, pp. 367–8, 376 (Coutances). *DHGE.*, vol. xii, col. 551 (Chartres). *Visio monachi*, XLVII, p. 304 (Eynsham dream). On the black Virgin of Rocamadour, which still survives, see Rupin, pp. 114, 291. On that of Le Puy, which is known from drawings, A. Chassaing, *Chroniques d'Étienne Medicis*, vol. i, Le Puy, 1869, p. 29n.; *Chron. Lemovicense*, *RHF.* xxi. 768 (disaster of 1255), cf. *GC.*, vol. ii, p. 716.

278 Fitzralph's sermon: Owst, pp. 140–1.
Abrupt origins of pilgrimages to statues: *Mirac. B.V.M. in Beverne*, in *Anecdota Gielemans*, III. 3, pp. 102–3. *De Imagine B.V.M. in sabulo Bruxellensi*, in *ibid.*, III. 14, p. 363 (Antwerp statue repainted). *Chartulary of Bridlington*, pp. 448–9 (Kernetby). *Concilia Magnae Britaniae*, ed. D. Wilkins, vol. ii, London, 1737, pp. 423–4 (Foston). John of Trittenheim, *De Mirac. B.V.M. prope Dietelbach*, I. 6, p. 1084 (Trier). John of Trittenheim, *De Mirac. B.V.M. Helbrunnensis*, II. 2–4, pp. 1160–2.

279 Legends follow: *DHGE.*, vol. x, cols. 92–4 (Boulogne). Toussaert, pp. 269–70 (Rozebeke). Misset, pp. 6, 43 (l'Épine).
Wurzburg sanctuaries: John of Trittenheim, *De Mirac. B.V.M. prope Dietelbach*, I. 6, 8, pp. 1083, 1087–8.
'Simple people of Christ': *Ibid.*, I. 9, 12, pp. 1091–2, 1097.
Walsingham offerings: Savine, p. 103. Wright (ed.), *Letters*, p. 138.
Buxton and Cardigan: Wright, *op. cit.*, pp. 143, 186.

280 Gregory VII: *Reg.*, VIII. 21, p. 559.
St. Charlemagne: see R. Folz, *Études sur le culte liturgique de Charlemagne dans les eglises de l'Empire*, Paris, 1951.
St. Canute: *Aa. Ss.* July, vol. iii, pp. 118–49. Kemp, pp. 69–70.

281 St. Leger: *DACL.*, vol. viii, cols. 2487–93. Guibert, *De Vita sua*, III. 20, pp. 231–2.
Thomas of Lancaster: J. R. Madicott, *Thomas of Lancaster, 1307–1322*, Oxford, 1970, pp. 329–30.
Edward II: *The diplomatic correspondance of Richard II*, ed. E. Perroy, Camden Soc., 3rd. series, vol. xlviii, London, 1933, pp. 62–3 (no. 95). E. Perroy, *L'Angleterre et le grand schisme d'occident*, Paris, 1933, pp. 330, 341–2.
Simon de Montfort: Stubbs, *Charters*, p. 409 (dictum of Kenilworth). *Mirac. Simonis de Montford*, ed. J. O. Halliwell, Camden Soc., O.S., vol. xv, London, 1840, pp. 67–110, esp. pp. 83–4.

282 Crowds at Gloucester: *Hist. mon. S. Petri Gloucestriae*, ed. W. H. Hart, vol. i, *RS.*, London, 1863, pp. 44–5, 46.
Wilsnack legend: oldest (15th-cent.) version ed. P. Heitz and W. L. Schreiber, *Das Wunderblut zu Wilsnack*, Strassburg, 1904, pp. 8–9.
'Sought from many a country . . .': *Book of Margery Kempe*, II. 4, p. 232.
Wilsnack was popular with English pilgrims, see *Lit. Cant.*, vol. iii, pp. 191–2; *Testamenta vetusta*, vol. i, p. 196.
Indulgences of 1384: Riedel (OS), pp. 140–3.
Mass-pilgrimage of 1387: Riddageshus, *Chron.*, ed. G. W. Liebnitz, *Scriptores rerum Brunswicensium*, vol. ii, Hannover, 1710, p. 81.
Wilsnack investigated: *Concilia Pragensia, 1353–1413*, ed. C. Höfler, Prague, 1862, p. 47. *Concilia Germaniae*, ed. J. F. Hartzheim, vol. v, Köln, 1763, pp. 35–6 (Magdeburg).

283 Disputes of 1446–51: indulgence of 1446 in Riedel (OS), pp. 149–51. Report in Breest, pp. 297–300. Citizens' complaint in Riedel (OS), pp. 144–5. Bull of 1451 in *ibid.*, pp. 152–6.

Children at Wilsnack: in 1475, Stolle, *Chron.*, pp. 376-9. In 1487 and after, Matthias Doring, *Chron.*, in F. A. Riedel, *Codex diplomaticus Brandenburgensis*, vol. iv (1), Berlin, 1862, p. 248.

284 'And men knew not . . .': Stolle, *Chron.*, pp. 377-8.
Child-pilgrims to Wilsnack criticized: pamphlet *On foolish people* in Wattenbach (ed.), 'Beiträge', pp. 605-7. Erfurt Augustinian in *ibid.*, pp. 607-8. *Das Tagebuch des Rathmeisters Marcus Spickendorff*, ed. J. O. Opel, Halle, 1872, p. 19.
Hosts burned: Kaweran, p. 350.

285 Children at S. Pierre-sur-Dive: Haimoin, *Lettre*, II, pp. 122-3. On children in popular religion, Alphandéry, vol. ii, pp. 135-48.
Children's crusade: Alphandéry, vol. ii, pp. 115-35.
'Many people . . .': *Annales Marbacenses*, p. 82.
Children at Mont-St.-Michel in 1333: Huynes, vol. i, pp. 98-114. On the *pastoureaux* of 1320, see Cohn, pp. 102-4.

286 In 1393 and 1441-2: Chomel, pp. 230-9.
In 1457: Jacques de Clercq, *Mémoires (1448-67)*, ed. A. Reiffenberg, vol. ii, Brussels, 1823, p. 276; John of Trittenheim, *Annales*, vol. ii, p. 431; Huynes, vol. i, pp. 123-7; Ekkehart Artzt, *Chron. Weissenburgense*, ed. C. Hoffman, *Quellen und Erörterungen zur bayerischen und deutschen Geschichte*, vol. ii, Munchen, 1862, pp. 147-8. On the children in Regensburg, Dupont (2), pp. 26-7. On hostile pamphlets, Delisle (2), p. 392.
Children at Monte Gargano: Haupt, pp. 673-4.
Nicklashausen: John of Trittenheim, *Annales*, vol. ii, pp. 486-91. Stolle, *Chron.*, pp. 380-3. Lorenz Fries, *Historie der Bischoffen zu Wurzburg*, Frankfurt, 1713, pp. 852-4. Documents in Barack (OS), pp. 50-2 (early history of statue), 53-4 (report of bishop's informer), 59, 66-79, 97-100 (prohibitions, interdict), 104-5 (destruction of church).

288 'Simple unlettered folk . . .': John of Trittenheim, *Mirac. B.V.M. prope Dietelbach*, I. 6, pp. 1083-4.

XVI. MEDIAEVAL CHRISTIANITY: RELIGION TO RITUAL

289 Latimer on Hailes: *Sermons and remains*, ed. G. E. Corrie, Parker Soc., iii, London, 1844-5, vol. ii, p. 364.
Conc. Châlons: *MC*. xiv. 96. Cf. Boniface, *Ep.* L, pp. 83-5.
Licence to sin: Langland, *Piers Plowman*, B. prol. 46-52, p. 3. Poitevin author quoted in E. Ginot, *Dix siècles de pèlerinage à Compostelle. Les chemins de Saint-Jacques en Poitou*, Poitiers, 1912, p. 40.
Criticized by moral reformers: Berthold, *Predigten*, XXVIII, vol. i, pp. 459-60. A. Franz (ed.), *Drei deutscher Minoriten-prediger aus dem 13 und 14 Jahrhundert*, Freiburg i. B., 1907, p. 69 ('did any of you try . . .'). Giordano da Rivalto, *Prediche inedite*, Bologna, 1867, p. 109; cf. *Prediche recitate in Firenze dal MCCCIII al MCCCVI*, vol. i, Firenze, 1831, pp. 252-3. See also Samouillan, pp. 306-8.

290 Langland: *Piers Plowman*, B.V. 57-8, 514-612, pp. 57-8, 85-9.
Gascoigne on indulgences: *Loci e libro veritatum*, ed. J. E. Thorold Rogers, Oxford, 1881, p. 123.

291 Petitions from French churches: collected in Denifle, vol. i.
Sale of crusading indulgence: *Hist. Compostellana*, II. 78, p. 429 (synod of 1125); William of Newburgh, *Hist. rerum Anglicanum*, III. 24, ed. R. Howlett, *Chronicles of the reigns of Stephen, Henry II, and Richard I*, RS., vol. i, London, 1884, pp. 274-5. On commutation of vows, see above, ch. IX. On sale of Roman Jubilee indulgence, see above, ch. XIII.
Sale of right to commute vows: *CPR. Letters*, vol. v, pp. 548-9 (Mattersley), but it was almost immediately cancelled, *ibid.*, p. 549. *Lit. Cant.*, vol. iii, p. 255 (no. 1064) (Canterbury in 1470).

292 Sale of dispensations for Rome, Santiago, etc.: Walsingham, *Hist. Anglicana*, ed. H. T. Riley, RS., London, 1863-4, vol. i, p. 452. Arch. Vat. Reg. Vat. 347, fols. 132-4 (Germany, 1390). Arch. Vat. Reg. Vat. 313, fol. 48 (Castile, 1391).
Price of dispensation: E. Göller, 'Die Einnahmen der apostolischen Kammer unter Johann XXII', *Görres-Gesellschaft. Verbindung mit ihrem historischen Institut in Rom*, vol. i, Paderborn, 1910, pp. 353, 361 (prices in 1330-1). L. Célier, *Les dataires du xvᵉ siècle et les origines de la daterie apostolique*, BEFAR., ciii, Paris, 1910, p. 153 (late 15th. cent.). *Letters and papers illustrative of the reigns of Richard III and Henry VII*, ed. J. Gairdner, RS., vol. ii, London, 1863, pp. 97-8.
Indulgences *ad instar*: S. Mancherini, *Codice diplomatico della Verna e delle SS. Stigmate*, Firenze, 1924, pp. 64-8 (no. 48). A. Mercati, 'Indulgenze della Porzioncola e della Verna concesse fuori dell'ordine francescano', *Archivum franciscanum historicum*, xliii (1950), pp. 337-59. *CPR. Letters*, vol. iv, p. 349, and see index s.v. 'Indulgences; of the Portiuncula'. On indulgences *ad instar* those of St. Mark's see, e.g., Jansen, p. 165 (Meissen, Erfurt, Paderborn, Benedictsbeuren, Bamberg); *CPR. Letters*, vol. v, pp. 384, 489, 590 (Bromholm, etc.).
Withdrawn in 1402: T. van Ottenthal, *Regulae cancellariae apostolicae*, Innsbruck, 1888, p. 76.

293 Not granted thereafter: This conclusion is based on papal bulls relating to England, the only ones which have been systematically calendared. Two of Boniface's indulgences *ad instar* were confirmed by his successors in 1409 and 1411, *CPR. Letters*, vol. vi, pp. 151, 295. On St. Nicholas of Calais, *ibid.*, vol. xiii, pp. 448-9.
Effect: *Journal d'un bourgeois*, p. 384. *CJC.*, *Extrav. Comm.*, V. ix. 4, vol. ii, cols. 1307-8 (bull of 1473).
Franciscans accused: See, e.g., Simon of Cremona, *De indulgentiis Portiunculae*, I, pp. 87-8.
Cologne indulgence: Jansen, pp. 152-4.
Unauthorized Jubilees: Jean Juvenel des Ursins, *Hist. de Charles VI*, in *Mémoires pour servir à l'histoire de France*, vol. ii, Paris, 1836, p. 442 (Le Puy). *Traité sur le cinquième jubilé de S. Thomas*, I. 1, 4, III. 1-2, 5, pp. 119, 121-2, 140, 142.

294 Pardoners in Spain: J. Goni Gaztambide, 'Los cuestores en España', *Hispania Sacra*, ii (1949), pp. 1-43, 285-310. In England: Jusserand, pp. 175-91; Chichele, *Reg.*, vol. iii, pp. 92-3, 100-1.
Council of Vienne: decree on pardoners in *CJC.*, *Clem.*, V. ix. 2, vol. ii, cols. 1190-1.

Forged bull of 1350: see above, p. 240.

Bulls displayed: Langland, *Piers Plowman*, B. prol. 69, p. 4. Bartolus, *Tractatus*, XVIII, pp. 37–9 (Slavs at Ancona). Cf. Chaucer, *Canterbury Tales*, Pardoner's tale, ll. 7–16, p. 301.

Totiens quoties: Paulus (2), vol. i, p. 344. In Rome: Capgrave, *Solace*, II. 1, p. 63; Muffel, *Beschreibung*, p. 19.

Council of Constance: Hefele, vol. vii, pp. 503, 548.

295 Boniface criticized: Gobelinus Persona, *Cosmidromius*, ed. M. Jansen, Munster, 1900, pp. 144–6. Neuss chronicler quoted in Fredericq (ed.), *Codex*, p. 22.

Canterbury petition: Foréville, p. 191 (P. J. XXX).

Indulgences transferable: *Liber exemplorum ad usum praedicantium*, ed. A. G. Little, Aberdeen, 1908, pp. 98–9 (Ulsterman). Bartolus, *Tractatus*, XXIX, pp. 57–8.

296 Theory of indulgences for dead: Paulus (2), vol. ii, pp. 160–72. On crusading preachers, Conrad of Ursperg, *Chron.*, MGH. SS. xxiii. 379.

Offered at Portiuncula: Bartolus, *Tractatus*, XXI, XXIV, pp. 42–3, 45–7; cf. XXII, XXV–XXVI, XXXI–XXXIII, pp. 43–4, 45–54, 61–5.

297 And elsewhere: Bridget, *Rev.*, VII. 14, p. 550 (Jerusalem). Philip, *Liber de Terra Sancta* (1377), pp. 522, 524 (Rome).

Pilgrimages ordered in English wills: *Testamenta vetusta*, vol. i, p. 51 (William de Beauchamp). Sharpe, *Calendar of wills*, vol. i, pp. 454, 640–1, 664, 479, vol. ii, pp. 41, 163, 234, 335, etc. Chichele, *Reg.*, vol. ii, pp. 74, 488 (Thomas of Arundel, Thomas Poulton); cf. pp. 104, 124, 385, 485, 539. CPR. *Letters*, vol. iv, pp. 388–9 (Fryng). Gibbons (ed.), *Early Lincoln wills*, p. 29 ('Roger, my grandson . . .').

And in foreign wills: 'Testaments enregistrées au Parlement de Paris dans le règne de Charles VI', ed. A. Tuetey, in *Collection de documents inédits sur l'histoire de France, Mélanges historiques*, vol. iii, Paris, 1880, pp. 464, 496, 526, 556–7, 571–2, 577, 588, 622–3, 638. Pastor, vol. iv, p. 150n. (Pressburg). See also Vazquez de Parga *et al.*, vol. i, pp. 120–1; *Cartulaire de N-D. de Boulogne*, pp. 196–7 (nos. 117, 119).

298 Papal indulgences for dead: Alonso de Palencia, *Crónica de Enrique IV*, ed. A. Paz y Melia, *Collección de escritores Castellanos*, cxxvi, vol. i, Madrid, 1904, pp. 164, 219–21 (crusading indulgence of 1457). Lea (1), vol. iii, p. 593 (Tarragona). Paulus (2), vol. ii, pp. 381–2 (Franciscans). *Archives historiques de la Saintonge et de l'Aunis*, x (1882), pp. 56–69 (Saintes).

Vicarious pilgrimages (12th. cent.): William, *Mirac. S. Thomae*, II. 20, p. 177 (Ralph). Thomas of Monmouth, *Mirac. S. Willelmi*, IV. 5, p. 170. Benedict, *Mirac. S. Thomae*, III. 58, p. 158 (nun).

Cressewyc: CPR. *Letters*, vol. iv, p. 389. Cf. Gibbons, *Early Lincoln wills*, p. 62.

299 Isabel of Bavaria: Jean Chartier, *Chronique de Charles VII*, ed. Vallet de Viriville, Paris, 1858, pp. 276, 279, 284; Forgeais, *Plombs historiés*, vol. iii, p. 202 (Avallon). On her unusual piety, see Perdrizet, p. 126. No pilgrim, alternative disposition: e.g. Sharpe, *Calendar of wills*, vol. i, p. 657.

'Of honest condition': e.g. *Testamenta vetusta*, vol. i, p. 68; Sharpe, *Calendar of wills*, vol. ii, p. 41.

John of Brittany: H. Morice (ed.), *Mémoires pour servir de preuves à l'histoire de Bretagne*, vol. ii, Paris, 1744, col. 1068.

Scandinavian professionals: Riant (3), p. 381.

Bishop of Lincoln: *Book of Margery Kempe*, I. 15, p. 36.

Flagellation and Jubilee: Giles li Muisis, *Chron.*, pp. 353, 361 (flagellant preachers). P. Fredericq, 'Deux sermons inédits de Jean du Fayt', *Académie Royale de Belgique, Bulletin de la classe des lettres* (1903), p. 700. See Delaruelle (1), pp. 141–3.

300 Deguileville: *Le pèlerinage de la vie humaine*, ed. J. J. Sturzinger, Roxburghe Club, London, 1893.

Used as argument against all external observances: *Lanterne of light*, XII, pp. 85–7. *Examination of William Thorpe*, p. 138. Similar opinions were expressed by Sir John Oldcastle at his trial, Rymer, *Foedera*, vol. ix, p. 63. On the condemnation of the *Lanterne*, Chichele, *Reg.*, vol. iv, pp. 134–7.

Gerson on pilgrimage of life: *Super quotidiano peregrini testamento*, ed. Glorieux, vol. viii, pp. 5–9. On the popularity of this work, M. Lieberman, 'Chronologie Gersonienne', *Romania*, lxxxi (1960), pp. 359–60.

St.-Trond MS: ed. A. van d. Wyngaert, 'Een merkwardige Nederlandsche kruiswegoefening uit de xvᵉ eeuw', *Ons geestlijk Erf*, ii (1928), pp. 10–41; xii (1933), pp. 322–4.

301 Oxford tract of 1423: Latin version in Gerson (wrongly attributed), *Opera*, ed. du Pin, vol. ii, cols. 523–4. French version, ed. E. Vansteenberghe, 'Pèlerinage spirituelle', *Revue des sciences religieuses*, xiv (1934), pp. 387–91. On its origin and date, I follow M. Lieberman, 'Gersoniana', *Romania*, lxxviii (1957), pp. 158–66.

Geiler: *Christlichen Bilgerschaften zum ewigen Vatterland*, Basel, 1513, fol. 206ᵛᵒ.

Erasmus: *Peregrinatio religiosa*, col. 787.

Jan van Paesschen: *Een devote maniere om gheestelyck pilgrimagie*, Louvain, 1563. On editions and translations, see Brit. Mus. *Catalogue of printed books*, and editions listed in catalogue of Bodleian Library, Oxford and Bibl. Nat., Paris. These are probably by no means complete.

302 Reformation said to have killed pilgrimage: Erasmus, *Peregrinatio religiosa*, cols. 774–5. Affagart, *Rélation*, pp. 20–1.

Mediaeval survivals in Protestant societies: see Thomas.

BIBLIOGRAPHY

This is not a complete bibliography of mediaeval religion, but a guide to the sources used in this book. Other works will be found in the annual bibliographies produced by the Revue d'Histoire Ecclesiastique, *and in the following specialized bibliographies:*

BEAUNIER, and BESSE, J. M. *Recueil historique des archevêchés, évêchés, abbayes, et prieurés de France, Archives de la France Monastique*, vols. I, IV, VII, X, XII, XIV, XV, XVII, XIX, XXXVI, XXXVII, XLV, n.e., 12 vols., Namur, 1905–41.

Bibliotheca Hagiographica Latina. Brussels, 1898–9.

COTTINEAU, L. H. *Répertoire topo-bibliographique des abbayes et prieurés*, 2nd. ed., 2 vols., Mâcon, 1935–7.

JAFFÉ, P. and WATTENBACH, W. *Regesta Pontificum Romanorum*, 2 vols., 2nd. ed., Leipzig, 1885–8.

KOHLER, C. *Rerum et personarum quae in Actis Sanctorum Bollandianis obviae at orientem latinum spectant index analyticus*, ROL., v (1897), pp. 460–561.

LECLERCQ, H. 'Pèlerinage à Rome', *DACL.*, vol. xiv, cols. 40–65.

LECLERCQ, H. 'Pèlerinages aux Lieux Saints', *DACL.*, vol. xiv, cols. 65–176.

RIANT, P. 'Inventaire sommaire des manuscrits rélatifs à l'histoire et à la géographie de l'orient', *AOL.*, ii (1884), pp. 131–204.

RÖHRICHT, R. (1). *Bibliotheca Geographica Palaestinae*, Berlin, 1890.

RÖHRICHT, R. (2). *Die Deutschen im heiligen Lände*, Innsbruck, 1894.

RÖHRICHT, R. (3). *Deutsche Pilgerreisen nach dem heiligen Lände*, Gotha, 1889.

I. ORIGINAL SOURCES

ADAM, abbot of Eynsham. *Magna Vita S. Hugonis*, ed. D. L. Douie and H. Farmer, 2 vols., London, 1961–2.

ADAM OF USK. *Chronicon*, ed. E. M. Thompson, 2nd. ed., London, 1904.

ADAMNAN, abbot of Iona. *De Locis Sanctis*, G. *Itin.*, pp. 221–97.

ADÉMAR DE CHABANNES. *Chronique*, ed. J. Chavanon, Paris, 1897.

AFFAGART, GREFFIN. *Rélation de Terre Sainte (1533–1534)*, ed. J. Chavanon, Paris, 1902.

AIMOIN. *Vita S. Abbonis*, PL. cxxxix. 375–414.

ALBERIC OF ROSATE. *Dictionarium Iuris tam civilis quam canonici*, Venice, 1611.

ALBERT OF AIX. *Historia Hierosolymitana*, RHC. *Occ.*, iv. 265–713.

ALEXANDER III, pope. *Epistolae et privilegia*, PL. cc.

ALFONSO IX, king of Castile. *Las siete partidas de las leyes del sabio don Alonso el nono*, ed. G. Lopez de Touar, 9 parts, Madrid, 1610–11.

ALFONSO X, king of Castile. *Cantigas de S. Maria*, ed. Mqs. de Valmar, 2 vols., Madrid, 1889.

AMORT, E. *De origine, progressu, valore, ac fructu indulgentiarum*, 2 vols., Augsburg, 1735.

Anecdota Gielemans: Anecdota ex codicis hagiographicis Johannis Gielemans, Bruxelles, 1895.

Anglo-Saxon Chronicle. ed. D. Whitelock, D. C. Douglas, and S. I. Tucker, London, 1961.

Annales Altahenses Maiores. ed. W. Giesebrecht and L. B. Oefele, *MGH. Rer. Germ.*, Hannover, 1891.

Annales Marbacenses. ed. H. Bloch, *MGH. Rer. Germ.*, Hannover, 1908.

Annales Regni Francorum. ed. G. H. Pertz and F. Kurze, *MGH. Rer. Germ.*, Hannover, 1895.

ANTENORIS. *Vita S. Silvini, episcopi Alciaci, Aa. Ss.* Feb., vol. iii, pp. 29–32.

ANTONINUS OF PLACENTIA. *Itinerarium, G. Itin.*, pp. 159–218.

AQUINAS, THOMAS, St. *Opera Omnia*, 15 vols., Rome, 1882–1930.

Archives de Bruges: Inventaire des archives de la ville de Bruges, Section première: Inventaire des chartes, ed. L. Gilliodts-Van Severen, 9 vols., Bruges, 1871–85.

ARNOLD OF LUBECK. *Chronica Slavorum*, ed. I. M. Lappenberg, *MGH. Rer. Germ.*, Hannover, 1868.

ARNOLD, T. (ed.). *Memorials of St. Edmund's Abbey*, 3 vols., *RS.*, London, 1890–6.

AUGUSTINE OF HIPPO, St. *De Civitate Dei*, ed. E. Hoffman, *CSEL.* xl. 2 vols., Vienna, 1899–1900.

AUGUSTINE OF HIPPO, St. *De cura pro mortuis gerenda*, ed. J. Zycha, *CSEL.* xli, Vienna, 1900.

AUGUSTINE OF HIPPO, St. *Epistolae*, ed. A. Goldbacher, *CSEL.* xxxiv, xliv, xlvii, lvii, 4 vols., Vienna, 1895–1923.

AUGUSTINE OF HIPPO, St. *Sermones, PL.* xxxviii–xxxix.

BALUZE, S. (ed.). *Vitae paparum Avinionensium*, n.e., ed. G. Mollat, 4 vols., Paris, 1916–28.

BARACK, K. A. (ed.). 'Hans Böhm und die Wallfahrt nach Nicklashausen im Jahre 1476', *Archiv des historischen Vereines von Unterfranken und Aschaffenburg*, xiv (3) (1858), pp. 1–108.

BARAUT, C. (ed.). 'Textos homilectics i devots del *Libre Vermell* de Montserrat', *Analecta Sacra Tarraconensia*, xxviii (1955), pp. 25–44.

BARTOLUS, FRANCIS, friar of Assisi. *Tractatus de indulgentia S. Mariae de Portiuncula*, ed. P. Sabatier, *Collection d'études et de documents sur l'histoire religieuse et littéraire du moyen age*, iii, Paris, 1900.

BEAUMANOIR, PHILIPPE DE REMI, SIRE DE. *Coutumes de Beauvaisis*, ed. A. Salmon, 2 vols., Paris, 1899–1900.

Becket Materials: Materials for the history of Thomas Becket, archbishop of Canterbury, 7 vols., *RS.*, London, 1875–85.

BEDE. *Ecclesiastical history of the English people*, ed. B. Colgrave and R. A. B. Mynors, Oxford, 1969.

BEDE. *De Locis Sanctis, G. Itin.*, pp. 301–24.

BEDE. *Vita S. Cuthberti*, ed. B. Colgrave, *Two lives of St. Cuthbert*, Cambridge, 1940.

BELLORINI, T. and HOADE, E. (ed.). *Visit to the Holy Places of Egypt, Sinai, Palestine, and Syria, in 1384, by Frescobaldi, Gucci, and Sigoli*, Publications of the Studium Biblicum Franciscanum, no. 6, Jerusalem, 1948.

'BENEDICT' (i.e. ROGER OF HOWDEN). *Gesta regis Henrici Secundi*, ed. W. Stubbs, 2 vols., *RS.*, London, 1867.

BENEDICT, canon of St. Peter's, Rome. *Liber Politicus*, in *Liber Censuum, ed. cit.*, vol. ii, pp. 139–77.

BENEDICT OF PETERBOROUGH. *Miracula S. Thomae Cantuariensis, Becket Materials*, vol. ii, pp. 21–281.

BENINCASA. *Vita S. Rayneri Pisani, As. Ss.* June, vol. iii, pp. 423–66.

BERNARD. *Itinerarium Bernardi monachi Franci, TM. Itin.*, vol. i, pp. 307–20.

BERNARD OF CLAIRVAUX, St. *Epistolae, PL.* clxxxii.

BERTHOLD OF REGENSBURG. *Predigten*, ed. F. Pfeiffer, 2 vols., Vienna, 1862–1880.

BERTRANDON DE LA BROQUIÈRE. *Voyage d'outremer*, ed. C. Schefer, *Recueil de voyages et de documents pour servir à l'histoire de la géographie*, xii, Paris, 1892.

Bibliotheca Cluniacensis. ed. M. Marrier, Paris, 1614.

BIELER, L. (ed.). *The Irish penitentials, Scriptores Latini Hiberniae*, v, Dublin, 1963.

Black Book of the Admiralty. ed. T. Twiss, 4 vols., *RS.*, London, 1871–6.

BONDURAND, M. (ed.). 'Détresse de l'abbaye de St.-Gilles pendant le schisme d'occident (1417)', *BHP.* (1899), pp. 435–45.

BONIFACE VIII, pope. *Régistres*, ed. A. Thomas, G. Digard, M. Faucon, *et al.*, *BEFAR.*, 2nd. series, vol. iv, 4 vols., Paris, 1884–1939.

BONIFACE and LULLUS. *Briefe*, ed. M. Tangl, *MGH. Epp. Sel.* i, Berlin, 1916.

Book of Margery Kempe. ed. S. B. Meech and H. B. Allen, *EETS.*, O.S., vol. 212, Oxford, 1940.

BRASCA, SANTO. *Viaggio in Terra Santa, 1480*, ed. A. L. Momigliano Lepschy, Milan, 1966.

BREWYN, WILLIAM. *A XVth. century guide-book to the principal churches of Rome*, ed. C. E. Woodruff, London, 1933.

BREYDENBACH, BERNARD VON. *Reiseinstruction, RM. Pilg.*, pp. 120–45.

BREYDENBACH, BERNARD VON. *Sanctarum peregrinationum in Montem Syon, ad venerandum Christi Sepulchrum in Jerusalem, et in Montem Sinai*, Mainz, 1486.

BRIDGET OF SWEDEN, St. *Revelationes*, ed. C. Durant, Antwerp, 1611.

BRYGG, THOMAS. *Itinerarium in Terram Sanctam domini Thomae de Swynburne*, ed. P. Riant, *AOL.*, ii (1884), pp. 378–88 (documents).

BUCCIO DI RANALLO. *Cronaca Aquilana rimata*, ed. V. de Bartholomaeis, *Fonti*, Rome, 1907.

Bull. Dipl.: Bullarium, diplomatum, et privilegium sanctorum Romanorum pontificum, ed. S. Franco and H. Dalmezzo, 23 vols., Turin, 1857–72.

Bull. Vat.: Collectio bullarum sacrosanctae basilicae Vaticanae, 3 vols., Rome, 1747–52.

BURCHARD OF MOUNT SION. *Descriptio Terrae Sanctae, L. Peregr.*, pp. 3–100.

BURTON, THOMAS. *Chronica monasterii de Melsa*, ed. E. A. Bond, 3 vols., *RS.*, London, 1866–8.

CAESARIUS OF HEISTERBACH. *Dialogus miraculorum*, ed. J. Strange, 2 vols., Cologne, 1851.

CAPGRAVE, JOHN. *Ye Solace of pilgrimes. A description of Rome, circa A.D. 1450*, ed. C. A. Mills and H. M. Bannister, London, 1911.

Capitula de miraculis et translationibus S. Cuthberti. in Symeon of Durham, *Opera Omnia, ed. cit.*

Capitularia Regum Francorum. ed. A. Boretius and V. Krause, *MGH. Leges*, sect. ii, 2 vols., Hanover, 1881–97.

CAPODILISTA, GABRIELE. *Itinerario in Terra Santa*, in Brasca, *op. cit.*, pp. 159–237.

Carmen de translatione S. Bartholomaei. ed. B. Sepp, *Neues Archiv der Gesellschaft für ältere deutsche Geschichtskunde*, xxii (1896), pp. 571–5.

Cartulaires du châpitre de l'église metropolitaine Sainte-Marie d'Auch. ed. C. Lacave la Plagne Barris, *Archives Historiques de la Gascogne*, ser. ii, fascs. iii–iv, Paris, 1899.

Cartulaire de l'eglise abbatiale Notre-Dame de Boulogne-sur-Mer, 1067–1567. ed. D. Haignéré, *Memoires de la Soc. Académique de Boulogne-sur-Mer*, xiii (1882–6), pp. 89–360.

Cartulaire du prieuré de La Charité-sur-Loire. ed. R. de Lespinasse, Nevers, 1887.

Cartulaire de l'abbaye de Conques en Rouergue. ed. G. Desjardins, Paris, 1879.

Cartulaire de l'abbaye cardinale de la Trinite de Vendôme. ed. C. Metais, 5 vols., Paris, 1893–1900.

CASOLA, PIETRO. *Canon Pietro Casola's pilgrimage to Jerusalem in the year 1494*, tr. M. M. Newett, Manchester, 1907.

CHARLIER, GILLES. *Oratio in concilio Basileensi de corrigendis peccatis publicis*, in H. Canisius and J. Basnage, *Thesaurus monumentorum ecclesiasticorum et historicorum*, vol. iv, Antwerp, 1725, pp. 566–627.

Chartes de Cluny: Recueil des chartes de l'abbaye de Cluny, ed. A. Bernard and A. Bruel, 6 vols., Paris, 1876–1903.

Chartes de Namur: Inventaire des chartes des comtes de Namur, ed. C. Piot, Brussels, 1890.

Chartulary of Bridlington priory. ed. W. T. Lancaster, Leeds, 1912.

CHAUCER, GEOFFREY. *The Canterbury Tales*, in *Complete Works*, ed. W. W. Skeat, vol. iv, Oxford, 1894.

CHICHELE, HENRY, archbishop of Canterbury. *The Register of Henry Chichele, archbishop of Canterbury, 1414–43*, ed. E. F. Jacob, Canterbury and York Society, xlv, 4 vols., Oxford, 1937–47.

Chronicon abbatiae de Evesham ad annum 1418. ed. W. D. Macray, *RS.*, London, 1863.

Chronica monasterii Casinensis. MGH. SS. vii. 551–844.

CLAES VAN DUSEN. *Waerachtighe Beschrijvinge der steden ende Plaetsen geleghen op den Wegh van Venetien na den H. Lande ende Jerusalem*, in Conrady (ed.), *Rheinische Pilgerschriften*, pp. 182–301.

CLEMENT VI, pope. *Lettres closes, patentes, et curiales se rapportant à la France*, ed. E. Déprez, *BEFAR.*, 3rd. series, vol. iii, 3 vols., Paris, 1901–61.

CLEMENT VI, pope. *Lettres closes, patentes, et curiales interessant les pays autres que la France*, ed. E. Déprez and G. Mollat, *BEFAR.*, Paris, 1960–1.

CONRADY, L. (ed.). *Vier rheinische Palaestina-Pilgerschriften des xiv, xv, und xvi Jahrhunderts*, Wiesbaden, 1882.

Coutumes du Namur et Coutume de Philippeville. ed. J. Grandgagnage, 2 vols., Brussels, 1869–70.

Coutumes du pays de Liège. ed. J. J. Raikem and M. L. Polain, vols. i–ii, Brussels, 1870–3.

DANIEL, Russian abbot. *Vie et pèlerinage,* in Khitrowo (ed.), *Itinéraires Russes,* pp. 1–83.

DELISLE, L. (ed.). 'Enquête sur la fortune des établissements de l'ordre de S. Benoît en 1388', *Notices et extraits des manuscrits de la Bibliothèque Nationale,* xxxix (1909), pp. 359–408.

Detectio corporis S. Areopagiticae Dionysii circiter anno 1050. in Félibien, *op. cit.* (MW), pièces justificatives, pp. 165–72.

DIETRICH OF NIEM. *De Scismate,* ed. G. Erler, Leipzig, 1890.

DU CANGE, C. *Glossarium mediae et infimae latinitatis,* 10 vols., Niort, 1883–7.

DUGDALE, W. *Monasticon Anglicanum,* 6 vols. in 8, London, 1817–30.

DUPLÈS-AGIER, H. (ed.). *Chroniques de Saint-Martial de Limoges,* SHF., Paris, 1874.

EADMER, monk of Canterbury. *De Sanctorum veneratione et obsecratione,* ed. A. Wilmart, *Revue des Sciences Religieuses,* xv (1935), pp. 184–219, 354–79.

EADMER, monk of Canterbury. *Vita S. Anselmi, archiepiscopi Cantuariensis,* ed. R. W. Southern, London, 1962.

EHINGEN, GEORGE VON. *Reisen nach der Ritterschaft,* ed. F. Pfeiffer, *BLVS.* i, Stuttgart, 1842.

EINHARD. *Translatio et Miracula S. Marcelini et Petri, MGH. SS.* xv. 238–64.

EINHARD. *Vita Karoli Magni Imperatoris,* ed. L. Halphen, Paris, 1938.

Epistolae quatuor de cultu S. Martini apud Turonenses extr. sec. xii, An. Boll., iii (1884), pp. 216–57.

ERASMUS, DESIDERIUS. *Peregrinatio religionis ergo,* in *Opera Omnia,* ed J. Clericus, vol. i, Leyden, 1703, cols. 774–87.

ERNOUL. *Chronique d'Ernoul et de Bernard le Tresorier,* ed. L. de Mas Latrie, SHF., Paris, 1871.

ETHERIA. *Peregrinatio ad Loca Sancta, G. Itin.,* pp. 35–101.

ÉTIENNE DE BOURBON. *Anecdotes historiques, légendes, et apologues,* ed. A. Lecoy de la Marche, SHF., Paris, 1879.

EUSEBIUS OF CAESAREA. *Historia Ecclesiastica (Kirchengeschichte),* ed. T. Mommsen, *Die Griechischen Christlichen Schriftsteller der ersten drei Jahrhunderte, Eusebius Werke,* vol. ii, Leipzig, 1903–9.

Examination of Master William Thorpe, priest, of heresy. in A. W. Pollard (ed.), *Fifteenth century prose and verse,* London, 1903, pp. 97–174.

FABER, FELIX. *Evagatorium in Terrae Sanctae, Arabiae, et Egypti Peregrinationem,* ed. C. D. Hassler, *BLVS.,* ii–iv, Stuttgart, 1843–9.

FAILLON, E. M. (ed.). *Monuments inédits sur l'apostolat de Sainte Marie Madeleine en Provence,* 2 vols, Paris, 1848.

FARSIT, HUGHES. *De Miraculis S. Mariae in urbe Suessionensis, PL.* clxxix. 1777–1800.

FONTANINI, J. (ed.). *Codex constitutionum quas summi pontifices ediderunt in solemni canonisatione sanctorum,* Rome, 1729.

FORÉVILLE, R. (ed.). *Un procés de canonisation à l'aube du xiiiᵉ siècle (1201–2). Le Livre de Saint Gilbert de Sempringham,* Paris, 1943.

FORGEAIS, A. *Collection de plombs historiées trouvés dans la Seine,* 5 vols., Paris, 1863.

FREDERICQ, P. *Codex documentorum sacratissimarum indulgentiarum Neerlandicarum* (*1300–1600*), Rijks Geschiedkundige Publicatiën, Kleine Serie, xxi, 'S-Gravenhage, 1922.

FRESCOBALDI, LIONARDO DI NICCOLO. *Viaggio in Egitto e in Terra Santa*, in Bellorini and Hoade, *op. cit.* (OS), pp. 29–90.

FRETELLUS, archdeacon of Antioch. *De situ urbis Jerusalem et de locis sanctis intra ipsam urbem sive circumjacentibus*, in C. M. de Vogué, *Les églises de la Terre Sainte*, Paris, 1860, pp. 412–33.

GERALD OF WALES. *Opera*, ed. J. S. Brewer and J. F. Dimock, 8 vols., *RS.*, London, 1861–91.

GERSON, JEAN. *Opera Omnia*, ed. L. E. du Pin, 5 vols., Antwerp, 1706.

GERSON, JEAN. *Oeuvres Complètes*, ed. P. Glorieux, Paris, 1960– (in progress).

Gesta abbatum S. Trudonensium. ed. C. de Borman, *Chronique de l'abbaye de Saint-Trond*, 2 vols., Liège, 1877.

Gesta consulum Andegavorum, ed. P. Marchegay and A. Salmon, in *Chroniques des comtes d'Anjou*, vol. i, *SHF.*, Paris, 1856.

Gesta Francorum et aliorum Hierosolymitanorum, ed. R. Hill, London, 1962.

GHILLEBERT DE LANNOY. *Voyages et ambassades*, in *Oeuvres*, ed. C. Potvin, Louvain, 1878, pp. 9–178.

GHISTELE, JOSSE VAN. 'Le Voyage en orient de Josse van Ghistele (1481–5), *Revue Generale*, xxxvii (1883), pp. 723–64; xxxviii (1883), pp. 46–71, 193–210.

GIBBONS, A. (ed.). *Early Lincoln wills*, Lincoln, 1888.

GILES LI MUISIS. *Chronica*, ed. J. J. de Smet, *Corpus Chronicorum Flandriae* (*Collection de chroniques Belges inédites*), ii, Brussels, 1841.

GIRNAND VON SCHWALBACH. *Pilgerschrift*, *RM. Pilg.*, pp. 97–9.

GLABER, RADULPH. *Historiae*, ed. M. Prou, Paris, 1886.

GRANDISON, JOHN DE. *The Register of John de Grandison, bishop of Exeter* (*A.D. 1327–1369*), ed. F. C. Hingeston-Randolph, London, 1894–9.

Graphia Aureae Urbis. VZ., vol. iii, pp. 67–110.

GREGORY, Master. *De Mirabilibus urbis Romae*, ed. M. R. James, *EHR.*, xxxii (1917), pp. 531–4.

GREGORY I, pope. *Dialogi*, Lib. II, *PL.* lxvi. 125–204; Libs. I, III–IV, *PL.* lxxvii. 149–430.

GREGORY I, pope. *Registrum epistolarum*, ed. P. Ewald and L. M. Hartmann, *MGH. Epp.* i–ii, 2 vols., Berlin, 1891–9.

GREGORY VII, pope. *Registrum*, ed. E. Caspar, *MGH. Epp. Sel.* ii, Berlin, 1920–3.

GREGORY IX, pope. *Régistres*, ed. L. Auvray, *BEFAR.*, 2nd. series, vol. ix, 4 vols., Paris, 1890–1955.

GREGORY OF TOURS. *Historia Francorum*, ed. B. Krusch and W. Levison, *MGH. Merov.* i (1), 2nd. ed., Hanover, 1937–51.

GREGORY OF TOURS. *Miracula et opera minora*, ed. B. Krusch, *MGH. Merov.* i (2), Hanover, 1885.

GUCCI, GIORGIO. *Viaggio ai Luoghi Santi*, in Bellorini and Hoade, *op. cit.* (OS), pp. 91–156.

GUÉRIN, P., and CÉLIER, L. (ed.). *Recueil des documents concernant le Poitou contenus dans les registres de la chancellerie de France*, 14 vols., *Archives Historiques du Poitou*, xi (1881), xiii (1883), xvii (1887), xix (1888), xxi

(1891), xxiv (1893), xxvi (1896), xxix (1898), xxxii (1903), xxxv (1906), xxxviii (1909), xli (1914–19), l (1938), lvi (1958).

GUI, BERNARD. *Practica inquisitionis heretice pravitatis*, ed. C. Douais, Paris, 1886.

GUIBERT OF NOGENT. *De pignoribus sanctorum*, PL. clvi. 607–80.

GUIBERT OF NOGENT. *Gesta Dei per Francos*, RHC. Occ. iv. 115–263.

GUIBERT OF NOGENT. *Histoire de sa vie (1053–1124)*, ed. G. Bourgin, Paris, 1907.

Guide: Guide du pelerin de Saint-Jacques de Compostelle, ed. J. Vielliard, 4th. ed., Mâcon, 1969.

GUILLAUME DE DEGUILEVILLE. *Le pélerinage de la vie humaine*, ed. J. J. Sturzinger, Roxburghe Club, London, 1893.

GUILLAUME DE SAINT-PATHUS. *Les Miracles de S. Louis*, ed. F. B. Fay, Paris, 1932.

HADDAN, A. W., and STUBBS, W. (ed.). *Councils and ecclesiastical documents relating to Great Britain and Ireland*, 3 vols., Oxford, 1869–71.

HAIMOIN, abbot of St.-Pierre-sur-Dive. 'Lettre sur la construction de l' église de Saint-Pierre-sur-Dive, en 1145', ed. L. Delisle, BEC., xxi (1860), pp. 113–39.

HARFF, ARNOLD VON. *Die Pilgerfahrt des Ritters Arnold von Harff in den Jahren 1469 bis 1499*, ed. E. von Groote, Cologne, 1860.

HERMAN, monk of Bury. *De Miraculis S. Eadmundi*, in Arnold, op. cit. (OS), vol. i, pp. 26–92.

HERMAN, canon of Laon. *De Miraculis S. Mariae Laudunensis*, PL. clvi. 961–1020.

Histoire versifié de l'abbaye de Fécamp. ed. A. Längfors, *Annales Academiae Scientiarum Fennicae*, ser. B, xxii, Helsinki, 1928.

Historia Compostellana. ES. xx.

Hodoeporicon S. Willibaldi. TM. Itin., vol. i, pp. 241–97.

HUGH OF FLAVIGNY. *Chronicon*, MGH. SS. viii. 288–502.

HUS, JOHN. *De Sanguine Christi*, ed. W. Flajshans in *Opera Omnia*, vol. i (3), Prague, 1904.

INNOCENT III, pope. *Regesta sive epistolae*, PL. ccxiv–ccxvii.

INNOCENT IV, pope. *Régistres*, ed. E. Berger, BEFAR., 2nd. series, vol. i, 4 vols., Paris, 1881–1919.

Innominatus I. in *Gesta Francorum*, ed. cit., pp. 98–101.

Innominatus V. ed. W. A. Neumann, *Oesterreichische Vierteljahresschrift für katholische Theologie*, v (1866), pp. 211–82.

Innominatus VI (Pseudo-Beda). ed. W. A. Neumann, *Oesterreichische Vierteljahresschrift für katholische Theologie*, vii (1868), pp. 397–438.

Inventio et miracula S. Wulfranni. ed. J. Laporte, *Mélanges de la Soc. de l' histoire de Normandie*, xive serie, Rouen, 1938, pp. 1–87.

Itinerarium cuiusdam Anglici Terram Sanctam et alia loca sancta visitantis (1344–45), BBB., vol. iv, pp. 427–60.

JACOB OF VORAGINE. *Legenda Aurea*, ed. T. Graesse, 3rd. ed., Dresden, 1890.

JACQUES DE VITRY. *Exempla et sermones vulgares*, ed. T. F. Crane, *Publications of the Folk-lore Society*, xxvi, London, 1890.

JACQUES DE VITRY. *Historia Hierosolymitana*, ed. J. Bongars, *Gesta Dei per Francos*, Hanover, 1611, vol. i, pp. 1047–1124.

JEAN DE MEUNG. See *Roman de la rose.*

JEROME, St. *Contra Vigilantium*, PL. xxiii. 339–52.

JEROME, St. *Epistolae*, ed. I. Hilberg, *CSEL.* liv–lvi, 3 vols., Vienna, 1909–18.

JOHN THE DEACON. *Descriptio Lateranensis Ecclesiae*, *VZ.*, vol. iii, pp. 319–73.

JOHN OF COUTANCES. *Miracula Ecclesiae Constantiensis*, in E-A. Pigeon, *Histoire de la cathedrale de Coutances*, Coutances, 1876, pp. 367–83.

JOHN OF SALISBURY. *Historia Pontificalis*, ed. M. Chibnall, London, 1956.

JOHN OF TRITTENHEIM (TRITHEMIUS). *Annales Hirsaugienses*, 2 vols., Saint-Gall, 1690.

JOHN OF TRITTENHEIM (TRITHEMIUS). *Opera pia et spiritualia*, ed. J. Busaeus, Mainz, 1604.

JOHN OF WURZBURG. *Descriptio Terrae Sanctae*, in T. Tobler (ed.), *Descriptiones Terrae Sanctae ex saeculo viii, ix, xii, et xv*, Leipzig, 1874, pp. 108–92.

JOINVILLE, JEAN SIRE DE. *Histoire de S. Louis*, ed. N. de Wailly, 2nd. ed., Paris, 1874.

Journal d'un bourgeois de Paris. ed. A. Tuetey, Paris, 1881.

KAJAVA, O. (ed.). *Etudes sur deux poemes francais rélatifs a l'abbaye de Fécamp, Annales Academiae Scientiarum Fennicae*, ser. B, xxi, Helsinki, 1928.

KHITROWO, B. de (ed.). *Itinéraires Russes en orient*, *SOL.*, v, Geneva, 1889.

KJELLMAN, H. (ed.). *La deuxieme collection Anglo-Normande des miracles de la Sainte Vierge*, Paris, 1922.

LAMBERT OF HERSFELD. *Opera*, ed. O. Holder-Egger, *MGH. Rer. Germ.*, Hanover, 1894.

LANFRID OF WINCHESTER. *Translatio et miracula S. Swithuni*, Lib. I, Lib. II, caps. 46–54, ed. E. P. Sauvage, *An. Boll.*, iv (1885), pp. 367–410; Lib. ii, caps. 1–45, *Aa. Ss.* July, vol. i, pp. 331–7.

LANGLAND, WILLIAM. *The Vision of William concerning Piers the Plowman*, Text B, ed. W. W. Skeat, *EETS.*, O.S., xxxviii, London, 1869.

Lanterne of light. ed. L. M. Swinburn, *EETS.*, O.S., cli, London, 1917.

LENGHERAND, GEORGES. *Voyage à Venise, Rome, Jerusalem, Mont Sinai, et le Kayre, 1485–6*, ed. Mqs. de Godefroy Menilglaise, Mons, 1861.

LE SAIGE, JACQUES. *Voyage de Jacques le Saige de Douai à Rome, Notre-Dame de Lorette, Venise, Jerusalem, et autres lieux saints*, ed. H-R. Duthilloeul, Douai, 1851.

Letters and papers, foreign and domestic, of the reign of Henry VIII, ed. J. S. Brewer, J. Gairdner, *et al.*, 21 vols. in 35, London, 1864–1920.

Liber Censuum: Le Liber Censuum de l'Eglise Romaine, ed. P. Fabre and L, Duchesne, *BEFAR.*, 2nd. series, vol. vi, 3 vols., Paris, 1910–52.

Liber Confraternitatis B. Mariae de Anima Teutonicorum de Urbe, ed. C. Jaenig, Rome, 1875.

Lib. Pont.: Liber Pontificalis, ed. L. Duchesne, *BEFAR.*, 2nd. series, vol. iii (1, 4), 2 vols., Paris, 1886–92.

Liber S. Jacobi, Codex Calixtinus. vol. i (Texto), ed. W. M. Whitehill, Santiago de Compostella, 1944.

Lit. Cant.: Literae Cantuarienses. The letter-book of the monastery of Christ Church, Canterbury, ed. J. B. Sheppard, 3 vols., *RS.*, London, 1887–9.

LUCHINO DEL CAMPO. *Viaggio a Gerusalemme di Niccoló da Este*, ed. G. Ghinassi, *Collezione di opere inedite o rare dei primi tre secoli della lingua*, i, Turin, 1861, pp. 99–160.

LUDOLPH OF SUCHEM. *De itinere Terrae Sanctae*, ed. F. Deycks, *BLVS.*, xxv, Stuttgart, 1851.

MABILLON, J. (ed.). *Vetera analecta*, 2nd. ed., Paris, 1723.

MC.NEILL, J. T., and GAMER, H. M. (ed.). *Medieval handbooks of penance. A translation of the principal 'Libri Penitentiales' and selections from related documents*, N.Y., 1938.

MALLIUS, PETER. *Descriptio basilicae Vaticanae*, *VZ.*, vol. iii, pp. 375–442.

Mandeville's Travels. ed. M. Letts, Hakluyt Soc., series ii, vols. ci–cii, London, 1953.

MANETTI, J. *Vita Nicolai V*, *RISS* (1). iii (2). 907–68.

Manuscrit de Rothelin. RHC. Occ., vol. ii, pp. 483–639.

MARCHEGAY, P., and MABILLE, E. (ed.). *Chroniques des églises d'Anjou, SHF.*, Paris, 1869.

MARIANO DA SIENA. *Viaggio in Terra Santa*, in *I Viaggi in Terra Santa di Simone Sigoli Fiorentino e ser Mariano da Siena*, Parma, 1865, pp. 107–90.

MASTRO, PAOLO DI BENEDETTO DI COLA DELLO. *Memoriale*, ed. M. Pelaez, *ASRSP.*, xvi (1893), pp. 41–130.

Mirabilia Urbis Romae. VZ., vol. iii, pp. 3–65.

Miracles de Notre-Dame de Rocamadour au xiie siècle. ed. E. Albe, Paris, 1907.

Miracula S. Benedicti. ed. E. de Certain, *SHF.*, Paris, 1858.

Miracula S. Columbani Bobbiensis. MGH. SS. xxx. 993–1015.

Miracula S. Eadmundi (MS. Bodley 240). in Arnold, *op. cit.* (OS), vol. i, pp. 359–77, vol. ii, pp. 362–8, vol. iii, pp. 318–48.

Miracula B. Egidii. caps. 1–9, 16–8, *MGH. SS.* xii. 316–23; caps. 12–15, 19–30, *An. Boll.*, ix (1890), pp. 393–422.

Miracula S. Eutropii Santonensis. Aa. Ss. April, vol. iii, pp. 736–44.

Miracula S. Fidis. ed. A. Bouillet, Paris, 1897.

Miracula S. Gilberti. in Foréville, *op. cit.* (OS), pp. 42–73.

Miracula S. Mariae in Carnotensi ecclesia facta. ed. A. Thomas, *BEC.*, xlii (1881), pp. 505–50.

Miracula S. Mariae Magdalenae Viziliaci facta. caps. 1–16 in Faillon, *op. cit.* (OS), vol. ii, pp. 735–42; cap. 17, *CCH.* (Bruxelles), vol. i, p. 214 (no. 44); cap. 18, *CCH.* (Paris), vol. i, p. 587 (no. 13).

Miracula S. Mariae Magdalenae Viziliaci facta (editio altera). Praefat., *CCH.* (Bruxelles), vol. i, p. 32 (no. 46); cap. 1, *CCH.* (Paris), vol. ii, pp. 292–3 (no. 2); cap. 2, *An. Boll.*, xvii (1898), p. 177 (no. 1); cap. 3, *CCH.* (Paris), vol. ii, p. 292 (no. 1); caps. 4–6, *An. Boll.*, xvii (1898), pp. 177–9 (nos. 2–4).

Miracula S. Mariae Magdalenae in vico S. Maximini in Provincia. CCH. (Paris), vol. iii, pp. 287–94.

Miracula S. Martialis anno 1388 patrata. ed. V. V. F. Arbellot, *An. Boll.*, i (1882), pp. 411–46.

Miracula S. Michaelis in Periculo Maris. ed. E. de R. de Beaurepaire, *Mémoires de la Soc. des Antiquaires de Normandie*, 3rd. series, ix (1877), pp. 864–98.

Miracula S. Wulfstani. ed. R. R. Darlington, Camden Soc., 3rd. séries, vol. xl, London, 1928, pp. 115–80.

MONTSABERT, D. P. de (ed.). *Chartes et documents pour servir à l'histoire de l' abbaye de Charroux, Archives Historiques du Poitou*, xxxix (1910).

MORE, SIR THOMAS. *A dyalogue of the veneration and worshyp of ymages and relyques, praying to saints and goyng on pylgrymage*, London, 1529.

MUFFELS, NIKOLAUS. *Beschreibung der stadt Rom*, ed. W. Vogt, *BLVS.*. cxxviii, Tübingen, 1876.

NAGL, F. (ed.). 'Urkundliches zur Geschichte der Anima in Rom', *Römische Quartalschrift*, Supplementheft xii, Rome, 1899, pp. 1–88.

NICCOLO DA POGGIBONSI. *Libro d'oltramare*, ed. A. Bacchi della Lega, *Scelta di curiosità letterarie inedite o rare dal secolo xiii al xvii*, clxxxii, 2 vols., Bologna, 1881.

NICEPHORUS. *Translatio S. Nicolai in Barum, An. Boll.*, iv (1885), pp. 169–92.

NICOLAS III, pope. *Régistres*, ed. J. Gay and S. Vitte, *BEFAR.*, 2nd. series, vol. xiv, Paris, 1898–1938.

NICOLAS IV, pope. *Régistres*, ed. E. Langlois, *BEFAR.*, 2nd. series, vol. v, Paris, 1886–93.

NICOLAS OF CLAMANGES. *Opera Omnia*, Leyden, 1613.

NOMPAR II, SEIGNEUR DE CAUMONT. *Voyaige d'outremer en Jherusalem par le seigneur de Caumont, l'an MCCCCXVIII*, ed. Mqs. de la Grange, Paris, 1859.

ODO, abbot of Cluny. *Vita S. Geraldi Auriliacensis comitis, PL.* cxxxiii. 639–710.

ODO OF DEUIL. *De profectione Lodovici VII in orientem*, ed. H. Waquet, *Documents rélatifs à l'histoire des croisades*, iii, Paris, 1949.

OGIER VIII, SEIGNEUR D'ANGLURE. *Le saint voyage de Jerusalem du seigneur d'Anglure*, ed. F. Bonnardot and A. Longnon, *SATF.*, Paris, 1878.

ORDERIC VITALIS. *The Ecclesiastical History*, books III–VIII, ed. M. Chibnall, vols. ii–iv, Oxford, 1969–73; other books, ed. A. Le Prévost, *SHF.*, 5 vols, Paris, 1838–55.

Ordonnances: Ordonnances des rois de France de la troisième race, 22 vols., Paris, 1723–1847.

O Roma nobilis! ed. L. Traube, *Bayerischen Akademie der Wissenschaften, Abhandlungen*, xix (1891), pp. 297–309.

OTTO OF FRIESING. *De duabus civitatibus*, ed. A. Hofmeister, *MGH. Rer. Germ.*, Hanover, 1912.

PALLADIUS, bishop of Helenopolis. *Historia Lausiaca*, ed. C. Butler, *Texts and Studies*, ed. J. Armitage Robinson, vol. vi, 2 vols., Cambridge, 1904.

PARDESSUS, J. M. (ed.). *Collection de lois maritimes antérieures au xviiie siècle*, 6 vols., Paris, 1828–45.

PARIS, MATTHEW. *Chronica Majora*, ed. H. R. Luard, 7 vols., *RS.*, London, 1872–83.

PAULINUS OF NOLA. *Carmina*, ed. W. von Hartel, *CSEL.*, xxx, Vienna, 1894.

PAULINUS OF NOLA. *Epistolae*, ed. W. von Hartel, *CSEL.*, xxix, Vienna, 1894.

PECOCK, REGINALD. *The Repressor of over-much blaming of the clergy*, ed. C. Babington, 2 vols., *RS.*, London, 1860.

Pèlerinage en Palestine de l'abbesse Euphrosine, princesse de Polotsk (1173). ed. B. de Khitrowo. *ROL.*. iii (1895), pp. 32–5.

Pèlerinages por aler en Iherusalem. MR. Itin., pp. 87–104.

Pèlerinages et pardouns d'Acre. MR. Itin., pp. 227–36.

PETER THE DEACON. *Historica relatio de corpore S. Benedicti, Aa. Ss.* March, vol. iii, pp. 288–97.

PETER THE VENERABLE, abbot of Cluny. *De Miraculis, PL.* clxxxix. 851–954.

PETER THE VENERABLE, abbot of Cluny. *The Letters of Peter the Venerable*, ed. G. Constable, 2 vols., Cambridge, Mass., 1967.

PETRARCH, FRANCESCO. *Le Familiari*, ed. V. Rossi, *Edizione nazionale delle opere di Francesco Petrarca*, vols. x–xiii, 4 vols., Florence, 1933–42.

PHILIP. *Descriptio de Terra Sancta* (*c. 1285–91*), ed. W. A. Neumann, *Oesterreichische Vierteljahresschrift für katholische Theologie*, xi (1872), pp. 1–78, 165–74.

PHILIP. *Liber de Terra Sancta* (*1377*), ed. J. Haupt, *Oesterreichische Vierteljahresschrift für katholische Theologie*, x (1871), pp. 511–40.

PHILIP, prior of St. Frideswide's, Oxford. *Miracula S. Frideswidae, Aa. Ss.* Oct., vol. viii, pp. 567–90.

PHOCAS, JOHN. *De Locis Sanctis, PG.* cxxxiii. 925–62.

POSSOT, DENIS. *Voyage de la Terre Sainte*, ed. C. Schefer, *Recueil de voyages pour servir à l'histoire de la géographie*, xi, Paris, 1890.

POWICKE, F. M., and CHENEY, C. R. (ed.). *Councils and synods, with other documents relating to the English Church*, vol. ii (1205–1313), Oxford, 1964.

PRUDENTIUS, AURELIUS CLEMENS. *Carmina*, ed. J. Bergman, *CSEL.*, lxi, Vienna, 1926.

PURCHAS, SAMUEL. *Purchas his pilgrimes*, Lib. VIII, cap. 5, vol. vii, Glasgow, 1905, pp. 527–72.

Quinze (*Les*) *joies de mariage*. ed. J. Rychner, Geneva, 1963.

RAYMOND OF AGUILERS. *Historia Francorum, RHC. Occ.*, vol. iii, pp. 231–309.

RAYNALD, O. *Annales Ecclesiastici*, ed. J. D. Mansi, 15 vols., Lucca, 1747–56.

REBDORF, HEINRICH VON. *Annales imperatorum et paparum*, ed. J. F. Boehmer, *Fontes rerum Germanicarum*, iv, Stuttgart, 1868.

REGINALD OF DURHAM. *De admirandis B. Cuthberti virtutibus*, Surtees Soc., i, London, 1835.

REGINALD OF DURHAM. *De Vita et miracula S. Godrici, heremitae de Finchale*, ed. J. Stephenson, Surtees Soc., xx, London, 1847.

Reisebuch der Familie Rieter. ed. R. Röhricht and H. Meisner, *BLVS.*, clxviii, Tübingen, 1884.

RIANT, P. (ed.). 'Pièces rélatives au passage à Venise de pèlerins de Terre Sainte', *AOL.*, ii (1884), pp. 237–49.

RICOLDO OF MONTE CROCE. *Liber peregrinationis, L. Peregr.*, pp. 101–41.

RIEDEL, F. A. (ed.). *Codex diplomaticus Brandenburgensis*, vol. i (2), Berlin, 1842, pp. 121–84 ('Die Stadt Wilsnack').

RIGAUD, ODO, archbishop of Rouen. *Regestum visitationum archiepiscopi Rothomagensis. Journales des visites pastorales d'Eudes Rigaud, 1248–69*, ed. T. Bonnin, Rouen, 1852.

RIGORD. *Oeuvres de Rigord et de Guillaume le Breton*, ed. H-F. Delaborde, *SHF.*, Paris, 1882.

RINDFLEISCH, PETER. *Walffartt, RM. Pilg.*, pp. 315–48.

ROBERT OF TORIGNY, abbot of Mont-St.-Michel. *Chronique*, ed. L. Delisle, 2 vols., Rouen, 1872–3.

Roman de la Rose. (by Guillaume de Lorris and Jean de Meung), ed. F. Lecoy, 3 vols., Paris, 1965–70.

ROSSI, G. B. de. *Instriptiones Christianae urbis Romae*, 2 vols., Rome, 1857–88.

ROT, HANS and PETER. *Pilgerreisen*, ed. A. Bernoulli, *Beiträge zur vaterländische Geschichte*, Neue Folge, i (1882), pp. 329–408.

RUCELLAI, GIOVANNI. *Il Giubileo dell' anno 1450*, ed. M. Giuseppe, *ASRSP.*, iv (1881), pp. 563–80.

RUDOLFUS, monk of Fulda. *Miracula sanctorum in Fuldenses ecclesias transtorum*, *MGH. SS.* xv. 328–41.

RYMER, T. (ed.). *Foedera et conventiones, literae, et acta publica*, 20 vols., London, 1704–35.

SACCHETTI, FRANCO. *I sermoni evangelici. Le lettere*, ed. O. Gigli, Florence. 1857.

SAEWULF. *Relatione de peregrinatione Saewulfi ad Hierosolymam et Terram Sanctam*, tr. W. Brownlow, *PPTS.*, London, 1892.

SAMSON, abbot of Bury. *De Miraculis S. Eadmundi*, in Arnold, *op. cit.* (OS), vol. i, pp. 105–208.

SHARPE, R. R. *Calendar of wills proved and enrolled in the Court of Husting*, London, *A.D. 1258–A.D. 1668*, 2 vols., London, 1889–90.

SIGNORILI, N. *Descriptio urbis Romae eiusque excellaentiae*, *VZ.*, vol. iv, pp. 151–208.

SIGOLI, SIMONE. *Viaggio in Terra Santa*, in Bellorini and Hoade, *op. cit.* (OS), pp. 157–201.

SIMON OF CREMONA. *De Indulgentiis Portiunculae*, ed. D. Trapp, 'The Portiuncula discussion of Cremona (ca. 1380). New light on 14th. century disputations', *Recherches de théologie ancienne et mediévale*, xxii (1955), pp. 79–94.

Stacions (The) of Rome and the Pilgrim's sea-voyage. ed. F. J. Furnivall, *EETS.*, O.S., xxv, London, 1867.

STEFANESCHI, JAMES, cardinal. *De Centesimo seu Jubileo anno*, ed. D. Quattrocchi, *Bessarione*, vii (1900), pp. 291–317.

STOLLE, KONRAD. *Thuringische-erfurtische Chronik*, ed. R. Thiele, *Geschichtsquellen der Provinz Sachsen*, xxxix, Halle, 1900.

STUBBS, W. (ed.). *Select Charters*, 9th. ed., Oxford, 1913.

SUGER, abbot of St.-Denis. *De Consecratione ecclesiae S. Dionysii*, in *Oeuvres Complètes*, ed. A. Lecoy de la Marche, *SHF.*, Paris, 1867, pp. 211–38.

SUGER, abbot of St.-Denis. *De Rebus in administratione sua gestis*, in *ibid.*, pp. 151–209.

SUGER, abbot of St.-Denis. *Vita Lodovici VI*, ed. H. Waquet, Paris, 1929.

SULPICIUS SEVERUS. *Libri qui supersunt*, ed. C. Halm, *CSEL.*, i, Vienna, 1866.

SURIANO, FRANCESCO. *Il Trattato di Terra Santa e dell' oriente*, ed. G. Golubovich, Milan, 1900.

SYMEON OF DURHAM. *Opera omnia*, ed. T. Arnold, *RS.*, 2 vols., London, 1882–5.

TAFUR, PERO. *Andancas e viajes por diversas partes del mundo avidos (1435–1439)*, ed. D. Marcos Jiménez de la Espada, *Coleccion de libros espanoles raros o curiosos*, viii, Madrid, 1874.

TARDIF, E-J. (ed.). *Coutumiers de Normandie*, Soc. de l'Histoire de Normandie, 2 vols., Rouen, 1881–96.

Testamenta vetusta. ed. Sir N. H. Nicolas, 2 vols., London, 1826.

THEODERIC OF WURZBURG. *De Locis Sanctis*, ed. T. Tobler, Saint-Gall, 1865.

THEODORET, bishop of Cyrus. *Graecarum affectionum curatio*, *PG.* lxxxiii. 775–1152.

THEOFRID OF EPTERNACH. *Flores epitaphium sanctorum*, *PL.* clvii. 313–404.

THIEL, A. (ed.). *Epistolae Romanorum pontificum genuinae a S. Hilario usque ad Pelagium II*, vol. i (461–523), Brunsberg, 1868.

THOMAS OF MONMOUTH. *Vita et miracula S. Willelmi Norwicensis*, ed. A. Jessop and M. R. James, Cambridge, 1896.

TOULMIN SMITH, J. (ed.). *Expeditions to Prussia and the Holy Land made by Henry, earl of Derby. The accounts kept by his treasurer during two years*, Camden Soc., 2nd. series, lii, London, 1894.

Traité sur le cinquième jubilé de Saint Thomas Becket (1420). in R. Foréville, *op. cit.* (MW), pp. 99–160.

URBAN II, pope. *Epistolae et privilegia*, PL. cli.

VAN DEN BUSSCHE, M. (ed.). 'Roc-Amadour. Les pèlerinages dans notre ancien droit penal. Collection de documents inédits des xive, xve, et xvie siècles', *CRH.*, 4th. series, xiv (1887), pp. 19–74.

VENTURA, WILLIAM. *Chronicon Astense, RISS (1)*. xi. 139–268.

VERGERIO, PAOLO. *Epistolario*, ed. L. Smith, *Fonti*, Rome, 1934.

VICTRICIUS, St., bishop of Rouen. *De Laude sanctorum*, PL. xx. 443–58.

Vie de Sainte Mélanie. ed. D. Gorce, *Sources Chrétiennes*, xc, Paris, 1962.

VILLANI, GIOVANNI. *Historie Fiorentine, RISS (1)*. xiii. 1–1002.

VILLANI, MATTEO. *Istorie, RISS (1)*. xiv. 1–728.

Visio monachi de Eynsham. ed. H. Thurston, *An. Boll.*, xxii (1903), pp. 225–319.

Vita Lietberti episcopi Cameracensis. in L. d'Achéry, *Veterum aliquot scriptores spicilegium*, Paris, 1657–77, vol. ix, pp. 675–733.

Vita Richardi, abbatis S. Vitoni Viridunensis. MGH. SS. xi. 281–90.

Vita S. Sigiranni. An. Boll., iii (1884), pp. 378–407.

Voyage de la Saincte Cyté de Hierusalem, fait l'an 1480. ed. C. Schefer, *Recueil de voyages et de documents pour servir à l'histoire de la géographie*, ii, Paris, 1882.

WACE. *Le Roman de Rou*, ed. A. J. Holden, SATF., 3 vols., Paris, 1970– (in progress).

WALTHER, PAUL, VON GUGLINGEN. *Itinerarium in Terram Sanctam et ad Sanctam Catharinam*, ed. M. Sollweck, BLVS., cxcii, Tübingen, 1892.

WASSERSCHLEBEN, F. W. H. (ed.). *Die Bussordnungen der abendländischen Kirche nebst einer rechtsgeschichtlichen Einleitung*, Halle, 1851.

WATTENBACH, W. (ed.). 'Beiträge zur Geschichte der Mark Brandenburg aus Handschriften der königlichen Bibliothek', *Sitzungsberichte der königlich preussischen Akademie der Wissenschaften* (1882), pp. 587–609.

WEY, WILLIAM. *The Itineraries of William Wey, fellow of Eton College, to Jerusalem, A.D. 1458 and A.D. 1462: and to Saint James of Compostella*, Roxburghe Club, London, 1857.

WILLIAM OF CANTERBURY. *Miracula S. Thomae Cantuariensis, Becket Materials*, vol. i, pp. 137–546.

WILLIAM OF JUMIÈGES. *Gesta Normannorum ducum*, ed. J. Marx, Soc. de l' Histoire de Normandie, Paris, 1914.

WILLIAM OF MALMESBURY. *De Gestis pontificum Anglorum*, ed. N. Hamilton, RS., London, 1870.

WILLIAM OF MALMESBURY. *De Gestis regum Anglorum*, ed. W. Stubbs, RS., London, 1887–9.

WILLIAM OF TYRE. *Historia rerum in partibus transmarinis gestarum, RHC. Occ.*, vol. i.

WRIGHT, T. (ed.). *Letters relating to the suppression of the monasteries*, Camden Soc., xxvi, London, 1843.

WYCLIF, JOHN. *De Ecclesia*, ed. J. Loserth, London, 1886.

WYCLIF, JOHN. *Sermones*, ed. J. Loserth, 4 vols., London, 1887–90.

YVO OF CHARTRES. *Decretum, PL.* clxi. 9–1022.

II. SECONDARY WORKS

ABBOT, E. A. *St. Thomas of Canterbury. His death and miracles*, 2 vols., London, 1898.

ABEL, F. M. 'Saint Jerome et Jerusalem', *Miscellanea Geronimiana publicati nel xv centenario dalla morte di san Girolamo*, Rome, 1920, pp. 131–55.

ALPHANDÉRY, P. *La Chrétienté et l'idée de la croisade*, 2 vols., Paris, 1954–1959.

ANDRIEU, M. 'Les églises de Rome au moyen age', *Revue des sciences religieuses*, ix (1929), pp. 540–74.

ATIYA, A. S. *The crusade in the later middle ages*, Cambridge, 1938.

AUDIAT, L. 'Pèlerinages en Terre Sainte au xve siècle', *Revue historique nobiliaire et biographique*, N.S., vi (1870–1), pp. 49–61.

BARLOW, F. 'Cnut's second pilgrimage', *EHR.*, lxxiii (1958), pp. 650–1.

BARTHÉLÉMY, A. de. 'Pèlerins Champenois en Palestine', *ROL.*, i (1893), pp. 354–80.

BATTISCOMBE, C. F. (ed.). *The relics of Saint Cuthbert*, Oxford, 1956.

BAYNES, N. H. 'The supernatural defenders of Constantinople', *An. Boll.*, lxvii (1949), pp. 165–77.

BÉDIER, J. *Les légendes épiques. Recherches sur la formation des chansons de geste*, 4 vols., 3rd. ed., Paris, 1926.

BEISSEL, S. (1). *Die Aachenfahrt. Verehrung der Aachener Heiligtumer seit den Tagen Karls des grossen bis in unsere zeit*, Stimmen aus Maria Laach, Erganzungsheft lxxxii, Freiburg i. B., 1902.

BEISSEL, S. (2). *Geschichte der Verehrung Marias in Deutschland wahrend des Mittelalters*, Freiburg i. B., 1909.

BEISSEL, S. (3). *Die Verehrung der Heiligen und ihrer Reliquien in Deutschland bis zum Beginne des 13 Jahrhunderts*, Freiburg i. B., 1890.

BENOIT, A. 'Les pèlerinages de Philippe le Bon à Notre-Dame de Boulogne', *Bulletin de la Soc. d'Études de la Province de Cambrai*, xxxvii (1937), pp. 119–23.

BERLIÈRE, U. 'Les pèlerinages judiciaires au moyen age', *Revue Bénedictine*, vii (1890), pp. 520–6.

BERNOULLI, C. A. *Die Heiligen der Merowinger*, Tübingen, 1900.

BETHELL, D. 'The making of a twelfth century relic collection', in Cuming and Baker, *op. cit.*, pp. 61–72.

BISCHOFF, B. 'The study of foreign languages in the middle ages', *Speculum*, xxxvi (1961), pp. 209–24.

BONDOIS, M. *La Translation des saints Marcellin et Pierre. Étude sur Einhard et sa vie politique de 827 a 834*, BEHE., clx, Paris, 1907.

BONSER, W. *The Medical background of Anglo-Saxon England. A Study in history, psychology and folklore*, London, 1963.

BREEST, E. 'Das Wunderblut von Wilsnack (1383–1552). Quellenmässige

Darstellung seiner Geschichte', *Märkische Forschungen*, xvi (1881), pp. 131–301.

BRUNDAGE, J. A. 'Cruce Signari: the rite for taking the cross in England', *Traditio*, xxii (1966), pp. 289–310.

CAPPARONI, A. 'L'ospedale di sant' Antonio dei Portughesi in Roma', *Atti del primo congresso Europeo di storia ospitaliers (1960)*, Reggio Emilia, 1962, pp. 278–85.

CAROLUS-BARRÉ, L. 'Saint Louis et la translation des corps saints', *Études d'histoire du droit canonique dediées à Gabriel Le Bras*, vol. ii, Paris, 1965, pp. 1087–112.

CARRERAS Y CANDI, F. 'Visites de nostre reys a Montserrat', *Boletín de la Real Academía de Buenas Letras de Barcelona*, ii (1903–4), pp. 339–88.

CATTANEO, E. 'La "statio" piccolo pellegrinaggio', in *Pellegrinaggi*, pp. 245–59.

CAUWENBERGHE, E. VAN. *Les pèlerinages expiatoires et judiciaires dans le droit commun de la Belgique au moyen age, Recueil de travaux de l'université de Louvain*, xlviii, Louvain, 1922.

CHAMARD, F. *Les réliques de Saint Benoit*, Paris, 1882.

CHAPEAU, G. (1). 'Les grandes réliques de l'abbaye de Charroux. Étude d' histoire et d'archéologie', *Bulletin de la Soc. des Antiquaires de l'Ouest*, 3rd. series, viii (1928), pp. 101–28.

CHAPEAU, G. (2). 'Un pèlerinage noble à Charroux au xie siècle. La fondation des prieurés d'Ham et d'Ardres, dépendances de Charroux', *Bulletin de la Soc. des Antiquaires de l'Ouest*, 3rd. series, xiii (1942–5), pp. 250–71.

CHEVALIER, C. U. *Notre-Dame de Lorette. Étude historique sur l'authenticité de la Santa Casa*, Paris, 1906.

CHOMEL, V. 'Pèlerins Languedociens au Mont-Saint-Michel à la fin du moyen age', *Annales du Midi*, lxx (1958), pp. 230–9.

COHN, N. *The pursuit of the millennium. Revolutionary millenarians and mystical anarchists of the middle ages*, 2nd. ed., London, 1970.

COLGRAVE, B. 'Bede's miracle stories', in *Bede. His life, times, and writings*, ed. A. H. Thompson, Oxford, 1935, pp. 201–29.

COULTON, G. G. *Five centuries of religion*, 4 vols., Cambridge, 1923–50.

CROKE, W. J. D. 'The national English institutions in Rome during the fourteenth century. A guild and its popular initiative', *Atti del Congresso Internazionale di Scienze Storiche (Rome, 1903)*, vol. iii, Rome, 1906, pp. 555–72.

CUMING, G. J., and BAKER, D. (ed.). *Popular belief and practice. Papers read at the ninth summer and tenth winter meetings of the Ecclesiastical History Society*, Studies in ecclesiastical history, viii, Cambridge, 1972.

DAUPHIN, H. *Le bienheureux Richard, abbé de Saint-Vanne de Verdun*, Louvain, 1946.

DAVID, P. *Études sur le Livre de Saint-Jacques attribué au pape Calixte II*, 4 vols., Lisbon, 1946–9.

DAVIES, H. W. *Bernhard von Breydenbach and his journey to the Holy Land, 1483–4. A Bibliography*, London, 1911.

DAVIS, J. F. 'Lollards, reformers, and St. Thomas of Canterbury', *University of Birmingham Historical Journal*, ix (1963–4), pp. 1–15.

DEFOURNEAUX, M. *Les Francais en Espagne aux xie et xiie siècles*, Paris, 1949.

DELARUELLE, E. (1). 'Les grandes processions de pénitents de 1349 et 1399', in *Disciplinati*, pp. 109–45.

DELARUELLE, E. (2). 'La spiritualité du pèlerinage de Rocamadour au moyen age', *Bulletin de la Soc. des Études Litteraires, Scientifiques, et Artistiques du Lot*, lxxxvii (1966), pp. 69–85.

DELARUELLE, E. (3). 'La spiritualité des pèlerinages à Saint-Martin de Tours du ve au xe siècle', in *Pellegrinaggi*, pp. 199–243.

DELARUELLE, E., LABANDE, E-R., and OURLIAC, P. *L'Église au temps du grand schisme et la crise conciliaire (1379–1449)*, Histoire de l'Église, ed. A. Fliche and V. Martin, vol. xiv, Paris, 1962–4.

DELAUNAY, P. *La médecine et l'Église. Contribution a l'histoire de l'exercice médical par les clercs*, Paris, 1948.

DELEHAYE, H. (1). *Les légendes hagiographiques*, Bruxelles, 1905.

DELEHAYE, H. (2). 'Les lettres d'indulgence collectives', *An. Boll.*, xliv (1926), pp. 342–79; xlv (1927), pp. 97–123, 323–44; xlvi (1928), pp. 149–57, 287–343.

DELEHAYE, H. (3). 'Loca sanctorum', *An. Boll.*, xlviii (1930), pp. 5–64.

DELEHAYE, H. (4). *Les origines de la culte des martyrs*, 2nd. ed., Brussels, 1933.

DELEHAYE, H. (5). 'Le pèlerinage de Laurent de Pasztho au Purgatoire de S. Patrice', *An. Boll.*, xxvii (1908), pp. 35–60.

DELEHAYE, H. (6). 'Les premiers "libelli miraculorum"', *An. Boll.*, xxix (1910), pp. 427–34.

DELEHAYE, H. (7). 'Les recueils antiques des miracles des saints', *An. Boll.*, xliii (1925), pp. 5–85, 305–25.

DELEHAYE, H. (8). *Sanctus. Essai sur le culte des saints dans l'antiquité*, Brussels, 1927.

DELISLE, L. (1). 'Authentiques de réliques de l'époque Mérovingienne', *MAH.*, iv (1884), pp. 3–8.

DELISLE, L. (2). 'Pèlerinages d'enfants au Mont-St.-Michel', *Mémoires de la Soc. des Antiquaires de Normandie*, 2nd. series, vii (1847), pp. 388–94.

DENIFLE, H. *La désolation des églises, monastères, at hôpitaux en France pendant la guerre de cent ans*, 2 vols., Paris, 1897–9.

DICKINSON, J. C. *The shrine of Our Lady of Walsingham*, Cambridge, 1956.

Disciplinati: Movimento (Il) dei disciplinati nel settimo centenario dal suo inizio, Deputazione di Storia Patria per l'Umbria, appendice al bolletino no. 9, Perugia, 1962; with index, 1965.

Divine healing and co-operation between doctors and clergy. British Medical Association, London, 1956.

DÖLGER, F. X. J. *Antike und Christentum. Kultur- und religionsgeschichtliche Studien*, 2 vols., Munster, 1929–30.

DONNET, A. *Saint-Bernard et les origines de l'hospice de Mont-Joux*, St.-Maurice, 1942.

DOSSAT, Y. 'De singuliers pèlerins sur la chemin de Saint-Jacques en 1272', *Annales du Midi*, lxxxii (1970), pp. 209–20.

DUBY, G. *La société aux xie et xiie siècles dans la région Mâconnaise*, Paris, 1953.

DU CANGE, C. 'Dissertation de l'escarcelle et du bourdon des pèlerins de la Terre Sainte', in *Observations et dissertations sur l'histoire de Saint Louys*, Paris, 1668, pp. 535–8.

DUCHESNE, L. 'Saint-Jacques en Galice', *Annales du Midi*, xii (1900), pp. 145–79.

DUPONT, E. (1). 'Les pèlerinages au Mont-St.-Michel du viiie au xixe siècle', *Annales de la Soc. Historique et Archéologique de Saint-Malo* (1909), pp. 179–242.

DUPONT, E. (2). 'Les pèlerinages d'enfants allemands au Mont-St.-Michel (xve siècle). Le recit de Baudry, archevêque de Dol', *Annales de la Soc. Historique et Archéologique de Saint-Malo* (1906), pp. 19–60.

DURAND-LEFEBVRE, M. *Étude sur l'origine des vierges noires*, Paris, 1937.

EBERSOLT, J. *Sanctuaires de Byzance. Recherches sur les anciens trésors des églises de Constantinople*, Paris, 1921.

ECKENSTEIN, L. *A history of Sinai*, London, 1921.

EICKEN, H. VON. 'Die Legende von der Erwartung des Weltunterganges und der Wiedersehr Christi im Jahre 1000', *Forschungen zur deutschen Geschichte*, xxiii (1883), pp. 303–18.

ELORDUY, E. 'La tradición Jacobea de Galicia en el siglo ix', *Hispania*, xxii (1962), pp. 323–56.

ELTON, G. R. *Policy and police. The enforcement of the Reformation in England in the age of Thomas Cromwell*, Cambridge, 1972.

ERDMANN, C. 'Endkaiserglaube und Kreuzzugsgedanke im XI Jahrhundert', *Zeitschrift für Kirchengeschichte*, li (1932), pp. 384–414.

EWIG, E. 'Le culte de Saint Martin à l'époque Franque', *Revue d'histoire de l'Église de France*, xlvii (1961), pp. 1–18.

FABRE, P. 'Les offrandes dans la basilique Vaticane en 1285', *MAH.*, xiv (1894), pp. 225–40.

FÉLIBIEN, M. *Histoire de l'abbaye royale de Saint-Denys en France*, Paris, 1706.

FICHTENAU, H. 'Zum Reliquienwesen im früheren Mittelalter', *Mitteilung des Instituts für österreichische Geschichtsforschung*, lx (1952), pp. 60–89.

FITA, F. 'El Jubileo del año 1300 su recuerdo monumental en el Rosellón. Observaciones sobre la metrica rimada de aquel tiempo', *Boletín de la Real Academía de la Historia*, xlvi (1905), pp. 301–5.

FLAHAULT, R. 'Notre-Dame de la Visitation à Bollezeele. Notes et documents', *Annales du Comité Flamand de France*, xxv (1900), pp. 93–171.

FÖRSTER, W. 'Le Saint-Vou de Lucques', *Romanische Forschungen*, xxiii (1907), pp. 1–56.

FORÉVILLE, R. *Le jubilé de Saint Thomas Becket, du xiiie au xve siècle (1220–1470). Étude et documents*, Paris, 1958.

FRANZ, A. (1). *Die kirchlichen Benediktionen im Mittelalter*, 2 vols., Freiburg i. B., 1909.

FRANZ, A. (2). 'Die strafe der Pilgermörder im mittelalterlichen Legenden', *Historisch-politischer Blätter für das katholische Deutschland*, cxxiii (1899), pp. 708–27.

FROLOW, A. *La rélique de la vraie croix. Recherches sur le developement d'un culte*, Archives de l'orient Chrétien, vii, Paris, 1961.

GAIFFIER, B. DE (1). 'Hagiographie Salernitaine. La translation de S. Matthieu', *An. Boll.*, lxxx (1962), pp. 82–110.

GAIFFIER, B. DE (2). 'Sainte Ide de Boulogne et l'Espagne. A propos de réliques Mariales', *An. Boll.*, lxxxvi (1968), pp. 67–82.

GAMBACORTA, A. 'Culto e pellegrinaggi a San Nicola di Bari fino alla primera crociata', in *Pellegrinaggi*, pp. 485–502.

GARRISON, F. 'A propos des pèlerins et de leur condition juridique', in *Études d'histoire du droit canonique dediées à Gabriel Le Bras*, vol. ii, Paris, 1965, pp. 1165–89.

GASNAULT, P. 'Le tombeau de Saint Martin et les invasions Normandes dans l'histoire et dans la légende', *Revue d'histoire de l'Église de France*, xlvii (1961), pp. 51–66.

GEBHARD, T. 'Die marianischen Grabenbilder in Bayern. Beobachtungen zur Chronologie und Typologie', *Festschrift Gustav Gugitz, Veröffentlichungen des oesterreichischen Museums für Volkskunde*, v, Vienna, 1954, pp. 93–116.

GÖLLER, E. *Die papstliche Poenitentarie von ihrem Ursprung bis zu ihrer Umgestaltung unter Pius V*, 2 vols. in 4, Rome, 1907–11.

GORCE, D. *Les voyages, l'hospitalité et le port des lettres dans le monde Chrétien des ive et ve siècles*, Paris, 1925.

GOUGAUD, L. *Les Chrétientés Celtiques*, Paris, 1911.

GREGOROVIUS, F. *History of the city of Rome in the middle ages*, 8 vols., London, 1894–1902.

GRETSER, J. *De sacris et religiosis peregrinationibus*, Ingolstadt, 1606.

GUDIOL, J. 'De peregrins i peregrinatges religiosos Catalans', *Analecta Sacra Tarraconensia*, iii (1927), pp. 93–119.

GUIRAUD, J. 'Le commerce des réliques au commencement du xie siècle', *Mélanges G. B. de Rossi*, Supplement au *MAH.*, xii (1892), pp. 73–95.

GUTH, K. *Guibert von Nogent und die hochmittelalterliche Kritic an der Reliquienverehrung, Studien und Mitteilungen zur Geschichte des Benediktinerordens*, xxi, Ottobeuren, 1970.

HARRIS, S. M. 'Our Lady of Cardigan', *Cymdeithas Ceredigion Llundain, Llawlyfr*, viii (1952–3), pp. 33–9.

HASKINS, C. H. 'A Canterbury monk at Constantinople, c. 1090', *EHR.*, xxv (1910), pp. 293–5.

HAUPT, H. 'Zur Geschichte der Kinderwallfahrten der Jahre 1455–1489', *Zeitschrift für Kirchengeschichte*, xvi (1896), pp. 671–5.

HAUPTS, H. 'Frankreich und die aachener Heiligtumsfahrt', *Zeitschrift des aachener Geschichtsvereins*, lxiii (1950), pp. 112–14.

HAUSMANN, M. *Geschichte der päpstlichen Reservatsfälle*, Regensburg, 1868.

HEFELE, C-J. *Histoire des conciles*, ed. H. Leclercq *et al.*, 8 vols, in 16, Paris, 1907–21.

HÉLIOT, P. and CHASTANG, M-L. 'Quêtes et voyages de réliques au profit des églises francaises du moyen age', *Revue d'histoire ecclesiastique*, lix (1964), pp. 789–822; lx (1965), pp. 5–32.

HENNIG, B. 'Kurfurst Friedrich II und das Wunderblut zu Wilsnack', *Forschungen zur brandenburgischen und preussischen Geschichte*, xix (1906), pp. 391–422.

HEYD, W. 'Les consulats établis en Terre Sainte au moyen age pour la protection des pèlerins', *AOL.*, ii (1884), pp. 355–63.

HÜFFER, H. F. 'Die spanische Jacobusverehrung in ihren Ausstrahlungen auf Deutschland', *Historisches Jahrbuch*, lxxiv (1955), pp. 124–38.

HUGHES, K. 'The changing theory and practice of Irish pilgrimage', *Journal of ecclesiastical history*, xi (1960), pp. 143–51.

HUIDOBRO Y SERNA, L. *Las peregrinaciones Jacobeas*, 3 vols., Madrid, 1949–51.

HUIZINGA, J. *The waning of the middle ages. A study of the forms of life, thought, and art in France and the Netherlands of the xivth. and xvth. centuries*, tr. F. Hopman, London, 1924.

HULBERT, J. 'Some medieval advertisements of Rome', *Modern Philology*, xx (1922–3), pp. 403–24.

HUYNES, J. *Histoire générale de l'abbaye du Mont-St.-Michel au Péril de la Mer* (1638), ed. E. de R. de Beaurepaire, Soc. de l'histoire de Normandie, 2 vols., Rouen, 1872–3.

JANSEN, M. *Papst Bonifatius IX (1389–1404) und seine Beziehungen zur deutschen Kirche*, Frieburg i. B., 1904.

JOERGENSEN, J. *Saint Bridget of Sweden*, tr. I. Lund, 2 vols., London, 1954.

JONES, G. H. *Celtic Britain and the pilgrim movement*, London, 1912.

JORANSON, E. (1). 'The great German pilgrimage of 1064–1065', in *The crusades and other historical essays presented to Dana C. Monro*, ed. L. G. Paetow, N.Y., 1928, pp. 3–43.

JORANSON, E. (2). 'The Palestine pilgrimage of Henry the Lion', in *Medieval and historiographical essays in honor of James Westfall Thompson*, Chicago, 1938, pp. 146–225.

JUSSERAND, J. J. *English wayfaring life in the middle ages*, tr. L. Toulmin Smith, 4th. ed., London, 1950.

KAMANN, J. 'Die Pilgerfahrten Nurnberger nach Jerusalem in 15 Jahrhundert', *Mitteilung des Vereins für Geschichte der Stadt Nurnberg*, ii (1880), pp. 78–163.

KAWERAN, G. 'Wilsnack', *Realencyclopädie für protestantische Theologie und Kirche*, vol. xxi, Leipzig, 1908, pp. 346–50.

KEMP, E. W. *Canonisation and authority in the western Church*, Oxford, 1948.

KÖTTING, B. (1). *Der frühchristliche Reliquienkult und die Bestattung in Kirchengebäude*, Arbeitsgemeinschaft für Forschung des Landes Nordrhein-Westfalen, Geisteswissenschaften, cxxiii, Köln, 1965.

KÖTTING, B. (2). 'Gregor von Nyssas Wallfahrtskritic', *Texte und Untersuchungen zur Geschichte der altchristlichen Literatur*, lxxx (1962), pp. 360–7.

KÖTTING, B. (3). *Peregrinatio religiosa. Wallfahrten in der Antike und das Pilgerwesen in den alten Kirche*, Regensburg, 1950.

KRAUS, F. X. 'Das anno santo', in *Essays*, vol. ii, Berlin, 1901, pp. 217–336.

KROGH, F. *Christian des Förstes Romerreise*, Copenhagen, 1872.

KRONENBURG, J. A. F. *Maria's Heerlijkeit in Nederland. Geschiedkundige schets van de Vereering der H. Maagd in ons Vaderland ven de eerste tijden tot op onze dagen*, 8 vols., Amsterdam, 1904–14; index, Roermond, 1931.

LABANDE, E-R. (1). ' "Ad limina". Le pèlerin mediévale au terme de sa démarche', in *Mélanges Réné Crozet*, Poitiers, 1966, vol. i, pp. 283–91.

LABANDE, E-R. (2). 'Éléments d'une enquête sur les conditions de déplacement du pèlerin aux xe–xie siècles', in *Pellegrinaggi*, pp. 95–111.

LABANDE, E-R. (3). 'Recherches sur les pèlerins dans l'Europe des xie et xiie siècles', *Cahiers de civilisation mediévale*, i (1968), pp. 159–69, 339–47.

LACARRA, J. M. 'Espiritualidad del culto dei santi y de la peregrinación a Santiago antes de la primera cruzada', in *Pellegrinaggi*, pp. 113–44.

LAMBERT, E. (1). 'Études sur le pèlerinage de Saint-Jacques de Compostelle', in Lambert, *Études Mediévales*, vol. i, Paris, 1956, pp. 119–271.

LAMBERT, E. (2). 'Ordres et confréries dans l'histoire du pèlerinage de Compostelle', *Annales du Midi*, liv–lv (1942–3), pp. 369–403.

LARSEN, L. M. *Canute the great, 995 (circ.)–1035*, London, 1912.

LASLOWSKI, E. *Beiträge zur Geschichte des spätmittelalterlichen Ablasswesens, Breslauer Studien zur historischen Theologie*, xi, Breslau, 1929.

LEA, H. C. (1). *A history of auricular confession and indulgences in the Latin Church*, 3 vols., London, 1896.

LEA, H. C. (2). *A history of the inquisition of the middle ages*, 3 vols., N.Y., 1888.

LE BLANT, E. 'Le vol des réliques', *Revue archéologique*, 3rd. series, ix (1887), pp. 317–28.

LECLERCQ, J. 'Mönchtum und Peregrinatio im Frühmittelalter', *Römische Quartalschrift*, lv (1960), pp. 212–25.

LECOY DE LA MARCHE, A. *La chaire francaise au moyen age, spécialement au xiiie siècle*, 2nd. ed., Paris, 1886.

LEFEBVRE, F-A. *Histoire de Notre-Dame de Boulogne et de son pèlerinage*, Boulogne, 1894.

LEFRANC, A. 'Le traité des réliques de Guibert de Nogent et les commencements de la critique historique au moyen age', in *Études d'histoire du moyen age dediées a Gabriel Monod*, Paris, 1896, pp. 285–306.

LE GRAND, L. 'Les pèlerinages en Terre Sainte au moyen age', *Revue des questions historiques*, xxxviii (1904), pp. 383–402.

LEROY, L. *Histoire des pèlerinages de la Sainte Vierge en France*, 3 vols., Paris, 1873–5.

LE ROY, T. *Les curieuses recherches du Mont Sainct Michel* (1647), ed. E. de R. de Beaurepaire, *Mémoires de la Soc. des Antiquaires de Normandie*, 3rd. series, ix (1877), pp. 223–833.

LLEWELLYN, P. *Rome in the dark ages*, London, 1970.

LOOMIS, C. G. *White magic. An introduction to the folklore of Christian legend*, Cambridge, Mass., 1948.

LOUIS, R. 'Le Codex Calixtinus', *Bulletin de la Soc. Nationale des Antiquaires de France* (1948–9), pp. 80–97.

LOPEZ FERREIRO, A. *Histoire de la S. A. M. iglesia de Santiago de Compostela*, 11 vols., Santiago, 1898–1909.

LUCHAIRE, A. 'Le culte des réliques', *Revue de Paris*, July–August 1900, pp. 189–98.

MABILLON, J. *Annales ordinis S. Benedicti*, 5 vols., Paris, 1703–13.

MAGNIN, E. 'Indulgences', *DTC.*, vol. vii, cols. 1594–1636.

MÂLE, E. *L'art réligieux du xiie siècle en France. Étude sur les origines de l'iconographie du moyen age*, 6th. ed., Paris, 1953.

MARIGNAN, A. *Le culte des saints sous les Mérovingiens (Études sur la Civilisation francaise, vol. ii)*, Paris, 1899.

MAXE-WERLY, L. 'Moules d'enseigne de pèlerinage', *Bulletin de la Soc. Nationale des Antiquaires de France*, 5th. series, vi (1885), pp. 194–9.

MISSET, E. *Notre-Dame de l'Épine, près Chalons-sur-Marne. La légende, l'histoire, le monument, et le pèlerinage*, Paris, 1902.

MOLINIER, C. *L'inquisition dans le midi de la France, au xiiie et au xive siècle. Étude sur les sources de son histoire*, Paris, 1880.

MOLLAT, G. 'Le Jubilé de 1350', *Journal des savants*, July–September 1963, pp. 191–5.

MOORE, W. J. *The Saxon pilgrims to Rome and the Scola Saxonum*, Fribourg, 1937.

MORAND, S-J. *Histoire de la Ste.-Chapelle Royale du palais*, Paris, 1790.

MOREAU, E. DE. *Histoire de l'Église en Belgique*, 2nd. ed., 5 vols., Brussels, 2.

MORRIS, C. 'A critique of popular religion. Guibert of Nogent on the relics of the saints', in Cuming and Baker, *op. cit.*, pp. 55–60.

MUSSAFIA, A. 'Studien zu den mittelalterlichen Marienlegenden', *Sitzungsberichte der königliche akademie der Wissenschaften zu Wien (phil.-hist. Kl.)*, cxiii (1886), pp. 719–94; cxv (1888), pp. 5–92; cxix (1889), Abh. ix, pp. 1–66; cxxiii (1891), Abh. viii, pp. 1–85; cxxxix (1898), Abh. viii, pp. 1–74.

MUSSET, L. 'Recherches sur les pèlerins et pèlerinages en Normandie jusqu'à la première croisade', *Annales de Normandie*, xii (1962), pp. 127–50.

NEEFS, E. 'Un voyage au xvᵉ siècle. Vénétie, Terre Sainte, Egypte, Arabie, Grandes Indes', *Revue Catholique*, N.S., ix (1873), pp. 268–91, 321–36, 425–51, 553–81.

NEWETT, M. M. *Canon Pietro Casola's pilgrimage to Jerusalem in the year 1494*, Manchester, 1907 (see OS).

OURSEL, R. *Les pèlerins du moyen age. Les hommes, les chemins, les sanctuaires*, Paris, 1963.

OWEN, D. M. 'Bacon and eggs. Bishop Buckingham and superstition in Lincolnshire', in Cuming and Baker, *op. cit.*, pp. 139–42.

OWST, G. R. *Literature and pulpit in medieval England. A neglected chapter in the history of English letters and of the English people*, 2nd. ed., Oxford, 1961.

PARKS, G. B. *The English traveller to Italy*, vol. i, *The middle ages (to 1525)*, Rome, 1954.

PASTOR, L. *The history of the popes from the close of the middle ages*, vols. i–vi, tr. F. I. Antrobus, various editions, London, 1949.

PAUL, J. B. 'Royal pilgrimages in Scotland', *Transactions of the Scottish Ecclesiological Society* (1905), pp. 147–55.

PAULUS, N. (1). 'Bonifatius IX und der Ablass von Schuld und Strafe', *Zeitschrift für katholische Theologie*, xxv (1901), pp. 338–43.

PAULUS, N. (2). *Geschichte des Ablasses im Mittelalter vom Ursprunge bis zur Mitte des 14 Jahrhunderts*, 2 vols., Paderborn, 1922–3.

PAULUS, N. (3). 'Das Jubilaeum vom Jahre 1350', *Theologie und Glaube*, v (1913), pp. 461–74, 532–41.

Pellegrinaggi: *Pellegrinaggi e culto dei santi in Europa fino alla 1ᵉ crociata*, *Convegni del Centro di Studi sulla Spiritualità Medievale*, iv, Todi, 1963.

PERDRIZET, P. *Le calendrier Parisien à la fin du moyen age d'après le bréviaire et les livres d'heures*, Paris, 1933.

PEREZ DE URBEL, J. 'Origenes del culto de Santiago en Espana', *Hispania Sacra*, v (1952), pp. 1–31.

PETIT, E. 'Raoul Glaber', *Revue historique*, xlviii (1892), pp. 283–99.

PETRUCCI, A. 'Aspetti del culto e del pellegrinaggio di san Michele Arcangelo sul Monte Gargano', in *Pellegrinaggii* pp. 145–80.

PLAINE, F. 'Les prétendues terreurs de l'an mille', *Revue des questions historiques*, xiii (1873), pp. 145–64.

PLETZ, J. C. 'Eleventh century pilgrimages from western Europe to the Holy Land', Unpublished M.A. thesis, Chicago, Dec. 1938.

PLUMMER, C. *Venerabilis Bedae opera historica*, vol. ii (*Commentarium*), Oxford, 1896.

POCQUET DU HAUT-JUSSÉ, B. 'La compagnie de Saint-Yves des Bretons à Rome', *MAH.*, xxxvii (1918–19), pp. 201–83.

PONCELET, A. 'La plus ancienne vie de S. Géraud d'Aurillac (d. 909), *An. Boll.*, xiv (1895), pp. 89–107.

PRÉVOST, L. (ed.). *Le Sinai, hier . . . aujourd'hui. Étude topographique, biblique, historique, archéologique*, Paris, 1937.

RACKHAM, B. *The ancient glass of Canterbury cathedral*, London, 1949.

RATZINGER, G. *Geschichte der kirchlichen Armenpflege*, Freiburg i. B., 1884.

RE, E. 'The English colony in Rome during the fourteenth century', *Transactions of the Royal Historical Soc.*, 4th. series, vi (1923), pp. 73–92.

RÉMY, F. *Les grandes indulgences pontificales aux Pays-Bas à la fin du moyen age, 1300–1531. Essai sur leur histoire et leur importance financière*, Louvain, 1928.

RIANT, P. (1). 'Des dépouilles réligieuses enlevées à Constantinople au xiiie siècle, et des documents historiques nés de leur transport en occident', *Mémoires de la Soc. Nationale des Antiquaires de France*, 4th. series, vi (1875), pp. 1–214.

RIANT, P. (2). 'La donation de Hughes, marquis de Toscane, au Saint-Sépulchre, et les établissements latins de Jerusalem au xe siècle', *Mémoires de l'Academie des Inscriptions et Belles Lettres*, xxxi (1884), 2e partie, pp. 151–95.

RIANT, P. (3). *Expeditions et pèlerinages des Scandinaves en Terre Sainte au temps des croisades*, Paris, 1865.

RIANT, P. (4). 'Inventaire critique des lettres historiques des croisades', *AOL.*, i (1881), pp. 1–224.

RODOCANACHI, E. 'Le premier Jubilé (1350)', in *Études et fantaisies historiques*, Paris, 1912, pp. 153–64.

ROHAULT DE FLEURY, C. *Mémoire sur les instruments de la passion de N-S. J-C.*, Paris, 1870.

RÖHRICHT, R. See bibliographies cited above.

ROMANI, M. *Pellegrini e viaggatori nell' economia di Roma dal xiv al xvii secolo*, Milan, 1948.

RUNCIMAN, S. (1). 'The Holy Lance found at Antioch', *An. Boll.*, lxviii (1950), pp. 197–209.

RUNCIMAN, S. (2). 'Some remarks on the Image of Edessa', *Cambridge historical journal*, iii (1929–31), pp. 238–52.

RUPIN, E. *Roc-Amadour. Étude historique et archéologique*, Paris, 1904.

RUSHFORTH, G. Mc.N. 'Magister Gregorovius de Mirabilibus Urbis Romae. A new description of Rome in the twelfth century', *Journal of Roman studies*, ix (1919), pp. 14–44.

SACHET, A. *Le pardon annuel de la Saint-Jean et de la Saint-Pierre de Lyon, 1392–1790*, 2 vols., Lyon, 1914–18.

SAIGE, G. 'De l'ancienneté de l'hôpital de S. Jean de Jerusalem. Donations dans l'Albigeois antérieures à la première croisade', *BEC.*, 5th. series, v (1864), pp. 552–60.

SAINT-GÉNOIS, J. DE. *Les voyageurs Belges du xiiie au xviie siècle*, Brussels, 1846.

SAMOUILLAN, A. *Olivier Maillard. Sa prédication et son temps*, Paris, 1891.

SAVINE, A. *The English monasteries on the eve of the dissolution, Oxford studies in social and legal history*, ed. P. Vinogradoff, i, Oxford, 1909.

SAXER, V. *Le culte de Marie Madeleine en occident des origines à la fin du moyen age*, Paris, 1959.

SCHMIDLIN, J. *Geschichte der deutschen Nationalkirche in Rom, S. Maria dell' Anima*, Freiburg i. B., 1906.

SCHREIBER, G. (ed.). *Wallfahrt und Volkstum in Geschichte und Leben*, Düsseldorf, 1934.

SEJOURNE, P. 'Réliques', *DTC.*, vol. xiii, cols. 2312–76.

SILVESTRE, H. 'Commerce et vol de réliques au moyen age', *Revue Belge de philologie et d'histoire*, xxx (1952), pp. 721–39.

SOUTHERN, R. W. 'The English origins of the "Miracles of the Virgin"', *Mediaeval and renaissance studies*, iv (1958), pp. 176–216.

SPRINGER, O. 'Mediaeval pilgrim-routes from Scandinavia to Rome', *Mediaeval studies*, xii (1950), pp. 12–122.

STIENNON, J. 'Le voyage des Liègeois à Saint-Jacques de Compostelle en 1056', in *Mélanges Felix Rousseau*, Brussels, 1958, pp. 553–81.

STORRS, C., and CORDERO CARRETE, F. R. 'Peregrinos Ingleses a Santiago en el siglo xiv', *Cuadernos de estudios Gallegos*, xx (1965), pp. 193–224.

STÜCKELBERG, E. A. *Geschichte der Reliquien in der Schweitz, Schriften der Schweitzerischen Gesellschaft für Volkskunde*, i, v, 2 vols., Basel, 1902–8.

THOMAS, K. *Religion and the decline of magic. Studies in popular beliefs in sixteenth and seventeenth century England*, London, 1971.

THURSTON, H. *The Holy Year of Jubilee. An account of the history and ceremonial of the Roman Jubilee*, London, 1900.

TOMMASINI, A. M. *I santi Irlandesi in Italia*, Milan, 1932.

TOUSSAERT, J. *Le sentiment religieux en Flandre à la fin du moyen age*, Paris, 1963.

TOYNBEE, M. R. *S. Louis of Toulouse and the process of canonisation in the fourteenth century*, Manchester, 1929.

VAES, M. (1). 'Les fondations hospitalières Flamandes à Rome du xve au xviiie siècle', *Bulletin de l'Institut Historique Belge de Rome*, i (1919), pp. 161–371.

VAES, M. (2). 'Hospice de Saint-Julien les Flamands à Rome. Les statuts de 1444', *Annales de la Soc. d'Émulation de Bruges*, lxvii (1924), pp. 65–96.

VALLA, M. 'Les Lyonnais à Compostelle', *BHP.* (1964), pp. 231–50.

VAN DE WALLE, B. 'Sur les traces des pèlerins Flamands, Hennuyers, et Liègeois au monastère Sainte-Catherine du Sinai', *Annales de la Soc. d'Émulation de Bruges*, ci (1964), pp. 119–47.

VAN ORTROY, F. 'Note sur l'indulgence de la Portioncule', *An. Boll.*, xxi (1902), pp. 372–80.

VAZQUEZ DE PARGA, L., LACARRA, J., and URÍA RÍU, J. *Las peregrinaciones a Santiago de Compostela*, 3 vols., Madrid, 1948–9.

VIELLIARD, J. (1). 'Notes sur l'hospice Saint-Nicholas des Catalans à Rome au moyen age', *MAH.*, 1 (1933), pp. 183–93.

VIELLIARD, J. (2). 'Pèlerins d'Espagne à la fin du moyen age', in *Homenatge a Antonio Robió i Lluch*, vol. ii, Barcelona, 1936, pp. 265–300.

VIELLIARD, R. *Recherches sur les origines de la Rome Chrétienne. Essai d' urbanisme Chrétien*, Mâcon, 1941.

VIGNERAS, L-A. 'L'abbaye de Charroux et la légende du pèlerinage de Charlemagne', *Romanic review*, xxxii (1941), pp. 121–8.

VILLEY, M. *La croisade. Essai sur la formation d'une théorie juridique*, Paris, 1942.

VINCENT, H. and ABEL, F-M. (1). *Bethléem. Le sanctuaire de la Nativité*, Paris, 1914.

VINCENT, H. and ABEL, F-M. (2). *Jerusalem. Recherches de topographie, d'archéologie, et d'histoire*, vol. ii (*Jerusalem nouvelle*), 2 vols., Paris, 1914–26.

VINCKE, J. (1). 'Espanya i l'any sant al segle xiv', *Analecta sacra Tarraconensia*, x (1924), pp. 61–73.

VINCKE, J. (2). 'Geleitbriefe für deutsche Pilger in Spanien', in Schreiber, *op. cit.*, pp. 258–65.

VINCKE, J. (3). 'Zur Frühgeschichte der Jubilaeumswallfahrt', in *ibid.*, pp. 242–57.

VINCKE, J. (4). 'Der Jubilaeumsablass von 1350 auf Mallorca', *Römische Quartalschrift*, xli (1933), pp. 301–6.

VIVES, J. 'Andancas e viajes de un hidalgo Espanol (1436–1439), con una descripción de Roma', *Gesammelte Aufsätze zur Kulturesgeschichte Spaniens*, vii (1938), pp. 127–206.

VOGEL, C. (1). 'La discipline pénitencielle en Gaule des origines au ixe siècle. Le dossier hagiographique', *Revue des sciences religieuses*, xxx (1956), pp. 1–26, 157–86.

VOGEL, C. (2). 'Le pèlerinage pénitencielle', in *Pellegrinaggi*, pp. 37–94.

WAAL, A. DE (1). *Das böhmische Pilgerhaus in Rom*, Prague, 1873.

WAAL, A. DE (2). 'Die Nationalstiftungen des deutschen Volkes in Rom', *Frankfurter zeitgemässe Broschüren*, i (1880), pp. 75–106.

WADDING, L. *Annales minorum*, ed. J. M. Fonseca, 2nd. ed., 19 vols., Rome, 1731–3.

WILMART, A. 'La Trinité des Scots à Rome et les notes du Vat. Lat. 378', *Revue Bénédictine*, xli (1929), pp. 218–30.

WOHLHAUPTER, E. (1). 'Beiträge zum Recht der Personenbeförderung über See im Mittelalter', *Historisches Jahrbuch der Görres-Gesellschaft*, lvii (1937), pp. 339–57.

WOHLHAUPTER, E. (2). 'Wallfahrt und Recht', in Schreiber, *op. cit.*, pp. 217–42.

WOODRUFF, C. E. 'The financial aspect of the cult of St. Thomas of Canterbury', *Archaeologia Cantiana*, xliv (1932), pp. 13–32.

WORMWALD, F. 'The rood of Bromholm', *Journal of the Warburg Institute*, i (1937–8). pp. 31–45.

ZEDELGEM, A. DE. 'Apercu historique sur la dévotion de la croix', *Collectanea Franciscana*, xix (1949), pp. 45–112.

ZETTINGER, J. *Die Berichte über Rompilger aus dem Frankreiche bis zum Jahre 800, Römische Quartalschrift*, Supplementheft xi, Rome, 1900.

INDEX

Aachen, 279, 280
Aasche, 47
Abbo, abt. of Fleury, 103, 133
Adalbert, St.: relics, 29
Adam, Guillaume, O.P., 188
Adam of Usk, 248
Adhemar, bp. of Le Puy, 27
Adrevald, monk of Fleury, 32–3, 34
Adso, abt. of Montiérender, 132
Aerts, Jan, 189
Affagart, Gréffin, 192, 204, 259, 264
Aganon, bp. of Autun, 119
Agelwy, abt. of Evesham, 198
Aibert, St., 127
Ailred, St., of Rievaulx: miracles, 62
Aimeric II, count of Fézensac, 169
Alberic of Rosate, 240–1
Albigensian heretics, 19, 58–9
Aldhelm, St.: miracles, 41, 86
Alexander, bp. of Jerusalem, 88
Alexander, St.: relics, 220
Alfonso VI, king of León and Castile, 116
Alkerton, Richard, 20, 168, 171
Ambrose, St., bishop of Milan, 26
Amiens, cathedral, 161
Andrew, St., 77, 249
Angers, 37, 141–2, 164
Anselm, St., abp. of Canterbury, 120, 172
Anselm of Ardres, 183
Anthony, St., 95; life of, by Athanasius, 16, 94, 146
Antioch, 27, 28
Antwerp, 46, 278
Aquinas: see Thomas Aquinas
Arculf, 91–2

Arles: christian cemetery, 131
Arnaldo de Monte, monk of Ripoll, 120
Arnold von Harff, 195–6, 216, 251, 261
Arnoul, St.: relics, 40; miracles, 79
Arques, treaty of (1326), 108
Aubert, St.: skull, 83
Aubrac: hospice, 200–1
Augustine, St., of Canterbury, 29, 57
Augustine, St., of Hippo, 18, 26, 198, 211; on dreams and visions, 26, 27; on miracles, 57, 65–6; on relics, 23, 25
Austremoine, St., 228
Autun, 17, 119, 135
Avallon: St. Lazare, 299
Avignon: pilgrimages to, 108
Avioth, 161

badges, 161, 174–5, 249–50
Baldwin, abt. of Bury, 84
Baldwin, latin emperor of Constantinople. 32
banditry, 177–82
Barcelona, Franciscan prior of, 47
Bari: St. Nicholas, 32
Bartholomew, St.: relics, 31, 165
Bartolus of Assisi, 295, 296
Basques, 177, 192–3
Battle abbey, 198
Bayeux, 50
Beaumanoir, Philippe de Rémy sire de, 107, 168
Bede: on 'conversion', 18; on diabolical possession, 79; on hell, 20–1